THE ILLUSTRATED ENCYCLOPEDIA OF

# DINOSAURS

AN ORIGINAL AND COMPELLING INSIGHT INTO LIFE
IN THE DINOSAUR KINGDOM

Dr David Norman & Dr Peter Wellnhofer

PUBLISHED BY
SALAMANDER BOOKS LIMITED
LONDON

## A Salamander Book

Published by Salamander Books Ltd
8 Blenheim Court
Brewery Road
London N7 9NT
United Kingdom



A member of the Chrysalis Group plc

**ISBN 1 84065 204 7**



All correspondence concerning the content of this volume should be addressed to Salamander Books Ltd.

## Credits

**Editor:** Philip de Ste. Croix

**Contributing editors:** Amanda O' Neill and Stella Caldwell

**Contributing authors:** (captions): Dr Michael Benton, Dr Gillian King

**Designers:** Nick Buzzard, Carol Warren, Roger Hyde, Jill Coote, John Heritage

**Colour dinosaur and pterosaur artwork:** John Sibbick
© Salamander Books Ltd

**Skeletal artwork (dinosaurs):**
Denise Blagden and David Nicholls
© Salamander Books Ltd

**Skeletal artwork and black and white restorations (pterosaurs):**
© Peter Wellnhofer

**Diagram artwork (dinosaurs):**
Bob Chapman, Alan Hollingbery, Greg Jones, Bernard Robinson, Tim Widdall
© Salamander Books

**Diagram artwork (pterosaurs):**
Peter Wellnhofer and Geoff Denney
© Salamander Books Ltd

**Text translation from German (pterosaurs text):** Michael Robinson

**Filmset:** Modern Text typesetting Ltd, England and SX Composing Ltd, England

**Colour and monochrome reproductions:** Culver Graphics Ltd, England, Scantrans PTE Ltd and Singapore and Contemporary Litho Ltd, England

Printed in Spain

## The Authors

Dr David Norman is a lecturer in zoology at Brasenose College, Oxford, and also a Research Fellow of the University Museum, Oxford, where he specialises in researching the evolution of and the relationships between dinosaurs. He graduated from Leeds University in 1973 and conducted postgraduate research at King's College, London and the British Museum (Natural History). He held a Royal Society Fellowship in Brussels for one year. David Norman has actively been involved in many important palaeontological finds, and participated in an expedition to the 'outback' of Australia in 1978 which resulted in the discovery of a small armoured dinosaur. He is a research consultant at an excavation at Nehden in Germany and is generally regarded as the world's foremost authority on *Iguanodon*. In addition to his technical and academic writing, on a more popular level he has written a *Spotter's Guide to Dinosaurs* and contributed to *Collins Guide to Dinosaurs*.

Dr Peter Wellnhofer is Hauptkonservator at the Bavarian State Collection of Palaeontology and Historical Geology, an institution that houses some of the finest pterosaur fossil remains in the world. He has worked in this field of research for more than 20 years and is recognised as a leading authority worldwide. Apart from his numerous scientific publications, he also prepared the volume on pterosaurs for the *Encyclopedia of Palaeoherpetology* and is the author of an illustrated booklet on pterosaurs and early birds from the Solnhofen limestone, *Solnhofer Plattenkalk: Urvögel und Flugsaurier*.

## The Artist

John Sibbick undertook his art training in the early 1970s at Guildford Art School, Surrey, where he studied graphic design and latterly, illustration. He subsequently spent four years in various art studios in London before going fully freelance. He has always been interested in prehistoric animals, and has worked on a number of books concerned with dinosaurs and their contemporaries. Apart from his publishing commissions, he also works regularly for galleries and museums, and has been involved in producing artwork for use in television documentary programmes about the world before man.

# ACKNOWLEDGEMENTS

FOR THEIR HELP in various aspects of this book, grateful thanks are due to Natalia Bakhurina, Moscow, Russia; Christopher Bennett, Lawrence, Kansas, USA; Dr Michael Benton; Leonhard Bimmer, Munich, Germany; Denise Blagden; Dr. José Bonaparte, Buenos Aires, Brazil; Nick Buzzard; Martyn Cowley, Simi Valley, California, USA; Harry Coussins; Philip de Ste. Croix; Prof Dr Dong Zhiming, Beijing, China; Dr Burkard Engesser, Basel, Switzerland; Karl A. Frickhinger, Gräfelfing, Germany; Rolf B. Hauff, Holzmaden, Germany; Prof Dr Dietrich Herm, Munich, Germany; Franz Höck, Munich, Germany; Alexander W.A. Kellner, Rio de Janeiro, Brazil; Dr Gillian King; Dr Heinz A. Kollman, Vienna, Austria; Dr Theo Kress, Solnhofen, Germany; Prof Dr Wann Langston, Jr, Austin, Texas; Renate Liebreich, Munich, Germany; Dr John G. Maisey, New York, USA; Dr Helmut Mayr, Munich, Germany; Dr Angela Milner, London, England; Dr Ralph Molnar, Fortitude Valley, Queensland, Australia; David Nicholls; Dany Oppliger, Basel, Switzerland; Prof Dr John H. Ostrom, New Haven, Connecticut, USA; Dr Colin Pennycuik, Miami, USA; Prof Dr Giovanni Pinna, Milan, Italy; Dr Georg Plodowski, Frankfurt, Germany; Ernst Schmieja, Munich, Germany; John Sibbick; Matt B. Smith, Bozeman, Montana, USA; David Unwin, Reading, England; Dr Günter Viohl, Eichstätt, Germany; Ingrid Wellnhofer; Prof Dr Frank Westphal, Tübingen, Germany, and Dr Rupert Wild, Stuttgart, Germany.

# CONTENTS

## SECTION ONE

# DINOSAURS

David Norman

# INTRODUCTION TO DINOSAURS

The name 'dinosaur' was first coined by Richard Owen (later Sir Richard), a famous British anatomist in 1841. The occasion was an annual meeting of the British Association for the Advancement of Science held at Plymouth (England). Owen had been asked to review all the fossil reptiles that had been described to that date from the British Isles. As a result of his anatomical training and expertise he was able to recognise from their meagre remains that three fossil reptiles, *Megalosaurus, Iguanodon* and *Hylaeosaurus,* were totally unlike any other fossil or living types. They were all very large (approximately elephant-sized), land-living creatures which had pillar-like legs that were tucked in beneath the body; this leg position was totally different from the splayed position of the legs typical of reptiles. Comparisons that Owen was able to make at the time suggested to him that these peculiar reptiles, which he named dinosaurs after the Greek words *deinos* and *sauros* or 'terrible reptiles', seemed to anticipate the form of the large pachydermal mammals (e.g. elephants, rhinoceroses and hippopotamuses) of today. Dinosaurs thus came to be regarded as the acme of the reptilian type of animal. The alleged similarity between the anatomical design of dinosaurs and large mammals seemed amply to confirm this view.

As it eventually transpired, Owen's model of the dinosaur proved rather inaccurate, although he was absolutely correct about the posture of these reptiles. Nevertheless, whatever the faults of his argument, Owen introduced dinosaurs to the world at large. Since that time (the 1840s) dinosaurs have held a deep and continuing fascination for generation after generation.

For the great majority of us it is a fascination that is intense but temporary: restricted to those formative years of childhood. Often it is the result of a first trip to a Museum, or a school project, or the purchase of a first picture book on dinosaurs. Whatever the stimulus, dinosaurs certainly make a big impression on children who very quickly learn their jaw-cracking names, their appearance, and even their feeding habits, as many parents and teachers will testify. The nature of their appeal obviously varies from individual to individual: it may be simply their immense size, or the grotesque appearance of their skeletons, or the inevitable associations that are drawn with a violent or blood-thirsty life-style. Whatever the cause, for a brief period the imagination of children all over the world (this is certainly not a phenomenon associated with just the western world) is kindled by these dramatic and awe-inspiring creatures. Today many museums have fine dinosaur skeletons on display to the public, so that their visual impact is immediate. However, even in the middle of the last century, before complete dinosaur skeletons had been discovered, interest in these former inhabitants of our world was intense.

For most of us though, the childhood fascination with dinosaurs is transient — it fades with the passing of the years. School curricula naturally demand skills other than the ability to recite the names and attributes of dinosaurs. Interest in dinosaurs, however, rarely dies completely — they are associated with crucial years in a child's development. I think that this is amply confirmed by the quite frequent appearance of 'dinosaur-inspired' stories in the media. New theories or discoveries concerning dinosaurs are still considered newsworthy even by the most sombre or serious-minded of newspapers or television programmes; dinosaurs even figure in advertising campaigns, though they almost always symbolise the epitome of something that is out-dated, badly-designed or inefficient (a view that will be firmly refuted in this book).

So, what is it that makes dinosaurs so innately interesting? Surely, so the argument goes, we should find something more relevant to our world instead of harking back to the ancient past. Why bother with creatures that lived over 64 million years ago when we have so many urgent and pressing problems in present-day society. Is it escapism — a way of taking our minds off the horrendous problems that face us from day to day? Many palaeontologists who have devoted their lives to the study of dinosaurs or other fossil creatures may sympathise with this point of view but would be tempted to offer the following rather more dispassionate scientific explanation.

We live in an incredibly complex biological world and have become (particularly through environmental issues) generally aware of our potential to affect the delicate balance of nature upon which we depend. The world that we now inhabit has taken at least 4,500 million years to reach its present state. During this time it has been altered by geological processes and

**Above:** Richard Owen, (1804-1892) who first coined the term *Dinosauria.* A leading comparative anatomist, he became the first superintendent of the British Museum (Natural History).

**Below:** Children are nearly always fascinated by dinosaurs. Here a crowd has gathered to watch the excavation of a large fossil reptile in the 'outback' of Queensland, Australia.

**Hip Structure (right)**
Top right is the pelvis of an early ornithischian dinosaur (*Heterodontosaurus*). Note the position of the pubis (in red). Below left is a typical saurischian pelvis (*Compsognathus*).

**Below:** This haunting reconstruction of *Diplodocus* is displayed in the Smithsonian Institution, Washington D.C. The eerie quality of the lighting in the photograph emphasises the aura of mystery and fascination that surrounds dinosaurs in general.

the organisms that have lived on this planet before us. Dinosaurs form a part, and quite a significant one since they lasted for over 140 million years, of the history of this planet. Perhaps by studying the rise, flourishing and eventual decline and extinction of this group we may learn more not only about long term evolutionary processes, but also about the complex interactions between these organisms and the Earth that they inhabited. We should perhaps be able to learn, from the example of the dinosaurs, how better to manage this world and so perhaps avoid the eventual fate of the dinosaurs. It also gives us an element of perspective about ourselves and the Earth. We are very probably temporary custodians of this planet, an integral part of the history of the Earth which has not only a past but a future. We should therefore concern ourselves with what we are doing to the planet at the present time and to what extent it will affect future generations and inhabitants, rather than selfishly pursuing short-term aims.

There is indeed a great deal of fundamental truth in these arguments. They do, however, run the risk of becoming very profound intellectually and at the same time potentially highly political.

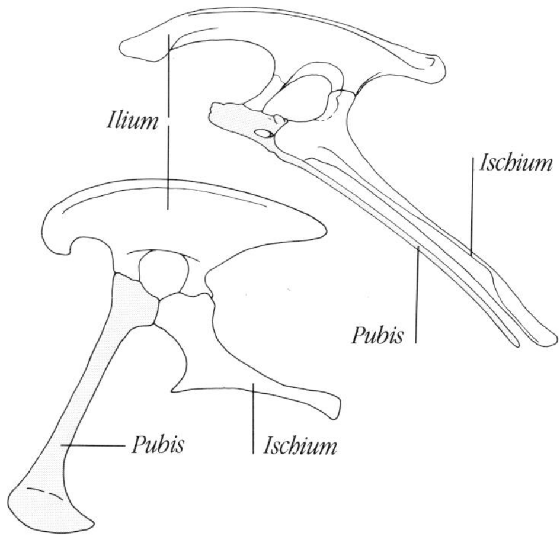


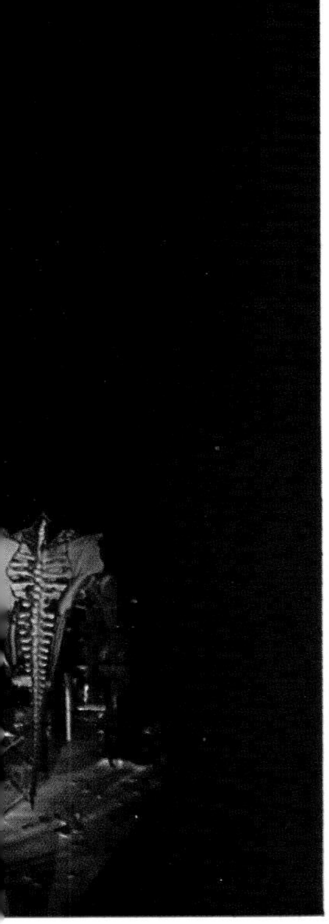

**Below:** Even in today's 'high technology' culture, dinosaurs frequently catch the headlines in the world's press — particularly when the find is especially large or dramatic. This is again an indication of the powerful impression that they make on the human mind.

I do not particularly wish to avoid these issues but I do feel that another argument, concerned with human emotions and psychology, is probably of greater immediacy to the issue of why bother about dinosaurs.

Dinosaurs are very big — even awe-inspiring — and are all extinct; they are also the virtual personification of 'dragons' or other 'mythical beasts' that are associated with folk-lore traditions dating back long before dinosaurs were first described. This common factor of a human obsession with 'dragons', 'mythical beasts' or dinosaurs may be a key feature relating to the very essence of the human condition: the imaginative and creative aspects of the human intellect.

Dinosaurs, like other mythical beasts, require us to exercise both *imagination* and *creativity* in order to bring these extinct creatures back to life and give them a feeling of reality. One of the key features of Man is his ability to use his imagination and creativity in order to think ahead, predict or anticipate — from planning how to trap a rabbit for food, to designing a piece of industrial machinery or a new silicon 'chip'. All these and many other day-to-day activities are central to our ability to co-ordinate and regulate our lives.

Like many other skills, imagination and creativity are partly innate and partly learned, and all require *stimulation* to grow and develop. Perhaps it is in this area that dinosaurs have a limited but important rôle to play in stimulating the innate imaginative and creative potential in ourselves, particularly during those vital childhood years. It seems to me that dinosaurs (just like fairy tales, mythologies, space adventures, science fiction, etc) fall into this category of stimuli for the human imagination. None is *necessarily* relevant to the material needs of our present society but all may be of some importance in the maintenance of our essential humanness.

## What Were Dinosaurs?

Before considering the dinosaurs as a whole, a few words of introduction should be offered on behalf of the dinosaurs themselves. There are very widespread misconceptions about the nature of dinosaurs, ranging on one hand from them being regarded as just any gigantic prehistoric animal to the notion that they are just one type of fossil animal. The truth is somewhere between these two extreme views.

Dinosaurs lived during the so-called Mesozoic Era of Earth history. The Mesozoic (literally 'middle life') comprises the Triassic, Jurassic and Cretaceous Periods which lasted from about 225 until 64 million years ago. Thus animals that lived either before or after the Mesozoic are *not* dinosaurs. For example, giant woolly mammoths which went extinct within the last million years or so are not dinosaurs, nor are the large sail-backed reptiles of the Permian Period such as *Dimetrodon*.

Dinosaurs are also *reptiles* so that any fossil animals from the Mesozoic Era that are not reptiles (that is to say fish, amphibians, birds or mammals) cannot be dinosaurs either. To be even more precise dinosaurs were a rather special group of reptiles. All of them were land-living creatures. Of course a few ventured into shallow swamps to wallow, much as elephants do today, but none were particularly powerful swimmers or habitually lived in the sea. Thus the gigantic sea monsters of the Mesozoic, the plesiosaurs, ichthyosaurs and mosasaurs were not dinosaurs.

Similarly no dinosaurs were airborne fliers, so that the extraordinary flying reptiles of the Mesozoic, the pterosaurs, were not dinosaurs.

Dinosaurs are in fact members of a group of reptiles known as archosaurs ('ruling reptiles') which include well-known creatures like crocodiles, the extinct pterosaurs and those well-known archosaur descendants, the birds, as well as other less well-known extinct creatures such as the thecodontians.

The dinosaurs are distinct from other archosaurs for one main reason which is (as Owen rightly pointed out in 1841) that they are able to walk and run extremely efficiently; their legs are tucked in beneath the body rather than being held out from the sides. This change has left tell-tale marks in the form of changes in the structure of the hip, knee and ankle joint in their fossilised remains that serve to distinguish fairly clearly dinosaur remains from those of other archosaurs (see pages 36-37).

## Hip Structure

Since the last half of the nineteenth century the dinosaurs have been split into two distinct groups, the *saurischian* ('reptile hipped') and *ornithischian* ('bird-hipped') dinosaurs. As their names suggest the hip structure of these two types is different.

Saurischian dinosaurs have hip bones arranged as shown in the diagram. The three bones on each side of the hip radiate outward from the hip socket. The upper bone (ilium) contacts the backbone forming a very firm attachment while the two lower bones (pubis and ischium) point forward and backward respectively and provide areas for the attachments of large leg-moving muscles. Examples of saurischian dinosaurs are the large plant-eating sauropods such as *Diplodocus* and *Brachiosaurus* and the meat-eating theropods such as *Allosaurus* and *Tyrannosaurus*.

Ornithischian dinosaurs have a rather differently shaped pelvis in which the pubis lies back against the ischium: an arrangement similar to that seen in birds (see diagram). In early ornithischians the hip bones are exactly as shown, but later on many seem to develop a new forwardly-directed pubis almost as if they were trying to replace the one they had lost. Ornithischians were *all* herbivores so far as we can tell and also tended to have a distinctive turtle-like beak at the tips of the jaws. Examples range from ornithopods such as *Hypsilophodon* to rather bizarre creatures such as the ceratopians (*Triceratops*), stegosaurs (*Stegosaurus*), ankylosaurs (*Euoplocephalus*) and 'bone-heads' such as *Pachycephalosaurus*.

**Right:** Baron Georges Cuvier (1769-1832) was the father of modern palaeontology and comparative anatomy. His description of the jaws of *Mosasaurus* paved the way for the scientific acceptance of extinction, and the first descriptions of dinosaurs by Buckland and Mantell.

**Below:** Deep in a chalk mine near Maastricht in Holland the jaws of the mighty *Mosasaurus* were unearthed in 1770. They provoked much interest and controversy, Cuvier eventually proving that they belonged to an extinct marine reptile.

**Left:** Dean William Buckland (1784-1856). Originally a scholar at Corpus Christi College, Oxford, he was appointed a Reader in Geology in 1818, and eventually became Dean of Westminster. It was he who described the remains of *Megalosaurus* in 1824.

**Right:** A portion of the lower jaw of *Megalosaurus bucklandi* which was part of the remains of this large carnivorous dinosaur, first described by Buckland. The remains are on view to this day at the University Museum, Oxford.

**Below:** *Scrotum humanum* was the caption provided for this piece of bone by R. Brooks in 1763. It was first illustrated by Robert Plot in 1676 who thought it belonged to a giant human. Though now lost, it may have been the lower end of the thigh bone of *Megalosaurus*.

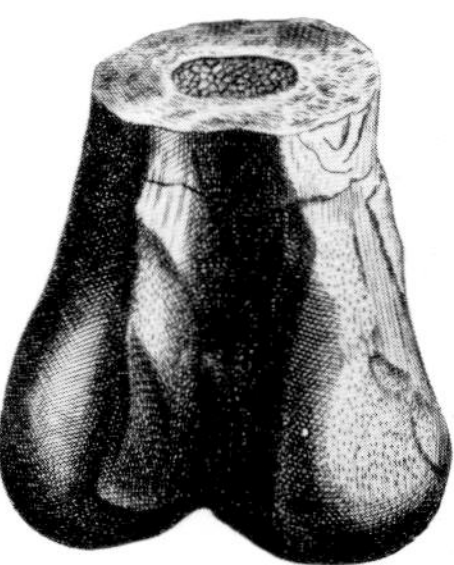

**Right:** Gideon Mantell (1790-1852), a country doctor in Sussex, described the first remains of *Iguanodon* (some teeth discovered by his wife) in 1822 before naming them in 1825.

## The Discovery of Dinosaurs

The first descriptions of true dinosaurs date back to the 1820s and the work of the Revd. William Buckland and Gideon Mantell. However, several significant events led up to these discoveries which are instructive because they reveal why it was that such giant fossil reptiles remained 'undiscovered' until such a late date. Dinosaur skeletons must have been weathering out of the rocks for longer than Man has existed on Earth. The reason for the delay in finding them was essentially a religious one. Religious beliefs in the early nineteenth century and earlier included a concept known as the *plenum*. This supposed that God must have populated the Earth with every conceivable type of organism. Bearing this in mind, it seemed inconceivable that he would have allowed any of his creatures to become extinct. The discovery of fossilised animals in rocks therefore presented a potential problem because fossils may prove the reality of extinction. For the most part early fossil discoveries were regarded as dead members of presently existing species. However, in 1770 a remarkable discovery, the jaws of a huge fossil animal, was made in a chalk quarry in Maastricht (Holland). After much difference of opinion the jaws were eventually recognised by the eminent French anatomist Baron Georges Cuvier as those of a gigantic marine lizard (*Mosasaurus*—'Meuse reptile'). This was a clear example of a long extinct creature and supported Cuvier's long-held belief that there had been repeated extinctions of animals in earlier times.

The dramatic size and appearance of these mosasaur jaws seems to have stimulated much interest in gigantic extinct fossil reptiles in subsequent years and was probably a major contributory factor to the discovery and acceptance of the giant fossil reptiles discovered by Mantell and Buckland.

## Mantell and Buckland

In the early 1820s Gideon Algernon Mantell was a family doctor in practice at Lewes in Sussex (England). He was also an extremely enthusiastic amateur geologist who had spent much of his early life exploring and collecting fossils from rocks in the South Downs area of Sussex. Indeed he even had a small geological museum of the specimens he had collected arranged in his house. In about 1822, or perhaps a little earlier, several large and rather unusual teeth came into his collection. He actually described these teeth quite accurately in a large book that he published in 1822 called *The Fossils of the South Downs* and noted that it was his wife, Mary Ann Mantell, who had discovered them in some gravel. A rather appealing but unsubstantiated story has frequently been told of Mary Mantell discovering the teeth in piles of gravel on the roadside while accompanying her husband on one of his many doctor's calls to patients in the countryside. Whatever the actual events, the important point was that they eventually fell into Mantell's hands. He was able to trace the gravel, in which the teeth were embedded, to quarries in the Cuckfield area of Tilgate Forest and soon discovered more fragmentary remains.

At first Mantell was at a loss to identify these teeth. When shown to eminent anatomists of the time, such as William Buckland at Oxford and Georges Cuvier in Paris, they were sceptical about the supposed age of the rocks and regarded the teeth as being of no particular interest; perhaps they belonged to a large fish, or mammal such as a rhinoceros of fairly recent origin. Despite these authoritative comments Mantell suspected that Buckland and Cuvier were wrong. He *knew* that the teeth were from 'secondary' (Mesozoic) rocks and therefore really ought to be reptilian. Further work of his own, comparing his fossil teeth, revealed at last that they were similar to those of a South American lizard, the iguana. Thus it was that in 1825 Mantell finally published his description of these teeth as those of a gigantic, 40ft (12m) long herbivorous fossil lizard named *Iguanodon* ('iguana-tooth'), an extinct relative of the living iguana. The article included a handsome admission by Cuvier of his faulty earlier determination.

A year earlier (1824) William Buckland described the partial remains of a large carnivorous reptile (including the partial jaw bone illustrated above right) which was discovered near Stonesfield in north Oxfordshire and named *Megalosaurus* ('big reptile').

Both of these gigantic lizards seemed to fall into the *Mosasaurus* category of fossil reptile, except that both were land-dwellers rather than marine. Thus, although they were notable discoveries, their true significance was not fully appreciated. The same also applies to the partial skeleton of another reptile, this time armoured, named *Hylaeosaurus*. It was described by Mantell in 1833. Throughout the 1830s more fragments of these reptiles were discovered although no complete skeletons were found at this time.

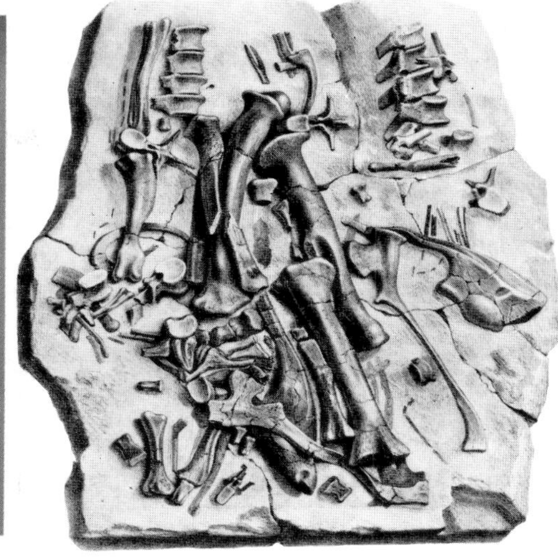

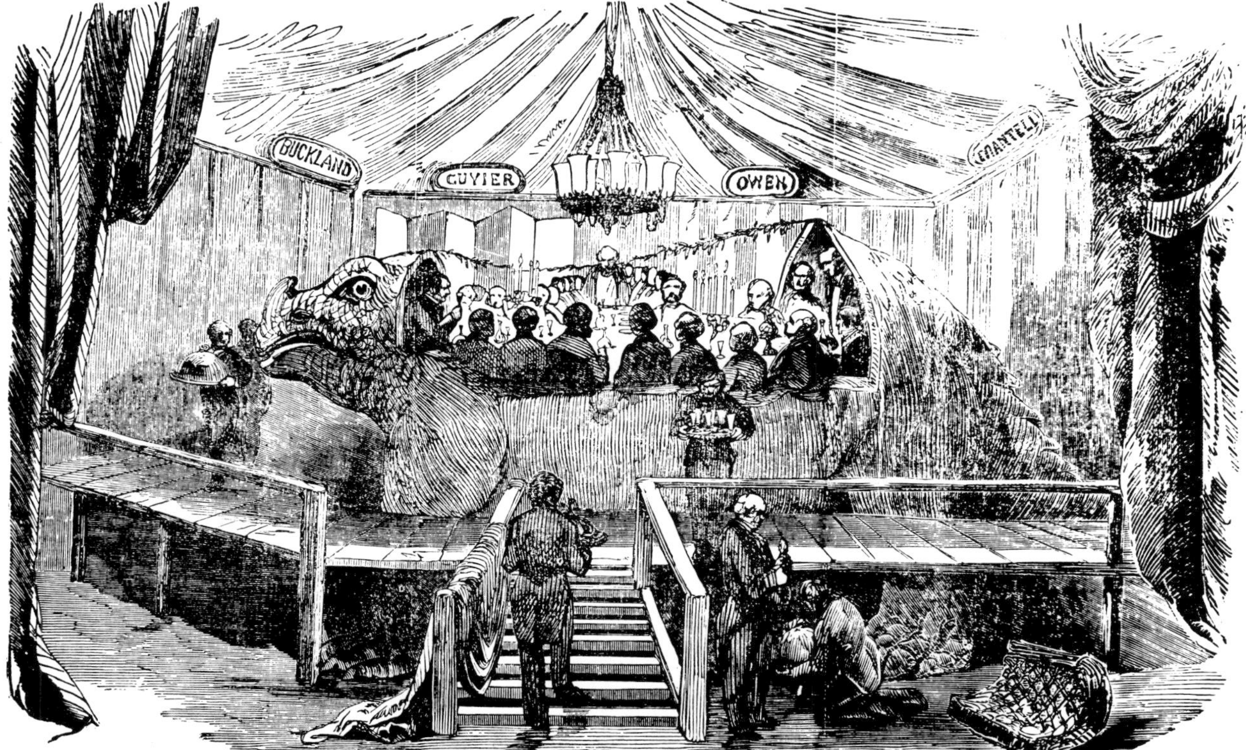


**Above:** This lithograph, from Owen's review of British fossil reptiles, is of the partial skeleton of *Iguanodon* found in a quarry at Maidstone in Kent. It was bought by friends for Gideon Mantell for the then princely sum of £25. These bones formed the basis of Mantell's early restoration of *Iguanodon* as a sort of giant lizard.

**Left:** Between 1852 and 1854 Richard Owen and the sculptor Waterhouse Hawkins produced several life-sized restorations of dinosaurs and other prehistoric animals for the grounds of the Crystal Palace exhibition centre at Sydenham. Just before they completed their task, Owen and Hawkins organised a special dinner party for 20 inside the incomplete body of an *Iguanodon*. As can be seen from the engraving of the occasion, the guests were rather cramped!

## Richard Owen's Dinosauria

In 1841 Richard Owen, another comparative anatomist who had been inspired by the work of Cuvier, entered the scene. His review of British fossil reptiles revealed that *Iguanodon, Megalosaurus* and *Hylaeosaurus* were so unlike living lizards, with which they had been compared, that they deserved to be recognised as a separate 'tribe or suborder' as he called them – namely the *Dinosauria* ('terrible reptiles'). Owen's conception of the dinosaurs as huge elephantine reptiles proved extraordinarily powerful, generating interest in the group among the scientific community and the general public that has endured right up to the present day.

As our understanding of dinosaurs has gradually improved over the years, it has become clear that dinosaurs had been inadvertently discovered many years earlier than Mantell and Buckland's works. Robert Plot, a clergyman at Oxford University and Keeper of the Ashmolean Museum, described and illustrated part of a thigh-bone in 1676 which he thought must have belonged to a giant human. The drawing looks remarkably like a thigh-bone of Buckland's *Megalosaurus*. Unfortunately there is now no trace of this bone. During the eighteenth century there are several reports of giant fossil bones having been discovered in rocks that have since yielded dinosaur remains.

In 1807-1809 fossil bones were recovered from Cuckfield in Sussex by William Smith during his geological survey of the British Isles. These have since been relocated in collections at the Institute of Geological Sciences in London by Dr Alan Charig and I was able to confirm that they belong to *Iguanodon*. This seems to be one of the earliest properly documented records of a dinosaur discovery.

Owen's view of dinosaurs as elephantine reptiles gained particular prominence in the early 1850s shortly after the Great Exhibition at Hyde Park of 1850-51. The enormous Crystal Palace in which the exhibition was held was moved to Sydenham Park in south-east London and Owen was asked to provide life-sized models of his prehistoric animals which could be placed in the park grounds. These models atracted enormous publicity at the time and are still standing today, and, inaccurate though we know them to be, they still create a strong impression on the viewer.

## American Discoveries

Not long after Owen's elephantine models of his dinosaurs had been finished at Sydenham, discoveries of dinosaurs began to be made in North America. Scattered teeth found in 1855 in Montana seemed to resemble those of *Iguanodon* and *Megalosaurus* from Britain. Joseph Leidy named these teeth *Trachodon* and *Deinodon* respectively. A little later in 1858 Leidy examined a partial skeleton from Haddonfield, New Jersey. Very fortunately this creature, named *Hadrosaurus* (again with teeth reminiscent of those of *Iguanodon*), had both its fore and hindlimbs preserved intact. Leidy realised that unlike Owen's 'elephantine' dinosaurs, his *Hadrosaurus* must have had a more kangaroo-like posture and at a stroke took *Hadrosaurus* far closer to an accurate picture of this type of dinosaur than over 30 years of work by Mantell, Buckland and Owen had managed. Life-sized models of *Hadrosaurus* and a carnivore named *Laelaps* were constructed in kangaroo-pose in the newly created Central Park of New York in 1868 by Waterhouse Hawkins (the man who had assisted Owen with his Sydenham dinosaurs).

**Above left:** Across the Atlantic, Hawkins was commissioned to build models of the dinosaurs described by Joseph Leidy. This is the *Hadrosaurus* skeleton in the Philadelphia Academy of Sciences in 1868.

**Above:** The son of a Quaker family, Edward Drinker Cope (1840-1897) was a precocious child with a brilliant intellect. His scientific reputation was great even before he became interested in dinosaurs in the 1870s.

**Above:** Less brilliant than Cope, Othniel Charles Marsh (1831-1899) was fortunate to have George Peabody as his uncle. With his support Marsh became a professor at Yale College with ample time to study dinosaurs.

Thus from early in their history dinosaurs had made a large public impact through the models in London and in New York, and the added 'spice' of a certain element of disagreement over the actual form of these animals. By the late 1870s further publicity was given to the dinosaurs as a result of virtually coincidental dinosaur discoveries in Europe and North America.

## Bernissart

In April, 1878 miners excavating a coal seam 1,056ft (322m) below ground at the small Sainte Barbe pit in the village of Bernissart (south-west Belgium) entered a clay-filled fissure. From this site were recovered the remains of almost 40 complete or partial *Iguanodon* skeletons. Excavation of these dinosaurs was handed over to research workers of the then Royal Museum of Natural History in Brussels (since re-named the Royal Institute of Natural Sciences). The recovery of these dinosaurs was the responsibility of Louis Depauw and the scientific description of these skeletons fell to Louis Dollo. Dollo was for the first time able to provide an accurate reconstruction of one of Owen's dinosaurs: *Iguanodon*. This finally confirmed that Leidy's views rather than Owen's were the more correct. Today over 30 of the Bernissart dinosaurs are exhibited to the public in enormous glass enclosures at the Royal Institute of Natural Sciences in Brussels (see also the following chapter 'To Study a Dinosaur').

## Cope and Marsh

In 1877, just before the Bernissart discoveries were made, even richer deposits were discovered in Colorado. These dinosaur fossils were discovered quite independently by two school masters: one, Arthur Lakes, found bones on a ridge at Morrison, Colorado and sent them to Othniel Charles Marsh, a Professor at Yale College (later to become Yale University), while the other, O. W. Lucas, found his fossils in similarly aged rocks near Canyon City, Colorado and sent his fossils to Edward Drinker Cope in New Jersey.

The coincidence of these discoveries was remarkable for in the late 1870s Marsh and Cope were already great rivals. The starting point of their rivalry was, according to Adrian Desmond, an occasion in 1870 when Cope showed Marsh the skeleton of *Elasmosaurus*, a plesiosaur from Kansas that Cope had described

**Below:** In the early 1880s the dinosaur skeletons collected at Bernissart began to be reassembled in St George's Chapel, Brussels. Here we see the completion of the first skeleton, and the men involved.

**Right:** The dinosaurs of China have rightly gained much attention in recent years. Seen here is the dinosaur hall at Beipei Museum with the fine skeletons of the stegosaur *Tuojiangosaurus* in the foreground, and the large sauropod *Omeisaurus* behind.

**Below:** In the 1920s several nests of eggs and young *Protoceratops* were found by the Central Asiatic expedition organised by the American Museum of Natural History. In recent years further Polish-Mongolian expeditions to this area have revealed more nests, like the one seen here.

a few years earlier. Upon examination Marsh noted that the head of the animal had been placed on the wrong end of the skeleton — a fairly dramatic error on Cope's part! Cope being a brilliant, but rather quick-tempered individual never forgave Marsh for pointing out this error and so their rivalry began.

The feud between Cope and Marsh was fuelled by these new dinosaur discoveries and the desire to be the first to describe any new dinosaur remains. From these beginnings in Colorado, teams of explorers hired by Marsh and Cope extended their excavations into Wyoming at Como Bluff (alongside the original Union Pacific Railroad) to Montana, the Connecticut Valley and New Mexico. Between 1877 and the late 1890s Cope and Marsh, driven by their intense rivalry, described about 130 new species of dinosaur, a veritable avalanche of types. Many of these fossils found their way into North American Museums, notably the Peabody Museum at Yale University, the Smithsonian Institution in Washington and the American Museum of Natural History (New York). Today they provide a testament to their mighty labours. The deaths of Cope in 1897 and Marsh in 1899 saw a change to much more careful and co-ordinated exploration of these North American localities.

In 1897/8 new expeditions to Como Bluff, Wyoming were undertaken by the American Museum of Natural History; these proved only moderately succesful but in 1898 a new locality, Bone Cabin Quarry, was discovered. The unusual name comes from the fact that a shepherd had built himself a small cabin out of the dinosaur bones that were strewn across the area. Between 1878 and 1905 the AMNH removed hundreds of bones of dinosaurs from this site.

In 1909 Earl Douglass of the Carnegie Museum (Pittsburgh) found one of the richest deposits of dinosaur skeletons that the world has ever known. The locality is in Utah, near Vernal in the Uinta mountains. This site was excavated from 1909-1923 by the Carnegie Museum and revealed magnificent skeletons of *Diplodocus, Apatosaurus, Camarasaurus, Stegosaurus, Allosaurus* and many other dinosaurs. In 1915 it became, by Presidential decree, Dinosaur National Monument' and today a working museum stands on the site. The steeply tilted fossil-bearing rocks form a mural with the fossils visibly in place.

## Dinosaurs in Canada

The first Canadian dinosaur remains were discovered during geographical surveys of the Canadian border in the early 1870s. In 1884 Joseph Tyrrell made the first important discovery of a skull of the carnivorous dinosaur *Albertosaurus* in the valley of the Red Deer River, Alberta. By the late 1880s it was realised that the only way to collect dinosaurs in this area was by using a boat to travel down river. This procedure was used with moderate success through the late 1890s into the first decade of the twentieth century when the real Canadian dinosaur rush began.

In 1910 Barnum Brown of the American Museum of Natural History (New York) launched a broad-beamed barge on the Red Deer River, equipped with a large tent and fully equipped for an expedition. Using this as a base camp, Brown navigated the river stopping at points to explore the terrain and collect fossils systematically. The results were remarkably good and form an impressive record of late Cretaceous dinosaurs from North America. Two years after Brown started his collecting trip by boat, Canadians joined in. The Sternberg family, Charles H. (senior) and his three sons, Charles, Levi and George, built a similar barge and began prospecting in the same area of the Red Deer River. Both groups were very successful during the period 1912-1917 finding many fine dinosaur specimens which are now on display in museums both in North America and elsewhere around the world.

## The African Dinosaur Rush

1907 saw the discovery of large dinosaur remains at Tendaguru in German East Africa (now known as Tanzania). These were excavated largely by native Africans under the supervision of scientists (Edwin Hennig and Werner Janensch) from the Berlin Museum of Natural History, during the period 1908-1912. Working under much more difficult conditions than those experienced in North America, the expedition recovered some remarkable dinosaurs including the gigantic, giraffe-like *Brachiosaurus*, as well as *Dicraeosaurus* and the armoured dinosaur *Kentrosaurus*.

A British Museum expedition also went to Tanzania in the 1920s and recovered more dinosaur remains, but these were rather more fragmentary than the German discoveries.

## Dinosaurs in Central Asia

In the early 1920s, following on from the phenomenal success that dinosaur collectors had had in North America through the preceding 40 years since the time of Cope and Marsh, an ambitious plan was hatched to send an expedition from the American Museum of Natural History into Mongolia.

The main aim of the expedition was to find more evidence concerning the origin of Man. The expedition (led by Roy Chapman Andrews, Henry Fairfield Osborn and Walter Granger) entered Mongolia for the first time in 1922. In the Gobi Desert they found some mammal remains, but by far the most significant discoveries made were of dinosaurs. Between 1922 and 1925 four expeditions managed to reach the Gobi and collected a fine array of dinosaurs: *Protoceratops, Pinacosaurus, Saurornithoides, Oviraptor, Velociraptor,* all of which were new to science. Most renowned of all these discoveries though were the nests of *Protoceratops* eggs — the first of any dinosaur to be discovered.

Political events in China in the 1920s and world events in the 1930s and 1940s prevented further exploration of Mongolia. However, in 1946 and 1948/9 Russian expeditions went back to Mongolia, led by I. Efremov and A. K. Rozhdestvensky. These revealed not only more *Protoceratops* and armoured dinosaurs, but also extended exploration into the Nemegt Basin where they found hadrosaurids like the North American *Saurolophus*, and *Tarbosaurus*, a form very close to the great North American *Tyrannosaurus*.

Further work in Mongolia followed in the 1960s and 1970s with the setting up of joint Russian-Mongolian and Polish-Mongolian collaborative expeditions to the Nemegt Basin and elsewhere; these have resulted in yet more new and interesting fossils being discovered, including not only abundant and varied dinosaurs, but also well-preserved and important early mammal remains.

## Dinosaurs in China

Records of 'dragon bones' from Sichuan in China, where dinosaur remains are known to be abundant today, have been traced back almost to the time of the birth of Christ A.D. 265-317. However, the study of dinosaur fossils in China dates back to 1902 with the collection by a Russian colonel (Manakin) of large fossils that had been discovered by fishermen in northern China. This site was excavated by Russians in 1915-17 and produced the hadrosaurid *Mandschurosaurus*, a well-preserved skeleton of which is now in Leningrad.

After this time several expeditions ventured into China, notably Sino-French, Sino-Swedish and the AMNH on their way to Mongolia. However, from 1933 onward the Chinese have been the primary explorers of their country. Led by the German-trained Professor Yang Zhong-jian (C. C. Young to western palaeontologists!), explorations were carried out in Sichuan,

Yunnan, Xinjiang and Gansu and led to the discovery of the prosauropod *Lufengosaurus*.

After the People's Republic was formed in 1949, all research was concentrated on the Institute of Vertebrate Palaeontology at Beijing (Peking) which co-ordinated much of the palaeontological work done in China. 1950 saw the discovery of the remarkable hadrosaurid *Tsintaosaurus* in Laiyang, and 1952 and 1957 skeletons of the diplodocid *Mamenchisaurus* in Sichuan. In the 1960s the huge hadrosaurid *Shantungosaurus* was excavated in Shandong. In the 1970s Xigong Province yielded many new and interesting forms, *Omeisaurus*, *Szechuanosaurus* and the stegosaur *Tuojiangosaurus*, and then the rich fossil deposits of Sichuan were discovered; these latter deposits have yielded literally hundreds of dinosaurs, many of which are to this day still being excavated. In many ways China is now the area of the present 'dinosaur rush', its finds being as important as those in North America around the turn of the century.

## South America and Australia

Dinosaur remains have been known in both South America and Australia for many years but there has been a significant rise in the number of finds in South America, particularly through the work of José Bonaparte (Argentina) and his collaborators, and in Australia through the work of Ralph Molnar, Tony Thulborn and colleagues in Brisbane, Sydney and Melbourne. All this points to the likelihood of new and dramatic discoveries in the near future. For example, one locality in southern Queensland has revealed literally hundreds of dinosaur tracks. Dinosaurs were obviously there in great abundance; it is surely just a matter of time before good fossil-bearing rocks are found.

## The Geological Timescale

Dinosaurs are found only in the so-called Mesozoic Era. To explain what the Mesozoic Era was in terms of Earth history we have illustrated here the Geological Timescale.

It has been estimated that the Earth is about 4,600 million years old. The oldest rocks so far discovered are about 3,600 million years old; however, there must have been a considerable period of time before this when the hot molten Earth cooled sufficiently for a crust of rocks to form. By dating meteorites which were probably formed at the same time as the rest of our Solar System, a generally agreed upon age of the Earth of 4,600 million years has been arrived at.

Precise dating of rocks is obviously of great importance to palaeontologists because it tells them the age of the fossilised organisms. Herein lies a major problem. There are only two ways of dating rocks, *comparative* dating and *absolute* dating.

Comparative dating, as the name implies, involves comparisons. In this case the characteristic fossils of one rock sample are compared with those of another area. If they are found to be broadly similar then it would seem a fair supposition that they were of similar age. By drawing comparisons between many rock and fossil types the *degree* of similarity can be assessed. For example fossil sequences from different areas may have overlapping ranges of fossils so that a comparative sequence of ages can be arrived at. Fine though these comparative series are, they give no idea of precisely how old the fossils are. For this absolute dating techniques are employed.

Absolute dating of rocks can be done by analysing radioactive isotopes. many elements have radioactive isotopes; these isotopes are known to *decay* at an established rate so that half of the isotope breaks down into a more stable element in a fixed time (the 'half-life'). Therefore if we know in what proportions the radioactive isotope and its stable version were first formed and can analyse their proportions at the present time, we can calculate how long the rocks have been formed. One of the best isotopes for dating rocks from the age of dinosaurs is Potassium 40; this decays to produce Argon 40. The half-life for this decay is about 1,300 million years. However the ratio of Potassium 40-Argon 40 can only be measured in volcanic lava. In order to arrive at agreed dates for the Mesozoic we have to rely on a combination of Potassium-Argon absolute dating of the occasional lava rock sample in dinosaur-bearing rocks, and comparative dating of fossil sequences in the rocks between these absolute dates. As a result of these two methods we have arrived at this generally agreed geological timescale illustrated here.

As can be seen from the timescale dinosaurs were not the oldest known fossils. The oldest forms of life so far discovered are tiny bacteria-like creatures whose remains have been preserved in rocks 3,100 million years old. More complicated forms of life appear about 2,500 million years later. Some of these fossils, form the so-called Ediacara shales of Australia, include sea-living worm-like animals, jellyfish and primitive corals. This vast expanse of time before the first complex organisms start to appear is known as the Precambrian ('before the Cambrian'). Beyond the Precambrian, the last 600 million years of life on Earth is termed the Phanerozoic ('visible life') which is in turn divided into three Eras: these are known as the Palaeozoic ('ancient life'), Mesozoic ('middle life'), and Cenozoic—or Kainozoic—('recent life').

The **Palaeozoic Era** (600-225 million years ago) marks the appearance of most of the major groups of animals and plants that we recognise today, such as shellfish, insects, spiders, fish, amphibians, reptiles, and most plant types except for the flowering plants.

The **Mesozoic Era** (225-64 million years ago) marks the arrival of several modern groups, notably the mammals and birds as well as flowering plants and many modern groups of insect. More importantly from our point of view, the Mesozoic marks the arrival of dinosaurs and their rise to dominance throughout this Era.

The Mesozoic Era is divided into three Periods: the Triassic Period (225-200 million years ago), the Jurassic Period (200-135 million years ago) and the Cretaceous Period (135-64 million years ago). At the start of the Triassic there were no dinosaurs. Mammal-like reptiles were particularly abundant; these, however, died out toward the end of the Triassic to be replaced by the dinosaurs. Many kinds of dinosaur appeared throughout the remaining 140 million years of the Jurassic and Cretaceous Periods but they all mysteriously became extinct at the end of the Cretaceous Period 64 million years ago.

The **Cenozoic (Kainozoic) Era** (64 million years ago up to the present) saw the change to animals and plants more typical of today. Mammals, birds, insects and flowering plants are everywhere and, quite importantly, so far as we are concerned the first humans appear. Early Man however did not appear on Earth until a *mere* 2-3 million years ago—long after the dinosaurs went extinct!

## Plate Tectonics

Ever since the first crude maps of the world were drawn, it must have seemed obvious that the continents could fit snugly together like the pieces of a gigantic jigsaw puzzle. For example the coastlines of North and South America seem remarkably similar to those of Europe and Africa on the other side of the Atlantic Ocean. No-one, however, took these observations to be particularly important because continents seem such firm and immovable things. Despite this, in 1915 Alfred Wegener proposed that the continents had in fact moved during the millions of years of Earth history: Europe and Africa had *drifted* apart from North and South America. He went on to show that if the continents were fitted back together, the rock types and mountain ranges often fitted together very neatly.

The notion of Continental Drift had one major problem in that it lacked a mechanism. What forces could have been responsible for

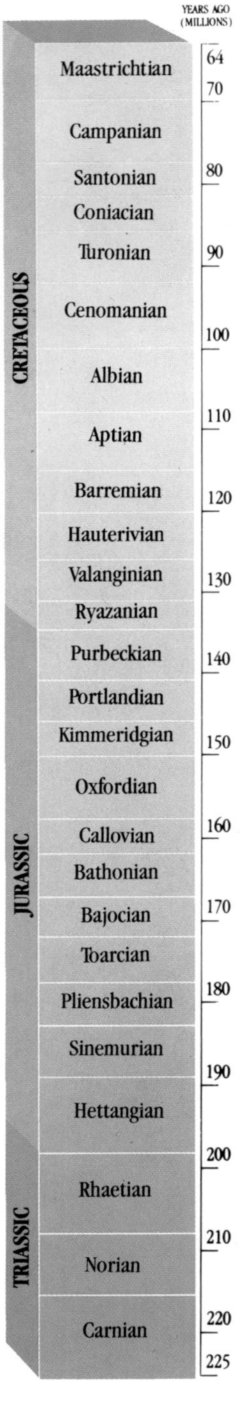

**The Geological Timescale (right and left)**
The spiral (right) is an attempt to compress the immense age of the Earth into a meaningful form. Each twist of the spiral covers 570 million years! Starting at the bottom, the formation of the Earth from a cloud of dust occurred about 4,500 million years ago. The Earth then cooled allowing a crust to form, and large amounts of gas and water vapour were expelled to form a primitive atmosphere of dense cloud and poisonous gas. By about 3,000 million years ago the crust and atmosphere were sufficiently stable for the first living organisms to appear—simple, single-celled bacteria. The next 2,400 million years were dominated by relatively simple forms of life, mainly bacteria that fed on simple chemicals, and others ('blue-greens') that were able to use sunlight to make oxygen. The blue-green algae formed huge reef-like structures, stromalites, in these ancient oceans. The first complex organisms appeared about 600 million years ago after which evolution proceeded more rapidly as can be seen from the annotated events marked on the diagram. The age of the dinosaurs (225-64 mya) is visible on the topmost layer, and this period is shown in expanded form in the time chart (left). The individual geological stages marked are scientifically-agreed time zones. This chart figures on the opening spread of each dinosaur family group later in the book, where the distribution in time of the dinosaur genera is duly indicated.

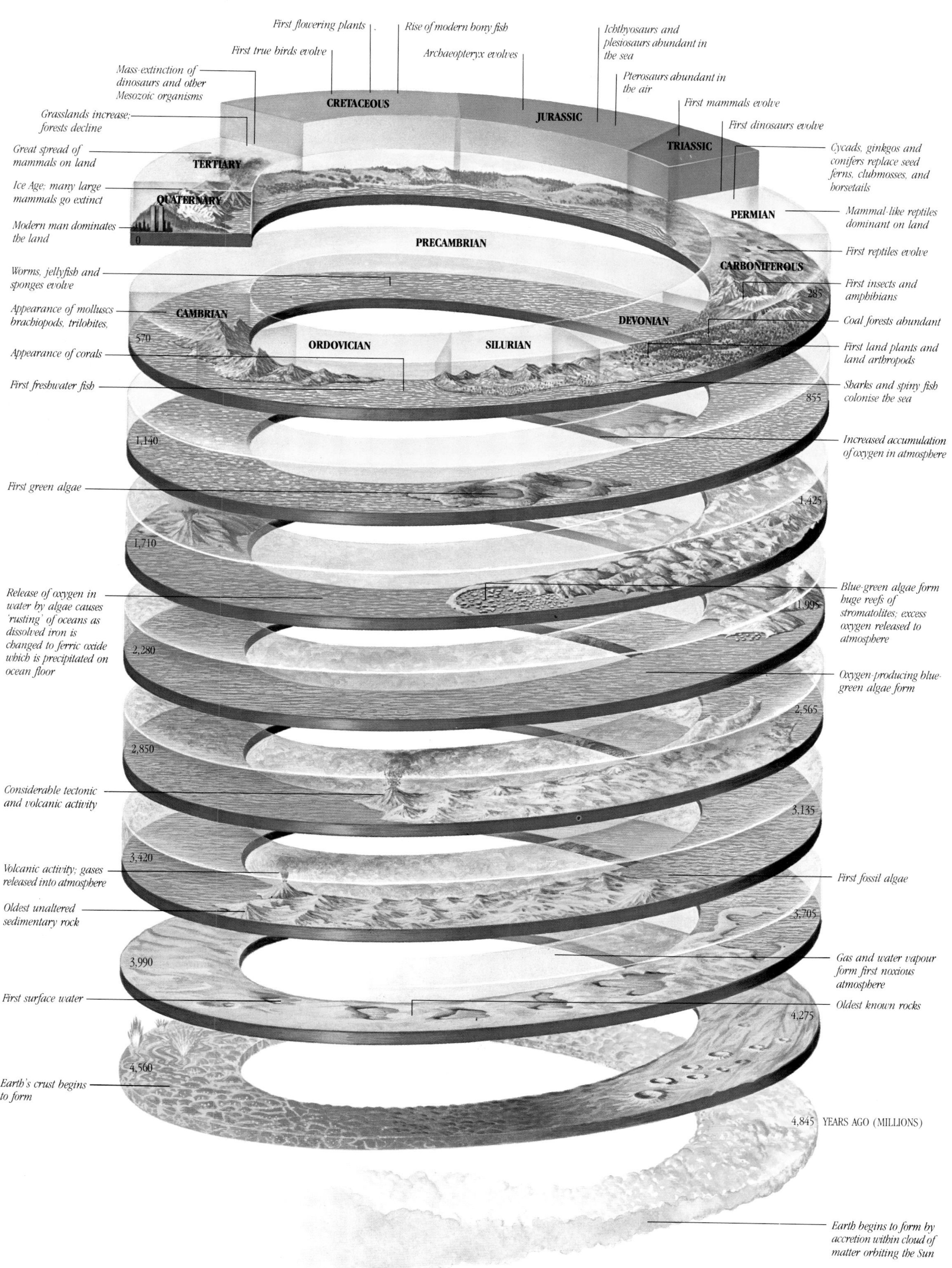
First flowering plants
Rise of modern bony fish
First true birds evolve
Archaeopteryx evolves
Ichthyosaurs and plesiosaurs abundant in the sea
Pterosaurs abundant in the air
Mass-extinction of dinosaurs and other Mesozoic organisms
CRETACEOUS
JURASSIC
First mammals evolve
First dinosaurs evolve
Grasslands increase; forests decline
TRIASSIC
Great spread of mammals on land
TERTIARY
Cycads, ginkgos and conifers replace seed ferns, clubmosses, and horsetails
Ice Age; many large mammals go extinct
QUATERNARY
PERMIAN
Mammal-like reptiles dominant on land
Modern man dominates the land
0
PRECAMBRIAN
First reptiles evolve
Worms, jellyfish and sponges evolve
CARBONIFEROUS
First insects and amphibians
285
Appearance of molluscs brachiopods, trilobites,
CAMBRIAN
DEVONIAN
Coal forests abundant
570
ORDOVICIAN
SILURIAN
First land plants and land arthropods
Appearance of corals
First freshwater fish
Sharks and spiny fish colonise the sea
855
1,140
Increased accumulation of oxygen in atmosphere
First green algae
1,425
1,710
Release of oxygen in water by algae causes 'rusting' of oceans as dissolved iron is changed to ferric oxide which is precipitated on ocean floor
Blue-green algae form huge reefs of stromatolites; excess oxygen released to atmosphere
1,995
2,280
Oxygen-producing blue-green algae form
2,565
2,850
Considerable tectonic and volcanic activity
3,135
3,420
Volcanic activity; gases released into atmosphere
First fossil algae
Oldest unaltered sedimentary rock
3,705
3,990
Gas and water vapour form first noxious atmosphere
First surface water
Oldest known rocks
4,275
4,560
Earth's crust begins to form
4,845 YEARS AGO (MILLIONS)
Earth begins to form by accretion within cloud of matter orbiting the Sun

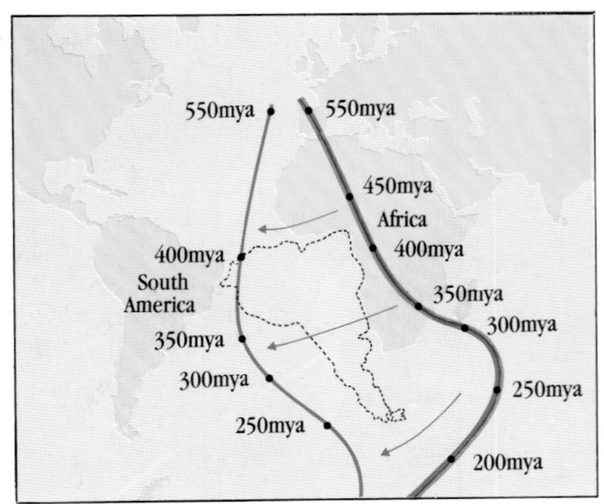


**Palaeomagnetism (left)**
When plotted, the polar bearings of South America and Africa follow curved paths. Between 550 and 270 million years ago these curves were identical: the continents were joined then.

**Sea-Floor Spreading (right)**
Molten rock in the mantle rises to form a mid-ocean ridge, pushing the sea-floor apart before descending at a 'trench' along a land margin.

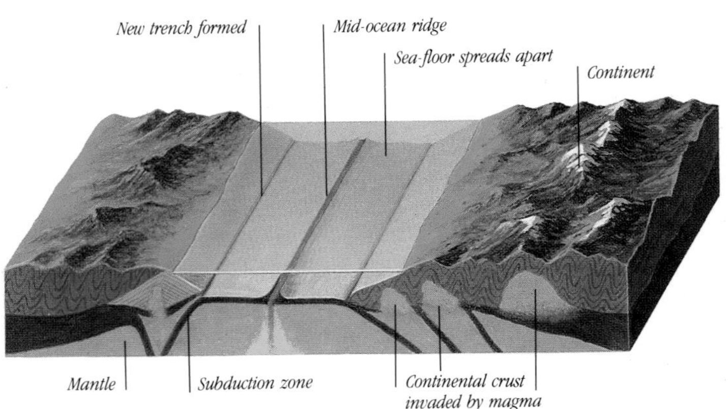


**Right:** Viewed from space, the Sinai peninsula, Red Sea, Egypt and Saudi Arabia show dramatically how areas of the Earth are splitting apart driven by convection in the the mantle. The Red Sea is the site of a new ocean which in several million years time may be as great as the Atlantic Ocean.

**Below:** This topographic relief map, produced from radar altimeter data from the Seasat satellite, lets us see the effects of sea-floor spreading. Note the deep ocean trenches off the coast of south-east Asia and the prominent mid-oceanic ridge in the Atlantic.

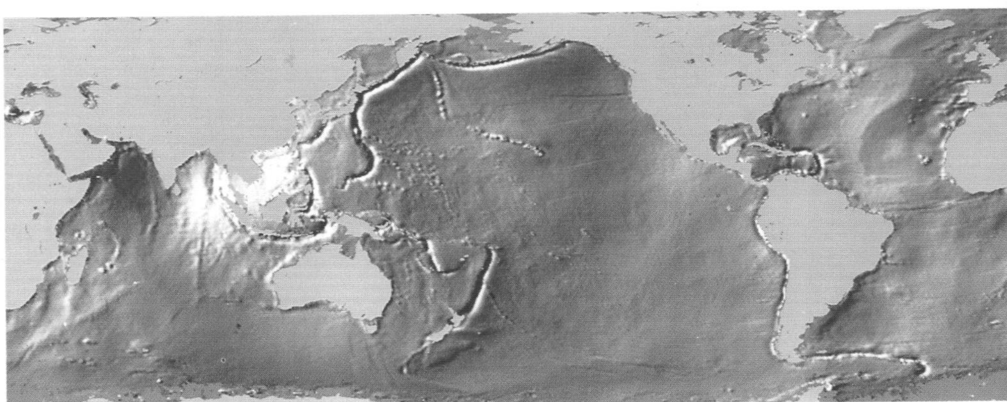

the movement of entire continents? At the time of Wegener no such forces were known, and so his theory was ignored or dismissed as preposterous. Since the early 1960s, however, much evidence has accumulated to support Wegener's ideas of Continental Drift. Notable among these are evidence of palaeomagnetism and sea-floor spreading.

Palaeomagnetism relies on the fact that some rocks contain magnetic iron particles. While these rocks are still molten, the particles point toward the magnetic pole just like compass needles. Once the rock has solidified, this magnetic bearing is preserved permanently. By studying such rocks the direction of the magnetic pole can be plotted. Obviously we would expect these 'fossil compasses' to point toward the present magnetic pole: but they do not! If we look at a series of differently aged rocks the 'compasses' point in a variety of directions which seem to plot the movement of the pole. In fact what it shows is the movement of the continent relative to the pole.

Sea-floor spreading observations have come from detailed studies of the sea-floor. These have shown that the oceans are divided up by a system of enormous underwater mountain ranges or 'ridges' and deep oceanic 'trenches'. These 'ridges' represent areas where new crust is being formed from molten rock rising from the centre of the Earth, while the 'trenches' are areas where the Earth's crust is slipping back downward into the molten mantle.

The great sheets of the Earth's crust (known as tectonic plates) are rather like gigantic, incredibly slow-moving (a few centimetres a year) conveyor belts; these carry the continents about on them. Incredible though it seems, the continents upon which we live are quite light compared with the Earth's crust and so are able to float along on their respective tectonic plates. The whole system appears to be powered by heat at the Earth's core; this causes the molten rock of the mantle to circulate, the movement of which in turn drags the Earth's crust along by friction.

The result of these remarkable revelations is that Wegener has now been proved to be quite correct, the continents have moved around quite considerably in geological time. This phenomenon can be demonstrated by looking at the positions of the continents during the Mesozoic Era.

In the Triassic Period the various continental blocks had, by pure chance, all bumped together to form the so-called supercontinent of Pangaea. Evidence for the existence of Pangaea comes from palaeomagnetic analysis and is strongly supported by the animals living on land in the Triassic. The strange, pig-like dicynodont *Lystrosaurus* is found in Australia, South Africa, India, China and Antarctica in the Triassic Period. Many other reptiles are very widely distributed across the continents; all of which points to their being able to disperse across dry land, rather than breast great oceans! Early dinosaurs seem also to be widely distributed at the end of the Triassic.

The Jurassic Period does not seem to have allowed the continents to remain in contact for very long. Pangaea began to split into several large fragments. The southern continents, South America, Africa, India, Antarctica and Australia began to pull away from Europe and North America with the formation of a narrow sea-way. Despite this there must have been significant contact between these areas because various Jurassic dinosaurs, diplodocids (page 80), brachiosaurids (page 86) and iguanodontids (page 110), are found to be practically the same in Africa and North America in late Jurassic times. In addition to this sea-barrier, another sea (Turgai Sea) separated Europe from Asia in middle Jurassic times; However, this was not before a significant fauna of dinosaurs had begun to develop in Asia.

By early Cretaceous times the Atlantic Ocean had begun to develop and the northern and southern continents were completely separated and India began to separate from Africa. At this time we start to find that some dinosaur groups seem to show a restricted distribution, particularly those that evolved in the early Cretaceous. For example the dromaeosaurids (page 56) are restricted to the northern continents, which is presumably where they evolved. Thus we begin to see how geological events can affect the evolutionary history of particular groups of animals.

By late Cretaceous times the continents were beginning to move into more familiar positions. Africa and South America had begun to drift apart and India was rafting across the Indian Ocean. The northern continents, while not greatly separated physically, were nevertheless very subdivided by oceans in such a way that western North America and eastern Asia were in contact across the Bering Straits, while Europe and eastern North America were still in

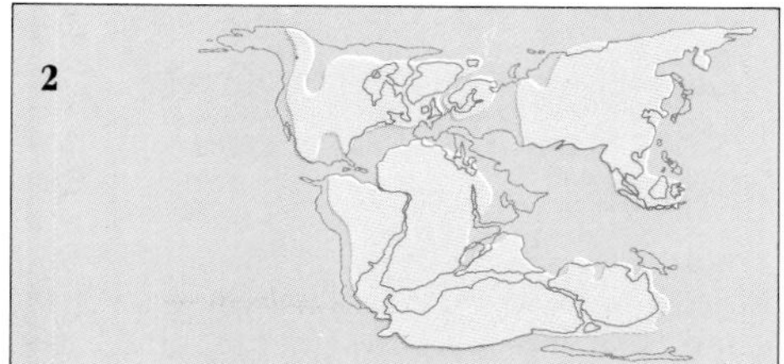


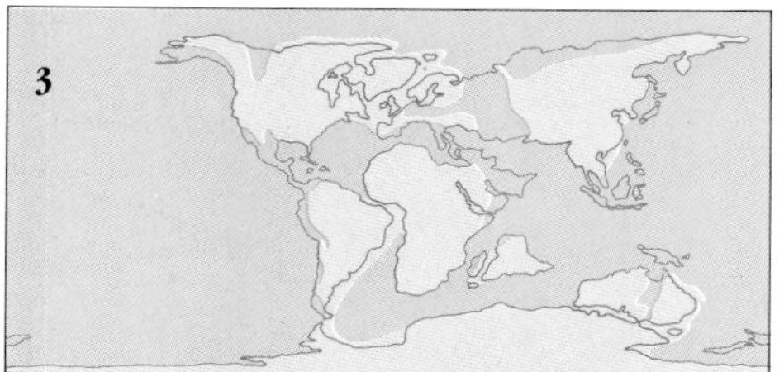


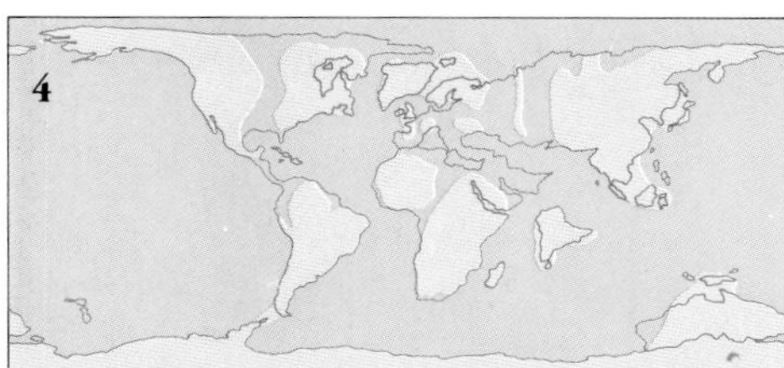


**Palaeogeographic Maps (left)**
The study of continental drift has made possible the production of a series of maps showing continental positions as they were in the Mesozoic Era. In the Triassic Period (**1**) all the continents were joined together to form the supercontinent of Pangaea. This began to split in the Jurassic Period (**2**); a narrow Atlantic Ocean formed and sea separated Europe and Asia. By the time of the early Cretaceous (**3**), the continents were further removed, and shallow seas started to divide the southern continents. By late Cretaceous times (**4**), South America and Africa had begun to separate, India was rafting away across the Indian Ocean and Europe and North America were moving apart. Seaways also divided Europe and Asia, *and* western from eastern North America. This resulted in some curiously isolated fauna.

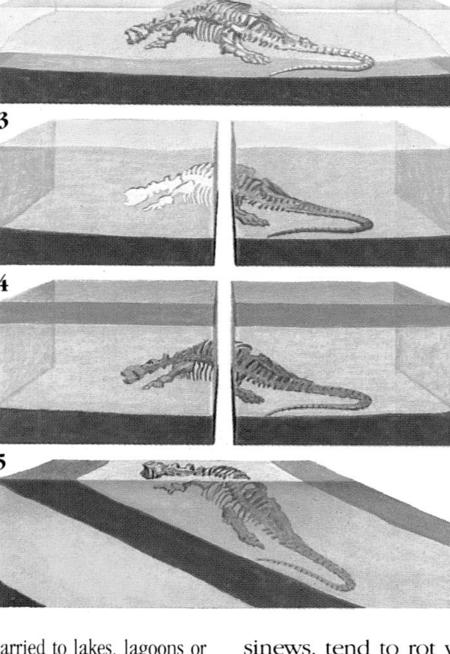


**Fossilisation (left)**
An essential requirement for the formation of a fossil is that after the organism dies (**1**) and the soft tissue rot away leaving (in this example) the bony skeleton, it should be rapidly buried by sediment (**2**). This normally occurs in rivers, lakes, or the sea into which the carcasses of land-living animals may be washed. Two processes may then occur (**3**). The organic material in the bones decays and may be replaced by minerals from water percolating through the sedimentary rocks: permineralisation (**left**). The bony structure may even be replaced entirely by minerals: petrification. Alternatively the bones may dissolve leaving a hollow mould (**right**) which may be filled later by minerals which form a solid replica of the bone: a natural cast (**4 right**). Land movements and erosion may then lead to exposure of the fossil (**5**).

**Sedimentation (below)**
Weathering of upland areas is responsible for the formation of sedimentary rocks. Wind, water, rain and ice action erode exposed rock; the silt is carried to lakes, lagoons or deltas where it may be deposited in layers. Land-living animals are most likely to be buried and fossilised in such areas.

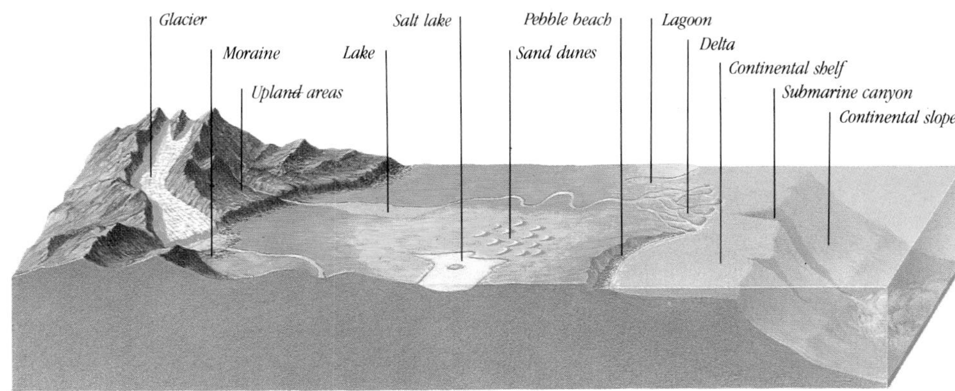


contact with each other. We find that dinosaur distributions reflect these connections with, for example, ankylosaurids (page 164), ceratopians (page 128) and advanced hadrosaurids (page 122) evolving in Asia and western North America, while nodosaurids (page 160), iguanodontids (page 110) and primitive hadrosaurids (page 116) persist in Europe and eastern North America.

The history of the continents and their geographic positions can thus be seen to play an important part in the evolutionary history of the dinosaurs. Without our knowledge of plate tectonics and continental drift some of their distribution would be very difficult to explain.

## Fossilisation

The word fossil used to mean literally *anything* that was dug out of the ground. Nowadays its meaning has become more restricted to the preserved traces or remains of ancient organisms.

The essential requirement for fossilisation is that the organism (be it plant or animal) or evidence of its activities (such as footprints, droppings, gnawings, pollen grains etc.) should be covered in sediment of some kind before scavenging animals or the natural processes of erosion or decay completely destroy them. Rapid burial of this kind is most likely to occur in the sea where a continuous rain of debris (silt and fine sands) falls on to the sea floor. As a result there is a very strong bias in the Fossil Record toward sea creatures. Land-dwelling creatures such as the dinosaurs also get preserved as fossils when their carcasses are washed into lakes or into the sea and buried; this is a rather chancy affair, yet despite this fossilised dinosaur remains are in some cases (as will be seen later) surprisingly abundant. Some have even been preserved in sand-dunes.

It is usual for only the hard parts, shells, teeth and bones, to be preserved as fossils since these are the things that are most resistant to decay. Soft tissues, such as skin, muscles and sinews, tend to rot very quickly. However, on rare occasions even these may be fossilised. For example soft-bodied jellyfish and worms have been preserved as imprints on rocks that are 530 million years old (the Burgess Shales of British Columbia). These remarkable fossils were apparently formed as a result of mud-slides from underwater cliffs which buried animals living on the sea-floor – such preservation is extremely rare.

Hard parts such as bones and teeth can be preserved in a number of ways. Teeth are particularly resistant and are frequently preserved in their original state. Most other hard parts are changed to a greater or lesser extent. Bones have a considerable amount of organic material in them; when buried the organic material (mostly collagen) decays or is dissolved away. Relatively recent fossil bones are often found in this state and are very light and crumbly. In older fossils the spaces around the bone crystals are filled with new minerals from water seeping through the rocks. These can be minerals such as silica, calcite or iron pyrites. This process of mineral replacement is known as permineralisation and makes the bones much harder and heavier.

On occasions, the original mineral structure of the bone can be replaced by the minerals in the percolating ground waters. The bone is then said to have been petrified or turned to stone. Permineralised *and* petrified bones retain their original structure as can be seen if examined microscopically. This presumably reflects the fact that the percolating minerals replace the bone minerals virtually molecule for molecule.

Sometimes the original bone material may be completely dissolved by the percolating minerals, leaving a hollow mould. Although a mould is not part of the original animal, it is nevertheless still a fossil because it tells us a great deal about the original animal. Sometimes moulds such as this are filled at a later date by another mineral. The mineral will then take on the form of the original object and it will again become a petrified fossil. Fossils formed in this way are known as natural casts.

## Trace Fossils

In addition to these conventional types of fossil there is also a group of fossils known as trace fossils. Trace fossils are those that reveal the former presence and activities of organisms, but not the organisms themselves. Trace fossils range from fossilised dung (*coprolites*) to gnawings, burrows and tubes. Some of the most abundant trace fossils are footprints and trackways, especially those of dinosaurs. In fact an entire sub-branch of palaeontology known as ichnology ('the study of footprints') has arisen solely devoted to the interpretation of fossilised footprints and tracks. Despite the fact that the makers of the trackways can never be identified with certainty, nevertheless a great deal can be learned from footprints. For example: whether it was a dinosaur that made them, whether they were four-footed (quadrupedal) or two-footed (bipedal), how heavy they were, how fast they were moving, whether they were showing herding behaviour, etc.

## Discoveries and Excavations

Palaeontology, like other sciences, is based upon factual information; in this case, the raw material for these facts are the fossils themselves. The science of palaeontology today, however, is not limited by the rate of discovery of new fossil specimens. As will be made obvious in Chapter 2 a considerable amount of scientific work can be done on material that was discovered a long time ago. Techniques of fossil preparation have improved immeasurably over the last half century. Thus specimens studied by palaeontologists in the 1920s or earlier can be further prepared to reveal new and important facts about the structure of dinosaurs. Scientific approaches have also changed over the years. Different sorts of investigatory approaches are used and new interpretations can result from examining old materials.

However interesting it might be to re-study old material, there is always a need for new or better preserved specimens to add to our gradually accumulated picture of the history of life on our planet. New fossil material comes from a wide range of sources from accidental discoveries to the activities of highly organised fossil collecting expeditions.

## Where To Look

Dinosaur fossils are obviously not just found anywhere. In order to understand where to look, we need to remember how and where fossils are most likely to form in the first place. If we know this then we should be able to predict where to look.

Dinosaurs were land-living creatures for the most part and the majority of these would be scavenged and their remains completely destroyed when they died. Events such as burial in volcanic ash (as at Pompeii) or sand dunes would preserve their remains, but are exceedingly rare. Occasionally animals may have died in or near water where their remains might be washed down-stream to be buried in lake sediments – some may even get washed out to sea before burial. In these sediments their remains are likely to become fossilised in the ways described.

So we should look in *sedimentary* rocks: clays, mudstones, limestones and sandstones; and preferably those that were deposited in rivers and lakes if we are looking for land-living animals. It is also important to look in rocks of the right age; it is obviously no use looking for dinosaurs in rocks of Permian age. Finally it is necessary to find *exposures* of sedimentary rock. It is again of no use if the sedimentary rocks that contain dinosaurs are buried thousands of feet beneath the ground. We are helped here in a number of ways. Erosion by wind and rain wears away rock exposing lower layers; this process is assisted by earth movements. Tectonic activity results in the Earth's crust being folded and buckled in places, bringing deep layers of rock to the surface. Rivers cut into rocks exposing layer upon layer of earlier rocks; a similar thing is found on the sea-shore, where wave action batters and erodes the cliffs at a very rapid rate continually exposing new rocks. Man is also a fairly effective agent in rock exposure. Quarrying, cutting roads, railway lines and foundations for buildings all expose new rocks.

So, in order to find fossilised dinosaurs we need to be well-prepared in advance. It is necessary to know where to find sedimentary rocks of the right type (lake or river sediments), the right age (Mesozoic), and where they are exposed and preferably being eroded. All this information can be provided by the detailed work of geologists who have been involved for the last two centuries in studying and mapping the distribution of rock types all over the World.

## Expeditions and Discoveries

All the back-up information indicated above can be used by palaeontologists and geologists in order to plan expeditions to find dinosaurs. Nowadays many expeditions tend to be large, expensive, often multinational projects involving teams of scientists. As such they require a great

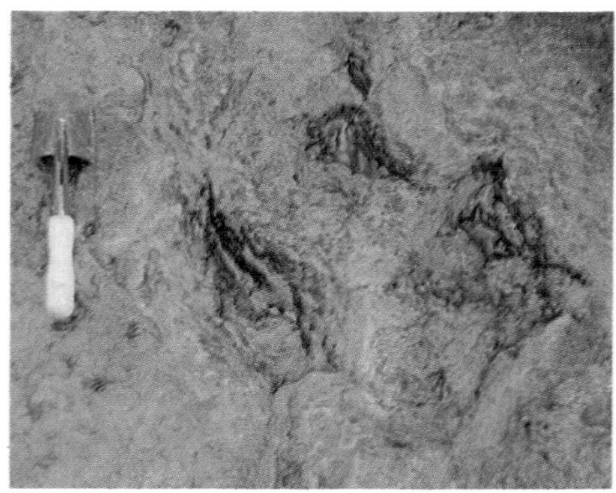

**Above:** We see clearly here the impression of a three-toed foot preserved in a rock. As can be appreciated from the size of the trowel, it is quite large and was probably made by *Iguanodon*, remains of which have been found in these rocks.

**Right:** Moving *Iguanodon* footprints can be quite a strenuous activity! This one literally fell out of the cliffs on the Isle of Wight, but such finds have to be collected quickly before they are pounded up by the action of the waves.

deal of co-operation, not only among the scientists but also between the relevant Governments of the countries involved. Providing that these potential difficulties are successfully overcome then the 'nitty gritty' of prospecting and collecting can proceed.

In the 'field' likely exposures of rock are visited by teams of people who spend their time scouring the rocky outcrops for slivers of fossil bone or other tell-tale signs. This can be very disheartening—days can go by with nothing being found; this is partly because it takes some time to get your 'eye in'—that is to become able to recognise those tell-tale signs of fossil fragments.

One fairly standard way of looking for fossils is to walk along the bottom of exposures, cliffs or valleys, looking for bits of bone. If some are found then it is a matter of scrambling up the exposures to see where they have come from; with luck this may lead to the discovery of a skeleton or part of a skeleton weathering out of the cliff-face.

Expeditions are not the only way to discover fossils. The most frequent, and often the most rewarding discoveries are made either by accident, or as a result of the activities of a dedicated and highly skilled band of amateur collectors.

Accidental discoveries are made by all sorts of people: quarrymen and miners, people building roads or digging foundations, farmers, holiday makers, or geologists during normal geological survey work. Most of these finds are reported back to museums for identification. Some of these may eventually lead to rather dramatic discoveries (such as Bill Walker's 'super claw'—see page 61).

Some other fossil discoveries result from the activities of fossil-collecting enthusiasts who spend their free time walking across well-known exposures on the look-out for new fossils. These 'amateurs' ('amateur' is hardly an appropriate term for these able, highly skilled enthusiasts) are extremely valuable to museums all over the world because they act as their 'eyes' and 'ears': keeping them in touch with the new finds and alerting them to new exposures. After all, museums cannot afford to keep their own staff on duty in this way. In many ways this dedicated band is continuing the work of early enthusiasts such as the pioneering figure of Gideon Mantell (see page 10).

**Left:** Successful expeditions require a lot of planning. Seen here are the closing phases of the excavation of the *Coelophysis* bone-bed in New Mexico. Large slabs of rock bearing the bones of this dinosaur have been exposed, lifted, coated in plaster-of-Paris, and are now being hauled away for the trip to the laboratory.

**Above:** Excavation of large specimens is complicated and laborious. Cyril Walker (BMNH) is here digging away the rock beneath a large ichthyosaur skeleton. Once this stage is completed, sections of the upper surface can be plastered, then the pillars broken and the fossil inverted so the underside can be plastered in turn.

**Below:** This old barracks on the upper University of Utah campus—the now defunct 'bone barn'—was the first home of the extensive collection of bones from the Cleveland-Lloyd Quarry. Often it is problems such as the storage of large numbers of fossils that can cause the biggest headaches after especially rich discoveries.

## Excavation Techniques

Having located a fossil skeleton the next problem is how to remove it without damage so that it can be prepared under laboratory conditions. The techniques adopted vary depending upon the size of the fossil. Small fossils are relatively easy to excavate. The important point to remember is not to get carried away in the excitement of your discovery. Ideally it should be labelled and then photographed in position in the rock, or at least careful notes and drawings made of its position; these may be of enormous value to palaeontologists at a later date (and also to you if some pieces become detached later).

Having recorded the position of the bone (or bones), the fossil is then prepared for removal. Usually some treatment is needed before it can be lifted. Often the remains are cracked or crumbly and need to be hardened using quick-setting resins or glues that can be painted or sprayed on. The fossils can then be either wrapped in paper and stored in sample bags, or if the bones are fragile protected in plaster or polyurethane foam jackets, so that they can be moved in relative safety.

Large fossils, such as dinosaur skeletons, are much more laborious to excavate. Quite often only a part of the skeleton is exposed on a cliff-face. To expose the skeleton completely, the 'overburden'—the rock lying above it—has first to be removed using picks, shovels and sometimes power hammers or even explosives! The overburden is removed to about 2-3in (5-8cm) above the level of the fossil and then fine hand-held tools are used to expose the upper surface of the skeleton. When fully exposed, the skeleton is then photographed and sketched and carefully labelled so that all of its parts can be clearly identified. The skeleton, since it cannot be lifted whole, is then carefully divided into blocks of manageable size each of which is plastered, re-labelled for identification back in the laboratory, and then removed.

## Laboratory Preparation

The arrival in the museum laboratory of new specimens collected on expeditions marks the next phase of work. This involves careful removal of protective packaging and then painstaking preparation of the fossils from the rock so that detailed study can begin. Various techniques are used to remove the rock ranging from fine hand-held needles, to electrically powered vibropens, small pneumatic chisels or ultrasonic probes, or in some cases chemical techniques such as acid treatment to dissolve the encrusting sediments.

In some cases this treatment can produce magnificent specimens that resemble the freshly prepared skeletons of living animals rather than those of 100-million-year-old fossils.

## Classification

There are enormously large numbers of organisms living in the world today and countless millions have lived in the past. Faced with such a bewildering diversity of life we might be tempted to throw up our hands in horror and say it is just impossible to understand either the nature of life or the reasons why there should be such diversity in Nature. This is not the case, however. Many thousands of biologists devote their lives to this very set of problems; surely they cannot all be wrong!

One of the great advances in our attempt to understand Nature has come from the activities of people interested in classification; this is the art of listing or cataloguing organisms. There are a variety of ways in which this can be done. For example they could be catalogued in the order in which they were discovered, or perhaps by size. Such lists, however, would not tell us anything about the qualities of the individual organisms. In practice, these sorts of systems have not been adopted by biologists for this very reason. Instead a system was developed through the work of people such as Carolus von Linné or Linnaeus (in the middle of the eighteenth century) which relied upon measuring the degree of resemblance between different organisms. A careful and detailed survey of living organisms revealed that certain of them shared features in common which could be used to cluster them together into related sets or groups.

To take a familiar example, a large group of animals possess a bony backbone (known as a vertebral column). This particular feature is found only in fish, amphibians, reptiles, mammals and birds and allows them to be grouped together and called 'vertebrates'. In similar fashion if we look within the vertebrates we find that amphibians, reptiles, mammals and birds have four limbs (while the fish have fins) and can be grouped together as 'tetrapods' (four-footed vertebrates). Furthermore if we look within the tetrapods, we find that reptiles, mammals and birds all bear young that develop inside an egg-membrane known as the amnion, while the amphibians do not. The former types are therefore grouped together as 'Amniotes'. All organisms can be grouped together into larger or smaller sets on the basis of the shared possession of certain characters. Looking at as many organisms as possible it is possible to build up, using this classificatory procedure, an hierarchical tree-like picture of the relationships of all organisms. The demonstration of this rather 'organised' pattern of relationships in nature by Linnaeus in the 1750s gave rise to the belief that God had created this pattern of life. Therefore, by studying this 'tree of life' and clarifying any ambiguities, philosophers believed that they might get closer to an understanding of the mind of God.

These views were challenged on many occasions by various scientists in subsequent years, but with little effect until 1858-59 when Charles Darwin published his theory of evolution through natural selection. This flew in the face of orthodox religious beliefs in that it implied that organisms had not been placed on Earth in one divine act of Creation, but had gradually changed or evolved over an immense period of time through a mechanism called 'Natural Selection' (survival of the fittest).

Natural selection is a mechanism which relies on a number of factors. First, all organisms in a species tend to vary — no two human beings are identical (apart from rare identical twins of course). Given this variation within a species, then it is likely that under certain (perhaps harsh) environmental conditions some individuals will by chance possess features that allow them to survive better than others. Given long enough under these conditions, and provided that the favourable traits are inherited by their offspring, the organisms in the population of this species may exhibit a change in character (evolve): this is because surviving organisms will tend to be those with the favourable traits. Thus an environmental change can be seen to be one way of introducing a change in the characteristics of a species. Given that this seems to be a not unreasonable set of circumstances, effects such as this could result in change (or evolution) within a species in a few generations (think, for instance, of the resistance that some bacteria have evolved to antibiotics, or rats to the poison warfarin). If we then extrapolate from these small changes that have taken place in a short space of time to the millions of years that have elapsed since the origin of life (about 3,100 million years), then the possibility of dramatic changes in the form of organisms seems very reasonable.

**Above:** Charles Darwin's theory of evolution (1858-9) envisaged natural selection as a mechanism for evolutionary change. This proposition allowed the tree of life to be interpreted as a genealogical tree instead.

Thus, with the advent of Darwin, the tree of life became, instead of just an interesting philosophical problem, a potential genealogy — literally the family tree of life. The prospect then arises of our being able to understand the pattern revealed in nature through the hierarchical classificatory scheme as a result of the evolution of one group from another in the course of time.

Up to this point, there had been no need to consider fossil organisms at all because the pattern of the classificatory tree was viewed as a static thing created by God in his infinite wisdom. However, if the tree of life could have been arrived at as a result of evolutionary events in the distant past, fossil organisms may provide clues to the process of evolution; they may even catch evolution 'in the act'.

Thus classification, often regarded as a dry and exceedingly boring branch of biology, can be seen to be an activity that is of considerable value to all those who are interested in the nature of the relationships between organisms. The following pages are devoted to the classification of the reptiles in general and the dinosaurs in particular.

## The Reptile Family Tree

As was mentioned earlier, the reptiles are classified along with the mammals and birds as Amniotes because their young develop within the so-called amniotic membrane. Excellent though this characteristic is if we consider living tetrapods, it is practically useless when it comes to distinguishing fossil amniotes from amphibians. Soft anatomical features like egg-membranes are simply not fossilised. As a result a series of additional characters has to be agreed upon in order to distinguish fossil amphibians and reptiles. For example, some fossil amphibians have been preserved with gilled larvae or sensory grooves on the skull; both of these features are only found in amphibian tetrapods. Failing these, then a range of skeletal characters are used but these are open to much disagreement among palaeontologists.

At the present time there is general agreement that one of the earliest known reptiles was *Hylonomus* from the very earliest part of the late Carboniferous Period. This was a small (12in, 30cm long) lizard-like creature which probably fed on insects which it crunched up between the spiky teeth in its jaw. It also acts as an excellent starting point for the family tree of reptiles.

There are about 16 Orders of reptile currently recognised of which only four have survived to the present day (the crocodiles, lizards and snakes, *Sphenodon,* and turtles and tortoises). The sixteen Orders are divided into four major groupings or subclasses: the anapsids, synapsids, euryapsids and diapsids (see illustration). These subclasses are recognised by the pattern of openings that is developed at the back of the head, immediately behind the eye cavity.

**Anapsids** are generally regarded as the most primitive of reptiles, and have no opening in the skull roof at all. This is the condition seen in *Hylonomus* and also with a little modification in the skulls of turtles and tortoises, the only living representatives of this group. The earliest turtles date back to the late Triassic since when they have changed little. It would appear that the heavily armoured shell provided an exceptionally safe haven from all predators but rather hampered their chances of evolving into anything more exotic.

The **synapsids** or mammal-like reptiles are all extinct. They have skulls with a single opening relatively low down on the side of the skull. The earliest members of this group appear in the late Carboniferous as lizard-like creatures very similar to the anapsid *Hylonomus.* Synapsids reached their heyday in the late Permian and early Triassic times when they were by far the most abundant of terrestrial vertebrates. Towards the end of the Triassic they declined in number and variety becoming extinct at the close of that Period.

**Euryapsids** are characterised by having a single opening on the side of the skull, but higher in position than in the synapsid condition. The least satisfactory subclass, many palaeontologists believe that they are an unnatural group of reptiles that just happen to share this euryapsid condition by chance, rather than because of more fundamental genealogical reasons. Euryapsids are all marine reptiles and include the plesiosaurs, ichthyosaurs, placodonts and nothosaurs of the Mesozoic Era.

The **diapsids** have a pair of openings behind the skull and are one of the most diverse reptile groups. Again the earliest diapsid reptiles are known from the late Carboniferous Period. Diapsids include not only the highly successful

**The Reptile Family Tree (right)**
Reptiles can be subdivided into four major groups on the basis of the pattern of openings in the back of the skull. These are anapsids, synapsids, diapsids and euryapsids (see drawings below and main headings on chart). Anapsids seem to be the most primitive types of reptile since they have no special skull openings and appear earliest in the fossil record. *Hylonomus* is one of the earliest definite reptiles; it comes from late Carboniferous deposits of Nova Scotia. The only surviving anapsids are the turtles and tortoises. Synapsids have an impressive fossil record. The earliest forms, pelycosaurs, appeared in the late Carboniferous and are followed by the therapsids and cynodonts of the Permian and Triassic. Synapsid reptiles went extinct in the late Triassic or early Jurassic, but gave rise to the earliest mammals which survived the reign of the dinosaurs and then evolved rapidly. Diapsids can be divided into two groups: lepidosaurs (lizards and snakes) and archosaurs (crocodiles, dinosaurs and their kin). The archosaurs date back to the late Permian proterosuchians which were followed by the late Triassic phytosaurs and true crocodiles. The Triassic was the time of origin of all major archosaur groups from the thecodontians to the aerial pterosaurs and the dinosaurs (for whose family tree see page 23). Note that the birds are here related to theropod dinosaurs. Euryapsids are an uncertain group including the placodonts, ichthyosaurs, and plesiosaurs, all of which were swimming forms.

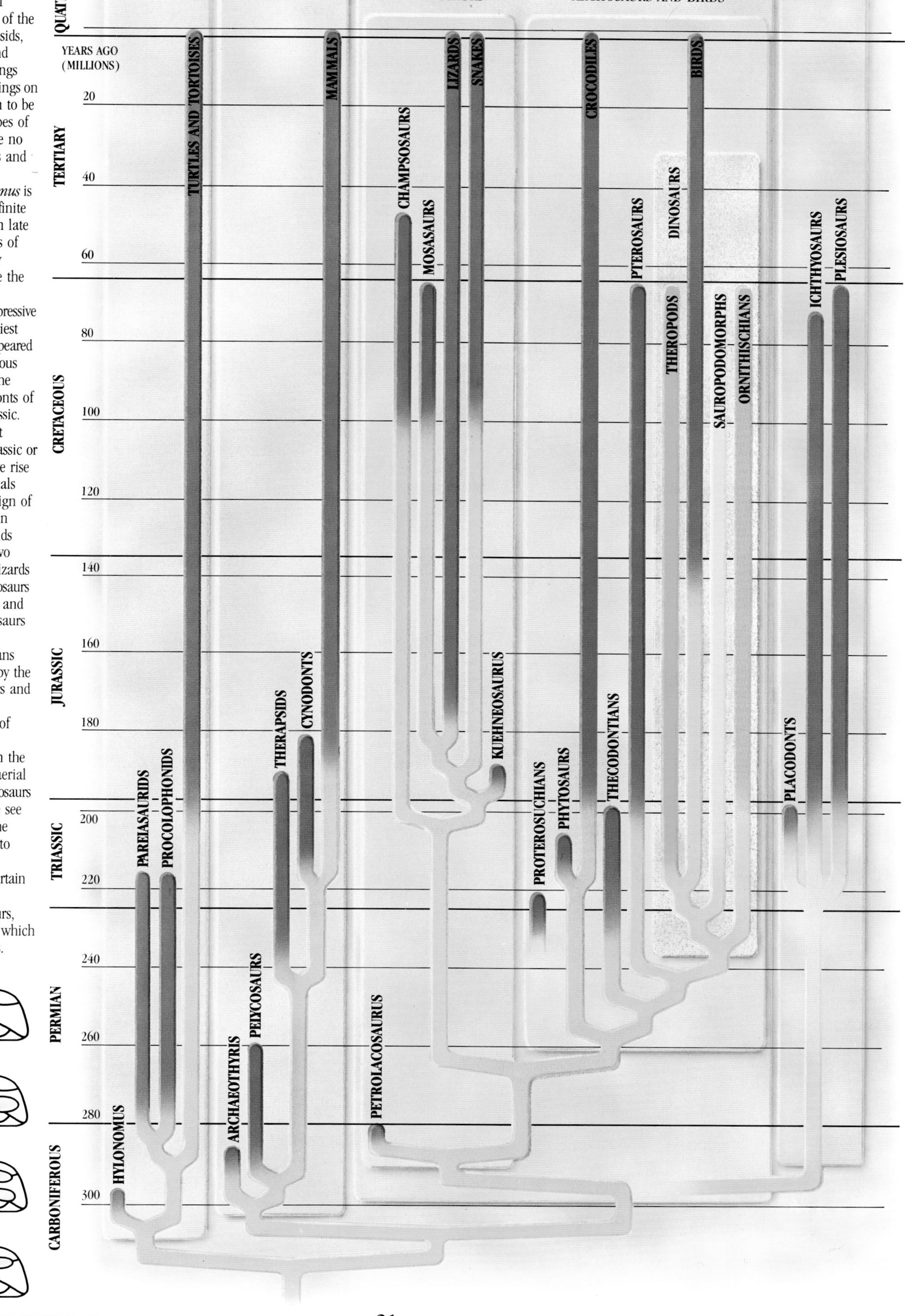

living forms, the lizards and snakes, but also the archaic lizard-like *Sphenodon* from New Zealand and the other great group the archosaurs ('ruling reptiles') represented today by the crocodiles and in the past by among others, the dinosaurs.

The archosaurs, dinosaurs on land and pterosaurs in the air, were particularly abundant and diverse during the Mesozoic Era, but suffered a major setback in the late Cretaceous when most non-crocodilian archosaurs went extinct. Since the end of the Cretaceous, the lizards and snakes have diversified and are now by far the most successful group of reptiles.

## Skull Openings

The characteristic development of openings in the rear part of the skulls of reptiles was for a long time explained as providing areas for the muscles of the jaws to bulge when they contracted. Although this is indeed the case in living reptiles, it seems unlikely that this was the reason for their development in early anapsid reptiles. Tom Frazzetta provided an interesting alternative explanation that has been accepted by most. The openings are regarded as developing in order to lighten the skull to make it more flexible and manoeuvrable, and to provide areas for much more effective muscle attachment around the edges of the holes. So rather paradoxically the appearance of holes in the skull roof probably strengthened rather than weakened the bite of these reptiles!

## The Dinosaur Family Tree

Dinosaurs, as mentioned above, are members of the archosaur group of reptiles; this includes the primitive thecodontians of the Permian and Triassic as well as the pterosaurs, crocodiles and dinosaurs which appear to have evolved from thecodontians. The archosaurs are recognised as such because they share several distinctive features that are not found in other diapsids. For example, the skull has, in addition to the 'diapsid' skull openings, another large triangular opening in front of the eye cavity and an opening in the side of the lower jaw as well. Archosaurs also tend to have rows of bony armour running down the middle of the back and, more often than not, have large, powerful back legs for running.

Turning to the dinosaurs, we can see from the family tree that dinosaurs are in fact divided into two distinct groups: the *Saurischia* ('reptile hipped') and the *Ornithischia* ('bird-hipped'). For many years after Richard Owen had christened the dinosaurs in 1841, they were regarded as a single group of reptiles. However, by 1887 enough material had been discovered to make it clear to Harry Govier Seeley that dinosaurs had either one type of hip arrangement or another, and so he coined these new names (see diagrams on page 9). The hip bones of saurischian dinosaurs do not differ very much from those of normal reptiles. Ornithischians by contrast have an unusual arrangement of hip bones whereby the pubis, which points forward and downward in reptiles, has swung backward to lie against the ischium. Curiously although this is the pattern seen in some early ornithischians, in later ornithischians (such as hadrosaurids or ceratopians) the pubis seems to develop a new forwardly-directed process; it is almost as if it were replacing the one that it had originally lost.

In addition to this very obvious difference in the structure of the pelvis, the two dinosaur groups differ in other ways. Notably the ornithischians are all herbivorous dinosaurs, while saurischians are represented by both carnivorous and herbivorous types. Also the ornithischians are 'peculiar' in that unlike any other animal they have a predentary bone, a crescent-shaped piece of bone at the front of the lower jaw. The predentary has a sharp, toothless edge and was undoubtedly covered in horn (like a turtle's beak). Ornithischians are also unusual in that they have bony ligaments that form a trellis-like arrangement across the spines of the back.

The family tree indicates that in addition to this basic division into saurischians and ornithischians, dinosaurs can be further subdivided. The saurischians form a 'natural' division into mainly meat-eating theropods and plant-eating sauropodomorphs.

The theropods are nearly all bipedal animals which can be separated out into rather distinctive types. Just as today we recognise felids (cat-like meat-eating mammals), and canids (dog-like meat-eaters) and several other categories such as bears and weasels, so it is with the theropods. On the one hand there are the gigantic tyrannosaurids and at the other extreme there are the slender 'coelurosaurs', or yet again the peculiar toothless ostrich dinosaurs (ornithomimosaurs). These various subdivisions are represented here.

Similarly the herbivorous sauropodomorphs can be divided into clearly distinctive groups such as medium-sized prosauropods and gigantic sauropods and then further into more closely-related groups or families such as the diplodocids and brachiosaurids.

**Above:** *Tyrannosaurus*' skull clearly shows the development of window-like openings in its sides characteristic of reptiles. These both lightened the head, and also improved the attachment areas for the jaw muscles, thereby increasing the power of the bite.

**Below:** This photograph shows the underside of the skull of one of the *Iguanodon* skeletons that were discovered at Bernissart in Belgium. The predentary bone characteristic of all ornithischian dinosaurs can be seen at the tip of the lower jaw.

The ornithischians (despite their name) do not appear to be at all closely related to birds — in fact birds may be very closely related to saurischian theropods. The ornithischians are divided into several clearly distinct groups. There are the ornithopods ('bird feet') — a rather misleading name since their feet are not particularly bird-like! Most of these are bipedal though on occasions they were capable of walking on 'all-fours'. One rather distinctive group which may be close relatives of the ornithopods (there is some dispute about this) is the pachycephalosaurs ('thick headed reptiles').

There are also the stegosaurs ('plated reptiles'), the ankylosaurs ('fused [welded] reptiles') and the ceratopians ('horned faces'). Unlike the ornithopods these were predominantly quadrupedal (except for a few ceratopians).

The relationships between these dinosaur groups are indicated at right, and provide a framework for the cladograms that appear with the colour drawings of dinosaurs later in the book. (Cladograms are the family-tree-type drawings representing the possible evolutionary relationships of the dinosaurs).

## Notes on Nomenclature

A variety of different names is used here for the various groupings of dinosaurs. These are arrived at as follows. The scheme starts with the species which are recognisable animal 'types', to put it rather simply. An example of this is the domestic cat, the scientific name for which is *Felis catus*. This consists of its 'particular' or species name, *catus*, and its 'group' or generic name, *Felis*. The generic, or genus, name indicates that domestic cats are members of a group of species of cat-like animals, such as the wild cat (*Felis sylvestris*) and the African bush cat (*Felis lybica*). Furthermore this genus *Felis* shows strong similarities to other cat-like carnivores such as the lion (*Panthera leo*) and the cheetah (*Acinonyx jubatus*); these can all be grouped together in the family *Felidae*.

We group related species of dinosaurs together in just the same way. For example *Iguanodon bernissartensis* is a particular *species* of ornithopod dinosaur. Other species of the genus *Iguanodon* are known: *I. mantelli, I. fittoni, I. dawsoni*. The genus *Iguanodon* is very similar to others such as *Camptosaurus, Ouranosaurus* and *Probactrosaurus*, so these are grouped together in the family *Iguanodontidae* (see the iguanodontids page 110). Beyond this level of grouping, the iguanodontid family shares features in common with several other families such as the hadrosaurids, hypsilophodontids and fabrosaurids and they are in turn grouped together in the Order Ornithopoda.

Thus we have a fairly clear hierarchy:

**Order : Family : Genus : Species**

In this book we will concentrate on these particular groupings: the Theropoda, and Sauropodomorpha of the Order Saurischia, and the Ornithopoda, Ceratopia, 'Pachycephalosaurs', Stegosauria and Ankylosauria in the Order Ornithischia. Within each of these major groupings the dinosaurs have, where possible, been clustered together into families (e.g. tyrannosaurids, hypsilophodontids etc.). Unfortunately this has not been possible in all groups as precise classification is currently almost impossible, and in this case the informal terms placed in quotation marks such as 'coelurosaurs' and 'carnosaurs' have been used. The reasons for this are explained in the relevant sections.

**The Dinosaur Family Tree (right)**
The major division of the dinosaurs is into the *Saurischia* and *Ornithischia;* it is based primarily on the differences in hip structure (see page 9). The *Saurischia* are further subdivided into *Theropoda* and *Sauropodomorpha.* The theropods included a wide variety of carnivorous dinosaurs all of which were bipedal. They range from small fast runners such as 'coelurosaurs', to the larger 'carnosaurs' and tyrannosaurids of the late Cretaceous. The sauropodomorphs were the large plant-eating dinosaurs of the Mesozoic. They include the partially bipedal prosauropods of the late Triassic and early Jurassic, and the massive quadrupedal sauropods of the later Jurassic and Cretaceous.

The *Ornithischia* were all herbivores. They can be further divided into a series of distinctive types: *Ornithopoda, Ceratopia, 'Pachycephalosaurs', Stegosauria* and *Ankylosauria.* Ornithopods first appeared in the early Jurassic with small, lightly-built creatures such as the fabrosaurids. They culminate in the late Cretaceous hadrosaurids. Ceratopians were a late Cretaceous group characterised by peculiar parrot-like beaks, horns and frills. Pachycephalosaurs were a strange group with oddly thickened skulls, while the stegosaurs and ankylosaurs were distinctively armoured types.

As can be seen, the various family groups have been given distinctive coloured bands (keyed below). They correspond to the colour bands across the top of the pages in the dinosaur section. The length of the coloured 'fingers' in this diagram corresponds to the geological time range in which we have found members of the family group.

THEROPODA
SAUROPODOMORPHA
ORNITHOPODA
CERATOPIA
'PACHYCEPHALOSAURS'
STEGOSAURIA
ANKYLOSAURIA

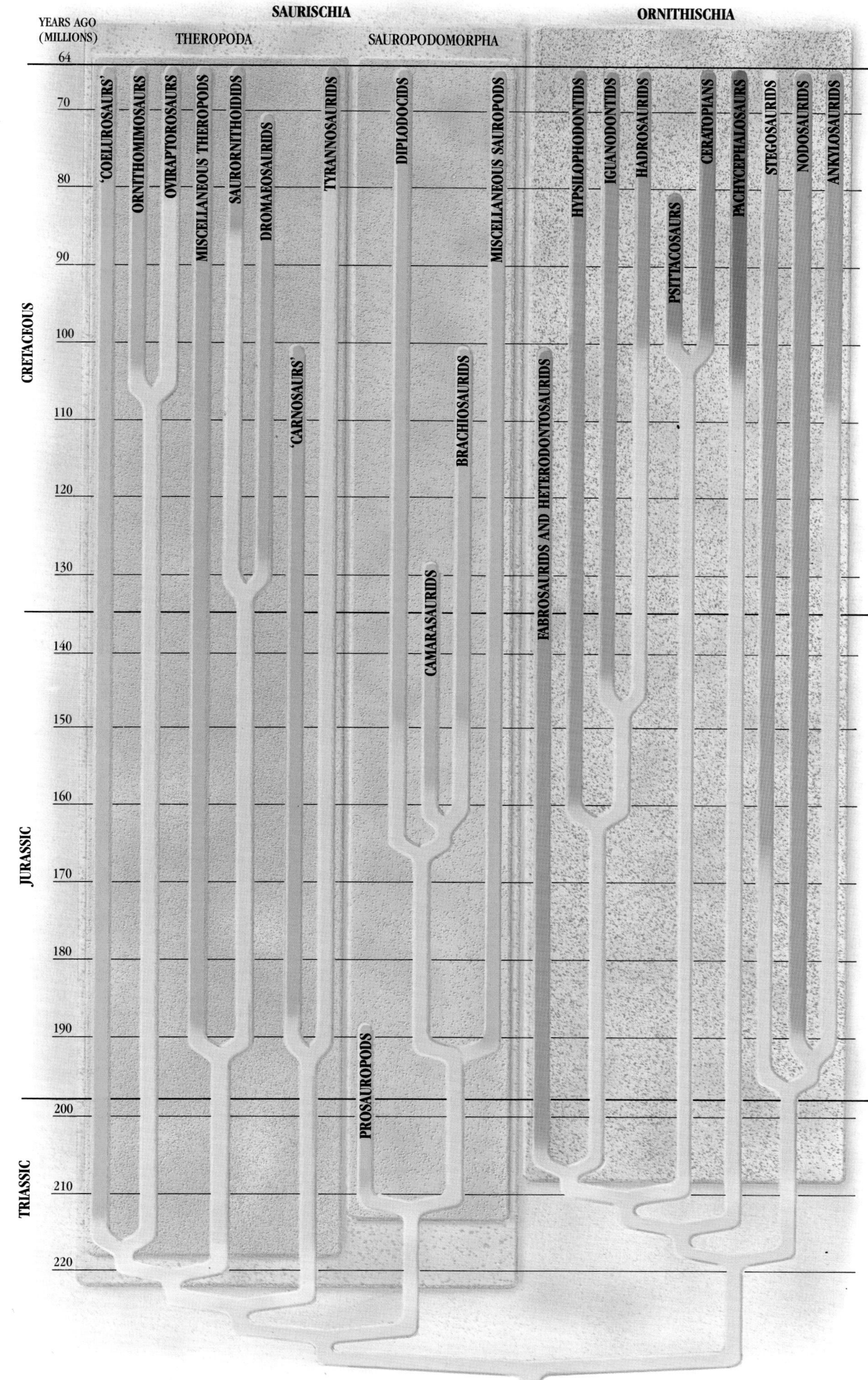

# TO STUDY A DINOSAUR

In this chapter we shall examine how a palaeontologist sets about studying a dinosaur, in this case *Iguanodon*, and show how research proceeds in a step-by-step way that involves several levels of intellectual activity in a fixed hierarchy. On the first level, the scientist analyses the fossils, taking into account the significance of where they were found, how they were excavated, and how they were prepared in the laboratory. By studying his laboratory specimens he can undertake the basic descriptive anatomy of the bones. From this stage, he can proceed to level two and make further anatomical deductions, such as how the skeleton might be put together and what this can tell us about the animal's musculature, its age, its nervous and blood systems, and likely methods of feeding and locomotion. Finally, the evidence from levels one and two is used to support higher level interpretations which may be concerned with how the dinosaur is related to other species, how this fits into the wider evolutionary framework, and what speculations we can make about the dinosaur as a living creature. So, let us proceed to study *Iguanodon*, starting at the first level outlined above.

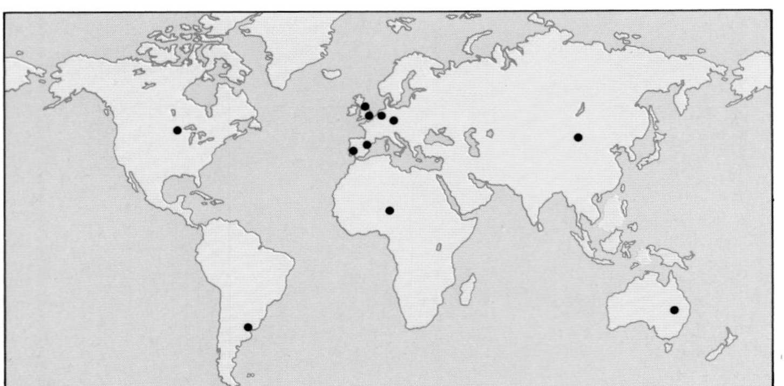

**Iguanodon Finds (left)**
The distribution of *Iguanodon* fossils has been reported to be very wide. However, on closer inspection many of the reports are found to be based on inadequate or misidentified specimens — for example, *Ouranosaurus* from Niger and *Muttaburrasaurus* from Australia. Definite *Iguanodon* remains are known in western Europe with possible (unsubstantiated) finds in Asia and North America.

## Where is Iguanodon found?

*Iguanodon* remains are typically found in rocks which are of the Lower Cretaceous Period (about 100 million years ago — mya). However, although rocks of this age are known from every continent in the world, those containing remains that are definitely of *Iguanodon* are only known across Europe and Asia (see map). There have been many other reports of *Iguanodon* in other countries, for example Spitzbergen in Norway, various parts of Africa, North America, South America and Australia, but these have been based on rather uncertain evidence such as footprint trackways (in Spitzbergen and South America) which are not diagnostic, or imperfect fragments of fossil bone, or teeth (in Africa). The evidence for *Iguanodon* in Australia was based on a partial skeleton of a dinosaur rather like *Iguanodon*, which on further inspection proved to be so different that it was given the name *Muttaburrasaurus* (see pages 110-111). The North American material is intriguing, but so far inconclusive. The material consists of a small piece of upper jaw with two teeth in it, and the end of a thigh bone (femur). Both of these specimens do indeed look rather like those of *Iguanodon*. Unfortunately there are several other known iguanodontids that also have such teeth and leg bones (*Camptosaurus* and *Ouranosaurus*) so at the moment we cannot be completely sure whether the North American specimens are of *Iguanodon*. This might seem to be an excessively cautious attitude to take to the evidence. However, as we shall see shortly, evidence such as the distribution of certain dinosaurs can be used to build up a much larger theoretical picture of the evolution and ecology of dinosaurs, and if the data base is not certain, this must be emphasized, otherwise it is possible that a completely inaccurate interpretation may be produced. The confusion resulting from this may take many years to resolve.

Looking in rather more detail at one of the areas where *Iguanodon* has been discovered, we can see that a considerable number of sites have yielded remains of this animal; these may range from isolated fragments of bone in some places, to partial or even complete skeletons in others. This locality data can reveal some interesting information. For example, if all the localities are plotted onto a geological map of the area, it can be seen that certain Wealden rocks, such as the Wadhurst Clay, the Tunbridge Wells Sand and the Weald Clay are the ones which tend to produce most of the fossils. We can, therefore, use this information to decide where to prospect for new fossil sites , and also take note of the range of time during which the fossils were laid down. For example, the Wadhurst Clay contains fossils of animals that lived much earlier than those of the Weald Clay, so we can ask whether there are any differences between the *Iguanodon* from these two periods which may reflect evolutionary changes.

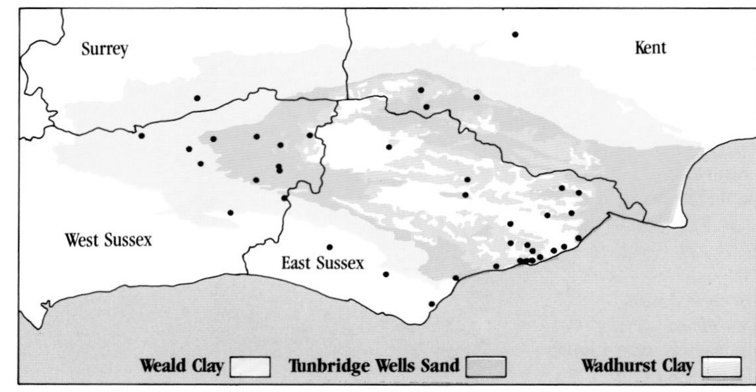


**The Wealden Area (right)**
Illustrated here is a map of the Wealden area of south east England which includes parts of Sussex, Surrey and Kent. Plotted on the map are the sites where *Iguanodon* remains have been discovered as well as the geological formation from which they came. *Iguanodon* remains occur mainly in the Weald Clay (yellow) and Wadhurst Clay area (red). Orange signifies Tunbridge Wells Sand.

In addition to the remains of *Iguanodon*, numerous other fossils have been discovered at these sites: other types of dinosaur, other reptiles, fish, even tiny shrew-like mammals and a vast array of plant remains. All of the latter information can be used to place *Iguanodon* into an ecological context. In attempting to reconstruct the environment in which *Iguanodon* might have lived, the geological nature of the deposits must be carefully reviewed to reassure ourselves that what we are seeing is in fact a true community of animals and plants, and not the chance accumulation of these remains which have been washed together from their natural habitats which may have been widely separated.

## What Fossils are They?

*Iguanodon* fossils come in a wide range of types which depend mainly upon the history and nature of the geological deposits in which they have been discovered. Wealden fossils were deposited in an area that we are confident was a fertile lowland plain across which many rivers and streams ran from upland areas to the north-east and south-west. At various times the land rose and fell, so that the Weald became periodically more marshy or lake-like. The dinosaurs living in the surrounding countryside naturally died and their remains may, or may not, have been washed into the river system and buried. As a result many fossils tend to be fragmentary, water-rolled specimens that are often quite hard to identify; these have undoubtedly come from rotted carcasses that

**Right:** This is an original drawing made by the mine workers (possibly even by Louis Depauw) at Bernissart. It is a carefully-drawn plan of a skeleton as it appeared when excavated.

**Far right:** Another drawing, this time by the artist Lavalette, made at the Museum in Brussels once the specimen (near right) had been reassembled and cleaned in the laboratories.

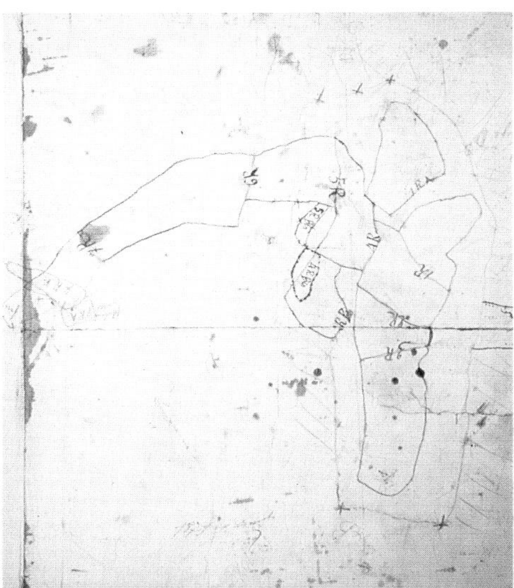

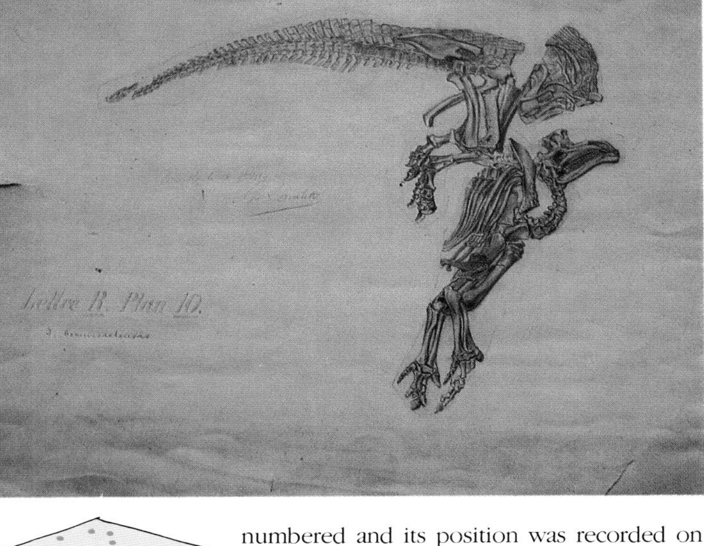

**Above:** This picture taken from Hanover Point beneath the cliffs on the southern coast of the Isle of Wight shows clearly the layers of Wealden rock that are being weathered away by wave action. Out of these rocks, which date from the Cretaceous Period, have fallen the remains of dinosaurs such as *Iguanodon, Polacanthus* and *Hypsilophodon,* as well as large sauropod and theropod dinosaurs.

**Nehden Excavations (below and right)**
Below we see early stages in the excavation of the new dinosaur quarry at Nehden in W. Germany. Beneath the protective awning, the clay deposit from which fossils have been recovered is being excavated systematically. The white posts act as markers so that a reference point can be given to each fossil as it is discovered and excavated prior to return to the Museum. Four plan drawings (right) taken at different levels within the quarry have here been super-imposed, using the original marker posts as reference points for each plan. The round dots on each level show the position of the remains of a baby *Iguanodon* which was evidently relatively undisturbed but scattered *vertically* rather than *horizontally,* as might have been expected.

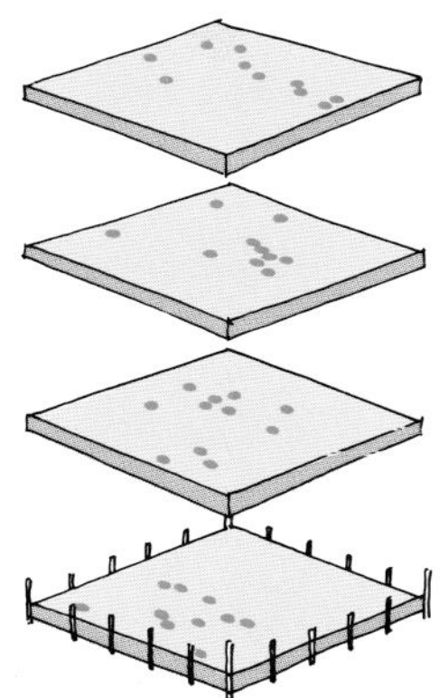

have been washed into a river and eventually fallen into pieces and the bones scattered and rolled among the pebbles and gravel of the river-bed. It is very rare that anything more complete than this is found; if it is, then it is almost invariably in the soft clays deposited under marshy conditions or in a lake. In this case, a carcass must have been rapidly washed downstream before sinking in a lake, and then being buried quickly in thick soft mud.

Much of the Wealden area has produced rather scrappy fragments, which caused early workers such as Mantell and Owen (see Chapter 1) so many problems. However, as early as 1871, an almost complete skeleton of an *Iguanodon* was discovered in the soft Wadhurst Clay near Hastings. Owen described various bits of it—but never realised that it was all part of the same animal! Unfortunately Owen, who never visited the site of the discovery relied on the amateur fossil collector, Samuel Beckles, to collect the skeleton, which consequently became rather mixed up. The specimen, now in the British Museum (Natural History) has lain unrecognised for over a century, yet it could have anticipated much of Dollo's work on *Iguanodon* (see below).

Two other types of fossil discovery deserve mention: one of these at Nehden in West Germany is very recent (1980), the other at Bernissart is relatively old (1878).

## The Find at Nehden

An abandoned open-cast quartz and gypsum quarry, near the village of Nehden, was found to contain, in a pocket of clay at its far end, some fragments of fossil bone. Eventually some teeth were found by Karl-Heinz Hilpert of the University Museum at Münster and identified as *Iguanodon.* Between 1980 and 1982 excavations were carried out at the new dinosaur site. They quickly revealed extremely rich fossil deposits. Much of the fossil bone, however, was disassociated. As a result it was decided to proceed with the excavations by removing horizontal layers of clay. The area to be excavated was mapped out using a grid of wooden posts at 20in (50cm) intervals and as each layer was excavated, each bone was numbered and its position was recorded on plan drawings. Study of this large quantity of material and the plan drawings has demonstrated that although the fossils were scattered, nevertheless if the position of the fossil remains of one small, probably baby, dinosaur is replotted on the plans, it seems that all of its remains were quite close together, but scattered *vertically* in the layers of clay. This is a fine demonstration of how useful it is to keep good, accurate records of what may seem at first sight to be most unpromising excavations. Certainly it was the case that the scattered and apparently totally jumbled nature of all the fossils was disheartening to the original excavators, who were presumably hoping to find a complete skeleton.

## Earlier Discoveries at Bernissart

An exceptional discovery was that made in 1878 at Bernissart, a small mining village in the Mons coal-field of south-west Belgium. The miners discovered a clay-filled fissure across a coal seam which was literally packed full of dinosaurs. However, rather than being fragmentary (as in the Wealden), or scattered (as at Nehden), the Bernissart fossils were of *complete* dinosaurs—as well as a whole range of fish, other reptiles and plant remains. These were discovered at a depth of 1,056ft (322m) in the mine. The remains of thirty-nine *Iguanodon,* many of them complete skeletons, were discovered at this site, before excavations were stopped in 1881. During the 1914-18 war, Bernissart was occupied by German forces, and the palaeontologist Otto Jaekel was sent from Berlin to supervise the reopening of the mine and the excavation of a new gallery. Just as the first fossiliferous layer was about to be uncovered, the Allies relieved Bernissart and work stopped. After the war, attempts were made to continue excavation, but regrettably the necessary money was not forthcoming and the mine had to be abandoned in 1921, after which it rapidly flooded. Many other skeletons, therefore, may still be buried underground.

As was the case at Nehden, very detailed records of the excavations undertaken between 1878 and 1881 were made. As each skeleton was discovered, it was given a letter of identification and its position in the mine was carefully drawn, so that it could then be divided up into manageable blocks which could be lifted. These were carried to the pit-head and then transferred by rail to the Royal Museum of Natural History in Brussels where each entire animal was reassembled, rather in the manner of a giant jigsaw puzzle.

The detailed records that were made of both the position of each dinosaur in the mine, and of the geology of the mine itself, were kept in the archive and they have made it possible to reconstruct the arrangement of the dinosaurs in the mine and their relative geological positions. This entirely new analysis of all the data that was so carefully collected so many years ago has revealed some interesting details about the mode of deposition of these dinosaurs which as we shall see later has implications for most published comments on Bernissart and its *Iguanodon* collection.

## Preserving Fossil Specimens

Preservation and conservation are subjects which do not normally receive much attention when dinosaur discoveries are discussed because fossilised bones are frequently both hard as stone and very stable. However, this is not always the case, as we shall see below. In the case of *Iguanodon,* these topics loom very large because the fossils recovered from both Bernissart and Nehden suffer, or have suffered in the past, from 'pyrite disease'. This is a condition in which the fossilised bone of the specimens appears spontaneously to crack and crumble away into fine pale-yellow powder. In earlier days this disastrous condition was thought literally to be caused by a disease that had 'infected' the fossil bones; thus various medical-type treatments were used in an attempt to 'kill' the infection. Such was the case at Bernissart. After the fossils had been excavated and were being transferred to Brussels between 1878 and 1881, they were constantly in danger of such decay. The procedure that was adopted to prevent and, it was hoped, cure the condition was to kill the 'disease' in the laboratories of the Museum in Brussels by using a rather dangerous mixture of alcohol saturated with arsenic and shellac – in order simultaneously to penetrate (alcohol), kill (arsenic), and harden (shellac) the fossils.

The record which was kept on the general state of preservation of the skeletons informs us that this attempt was not particularly successful. Between 1884 and 1890 the fossils continued to decay in their glass enclosure at the Museum and eventually all had to be returned to the laboratories for re-treatment.

We now know that the cause of 'pyrite disease' is *iron pyrites* (or 'fool's gold'), the chemical iron sulphide ($FeS_2$). At Bernissart (and at Nehden) the water in the clays where the dinosaurs were found contained this chemical which penetrated the bones. While the skeletons remain buried in the clay, they are relatively stable; there is no serious pyritic decay, although there can be the occasional growth of crystals of iron pyrites. However, once the fossils are removed from the clay during excavation, they begin to dry out. As a result the water content in the fossil bone falls from the usual level of saturation. At about 60% relative humidity some of the iron pyrites in the fossil (particularly the micro-crystalline variety) becomes unstable and is spontaneously converted to iron sulphate (the pale-green powder); free acids are also produced. Thus the 'disease' that affects these fossils is really a simple chemical process which is dependent only upon the amount of moisture in the air. What was happening in Brussels after the 'treatment' was that the alcohol-arsenic-shellac mixture helped to strengthen the fossils, but at the same time it trapped moisture within the bones, so that instead of the bones drying out quite quickly with a small amount of pyritic decay taking place, the whole process was extended over a period of probably twenty to thirty years so that considerable damage was done. It is a great pity that the method that was used to preserve the marvellous collections of fossils from Bernissart actually resulted in their suffering more from the effects of 'pyrite disease' rather than less. However, at the time when this was done, nobody knew any better way of treating them. We can all be wise with hindsight. Having eventually 'dried out', the Bernissart material on display at the Royal Institute of Natural Sciences in Brussels (formerly the Royal Museum of Natural History) is now perfectly stable. In addition, large glass enclosures were built around the display in the 1930s which serve to stabilise the humidity around the specimens.

Nehden, the newest find of *Iguanodon,* presented the same problems as those faced at Bernissart: pyritic decay. The treatment of these fossils has been significantly different and reflects modern techniques of conservation. As soon as a fossil was exposed, it was coated with a weak epoxy-resin to prevent too much evaporative water loss. The specimen was then removed by cutting it out in a jacket of clay, and wrapping the whole in hessian cloths. In the laboratory the fossils were unwrapped and then placed in a large, purpose-built vacuum impregnator with polyethylene glycol granules. The vacuum pump dehydrates the specimens, and the temperature is gradually raised to 60°C to drive off any remaining moisture and to melt the polyethylene glycol which penetrates, seals and greatly strengthens the fossils, as well as the clay matrix. The latter has then to be removed rather laboriously using air- and/or electrically powered vibrating hammers. The resulting fossils, when full prepared, are extremely tough and very stable with a slightly 'waxy' feel.

## Studying the Bones

The last, and in many ways the most important but also the most tedious, part of the process of collecting information about a fossil animal such as *Iguanodon* takes place in the laboratory.

The bones have to be sorted and glued together where necessary, and carefully cleaned; the latter may take a considerable amount of time if they are embedded in very hard rock and need to be prepared by mechanical or chemical means. However, when this is finally completed, the specimen is ready to be described. This is one of the most important stages in the study of any fossil species because it is the detail and accuracy of the description that will allow other scientists who are interested in similar animals to compare them closely and perhaps draw conclusions about their relatedness or about their general biology.

The scientific description takes the form of detailed drawings and photographs of individual bones in various views (dorsal, medial, ventral, lateral, proximal and distal) and in the case of some complicated specimens or teeth with much fine detail that are very difficult to draw, photographs in stereo pairs may be used so that the researcher, with the appropriate viewer, can see a three-dimensional picture of the specimen in question. The various illustrations are accompanied by a great deal of technical language which is used to describe particular important features of the bones, and also to make comparisons with other dinosaurs in order to demonstrate their similarities or differences.

In addition to the bone-by-bone description of the skeleton, various drawings are usually made of the reconstruction of certain parts of the body. This helps considerably to clarify the description. For example, it is all very well to describe each bone of the skull in minute detail, but it is practically impossible to fit these all together in your mind to visualise a complete skull.

All this rather dry and dusty work gives a very detailed knowledge of bony structures which does, on occasions, have rather unexpected benefits. A rather large, non-descript bony fragment, which had been discovered in a quarry in the Wealden, was unidentifiable until I re-discovered it. My detailed descriptive work meant that I immediately recognised it as a part of the rear of the head of a large *Iguanodon,* including the braincase. The fossil bone of the head was extremely poorly preserved but it was

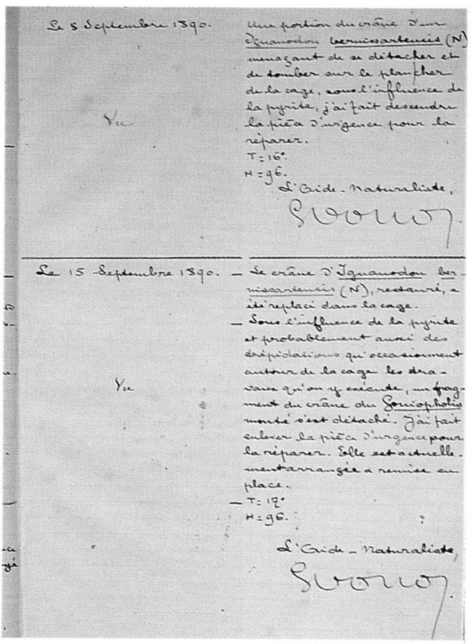

Le 5 Septembre 1890. | Vu

Une portion du crâne d'un Iguanodon bernissartensis (N) menaçant de se détacher et de tomber sur le plancher de la cage, sous l'influence de la pyrite, j'ai fait descendre la pièce d'urgence pour la réparer.
T=16°.
H=96.
L'Aide-Naturaliste,
L Dollo.

Le 15 Septembre 1890. | Vu

— Le crâne d'Iguanodon bernissartensis (N), restauré, a été replacé dans la cage.
— Sous l'influence de la pyrite et probablement aussi des trépidations qu'occasionnent autour de la cage les travaux qu'on y exécute, un fragment du crâne du Goniopholis monté s'est détaché. J'ai fait enlever la pièce d'urgence pour la réparer. Elle est actuellement arrangée et remise en place.
— T=17°
H=96.
L'Aide-Naturaliste,
L Dollo.

**Above:** The detailed records that were kept by Louis Dollo of the condition of the Bernissart fossils that were put on display in the museum courtyard tell a sad story of continual pyritic decay.

**Right:** Once the fossil has been collected and brought back to the Museum, the long task of preparation begins. More often than not the fossil is embedded in a slab of rock, with just a small portion exposed. The job then is carefully to remove the rock at the same time avoiding damage to the fossil. One of the standard preparatory tools is an electrically-powered vibrating needle which is being used here delicately to chip away the rock.

**Below:** At Münster University, the fossils from Nehden were treated in a vacuum impregnator. This vertebra of *Iguanodon* has just been treated and shows the 'waxy' protective coating of polyethylene glycol covering it.

embedded in very hard rock so I decided to have the specimen sectioned in the hope that it might reveal parts of the endocranial cavity (the cavity for the brain). The specimen did indeed show evidence of the brain cavity; but more than this, further preparation revealed the presence of a brain cast, the cranial nerves, the blood system surrounding the brain and the structure of the inner ear (where the hearing and balancing senses are located). This exciting find would not have been made if it had not been for the underlying, painstaking work that had gone into studying the bones.

Having thus established a data-base, a 'body' of solid evidence concerning the detailed structure of *Iguanodon,* this evidence can then be 'used' in order to gain a more comprehensive idea of the way in which the animal lived—its biology—as far as possible. This is done largely by using comparisons with living animals and a measure of elementary mechanics and common sense. Let us see to what extent we can use these principles to understand more about the biology of *Iguanodon.*

## The Shape of the Skeleton

In that there are complete skeletons of *Iguanodon* known from Bernissart, it is possible to build up quite an accurate picture of its general shape. It is frequently the case that palaeontologists have rather more fragmentary remains to deal with, so that their attempts must be inevitably more tentative.

It is surprising to see how much our idea of the general body-shape of *Iguanodon* has changed over the years. As we saw earlier, the first conception of *Iguanodon* as a gigantic lizard was very inaccurate and reflected the very fragmentary nature of the material at hand. Similarly Owen's conception (following the idea of Cuvier) that *Iguanodon* was a reptilian rhinoceros was wrong, but understandable at the time. The first restoration of the skeleton of *Iguanodon* based on complete skeletons was that of Louis De Pauw and Louis Dollo, which has become the standard restoration up to the present day. As we shall see below, I think that there are good reasons why the De Pauw-Dollo restoration is not correct; however, first of all let us consider why it was that De Pauw and Dollo chose this particular form for the body.

Between 1878 and 1882 (1882 was when the first restoration of *Iguanodon* was produced) Dollo and De Pauw had many complete skeletons and detailed drawings to study so that the anatomy was very clear. The prevailing scientific influence at that time was from the work of Thomas Henry Huxley (an influential

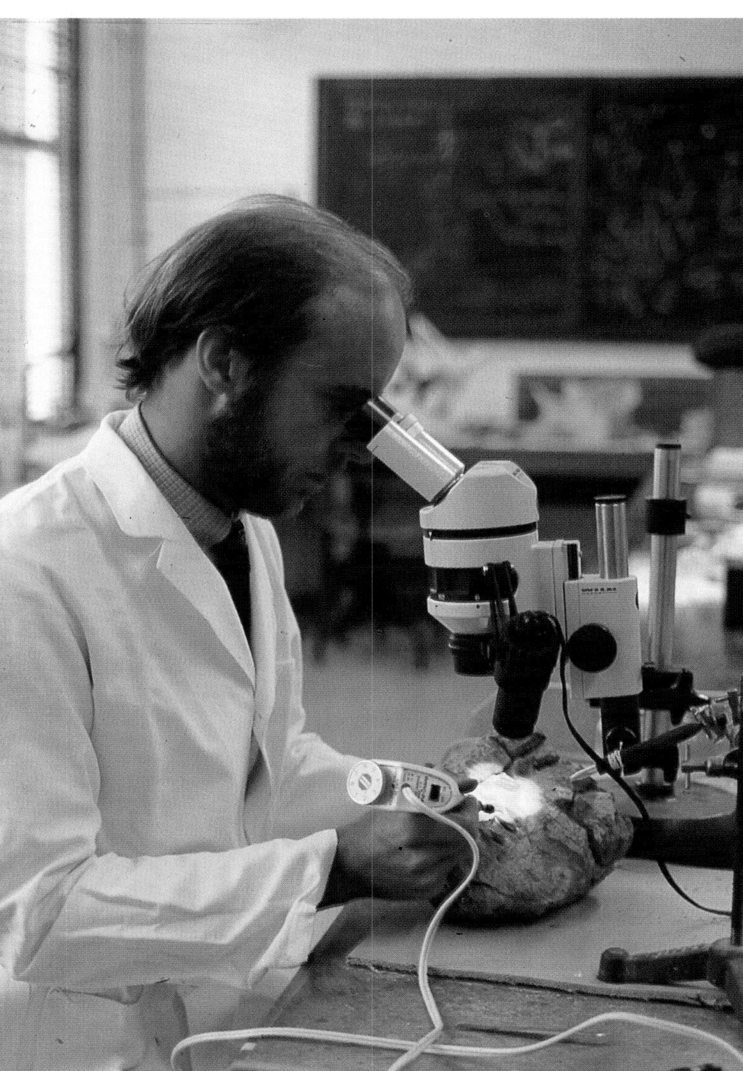

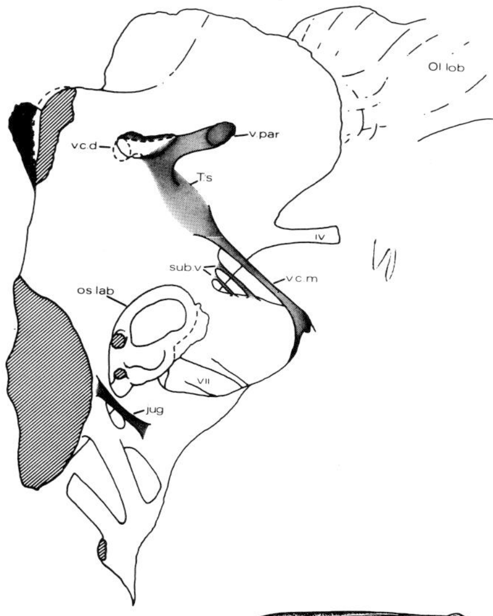


**Endocranial Cast (right and below right)**
This photograph shows the endocranial cast of *Iguanodon* after careful preparation. The specimen is seen here looking down on it from above and slightly behind the right ear of the dinosaur. The brain cast is the portion on the left side of the photograph. Various narrow pipes or tubes can be seen running to and from the brain cast and represent the passages for nerves and blood vessels. An outline drawing of the photograph shows more clearly some of the parts of the brain cast. The labels identify many of the parts. For example, os. lab. = osseus labyrinth, the cavity of the inner ear; jug = jugular vein; ol. lob. = olfactory lobes; vcd, v. par, Ts, vcm and sub. v refer to other blood vessels and the Roman numerals to nerves.

**Iguanodon Skull (below)**
This detailed drawing (a longitudinal section) shows the arrangement of bones inside the skull of *Iguanodon* and has been made possible by careful and painstaking work on lots of isolated bony fragments; these have been put together rather like a difficult jigsaw puzzle. At the top right is the area of the braincase, with the outline of the brain shown quite clearly.

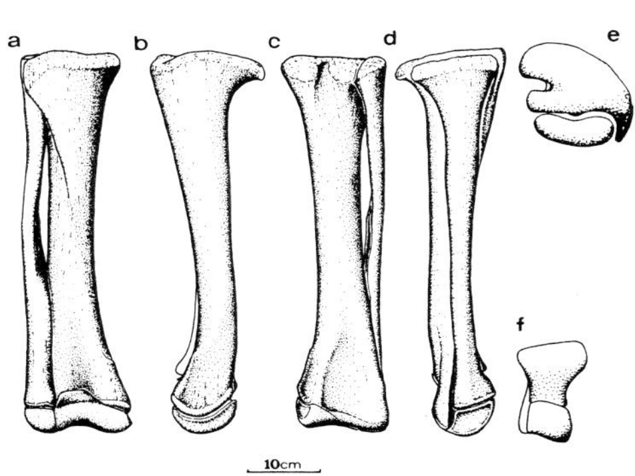


**Detailed Drawings (right)**
These drawings are of the shin and ankle bones of *Iguanodon.* As can be seen these have been drawn in various views: a = dorsal, b = medial, c = ventral, d = lateral, e = proximal, f = distal. In this way a fairly detailed picture of the anatomy of the dinosaur can be built up and used for comparisons with other dinosaurs.

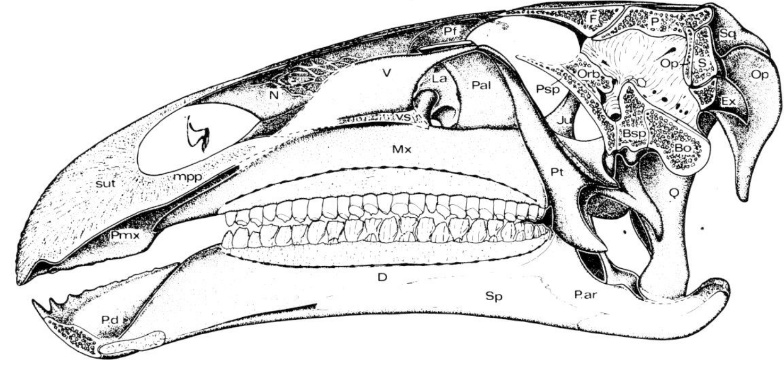

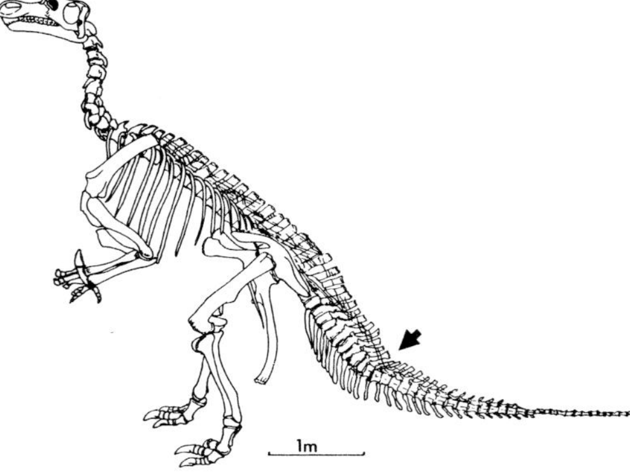


**Left:** This photograph taken in 1879/80 shows the first attempt to reconstruct the skeleton of *Iguanodon* from material at Bernissart. Note the small emu and wallaby skeletons for guidance. This workshop was in the Chapel of St George in Brussels, near the Natural History Museum.

**The Bernissart Iguanodon (above)** This finished version of *Iguanodon* was completed in about 1882 after the first attempts of 1878. This reconstruction was first published by Dollo in 1882. Note that the tail was broken in the area arrowed.

evolutionary biologist and palaeontologist). A decade earlier (in 1870), Huxley had been able to demonstrate that dinosaurs showed certain affinities with birds in the construction of the hip bones and hind leg, rather than with large pachydermal mammals as Owen believed. So Dollo and De Pauw not surprisingly chose an emu skeleton as one model upon which to base the reconstruction, because *Iguanodon* showed clearly the bird-like pelvis and the rather bird-like hind leg as Huxley had predicted. However, the resemblance was far from complete; unlike a bird, *Iguanodon* had a massive bony tail, and large forelimbs and hands. The only other living animals that fit these general proportions are members of the kangaroo family. Thus we see in photographs of the time the skeletons of an emu and a wallaby dwarfed alongside the massive bones and skeleton of the first *Iguanodon.* Not surprisingly then, the final version of the restored skeleton resembled, if anything, a giant wallaby, with a hint of emu in its bird-like neck. And indeed, this is how *Iguanodon* has been restored ever since, both as a skeleton and also as flesh restorations.

There are however, in my opinion, several anatomical features which suggest that all is not well with this particular restoration. Let us consider them point by point.

**The tail** As can be seen from the beautiful drawings made at the time, and also in several of the skeletons in Brussels today which are laid out as they were found in the mine, the tail was normally held out in a straight line behind the hips; it was held straight by a series of long bony rods (the remnants of long tendons of the muscles of the back). However, if we look at the De Pauw—Dollo restoration we can see the kangaroo-like sweep of the tail. Looking carefully at the original skeleton it is possible to see that the tail of *Iguanodon* has been artificially curved. This point is very important because straightening the tail produces great changes in the form of the body. If the tail is straightened, the front part of the body has to be lowered so that the backbone is more horizontal and the animal is balanced at the hips; this in turn explains why the long bony tendons of the back are continued into the tail: they acted as powerful cable-like hawsers to prevent the backbone from sagging while the long, heavy tail counterbalanced the front end of the body. This cantilevered design is a very simple and yet mechanically efficient system of support which would undoubtedly have been necessary for an animal measuring between 30 and 33ft (9-10m) in length and weighing somewhere between 1·5 and 2 tonnes.

The repercussions caused by altering the posture to one in which the vertebral column was held more horizontally are interesting. The first consideration relates to the forelimbs. If the front end of the vertebral column is lowered, the forelimb is brought quite close to the ground, certainly close enough to touch the ground with ease. The question then is whether *Iguanodon* was able to use its front legs for walking, or whether it tucked them out of the way, rather like a kangaroo does when it is hopping at speed. To try to solve this question we can use various lines of investigation. Here we will concentrate on a few areas.

**The hand** The structure of the hand may well indicate the range of ways in which it can be used. As can be seen from the diagram, the hand of *Iguanodon* is the normal five-fingered structure with which we are already familiar in our own hands. However, if we look a little closer, then we can appreciate several rather unusual characteristics. Firstly the thumb is modified into a large, conical spike which sits upon the side of the wrist. In fact it can only move across the wrist in a sweeping movement,

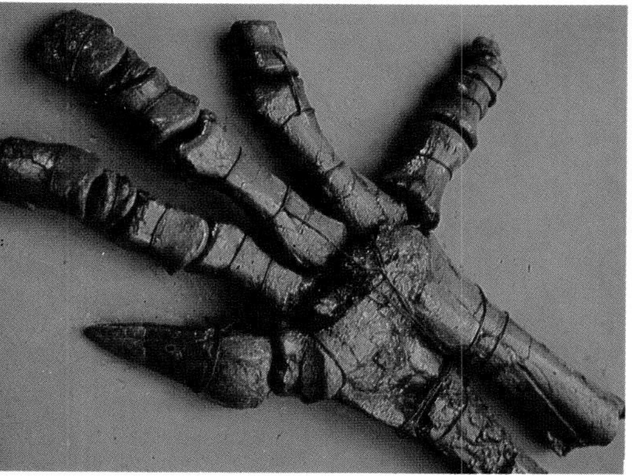

**Above:** This isolated hand found in the mine at Bernissart is very well-preserved and clearly shows some of the unusual features of the hand: note particularly the large spike on the thumb, the broad hooves on its middle fingers, and its slender fifth finger.

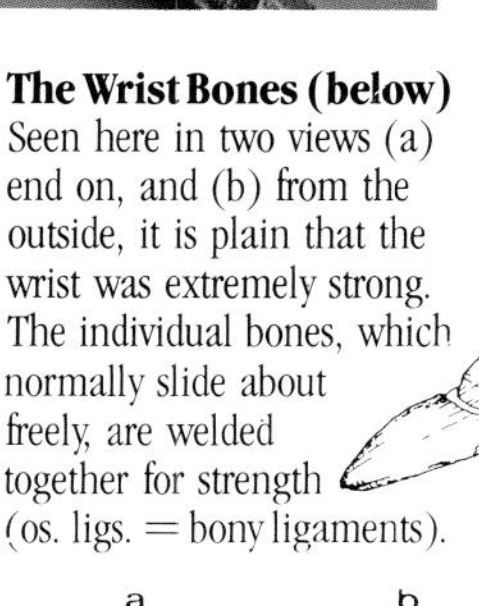

**The Wrist Bones (below)** Seen here in two views (a) end on, and (b) from the outside, it is plain that the wrist was extremely strong. The individual bones, which normally slide about freely, are welded together for strength (os. ligs. = bony ligaments).

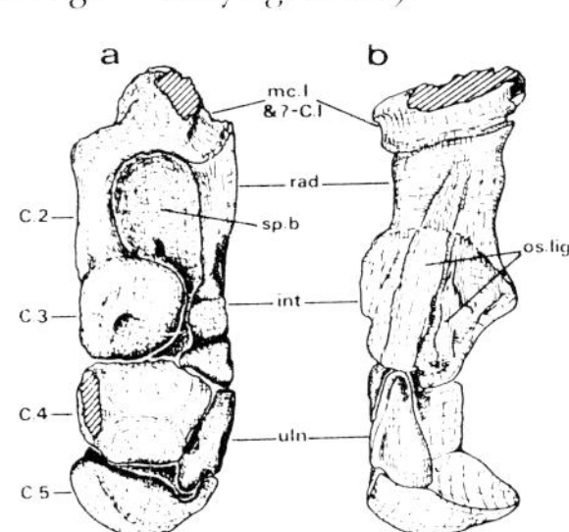


**Flexing the Hand (above)** By adjusting the bones of the hand, it can be arranged in a 'fully-flexed' position as shown here. The fingers cannot be closed properly to make a 'fist', although the 5th finger can be flexed across the hand quite well, as shown here.

**The Walking Hand (left)** By contrast, the middle three fingers can be hyperextended and form a very effective weight-supporting arrangement. The broad and rather twisted hooves on these fingers seem well adapted for walking on, rather than for grasping objects.

**Left:** In Brussels Natural History Museum two large glass enclosures are used to display the *Iguanodon* skeletons from Bernissart. In one there are 11 skeletons mounted in standing position, while the other (seen here) has the remains of 20 skeletons laid out roughly in the positions that they were found.

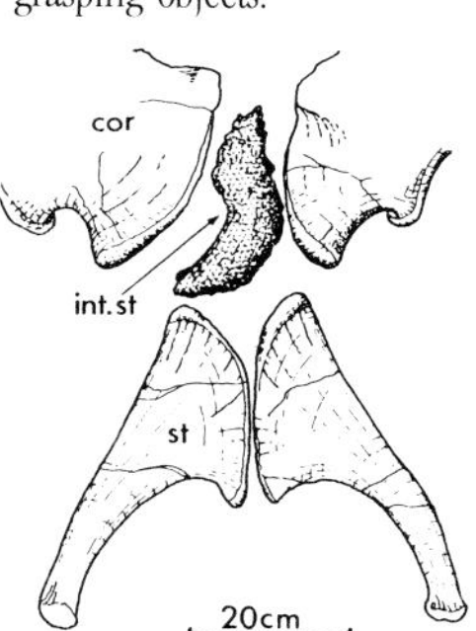


**Chest Bones (right)** Looked at from beneath, the bones of the shoulders and chest are clearly visible. The two hatchet-shaped bones lie in the area of the breast, while the two saucer-shaped bones are parts of the shoulders. Between these lies an irregular bone which may have strengthened the chest for walking on all-fours.

and it seems to have nothing to do with the other fingers which it cannot touch. The second, third and fourth fingers are also rather oddly arranged. The three long bones that form the palm of the hand are held together very rigidly and the toes on the ends tend to splay outward, away from one another towards their tips. In addition, and perhaps most significantly, if the joints between the finger bones are analysed for movement it can be seen that these fingers cannot be closed to make a tight 'fist' for holding objects (plant food etc.) but they can be bent backwards (hyperextended) on themselves. Finally, the tips of the second and third fingers are not narrow and curved as they are in typical prehensile hands, but are broad, flattened and twisted, in this way they resemble the toe bones of the walking legs of animals such as the rhinoceros or hippopotamus.

Unlike the others, the fifth finger is quite long and, judging by the way the individual bones are jointed together, very flexible. Certainly this would have been much more finger-like in our sense than any of the other fingers; perhaps it was used to hook up or manipulate pieces of foliage into the mouth.

As can be seen in the diagram, the hand can be reconstructed both in a grasping position (rather unconvincing because the fingers do not meet, but rather diverge) or in a splayed position, as if resting on the ground. The latter position, with fingers splayed is so similar to the splayed, weight-bearing arrangement in the foot that this seems to be the most reasonable position.

**The wrist** In a mobile, grasping hand, the wrist bones are usually well-developed and allow considerable movement to take place between the hand and the forearm. Obviously the hand should be as flexible as possible. In a hand used for walking upon, the bones of the wrist perform the function of shock absorbers and tend to be quite flattened, and reduce the range of movement between hand and forearm to that of a simple hinge so that the likelihood of dislocating the wrist while running, or even walking, is minimised.

In *Iguanodon* the wrist bones are quite extraordinarily modified. The individual wrist bones can just about be distinguished, but they are all cemented together by the growth of a lot of spongy bone and the alteration of the normally tough, cord-like ligaments which wrap around the wrist, into sheets of bony fibres. The hand and forearm bones are wedged into the wrist to create quite a firm structure with a very limited range of movement.

**The forearm and upper arm** These are quite stout bones and are also proportionally rather long (ie 70% of the length of the back leg). The stoutness and length of the front legs are not typical of an animal which uses its hands to pick up objects; again, those bones tend to be rather light and slender so that the arms are more mobile.

**The shoulders** Again, the shoulder bones are very large, reflecting the size of the arm and hand. However, although we would expect the shoulder bones to be quite large in such animals whether they were walking on two or four legs, there is one peculiarity in the shoulder girdle of *Iguanodon*. In several of this specimens from Bernissart in Belgium, there is a peculiar irregular bone in the centre of the chest (see diagram). This completely novel bone, not usually found in dinosaurs of this type, requires some explanation. If we add together the information from above, then there is one possible explanation at least for why it is there.

Putting all the information together, we have an animal with a hand that is incredibly specialised. The thumb is stiletto-like and was most probably used rather like a gangster's stiletto-knife for fighting at close-quarters with large predatory dinosaurs such as *Megalosaurus* (pages 62-67). The middle three fingers formed a solid centre to the hand, and were hoofed and able to bend backward to form a weight-supporting arrangement. Finally, the fifth finger was a highly mobile, prehensile structure which may indeed have been used to grasp objects. Add to this the stiff wrist, the long, powerful arm bones and shoulders and it seems almost inevitable that *Iguanodon* used to walk on all-fours at least for part of the time. Obviously it must also have been able to use its front legs as ordinary hands, by swinging the front part of the body upwards, perhaps to browse on foliage, or to defend itself against predators. However, I suspect that fully-grown animals may have spent much of their time on 'all-fours' because this would account for the peculiar bone found in the centre of the chest. The knobbly texture of this bone, and its rough and quite variable shape suggests that it may be a pathological development. I think that this bone may well have formed because the fully-grown animals were walking on their front legs for considerable periods of time. The weight carried by the front legs, during walking especially, would be transmitted alternately through the left and right halves of the shoulder bones at each stride; this would inevitably cause twisting across the chest between the shoulders, where the tissues were probably of cartilage and, compared with bone, quite weak. The new bone may therefore have formed in the cartilage of the chest to help prevent the chest from being literally pulled apart while walking. You may well ask, why don't other four-footed dinosaurs have this problem and also develop peculiar chest bones? The answer seems to be that at least some did; it has recently been reported that some ankylosaurs have similar irregular chest bones.

As was mentioned earlier, it seems that the nearer to full adult size that *Iguanodon bernissartensis* grew, the more likely it was to walk or rest on all-fours. This implies that smaller and presumably younger individuals spent more of their time walking bipedally. The reason for believing this can be found by looking at leg and arm proportions in small and large *Iguanodon* skeletons. Curiously if the lengths of the forelimb and hindlimb are compared in small and large specimens, the small individuals seem to have proportionally shorter arms than the larger specimens! Therefore as the animals grew to full size, their front legs got longer as if they were anticipating being used to walk upon. This rather strange observation may perhaps be explained by the way of life of the animal. As relatively peaceable plant eaters, *Iguanodon* undoubtedly fell prey to the large, predatory dinosaurs of the time such as *Megalosaurus* or *Altispinax* (pages 62-67) or even 'super-claw' (pages 56-61). Small *Iguanodon* would probably not have had the physical strength to defend themselves against large predators, and probably relied upon their agility and speed to escape. The larger, heavier and less agile adults would have used an alternate strategy; they were large and powerful and could have stood their ground against predators, using the stiletto-like thumb-spike as a devasting weapon at close-quarters.

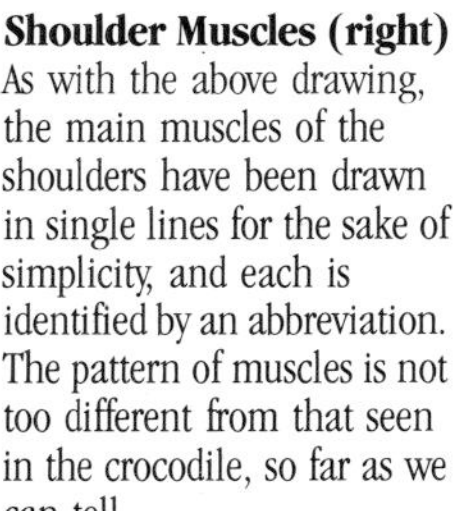

**Hip Muscles (left)**
Careful study of the surface of the pelvis and leg bones makes it possible to attempt a reconstruction of the main hip muscles of *Iguanodon.* In this diagram, the main muscles are indicated as lines and their names are given in abbreviated form. The arrangement is quite like that of birds and crocodiles.

**Shoulder Muscles (right)**
As with the above drawing, the main muscles of the shoulders have been drawn in single lines for the sake of simplicity, and each is identified by an abbreviation. The pattern of muscles is not too different from that seen in the crocodile, so far as we can tell.

## Reconstructing Muscles

In addition to analysing the skeletons to make bone-by-bone reconstructions, it is also possible to study certain areas of the body (the hips, shoulders and head in particular) for evidence of muscle attachment. This is possible because areas where muscles and ligaments are attached to bone frequently develop characteristic surface markings or muscle scars. Some muscles even cause the development of ridges or crests of bone especially for their attachment. In areas of the body where large and powerful muscles are attached, such as around the hips, shoulders and head, the pattern of muscle scars can be quite distinctive, even in fossil bone. So, how do we interpret the muscle scars? Well, just as in the case with the reconstruction of the skeleton from its bones, we use a judicious mixture of comparison with modern living relatives, and a certain amount of commonsense.

**The hips** As can be seen in the diagram the muscles of the hip of *Iguanodon* can be reconstructed to show remarkable complexity. The basis for this is firstly the pattern of muscle scars on hip and femur. These are then compared with the known arrangement of muscle attachments of hip and leg muscles in living crocodiles and birds. The reasons for using these two groups for comparison are as follows: crocodiles, as archosaurs, are the only living reptilian relatives of the dinosaurs (see pages 20-21) and would therefore perhaps be expected to show some fundamental resemblances in muscle arrangement with a dinosaur such as *Iguanodon*; birds seem also to be not only extremely close relatives of the dinosaurs (pages 175-174) but also show a very similar arrangement of their hip bones (*Iguanodon* being after all an ornithischian or 'bird-hipped' dinosaur).

Of course the pattern of muscle scars on the hips of *Iguanodon* does not *exactly* conform to the pattern seen in either the crocodile or the bird, so the final reconstruction represents a compromise which, in the opinion of the expert, seems to be the most reasonable interpretation of the evidence available. Obviously the skeletal reconstruction and proposed method of locomotion will influence the final choice. I should say that bearing all these factors in mind, the final interpretation should not be too far from the truth.

**The shoulders** Exactly the same technique is used to interpret the muscles of the shoulder region as well. However this time we cannot use the crocodile *and* the bird for comparison. The bird would be a very unwise choice for comparison because it has forelimbs that are modified into wings. This means that although the pattern of bones in the arm and shoulder are roughly comparable with those of *Iguanodon,* the muscles are highly modified for flapping—a movement that is not very important to a terrestrial animal.

Again, as in the hip region, it is possible to come up with a fairly clear pattern of muscles, which should be consistent with the proposed way of life of the animal.

**The head** The muscles of the head are principally those necessary for feeding. In most cases these muscles are quite complicated in their arrangement. The reason for this is that the majority of animals bite their food quite precisely (just think how carefully and delicately or powerfully you can move your teeth and jaws); to do this many different muscles are needed (the more the better, it would seem!). The illustrations show details of the structure of *Iguanodon*'s head.

## Feeding Habits

Just as the muscles of the hips can be useful to support or confirm ideas about the method of locomotion of an animal, so too can the jaw muscles help to work out how such an animal chewed its food. In the case of carnivores the teeth and jaws are mainly concerned with killing (large stabbing teeth) and biting off chunks of meat which can be swallowed quickly so that the flesh can be digested in the stomach. Herbivores face a much greater problem: plant food is far less nutritious than meat, which can be quickly broken down in the stomach, and therefore they have to spend a lot of time 'processing' it. That is to say pounding up the plant fibres so that they will release their nutrients, just as cows now 'chew the cud'.

By any standards *Iguanodon* was a large herbivore and would probably therefore have been quite efficient about the way in which it

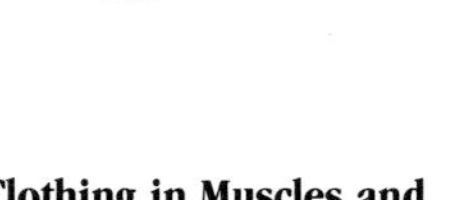


**Clothing in Muscles and Skin (left)**
It is possible to clothe the skeleton of *Iguanodon* in the muscles of the shoulders, hips and head from the analysis so far given. Add to this the general muscles of the neck, belly and tail (middle picture) and we can wrap it in skin and provide a restoration of the animal as a living creature. (From Mark Hallett's drawings.)

**Beak and Jaws (above)**
The diagrams above show the likely form of the horny beak that covered the front of the upper and lower jaws of *Iguanodon* in life. This sharp, continually-growing beak would have been very effective for nipping off tough twigs and shoots of horsetails, cycads and conifers that may well have been the staple diet of this herbivorous creature.

**Right:** A heavily worn tooth is seen near right. The upper, wider part is worn flat and the right hand side is broken off. Note the long, slender root. The middle tooth is a newly emerged crown; the surface is shiny with its hard enamel coating and the coarse serrations can be seen on its front and back edges. Far right is a partly worn tooth, and below are teeth embedded in the jaw.

dealt with its food. Looking at the skull we can see that the front of its jaws lacked teeth but had instead a turtle-like horny beak which would have been ideal for cropping vegetation, and has the added advantage of never wearing out! The teeth are very numerous (100 or so) and are found in parallel rows; the teeth in each row lock together to form a continuous cutting edge. The teeth are also inset, that is to say that there is a depression along the outside of both the upper and lower jaws which formed a cheek pouch. At the back of the lower jaw there is a large prong of bone, the coronoid process, to which many of the large jaw muscles were attached; behind this again the jaw drops down sharply to the jaw joint which means that all teeth would meet simultaneously as the jaws close.

The jaw muscles would close the jaws very powerfully, so that the teeth in each jaw meet and slide past one another. In doing this a most remarkable thing happens. Because the upper teeth slide at an angle past the *outside* of the lower teeth, the upper jaw on either side is pushed apart; it is able to do this because instead of its head being solid, as is usually the case, it has joints running down either side of it. The movement seems to have been controlled by special ligaments or muscles.

This extraordinary system whereby the upper jaw can move sideways is very interesting, and was probably very important to *Iguanodon* because it allowed this dinosaur to chew its food very efficiently. Large herbivorous mammals (cows or horses or people for example) chew their food by moving the *lower* jaw not only up and down but also from side-to-side in a rotatory movement. The side-to-side part of the movement is very important because it means that the lower teeth can grind against the upper teeth and so break up the plant fibres. Reptiles generally cannot chew food like this, and *Iguanodon* is no exception; they do not have the special muscles that allow mammals to move the lower jaw from side to side. However, although *Iguanodon* can only move its lower jaw simply up and down, because its upper jaw splays outwards, the upper teeth are able to make the all-important grinding movement against the lower ones. This is rather a fine example of a completely unexpected alternative solution developed by the dinosaurs to the problem of how to chew plants efficiently. As can be appreciated, the presence of the peculiar joints in the skull of *Iguanodon* may have remained completely inexplicable if we had not had the mammalian example of chewing for comparison.

**Above:** This specimen in Brussels is very well preserved and little disturbed. The shiny reflective surface of the bones is caused by coatings of preservative. Note here the shape of the skull with its large beak, long, tooth-lined jaws, inset teeth for a cheek pouch, low jaw joint and coronoid process, all of which helped it to chew tough plants.

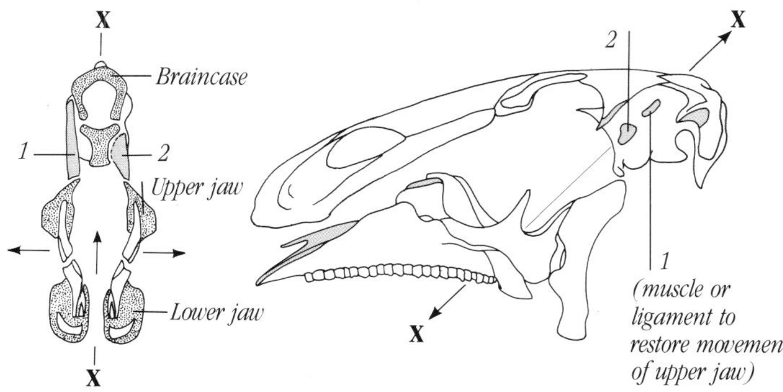


**Skull and Jaw Movements (above)**
These drawings attempt to show how these animals were able to chew tough plants very efficiently. Above, the lower jaw has been removed, and the remainder of the skull has been separated into two portions. One bears the teeth: the upper jaw and other attached bones; the other being the remainder of the skull roof and braincase. These two portions are jointed together along the blue areas so that the upper jaw on each side can swing in and out. Above left we see a cross-section along the line x-x in the previous diagram. It demonstrates how closing the jaws pushes the upper jaws apart, allowing the upper teeth to slide past the lower, so creating a grinding motion.

## Nervous and Blood Systems

The endocranial cast referred to earlier clearly shows the general shape of the brain cavity of *Iguanodon,* (as well as lots of other interesting details), which give an insight into aspects of the life of the animal that are very rare in any fossil species.

Careful analysis of the cast reveals the degree of development of the nervous system—the system that governed sensitivity (sight, hearing, taste etc), co-ordination and behaviour. This reveals that rather than being stupid, slow-witted creatures as is the popular image of dinosaurs, they had quite large brains by reptilian standards and were highly sensitive, well co-ordinated, and probably capable of quite elaborate behaviour. With regard to behaviour, many living reptiles, crocodiles especially, show remarkable complexity, particularly that associated with breeding and care of the young hatchlings.

In addition, the endocranial cast has brought to light unexpected details of the blood supply to the brain and surrounding tissues. All of this is really quite amazing detail when you consider that fossils of *Iguanodon* are over 100 million years old.

## Variability and Sex

One particular problem that bedevils palaeontological research is sexual dimorphism. That is to say if we find some differences between the fossilised skeletons of two otherwise very similar animals, can we prove that the differences are just (i) the normal range of variation for the species (just think of the range of shapes and sizes that human beings come in!), or (ii) that they show the differences to be expected between male and female of the same species, or (iii) that they are in fact truly different species?

These are virtually insoluble problems, because the ultimate solution could only be found if we had the living animals to study. In the end, decisions of this type are to some degree arbitrary, reflecting the opinion of the expert in question.

In the case of *Iguanodon* we again have a rather interesting situation. In Bernissart many skeletons were discovered at the same site, and therefore may represent a local 'population' or fauna of this species. It should therefore be possible to investigate the skeletons for tell-tale signs of normal individual variability or sexual differences. What has been discovered is that there are two different 'types' of *Iguanodon:* one named *Iguanodon bernissartensis* is very large, (30-33ft, 9-10m long) and stoutly built, as might be expected of an animal weighing about 2 tonnes; the other is named *Iguanodon mantelli* and is quite a lot smaller,

(16·5-20ft, 5-6m long) and more gracefully built (weighing about 0·7 tonne).

These two species can be distinguished by several anatomical differences: the shape of the skull, the bones of the hand, the pelvis and foot. So, what is the significance of these differences? Well, since they are consistent (even when you compare similar sized individuals), at first sight the differences can be used to propose that the skeletons are of separate species (therefore *I. bernissartensis* and *I. mantelli* are sufficiently distinct to be given names that recognise the differences). It does not seem reasonable to regard these two 'types' as representing variations within a single species (the differences are regarded as too great and too consistent for that). However, that leaves the last option, which is to decide whether they represent male and female versions of the same species. Here 'expert' opinions are divided, several workers have proposed that the two 'species' are male and female. Some regard the small type *(I. mantelli)* as the male, others regard it as the female (i.e. if we use modern reptiles for comparison, some male lizards and crocodiles are larger than the females, whereas female turtles are usually larger than the males).

The present interpretation that I shall give is rather ambiguous, because the answer is not clear. The anatomical differences between these specimens are sufficiently clear-cut to allow them to be defined as species. Therefore, I think that the names *I. bernissartensis* and *I. mantelli* should remain. However, in saying this I am proposing that two species of very similar-sized dinosaurs, which are obviously closely related, lived at the same time and probably in the same area. Is this reasonable from a biological and ecological point of view? The answer is a *probable* no! It would need to be demonstrated that the two 'types' of *Iguanodon* are separated ecologically, so that they were not competitors for the same niche.

Thus there are two outstanding problems: firstly, can the differences between the two 'types' of *Iguanodon* be proved to be sexual, and secondly, can the two 'types' be separated ecologically? Neither question can be answered satisfactorily. For the time being, therefore, the two types are recognised as species, but they may be sexual forms of just one species.

## Higher Level Interpretations

There are a number of ways in which the evidence that has been accumulated throughout this chapter can be brought together to help us draw more wide-ranging conclusions and generate new theories. I will elaborate a few of these.

**Anatomy and relationships** The detailed anatomical studies can be used for comparison with other dinosaurs of a similar type in order to get an idea of its evolutionary relationships with the other forms. The strictly anatomical data can be used to generate a pattern of relationships (see cladogram of iguanodontids on page 111). This can then be superimposed upon the geological timescale so that we can tie the relationships into an evolutionary pattern. By this means we can then begin to ask questions about how and why the pattern of relationships may have arisen through evolution, or indeed perhaps whether the relationships that have been proposed are indeed correct!

One way of using this sort of approach is to compare the pattern of relationships that have been deduced with the *geographical* distribution of the species involved. That is to say, is there any broad correlation between geographical separation of species (through continental drift for example) and the evolutionary pattern that has been deduced?

In the case of *Iguanodon* and related ornithopod dinosaurs, there does seem to be some measure of agreement between the evolutionary relationships that have been proposed and continental movements. The evolutionary pattern suggests that the hadrosaurids (pages 116-127) may have evolved from the iguanodontids (pages 110-115) in the Jurassic, with the latter being confined to Europe and the western continents, while the hadrosaurids evolving in the east spread back into the west sporadically in the Cretaceous.

**Ecology** Information on the local flora and fauna associated with *Iguanodon* can be used to build up a fairly comprehensive picture of the general life-style of the animal: the way it fitted into the ecology of the time and whether it is comparable with any modern animals in the sort of rôle which it fulfilled.

One rather misleading aspect of the way of life of *Iguanodon* relates to the discoveries at Bernissart. The concentration of skeletons at Bernissart has been used as evidence that these animals lived in herds, and in the case of Bernissart that they plunged into a ravine after being stampeded by a predator, or some other dramatic event. Unfortunately, appealing though the story is, it is certainly not what happened at Bernissart. Re-study of the material has shown that there was no ravine to fall into, the skeletons simply collected in a marshy or lake-like depression; furthermore there was no large herd, but rather there were separate phases of deposition, with carcasses being washed in and buried from time to time.

**Right:** This photograph gives a vivid impression of the incredible display of *Iguanodon* from Bernissart as they can be seen today behind vast glass panels at the Royal Institute of Natural Sciences in Parc Léopold. Most of these are *Iguanodon bernissartensis;* however the skeleton of *I. mantelli* is in the centre near the far side of the enclosure.

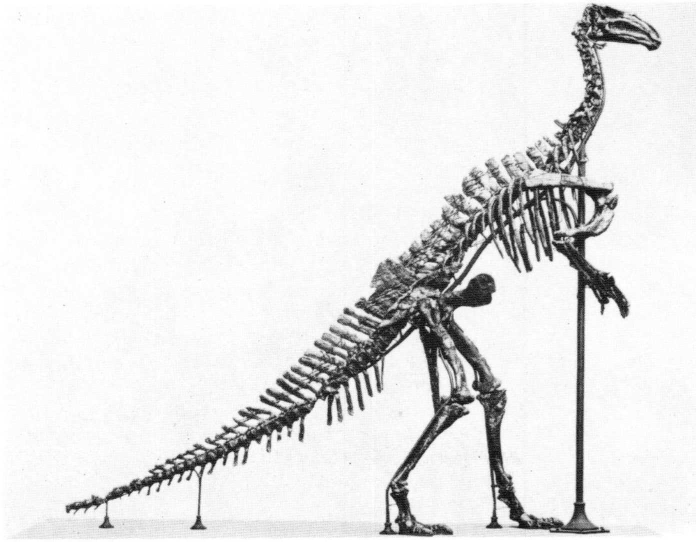

**Below:** Taken in 1883, this photograph, from Dollo's original account of the species, shows the one well-preserved skeleton of *Iguanodon mantelli* from Bernissart. This individual is 20ft (6m) long and appreciably more slender than the 33ft (10m) long *Iguanodon bernissartensis.*

**Bernissart Excavation (left)**
This map shows the position of the *Iguanodon* skeletons as found in the mine. They seem to have been deposited in two distinct orientations (red is the lower, older level) probably at different times. This may mean that the direction of the flow of current carrying the bodies altered between depositions.

**Patterns and processes** Another way of looking at evolutionary processes is to attempt to carry out population censuses (counting fossil specimens). This is admittedly rather a hazardous approach to use because the number of fossils that may be found at any one place at any one time must be subject to enormous variables. Nevertheless, sometimes undeniable patterns do emerge, which demand some attempted explanation. One such pattern reflects what appears to be the history of the ornithopod dinosaurs.

During much of the Jurassic Period the ornithopods were neither particularly numerous nor particularly diverse; they seem if anything to be relatively small to medium-sized herbivores when compared with the numerous giant sauropods. The Cretaceous Period, however, shows a major change in fortunes. The sauropods appear to decrease in number and variety, while the ornithopods increase quite dramatically. Not only are there several different types, but locally they can be very abundant. *Iguanodon* is, by any standards, very abundant in Europe. By the end of the Cretaceous Period the ornithopod hadrosaurids were clearly one of the most diverse and abundant groups, particularly in North America and Asia. What caused this remarkable change in the fate of the sauropods and ornithopods? One answer may be seen in the way that ornithopods chewed their food. The advanced ornithopods, such as the hypsilophodontids, iguanodontids and hadrosaurids, all show the development of the peculiar chewing mechanism described earlier for *Iguanodon*. It could well be that the replacement of the sauropods by ornithopods hinged on an ability to chew food. Sauropods had teeth that were used rather like 'rakes' to gather up leaves and twigs. These were swallowed without being chewed and then pounded up in a muscular gizzard which was lined with pebbles. It is quite possible that a vegetation change, perhaps linked to the rise of the flowering plants (angiosperms) which occurred at the beginning of the Cretaceous Period, promoted the decline of the stomach-grinding sauropods and the rise of the mouth-grinding ornithopods.

These are admittedly tenuous proposals, but I hope that it can be appreciated how such interesting broad-scale or *macroevolutionary* observations can arise from such mundane work as the counting of fossils!

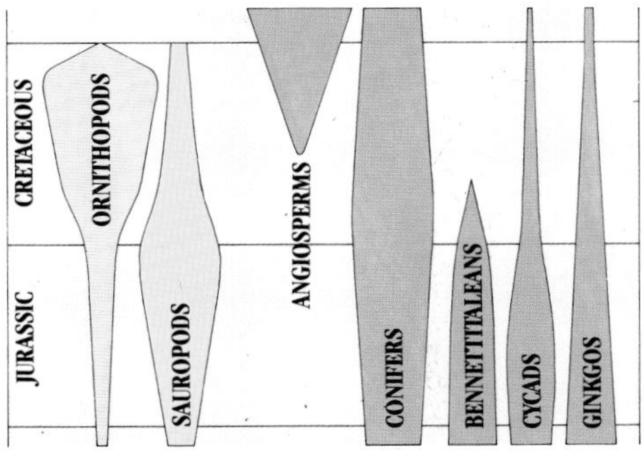


## Drawing Conclusions

As a result of all the foregoing work, we can build up a fairly—perhaps surprisingly—comprehensive picture of our fossil animal, in this case *Iguanodon*. Starting with our pile of bones, we have pieced them together to build a skeleton, deduced how it would have supported itself and moved around; clothed it in muscles and analysed the way in which it would have fed; we have also gained an insight into its intellectual abilities, and even pondered the problems of sex! Having built up a picture of *Iguanodon*, we have then taken all this information and 'processed' it in an attempt to bring this animal to life: discussing its ecology, relationships and evolution in time and space. One area of this research has led us to use the geological timescale to speculate upon a rather curious pattern of faunal replacement which seems to have occurred at about the time that *Iguanodon* lived (the replacement of the sauropods by ornithopods as abundant herbivores). The explanation for the replacement may have it origins in the rise of flowering plants and the rather peculiar way in which *Iguanodon* and other ornithopod dinosaurs chewed their food.

Therefore, we do seem to know a surprising amount about the general biology and way of life of this extinct animal. However, at this point it would be best to remind ourselves that there is also a considerable amount of information that we do not and cannot ever know about such animals. This can perhaps be best appreciated by comparing our information on *Iguanodon* with that available for a living lizard, the *Iguana* (see table at foot of column).

Thus we can learn virtually all there is to know about the *Iguana* because it is alive and amenable to study both in the 'field' (in its natural surroundings) and the laboratory. As soon as a species goes extinct, a considerable amount of information is lost. A very recently extinct *Iguana*, for example, would be not much better than *Iguanodon* (extinct 100 million years ago) from the point of view of information that can be retrieved. This should be borne in mind when looking at the rest of the book. The pictures represent our best attempt to bring them back to life, and rely on a combination of fact, interpretation, and scientifically inspired guesswork. For example, how do we know what colours they were? The answer is simply that we have no idea of their colour. However, by looking at animals around today we realise that colours are important and quite variable; they are used for camouflage (either by causing an animal to blend in with the background or by being disruptive to confuse a potential predator or prey), as warning colours, for sexual attractiveness, territorial behaviour, or more general social behaviour. The colours used here are, therefore, educated guesses based on a comparison with living forms.

**Comparative Knowledge**

| Iguana | | Iguanodon |
|---|---|---|
| | **Anatomy and Physiology** | |
| complete | bone structure | complete |
| complete | musculature | partial |
| complete | soft anatomy | very little |
| complete | locomotion | partial |
| complete | feeding and digestion | little |
| complete | sensory systems | very little |
| complete | reproduction | very little |
| complete | water balance | none |
| complete | blood systems | very little |
| complete | metabolism | none |
| | **Ecology** | |
| complete | field studies | none |
| complete | laboratory | none |
| | **Behaviour** | |
| complete | field studies | none |
| complete | laboratory | none |
| | **Evolution and** | |
| fairly complete | **relationships** | partial |

**Right:** *Conolophus*, the land-iguana of the Galapagos Islands, allows us a great opportunity to study all aspects of its biology. Many of these we can only guess at in the case of dinosaurs like *Iguanodon*.

**Large-scale Evolution (left)**
This chart shows how the fortunes of various groups varied during the Mesozoic Era. Sauropods were notably abundant in Jurassic times, but declined in the Cretaceous. The reverse seems true of the ornithopods. Is this linked to changes in plant types (near left) and food-processing techniques?

As described earlier, dinosaurs are related to a very large group of so-called 'two-arched' or diapsid reptiles. The diapsids are a very diverse group of reptiles ranging from dinosaurs to living forms such as lizards, snakes and crocodiles, as well as the extinct flying reptiles, the pterosaurs, and less well-known groups such as the thecodontians and rhynchosaurs.

In order to trace the history and origins of dinosaurs we must briefly dwell on some of these groups, because in them we find some clues to dinosaur ancestry.

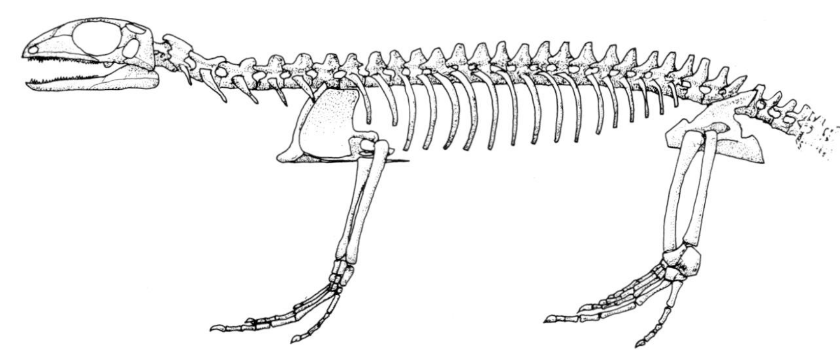

## The Earliest Diapsids

The first diapsid known is an animal named *Petrolacosaurus* which comes from the Carboniferous of Kansas in North America. It is a remarkably lizard-like creature with, if anything, rather disconcertingly long legs. These evidently agile animals very probably fed upon the insect life in the dry upland areas surrounding the coal-swamp forests which were very widespread at this time in the Earth's history. These were evidently very successful little animals because animals of just this type (modern lizards!) are still widespread and abundant, particularly in the tropics. However, the success of this early diapsid was of crucial importance because its survival acted as a springboard for the evolution of a considerable variety of diapsids in the Carboniferous and Permian Periods. It would appear from the study of the diapsids found in rocks of these times that there was an early separation into two quite distinctive groups of diapsid. One of these, the lepidosaurs, remained virtually unchanged as generally small, very lizard-like creatures; the other group, the archosaurs, were generally larger predatory creatures with heavier bodies, particularly powerful hindlimbs and tails, and a pronounced tendency to develop armour plating over the back. It is the latter group (the archosaurs) that particularly interest us, because it is from them that the dinosaurs finally evolved towards the end of the Triassic Period. However, before looking at the archosaurs let us briefly look at the lepidosaurs. After all, dramatic though the dinosaurs were, they went extinct, whereas the lepidosaurs (as lizards and snakes) have continued to evolve right through to the present day.

**The Lepidosaurs** Most of the history of lepidosaurs revolves around their small-size and insectivorous habit (with one particularly noteworthy exception). They can generally be said to live a very economical life-style. The heat of the sun is used to maintain body temperature within tolerable limits, and strong, widely-spread legs and sinuous body movements are combined to move extremely quickly over short distances – to catch prey and avoid predators. They also feed on small highly nutritious packets of food (i.e. insects). The main evolutionary innovation of the lepidosaurs is in fact an adaption linked to feeding. Comparing the skull of *Petrolacosaurus* with that of a modern lizard, we can see that the lower temporal arch has been lost: a feature peculiar to lepidosaurs. Its loss means that the skull bones can develop remarkable flexibility. As a result food can be manipulated with great precision while in the mouth. The skull mobility is thought to be one of the reasons for the continued success of lepidosaurs. The snakes have taken skull flexibility to almost ridiculous extremes in that their heads are so flexible that they can swallow prey much larger than their own heads (see also page 371).

**Petrolacosaurus Skeleton (above)**
This small reptile comes from the late Carboniferous rocks of Kansas. In its general proportions it resembles most other lizard-like reptiles, although its legs are rather long. Very probably *Petrolacosaurus* was a fast-moving predator of insects.

**Petrolacosaurus Skull (right)**
These views show the two openings behind the eye socket that characterise diapsid reptiles. The teeth are small and spiky, well suited to a diet of insects. The drawings are based on the work of Dr Robert Reisz.

**Petrolacosaurus Skull**

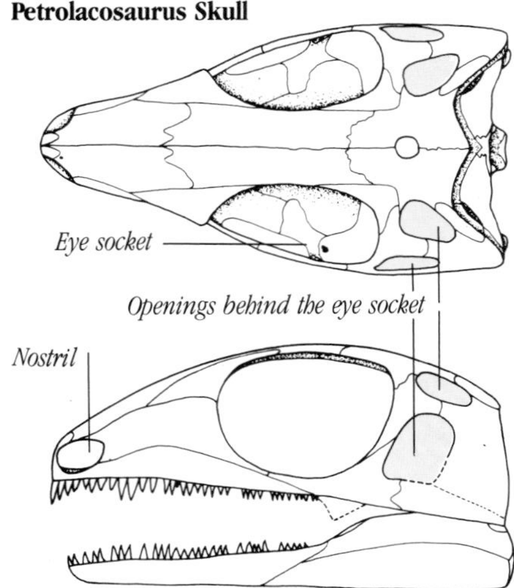


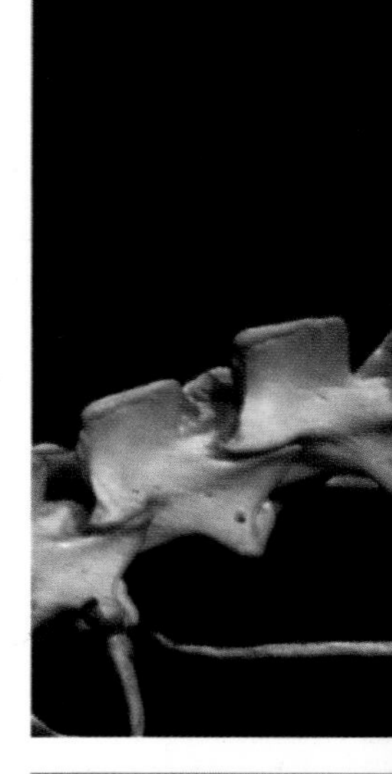

**Euparkeria Skull and Skeleton (right and below)**
*Euparkeria* is a good example of an early archosaur reptile. Based on the work of Dr Rosalie Ewer, this reconstruction shows a highly active creature which grew to about 3·3ft (1m) in length. As shown here, the tail is used to counter-balance the body for short sprints on its hind legs. The skull shows the typical archosaur pattern of openings in front of the eye and in the lower jaw.

**Euparkeria Skull**

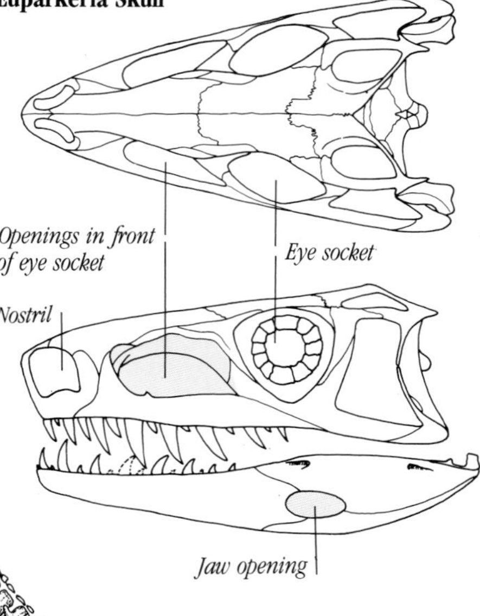

**Right:** This cast of the skull of *Riojasuchus*, a South American thecodontian, is in the collection of the British Museum (Natural History). As in the case of *Euparkeria* (below left), the typical archosaur skull openings in the upper and lower jaws are well shown. The powerful jaws and serrated teeth of both these creatures testifies to their predatory habits.

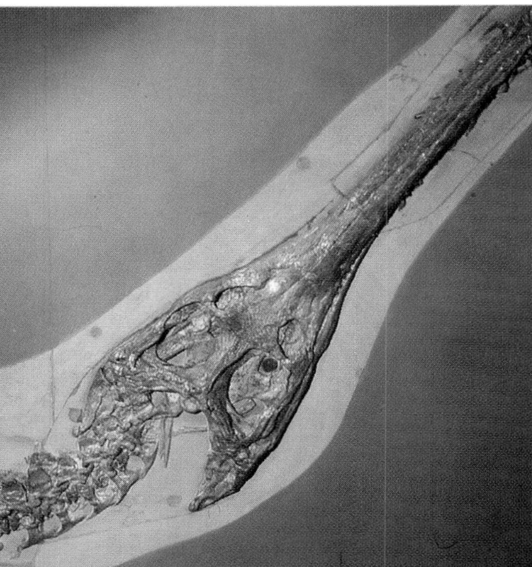

**Above:** The varanid lizards of today (the monitor lizards) appear to be distant living relatives of the gigantic mosasaurs of the late Cretaceous seas. This specimen shows very clearly the detailed structure of the skull. The loss of the lower temporal arch behind the eye allows such reptiles great jaw flexibility.

**Leg Postures (below)**
This sequence, adapted from Dr Alan Charig's work, shows the sprawling posture of most living reptiles (far left). In the centre is the semi-erect posture adopted by thecodontians and living crocodiles. On the right is the fully-erect posture typical of dinosaurs, birds and mammals.

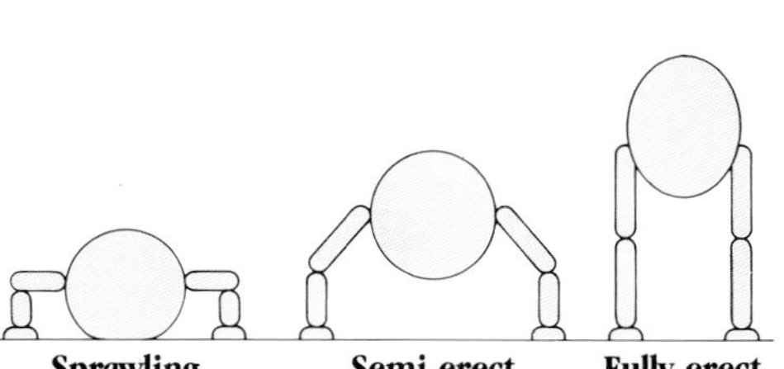


**Above:** The skull of a phytosaur, an early but short-lived group of archosaurs. These large aquatic reptiles looked very similar to crocodiles. They lived in late Triassic times only. They were predominantly fish-eating types with long, narrow snouts lined with sharply pointed teeth. One notable feature of these animals is that whereas crocodiles have nostrils at the tip of the snout, in phytosaurs they were situated on a mound just above their eyes.

The mosasaurs of the Cretaceous Period are one exception to the general rule that states that lepidosaurs are small. These were huge sea-going lizards which appear to have been giant relatives of the monitor lizards of Africa and South-East Asia. Most present-day lizards are adept swimmers, but the mosasaurs took this to an extreme because their legs had developed into broad paddles.

**The Thecodontians** The earliest archosaurs so far known are really quite large animals from the end of the Permian Period, such as *Proterosuchus* and *Erythrosuchus*. However, rather than use these as examples of a typical early archosaur, I shall use the relatively small Triassic thecodontian *Euparkeria*. This particular genus is well-known and well illustrates the principal attributes of all early archosaurs.

The skull of *Euparkeria* shows several of the distinctive characters of the archosaur: the head is relatively large and has deeply-rooted teeth with sharp serrated edges; there is also an additional opening, in the form of a broad depression on the side of the head immediately in front of the eye socket; there is another aperture in the side of the lower jaw as well. None of these features is found in typical lepidosaurs. Along the backbone, there is also a double row of bony plates—the beginnings of armour-plating, another archosaur feature. Finally and very importantly as we shall see shortly, there are some rather subtle rearrangements found in the hips and hind leg. These changes reflect an ability to alter the angle that the back leg makes between the body and the ground during a normal stride. The upper leg bone (femur) is distinctively curved and the hip-joint is socketed in such a way that the leg can be held either straight out from the side of the body as in a lizard or alternatively the leg can be held partly beneath the body. The latter position enables the belly of the animal to be raised from the ground so that it does not drag and walking is therefore more easy and efficient. The ability to use a so-called 'variable gait'—to hold the leg in positions other than just the typical sprawling posture—seems to have been of considerable importance to the evolution of the thecodontians as a whole and to that of their eventual successors, the dinosaurs, in particular.

Holding the legs at least partly beneath the body has one immediate advantage: it means that larger body-sizes can be attained because the weight of the body can be carried by the legs rather than through the belly resting on the ground. Thus, by altering the range of leg positions, the archosaurs immediately opened up a range of body sizes that could not possibly be achieved by lepidosaurs. However, large size does have its side-effects. In the case of the thecodontians it resulted in the modification of the ankle joint. With the legs held out from the sides of the body, as in typical lizards, the ankle is subjected to considerable twisting during the normal range of movement between foot and leg. While animals are relatively small, and the forces involved in moving are small, there is no particular requirement for great strength and stability in the ankle bones. However, large size and variable gait, as in thecodontians, demands much greater strength and stability of the ankle joint—to prevent unwanted dislocation for example. The solution found variously in thecodontians is to develop a rather unusual ankle joint with, instead of rows of small bones that slide past one another, a strong ball-and-socket joint between the ankle bones (see diagram on page 36). Ankles of this general type are found in all thecodontians and can be taken as a reflection of the greater power exerted by the hindleg on the foot.

Thus what we appear to see in early archosaurs is a suite of characteristics that distinguishes them from their 'cousins' the lepidosaurs—how did these new characters arise? The usual explanation offered is that the early thecodontians (*Proterosuchus* is a good example) became at least partially aquatic (generally crocodile-like) in their way of life. In water a powerful tail and large hind legs are advantageous for swimming powerfully to capture other animals and they can also grow larger because their weight is buoyed up by water. It is proposed therefore that these thecodontians became large aquatic predators with big tails and long back legs. Later on, these 'types' reverted to living on land, but although

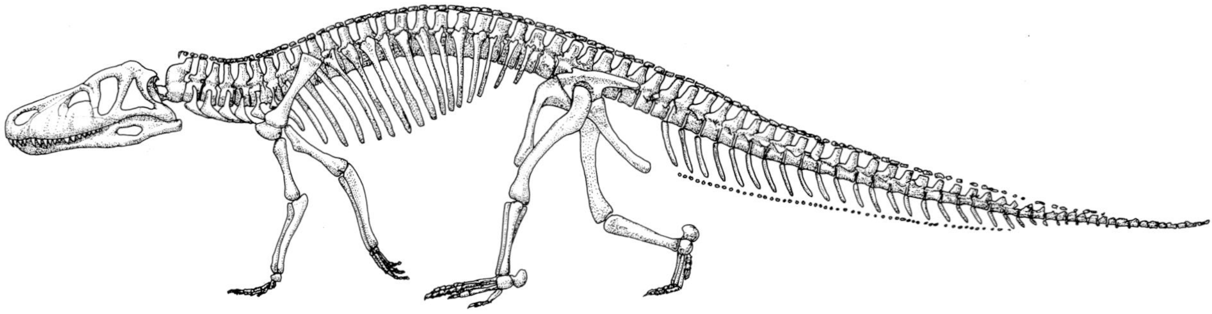

**Saurosuchus Skeleton (left)**
This large (10-16·4ft, 3-5m long) and heavily built carnivorous thecodontian lived towards the close of the Triassic Period. Such creatures were evidently the major land-living predators in the world prior to the appearance on the scene of the first large carnivorous dinosaurs.

**Left:** Rhynchosaurs like this were a short-lived but briefly very abundant group of reptiles in the late Triassic Period. Reaching a length of 3·3-6·6ft (1-2m), they seem to have been rather pig-like creatures using their tusks to root about for food.

**Ankle Structures (below)**
Associated with the changes in posture illustrated on page 35 were alterations in the ankle joint. On the left is shown a 'typical' semi-erect archosaur ankle. The hinge between leg and foot (red line) has a sharp twist to allow the foot to swivel. In the fully-erect dinosaur the hinge is simple as it does not have to withstand great twisting forces.

large, they had powerful back legs to support the body and a large counterbalancing tail which suited them well to a terrestrial rather than an aquatic way of life.

This theory fits in well with the known fossil record, but it does not strike me as a totally convincing explanation. I can much more readily imagine that the earliest archosaurs appeared in upland areas as small or medium-sized carnivores which had developed a variable gait as a means of moving more efficiently to catch prey, and simultaneously giving them the opportunity to grow into much larger predators. The early archosaur 'type' would then be a *Euparkeria*-like animal. The problem with *Euparkeria* being an actual animal of this type is that unfortunately it lived too late in time. I consider that similar active, predatory archosaurs must have existed in the upland areas in late Permian/early Triassic times, but as yet we just have not found them. If this is the case, *Proterosuchus* and other large aquatic thecodontians may then be seen as early representatives of an evolutionary radiation of archosaurs into the watery habitat; this was eventually to be colonised by the extremely successful archosaur group, the crocodiles. I therefore see the development of the archosaur ankle joint in particular as a consequence of developing a variable gait for more efficient locomotion and support on *land* rather than it developing in *water* as others have proposed. Clearly, the explanation that we can provide for archosaur origins is not clear-cut but relies on opinion and personal preference. However, what is not in doubt is the fact that archosaurs did possess the suite of anatomical features listed above and that their arrival coincided with a very noticeable change in the types of animal to be found in the world at this time.

## The Rise of the Dinosaurs

Throughout the Triassic a considerable variety of thecodontians are found almost world-wide, ranging from small *Euparkeria*-like animals to very large crocodile-sized forms such as *Saurosuchus* from Argentina or *Ticinosuchus* from Germany. All in all they seem to have been very successful carnivorous forms.

However, in order to understand the processes that were taking place in the Triassic and led to the appearance of the dinosaurs at the very end of the Triassic, we must briefly chart the events of the Triassic as a whole. In the early part of the Triassic, the thecodontians were not very abundant, but lived alongside a very diverse fauna of herbivorous (dicynodont) and carnivorous (cynodont) mammal-like reptiles. By the middle of the Triassic the dicynodonts had been replaced by diademodontoids (herbivorous cynodonts) and also by the rhynchosaurs, a short-lived but meanwhile very numerous group of diapsid reptiles. The thecodontians meanwhile persisted as generally large-bodied carnivores. At the end of the Triassic there was a rather abrupt change in fortunes: the majority of the mammal-like reptiles went extinct, as did the rhynchosaurs, while the dinosaurs and other late thecodontian groups rose to a dominant position. The age of the dinosaurs begins.

The explanations for the observed change in fortunes of the mammal-like reptiles and archosaurs at the close of the Triassic has provoked considerable debate. For the moment, we will merely accept the fact that it happened, although those that are interested may turn straight to page 170 for more information. However, before going on in the next chapter to

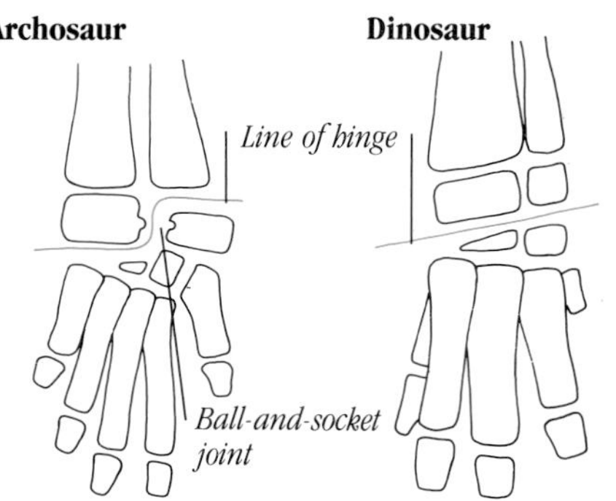


discuss in some detail the anatomy and biology of the dinosaurs that are presently known, a few more words about dinosaur anatomy are in order.

## Dinosaur Anatomy

To recap briefly on the distinction that was introduced in the 'dinosaur family tree' section of Chapter 1, the dinosaurs that evolved from the thecodontians at the end of the Triassic can readily be divided into two types: saurischian ('reptile-hipped') dinosaurs and ornithischian ('bird-hipped') dinosaurs.

Saurischian dinosaurs include both carnivorous and herbivorous representatives and are characterised by having a pelvis in which the three bones (ilium, ischium and pubis) radiate outwards from one another in different directions from the hip joint or socket like most other reptiles. However, unlike most other reptiles there is an opening in the hip socket and above the opening an outwardly-directed lip against which the femur was firmly pressed. Also, the pubis and ischium are very long and directed downward between the legs. The legs in turn are tucked in pillar-like beneath the

Lip
Ilium
'Head'
Opening in hip socket
Pubis
Ilium
1
1
Femur
Pubis

**Hip Joints (left)**
In semi-erect archosaurs (far left) the femur is angled inward against the hip socket and muscle 1 swings the leg forward quite easily. In dinosaurs the femur is upright and has a 'head' that fits against a lip on the socket. Muscle 1, which works well for the semi-erect archosaur, is too short to work effectively for the dinosaur.

**Dinosaur Hips (below)**
These diagrams, based on the ideas of Dr Alan Charig, attempt to explain the range of dinosaur hip structures (pubis: blue; muscles: red). In *Ticinosuchus* (far left), a thecodontian included for comparison, the normal hip muscles operate effectively because the femur is angled inward. In the quadrupedal sauropod *Diplodocus* muscle 1 still operates because the femur does not swing far forward. Muscle 1 works more effectively for a bipedal theropod like *Ceratosaurus* because the pubis is tilted up and away from the femur. In *Scelidosaurus,* an early quadrupedal ornithischian, the pubis has moved backwards and muscle 1 is attached to the ilium. In the bipedal *Hypsilophodon* a new pubic bone has grown for the attachment of muscle 1.

**Above left and above:** Seen here are an ornithischian dinosaur (*Stegosaurus,* above left), and a saurischian one (*Tarbosaurus,* above). The pelvis of *Stegosaurus* has a backwardly-pointing pubis, while that of *Tarbosaurus* points forward and down from the hip socket. However, *Stegosaurus,* like many late ornithischians, has also developed a new forwardly-pointing pubic bone.

**Ticinosuchus**

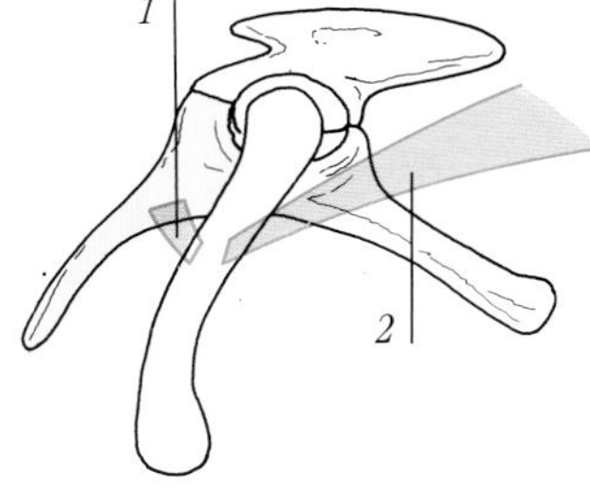

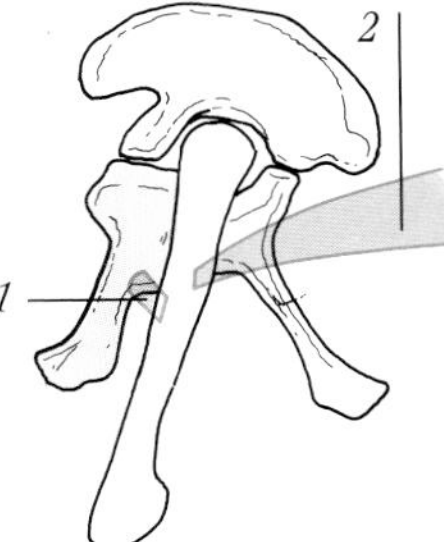


**Ceratosaurus**

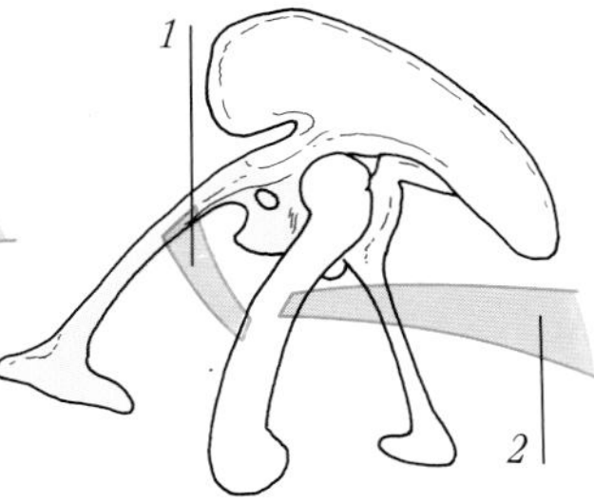


**Scelidosaurus**

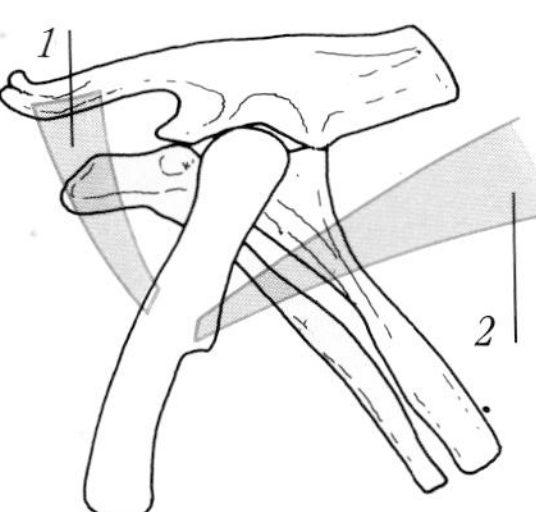


**Hypsilophodon**

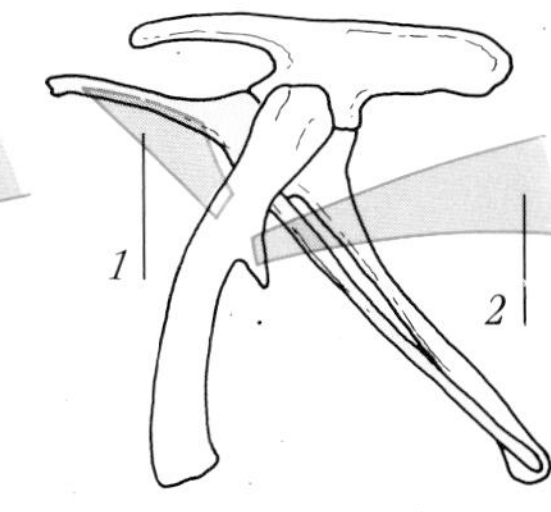


body and show several changes from the thecodontian plan. The femur has a distinct 'head' which sticks out at right-angles to the shaft. The 'head' fits into the deep hip socket, and rests against the lip. The knee joint is a simple hinge, as is the ankle joint. The ankle does not have to withstand the great twisting forces that were found in the variable-gaited thecodontians, so it can become a very strong, simple hinge, rather than having a complicated ball-and-socket joint as in the thecodontian.

The saurischian dinosaurs are in turn divided into two distinct groups, the theropods (bipedal carnivores of various sizes) and the sauropodomorphs (generally quadrupedal plant eaters of very large size).

Ornithischian dinosaurs resemble saurischian dinosaurs in the structure of the legs: they have a similarly off-set head to the femur as well as hinge-like knee and ankle joints. However, the pelvis, although it has a perforated socket, and a lip, is notably different. The pubis lies parallel to the ischium as it does in living birds (hence the name ornithischian). In some later ornithischians the pubis develops another anterior spine which resembles but should not be confused with the saurischian one. In addition to the difference in hip structure, ornithischians also possess a lattice of bony rods on either side of the spines of the back and a peculiar horn-covered bone (predentary) at the tip of the lower jaw. These three differences serve readily to distinguish ornithischian from saurischian dinosaurs. Ornithischians were *all* herbivorous and are represented by the more bizarre looking type of dinosaur, such as the plated stegosaurs, the tank-like ankylosaurs, the horned ceratopians and the crested hadrosaurs.

Why is it that dinosaurs have such distinctive hips? One novel explanation provided by Dr Alan Charig (London) (in fact the only one that has ever been put forward) is that it is to do with the way the leg muscles worked in thecodontians and dinosaurs. It is briefly as follows: in thecodontians the main leg moving muscles were attached to the pubis and to the tail (muscles 1 and 2 in diagram). Muscle 1 pulled the leg forwards, while muscle 2 pulled it back (the main walking muscle). However, if we imagine this arrangement operating in a dinosaur, then there are a couple of unexpected problems. The main one is that with the legs fully 'tucked-in', as in the typical dinosaur, the femur is brought very close to the pubis—in fact too close for muscle 1 to be able to work properly. Therefore the earliest dinosaurs seem to have been faced with a problem: how to avoid having the femur too close to the pubis. The dinosaurs seem to have 'solved' the problem in at least three different ways. The huge sauropodomorph saurischians simply stayed as they were and exploited the option of moving slowly with their legs acting as pillars and having a small range of leg movement. The theropod saurischians became bipedal and by doing so swung the body and pubis upwards and away from the femur so that the leg muscles continued to work effectively. The ornithischians seem to have 'decided' early on, to abandon the pubis altogether; it was therefore swung backwards out of the way against the ischium and the leg-moving muscle was moved to the long spike on the front end of the ilium. The redevelopment of a pubic spine in later ornithischians may well be associated with the development of bipedality which moves the anterior spike on the ilium to a rather unfavourable position for leg muscle 1.

# 'COELUROSAURS'

The saurischian dinosaurs are a fairly mixed group of animals which all share the general features associated with a re-organisation of the hindlimb and pelvis for a fully erect position (see pages 36-37). It is possible to break down the saurischians into at least two quite distinct groups: the **Theropoda** ('beast feet') and **Sauropodomorpha** ('reptile-type feet'). The theropods tend to be bipedal carnivores of various shapes and sizes, while the sauropodomorphs tend to be either omnivores (ie. eating a mixed diet) or herbivores. We shall use this division to look at the saurischian types over the next few pages: theropods (pages 38-73) and sauropodomorphs (pages 74-97).

The theropods are a group of carnivorous dinosaurs of bewildering variety. They are all grouped together because of their shared predatory habits and associated skeletal form. Unfortunately their relationships are not at all clear and can only be hinted at here in the

**Coelophysis (below)**
This is one of the earliest and most primitive dinosaurs. *Coelophysis* was very slim and it could have run on its hind legs, or walked on all-fours. The hands were equipped with three strong fingers that were probably used for attacking smaller prey animals such as the small lizard-like reptiles that lived at the same time. Some of the skeletons of *Coelophysis* that were found in a mass burial at Ghost Ranch, New Mexico, in 1947 contained the bones of juveniles of the same species. It was thought that these were babies ready to be born, but they are rather too big for that so *Coelophysis* may have been a cannibal.

**Compsognathus (below)**
One of the smallest dinosaurs of all, some *Compsognathus* reached a total length of only 28in (70cm) or so. Most of this length was made up by the long slender tail, so that an adult *Compsognathus* was no heavier than a hen. The tail was used as a balancing rod during fast running. The neck was quite long like that of *Coelophysis*, and *Compsognathus* had only two clawed fingers on its hand, an unusual feature.

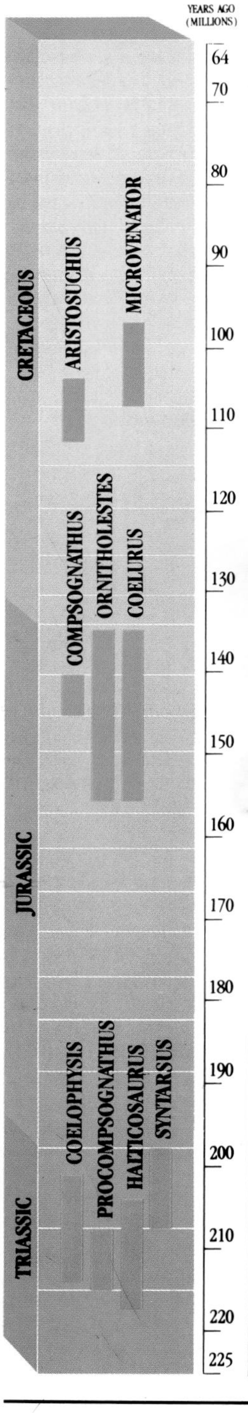

**Time Chart (left)**
This chart shows that there were lots of 'coelurosaur'-type theropods living throughout much of the reign of the dinosaurs, although they seem to show a fairly sharp decline towards the end of the Cretaceous Period.

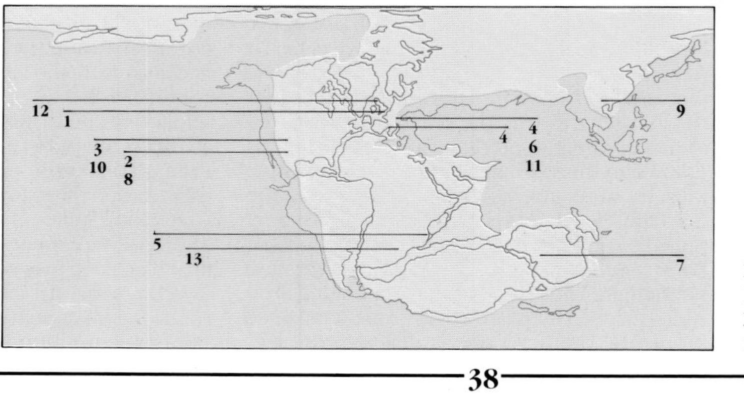

**Map (left)**
**1** *Aristosuchus*
**2** *Coelophysis*
**3** *Coelurus*
**4** *Compsognathus*
**5** *Elaphrosaurus*
**6** *Halticosaurus*
**7** *Kakuru*
**8** *Longosaurus*
**9** *Lukousaurus*
**10** *Ornitholestes*
**11** *Procompsognathus*
**12** *Saltopus*
**13** *Syntarsus*

vaguest way. The reason for this uncertainty is the relative rarity of good theropod fossils. There are many isolated theropod fossil bones and teeth, but (as we shall see) these tend to *add* to the confusion, rather than helping to clarify our understanding of the groups and their relationships. We shall be looking at good examples of 'coelurosaurs' (pages 38-43), ornithomimosaurs (pages 44-49), miscellaneous small theropods (pages 50-55), dromaeosaurids (pages 56-61), 'carnosaurs' (pages 62-67) and tyrannosaurids (pages 68-73). The terms 'coelurosaur' and 'carnosaur' are deliberately used in quotation marks as the precise relationships of the dinosaurs included in these groups are virtually impossible to untangle.

## 'Coelurosaurs'

As explained above, the first group of saurischian dinosaurs with which we shall be dealing are the theropods ('beast feet'). All theropods were carnivores (although there are one or two examples such as the ornithomimosaurs—pages 44-49—which lacked teeth and may have had a rather specialised diet); they also all tend to be two-legged (bipedal) runners. As you will see over the next few sections, this sort of body plan is surprisingly constant in all theropods. Comparing these creatures with living animals, it is difficult to find obvious counterparts. The most familiar living carnivores are the quadrupedal (four-footed) mammals such as the various dogs, bears and cats. The only two-legged carnivores are found among the birds (kestrels, kites, eagles, etc), but these winged and feathered animals can hardly be compared to the ground-dwelling theropods of the dinosaur era. This is an observation which poses an obvious but difficult question. Why was it that dinosaurs produced so many obviously successful ground-dwelling *bipedal* predators, whereas today the ground-dwelling predators are all *quadrupeds?* Before we try to answer this question, let us look at some representatives of the geat variety of theropod dinosaurs. Firstly there are the 'coelurosaurs' ('hollow-tailed reptiles').

The 'coelurosaurs' that we shall be looking at here are a rather odd mixture of generally small, lightly-built theropods. They are clearly not all close relatives when looked at in detail, but are described together in this section simply as a matter of convenience. All of these theropods are slender, fast-running predators with small heads (the jaws of which are lined with small, sharp teeth), long flexible necks and long arms with sharply-taloned grasping hands. Unfortunately, although animals of this general type must have been quite abundant throughout the 140 million year reign of the dinosaurs, the very fact that they were both small and lightly-built greatly reduces the probability of their being preserved at all well as fossils. Small animal carcasses tend to rot very quickly and their skeletal remains are liable to be scavenged and

**Comparative Sizes (left)**
**1** *Compsognathus*: l. 28in-4·6ft (70cm-1·4m).
**2** *Ornitholestes*: l. 6·5ft (2m).
**3** *Coelophysis*: l. 10ft (3m).

**Ornitholestes (left)**
This 'coelurosaur' was intermediate in size between the other two dinosaurs shown here, being about 6·5ft (2m) long. *Ornitholestes* was an active predator,and it may have fed on small animals like lizards, frogs and early mammals, all of which have been found in associated sediments. It had strong jaws and powerful grasping hands. The name *Ornitholestes* means 'bird robber', and it is just possible, although not very likely, that it could have captured early birds for food.

**Family Tree (below)**
This cladogram shows how we think 'coelurosaurs' are related to one another. The relatively primitive Triassic forms *Syntarsus* and *Coelophysis* (which may be linked to some of the early 'carnosaurs', page 62) are separated from the more advanced late Jurassic 'coelurosaurs'.

scattered, or completely destroyed. As a result, the fossil record of coelurosaur-type dinosaurs is extremely patchy. Their remains are found throughout the reign of the dinosaurs, but the vast majority of their fossils are isolated bones and teeth. This makes for great problems when it comes to looking at or trying to investigate their biology and relationships. It also creates problems which we will see recur throughout this section; these relate to the naming of dinosaurs. Quite often in the past, dinosaur names have been given to extremely scrappy pieces of fossil. In later years it has become obvious that the material is either so poor that it cannot be used for strictly scientific comparison with other more complete skeletons (*Monoclonius*—page 134—may be a good example of this); or it turns out that several names have been proposed for various pieces of just one dinosaur (*Brontosaurus* which is now known as *Apatosaurus*—pages 80-81—is a good example of this). In the case of the 'coelurosaurs' we shall concentrate on three, rather different, but nevertheless well-preserved specimens: *Coelophysis*, *Compsognathus* and *Ornitholestes*, in order to illustrate the main characteristics of this group of dinosaurs.

## Coelophysis Described

The remains of *Coelophysis* ('hollow form') were first discovered by an amateur fossil collector named David Baldwin. Baldwin was originally a collector of fossils employed by Othniel C. Marsh, but later in his career he began to work for Edward D. Cope. Compared with many of the North American fossil collectors of the late 19th century, Baldwin was unusual because he worked alone rather than in larger working parties. Baldwin collected fossils from New Mexico where there are good exposures of Permian and Triassic rocks. In Triassic rocks near Abiquiu in north-western New Mexico, Baldwin discovered some scraps of early dinosaurs in 1881. These bones were shipped back to Cope in Philadelphia who immediately recognised them as the bones of a small, very lightly-built carnivorous dinosaur. In fact he claimed that he was able to recognise *three* species of this dinosaur among these scrappy remains: *Coelophysis bauri*, *Coelophysis willistoni* (named after George Baur and Samuel Wendel Williston, both of whom were assistants of O.C. Marsh) and *Coelophysis longicollis*. These rather incomplete remains comprised various vertebrae, leg bones, and pieces of pelvis and rib, and they remained all that was known of one of the earliest discovered dinosaurs for the next sixty years. Then, in 1947, an expedition organised by the American Museum of Natural History re-visited the area of New Mexico explored by David Baldwin. From the field notes Baldwin made at the time, the expedition was able to discover the original *Coelophysis* locality, now on a property known as Ghost Ranch. The team

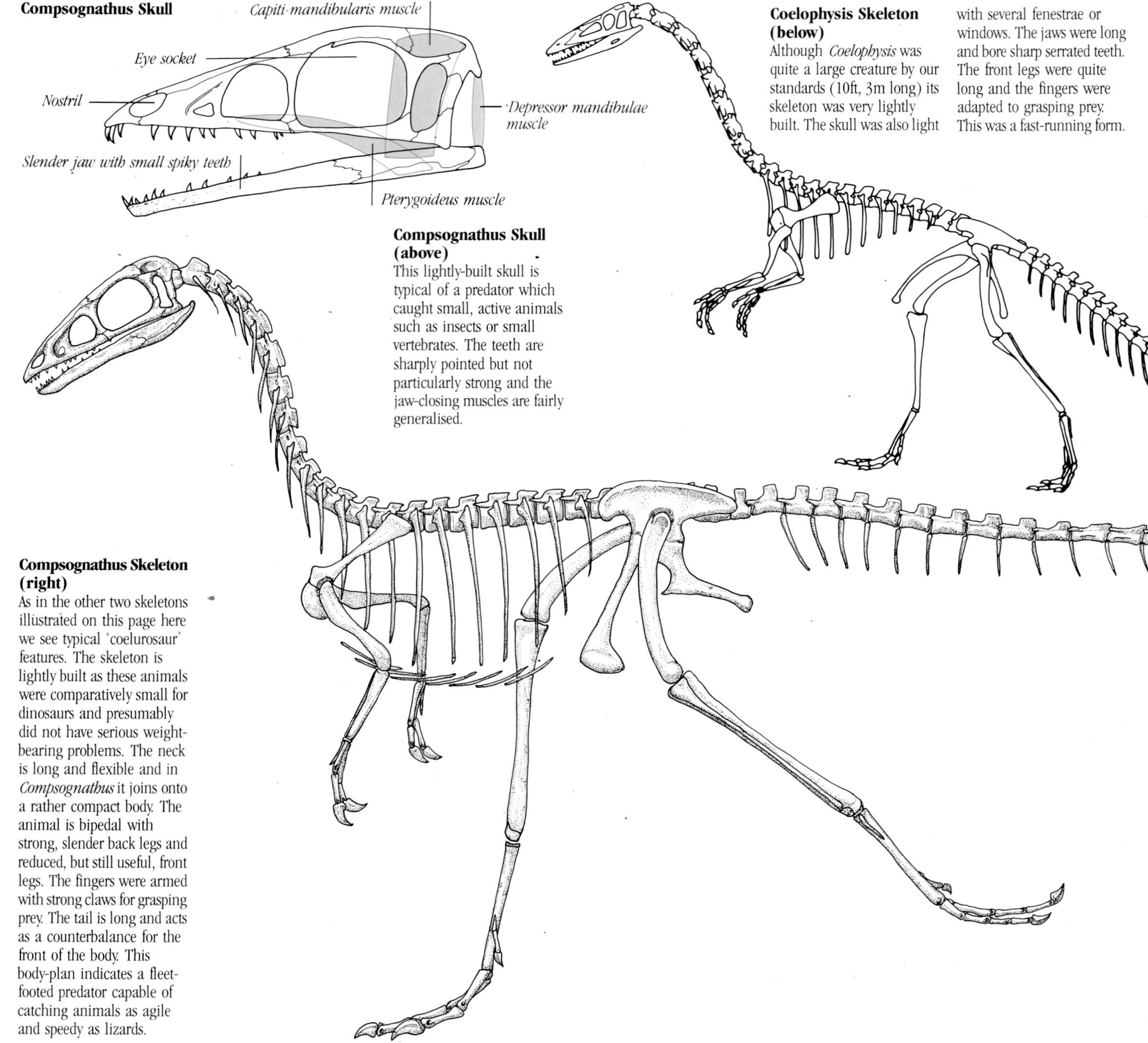


**Compsognathus Skull**

**Coelophysis Skeleton (below)**
Although *Coelophysis* was quite a large creature by our standards (10ft, 3m long) its skeleton was very lightly built. The skull was also light with several fenestrae or windows. The jaws were long and bore sharp serrated teeth. The front legs were quite long and the fingers were adapted to grasping prey. This was a fast-running form.

**Compsognathus Skull (above)**
This lightly-built skull is typical of a predator which caught small, active animals such as insects or small vertebrates. The teeth are sharply pointed but not particularly strong and the jaw-closing muscles are fairly generalised.

**Compsognathus Skeleton (right)**
As in the other two skeletons illustrated on this page here we see typical 'coelurosaur' features. The skeleton is lightly built as these animals were comparatively small for dinosaurs and presumably did not have serious weight-bearing problems. The neck is long and flexible and in *Compsognathus* it joins onto a rather compact body. The animal is bipedal with strong, slender back legs and reduced, but still useful, front legs. The fingers were armed with strong claws for grasping prey. The tail is long and acts as a counterbalance for the front of the body. This body-plan indicates a fleet-footed predator capable of catching animals as agile and speedy as lizards.

explored the area and found large numbers of bone fragments, but no good skeletons. Eventually it was decided to excavate a large section of the hillside, down to the layer where the bones seemed to be weathering out. As this layer was exposed, it revealed one of the most amazing dinosaur graveyards. Literally dozens of skeletons were discovered all lying across one another. It seems as though some local catastrophe had struck a herd of these animals; perhaps they were caught in a flash-flood and their carcasses were swept downriver on to a sand bar near the mouth of a river. Whatever the reason, the phenomenon has left for us some of the best evidence of any Triassic dinosaur. In this remarkable accumulation of skeletons can been seen animals of all ages from very young to fully-grown. These show that Cope was wrong to name three different species of *Coelophysis;* all that he had done was recognise the differences caused by growth between individuals.

As can be seen in the illustrations, *Coelophysis* was a slender creature; its skeleton was very lightly-built, with a long tail counterbalancing the front part of its body. The head was long and pointed, the eyes were large and the long jaws were armed with sharp, serrated teeth. As with all 'coelurosaurs', the neck was very slender and flexible. The arms were moderately long and had sharp clawed hands for grasping prey. The back legs were quite long and slender, and designed for running fast in pursuit of prey.

## Life-Style and Habits

The general life-style of *Coelophysis* is fairly obvious. With its lightly-built skeleton, long back legs, grasping hands and sharp tooth-lined mouth, it was undoubtedly a nimble predator of the late Triassic. Its potential victims were probably quite varied. Growing to a maximum length of 10ft (3m), *Coelophysis* may well have preyed upon the small, fleet-footed ornithopods of the time: *Lesothosaurus, Heterodontosaurus* and *Scutellosaurus* (see pages 98-99), all of which were no more than 3-5ft (1-1·5m) long. In fact they probably had a fairly varied diet, as many carnivores do today, taking large and small insects, amphibians and lizards.

The Ghost Ranch discoveries also give a rather gruesome insight into the feeding habits of *Coelophysis.* Some of the skeletons reveal the presence of small *Coelophysis* skeletons inside the ribcage of adult animals. At first it was supposed that the young skeletons were those of unborn infants. Unfortunately this is unlikely. All dinosaurs seem to have laid eggs, rather than bearing live young. The supposed embryos are, however, too large and well-formed to have been from embryos within eggs; they must therefore represent the last *meal* of the adult *Coelophysis!* This example of cannibalism probably reflects the fact that *Coelophysis* adults would tend to eat *any* small creatures that they could catch — even their own kind!

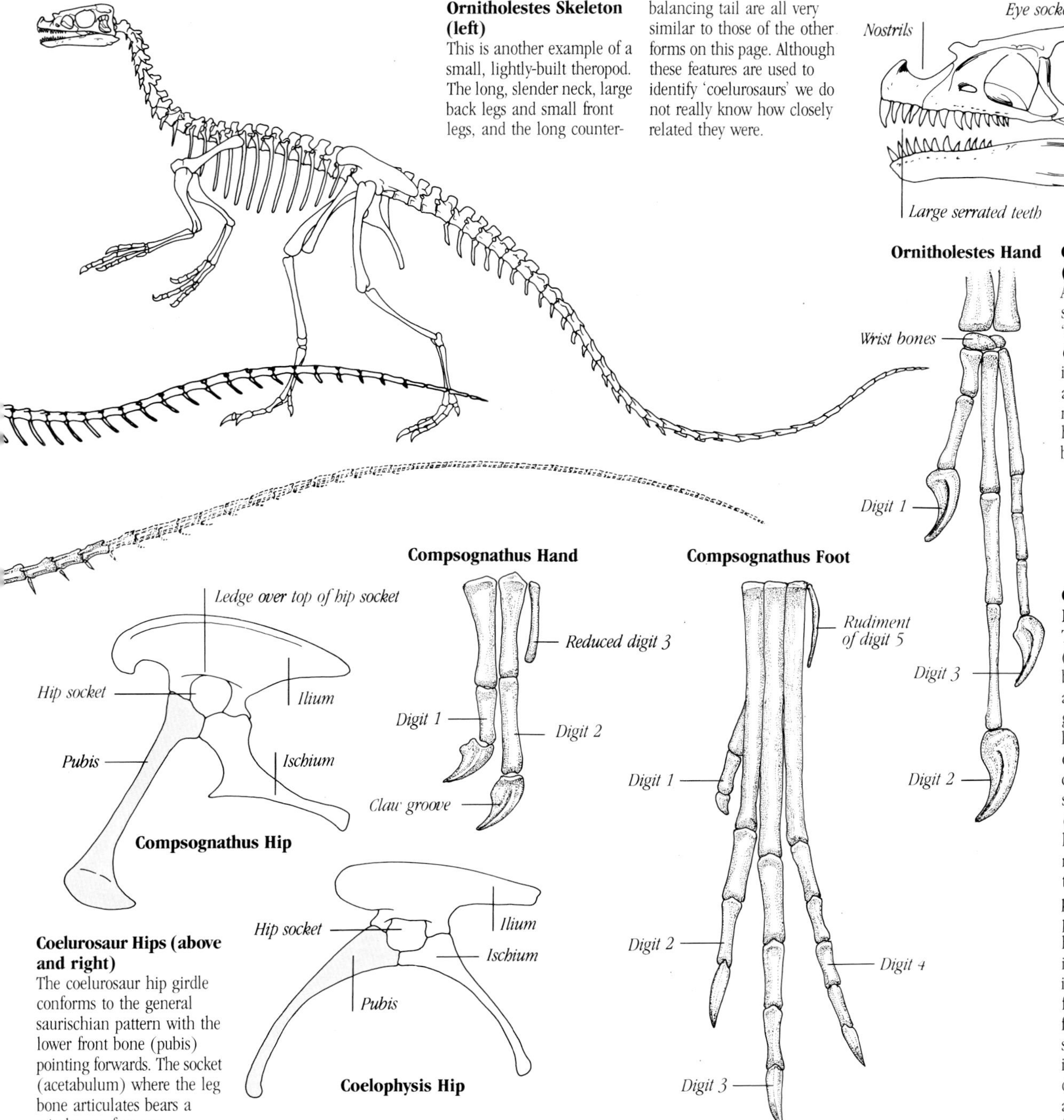


**Ornitholestes Skeleton (left)**
This is another example of a small, lightly-built theropod. The long, slender neck, large back legs and small front legs, and the long counter-balancing tail are all very similar to those of the other forms on this page. Although these features are used to identify 'coelurosaurs' we do not really know how closely related they were.

**Ornitholestes Skull (above)**
Although its skeleton is very similar to that of other 'coelurosaurs', the skull of *Ornitholestes* is rather different in being more heavily built and having shorter jaws and more robust teeth. It may have had a more powerful bite than other forms.

**Coelurosaur Hands and Feet (left)**
The hand of *Compsognathus* (far left) is rather peculiar in being so short, since an animal which presumably grasped its prey would need a longer hand to do so. Also only two of the fingers are clawed and the third is very small indeed. The foot of *Compsognathus* (middle left), however, is quite typical of most 'coelurosaurs' with three long, slender, forward-pointing toes and a fourth pointing backwards. The hand of *Ornitholestes* (left) is unusual for 'coelurosaurs' in having two especially long fingers and a short first finger. It is possible that this short finger could be turned in towards the others, as we do with our thumb, providing a very effective mechanism for gripping prey.

**Coelurosaur Hips (above and right)**
The coelurosaur hip girdle conforms to the general saurischian pattern with the lower front bone (pubis) pointing forwards. The socket (acetabulum) where the leg bone articulates bears a window or fenestra.

## The Discovery of Compsognathus

Another of the few well-preserved 'coelurosaurs', *Compsognathus* ('pretty jaw') remains have been discovered in rocks of late Jurassic age from southern Germany and France. It was a small creature, the remains so far discovered indicate an animal of between 28in and 4·6ft (70cm-1·4m) in length.

The first remains of *Compsognathus* to be discovered consisted of a beautifully preserved, virtually complete skeleton from the lithographic limestone of the Riedenburg-Kelheim area of southern Germany (Bavaria). The precise area where this was discovered is now unknown because Dr Oberndorfer who collected this specimen in the late 1850s was rather vague about where he had found it; this may have been because he did not want other amateur collectors to discover his locality. Many amateur fossil collectors in Germany scoured the lithographic limestone quarries because they produced some of the finest preserved fossils of pterosaurs and *Archaeopteryx* (see pages 175-177) which could be sold to State museums for a great deal of money. Since this time only two other specimens of *Compsognathus* have been reported. One consists of a few toe bones from the same area. The other is an almost complete skeleton discovered in rocks of a similar age near Nice in southern France in 1972.

The first *Compsognathus* skeleton is by far the best known specimen and has recently been redescribed by Professor John Ostrom (Yale). It represents an animal of about 28in (70cm) body length, preserved lying on its right-hand side. The skeleton is virtually undisturbed. (The hand bones are a little scattered, probably drifted in currents as the carcass rotted, and there is some evidence that the belly was breached, perhaps by the build up of gases within the decomposing cadaver.)

The death position of the animal is characteristic of many skeletons with the head and neck strongly arched over the back. The likely cause of this contorted posture is the contraction in *rigor mortis* of the neck muscles and ligaments which would have been very powerful in these long-necked animals.

As can be seen from the skeletal reconstruction, the proportions of *Compsognathus* are very similar to those of *Coelophysis*. A long tail counterbalances its front, and the hindlimbs are strong and slender, indicating that it was a fleet-footed biped. The back of the animal is relatively shorter than that of *Coelophysis*, giving it a more 'compact' appearance, but the neck and head are very similar in general shape.

The forelimbs deserve particular mention. Firstly, they are unusually short for an animal that presumably used them to grasp prey; and secondly, they exhibit only two clawed fingers on each hand, whereas *Coelophysis* has three, and a remnant of a fourth.

## Life-Style and Habits

The life-style of *Compsognathus* is reasonably self-evident. It was a fleet-footed, bipedal predator of small animals: presumably insects and small vertebrates of various types. Very fortunately, we can be more certain of the probable feeding habits and abilities of *Compsognathus* than of most other dinosaurs, because, like *Coelophysis*, the remains of its last meal are preserved within the ribcage of this animal as well.

John Ostrom was able to study the stomach contents of *Compsognathus* and showed that it consisted of the skeleton of a small lizard named *Bavarisaurus*. (O.C. Marsh, who first noted that stomach contents were present in the ribcage, suggested that they represented embryos.) Judged by the proportions of its limbs and its long tail, Ostrom deduced that *Bavarisaurus* must have been an extremely fast-running, agile ground-dwelling lizard. Since *Compsognathus* undoubtedly caught the *Bavarisaurus* we have a testimony to its abilities. In order to catch this type of creature it would need keen sight, rapid acceleration, high speed, manoeuvrability and quick reactions.

In 1972 a new species of *Compsognathus (C. corallestris)* was described, based on a fairly complete skeleton of a larger animal in almost the same preserved position. The new specimen was given the new specific name because it was larger than the German skeleton and also because it seemed to have flipper-like front legs. A flesh reconstruction of *Compsognathus corallestris* was produced in Dr Beverly Halstead's book *The Evolution and Ecology of the Dinosaurs* in 1975. It was envisaged that this species of *Compsognathus* lived in and around coral lagoons and that the 'flippers' on its forelimbs enabled it to swim more efficiently in the lagoons, either in pursuit of prey or to avoid predators.

Unfortunately the evidence upon which the 'flipper' reconstruction is based is extremely dubious. The forelimbs of this skeleton are quite poorly preserved, and the area around the forelimbs which is supposed to show the flipper impression does not look very different from other areas of the slab of rock upon which this animal is preserved. Careful comparison of the two good skeletons by Professor Ostrom proved fairly conclusively that the French specimen was simply a larger version of the same species of *Compsognathus* from Germany and that there was no good evidence for a flipper on the forelimb.

## The 'Bird Robber'

This third type of 'coelurosaur' — *Ornitholestes* ('bird robber') — was discovered in late Jurassic rocks at Bone Cabin Quarry near Como in Wyoming (North America) in 1900. This specimen, which consists of a partial skeleton including the skull, jaws and many other parts, was first described by Henry Fairfield Osborn in 1903 and in more detail in 1916. To this day it is still only known from this specimen and an incomplete hand from another individual.

Again a quick glance at *Ornitholestes*, *Coelophysis* and *Compsognathus* reveals the very strong similarity between all three of these dinosaurs. The body of *Ornitholestes* is similarly balanced at the hips and the neck is slender and flexible. The skull and forelimbs are, however, sufficiently different to merit some brief comments. The skull is rather more robustly constructed than the previous two examples, being both deeper and shorter-snouted. The teeth are also numerous and quite large. This arrangement of skull and teeth suggests greater mechanical strength and that *Ornitholestes* had a rather more powerful bite than either of the other two. Perhaps *Ornitholestes* was capable of tackling larger and more active prey than either *Compsognathus* or *Coelophysis*. The hand, which was represented by several finger bones in the original skeleton and two other complete fingers from another individual, is rather unusually proportioned. The second and third fingers are long, slender and almost equal in length while the first finger is very short. The arm is also relatively long in proportion to that of *Coelophysis* and *Compsognathus*. Both of these features suggest an enhanced prehensile ability of the forelimb for reaching and grasping prey more powerfully and effectively. The difference in length between the first and the second and third fingers is linked to the ability to turn the first finger inwards against the other two like a thumb. The hand could therefore grip its prey very powerfully indeed. The structure of the hand is rather similar to that of dromaeosaurids (pages 56-61).

## Other 'Coelurosaurs'

The three examples that we have looked at so far are fairly representative of a bewildering variety of lightly-built theropods that are found throughout the reign of the dinosaurs. We shall look at some of the more bizarre types of small theropod over the next few sections. There are, however, a considerable number of small theropods which are, for the most part, rather

**Above:** A reconstruction of the skeleton of *Ornitholestes* that has been prepared by the Tyrrell Museum of Palaeontology in Alberta. The skull is quite deep and obviously fairly robust, implying that *Ornitholestes* was a predator that was equipped with quite a powerful bite.

**Below:** This beautifully preserved specimen of *Compsognathus* is from the lithographic limestone of the Riedenburg-Kelheim area of Bavaria. We know something of the feeding habits of this nimble predator as the remains of *Bavarisaurus*, a lizard, were found in its stomach.

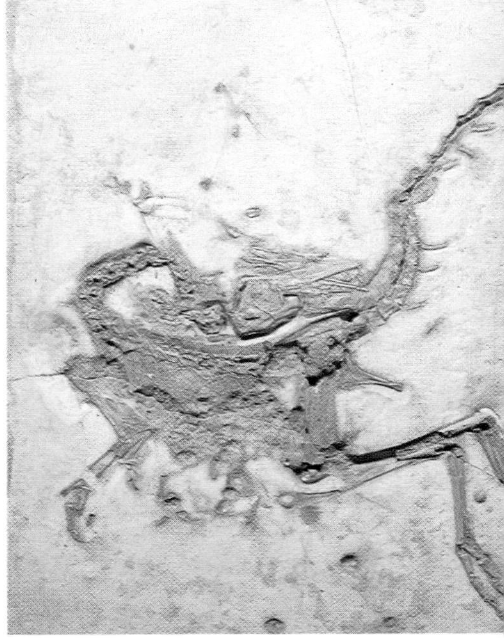

poorly known and whose biology and relationships to the above dinosaurs are naturally difficult to assess.

(i) Possible relatives of *Coelophysis* include *Procompsognathus* ('before pretty jaw') a very fragmentary fossil from the Triassic of West Germany, and *Halticosaurus* ('nimble reptile') a much larger but again rather poorly preserved skeleton from the same site, and *Longosaurus* ('Long's reptile') based on some of Cope's original *Coelophysis longicollis*. In addition to these species there are *Syntarsus* ('fused ankle'), a partial skeleton from the late Triassic of Zimbabwe; *Saltopus* ('leaping foot') which is an imperfectly known small form from the late Triassic of Scotland; and *Lukousaurus* ('Lu-Kou reptile') a peculiar horned form from the late Triassic of southern China.

Several other genera such as *Avipes* ('bird foot'), *Dolichosuchus* ('long crocodile') and *Velocipes* ('speedy foot') are dubious forms based on rather poor material. *Spinosuchus* ('spiny crocodile') from Texas is a thecodontian, not a dinosaur at all.

(ii) Relatives of *Compsognathus* are not presently known, although many authors have related *Compsognathus* to the *Ornitholestes*-type 'coelurosaurs' listed below.

(iii) Possible relatives of *Ornitholestes*, generally known as coelurids, include *Coelurus* ('hollow tail') from the late Jurassic of Wyoming in North America: *Aristosuchus* ('top crocodile'), a fragmentary type from the early Cretaceous of southern England; *Elaphrosaurus* ('light reptile'), a moderately well-preserved but headless skeleton from the late Jurassic of Tendaguru (Tanzania); *Microvenator* ('small hunter') from the early Cretaceous of Montana, as well as possibly *Stokesosaurus* ('Stokes' reptile') from the late Jurassic of Utah; *Iliosuchus* ('crocodile pelvis') from the late Jurassic of England; and *Kakuru* ('rainbow lizard'), a genus based on a tibia from South Australia. Relations may also exist with dromaeosaurid theropods.

## Dubious Genera

Numerous extremely dubious coelurids are known including: *Coeluroides* ('Coelurus form'), *Compsosuchus* ('pretty crocodile'), *Inosaurus* ('In reptile'), *Jubbulpuria* ('from Jabalpur'), *Laevisuchus* ('lucky crocodile'), *Ornithomimoides* ('Ornithomimus form'), *Sinocoelurus* ('Chinese hollow tail') and *Teinurosaurus* ('extended reptile'). The latter are all based on undiagnostic remains which may or may not be of small theropod dinosaurs.

An example of the problems that have been created as a result of the very poor state of some of these fossils is given by *Aristosuchus* from southern England. Fragmentary remains of this little creature have been given at least five different names over the years: *Calamosaurus, Calamospondylus, Thecocoelurus, Thecospondylus* and *Coelurus*. All of these are invalid, but cause enormous confusion to people studying these creatures.

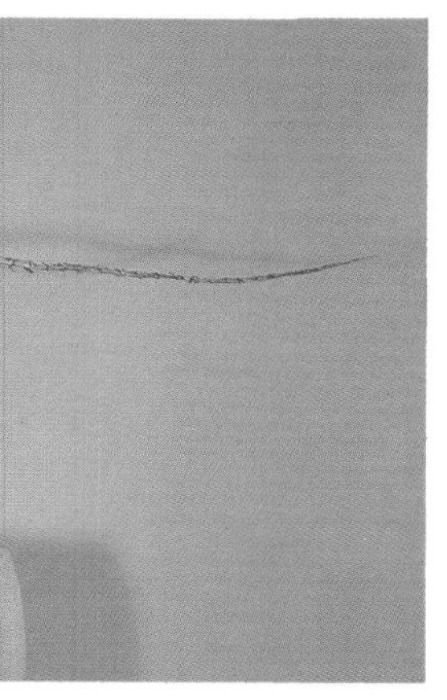

**Below:** It is not easy to find counterparts of the small theropods in the natural world today, but their behaviour may have paralleled that of the Secretary Bird seen here, which is also a long-legged, and fleet-footed predator the feeds upon ground dwelling reptiles.

**Above:** *Coelophysis* is a typical 'coelurosaur' with its long jaws, sharp teeth, and long, slender limbs. The curved-back position of the head was probably caused by the contraction of the neck muscles as *rigor mortis* set in.

**The Lagoon Dweller (below)**
An intriguing suggestion has been advanced that one species of *Compsognathus (C. corallestris)* may have been equipped with flipper-like forelimbs which would have allowed it to adopt an amphibious way of life, venturing into lagoons to find food or avoid its natural enemies, as below. Recent study of the skeleton, however, casts doubt on the evidence of flippers and seems to rule out this interpretation.

# ORNITHOMIMOSAURS & OVIRAPTOROSAURS

**Struthiomimus (right)**
This was a medium-sized ostrich dinosaur, being 10-13ft (3-4m) long. The proportions of the body of *Struthiomimus,* and many of the more detailed features of its anatomy are remarkably convergent with present-day ostriches. The limbs are very similar,and palaeontologists speculate that the ostrich dinosaurs could have run just as fast as a modern ostrich. The most obvious differences are that *Struthiomimus* had no feathers (as far as we know) and that it used its long tail for balancing while running. Ostriches use their reduced wings for this purpose.

Having introduced the theropods as fleet-footed predatory dinosaurs, it must seem a little odd to find that the very next example after the 'coelurosaurs' should be that of theropods that have lost their teeth! Nevertheless, both the ornithomimosaurs ('bird mimic reptiles') and the relatively less well-known oviraptorosaurs ('egg-stealing reptiles') have this rather dubious distinction.

## Ornithomimosaurs

Also known as 'ostrich dinosaurs' for fairly obvious reasons (see below), ornithomimosaur remains are reasonably abundant in late Cretaceous rocks of Western North America and East Asia (Mongolia). Ornithomimosaurs seem to be very similar in size and appearance, reaching body lengths of about 10-13ft (3-4m), and bearing a strong resemblance to modern ground-dwelling birds such as the ostrich or emu.

**Time Chart (left)**
The ornithomimosaurs are notable for their general appearance in the late Cretaceous, the earliest form seeming to date from the middle Cretaceous, provided it has been correctly identified. Some authors have proposed that they are related to *Elaphrosaurus* of the Late Jurassic. The oviraptorosaurs are exclusively late Cretaceous in age. Their origins are unknown.

**Family Tree (below)**
The relationships of the ostrich dinosaurs are not at all clear. The North American forms are all very similar and show strong affinities to *Gallimimus.* Ornithomimosaurs may have their origins in the middle Cretaceous from forms like *Archaeornithomimus.* The oviraptorosaurs occupy a related but separate branch of the cladogram.

The first ornithomimosaur remains consisted of the imperfect foot of a dinosaur which was discovered in 1889 by George Cannon in late Cretaceous rocks near Denver, Colorado. Marsh described this material in 1890 as *Ornithomimus velox* ('speedy bird mimic') and, in addition, named two other species *O. tenuis* (a partial foot and hindlimb) and *O. grandis* from other fragmentary remains. Both of the latter had been discovered by J. B. Hatcher in Montana, in the later 1880s. More fragmentary material was described by Marsh in 1892 *(O. sedens* and *O. minutus)* and he recognised from the remains of the pelvis of *Ornithomimus sedens* that these animals were not ornithopods (pages 98 to 127) as originally suspected, but theropods of a hitherto unknown sort. The precise relationships of these remains to other theropods were very uncertain; they represented relatively large animals and were therefore thought to belong to the carnosaurs rather than the smaller coelurosaurs.

A clear picture of the really unusual nature of these animals did not emerge, however, for several years. In 1902 Lawrence Lambe described another specimen from the late Cretaceous of Red Deer River, Alberta as *Ornithomimus altus;* this was again rather fragmentary, comprising hindlimbs, feet and pelvic bones. It was not until 1917 that the first reasonably complete skeleton of an ornithomimosaur was described by Henry Fairfield Osborn. This skeleton consisted of a more-or-less completely preserved animal, lacking only parts of the head, some of the vertebrae and a few limb bones. It allowed the first accurate skeletal reconstruction to be drawn.

On the basis of this fine specimen, Osborn proposed that it was virtually indistinguishable from Lambe's *Ornithomimus altus* but suggested that a new generic name *Struthiomimus* ('ostrich mimic') *altus* be used. Osborn claimed that *Struthiomimus* was from a geologically earlier period than *Ornithomimus*, and also differed in that *Struthiomimus* still had a small splint-like remnant of a fourth toe on its hindfoot which *Ornithomimus* lacked.

Osborn's description and discussion of the anatomy and biology of *Struthiomimus* was wide-ranging and perceptive. He recognised the very strong similarity between the proportions of *Struthiomimus* and the large running birds of today (small head, long neck, and legs) — although there is the obvious lack in living birds of a long, bony tail and long, clawed arms. The really unexpected characteristic of this form, however, was the absence of teeth in its jaws. The resemblance in shape and texture of the jaw bones to those of birds suggests that the jaws were sheathed in a horny beak.

The thin and light structure of ornithomimosaurs' skull bones makes it highly probable that the skulls of these creatures were *flexible*. Certainly many living birds are able to tilt the upper beak upward or downward while moving the lower jaw. This allows them to

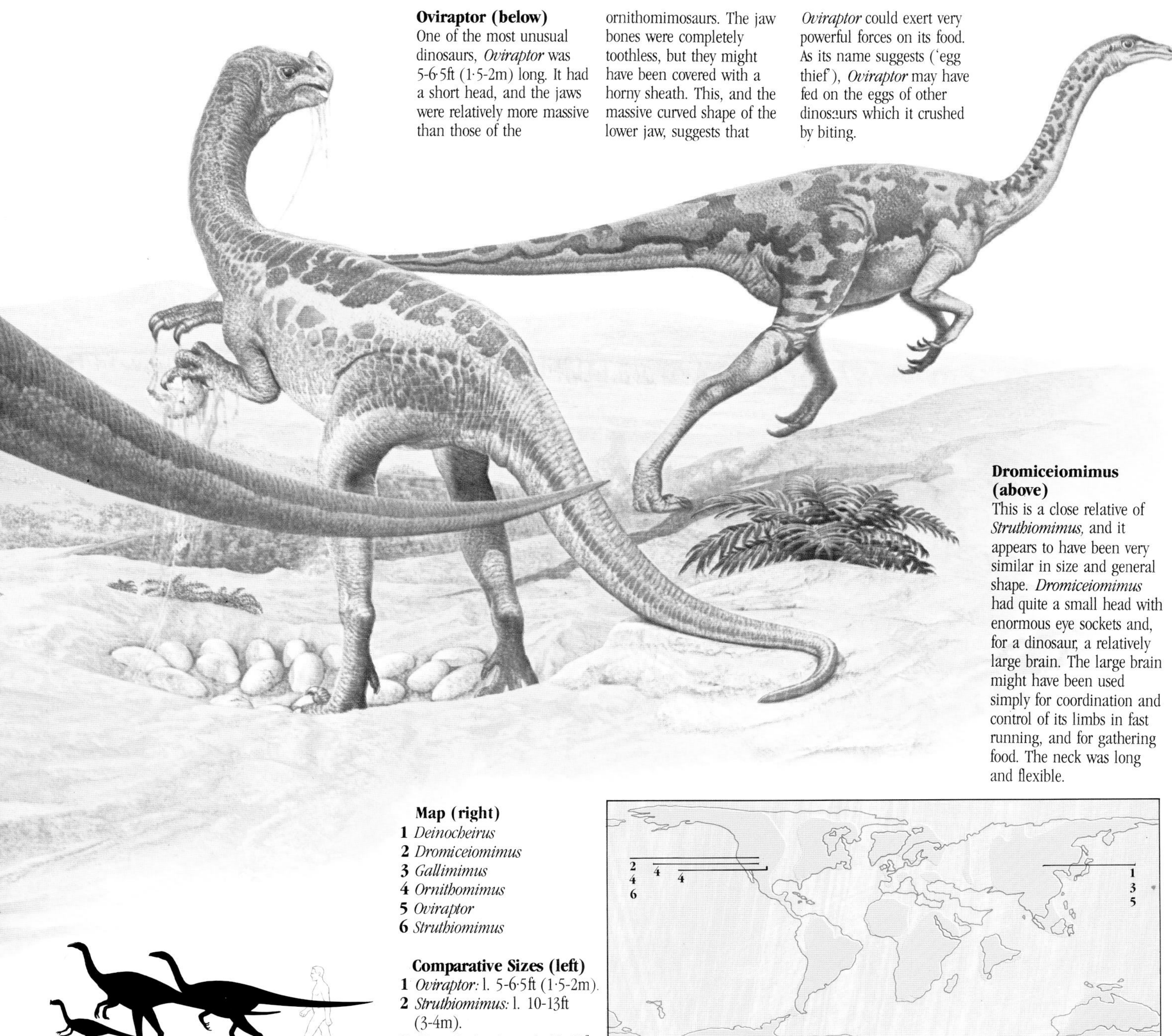


**Oviraptor (below)**
One of the most unusual dinosaurs, *Oviraptor* was 5-6·5ft (1·5-2m) long. It had a short head, and the jaws were relatively more massive than those of the ornithomimosaurs. The jaw bones were completely toothless, but they might have been covered with a horny sheath. This, and the massive curved shape of the lower jaw, suggests that *Oviraptor* could exert very powerful forces on its food. As its name suggests ('egg thief'), *Oviraptor* may have fed on the eggs of other dinosaurs which it crushed by biting.

**Dromiceiomimus (above)**
This is a close relative of *Struthiomimus*, and it appears to have been very similar in size and general shape. *Dromiceiomimus* had quite a small head with enormous eye sockets and, for a dinosaur, a relatively large brain. The large brain might have been used simply for coordination and control of its limbs in fast running, and for gathering food. The neck was long and flexible.

**Map (right)**
**1** *Deinocheirus*
**2** *Dromiceiomimus*
**3** *Gallimimus*
**4** *Ornithomimus*
**5** *Oviraptor*
**6** *Struthiomimus*

**Comparative Sizes (left)**
**1** *Oviraptor:* l. 5-6·5ft (1·5-2m).
**2** *Struthiomimus:* l. 10-13ft (3-4m).
**3** *Dromiceiomimus:* l. 10-13ft (3-4m).

manoeuvre food in the mouth with great precision. A good example is a parrot; parrots and budgies are able to hold nuts between their jaws and by carefully moving upper and lower beaks and tongue in unison, remove the unpalatable husks with great delicacy. Ornithomimosaurs seem to have had the same abilities, because their skulls were so light. Whether this allowed them to consume a wider range of food in their diet, or represented a special adaptation to a specific type of food is uncertain.

The neck was long and slender and the bones were very flexibly jointed to permit great mobility, whereas the back seems to have been held rather stiffly. The spines of the backbone are scarred by powerful ligaments which held them in place. The ribs are also well formed and were apparently connected to an extensive series of belly ribs (gastralia). The combination of ribs enclosing the entire chest and belly region, plus the stiffening ligaments of the back, undoubtedly conferred great rigidity upon this part of the body. The spine is jointed very firmly to the pelvis, and the tail, which was evidently long, is unusually modified towards its back end. The narrow prongs of bone (zygapophyses) which jut out from the top of the individual vertebrae and help to control the movements of the tail bones are unusually long. As a result of this, the end of the tail must have been held quite stiffly, although the part of the tail nearer the hips was quite normally flexible.

The front legs are remarkably slender and elongate, ending in three very long, clawed fingers. Compared with *Ornitholestes* (see page 41) the proportions of the fingers are different and the claws are much less sharply curved. Osborn was particularly struck by the similarity in proportion and arrangement between the forelimbs of *Struthiomimus* and those of the three-toed sloth *(Bradypus tridactylus)*.

The hindlimbs are remarkably long and slender, and obviously well designed for fast running. The feet, which are also long and slender, end in three toes with narrow, flattened claws, rather similar to those on the feet of large running birds.

## Habits of Struthiomimus

Osborn reviewed the various proposals that had been made up to then (1917) concerning the habits of ornithomimosaurs. These seemed to him to present certain problems. On the one hand *Struthiomimus* resembled ostrich-like running birds in the structure of its head, neck and legs; while on the other, its forelimbs were most similar to those of the sloths (which hang from branches).

That *Struthiomimus* was a running creature seems incontrovertible; its tail counterbalanced the front part of its body, the stiffening of its back end apparently most readily explained if it were used as a dynamic stabiliser for rapid changes of direction, as well as straight running. This particular adaptation seems to be quite

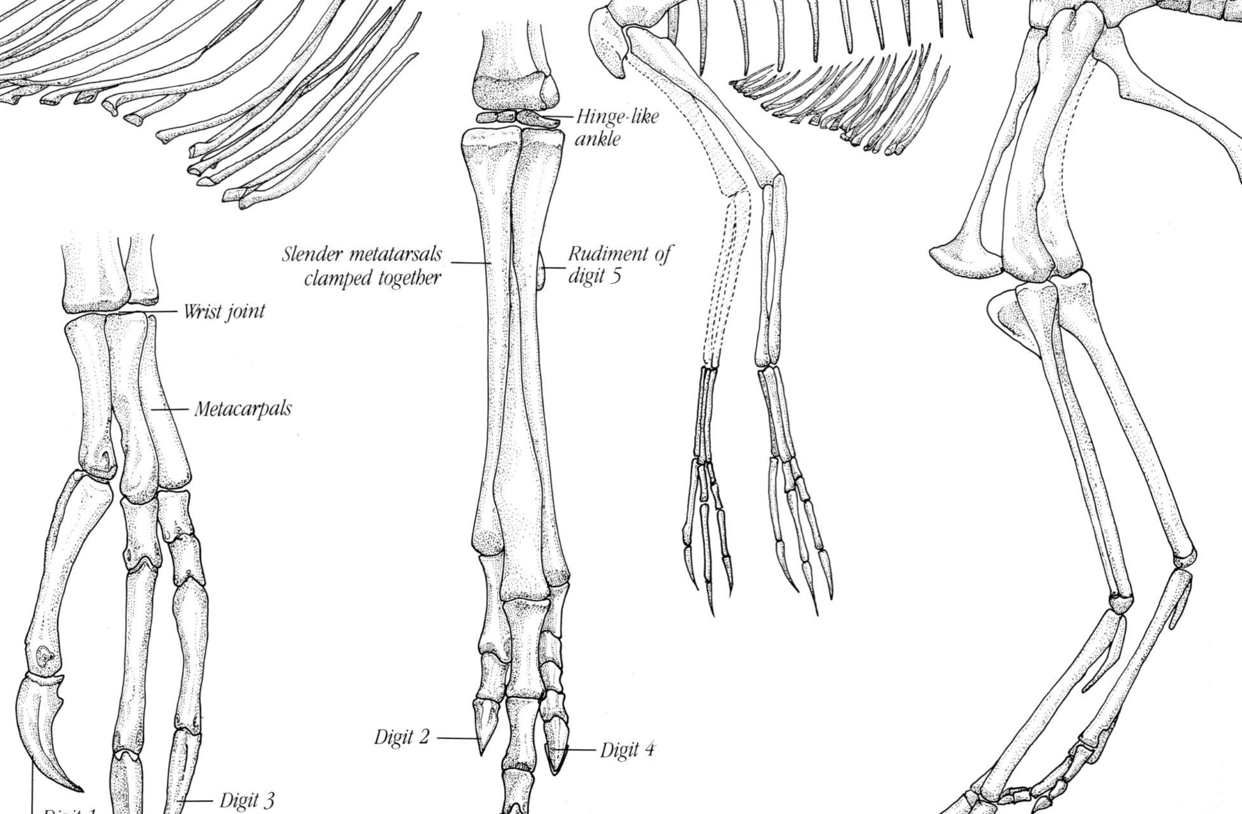


**Belly Ribs of Struthiomimus (below)**
Belly ribs, or gastralia, are found in various reptile groups although they are absent from mammals. They are not formed in the same way as vertebral ribs and should not strictly be called by the same name. No-one really knows what their function is but there have been several suggestions. They may help to support the abdomen, especially important in an herbivore with a large gut.

**Struthiomimus Skeleton (right)**
This skeleton is an odd mixture of rigidity and flexibility. The neck was long, slender and presumably highly mobile but the vertebrae of the back were held stiffly in place by strong ligaments. The end of the tail was also very stiff since the prongs of bone which joined the vertebrae together were very long and so restricted movement. The front legs were relatively long, and very slender.

**Struthiomimus Skull (left)**
The long slender, toothless jaw and large eyes give this skull a very bird-like appearance. It is also probable that the jaws were covered with horn. The lightness and thinness of the skull bones suggest that they may have been flexible, allowing movement in the skull, as in modern birds.

**Struthiomimus Hand and Foot (right)**
The foot (far right) provides evidence that *Struthiomimus* was a running creature. The toes are rather long and slender, but the upper foot bones (metatarsals) are very elongate. The foot bears an obvious resemblance to that of large running birds such as ostriches. The claws are narrow and flattened and may have provided traction with the ground to stop the foot slipping as it was thrust backwards during running. The hand is rather lightly built but looks as though it would form a useful gripping mechanism, perhaps for bending down the branches of trees, and so bringing them within range of *Struthiomimus*' slender toothless beak.

widespread among fleet-footed dinosaurs. Dromaeosaurids (pages 56-61) show an extreme development of stiffening rods of the sort seen in *Struthiomimus* while hypsilophodontids (pages 104-109) used a sheath of ossified tendons to achieve the same sort of structure.

As far as their likely diet is concerned, William Beebe proposed that ornithomimosaurs were insectivores, perhaps the equivalent of the anteaters of today. Osborn rejected this theory because the forelimbs of *Struthiomimus* were clearly not powerful enough to undertake the sort of digging activities needed to grub up anthills. Certainly there is no evidence of the powerful shoulder muscles characteristic of modern anteaters, nor was there any evidence of a long, sticky tongue. Furthermore the hindlimbs were adapted for fast running rather than digging.

Another theory arose when Barnum Brown noted that the remains of ornithomimosaurs are usually found in coastal shore deposits, and proposed that these creatures may have waded along shores feeding on small crabs and shrimps. They may then have used their forelimbs for scraping sand, moving rocks and probing crevices to catch these animals. Osborn also rejected this theory, although his reasons for doing so are not nearly as convincing as he obviously thought they were. Firstly, he suggested that the beak and hands were not adapted for catching shrimps and the like. This is obviously a matter of opinion, rather than being based on a logical argument. Secondly, he stated that the forelimbs were not adapted either for digging or holding struggling prey. Again in what sense this is supposed to provide a conclusive rebuttal of Brown's proposal is not obvious.

Thirdly, neither the structure of the beak nor that of the feet resembles that of living wading birds. This argument may have a little more weight because Osborn is at least making a statement of comparison. However, whether the structure and habits of small wading birds can be realistically compared with those of a 10-13ft (3-4m) long shore-dwelling dinosaur must be open to doubt.

Having reviewed and rejected previous theories, Osborn proposed his own—the ostrich theory—which was that *Struthiomimus* was a browsing herbivore. He suggested that the forelimbs were used as grapples for bending down branches, so that young shoots and buds could be bitten off. This type of life-style seems to explain the combination of long grasping hands and arms, and the long flexible neck which would have allowed the head to be moved with accuracy between branches and twigs, there to peck at food. The shape of the beak seems well suited to this type of feeding. And finally the feet are similar to those of the big ostrich-like birds.

A fourth interpretation of the habits of *Struthiomimus*, proposed by Dr William King

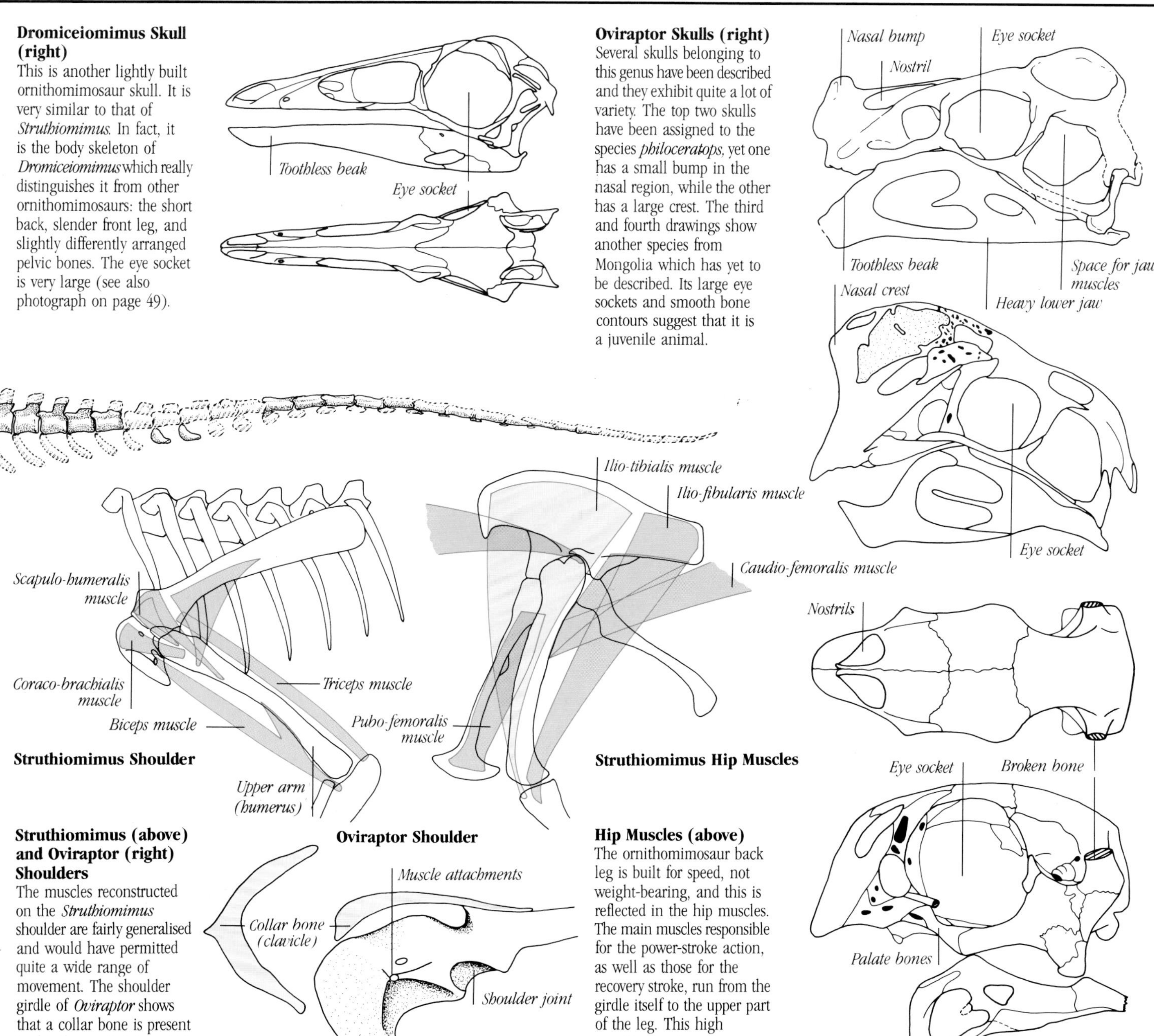


**Dromiceiomimus Skull (right)**
This is another lightly built ornithomimosaur skull. It is very similar to that of *Struthiomimus*. In fact, it is the body skeleton of *Dromiceiomimus* which really distinguishes it from other ornithomimosaurs: the short back, slender front leg, and slightly differently arranged pelvic bones. The eye socket is very large (see also photograph on page 49).

**Oviraptor Skulls (right)**
Several skulls belonging to this genus have been described and they exhibit quite a lot of variety. The top two skulls have been assigned to the species *philoceratops*, yet one has a small bump in the nasal region, while the other has a large crest. The third and fourth drawings show another species from Mongolia which has yet to be described. Its large eye sockets and smooth bone contours suggest that it is a juvenile animal.

**Struthiomimus Shoulder**

**Struthiomimus Hip Muscles**

**Oviraptor Shoulder**

**Struthiomimus (above) and Oviraptor (right) Shoulders**
The muscles reconstructed on the *Struthiomimus* shoulder are fairly generalised and would have permitted quite a wide range of movement. The shoulder girdle of *Oviraptor* shows that a collar bone is present in this theropod at least. It is shown in top view (near right) and in side view.

**Hip Muscles (above)**
The ornithomimosaur back leg is built for speed, not weight-bearing, and this is reflected in the hip muscles. The main muscles responsible for the power-stroke action, as well as those for the recovery stroke, run from the girdle itself to the upper part of the leg. This high insertion produces a more rapid swing of the leg, and thus more speed.

Gregory, is essentially similar to Osborn's, only differing in one or two respects. Gregory concurs with Osborn in envisaging these animals as very fast-running ground dwellers which used their arms and hands as grapples to obtain food. However, Gregory proposed a much more catholic diet for *Struthiomimus*, suggesting it was an omnivore, taking fruits and seeds as well as small vertebrates (mammals, reptiles, amphibians) and larger invertebrates (millipedes, flying insects etc). Gregory also came up with the novel suggestion that they may have had skin flaps (patagia) between the arms and body; these, he proposed, served to prevent the animal from toppling forward when running fast with arms outstretched. This last suggestion has never really been taken seriously, and it could only be proved if a well-preserved skin impression were to be found.

To sum up, although Brown's sea-shore theory has not been effectively disproved, the general consensus today supports the opinions of Osborn and Gregory. Ornithomimosaurs were probably ground-dwelling, omnivorous dinosaurs which were capable of running very fast—perhaps as fast as living ostriches (31 mph, 50 kph). Their fleetness of foot and probable great manoeuvrability permitted them not only to escape larger predators, but also to catch fast-moving prey, such as lizards, small mammals or flying insects.

## Recent Discoveries

Since the early years of this century, several significant discoveries of ornithomimosaurs have been made both in North America and Asia. In the early 1920s a fragmentary skeleton, *Struthiomimus brevitertius,* came to light. Then in 1926 a new specimen was discovered near Steveville on the Red Deer River, Alberta. This new find consisted of the front part of the skeleton (including a fine head) of an ornithomimosaur, which was described and named *Struthiomimus samueli* by William Parks in 1928. This was the first ornithomimosaur with a well-preserved skull. In the early 1970s Osmolska, Roniewicz and Barsbold described a completely new ornithomimosaur: *Gallimimus* ('chicken mimic') from Mongolia.

In 1972 Dale Russell (Ottawa) provided a much needed review of the North American ornithomimosaurs and reassessed the various species that had been proposed since the 1890s. This was valuable because many authors had tended to regard *Ornithomimus* and *Struthiomimus* as the same animal, and used *Struthiomimus* as the generic name for almost all the material.

Russell's research revealed that there were *three* genera of ornithomimosaurs in the late Cretaceous of North America:

(i) *Ornithomimus* (based on Marsh's original type material, *O. sedens,* and another fine skeleton lacking only the tail—originally named *Struthiomimus currelli*—from the Red Deer River). *Ornithomimus* is distinguished from the two other genera, *Struthiomimus* and *Dromiceiomimus,* by the length of its back, the proportions of its forelimbs (longer than *Struthiomimus*) and hindlimbs (shorter than both *Struthiomimus* and *Dromiceiomimus*) and the shape of its hands.

(ii) *Struthiomimus* (based primarily on the skeleton described by Osborn in 1917 and other related, but relatively poorly preserved, material) is distinguished from the other two genera by the length of its body, the proportions of its limbs (longer legs and shorter arms than *Ornithomimus*), and hand and pelvis shape.

(iii) *Dromiceiomimus* ('emu mimic'). This new genus, proposed by Dale Russell, is based on material from Alberta originally described as *Struthiomimus brevitertius* and *Struthiomimus samueli* by William Parks. *Dromiceiomimus* has a relatively short back, a comparatively slender and long forearm and hand, and somewhat differently arranged pelvic bones.

Russell also reviewed the possible habits of ornithomimosaurs and proposed that they may well have been solely carnivorous, perhaps feeding upon eggs and other small animal material obtained by scooping from the ground or digging. Since ornithomimids were defenceless, they would have relied upon their sprinting abilities (and possibly camouflage) to avoid predators which may well have been the more heavily built but less agile tyrannosaurids (pages 68-73).

Ornithomimosaurs may well have originated from the lightly-built theropods ('coelurosaurs') such as *Elaphrosaurus,* a relatively large, lightly-built theropod from the later Jurassic of Tanzania. Unfortunately the head of *Elaphrosaurus* is not known, so it is uncertain whether it possessed teeth in its jaws or had the horny bill typical of ornithomimosaurs. However, numerous small theropod teeth are known from the same locality. Another species, originally named *Ornithomimus asiaticus,* from the early Cretaceous of Mongolia, which has since been re-named *Archaeornithomimus* ('ancient bird mimic'), may also be an early ornithomimosaur, but at the moment this form is only known from a few fragmentary bones of the hand, foot and backbone.

*Gallimimus,* the Asian ornithomimosaur, comes from the late Cretaceous of Mongolia. It has been described from at least three quite well-preserved skeletons and differs from the North American forms in the shape of its skull and the proportions of its limbs.

*Garudimimus* (Garuda [a mythical bird] mimic') is another ornithomimosaur from the late Cretaceous of Mongolia. It is known from a well-preserved skull and other fragments described by Rinchen Barsbold in 1981. This dinosaur was placed in a group all of its own: the garudimimidae. This was because it had an unusually shaped beak, notched at its tip, and a peculiar bony ridge just above its eyes. It seems at this stage more probable that *Garudimimus* simply represents a distinctive ornithomimosaur rather than a totally new group of toothless dinosaurs.

*Deinocheirus* ('terrible hand') is a remarkable fossil from the late Cretaceous of Southern Mongolia. *Deinocheirus* consists of just two huge arms that were discovered by the Polish-Mongolian expedition (see photograph). In their general arrangement and proportions, these puzzlingly large arms most closely resemble those of the ornithomimosaurs. The arms are long, and for their size, relatively

**Above:** As its name suggests, *Struthiomimus* (and other ornithomimosaurs) probably resembled today's ostrich to some degree, both being fast-running and well balanced creatures.

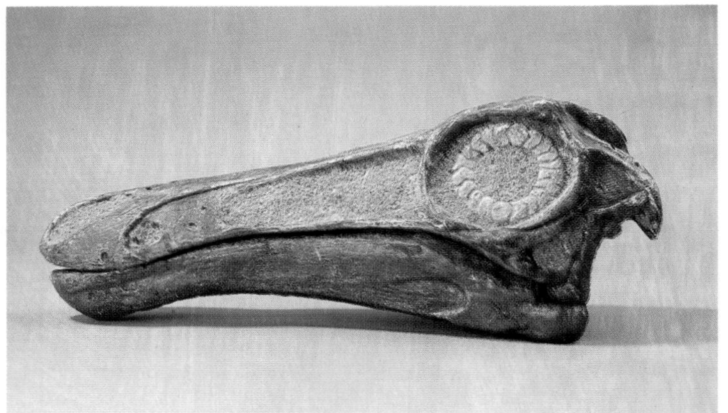

**Left:** A cast of a skull of the Mongolian ornithomimosaur *Gallimimus* in the British Museum (Natural History) collection. Note the long, toothless jaws and the relatively large size of the eye socket.

**Browsing Herbivores (right)**
A number of suggestions have been advanced with regard to the likely feeding habits of ornithomimosaurs. While it is impossible to be certain, their basic body shape would seem to be well adapted to a plant-eating life-style. The long arms and hands might be used to grasp branches while the beak could nip off buds and leaves. Of course these attributes would also suit a speedy omnivore with a wider and more catholic diet.

slender, and end in three-fingered hands. The fingers themselves are huge, but are of practically equal length, a characteristic of ornithomimosaurs. However, the first finger shows no obvious thumb-like ability to fold inwards to form an effective grip, as in ornithomimosaurs. Exactly what the rest of the animal looked like is a complete mystery.

## Oviraptorosaurs

These equally extraordinary creatures—egg-thieves as their name suggests—are at the moment rather poorly-known, toothless theropod dinosaurs. However, this situation should improve greatly in the next few years as new Mongolian material is described.

The first remains of fossils of this type of dinosaur were those named *Oviraptor* ('egg thief') and were discovered during the American Museum of Natural History—Mongolian expedition in the early 1920s. The remains consisted of one partial skull and skeleton discovered in 1923 by Mr George Olsen, at the *Protoceratops* (see pages 128-133) locality of Shabarakh Usu, Southern Mongolia. The skull (illustrated on page 47), although rather badly fractured, was preserved in a nodule of sandstone, so that a clear idea of its shape and the arrangement of its bone was obtained. It is notable for the large number of openings in its sides and the curious horn-like prong on the tip of its snout. As in the ornithomimosaurs (with which group these dinosaurs have been linked by many), this skull possesses no teeth and presumably compensated for this by having horn-covered jaws. However, unlike the skulls of ornithomimosaurs, this skull is rather short-snouted, with a very deep and strong lower jaw.

Associated with the skull, that was described by Osborn in 1924, was a partial skeleton consisting of fragmentary neck vertebrae, various ribs, the shoulder bones, left arm and hand, and most of the right hand. The hand was well enough preserved to reveal that there were three elongate fingers ending in large, sharp claws. However, the proportions of the fingers are different from those of ornithomimosaurs, in that they have more sharply-curved claws and the first finger is considerably shorter than the other two. In fact the hand is rather similar in shape to that of *Ornitholestes* (page 41) and the dromaeosaurids (pages 56-61). The arms and shoulders do not disclose much concerning the biology of this creature, but there is one unexpected bone preserved in the shoulder—a modified collar-bone or clavicle. A few years ago no dinosaur was supposed to possess a bony collar bone. It was believed that they had been lost early in the history of the reptile group from which dinosaurs were thought to have evolved.

Since the original description of this new dinosaur by Osborn, five better preserved skulls and skeletons of *Oviraptor* have been discovered by a joint Soviet-Mongolian expedition in 1972. These are to be described by Dr Rinchen Barsbold (Ulan Bator, Mongolia) in the near future. However, some preliminary comments and illustrations of these dinosaurs were published in 1983 which confirmed the presence of the unusual collar-bone in the shoulder. The curious feature is that instead of comprising a pair of bones, one on each side of the shoulder girdle, the two bones are welded together to form a single curved bone. This arrangement is strikingly like that seen in living birds whose collar bones are fused together to form the 'wish-bone' (furcula). This discovery has added much fuel to the debate over the origin and relationships of birds and dinosaurs (see pages 175-177).

According to Dr Barshold, the remainder of the skeleton of *Oviraptor* is very similar to that of most theropods, and this reassurance has formed the basis for the flesh restoration of *Oviraptor* on pages 44-45. Some inaccuracies will undoubtedly be revealed when full skeletal descriptions have been published.

Both the Polish-Mongolian expedition of 1970-71 and the Soviet-Mongolian expedition of 1972 recovered *Oviraptor* material. This has revealed quite a wide range of skull shape and degree of horn development. Many of these differences may be due to the degree of maturity of the specimen.

*Oviraptor* may also provide a clue to an unusual bird-like jaw from the late Cretaceous of Alberta, Canada. Originally this was described as the lower jaw of *Caenagnathus* ('recent jawless'), and was thought to be that of an unusual bird. The jaw was unlike anything previously described as bird-like. However, as Halszka Osmolska rightly pointed out in 1976, the jaw of *Caenagnathus* closely resembles that of *Oviraptor* and very probably represents a North American species of this unusual group of animals.

The circumstances of preservation of the original specimen of *Oviraptor* described by Osborn in 1924 provided the reason for its name: *Oviraptor philoceratops* ('egg thief, fond of ceratopian eggs'). Its skull and skeleton were found lying on top of a clutch of *Protoceratops* eggs! Perhaps the unfortunate creature had died at the very moment of robbing a nest, or its skull was crushed after being caught by an enraged parent. We shall never know. It is certainly possible that *Oviraptor* preyed upon ceratopian eggs, which it cracked open with its horny beak. Perhaps, like the ornithomimosaurs, they were general predators or scavengers of anything dead or alive.

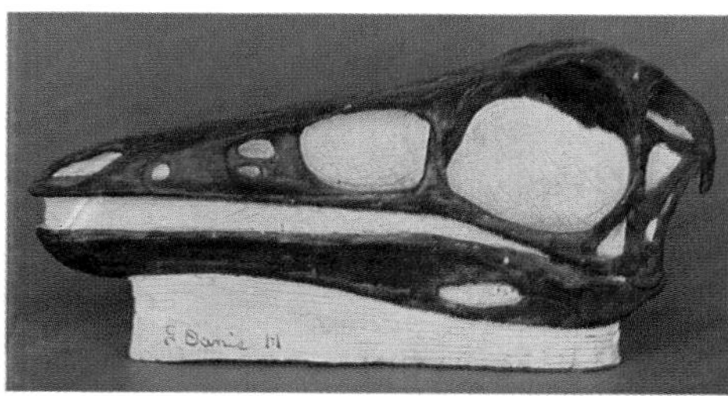

**Left:** *Dromiceiomimus* ('emu mimic') *brevitertius* is known from the late Cretaceous of Alberta in Canada. Again the size of the eye socket is really remarkable, and may imply that these creatures possessed a particularly acute sense of vision.

**Above:** The gigantic forearms of *Deinocheirus mirificus* being mounted at the Institute of Palaeobiology in Warsaw. We can only speculate what the rest of this remarkable creature may have looked like: very possibly a giant ornithomimosaur.

# Miscellaneous Theropods

Over the last decade in particular a large variety of enigmatic theropods have been discovered and described. For the most part these have been rather poor or incomplete specimens of dinosaurs which do not seem to fit readily into any of the groups currently recognised. Described below are *some* of these new and enigmatic animals. It is quite likely that when more and better preserved fossils of these creatures are recovered, many will fall into some of the better established groups; others, however, may prove to be totally new dinosaur types.

## Segisaurus

Discovered in 1933 in early Jurassic rocks of Arizona, *Segisaurus* ('reptile from Segi Canyon') was described by Dr Charles Camp in 1936. The fossil remains of this animal consist of a fragmentary, headless skeleton which includes a few back vertebrae, some ribs, the shoulder girdle, incomplete arms, legs and parts of the pelvis. The animal as reconstructed is small (about 3·3ft, 1m long) and ran on slender hind legs. The fore legs were apparently short, with sharp-clawed fingers. The feet and hands are reminiscent of those of 'coelurosaur'—type theropods. However, *Segisaurus* does have a collar bone (clavicle) preserved on one shoulder which, as we saw earlier (pages 48-49), is quite rare in dinosaurs. Until better material of *Segisaurus* is recovered it is probably best to regard it as a rather curious small theropod.

## Chirostenotes

*Chirostenotes* ('slender hand') consists of two imperfectly preserved, sharply-clawed hands which were discovered in late Cretaceous rocks of the Red Deer River, Alberta. The fingers are of unequal length and quite closely resemble those of the late Jurassic 'coelurosaur' *Ornitholestes* (see page 41) and the dromaeosaurids (pages 56 to 61). Indeed *Dromaeosaurus* is known from the same area, so this material may well belong to this genus. In addition to these two hands, several other teeth and a lower jaw were referred to *Chirostenotes*. These were found a few miles from the hands, so their reference to this genus is necessarily cautious, but they do, with the benefit of hindsight, resemble dromaeosaurid jaws.

## Macrophalangia

*Macrophalangia* ('large toes') is another theropod from the Red Deer River of Alberta. First described by Charles Sternberg in 1932, *Macrophalangia* is known from a partial foot which looks very much like that of an ornithomimosaur (see pages 44-49). It has long and slender toes ending in flattened but quite pointed claws. However, unlike the three-toed ornithomimosaur foot, the foot of *Macrophalangia* has four toes: three long, slender ones and a smaller first toe typical of the great majority of theropods. The question, therefore, is: does *Macrophalangia* represent a primitive type of ornithomimosaur? If it does, then its appearance in late Cretaceous rocks is unexpected. Alternatively, these remains may indicate a completely new group of slender-toed theropods in the late Cretaceous.

## Elmisaurus

*Elmisaurus* ('foot reptile'), another poorly preserved theropod, this time from the late Cretaceous of the Gobi Desert, was described in 1981 by Dr Halszka Osmolska. Known as it is from portions of hands, feet and odd leg bones, this new dinosaur may provide vital clues to the relations of both *Chirostenotes* and *Macrophalangia*. The hand of *Elmisaurus* seems, from its proportions, to resemble closely that of *Chirostenotes* (as well as that of *Ornitholestes* and dromaeosaurids). The foot, however, is most similar to that described as *Macrophalangia*; the toes are quite long and slender and are arranged very similarly to those of *Macrophalangia* and ornithomimosaurs, except that as in *Macrophalangia* there appear to be *four* toes. The interpretation that can be made from this combination of features is that the remains of *Chirostenotes, Macrophalangia* and *Elmisaurus* represent the remains of a new type of theropod in the late Cretaceous. Osmolska proposed that these all be referred to as elmisaurids, a new family of theropod dinosaurs. These dinosaurs seem to combine the grasping hands of the rapacious dromaeosaurids with the fleetness of foot of ornithomimosaurs. Unfortunately at the moment very little is known about the rest of the skeleton or the skull, so that accurate life-like restorations of these creatures are impossible.

## Avimimus

In 1981 Dr Kurzanov (Moscow) described the partial skeleton of a remarkably bird-like theropod dinosaur, *Avimimus* ('bird mimic'), discovered during the joint Soviet-Mongolian expedition. This dinosaur was of very slender build, with slim legs and long bird-like feet, as well as a long slender, bird-like neck. The tail was typically long and dinosaurian (unlike the short 'Parson's Nose' of a bird) so as to counterbalance the front part of the body. Dr Kurzanov noted that there were a considerable number of bird-like characters found in *Avimimus* and proposed that this was a small,

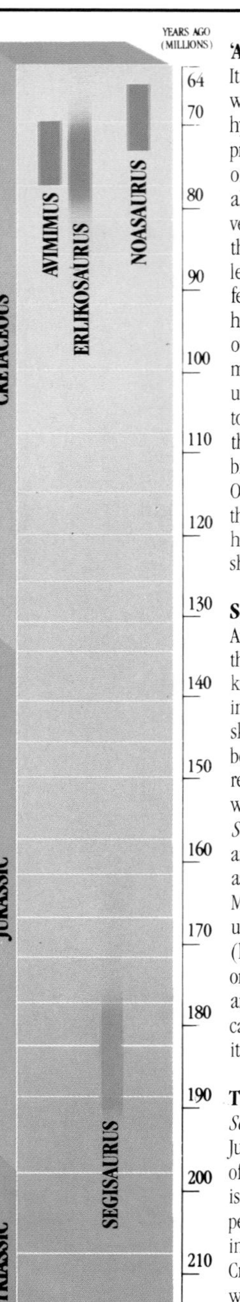

**'A Segnosaur' (right)**
It must be emphasized that what you see here is an hypothetical animal. At present we know the structure of the skull of *Erlikosaurus* along with some of its neck vertebrae and feet. Added to this we have part of a jaw, legs, a pelvis and hands and feet of *Segnosaurus*. These have been used to provide an outline of what a segnosaur may have looked like. The unusual combination of a toothless beak, bird-like hips, theropod hands and rather broad feet is most perplexing. One suggestion is that they were fish eaters and had webbed hind feet as shown here.

**Segisaurus (right)**
Another unusual theropod is the early Jurassic form known as *Segisaurus* found in Arizona. Unfortunately the skeleton was found to be headless though the remainder was reasonably well preserved. As seen here *Segisaurus* was quite small and was lightly constructed as a presumably agile runner. Most probably *Segisaurus* fed upon small vertebrates (lizards and amphibians) or larger insects. The teeth are not preserved so we cannot be absolutely sure of its diet.

**Time Chart (left)**
*Segisaurus* from the lower Jurassic is one of the earliest of these theropod forms; this is then followed by a range of peculiar theropods clustered into the late part of the Cretaceous Period which was possibly a time of 'experimentation' in theropod design—perhaps reflecting unusual climatic conditions at the time.

feathered, bird-like dinosaur of the late Cretaceous. Among the skeletal remains there is an incomplete forelimb which is of particular interest. Kurzanov analysed the bones of the forelimb in some detail and demonstrated that the humerus (upper arm bone) was extremely bird-like with all the ridges and bumps for attachment of the main flight muscles, and a wing-folding mechanism. In addition, and perhaps more intriguing still, Kurzanov demonstrated that one of the forearm bones (ulna) had a distinctive bony ridge running along its rear edge. No other theropod is known to possess such a bony ridge. Birds however do have a rather similar series of small bony 'pimples' running along this forearm bone. These 'pimples' are developed at the point of attachment of the flight feathers (secondaries). *Avimimus* does not have a series of pimple-like attachment points, but rather a long bony ridge; nevertheless such a structure is very suggestive of the presence of feathers on the forelimbs. As Dr Kurzanov rightly points out, there is no direct evidence of feathers as there is in the case of the famous fossils of *Archaeopteryx*, but the bird-like structure of the skeleton and the possible feather attachment ridge on the bone of the forearm are very suggestive. Kurzanov proposes that *Avimimus* was a member of a very late group of bird-like theropod dinosaurs named avimimids; these were small, fleet-footed creatures living perhaps upon insects. The feather covering is supposed to be associated primarily with body insulation rather than flight. Kurzanov believes that these were small highly-active creatures which would have generated their own body heat internally, rather than relying upon the Sun to keep them warm as reptiles usually do. Since they were small, avimimids would have needed some form of insulation to control the rate at which they lost heat, and feathers may have been what they used. As others have suggested in the past, a small, highly-active, ground-running creature such as this may have been a first stage in the origin of powered flight. Kurzanov visualises *Avimimus* occasionally fluttering into the air when pursuing flying insects, or alternatively using short airborne jumps as a way of avoiding larger fleet-footed predators.

*Avimimus* is obviously an interesting and highly controversial animal at this moment. As with most fossils, its remains are frustratingly incomplete. It would be nice to know what the complete structure of the head, the shoulder bones, the remainder of the arm and hand and the hips were like; all of which would help to clarify the true nature of this animal. If *Avimimus* was truly a *feathered* theropod dinosaur, then it would provide an extraordinary and unexpected insight into the process of evolution because it suggests that a structure as complicated as a bird's feather may have evolved twice: once producing true birds in the Jurassic, and a second time producing the avimimids of the late Cretaceous. Unless,

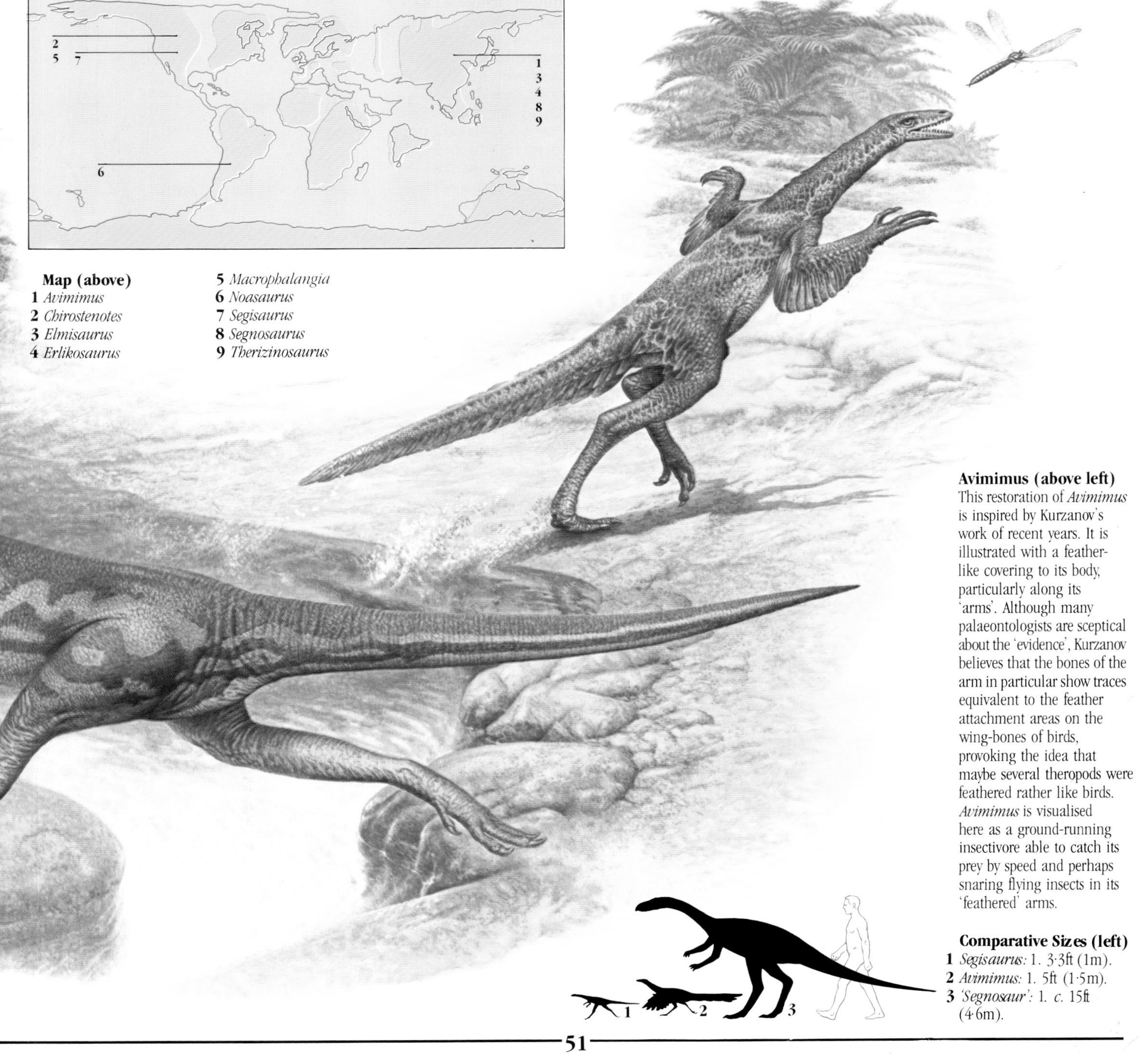


**Map (above)**
**1** *Avimimus*
**2** *Chirostenotes*
**3** *Elmisaurus*
**4** *Erlikosaurus*
**5** *Macrophalangia*
**6** *Noasaurus*
**7** *Segisaurus*
**8** *Segnosaurus*
**9** *Therizinosaurus*

**Avimimus (above left)**
This restoration of *Avimimus* is inspired by Kurzanov's work of recent years. It is illustrated with a feather-like covering to its body, particularly along its 'arms'. Although many palaeontologists are sceptical about the 'evidence', Kurzanov believes that the bones of the arm in particular show traces equivalent to the feather attachment areas on the wing-bones of birds, provoking the idea that maybe several theropods were feathered rather like birds. *Avimimus* is visualised here as a ground-running insectivore able to catch its prey by speed and perhaps snaring flying insects in its 'feathered' arms.

**Comparative Sizes (left)**
**1** *Segisaurus*: 1. 3·3ft (1m).
**2** *Avimimus*: 1. 5ft (1·5m).
**3** *'Segnosaur'*: 1. *c.* 15ft (4·6m).

of course, all small theropods were feathered! In the past most evolutionary biologists have argued that a structure as complex as a feather was very unlikely to have evolved more than once. At the moment I am rather sceptical of Dr Kurzanov's proposals.

## Segnosaurids

The first segnosaurid remains were described in 1979 by Dr Altangerel Perle and also by Dr Rinchen Barsbold (Ulan Bator, Mongolia) from material discovered during the Soviet-Mongolian expeditions. As with the previous examples, the fossil remains are incomplete and merely provide an interesting glimpse of other dinosaur types. So far three Mongolian segnosaurids have been named: *Segnosaurus* ('slow reptile'), *Erlikosaurus* ('King of the Dead [Erlik] reptile') and an un-named form, all of which come from the late Cretaceous Bayn Shireh horizon of south-eastern Mongolia.

*Segnosaurus,* the first of these dinosaurs to be described, was based on a partial skeleton including a lower jaw, parts of the legs and backbone, and a complete pelvis. Several other fragments including a forelimb have also been discovered in the same area which provide a little more evidence of the structure of this animal. Several features of *Segnosaurus* deserve mention. First and most obviously, the pelvis is very unusual for a theropod. As can be seen right, the pubis lies parallel to the ischium below the hip socket; this arrangement is very similar to that seen in ornithischian dinosaurs and birds. Secondly, the jaws are unusual for theropods in that the front part of the jaw was toothless and the teeth at the back of the jaw were quite small and pointed, rather than being like large serrated daggers. The front end of the jaws was probably covered by a horny beak, again rather like that of ornithischian dinosaurs. The head, at least as judged from the size of the jaw, was quite small relative to the size of the body. The forelimb was short and ended in three slender, clawed fingers. The hindlimb was quite sturdy and ended in a rather short and broad four-toed foot. Again the foot is most unusual for a theropod, the toes of which are usually slender and bunched together in a distinctly bird-like arrangement.

Clearly *Segnosaurus* was a most unusual theropod. The remains indicate an animal of 20-23ft (6-7m) in length with a small head, horny beak, small cheek teeth, short forelimbs, bird-like pelvis and stout, broad-footed hindlimbs. *Segnosaurus* must have been a rather slow-moving theropod with a very specific diet. One suggestion is that *Segnosaurus* was an aquatic fish eater; this may explain the small pointed teeth and broad (perhaps webbed) feet of this animal, though why it should possess a horny beak is a complete mystery.

*Erlikosaurus* from Baysheen Tsav in Mongolia is known from a skull, some neck vertebrae, a humerus and both feet. Smaller than *Segnosaurus, Erlikosaurus* was described by Barsbold and Perle in 1980. The skull shows the same toothless beak at the front of the jaws, and small, pointed teeth behind. The hind foot is rather similar to that of *Segnosaurus* in that there are four toes which are rather short, but end in sharp claws.

In general shape the jaws, neck vertebrae and feet of these two animals are very similar. However *Erlikosaurus* is smaller than *Segnosaurus,* has a greater number of teeth, a larger beak and narrower claws on its feet. The shape of the pelvis in *Erlikosaurus* is entirely unknown at present, but is assumed to have resembled that of *Segnosaurus.*

*'Un-named reptile'* from Khara Kutul consists of a pelvis alone. This resembles that of *Segnosaurus* except that it is slightly smaller; there are also a few differences in detailed structure including the welding together of pubis and ischium. These differences have been deemed sufficient to recognise the existence of another segnosaurid from the late Cretaceous of Mongolia. However, it is at present not sufficiently well known to exclude the possibility that it is either the pelvis of *Erlikosaurus* or a variation of *Segnosaurus,* so very wisely a name has not yet been given.

*Nanshiungosaurus* ('Nanshiung reptile') which has been referred to the segnosaurids is fragmentary material that may be of a sauropod.

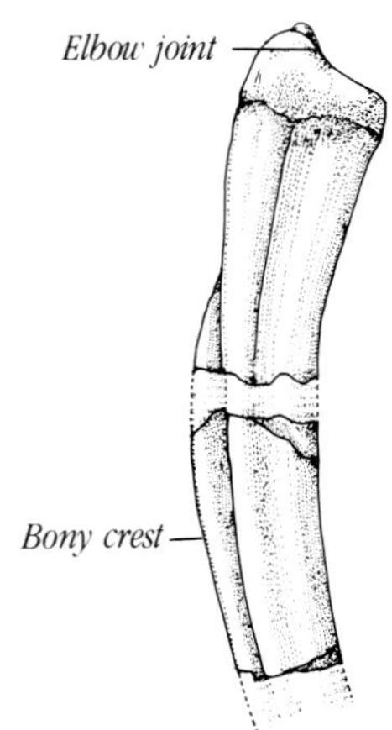


**Avimimus Arm Bone (above)**
This incomplete arm bone (the ulna) is one of the most interesting (and controversial) pieces of evidence relating to the biology of *Avimimus.* The crest of bone indicated has been interpreted as an area for the attachment of wing feathers.

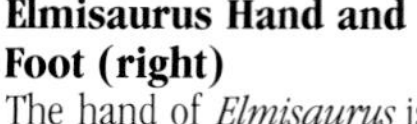

**Elmisaurus Hand and Foot (right)**
The hand of *Elmisaurus* is quite well preserved and in its proportions fairly closely resembles that of dromaeosaurids such as *Deinonychus.* It has a very powerful first finger and a long slender third finger. The foot by contrast is more similar to that of the ornithomimosaurs in that the toes are long and slender, and there is no enlargement of the second toe as a slashing claw.

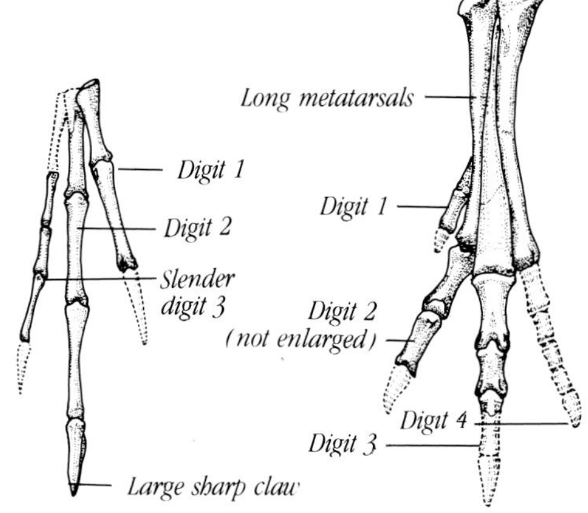

**Above:** The North American Road Runner is a very fleet-footed creature. It has long back legs somewhat like those of *Avimimus,* which may have had a similar life-style.

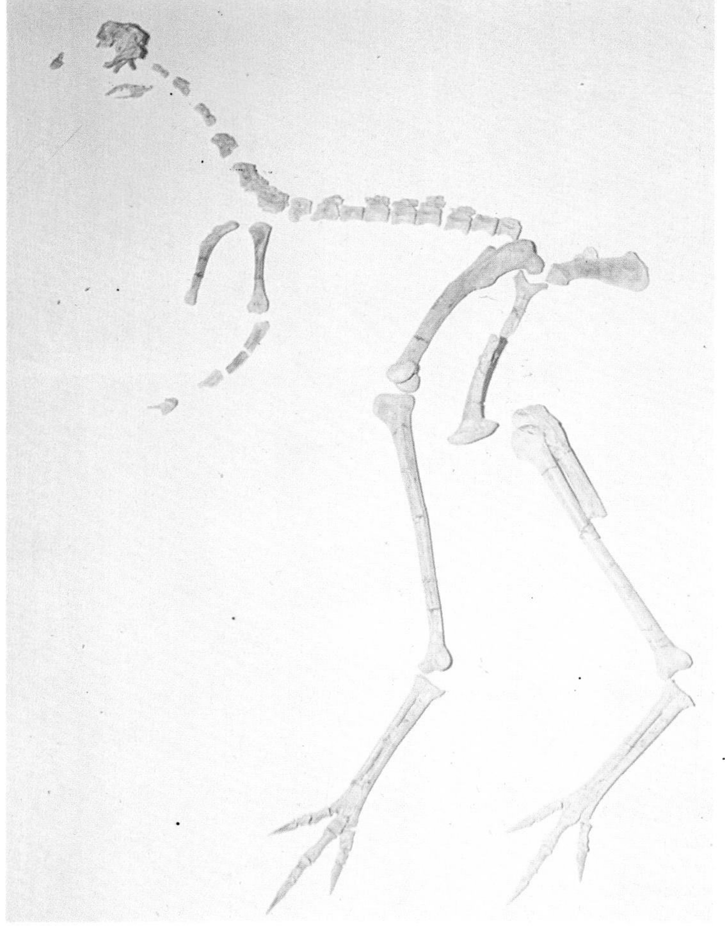

**Right:** This photograph of *Avimimus* was provided by Dr Kurzanov of the Moscow Academy of Sciences and is one of the most recent reconstructions of this creature. As seen here it is surprisingly bird-like with long back legs, long neck and no tail. The forelimbs are short, but rather poorly preserved. The apparent absence of a tail is most intriguing.

In 1985 Greg Paul made the rather controversial suggestion that segnosaurids may be late surviving relatives of early prosauropods and ornithischians. This is a contentious claim which is bound to provoke much argument.

## Noasaurids

Fragmentary remains of *Noasaurus* ('reptile from Noa'—Noa=N.W. Argentina) were described by José Bonaparte and Jaime Powell in 1980. They come from late Cretaceous rocks of the El Brete area of north-west Argentina and include parts of the skull, some vertebrae, and two foot bones—including a large claw. Careful comparison of these remains with those of known theropods seems to suggest that *Noasaurus* belongs to another new group of theropods: the noasaurids. However, this suggestion should be treated with great caution until better material is discovered. One rather interesting point noted by Bonaparte and Powell is that, if correctly identified, the foot claw seems to be of the large slashing type seen on the foot of dromaeosaurids (pages 56-61). However, the form of the claw is such that it could not have evolved from the type of claw seen in dromaeosaurids, but must have evolved quite independently.

## Therizinosaurids

A large amount of dinosaur material was collected by a Soviet-Mongolian expedition to the southern Gobi Desert in 1948 which included some very large bony claws. These latter were described as *Therizinosaurus* ('scythe reptile') and were associated with some large flattened ribs. Later in 1957, 1959 and 1960 more large claws were discovered in Khazakhstan, Transbaykalia and Inner Mongolia. The latter consisted of not only a large claw, but also a partial forelimb, the incomplete hindlimbs and a tooth. These remains were of a large theropod dinosaur and finally proved that the claws of *Therizinosaurus,* originally thought to belong to turtle, were those of a dinosaur. The large flattened ribs finally proved to be ribs of a large sauropod dinosaur. As was the case with *Deinocheirus* (page 49), the remains of *Therizinosaurus* hint at some extraordinary late Cretaceous dinosaur from Asia. One of the claws from the hand measures approximately 28in (70cm) in length—this does not include the horny part of the claw which would have made it even longer! Precisely what these huge claws were used for is a mystery. They may have been formidable weapons for slashing through the skin of their prey or, as has been suggested by others, they may have been used to tear open termitaria (anthills). However, it does seem rather hard to believe that such a large animal lived on just termites or ants! Once again we have a desperate need to discover more of these amazing and perplexing fossil creatures.

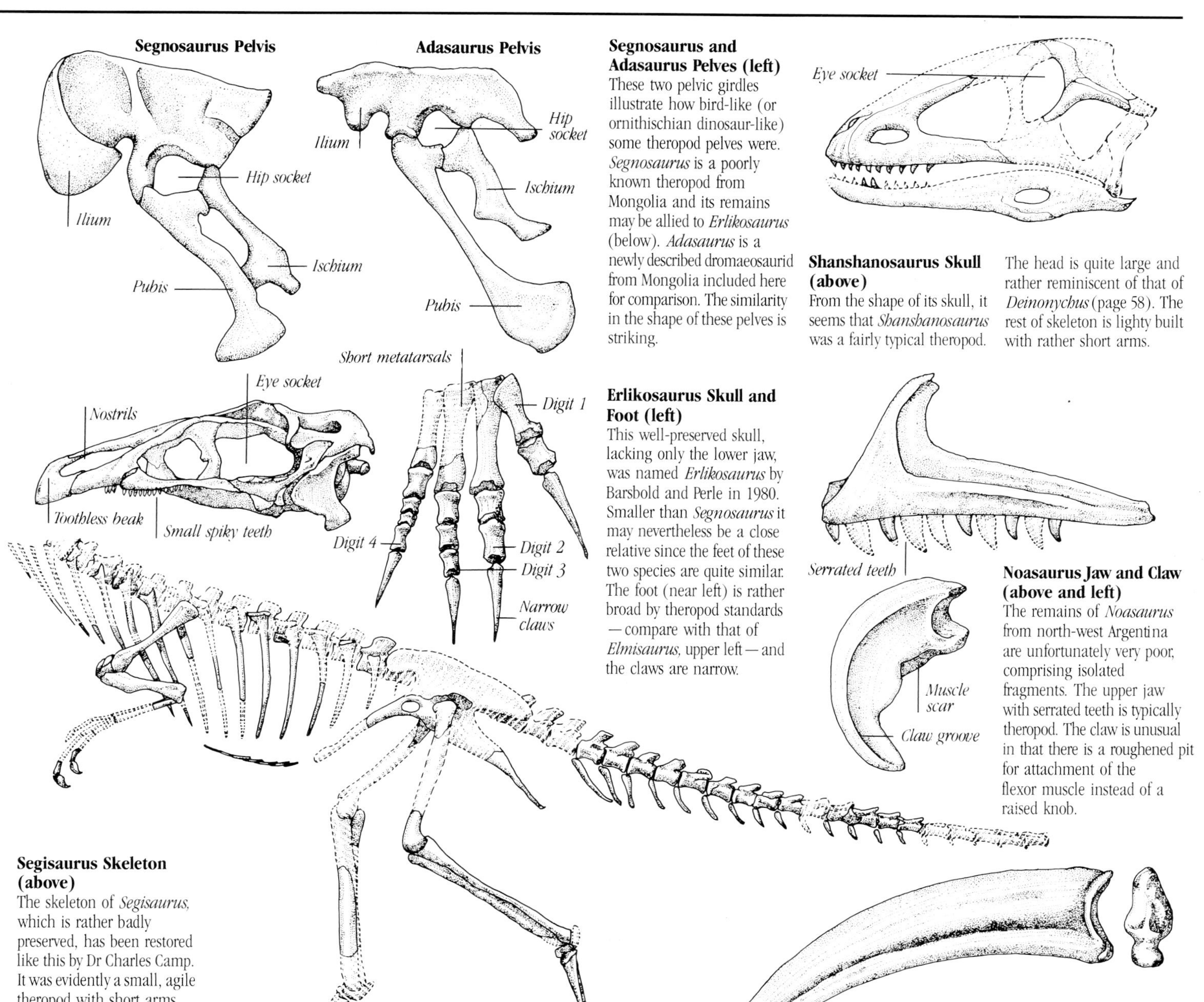


**Segnosaurus and Adasaurus Pelves (left)**
These two pelvic girdles illustrate how bird-like (or ornithischian dinosaur-like) some theropod pelves were. *Segnosaurus* is a poorly known theropod from Mongolia and its remains may be allied to *Erlikosaurus* (below). *Adasaurus* is a newly described dromaeosaurid from Mongolia included here for comparison. The similarity in the shape of these pelves is striking.

**Shanshanosaurus Skull (above)**
From the shape of its skull, it seems that *Shanshanosaurus* was a fairly typical theropod. The head is quite large and rather reminiscent of that of *Deinonychus* (page 58). The rest of skeleton is lighty built with rather short arms.

**Erlikosaurus Skull and Foot (left)**
This well-preserved skull, lacking only the lower jaw, was named *Erlikosaurus* by Barsbold and Perle in 1980. Smaller than *Segnosaurus* it may nevertheless be a close relative since the feet of these two species are quite similar. The foot (near left) is rather broad by theropod standards —compare with that of *Elmisaurus,* upper left—and the claws are narrow.

**Noasaurus Jaw and Claw (above and left)**
The remains of *Noasaurus* from north-west Argentina are unfortunately very poor, comprising isolated fragments. The upper jaw with serrated teeth is typically theropod. The claw is unusual in that there is a roughened pit for attachment of the flexor muscle instead of a raised knob.

**Segisaurus Skeleton (above)**
The skeleton of *Segisaurus,* which is rather badly preserved, has been restored like this by Dr Charles Camp. It was evidently a small, agile theropod with short arms and powerful grasping hands. The absence of the head is frustrating since it might have revealed its diet, and relationships to other early theropods.

**Therizinosaurus Claw (above)**
The claws from Mongolia that have been referred to *Therizinosaurus* are quite enormous. The one illustrated here measures 28in (70cm) in length. Whether these belonged to giant *Deinocheirus*-type dinosaurs (page 49) or some other type is uncertain

# SAURORNITHOIDIDS

In 1923 Henry Fairfield Osborn described the incomplete remains of a bird-like theropod dinosaur from late Cretaceous rocks at Bayn Dzak (=Shabarakh Usu) in the Gobi Desert. These included the major part of a skull found in one sandstone nodule and, a little way away from this, parts of the backbone, pelvis, legs and feet. All of these remains were collected in 1923 by a Chinese assistant on the Central Asiatic Expedition of the American Museum of Natural History.

This new dinosaur was named *Saurornithoides mongoliensis* ('bird-like reptile from Mongolia') and was at first supposed to be an early toothed bird, because its skull had a long, rather bird-like, narrow muzzle. In general shape and proportions the skull is rather similar to that of *Velociraptor* (page 56) which was incidentally described at the same time and came from the same area of Mongolia. However, the teeth (in particular) are rather different; those of *Saurornithoides* are smaller and more numerous with 38 teeth in the upper jaw, while *Velociraptor* had no more than 30 teeth. The teeth were also unusual in that only their back edges were serrated whereas both front and back edges of *Velociraptor's* were serrated. The incomplete hind foot showed that the toes were arranged in typical theropod fashion with a small, spur-like first toe and three longer walking toes. The original drawings of the specimen show that the second toe of the foot had a somewhat enlarged claw which could have been raised clear of the ground. However, this was not appreciated at the time when it was first described and its significance was realised only much later.

Osborn concluded that *Saurornithoides* must have been a small, carnivorous theropod which was neither as fleet-footed nor as voracious as *Velociraptor.*

Somewhat later (in 1932) some more bones were described by Charles Sternberg; these came from the late Cretaceous near Steveville on the Red Deer River, Alberta. The remains included a complete foot, several hand bones and a few vertebrae. The hand bones were rather similar to those of *Ornitholestes* (pages 46-47) and *Chirostenotes* (pages 50-51) with uneven finger lengths. The foot, however, was rather unusual because, although it showed the typical bird-like arrangement of toes, the second toe was somewhat shorter than the third and fourth toes and had an unexpectedly large, sharply-curved claw. The third and fourth toes were both quite long and almost equal in length with smaller but still sharply-curved claws. As was hinted at above in relation to the foot of *Saurornithoides,* the second toe was jointed in such a way that it could be held clear of the ground, instead of being used for walking upon. Again the significance of the unusual second toe and its claw was missed. At the time Sternberg concluded that this foot belonged to a new type of theropod which may have evolved from animals like *Ornitholestes;* he named this material *Stenonychosaurus* ('slender clawed reptile') *inequalis.*

It was not until the discovery of *Deinonychus* (see page 56) in the mid 1960s and the research work of Professor John Ostrom (Yale) that the possibility of a relationship between *Saurornithoides* and *Stenonychosaurus* was appreciated. Ostrom recognised that *Deinonychus* had a very large claw on the second toe of its foot; he believed that this was used as an offensive weapon. Detailed comparison with other theropod feet showed that *Saurornithoides* and *Stenonychosaurus* had smaller, but similar, offensive claws. At first, both of these dinosaurs were included with other dromaeosaurids. However, in 1974 Rinchen Barsbold (Ulan Bator, Mongolia) described more material of *Saurornithoides* which had been discovered at Bugeen Tsav in Mongolia. This material, ascribed the name *Saurornithoides junior* ('younger bird-like reptile'), was found in slightly earlier rocks and was 30 per cent larger than Osborn's species, while the number of teeth in the jaws was also greater. Apart from these differences, which may eventually prove to be simply due to growth, the two species seem remarkably similar.

The new *Saurornithoides* material included a well-preserved skull. The latter showed some rather curious swollen areas in the ear region and in the floor of the braincase. These features, plus the quite small size of the claw on the second toe of the foot, and the fact that their teeth were relatively smaller, more numerous and only serrated along their back edges, prompted Barsbold to propose that *Saurornithoides* and *Stenonychosaurus* should not be included in the dromaeosaurid family as proposed by Ostrom. Instead he placed them in a family of their own, and they became known as saurornithoidids. In 1978 Hans-Dieter Sues added another fragmentary form, *Saurornitholestes* ('reptile-like bird robber'), to the saurornithoidid group, although this small, lightly-built creature (found in Alberta, Canada) may in fact be a dromaeosaurid. Other supposed saurornithoidids include *Bradycneme* ('heavy shin') and *Heptasteornis* ('seven star bird') both from Rumania and originally thought to belong to birds; both of these are extremely dubious since they are based on very poor material. *Pectinodon* ('comb tooth') is another possible saurornithoidid.

## The 'Dinosauroid'

In 1982 Dale Russell and R. Séguin (Ottawa) published an interesting article on *Stenonycho-*

**Time Chart (left)**
Another of the exclusively late Cretaceous groups, the saurornithoidids are only known so far from western North America and East Asia. At this time the two areas were connected via the Bering Straits and many of their dinosaurs are similar. These forms will probably only be found in these parts of the world.

**Stenonychosaurus (right)**
This has been credited as the most intelligent dinosaur. Compared with most other dinosaurs, it had a relatively large brain, but most of this excess brain volume was probably not concerned with reasoning and other activities that we would call 'intelligence'. *Stenonychosaurus* had large eyes, slender flexible fingers, and a light body. The brain was probably concerned mainly with its highly developed senses, fine control of its limbs, and fast reflexes, which were used in hunting small and elusive prey.

**The 'Dinosauroid' (right)**
Is this what *Stenonychosaurus* might have looked like if it had continued evolving to the present day? Russell and Séguin assumed for it an enlarged brain, and the short neck and upright posture were arrived at as a way of balancing the head more efficiently. In turn, the vertical posture removed the need for a tail. The legs were modified by lowering the ankle to the ground and the foot was lengthened. Although fictional, given the right conditions, such changes would be quite feasible.

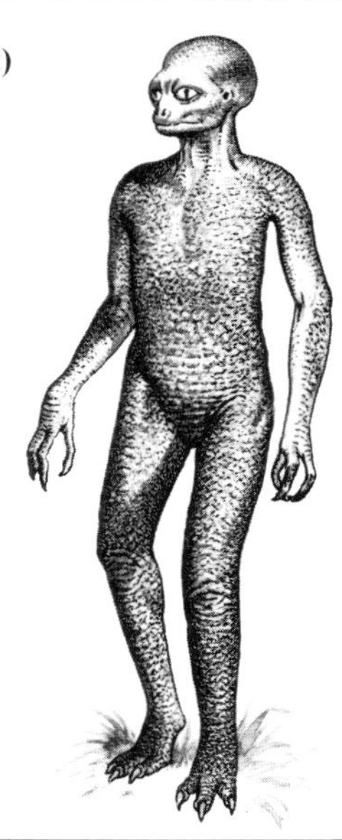

*saurus*. A new partial skeleton of this dinosaur was discovered in Alberta in 1967, and this provided the basis for the first skeletal and flesh restoration of *Stenonychosaurus*. The detailed work that went into building this first model was described and illustrated in Russell and Séguin's paper. However, in addition to this work, they also indulged in an imaginative thought experiment. They posed the question: what might these dinosaurs have looked like if they had continued to evolve and not gone extinct at the end of the Cretaceous Period?

*Stenonychosaurus* proved to be an interesting choice of dinosaur for this type of 'experiment' because it was one of the largest-brained and therefore presumably one of the most intelligent of all dinosaurs. The result of this experiment was the so-called 'dinosauroid' restoration seen here.

One interpretation of the probable habits of *Stenonychosaurus* (and saurornithoidids in general) is that they were lightly-built active hunters of small prey—perhaps small lizards and mammals. The long grasping hands, and the very large eyes which pointed partly forward and therefore gave reasonable stereoscopic vision, may indicate that these were nimble predators which were active at dusk or even at night, when many of the small nocturnal mammals of the time would have been active.

The 'dinosauroid' was constructed by extrapolating from these attributes. It was visualised as a highly intelligent and 'manipulative' dinosaur. What it would have lacked in fleetness of foot (since it is more 'flat-footed' than *Stenonychosaurus*) it would have made up for through its greater intellect. This would have allowed it to avoid potential predators by 'outwitting' them rather than by showing them a 'clean pair of heels'. As a predator it may have been able to catch prey both by endurance running and perhaps by making simple weapons—much as primitive man must have done. Such an idea is an obviously fanciful, though provocative thought.

**Saurornithoides (below)**
Like *Stenonychosaurus*, *Saurornithoides* had a large brain and a slender body. Its large saucer-like eyes might have been used for hunting small mammals at dusk, when other predatory dinosaurs would have been unable to see properly. *Saurornithoides* had small sharp teeth, but these were serrated only on the posterior edges. On its foot, there was a slightly enlarged claw which was normally folded back, but which could be used to slash at potential prey. In this it resembles *Deinonychus*.

**Map (right)**
1 *Saurornithoides*
2 *Saurornitholestes*
3 *Stenonychosaurus*

**Comparative Sizes (left)**
1 *Stenonychosaurus*: l. 6·5ft (2m).
2 *Saurornithoides*: l. 6·5ft (2m).

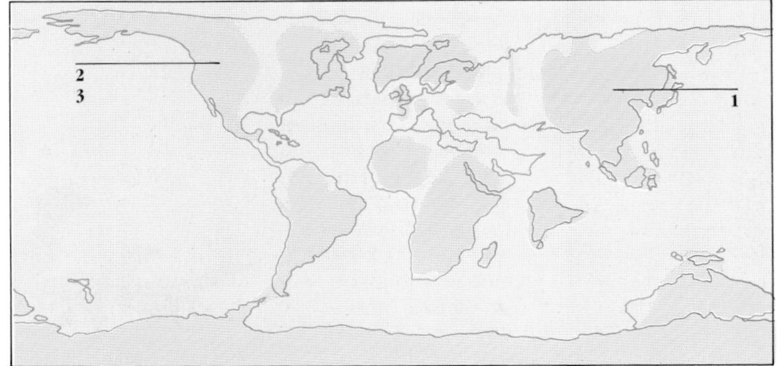

# DROMAEOSAURIDS

Our knowledge of the dromaeosaurids has until quite recently been rather patchy in nature. The first dromaeosaurid remains to be described were those of *Dromaeosaurus* ('running reptile') *albertensis*, which were discovered near the Red Deer River by Barnum Brown in 1914. Unfortunately, as is often the case with many fossil species, the specimen that Brown collected was far from complete; it consisted of the partial head, lower jaws and an assortment of foot bones of a small carnivorous dinosaur. During the next fifty years nothing more was discovered of this dinosaur. Many scientists referred to this specimen but were unsure of its real nature and relationship with the other types of carnivorous dinosaurs then known, because so many parts of its skeleton were still undiscovered. Consequently *Dromaeosaurus* was grouped by some people with the huge 'carnosaurs' (the tyrannosaurids or megalosaurs) while others suggested that it was related to the small, slender 'coelurosaurs'

**Deinonychus (below)**
To date this is the best known of all dromaeosaurids, several partial skeletons having been described in great detail by Professor Ostrom. The distinctive characteristics of dromaeosaurids are shown very clearly here. The head is large with backwardly curved teeth; the arms are long and powerful, and the feet have the extraordinary sickle-like second toe. As can be seen here, the 'terrible claw' is shown raised off the ground. It was, in life, in such a position to protect the sharp point of the claw.

**Velociraptor (below)**
Fossil remains of this dinosaur have been discovered in the Djadochta Formation of Shabarak Usa, in Mongolia. Although illustrated with *Dromaeosaurus* and *Deinonychus* here, remains of *Velociraptor* have not been found so far in geological deposits at the same sites as the other two, so in life they probably never met! *Velociraptor* can be distinguished from other dromaeosaurids by its very low and narrow head. The difference in head shape and size may well reflect differences in the diets.

YEARS AGO (MILLIONS)
64, 70, 80, 90, 100, 110, 120, 130, 140, 150, 160, 170, 180, 190, 200, 210, 220, 225

CRETACEOUS
JURASSIC
TRIASSIC

VELOCIRAPTOR
DROMAEOSAURUS
HULSANPES
DEINONYCHUS
'SURREY DINOSAUR'
PHAEDROLOSAURUS

**Time Chart (left)**
The dromaeosaurids are very restricted in their time of appearance in the fossil record. One of the earliest known, after *Phaedrolosaurus*, is the new 'Surrey dinosaur' which is still being prepared at the British Museum. It dates from rocks of latest Lower Cretaceous age. *Deinonychus* is known from rocks that are a little younger, and is followed onto the scene by *Velociraptor*, *Dromaeosaurus* and *Hulsanpes* in the Upper Cretaceous.

**Comparative Sizes (left)**
1 *Dromaeosaurus*: l. 6ft (1·8m).
2 *Velociraptor*: l. 6ft (1·8m).
3 *Deinonychus*: l. 10-11ft (3-3·3m)

(e.g. *Compsognathus* or *Coelurus*). If anything, its small size tended to favour the latter interpretation.

This rather unsatisfactory state of affairs was considerably improved by the discovery in 1964, by Grant Meyer and Professor John Ostrom of Yale University, of a new fossil locality in southern Montana. During the next two years excavations at this site unearthed several hundred bones of an entirely new carnivorous dinosaur: *Deinonychus* ('terrible claw') *antirrhopus*. The study of this dinosaur, which is now known from several almost complete (or complimentary) skeletons, has revealed many new and exciting facts: not only about this extraordinary kind of dinosaur, but also about its kinship with *Dromaeosaurus*. The peculiarities of *Deinonychus* help to show why it had been so difficult for earlier researchers to pin-point its affinities with *Dromaeosaurus*. Both *Dromaeosaurus* and *Deinonychus* share characteristics with both 'carnosaurs' and 'coelurosaurs', as well as exhibiting features that are unique; hence the confusion. One of their most characteristic features is the huge, sickle-like claw on the second toe of the foot. Once the unusual nature of the feet of these dinosaurs was appreciated, it became possible to draw comparisons with another dinosaur known since 1924, *Velociraptor* ('speedy predator') *mongoliensis*, which also had a sickle-like claw on its hind foot. A remarkable discovery made more recently in Mongolia is that of an almost complete *Velociraptor* skeleton preserved, apparently in combat position, clutching the skull of a *Protoceratops* skeleton with its forelimbs; this may be one of the few pieces of real evidence we have of the feeding habits of predatory dinosaurs.

Dromaeosaurids are now known from well preserved remains of the Upper Cretaceous of North America (*Dromaeosaurus* and *Deinonychus* in particular) and Mongolia (*Velociraptor*). In addition, other rather fragmentary remains have been described; these are *Hulsanpes* ('foot from Khulsan') *perlei*, which consists only of the incomplete hind foot of a very small dromaeosaurid from the Upper Cretaceous of Mongolia, and *Phaedrolosaurus* ('gleaming reptile') *ilikensis* from the Lower Cretaceous of China. *Phaedrolosaurus* consists of some scattered teeth and leg bones which do not all derive from the same animal; none of these shows *clear* evidence that it comes from a dromaeosaurid and should therefore be ignored until better material is discovered. *'Adasaurus'* is another recently discovered dinosaur from southern Mongolia that is thought to be a dromaeosaurid. It has not yet been fully described.

One of the most exciting recent discoveries was made in southern England. In 1982 a quarryman, Bill Walker, discovered a very large, sickle-shaped claw in a quarry in Surrey. The claw (three-times larger than that of *Deinonychus!*) was taken to the British Museum

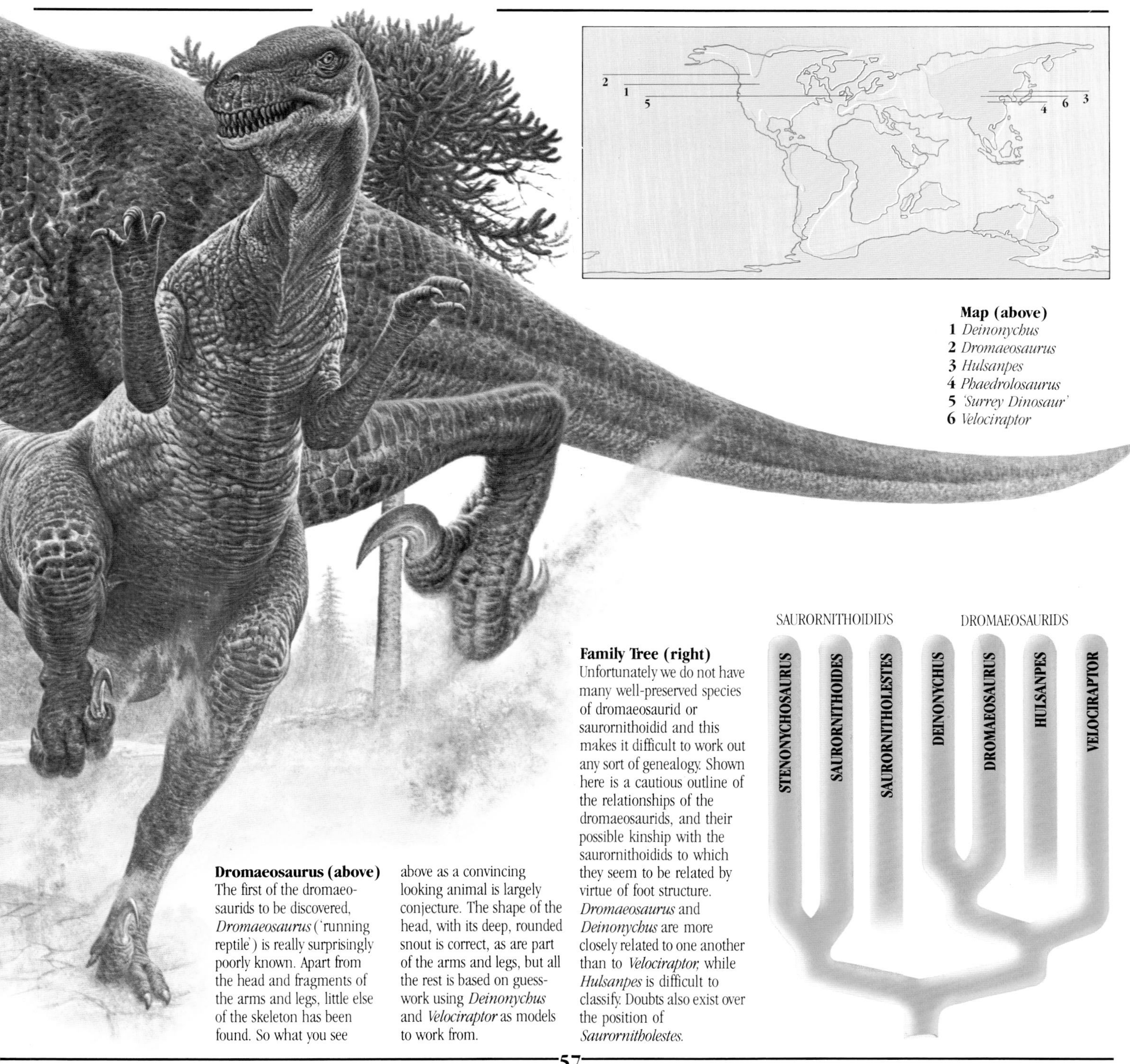


**Map (above)**
**1** *Deinonychus*
**2** *Dromaeosaurus*
**3** *Hulsanpes*
**4** *Phaedrolosaurus*
**5** *'Surrey Dinosaur'*
**6** *Velociraptor*

**Dromaeosaurus (above)**
The first of the dromaeosaurids to be discovered, *Dromaeosaurus* ('running reptile') is really surprisingly poorly known. Apart from the head and fragments of the arms and legs, little else of the skeleton has been found. So what you see above as a convincing looking animal is largely conjecture. The shape of the head, with its deep, rounded snout is correct, as are part of the arms and legs, but all the rest is based on guesswork using *Deinonychus* and *Velociraptor* as models to work from.

**Family Tree (right)**
Unfortunately we do not have many well-preserved species of dromaeosaurid or saurornithoidid and this makes it difficult to work out any sort of genealogy. Shown here is a cautious outline of the relationships of the dromaeosaurids, and their possible kinship with the saurornithoidids to which they seem to be related by virtue of foot structure. *Dromaeosaurus* and *Deinonychus* are more closely related to one another than to *Velociraptor*, while *Hulsanpes* is difficult to classify. Doubts also exist over the position of *Saurornitholestes*.

(Natural History) in London where it immediately attracted a great deal of interest. A team of scientists from the museum visited the site and in 1983 an excavation was arranged, which recovered the major part of a very large dromaeosaurid. At present the specimen is being carefully prepared in the palaeontology laboratory of the British Museum so that it can be scientifically described. Meanwhile the palaeontological world will have to wait patiently for the results of this work.

Turning to the distribution of dromaeosaurids, at present these dinosaurs are only known in the northern continents: North America, Europe and Asia; this suggests two possible explanations. Firstly these dinosaurs may have also lived on the southern continents, but have simply not been found there to date. Alternatively, and more likely to my mind, is the possibility that these dinosaurs are *restricted* to the northern continents. The earliest record we have of dromaeosaurids is from the approximate middle of the Cretaceous Period; at this time Tethys, a large ocean, separated Europe and Asia from Africa, Australia and India. Seaways also separated North from South America and had probably done so for several millions of years. Therefore, if dromaeosaurids had evolved in the northern hemisphere in Lower or Middle Cretaceous times, then they would have been able to spread across these continents relatively easily because they were still linked, but would have been less likely, or perhaps unable, to cross the seas and reach the southern continents. Thus their distribution may well be explicable in terms of their time of origin and the relative positions of continents then.

The relationship of dromaeosaurids to other carnivorous dinosaurs is still a vexed question. Their nearest relatives would seem to be the saurornithoidids (see pages 54-55); these are dinosaurs which also exhibit a smaller version of the peculiar sickle-shaped toe claw. However the saurornithoidids do not possess the peculiar stiffened tail or the same hips as dromaeosaurids, and are separated from them for these reasons. The general consensus regarding the relationships between dromaeosaurids and other carnivorous dinosaurs are indicated in the cladogram diagram. On balance the dromaeosaurids share slightly more characteristics with 'coelurosaurs' than with the 'carnosaurs' and could be thought of, perhaps, as rather special, highly predatory dinosaurs that evolved from simpler coelurosaurian ancestors.

## Deinonychus Described

The best example of the dromaeosaurid type of dinosaur is without doubt *Deinonychus*, because it is known from well preserved material and has been very thoroughly described by Professor John Ostrom. Detailed study of its anatomy has revealed a number of quite remarkable features.

**Head (below and right)**
Apart from the area around the jaws, where the teeth have to be firmly anchored in bone, the head of *Deinonychus* is composed of thin struts of bone which are arranged to make it both strong and light. The jaw muscles (1, 2 and 3) are confined to the back of the head and stretch down to the lower jaw. Muscle 1 (below) gives the jaw its powerful 'bite', while muscle 2 'snaps' the jaws shut quickly. Muscle 3 at the back of the head simply opens the jaws wide.

**Velociraptor Skull (left)**
This differs in shape from that of *Deinonychus;* it has a long, low, depressed snout. The eye sockets are large, and the irregular array of teeth are sharply serrated as one might expect in a carnivorous predator.

**Arm and Shoulder (below)**
This rather unusual diagram is drawn from a position looking down on the back of the animal from above its right shoulder. At the bottom are a row of vertebrae with part of the rib-cage, and the shoulder blade and arm in position. The shape and texture of the shoulder and arm bones show details of the shoulder muscles. Not surprisingly for an animal of this type which clutched its prey, the shoulders and arms were heavily muscled — some important muscles are illustrated in red.

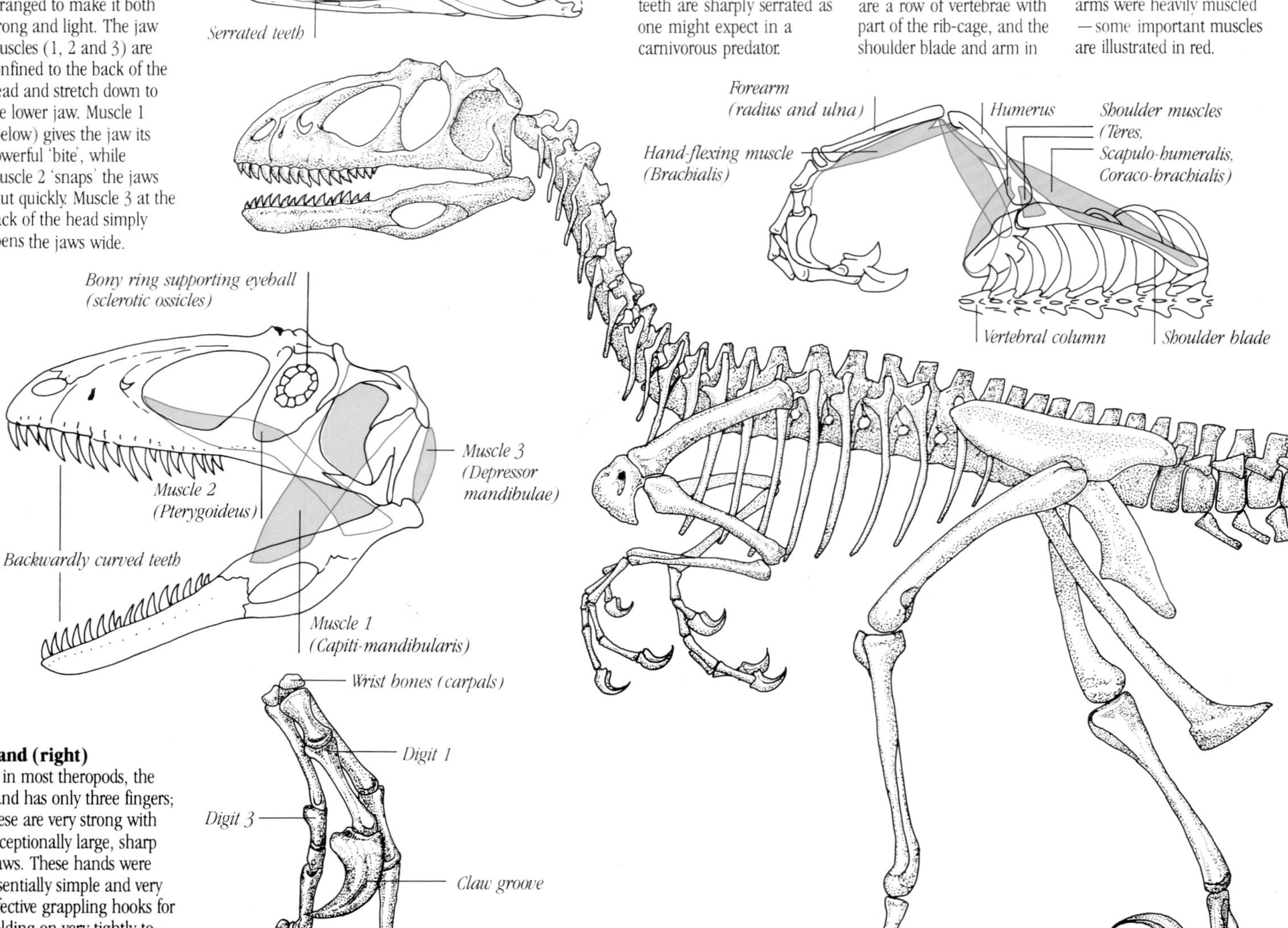


**Hand (right)**
As in most theropods, the hand has only three fingers; these are very strong with exceptionally large, sharp claws. These hands were essentially simple and very effective grappling hooks for holding on very tightly to prey. The small, pebble-like wrist bones are arranged so that the hand can be strongly flexed to improve grip.

Looking first at the skull, *Deinonychus* has a large head but it is a quite lightly built with large openings in its sides for the eyes and muscles of the jaws. The teeth are large, with serrated edges for cutting through flesh, and are curved backwards. Putting these facts together we can deduce that this animal was probably a sharp-eyed predator which used its large jaws and teeth to overcome and eat its prey very efficiently. The thin bony framework of the skull made it very light and manoeuvrable for its size, and also provided ample room for large jaw muscles to give the animal a fearsome bite. The muscles of the jaws were arranged so that one set (the capiti-mandibularis) was able to drive the jaws together really powerfully when they were nearly closed, while another set (the pterygoideus) worked best when the jaws were wide open and gave a sharp snapping bite. Both of these muscles were very large and powerful in *Deinonychus*. The backward curvature of the teeth also suggests that *Deinonychus* was able to tear large chunks of flesh from its prey by tugging backwards while it was biting. Unfortunately the top of the skull of *Deinonychus* is not well preserved. However in *Dromaeosaurus* a narrow hinge runs across the head just behind the eyes; this probably served as a shock-absorber which may even have prevented it from jarring its brain when it snapped its jaws together.

*Deinonychus'* neck is quite slender, sharply curved and flexible so that the head had a very wide range of movement. The back by contrast (and especially the tail, as we shall see later) was held quite stiffly by powerful ligaments; these were necessary because when the animal walked and ran, its back was held horizontally and needed constant support to prevent the animal from collapsing.

The arms are unusually long and the three-fingered hands are very large with powerful, sharply curved talons. The strong arms and hands were obviously used to catch and hold prey very firmly. The upper arm bone (humerus) is broad and has roughened areas for the attachment of powerful chest and arm muscles; this reinforces the supposition that the arms were used to hold actively struggling prey. Indeed the development of such powerful muscles and long arms may be explained by the extraordinary way in which these animals caught and killed their prey.

The hind leg of *Deinonychus* is clearly its most striking possession. Looking first at the leg as a whole, the upper leg bone (femur) is quite short, shorter than the shank (tibia and fibula), which is a feature usually associated with animals that are capable of running very fast. The foot bones are, however, short and stout – not as long as might be expected in a fast runner – but are modified, for a very good reason. Instead of having three forwardly pointing toes of roughly equal length as is usually the case, it has two toes (the third and fourth) which it used for walking, while toe

**Deinonychus Skeleton (below)**
The colour restoration of *Deinonychus* on the previous page is based on this detailed skeletal restoration. The large head is balanced on a slender, almost bird-like neck which was evidently very flexible. The chest was quite short and horizontal. The arms are shown held folded in their resting position against the flanks, rather like the wings of a bird at rest. The hip bones have been a matter of some controversy, especially the shape and size of the pubis. Early on, the pubis was not known at all, in fact a shoulder bone was accidentally put in its place! Now that the real pubis is known, its position is still not certain.

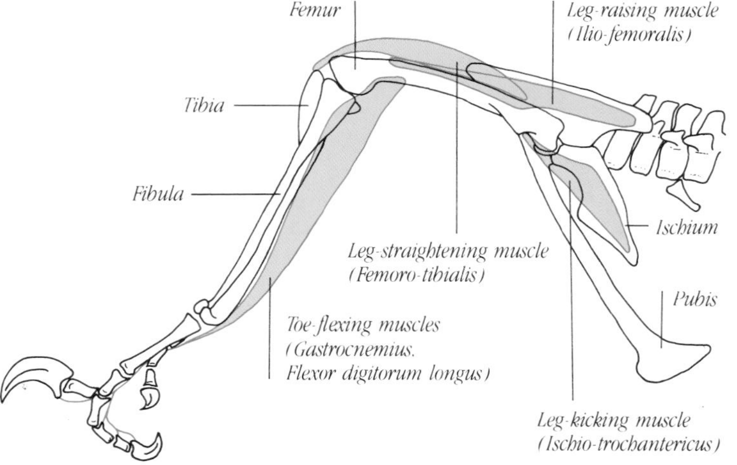


**Leg (left)**
*Deinonychus'* main weapon of attack would have been the leg with its huge claw, rather than the jaws and teeth of the typical predator. As can be seen (left) the muscles of the leg are quite complicated (these are just a few of them!) and most seem to have been arranged in a way that is typical for most dinosaurs. However, the femur has an unusual ridge near its top end. This may well have served as the point of attachment for a special leg-kicking muscle.

**Tail (below)**
As can be seen in the full skeleton (left) the part of the tail nearest the hips is quite normal in structure, with simple, block-like vertebrae. However, the remaining three-quarters of the tail is surrounded by a sheath of fine bony rods. As can be seen below, these rods are developed from each tail bone and served as muscle attachment sites and stiffeners. Muscles in the base of the tail attach to the bony rods so the tail may be held very still when running.

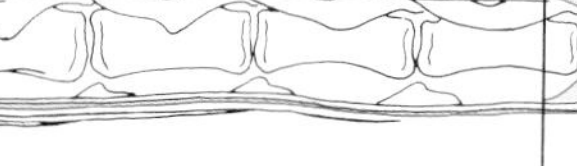

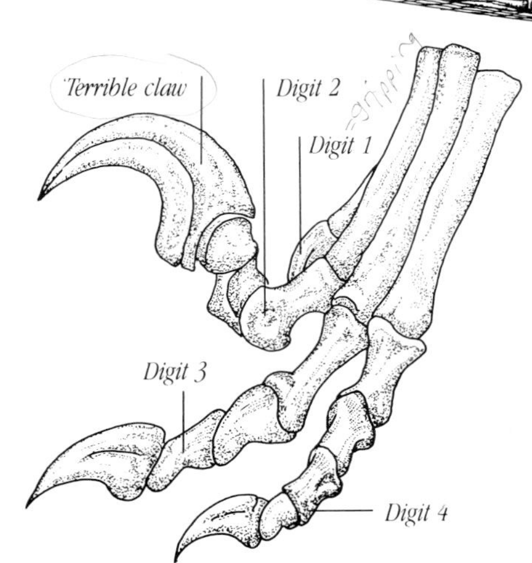


**The Foot and Claw (left)**
The foot of *Deinonychus* is one of the most extraordinary of any dinosaur. As can be seen (left) it has four toes. The first toe is a small spur-like one, and very similar to the first toe of most theropods; it was probably held clear of the ground and may have been used for gripping food or prey. The second toe is the most striking feature of the foot, with its enormous claw. The joints of this toe are specially enlarged so that the toe can be raised upward and backward to avoid damage while running. The other two toes are of roughly equal length and were the only ones used for running upon. The toes could be flexed through a very wide arc (far left) to penetrate the flesh of the prey.

number two is modified into a large sickle-shaped claw, and toe one is a small backward-pointing spur. The explanation for this large claw seems to be that it was used as a formidable weapon of attack. The drawing below shows how the hind leg may have been used. The femur has a special process (posterior trochanter) to which was attached a muscle which came from the ischium; this muscle was used specially for kicking backwards and downwards with the foot to slash open the soft belly of its prey. This special hip muscle may have been developed because had *Deinonychus* used its normal leg-pulling muscles, which are attached to the tail, it would have inevitably twitched its tail as it kicked, causing it to become unbalanced or perhaps to fall over!

## Deinonychus' Tail

Another unusual feature of *Deinonychus* is to be found in the tail. As can be seen, the tail bones near the hips have the usual set of short knobs and spines, so that they can move one against another without becoming dislocated. Farther back down the tail, however, the vertebrae change their appearance quite dramatically. Beneath and between each vertebra are small wedge-shaped bones called chevrons; these develop a pair of long, thin forwardly-pointing rods of bone, which overlap several vertebrae in front. Similarly, above the vertebrae processes which are normally quite short and stout are developed into enormously elongate forwardly-pointing rods. The effect of these rod-like structures is to produce a sheath of bony rods, where the rods of neighbouring vertebrae overlap, which almost completely surrounds the tail of the animal. Despite the fact that these bony rods seem almost to encase the tail bones, it nevertheless remains flexible because the joints between the individual vertebrae are still well developed and not welded together by bone. It seems most likely that the tail rods were formed from long, thin, tail muscles. Such muscles are found in the tails of living lizards and even long-tailed mammals such as kangaroos. In *Deinonychus* these long thin muscles, which are largely tendinous, appear to have been converted into bone. Such a conversion is not as remarkable as it sounds because a thin sheet of soft tissue, which covers the surface of bones and is continuous with muscles which are attached to bone, is the area where bone-forming cells are found and these can (and quite often do) readily migrate into the tendons of muscles. It would seem most probable that the ends of the bony rods in the tail of *Deinonychus* had muscles attached to them. Thus the tail was remarkably specialised: near the hips, the tail was quite flexible because there were no overlapping bony rods; the far end of the tail, however, could either be held extremely stiffly as the muscles attached to the bony rods pulled it taut or, conversely, relaxation of the tail-rod muscles would endow the tail with some slight flexibility. The reason for such complexity in the tail is very probably associated with its predatory life-style. First of all, the tail is long in order to counterbalance the weight of the front half of the body. Secondly, the stiffened tail may well have acted not only as a dynamic stabiliser when running at speed, but also as a means of allowing a rapid change of direction when chasing fleet-footed and evasive prey. Swift alterations of direction could be made by swinging the tail to one side and using it to rotate the front end of the body, even when running at full speed. Damage to the tail by 'whip-lash' while performing this manoeuvre would have been prevented by keeping the tail very stiff, using the tail rods and muscles.

## Patterns of Behaviour

So, what do all these observations tell us about the probable life-style of this animal. Well, they suggest a great deal about one aspect of its life as a predator. *Deinonychus* was apparently quite small, the total length of an adult may not have been much more than 10-11 feet (3-3·3m) judging by the remains found to date. Living at the same time as *Deinonychus* were herbivorous sauropods (titanosaurs), ankylosaurs (*Sauro-*

**Above:** A skeleton of *Dromaeosaurus* in the final stages of reconstruction at the Tyrrell Museum of Palaeontology, Alberta. The characteristic sickle-shaped claws on the hind feet are very evident.

**The Hunting Pack (left)** To overcome large prey like *Tenontosaurus*, *Deinonychus* may have hunted in predatory packs. Some would slow the potential victim by grasping its tail and hind quarters while others would aim lethal kicks at its underside.

**Hunting Hypsilophodon (below)** This sequence shows how an individual *Deinonychus* may have hunted a similarly fleet-footed prey, such as the ornithopod *Hypsilophodon*, in a one-to-one chase. Both animals are capable of high-speed running and jinking, but once *Deinonychus* has closed with its prey, it uses its arms and teeth to subdue the struggling creature. The *coup de grâce*, however, is administered by the fearsome claws on *Deinonychus'* hind feet.

*pelta*) and the hypsilophodontid *Tenontosaurus*, as well as other predators including a large 'carnosaur' and a small ornithomimosaur. All the herbivores were the potential prey of *Deinonychus* in one way or another: let us consider the various ways in which *Deinonychus* may have stalked and killed its prey.

(i) **Sauropods** Obviously fully grown, 65 feet (20m) long titanosaurs are unlikely to have been preyed upon by small *Deinonychus*. However, just as is the case today with the large cats hunting zebra and wildebeest in Africa, the usual target is not the strong adult, but the young, and old or sick individuals. Similarly *Deinonychus* may have stalked young titanosaurs in the same way as the big cats. There is much circumstantial evidence from footprint trackways of herding in sauropods, the young animals clustering at the centre of the herd protected by the adult individuals. One can imagine small predatory packs of *Deinonychus* waiting patiently for a young titanosaur to wander a little way from the main herd in search of more succulent vegetation where, unprotected by the adults, it might be pounced upon by a ferocious pack of *Deinonychus*.

(ii) **Ankylosaurs** A rather different proposition for *Deinonychus*, the nodosaurid *Sauropelta* (page 160) would have relied on its heavy dermal armour to resist attack. For the most part *Sauropelta* was probably impregnable. The only possible tactic would have been for *Deinonychus* to attempt to turn the animal on to its back to expose its relatively unprotected belly. Adult *Sauropelta* were sufficiently large and heavy to be beyond the scope of *Deinonychus*; however, as with the sauropods, young *Sauropelta* may well have fallen prey to *Deinonychus*.

(iii) **Ornithopods** The most numerous fossils found in the quarries that have yielded *Deinonychus* remains are those of *Tenontosaurus tilletti* (page 104); this was a medium-sized unarmoured herbivore, and would undoubtedly have been the main species upon which *Deinonychus* would have preyed. Both young and fully adult individuals of *Tenontosaurus* were likely targets, although the method of attack was probably different in each case.

Small *Tenontosaurus* were lightly built, agile creatures with relatively long slender legs and, curiously like *Deinonychus*, special tail-stiffening bony rods. These little animals were therefore quite nimble and fleet-footed; the stiffened tail would again have acted both as a dynamic stabiliser and as an inertial beam so that they could jink from side to side when running at high speed to evade predators. Lone *Deinonychus* are likely to have stalked young *Tenontosaurus* in order to get close enough to make a short sprint to catch them. If alerted, young *Tenontosaurus* probably stood a fair chance of escaping as it probably had a slightly greater top-speed. The reason for believing this is that *Deinonychus*' massive sickle-claw required a foot that was short and strong to absorb the stresses imposed by its very powerful kick (one specimen has been found with a toe bone [phalanx] of the big claw that had been broken and then healed during the life of the animal). *Deinonychus* could not therefore have such a slender ('fleet') foot as *Tenontosaurus*.

Larger, adult specimens of *Tenontosaurus* may well have attracted hunting packs of *Deinonychus*. Professor Ostrom noted when the first remains of *Deinonychus* were recovered that bones from three partial skeletons were found quite close to a skeleton of *Tenontosaurus*, and suggested that *Deinonychus* may have hunted in packs, rather like Cape hunting dogs. This seems to me a reasonable proposition. Certainly a fully grown *Tenontosaurus* was considerably larger than *Deinonychus* so it is unlikely that a single *Deinonychus* could bring down a *Tenontosaurus* alone. However, a concerted attack by several individuals would undoubtedly have resulted in success and large quantities of food as a reward.

*Deinonychus*' principal weapon was almost certainly its hind leg and claw. Small animals would have been grasped very securely by the large, powerful and very sharply taloned hand. Instead of being held close to the body so that it could be bitten, the prey would have been held out at arms' length. (The arms and hands of *Deinonychus* are extraordinarily long by the standard of most other theropods.) In this way the foot and its huge claw could be drawn forward so that it could be kicked against the belly of its prey. The arms and hand are therefore vitally important for not only grasping prey, but also holding it secure, keeping it at a distance to allow 'kicking room', and also to steady the prey against the impact of the kick. It seems likely, therefore, that the foot claw was used to kill the prey by disembowelling and that the teeth were used primarily for feeding. Most of the teeth are backwardly-directed, rather than being downwardly-pointing, stabbing-teeth as is the case in predators that use them to kill. Instead *Deinonychus*' teeth seem to have served for biting off large chunks of meat; this being effected by violent backward tugs of the head and body, while the jaws were clamped onto a piece of flesh.

All in all, *Deinonychus* (as well as the other dromaeosaurids) must be one of the most extraordinary predatory animals ever to have lived: its most remarkable feature of all being the enormous sickle-like claw on its hind foot which seems to have totally changed its method of attacking prey from that adopted by all other carnivorous dinosaurs.

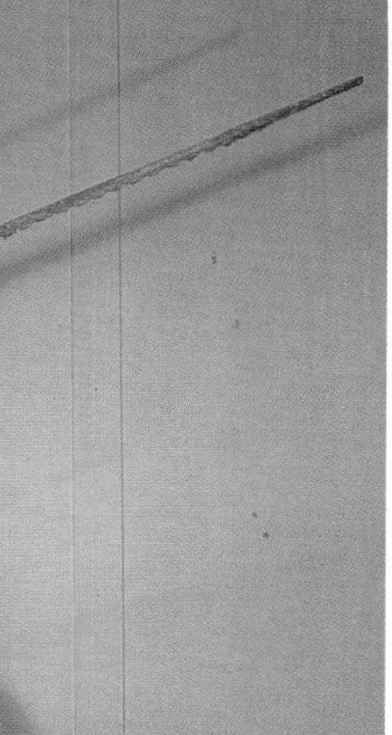

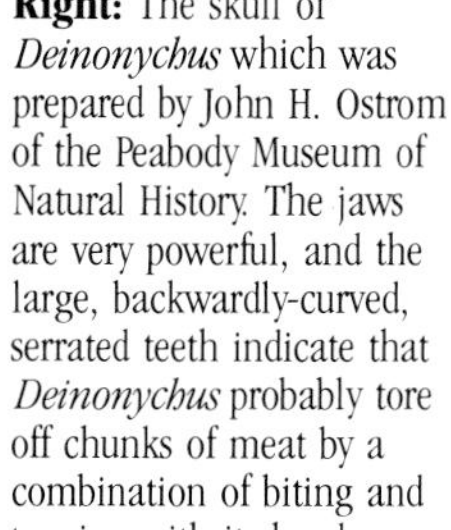

**Right:** The skull of *Deinonychus* which was prepared by John H. Ostrom of the Peabody Museum of Natural History. The jaws are very powerful, and the large, backwardly-curved, serrated teeth indicate that *Deinonychus* probably tore off chunks of meat by a combination of biting and tugging with its head.

**Right:** The awesome claw of the 'Surrey dinosaur' which measures 12in (31cm) around its outside edge. About half the skeleton of this theropod has been recovered including much of the skull, limbs and girdle.

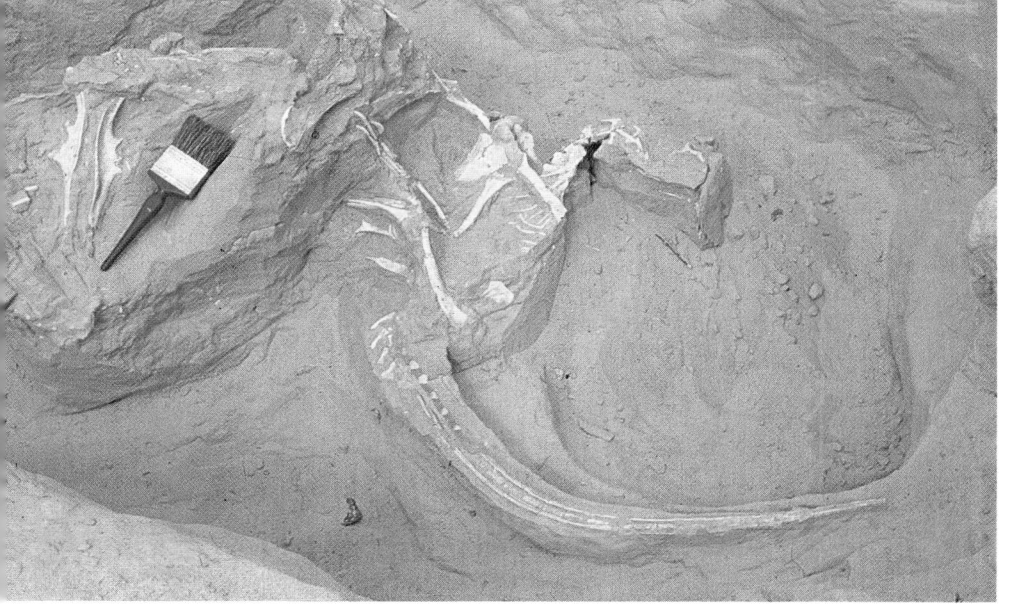

**Below:** This remarkable find was uncovered by the 1971 Polish-Mongolian expedition at Toogreeg in the Gobi Desert. It reveals the skeleton of *Velociraptor mongoliensis* interlocked with that of *Protoceratops andrewsi* (on the left, its skull being the triangular feature apparently gripped by *Velociraptor's* hands and feet). Did they die in combat, perhaps as *Velociraptor* was trying to plunder eggs from the ceratopian's nest?

# 'CARNOSAURS'

The 'carnosaurs' are, with the 'coelurosaurs', the other major group of theropod dinosaurs described in most popular dinosaur books. They differ quite markedly in their bodily proportions when compared with the various types of theropod that have been described over the previous pages. 'Carnosaurs' were typically large theropods, 20ft (6m) or more in length, and were heavily built, with stout, pillar-like hindlegs, rather feeble forelimbs and very large heads perched upon short, very powerful necks. Most of the 'carnosaurs' described over the next few pages share these characteristics. However, there is very little agreement among palaeontologists about the degree to which they are all related to one another. Part of this uncertainty stems from the fact that very few of these heavily-built theropods are known from anything like a complete skeleton. It is also quite likely that smaller theropods tend to share common design features (i.e. slender legs, long arms, small heads etc) while larger theropods all tend to have pillar-like legs, large heads and short arms. We may, therefore, simply be grouping together animals which share the same design constraints, rather than those which are closely related in a genealogical sense.

In order to cope with these problems, I shall describe some of the best-known examples of these large theropods ('carnosaurs') in order to provide some basic information about their structure and biology. Below can be seen life-like restorations of three quite well-known theropods: *Allosaurus* ('strange reptile'), *Ceratosaurus* ('horned reptile') and *Dilophosaurus* ('two-crested reptile'). All three are known from the Jurassic Period. *Allosaurus* and *Ceratosaurus* seem to have been contemporaries, their remains having been found in the same late Jurassic quarries of North America. *Dilophosaurus*, however, is one of the very few well-preserved early Jurassic dinosaurs. It also was found in North America.

*Allosaurus* ('strange reptile') has rather confused origins, like many other dinosaurs. The remains of an *Allosaurus*-like theropod were first discovered in 1869 by Dr Ferdinand Hayden in Grand County, Colorado. This consisted of a single broken tail bone, which was described in some considerable detail by Joseph Leidy in 1870. Leidy was able to show that this single broken bone resembled those of other large carnivorous dinosaurs known from Europe, and at first he referred to it as *Poicilopleuron* ('varying cavity') after a European genus. A little later Leidy gave this bone the new name *Antrodemus*. Somewhat later (in 1877) Benjamin Mudge, one of O. C. Marsh's trusted field assistants, discovered the partial remains of another large carnivorous dinosaur in Fremont County, Colorado. To these imperfect remains Marsh gave the name *Allosaurus*. Unfortunately Marsh then decided to abandon Mudge's quarry in Fremont County and return to Wyoming where better fossils were being

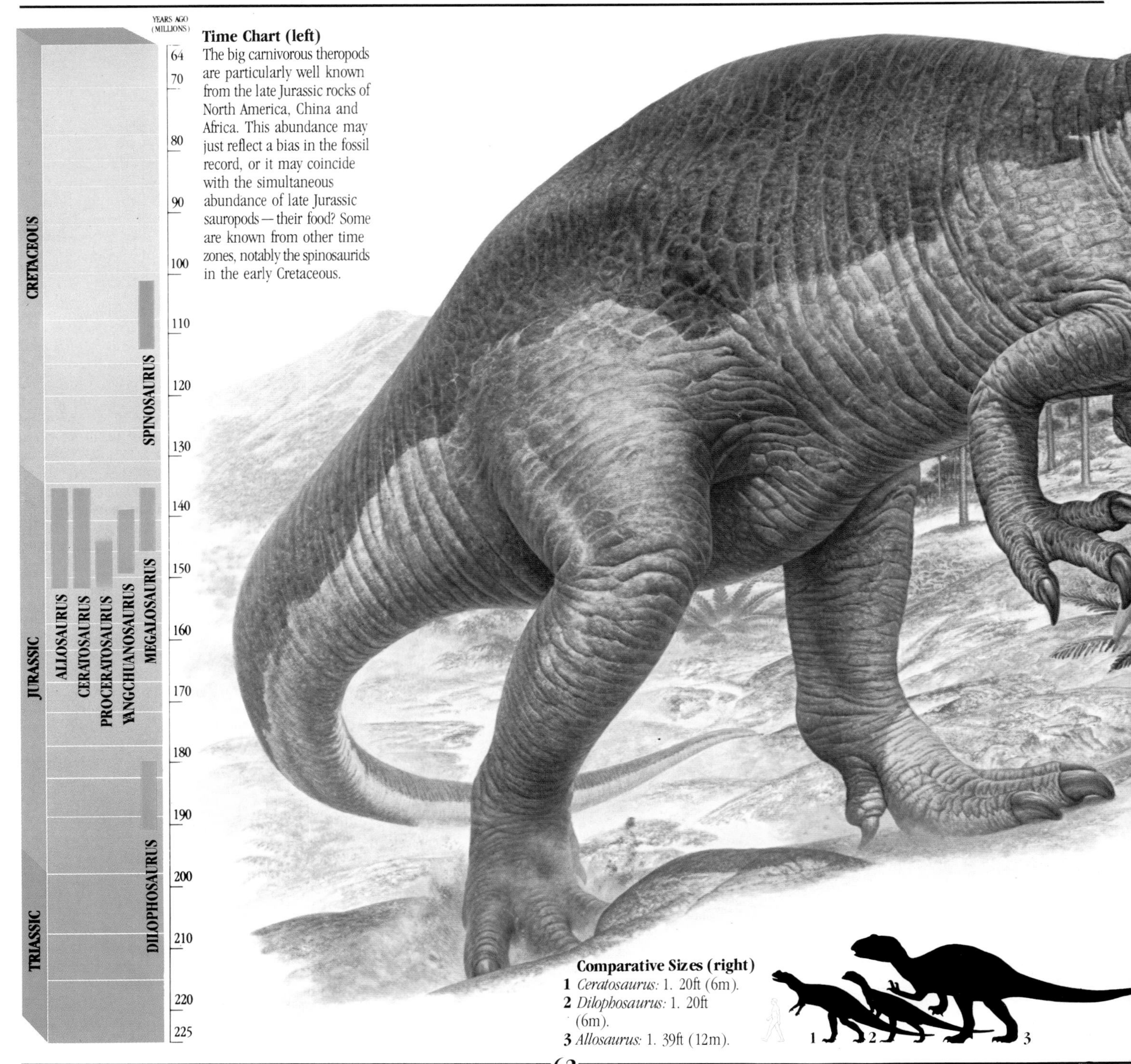


**Time Chart (left)**
The big carnivorous theropods are particularly well known from the late Jurassic rocks of North America, China and Africa. This abundance may just reflect a bias in the fossil record, or it may coincide with the simultaneous abundance of late Jurassic sauropods — their food? Some are known from other time zones, notably the spinosaurids in the early Cretaceous.

**Comparative Sizes (right)**
**1** *Ceratosaurus:* 1. 20ft (6m).
**2** *Dilophosaurus:* 1. 20ft (6m).
**3** *Allosaurus:* 1. 39ft (12m).

**Allosaurus (below)**
This large carnivore lived in North America at the same time as the first bird, *Archaeopteryx* (shown here) lived in Germany. An adult *Allosaurus* was up to 39ft (12m) long, and the skull could be 3ft (90cm) long. The jaws were lined with recurved dagger-like teeth which had serrated edges back and front, just like the blade of a steak knife. *Allosaurus* had strong claws on its hand and feet with which to hold down and tear at its prey.

found, so that little more of this animal was discovered. In 1883 another of Marsh's assistants (M.P. Felch) returned to the 'Garden Park' Quarry and resumed where Mudge had left off—with spectacular results.

Between 1883 and 1884 Felch excavated an almost complete *Allosaurus* skeleton from this quarry as well as several partial skeletons and various isolated fragments. Many of these remains were described by Marsh in subsequent years. Much of this material was carefully prepared in the early part of this century at the Smithsonian Institution in Washington and was finally described by Charles Gilmore in 1920 under the name of *Antrodemus!* Gilmore decided that the single fragment of backbone described by Leidy was diagnostic of this dinosaur and therefore referred all the material, including that described by Marsh as *Allosaurus*, to *Antrodemus*. Clearly Gilmore's decision was mistaken; he should not have based his dinosaur on such

**Dilophosaurus (above)**
This is the earliest large carnivorous dinosaur. *Dilophosaurus* had a crest on its head which was made from two thin ridges of bone situated side by side, and shaped rather like half dinner plates set up on end. *Dilophosaurus* was also different from the other two later 'carnosaurs' shown here since its jaws were weak and slender. They probably could not have withstood the stresses of dealing with struggling prey, and it has been suggested that *Dilophosaurus* was a scavenger rather than an active predator.

**Ceratosaurus (above)**
Similar to *Allosaurus* in some respects, *Ceratosaurus* was smaller, and had four-fingered hands. The most striking feature of *Ceratosaurus* is the fact that it had a sizeable bony bump on its snout which was shaped rather like a rhinoceros horn. The function of the bony bump is uncertain. It probably was not for protection against other predators, but may have been used by males in fighting each other for mates. *Ceratosaurus* has fewer teeth than *Allosaurus*.

**Map (below)**
**1** *Allosaurus*
**2** *Altispinax*
**3** *Ceratosaurus*
**4** *Dilophosaurus*
**5** *Eustreptospondylus*
**6** *Megalosaurus*
**7** *Priveteausaurus*
**8** *Proceratosaurus*
**9** *Spinosaurus*
**10** *Szechuanosaurus*
**11** *Yangchuanosaurus*

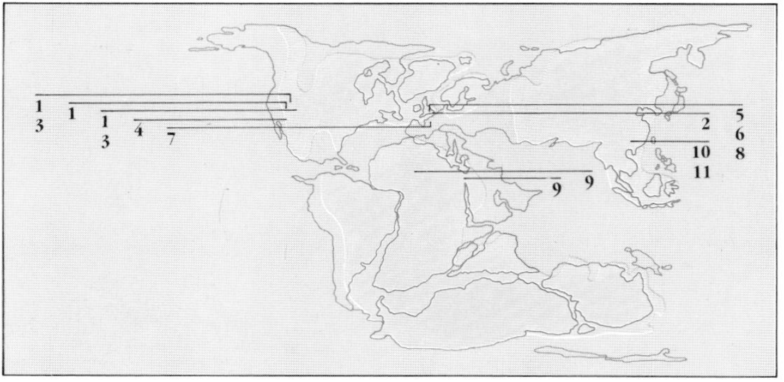


**Family Tree (right)**
The 'carnosaurs' have been split into the primitive *Ceratosaurus* group (which may have included early 'coelurosaurs'), and the more advanced spinosaurids, and *Allosaurus* and related theropods.

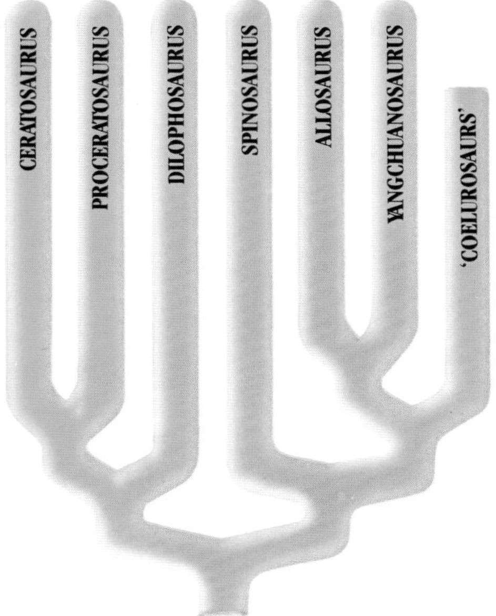

poor original material. Today the genus *Allosaurus* is the one that is recognised and is based on the virtually complete skeleton discovered by M. P. Felch in 1883. Since that time more *Allosaurus* material has been recovered from late Jurassic rocks of North America. One of the most spectacular of these discoveries was made in Utah in 1927 at the so-called Cleveland-Lloyd Dinosaur Quarry.

First exploration of this site by the University of Utah yielded over 800 dinosaur bones in just a few weeks, after which no further interest was shown. In 1939 further excavations by Princeton University resulted in the collection of a further 1,200 bones. Finally in 1960 the University of Utah, under the guidance of Dr Jim Madsen and William Stokes, organised a co-operative dinosaur project. By this means various institutions from around the world donated money or materials to aid an extensive series of excavations at the Cleveland-Lloyd Quarry (1960-1965) and received partial or complete dinosaur skeletons in exchange. In 1967 the Cleveland-Lloyd Quarry was designated a 'Natural Landmark' and is now protected by federal law through the United States Department of the Interior. A permanent working exhibit of the excavation site, rather similar to that created at Dinosaur National Monument (also in Utah) is planned for the near future.

To date the quarry has revealed a diverse fauna of dinosaurs: ornithopods, stegosaurs, ankylosaurs, sauropods and theropods of several types including *Allosaurus* and *Ceratosaurus*. Curiously, *Allosaurus* is by far the most common dinosaur, being represented by at least 44 individuals which range in size from 39ft (12m) in length down to juveniles 10ft (3m) long. The one unfortunate feature of the Cleveland-Lloyd Dinosaur Quarry is that all the skeletal material is scattered. There is not one articulated skeleton.

The skull of *Allosaurus* was far longer than that of any of the theropods described so far. Several skulls are known which range in length from 24-36in (60-90cm). The jaws are very large and lined with many long, curved, serrated teeth. Above the jaws, the skull, although large, is surprisingly lightly constructed. There are several large lateral spaces in front and behind the eye. These must have served a purpose and it seems most likely that they helped to lighten the skull so that it was easier for the animal to move its head around. There are really only two areas of skull that cannot be lightened much by removal of bone; these are the jaws, which have to anchor the teeth, and the area at the rear of the skull where the muscles that operate the jaws attach. Between these two areas of the skull there is a rather complicated series of bars or struts of bone which presumably served to transmit the forces exerted on the bones of the skull during biting and tugging at prey. It must seem a little curious that the very large skulls of predatory dinosaurs should have proportionately less bone in them than some of the smaller

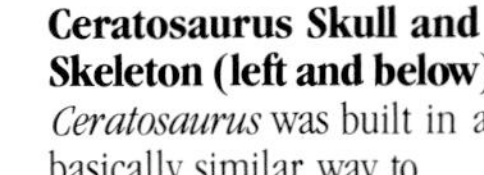

**Ceratosaurus Skull and Skeleton (left and below)** *Ceratosaurus* was built in a basically similar way to *Allosaurus* and exhibits typical 'carnosaur' features. The skull is rather large for the body and although it has a very robust lower jaw the rest of it is quite lightly built. The crest in the nasal region is a distinguishing feature of *Ceratosaurus*. The neck is rather short and although the back leg is powerful and pillar-like, the front leg is feeble. The tail is long and provides attachment for strong musculature and acts as a counterbalance.

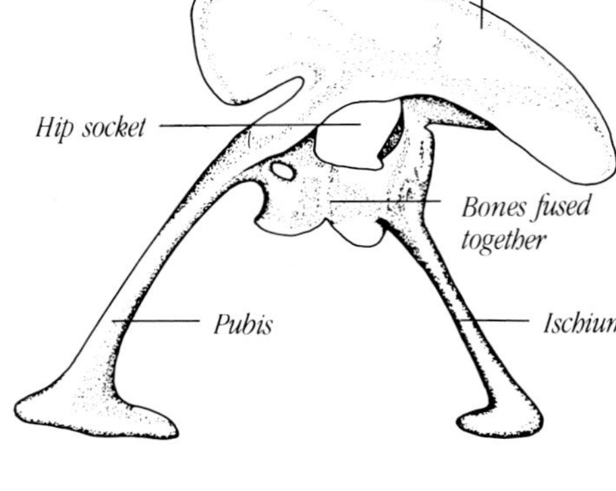


**Ceratosaurus Hip (right)** The hip of this 'carnosaur' shows the arrangement typical of saurischian dinosaurs with the front pelvic bone (pubis) pointing forwards. However, the hip of *Ceratosaurus* is unusual in that the individual bones are firmly welded together and the sutures (areas of contact of the bones) are obliterated.

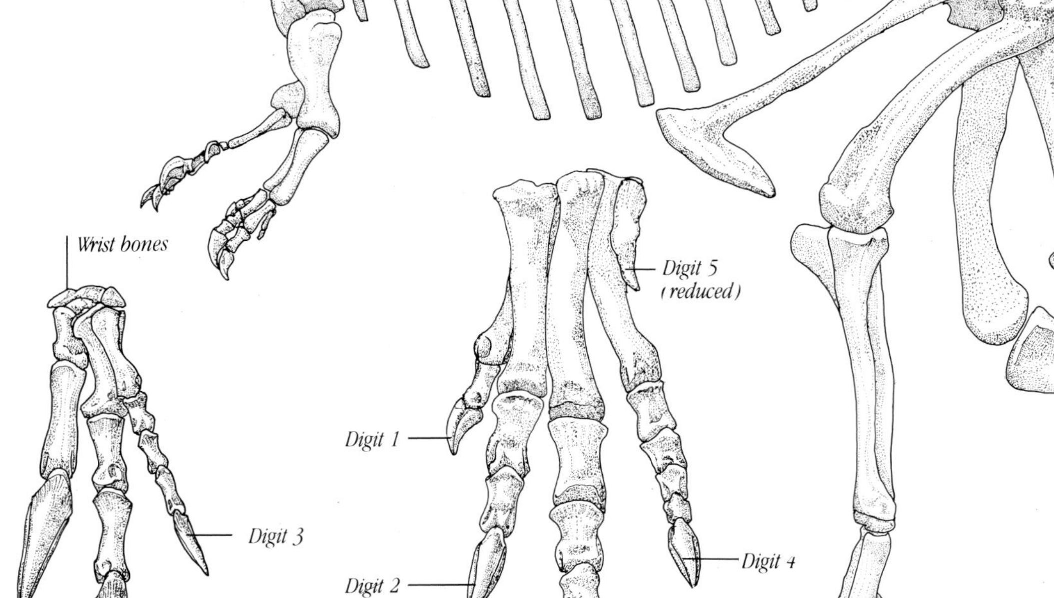


**Allosaurus Hand and Foot (right)** As in all 'carnosaurs' the front leg of *Allosaurus* is much weaker than the back one and this is reflected in the hand and foot. The hand (immediate right) has three fingers and although it is relatively small it bears three sharp, curved claws. It would have been very useful in helping to subdue prey and possibly also in tearing flesh off the bones of carrion. The feet (far right) are much larger and have four toes each. Toes 2, 3 and 4 face forwards while the first toe points backwards. This configuration would have provided a large surface area for the foot—an adaptation for bearing the weight of this large (up to 39ft, 12m long) lumbering theropod.

theropods. However, it does highlight the point that a skull of solid bone would have rendered the head incredibly heavy and unwieldy in life. Large size does have the added cost to the animal of greater weight and, as will be seen in some of the very large sauropod dinosaurs (pages 80-97), some went to extraordinary lengths in order to reduce the weight of bone in their bodies.

Another curious feature of *Allosaurus'* skull is the large roughened ridge just above and in front of the eye. The centre of this bone is hollowed out, but no-one is really sure why. It may have housed a salt gland or alternatively provided some sort of distinctive feature that allowed individual *Allosaurus* to recognise one another (unusual or elaborate head-gear is known in many dinosaurs—see the hadrosaurids and ceratopids for examples).

Behind the head the body was typically 'carnosaur'. The massive pillar-like legs supported the squat body which was balanced over the hips by the massive tail. The neck, although short, was strongly curved so that the head was held almost above the shoulders rather than extended forward. The long ribs and blunt roughened spines on the neck indicate that powerful muscles were attached here, which undoubtedly assisted with feeding. The back too was short and powerfully constructed, and the spines of each vertebra are broad and very roughened where powerful back muscles and ligaments were attached. The forelimbs are quite small compared with the hindlimbs but they were evidently very powerful, and ended in three viciously curved claws.

## Possible Life-Style

All in all, *Allosaurus* was an extremely well-equipped predatory dinosaur. The huge jaws were lined with large, stabbing and cutting teeth, both for killing and dismembering their prey. The powerful neck and back would have aided the jaws in tearing off large chunks of flesh, and the large claws on the hands and feet undoubtedly helped to subdue their victims. Precisely what their prey and predatory habits were is something of a mystery. Unlike the majority of 'coelurosaurs', these animals were not built for high-speed pursuit; they were much larger lumbering creatures. They probably fed upon the larger ornithischians such as *Camptosaurus* (page 110) and *Stegosaurus* (page 152) as well as the larger sauropods: *Diplodocus* and *Apatosaurus* (pages 80-81).

*Camptosaurus* was a moderate sized (16·5-23ft, 5-7m long) ornithopod which was presumably quite nimble although defenceless; it may well have been captured by ambush rather than hot pursuit tactics. *Stegosaurus* with its defensive tail spikes may have posed greater dangers to *Allosaurus* even though it was a much slower moving prey. The large sauropods could well have been attacked by *Allosaurus* operating in hunting groups. It seems possible

**Dilophosaurus Skeleton (below)**
*Dilophosaurus* was about 20ft or 6m long—about the same length as *Ceratosaurus*. Both were probably more agile than *Allosaurus* which was very much larger. Again in *Dilophosaurus* we see the typical 'carnosaur' features of the large head, weak front leg, powerful back leg and long tail. In this form the neck was longer and more flexible than usual, but it was still controlled by powerful muscles attached to the neck and ribs. These were probably necessary to support the large head.

**Dilophosaurus Skull (below)**
This is a typical 'carnosaur' skull, being large relative to the body and lightly built except for the strong lower jaw. The crests on the skull give this animal its name.

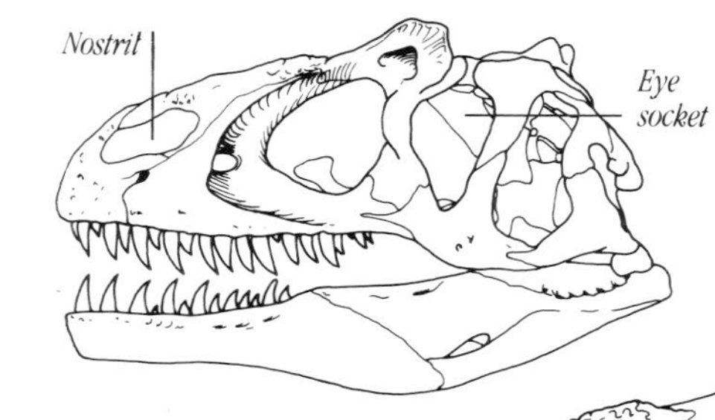


**Yangchuanosaurus Skull (below)**
This is the skull of a Chinese form from the Jurassic deposits of Sichuan. It is very similar to that of *Allosaurus* to which it might be related.

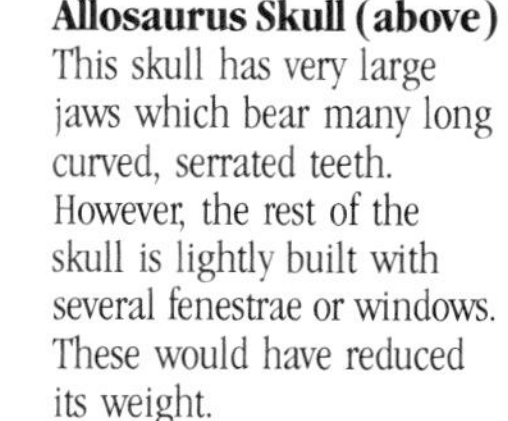

**Allosaurus Skull (above)**
This skull has very large jaws which bear many long curved, serrated teeth. However, the rest of the skull is lightly built with several fenestrae or windows. These would have reduced its weight.

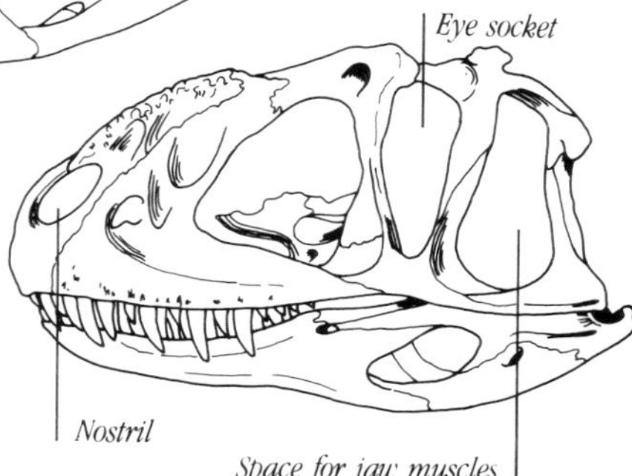


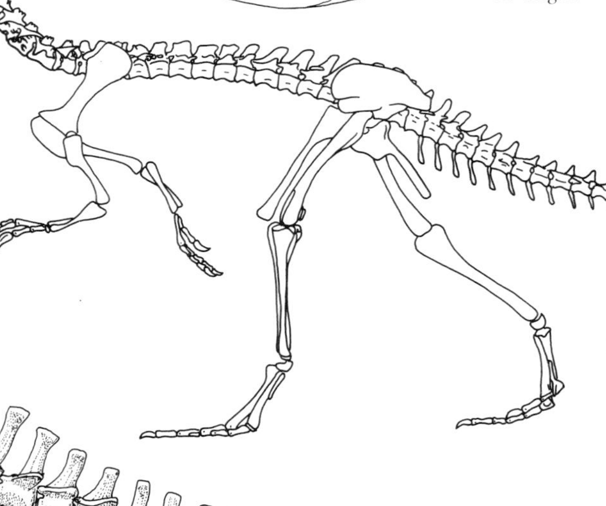

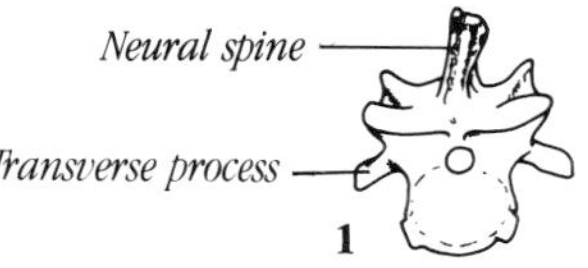


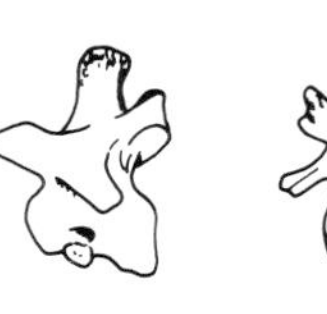

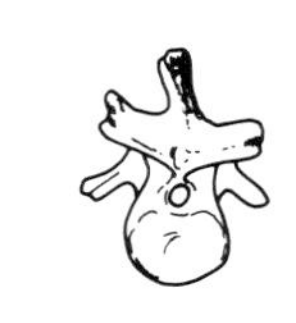

Muscle scar

2

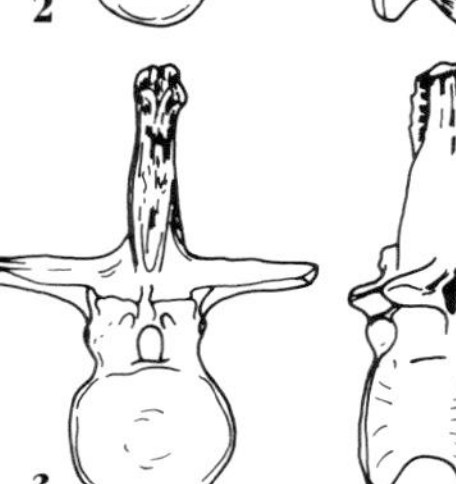

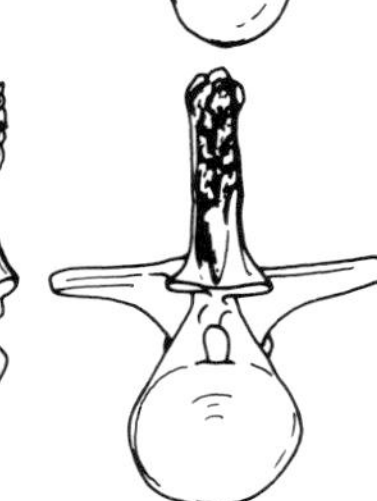

3

**Allosaurus Vertebrae (right)**
**1** The top row shows a vertebra from the neck region. It is relatively small and has a low neural spine and short transverse processes. Its design lets the neck move freely.

**2** The middle row shows a vertebra from the shoulder region. The neural spine is taller and shows muscle attachment scars. The rib is double-headed and contacts the transverse process and the body of the vertebra itself.

**3** The bottom row shows a vertebra from just in front of the hip region where the largest vertebrae occur. The tall neural spine is very rough where muscles attached. The transverse process is almost horizontal unlike that of the shoulder.

that several *Allosaurus* could bring down even the largest sauropods in a determined attack; although the main victims may well have been the less powerful juveniles. The evidence of strong herding tendencies among sauropods is probably a reflection of the threat posed by large predatory theropods such as *Allosaurus*.

Like the large predatory cats of today, *Allosaurus* were probably opportunistic scavengers of carrion—not only devouring long-abandoned carcasses, but also driving small theropods away from their own kills.

## Ceratosaurus Described

The first skeleton of *Ceratosaurus* ('horned reptile') was discovered in 1883/4 by M. P. Felch at the same quarry in which the fine skeleton of *Allosaurus* was excavated in Fremont County, Colorado. A large part of the skeleton of this theropod was recovered which provided O. C. Marsh with very good information with which to describe another new type of theropod, which was both smaller and clearly different from *Allosaurus*.

*Ceratosaurus* seems to have reached a maximum body length of 20ft (6m) and stood about 6·5ft (2m) high. In its general proportions *Ceratosaurus* resembles *Allosaurus*: it has a large head, a short neck, relatively short arms and pillar-like legs. However, there are several notable differences. In the skull the jaws are massive and the teeth are sharp and curved. Again the sides of the skull are cut away to produce large open spaces enclosed by a bony framework of struts. There is also a large, hollowed-out ridge just above the eye similar to that of *Allosaurus*. However, unlike *Allosaurus*, there is a very prominent bony horn on the snout; also there are fewer teeth in the jaws and the back of the skull is larger and deeper.

The remainder of the skeleton of *Ceratosaurus* also shows several subtle differences from that of *Allosaurus*. In particular the hand has four well-developed fingers, unlike *Allosaurus* which has only three. The bones of the pelvis are also rather unusual in that they are all firmly welded together by bone, rather than remaining separate as is normally the case. Rather unexpectedly, the *Ceratosaurus* skeleton was also found to possess the remains of a narrow row of bony plates which seem to have run down the middle of the back.

Compared with *Allosaurus*, *Ceratosaurus* would seem to have been a smaller, more lightly-built and agile predator. Skeletal remains of *Ceratosaurus* are quite rare in late Jurassic rocks, and most probably this implies that it was a more versatile and perhaps solitary predator, unlike the gregarious *Allosaurus*.

## The Discovery of Dilophosaurus

Unlike the two previous theropods, *Dilophosaurus* ('two-ridged reptile') is from the early Jurassic. Its remains were first discovered in 1942 during an expedition to Northern Arizona organised by the University of California. The team were led to the site by a Navajo Indian, Mr Jesse Williams, where they discovered the remains of three individuals: one was an almost complete 20ft (6m) long skeleton, the other two consisted of rather badly eroded fragments.

After careful preparation in the laboratory, this dinosaur was finally described by Dr Sam Welles in 1954 as a new species of *'Megalosaurus'*. *Megalosaurus* is a well known, but unfortunately very fragmentary, large theropod dinosaur from the late Jurassic of England (see later). First analysis of Welles' new dinosaur suggested strong similarities to the English theropod. In 1964 Welles returned to the area in which his *'Megalosaurus'* was found and was fortunate to discover another skeleton of a similar theropod. Unlike the previous examples, this skull was quite well preserved and revealed a pair of thin bony crests that ran along its top. Clearly this was no ordinary theropod, and in 1970 Welles gave it the new name of *Dilophosaurus* in recognition of the unusual crests on its head.

In 1984 Sam Welles published a very detailed description of *Dilophosaurus*. As seems typical of 'carnosaurs', the skull of *Dilophosaurus* is large in proportion to its body, and is quite delicately constructed. Welles concluded that the long slender teeth at the front of the snout were probably used for plucking and tearing at the flesh of their victims rather than biting, while the more posterior teeth were used for cutting and slicing flesh. The function of the tall crests on the skull remains a mystery; most likely they were associated with some aspect of the behaviour of the animal—perhaps visual signalling for recognition purposes.

The neck, although long and flexible, was controlled by powerful muscles attached to the ribs and spines. The long tail counterbalanced the animal so that it could walk and run on its hind legs which were long and powerful. The forelimbs were short but strong, and the hand had four fingers, the first three of which bore sharp claws. The first finger was shorter and more powerful than the other two.

## The Variety of 'Carnosaurs'

There are in addition to *Allosaurus*, *Ceratosaurus* and *Dilophosaurus* many other carnosaurs from the Jurassic and Cretaceous rocks of most countries. Unfortunately many of them are known from very scrappy material, such as odd serrated teeth or claws; this has led to the naming of large numbers of species on very dubious evidence indeed. One of the best examples of the problems created by imperfect or scrappy material causing a proliferation of names is the renowned dinosaur *Megalosaurus*.

*Megalosaurus* ('big reptile') is particularly famous because it was the first dinosaur to be named and scientifically described. The remains of *Megalosaurus (M. bucklandi* as it was later to be known) were discovered in a quarry at Stonesfield in Oxfordshire, England in the early years of the 19th Century; they represent parts of a large theropod dinosaur 23-26·2ft (7-8m) long that lived in late Jurassic times. The skeleton, first described by William Buckland in 1824, included parts of the jaws, several vertebrae, and parts of the pelvis and hindlimbs. In the years following the original description, any fragmentary remains of a carnivorous dinosaur found in Jurassic or Cretaceous rocks were referred to as *Megalosaurus!* Thus *Megalosaurus* remains were reported from Europe (France, Belgium, Germany, Portugal), Australia and North America (later to be renamed *Dilophosaurus!*). In fact much of this material is either obviously not referrable to *Megalosaurus* or too fragmentary to be diagnosed as anything more than 'the remains of a large theropod'.

For example, one well-preserved skeleton from Wolvercote, near Oxford, was for a long time referred to as another species of *Megalosaurus (M. cuvieri)*. It consisted of a considerable part of the skeleton of a 16·5-20ft (5-6m) long theropod. After detailed study of this and other material, Dr Alick Walker (Newcastle) was able to show that this species was totally unlike *M. bucklandi* and deserved a completely new name: *Eustreptospondylus oxoniensis* ('Oxford's true reversed backbone'). To add further confusion to the situation, Alick Walker referred another specimen (an incomplete braincase from Dives [France] from similarly aged rocks) to *Eustreptospondylus (E. divesensis)*. Re-study of this material led Dr Philippe Taquet and Sam Welles to propose that *E. divesensis* was so different from *E. oxoniensis* that it deserved to be renamed *Piveteausaurus divesensis* ('Piveteau's reptile from Dives')!

Another poorly known species of *Megalosaurus (M. dunkeri)* from the early Cretaceous near Hastings in Sussex is remarkable for the height of the spines on its backbones; these are quite unlike those on the back of *M. bucklandi*. In 1926 Friedrich Freiherr von Huene renamed this species *Altispinax* ('tall spines'). Yet another *Megalosaurus (M. parkeri)*, based on a partial skeleton from the Jurassic of Dorset, was also notable for its high spines and was later renamed *Metriacanthosaurus* ('long spined reptile') by Dr Alick Walker.

These are just a few examples of the confusion that has arisen through the unfortunately widespread use of *'Megalosaurus'* as a 'dustbin' for any large theropod remains; this arose primarily because most theropod fossils are isolated fragments and because the original *Megalosaurus* was a very imperfect specimen. Up to the present time at least 26 different names have been created for large, poorly-preserved *Megalosaurus*-like theropods. As we shall see later, such a profusion of names can cause great problems of classification.

## Spinosaurids

Spinosaurids ('spine reptiles') are a group of relatively tall-spined theropods. They include such forms as *Altispinax* and *Metriacanthosaurus*. The family was founded on the remains of *Spinosaurus* which come from the late Cretaceous of Niger (Africa) and Egypt. The original material is again somewhat incomplete, including parts of the jaw, and some neck, back and tail vertebrae, but it indicates a large

theropod 33-39·4ft (10-12m) long with spines up to 6ft (1·8m) long! *Acrocanthosaurus* ('top spined reptile') is yet another large 42·6ft (13m) high-spined theropod from the early Cretaceous of Atoka County, Oklahoma. *Saurophagus* ('reptile eater') from the same general area may well be referrable to *Acrocanthosaurus*.

Although relatively little is known of spinosaurids as a whole, the extraordinary height of the spines does require some explanation. Their exaggerated size has two likely explanations: they were either used as behavioural signals for recognition purposes (mates or rivals), or they may have served as solar panels or radiators of heat to regulate the body temperature. Standing sideways on to the Sun, blood passing through the skin of the sail-like array of spines would have been warmed to raise the body temperature. Alternatively, by facing into the Sun, the sail could have acted as a radiator to dissipate heat.

## Chinese Theropods

Since 1942, the only large theropod known from China was *Szechuanosaurus* ('reptile from Szechuan') described on the basis of four large serrated teeth dated at late Jurassic. Obviously this is insufficient material upon which to base a new species, but it at least records the existence of large theropods in China. The situtation has improved greatly in recent years as a result of the parties organised through Beijing (Peking), which have collected new fossils in various parts of China. In 1978 a new theropod was described as *Yangchuanosaurus* ('Yang-ch'uan reptile'). *Yangchuanosaurus* was based on a nearly complete skeleton from the late Jurassic of Sichuan Province. The skull and skeleton are very similar to that of *Allosaurus* and seem to indicate that these two forms are very closely related. Since then another skull and partial skeleton have been discovered which have also been referred to the genus *Yangchuanosaurus*, but in this particular instance as a new species.

## Other Large Theropods

Excluding the tyrannosaurids (pages 68-73), which are all late Cretaceous species and quite distinct from the majority of large theropods,a variety of 'carnosaur' names are commonly used; valid and dubious names are listed below.

Most of the dubious genera, although undoubtedly based on the remains of theropods, are not sufficiently well preserved for useful scientific comparisons to be made. Their only justification is in instances where they provide a record of theropods on other continents. For example **Rapator* is a theropod from the early Cretaceous of Australia and as such may provide useful evidence about the geographic distribution of theropods at this time. All those which provide this type of information are marked with an asterisk (*).

**Spinosaurus (left)**
Spinosaurids are an especially interesting group of 'carnosaurs' that developed long dorsal spines that seem to have acted as supports for a large sail of skin. We see here *Spinosaurus*, an *Allosaurus*-sized theropod known from Africa whose spines grew to a length of 6ft (1·8m). It is possible that the spinal sail acted as a heat exchanger allowing the dinosaur to warm its blood rapidly when standing in the Sun, or to dissipate heat when the sail was angled out of direct sunlight. Similar spines are found on the iguanodontid *Ouranosaurus*, also from Niger. Perhaps some climatic factor caused this common development.

**'CARNOSAUR' GENERA**

**Valid**
*Acrocanthosaurus*
*Allosaurus*
*Altispinax (?)*
*Ceratosaurus*
*Dilophosaurus*
*Dryptosaurus (?)*
*Erectopus*
*Eustreptospondylus*
*Marshosaurus*
*Megalosaurus*
*Metriacanthosaurus*
*Piatnitzkysaurus*
*Poekilopleuron*
*Priveteausaurus*
*Proceratosaurus*
*Spinosaurus*
*Torvosaurus*
*Yangchuanosaurus*

**'CARNOSAUR' GENERA**

**Dubious**
*Aggiosaurus*
*Antrodemus*
*(=Allosaurus)*
*Apatodon*
*(=Allosaurus)*
*Arctosaurus*
*Bahariasaurus*
*Carcharodontosaurus*
*Chienkosaurus*
**Chingkankousaurus*
*Coelosaurus*
*Colonosaurus*
*Creosaurus*
*(=Allosaurus)*
*Diplotomodon*
*Dryptosauroides*
**Embasaurus*
*Empaterias*
*(=Epanterias)*
*Epanterias*
*(=Allosaurus)*
*Epantherias*
*(=Epanterias)*
*Gwyneddosaurus*
*Kelmayisaurus*
*Labrosaurus*
*(=Allosaurus)*
*Laelaps*
*(=Dryptosaurus)*
*Macrodontophion*
*Majungasaurus*
*Orthogoniosaurus*
*Palaeosauriseus*
*Paronychodon*
*Pneumatoarthmus*
*Poicilopleuron*
*(=Allosaurus)*
*Polyodontosaurus*
**Rapator*
*Sarcosaurus*
*Saurophagus*
*(=Acrocanthosaurus?)*
*Szechuanosaurus*
*Tichosteus*
**Unquillosaurus*
*Walgettosuchus*
*(=Rapator?)*
*Zapsalis*

*=Significant geographically

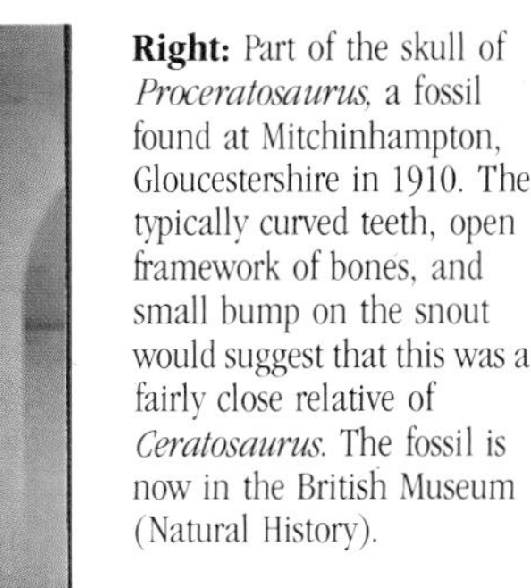

**Right:** Part of the skull of *Proceratosaurus*, a fossil found at Mitchinhampton, Gloucestershire in 1910. The typically curved teeth, open framework of bones, and small bump on the snout would suggest that this was a fairly close relative of *Ceratosaurus*. The fossil is now in the British Museum (Natural History).

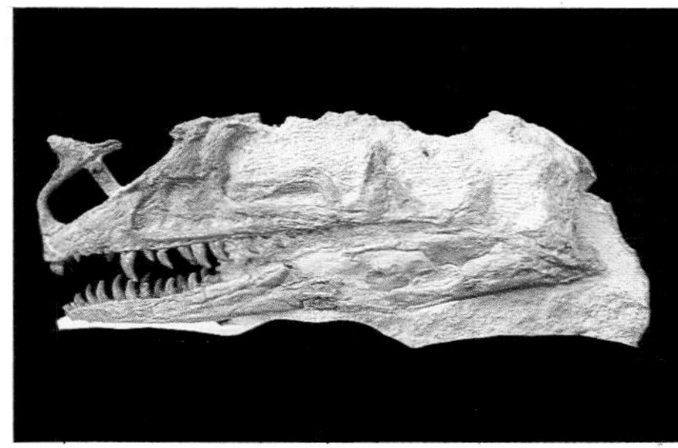

**Right:** *Yangchuanosaurus shangyouensis*, a 20ft (6m) long theropod from China now exhibited in Beipei Museum. The general shape of the skeleton suggests it is related to *Allosaurus*.

**Left:** *Allosaurus* attacking *Camptosaurus*, an iguanodontid. We can see clearly how massive the skull of *Allosaurus* is, but also how window-like openings are let into it to save weight. Note the three-fingered hand. This superb mount is in the Los Angeles County Museum.

# Tyrannosaurids

Tyrannosaurids, undoubtedly the best known of all dinosaurs, are a family of large (20-46ft, 6-14m long) theropod dinosaurs whose remains have been found in late Cretaceous rocks in North America and Central Asia. There are four well established species of tyrannosaurid: *Tyrannosaurus rex, Daspletosaurus torosus* and *Albertosaurus libratus,* which come from North America, and *Tarbosaurus bataar* from the Nemegt Basin of Mongolia.

The tyrannosaurids were not recognised as a distinct group of theropods until 1906, shortly after the first reasonably complete skeleton of *Tyrannosaurus* was discovered in Montana in 1902. Prior to this, numerous teeth and other generally indeterminate fragments of large theropods (probably tyrannosaurids) had been discovered in the middle and late part of the nineteenth century. The earliest of these was a selection of large theropod teeth collected from Montana in the 1850s. Joseph Leidy, the pioneering palaeontologist who described many of the early dinosaur finds from North America, described these teeth as *Deinodon horridus* ('horrifying terrible tooth'). A little later (1866) E. D. Cope renamed these teeth *Dinodon,* and then in 1869 Leidy selected some of these teeth, because they differed in shape, and decided that they came from a new form, *Aublysodon.* The names *Laelaps* and *Teinurosaurus* were also applied to this material in subsequent years. This welter of names represents an inauspicious beginning for such a renowned group of dinosaurs, and provides yet another example of how dangerous it can be to name new species on the basis of inadequate material. One of the problems with the *Deinodon* teeth was that some were from near the front of the jaws, while others were from the back. Because tyrannosaurid teeth tend to vary in shape along the length of the jaw, those from the front look markedly different from those at the back. In isolation it would seem reasonable to give differently shaped teeth different names (as Leidy did) in the belief that they came from different animals. If these scientists had resisted the temptation to name the teeth until better material, such as a skull and jaws has been discovered, much confusion would have been avoided.

*Tyrannosaurus* ('tyrant reptile') was first described by Henry Fairfield Osborn in 1905 from a partial skeleton discovered in late Cretaceous rocks in Dawson County, Northern Montana. The skeleton (discovered in 1902) consisted of the jaws and parts of the skull, back bones, shoulders, pelvis and the hindlimbs of a very large theropod. In addition to this material, another very large partial skeleton of a theropod was discovered in Wyoming; this was described as *Dynamosaurus* ('dynamic reptile'). Although equally as large as *Tyrannosaurus, Dynamosaurus* was at first regarded as a distinct species because there seemed to be some evidence of bony armour plating along its back like that

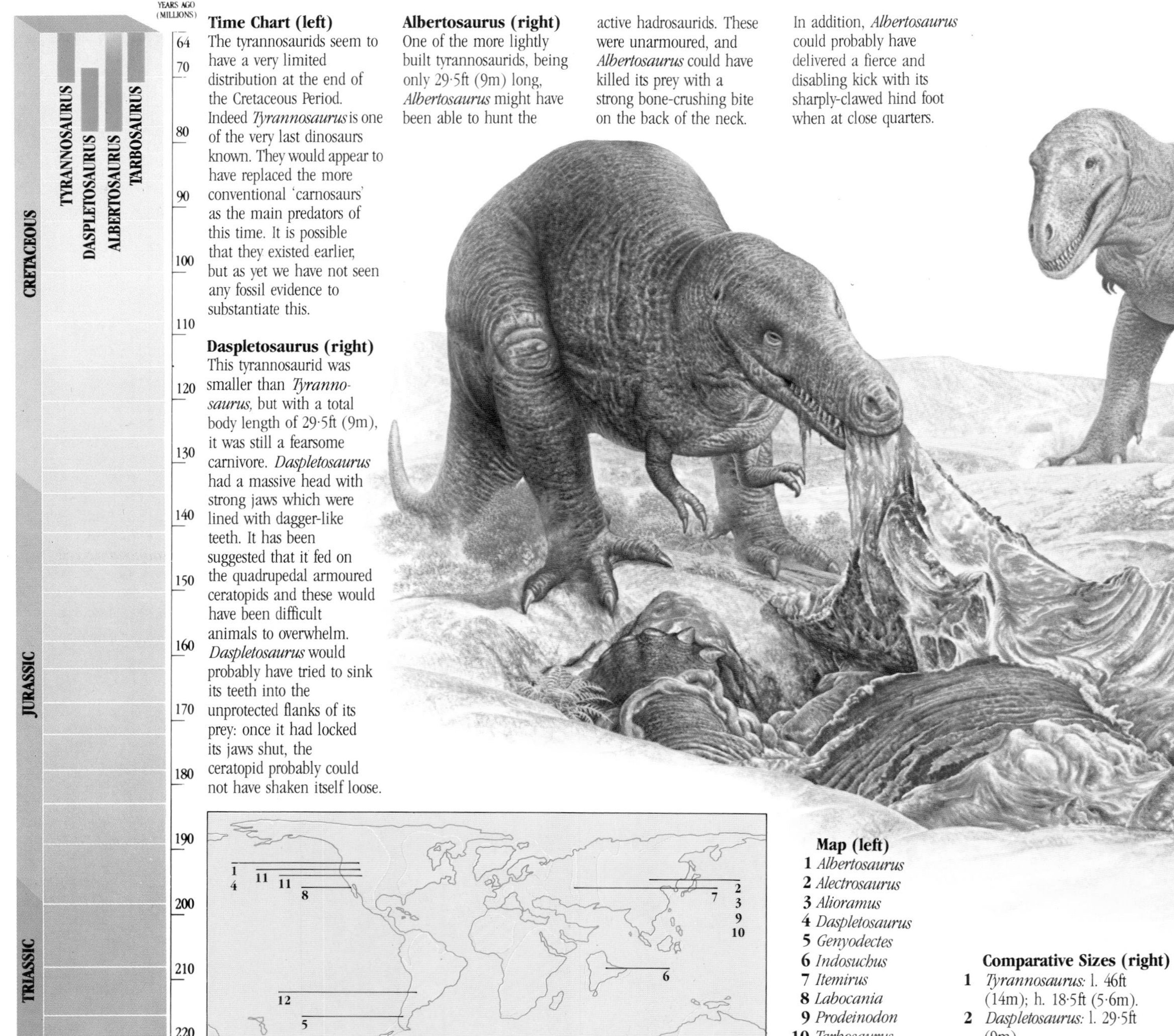


**Time Chart (left)**
The tyrannosaurids seem to have a very limited distribution at the end of the Cretaceous Period. Indeed *Tyrannosaurus* is one of the very last dinosaurs known. They would appear to have replaced the more conventional 'carnosaurs' as the main predators of this time. It is possible that they existed earlier, but as yet we have not seen any fossil evidence to substantiate this.

**Daspletosaurus (right)**
This tyrannosaurid was smaller than *Tyrannosaurus,* but with a total body length of 29·5ft (9m), it was still a fearsome carnivore. *Daspletosaurus* had a massive head with strong jaws which were lined with dagger-like teeth. It has been suggested that it fed on the quadrupedal armoured ceratopids and these would have been difficult animals to overwhelm. *Daspletosaurus* would probably have tried to sink its teeth into the unprotected flanks of its prey: once it had locked its jaws shut, the ceratopid probably could not have shaken itself loose.

**Albertosaurus (right)**
One of the more lightly built tyrannosaurids, being only 29·5ft (9m) long, *Albertosaurus* might have been able to hunt the active hadrosaurids. These were unarmoured, and *Albertosaurus* could have killed its prey with a strong bone-crushing bite on the back of the neck. In addition, *Albertosaurus* could probably have delivered a fierce and disabling kick with its sharply-clawed hind foot when at close quarters.

**Map (left)**
**1** *Albertosaurus*
**2** *Alectrosaurus*
**3** *Alioramus*
**4** *Daspletosaurus*
**5** *Genyodectes*
**6** *Indosuchus*
**7** *Itemirus*
**8** *Labocania*
**9** *Prodeinodon*
**10** *Tarbosaurus*
**11** *Tyrannosaurus*
**12** *Unquillosaurus*

**Comparative Sizes (right)**
**1** *Tyrannosaurus:* l. 46ft (14m); h. 18·5ft (5·6m).
**2** *Daspletosaurus:* l. 29·5ft (9m).
**3** *Albertosaurus:* l. 29·5ft (9m).

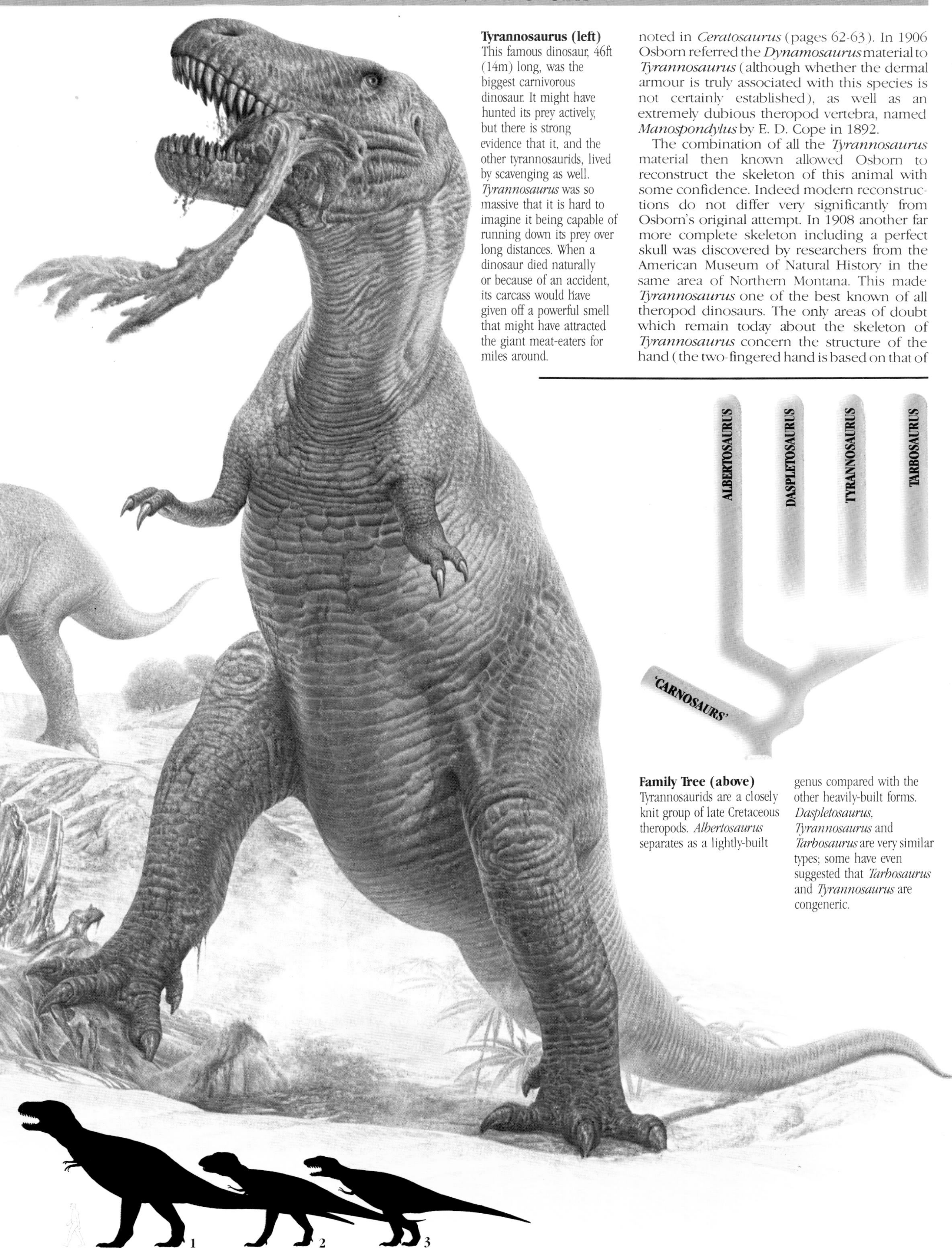


**Tyrannosaurus (left)**
This famous dinosaur, 46ft (14m) long, was the biggest carnivorous dinosaur. It might have hunted its prey actively, but there is strong evidence that it, and the other tyrannosaurids, lived by scavenging as well. *Tyrannosaurus* was so massive that it is hard to imagine it being capable of running down its prey over long distances. When a dinosaur died naturally or because of an accident, its carcass would have given off a powerful smell that might have attracted the giant meat-eaters for miles around.

noted in *Ceratosaurus* (pages 62-63). In 1906 Osborn referred the *Dynamosaurus* material to *Tyrannosaurus* (although whether the dermal armour is truly associated with this species is not certainly established), as well as an extremely dubious theropod vertebra, named *Manospondylus* by E. D. Cope in 1892.

The combination of all the *Tyrannosaurus* material then known allowed Osborn to reconstruct the skeleton of this animal with some confidence. Indeed modern reconstructions do not differ very significantly from Osborn's original attempt. In 1908 another far more complete skeleton including a perfect skull was discovered by researchers from the American Museum of Natural History in the same area of Northern Montana. This made *Tyrannosaurus* one of the best known of all theropod dinosaurs. The only areas of doubt which remain today about the skeleton of *Tyrannosaurus* concern the structure of the hand (the two-fingered hand is based on that of

**Family Tree (above)**
Tyrannosaurids are a closely knit group of late Cretaceous theropods. *Albertosaurus* separates as a lightly-built genus compared with the other heavily-built forms. *Daspletosaurus, Tyrannosaurus* and *Tarbosaurus* are very similar types; some have even suggested that *Tarbosaurus* and *Tyrannosaurus* are congeneric.

the related tyrannosaurid *Albertosaurus*—see below) and the length of the tail.

Some reconstructions of *Tyrannosaurus*, especially the later ones of Osborn, tend to show a very elongate tail dragging along the ground. However, as can be seen in the drawing of the skeleton, large sections of the end of the tail are unknown. As reconstructed here, the tail is given an 'average' length for a theropod and is shown held off the ground as a counterbalance. This pose was first proposed by Barney Newman (S. Africa) who was at one time involved in mounting the cast of a *Tyrannosaurus* skeleton in the original dinosaur gallery of the British Museum (Natural History).

## Tyrannosaurus Anatomy

The skull of *Tyrannosaurus* is not of the type seen in *Allosaurus* (page 65), a similarly-sized theropod of the Jurassic Period. The *Allosaurus* skull is notable for the large window-like openings which give it a very open, airy appearance, apparently combining strength and lightness as far as possible. *Tyrannosaurus* by contrast has a skull which is far more massive. The window-like openings are still present, but they are not nearly as large, and the bony framework that surrounds them is thick and heavy. Nature would not normally add such a weight of bone to the skull of such a creature without good reason, because such additions would be very costly to the animal in terms of the amount of energy that it would have to expend simply to carry such a heavy head around. The enormous weight and apparent great strength of the skull must be a reflection of the feeding habits of *Tyrannosaurus*, which are discussed below.

The massive head is supported by a very short powerful neck, the vertebrae of which are very thick and bear stout spines for the attachment of powerful ligaments and muscles used to hold the head in position. The ribs are also very long for the attachment of more muscles used to twist the neck and swing it from side to side. The bones of the back are larger and stronger than those of the neck and acted in life like a massive girder. The block-like bodies of each vertebra withstood enormous compression forces because of the great weight of the body, while the roughened and ridged edges and tops of the spines projecting from the top of each vertebra were the sites for attachment of extremely powerful ligaments and muscles; these would have acted rather like hawsers holding the bones in place, while at the same time allowing them to move within the normal range of body movements.

An indication of just how enormous these forces on the backbone must have been is provided by the skeleton itself. In the skeleton discovered in 1908, two pairs of vertebrae in the back have become welded together. This is not a normal condition but a pathological one; the great compression forces had evidently col-

**Tarbosaurus Skull (below)**
This skull was very powerfully built, possibly to withstand the impact caused when the animal hurtled into its prey. Flexible areas in the skull may have absorbed some of the shock of the impact. The muscles would produce a powerful bite.

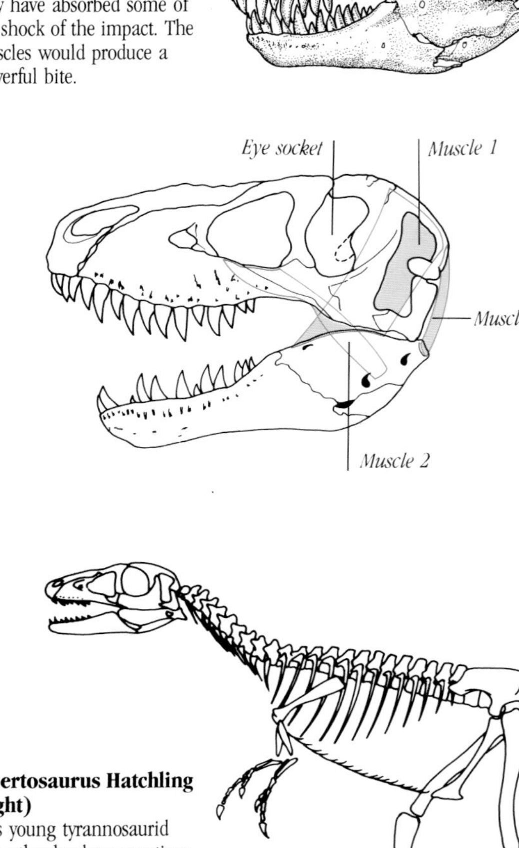


**Tyrannosaurus Skeleton (below)**
*Tyrannosaurus* was over 40ft (12·3m) long and might have weighed up to 7 tonnes, so its skeleton is a compromise between the need to bear this massive weight and to run around to catch food. The skull is much more massive than that of the 'carnosaurs' described earlier, built to withstand impact. It is supported by a stout neck which joins the compact back region. The bodies of the individual vertebrae are designed to withstand compression forces, while the stout ribs, joined by ligaments and muscles, would withstand tension. The hip girdle and back limb were extremely strong since they would take the animal's weight. As in other bipedal dinosaurs, the long tail counterbalanced the front of the body. The front legs were very small and feeble. The belly is lined with ribs—gastralia—which probably served to stiffen this area.

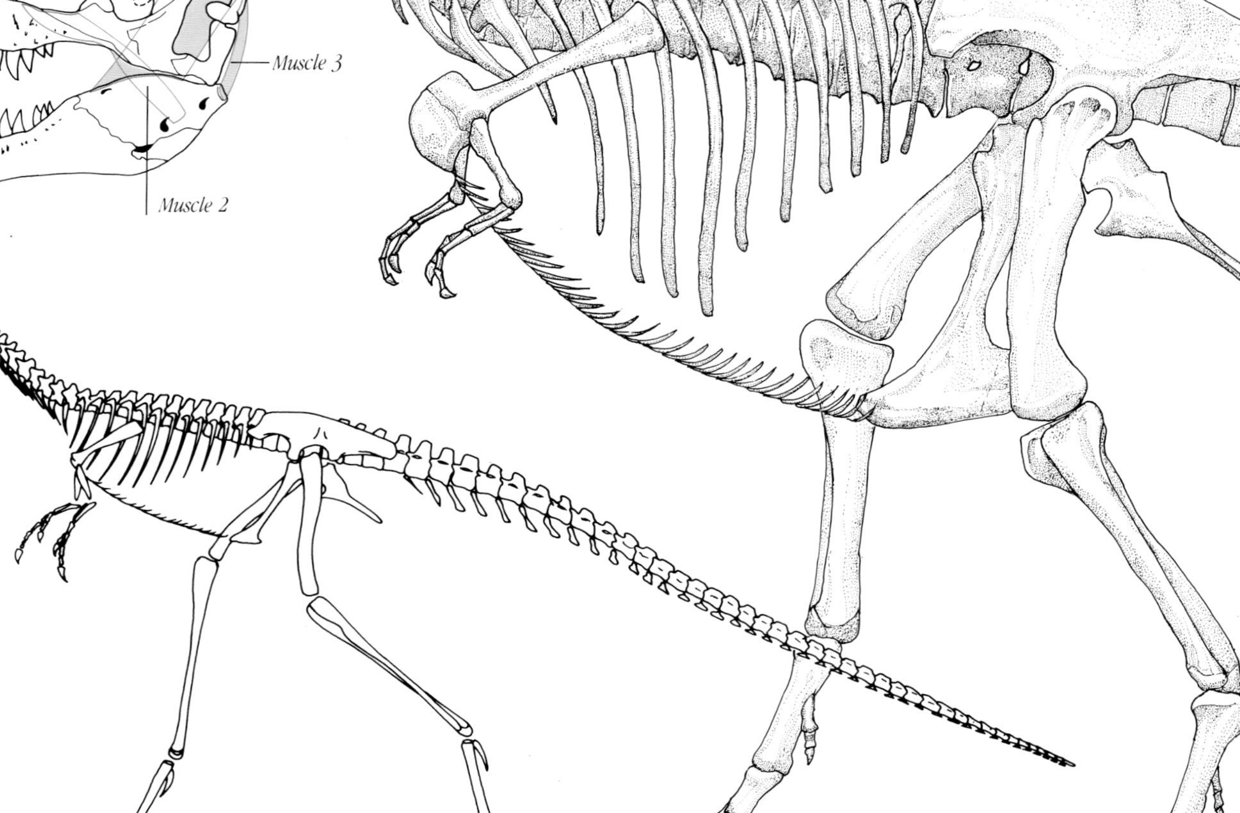

**Albertosaurus Hatchling (right)**
This young tyrannosaurid shows the slender proportions of the juvenile animal. It does not have the great weight of the adult to bear so it can be much more lightly built. Juvenile features are the slender jaws and snout, the relatively larger and rounder eye-socket, the elongated ankle region and the loosely joined bones of the skull. This little creature looks quite fleet-footed.

lapsed the originally flexible joints between these vertebrae so that these backbones began to rub together, causing no doubt severe arthritic pain, until the bones finally welded themselves together.

Despite the enormous forces acting on the bones of the back, several vertebrae at the base of both the neck and the back possess cavities in their sides (known as pleurocoels) which undoubtedly served to reduce the weight of bone in the back wherever possible.

The pelvic bones are very large to allow for the attachment of big leg muscles and also to provide a strong socket for the hip joint itself. The huge blade-like upper pelvic bone (ilium) has a rather complex pattern of ridges and rough-edged patches (see below) which mark the areas of attachment to the stout ribs (sacral ribs) of the backbone. Six bones of the back are welded together to produce a massive and strong bar of bone; this had to be strong because the entire weight of the body—perhaps 6-7 tonnes—had to be carried across this joint to the hindlimbs. The legs are naturally very large and heavy-boned in order to support the large body. The feet are quite broad with three forward-pointing toes which end in sharply-curved talons, and a small backwardly-directed spur-like first toe.

The arms and hands of *Tyrannosaurus* are one of its most bizarre features. We noted earlier that the forelimbs of 'carnosaurs' tend to be relatively short, certainly when compared with those of 'coelurosaurs'. In *Tyrannosaurus* and tyrannosaurids generally this trend seems to be taken to a ridiculous extreme. The shoulder bone is moderately large, but the limb is minute and ends in a small two-clawed hand.

As with most theropods there is an array of ribs lying in the wall of the belly; in life these probably connected via ligaments (or possibly directly) to the ends of the chest ribs enclosing the chest and belly, and thereby making this part of the body fairly stiff and inflexible.

## Other Tyrannosaurids

*Albertosaurus* ('reptile from Alberta') is another North American tyrannosaurid. Like *Tyrannosaurus* it has had a rather chequered history. Two partial skulls of large theropods were discovered on the Red Deer River of Alberta in the early 1890s; these were first referred to *Laelaps* by E. D. Cope (1892). Subsequently Lawrence Lambe transferred them to Marsh's genus, *Dryptosaurus* ('wounding reptile'). Both of these genera, as we have already seen, were based on inadequate material. However, in 1905 the remains of large theropods were reviewed by H. F. Osborn; in his article Osborn created yet another name for these remains: *Albertosaurus sarcophagus*. Knowledge of this type of dinosaur was greatly improved by C. H. Sternberg's discovery in 1913, near Berry Creek on the Red Deer River, Alberta, of a very well-preserved skeleton of a large theropod dinosaur. The remains included not

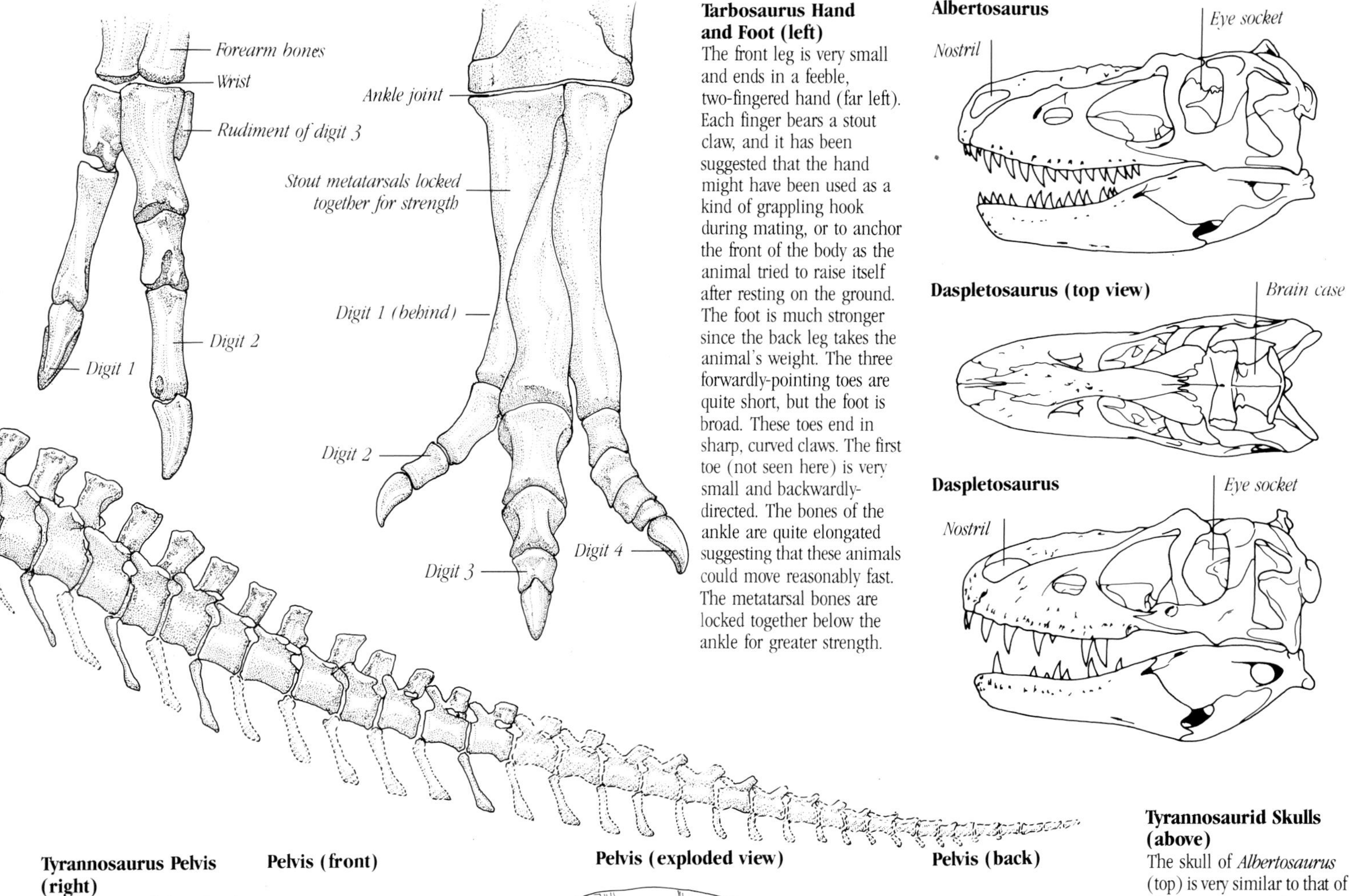


**Tarbosaurus Hand and Foot (left)**
The front leg is very small and ends in a feeble, two-fingered hand (far left). Each finger bears a stout claw, and it has been suggested that the hand might have been used as a kind of grappling hook during mating, or to anchor the front of the body as the animal tried to raise itself after resting on the ground. The foot is much stronger since the back leg takes the animal's weight. The three forwardly-pointing toes are quite short, but the foot is broad. These toes end in sharp, curved claws. The first toe (not seen here) is very small and backwardly-directed. The bones of the ankle are quite elongated suggesting that these animals could move reasonably fast. The metatarsal bones are locked together below the ankle for greater strength.

**Tyrannosaurid Skulls (above)**
The skull of *Albertosaurus* (top) is very similar to that of *Tyrannosaurus*. It is massively built with smaller skull windows surrounded by thicker struts of bone. The teeth are sharp and recurved (pointing backwards), typical of a carnivore. *Daspletosaurus* (middle and bottom) also has the typical tyrannosaurid build. It is distinguished by its teeth which, although fewer in number, are particularly large. All tyrannosaurid skulls show marked similarities.

**Tyrannosaurus Pelvis (right)**
In these views of the pelvis it is possible to see the upper pelvic bone (ilium) and the vertebrae which attach to it (sacral vertebrae). The lower pelvic bones are not shown. In the exploded view of the pelvis (middle, top and bottom) the wide, plate-like nature of the ilium is seen. This gives plenty of area for muscle attachment. The sockets for the sacral ribs (arrowed) are also visible in the middle drawing.

**Pelvis (front)**

**Pelvis (exploded view)**

**Pelvis (back)**

Ilium

Ilium

Hip socket

Sacral vertebrae

**Pelvis (top)**

**Pelvis (bottom)**

only a fine, if slightly squashed skull, but a major part of the remainder of the skeleton including the forelimb. In 1914 this skeleton was given the name *Gorgosaurus (Albertosaurus) libratus* ('free dragon reptile'). At this time the skeleton had only been partly prepared. However, the forelimb was sufficiently distinctive to merit some early comment.

In the majority of theropods (although see *Compsognathus* for an exception) the hand has three clawed fingers. In *Gorgosaurus (Albertosaurus)* Lambe note only two clawed fingers (digits 1 and 2) both of which were quite small and a remnant of the third finger (a small splint of bone pressed up against the base of the second one). The very small forelimb and reduced hand is now one of the characteristics that distinguish the tyrannosaurids as a whole.

In 1917 Lambe completed a detailed study of *Gorgosaurus* and provided a first skeletal reconstruction. This revealed a theropod which was a little smaller than *Tyrannosaurus,* but otherwise its proportions were very similar. It was not directly related to *Tyrannosaurus* at the time because (for one reason) Osborn had reconstructed the skeleton of *Tyrannosaurus* in 1916 with three clawed fingers on the hand. He had no evidence for this at the time, but was presumably simply copying the arrangement that he had already described in *Ornitholestes* (pages 40-41) and *Struthiomimus* (pages 46-47). Like *Tyrannosaurus* the skeleton of *Gorgosaurus* was that of a large and quite heavily-built theropod with a massive skull, short forelimbs and heavy, pillar-like legs ending in bird-like feet. Similarly the belly ribs were particularly well-developed, as was the lower end of the pubis in the pelvis; the end of this bone is distinctly enlarged ('footed') and this feature may be linked to the habits of these creatures.

In 1970, Dale Russell reviewed the large theropods of Western Canada. He concluded that the material of *Albertosaurus* originally described by Osborn as *A. sarcophagus* was practically the same as the *Gorgosaurus libratus* material described by Lawrence Lambe and therefore referred *Gorgosaurus* to the genus *Albertosaurus* as *A. libratus.* Another almost complete skeleton described as *Gorgosaurus sternbergi* in 1923 was also referred to as a juvenile of *A. libratus.* The differences between *A. libratus* and *G. sternbergi* included small size (*G. sternbergi* was only 60 per cent of the size of *A. libratus*), more slender jaws and snout, and a rounder eye socket. In addition the bones of the skull were not firmly joined together and the lower part of the leg was more elongated. All of these features are ones that can be associated with juvenility in this specimen. On this basis, and from the fragmentary remains of *Albertosaurus* collected throughout Canada, Russell was able to project backwards in time to estimate the size of a hatchling *Albertosaurus.* This shows the rather slender and delicate proportions of young tyrannosaurids (see page 70). *Albertosaurus sarcophagus* comes from geologically younger rocks in Western Canada and is therefore probably not referrable to *A. libratus* but may represent a descendant species.

*Daspletosaurus torosus* ('frightful flesh-eating reptile') comes from the Red Deer River near Steveville, Alberta. Most of the skeleton was found by C. M. Sternberg in 1921. At first this was referred to as *'Gorgosaurus'* being of about the same size (29·5ft, 9m long) as the specimen described by Lambe. However, the skeleton is that of a much more heavily-built animal than *Albertosaurus.* The forelimb, although small as in all tyrannosaurids, is larger than that of all other known species.

As Dale Russell pointed out, almost all *Daspletosaurus* remains are from large, presumably fully adult specimens, while the remains of more than half of the *Albertosaurus* skeletons found to date are of immature individuals. The coexistence of two species of large theropods may indicate that there were at least two discrete ecological niches for them. Dr Russell proposed that *Daspletosaurus* preyed upon the larger and heavier ceratopids (pages 134-145) while the lighter and perhaps more fleet-footed *Albertosaurus* preyed upon the smaller, more agile hadrosaurids (pages 116-127). It is certainly true that hadrosaurids and *Albertosaurus* are both very abundant at this particular time, while *Daspletosaurus* and the ceratopids are markedly less so, but whether these ratios are merely a matter of chance, or indicate the biological interactions suggested, is an open question.

*Tarbosaurus bataar* ('alarming reptile from Bataar'), a large tyrannosaurid from the Nemegt Basin of the Gobi Desert in Mongolia, was first described in 1955. The remains of at least seven individuals were collected by the Palaeontological Institute of the Academy of Sciences of the Soviet Union. In addition, at least six more skeletons were collected during the Polish-Mongolian expeditions. Although this dinosaur has not been described in detail, the information released to date suggests that *Tarbosaurus* was practically identical with *Tyrannosaurus,* although there are a few relatively minor differences in the structure of the skull bones that serve to distinguish the two forms. Apparently fully adult specimens never attained the size of the largest *Tyrannosaurus* specimens. Despite the relatively enormous distance that separates *Tyrannosaurus* and *Tarbosaurus* geographically, it is very tempting to place them in the same genus: this would certainly have been done had the *Tarbosaurus* remains actually come from Canada.

## Probable Life-Style

Lawrence Lambe was one of the first palaeontologists to offer comments on the likely life-style of a tyrannosaurid (*Albertosaurus*). He proposed that *Albertosaurus* was a very slow-moving creature of sluggish habits. He noted that the well-developed belly ribs and the large 'foot' on the pubis could have been adaptations for lying prone on the ground. When driven by hunger, *Albertosaurus* would raise itself to its feet and slowly pace about in search of food, relying principally upon scavenging the carcasses of dead animals. Such a view is held by some (but not all) palaeontologists today.

Looking at the skeleton of *Tyrannosaurus,* the impression gained is one of a fairly dynamic animal. The tail is massive and counterbalances the trunk and head very effectively; the legs are indeed pillar-like in construction, as is necessary in an animal of relatively great weight. This, however, does not necessarily mean that tyrannosaurids were slow, lumbering creatures. A rhinoceros also possesses pillar-like legs to support its immense body weight, yet it can run extremely fast (22-25mph, 35-40kph). The ability of an animal to run fast depends not only upon the proportions of its limbs, but also on their overall length. Longer-legged animals (such as tyrannosaurids) take long strides and are therefore able to cover the ground very quickly, even though their legs do not move as fast as a more fleet-footed creature.

In view of these factors it would seem that tyrannosaurids may well have been predators which were able to move quite quickly, but only over short distances. It is hard to imagine a 6 tonne tyrannosaurid chasing a hadrosaurid at speed for several kilometres in the way that a Cape Hunting Dog may pursue wildebeest on the African plains. What seems more probable is that tyrannosaurids were lurking predators waiting in ambush for their prey and catching them after a short chase.

The heavily reinforced skull of tyrannosaurids may also confirm the suggestion that these animals were devastating predators. The powerful structure of the skull probably implies that the head had to withstand the violent impact of the jaws against the body of the prey; the shock of a tyrannosaurid hitting a hadrosaurid at 12-20mph (20-30kph) would have been borne by the skull. Perhaps related to this method of hunting is the presence of regions of flexibility at the back of the skull

**Above:** This display in the British Museum (Natural History) emphasises the massive construction of *Tyrannosaurus'* skull, and the fearsome array of teeth that it possessed.

**Below:** This fine skeleton of *Tarbosaurus bataar* is in the Palaeontological Institute of Moscow. Its close kinship with *Tyrannosaurus* can readily be appreciated.

where the lower jaw is supported. These areas may have allowed the skull bones to move passively under great stress (either under impact, or as a result of the prey struggling violently), so that the very large forces experienced would not break the skull bones.

Once subdued, the prey would have been very rapidly dismembered. The jaws, armed with large serrated teeth, would have sliced through the skin and flesh of the carcass. Violent twisting and tugging of the head aided by the powerful neck and legs would have torn the most powerful of sinews, so that great chunks of flesh and bone could have been swallowed whole.

One persistent puzzle of tyrannosaurid anatomy has been the ridiculously small arms of these formidable creatures. The hands seem to be of little potential use for dismembering prey, unlike those of other large theropods (see *Allosaurus* pages 62-63). Neither does it seem likely that they could reach the creature's mouth. Two suggestions only seem feasible, both of which may have some merit. Osborn proposed that they may have been used as grapples during mating so that the male was able to hold on to the female; this could well have been important for relatively unstable two-legged creatures.

An alternative, or perhaps ancillary, function for the forelimb was proposed by Barney Newman. He suggested that if *Tyrannosaurus* were to adopt a prone position while resting—as Lambe suggested on quite reasonable evidence—then it may have been faced with a rather unexpected problem. When trying to raise itself from the ground, it would have needed to anchor the front part of the body against the ground, otherwise in attempting to straighten its legs it would have tended to pitch forward onto its nose. The front limbs therefore served to anchor the chest so that the legs could be straightened before the head and body were tilted backwards, allowing the upper part of the animal to be brought upwards into the normal standing position.

## Dubious Tyrannosaurids

A number of fragmentary fossil finds have been referred to the tyrannosaurid family, although the evidence for such a classification remains inconclusive. These dubious tyrannosaurids include *Genyodectes* ('received under jaw'): partial snout from the late Cretaceous of Patagonia; *Labocania* ('from La Bocana'): late Cretaceous of Baja California; *Indosuchus* ('Indian crocodile'): late Cretaceous of India; *Unquillosaurus* ('Unquillo reptile'): late Cretaceous of Argentina; *Prodeinodon* ('before terrible tooth'): late Cretaceous of Mongolia; *Alioramus* ('other branch'): late Cretaceous of Mongolia; *Alectrosaurus* ('single reptile') late Cretaceous of Mongolia; and *Itemirus* ('from Itemir'): late Cretaceous of central Kyzylkum, Central Asia.

**Right:** A skeleton of *Tarbosaurus bataar* being excavated from the late Cretaceous sandstone of Nemegt, Gobi Desert, during the 1970 Polish-Mongolian expedition.

**Below:** This view of *Albertosaurus* enables us to see particularly well the tiny forelimbs that are characteristic of tyrannosaurids, and the 'footed' lower end of the pubis in the pelvis.

**Hunting Methods (above)** Tyrannosaurid skulls are heavily reinforced, and this suggests that they may have attacked their prey, such as this hadrosaurid, by running into it jaws agape, the shock of such a collision being absorbed by the skull bones.

**Functional Arms (below)** The minute size of tyrannosaurid forelimbs is a puzzling phenomenon. One explanation envisages them being used as props to help the animal rise from a prone position. They would secure the front of the body while the rear legs were straightened; the upper body would then be tilted back to bring the tyrannosaurid upright.

# Prosauropods

Prosauropods are an interesting, but also rather puzzling group of saurischian dinosaurs. They existed in the late Triassic and early Jurassic and were distributed practically worldwide, their remains having been discovered on every continent except for Antarctica; they also tend to be found extremely abundantly in rocks of this age. In fact they seem to represent the first major evolutionary radiation among the dinosaurs—indeed among the archosaurs (dinosaurs, crocodiles, pterosaurs, thecodontians, etc)—to exploit plant food. Until the late Triassic the world had been dominated by various herbivorous types of mammal-like reptile. During the Permian and Triassic Period the archosaurs were, with very few exceptions, exclusively carnivores of various shapes and sizes.

The prosauropods were, therefore, a very important group of early dinosaurs which, in a sense, paved the way for the evolution of the gigantic and closely related sauropod dinosaurs.

The fossil record of prosauropods suffers many of the problems previously encountered in the theropods. Numerous species have been established upon totally inadequate fossil material. In order to learn something of the nature and biology of prosauropods we shall, therefore, consider a few of the better-known species. Prosauropods have been divided into three families: the anchisaurids, melanorosaurids and yunnanosaurids all of which are discussed below.

## Anchisaurids

The vast majority of all prosauropods known to date fall into this family which derives its name from *Anchisaurus* ('close reptile'), a small (8·2ft, 2·5m long), lightly-built prosauropod from early Jurassic rocks of the Connecticut Valley of eastern North America. The earliest discovery of *Anchisaurus* was made in 1818. These fragmentary remains, at first thought to be human, were not confidently identified as reptilian until 1855! And it was not until 1912, when Richard Swan Lull was reviewing the fossils discovered in the Connecticut Valley, that the material was referred to as those of the prosauropod dinosaur *Anchisaurus*. Between the time of the first discovery and its final identification, other material was discovered in adjoining areas of the Connecticut Valley. Edward Hitchcock (who collected large numbers of fossil footprints in this area) reported bones from Springfield, Massachusetts; this skeleton was named *Megadactylus polyzelus* by his son E. Hitchcock Jr, and subsequently renamed *Amphisaurus* by Marsh in 1882 (because another animal had already been named *Megadactylus*), and then again in 1885 renamed *Anchisaurus polyzelus* by Marsh because the name *Amphisaurus* was also preoccupied!

The most productive site in the Connecticut Valley proved to be a quarry near Manchester,

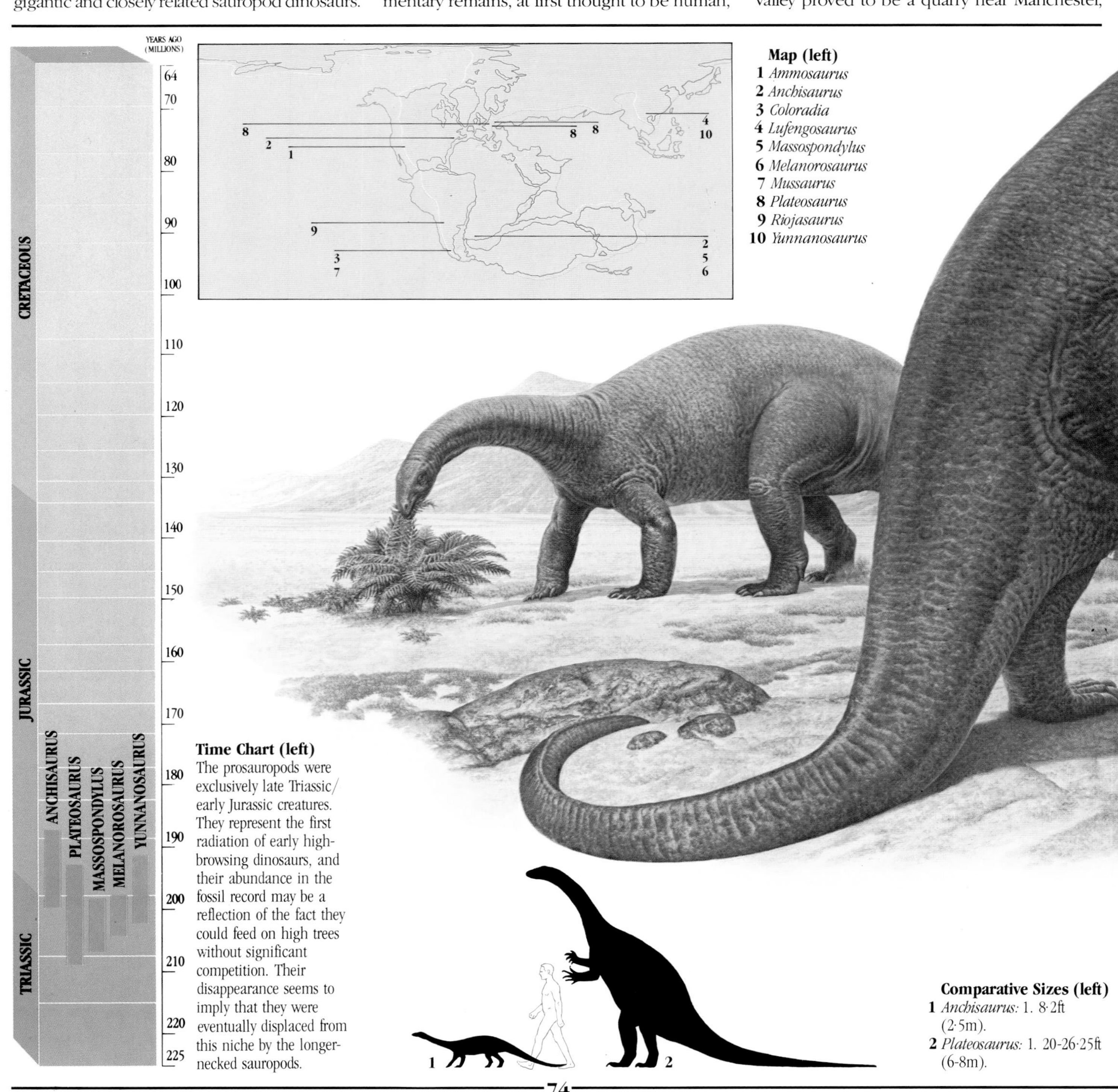


**Map (left)**
**1** *Ammosaurus*
**2** *Anchisaurus*
**3** *Coloradia*
**4** *Lufengosaurus*
**5** *Massospondylus*
**6** *Melanorosaurus*
**7** *Mussaurus*
**8** *Plateosaurus*
**9** *Riojasaurus*
**10** *Yunnanosaurus*

**Time Chart (left)**
The prosauropods were exclusively late Triassic/early Jurassic creatures. They represent the first radiation of early high-browsing dinosaurs, and their abundance in the fossil record may be a reflection of the fact they could feed on high trees without significant competition. Their disappearance seems to imply that they were eventually displaced from this niche by the longer-necked sauropods.

**Comparative Sizes (left)**
**1** *Anchisaurus:* l. 8·2ft (2·5m).
**2** *Plateosaurus:* l. 20-26·25ft (6-8m).

Connecticut, this produced three well-preserved prosauropod skeletons and a few other fragments. These skeletons were described in some detail by O. C. Marsh in the early 1890s as *Anchisaurus major, A. colurus* and *A. solus. A. major* was subsequently renamed *Ammosaurus major* and *A. colurus* became *Yaleosaurus colurus* just to add to the general confusion! Other prosauropod material comes from the Navajo Sandstone of northern Arizona and consists of the partial remains of *Ammosaurus* ('sand reptile').

*Anchisaurus* remains have also been described from the earliest Jurassic rocks of Orange Free State, South Africa. Originally described as *Hortalotarsus, Thecodontosaurus* and *Gyposaurus,* Drs Peter Galton and Mike Culver redescribed this partial skeleton of *Gyposaurus* and noted that it was virtually indistinguishable from the North American *Anchisaurus* and so renamed it *Anchisaurus capensis.*

**Plateosaurus (left)**
This was the first large dinosaur, reaching a length of up to 26·25ft (8m). *Plateosaurus* fed on plants at ground level and on leaves of tall trees. *Plateosaurus* could stand on its hind legs or on all-fours, and its long neck would have allowed it to seek food over a wide area. The hands are characterised by their strong fingers, and particularly the thumb which was furnished with a broad scythe-like claw. This thumb was probably used to rake up plants on the ground, or to tear leaves down from the trees, or possibly as a defensive weapon.

**Family Tree (above)**
*Anchisaurus* and its allies are generally slender, mostly bipedal forms. *Yunnanosaurus* may represent a group of prosauropods that developed sauropod-like teeth. *Melanorosaurus* represents a group of large sauropod-like prosauropods.

**Anchisaurus (above)**
One of the smaller prosauropods, the early Jurassic form *Anchisaurus* was a successful early herbivore. It had blunt pencil-shaped teeth spaced out along its jaw, and there have been long arguments about whether it ate meat, plants or both. The balance of evidence seems to favour a vegetarian diet. *Anchisaurus* was lightly built and probably agile, so that it could escape the attentions of the contemporary theropod predators.

The skeleton of *Anchisaurus,* based on material from the Connecticut Valley, consists of the major part of the skeleton lacking only the tail and much of the neck. As can be seen in the drawings the skull of *Anchisaurus* was quite small in proportion to the body, with a relatively long and slender snout. The teeth were quite slender and pencil-shaped and may well have had rough serrations down the front and back edges. These serrations are not like the fine, sharp serrations of typical theropod teeth, but rather large, coarse ridges which were evidently suited to shredding plant fibres.

The neck and back of *Anchisaurus* are reconstructed partly by reference to other prosauropods, such as the well-preserved *Plateosaurus.* The neck was probably long, slender and flexible, as was the back, giving these animals a rather long-bodied look—particularly when compared with theropods. The tail was undoubtedly long, and helped to counterbalance the front part of the body over the hips.

The limbs are of slightly unusual construction. The hindlimbs are relatively sturdy and were evidently well-designed to carry the bulk of the weight of the animal when walking. The foot also was quite broad with four well-developed toes and the rudimentary remains of the fifth. The forelimbs and shoulders, however, were also remarkably well-developed. The shoulders are stout and the arms relatively long and were evidently capable of touching or resting on the ground with ease; this suggests that *Anchisaurus* may have walked on all fours on occasions. The hand is rather curious in that the outer fingers (4th and 5th) are quite small and slender and may not have borne claws, while the inner fingers are well developed, particularly the first finger which has a much enlarged sharply-curved claw.

## Plateosaurus Described

Another of the anchisaurid-type of prosauropods, *Plateosaurus* ('flat reptile') was considerably larger (20-26·25ft, 6-8 m body length) and comes from the late Triassic rocks of western Europe (Federal Republic of Germany, the German Democratic Republic, France and Switzerland). Today *Plateosaurus* remains are known to occur in mass concentrations of relatively complete remains, notably at Trössingen in the FRG, Halberstadt in the GDR and La Chassagne in France.

The first remains of *Plateosaurus* were described by Hermann von Meyer in 1837 from fragments of a skeleton. However, during 1911-12, 1921-23 and in 1932 extensive excavations at Trössingen were carried out by the Palaeontological Institute of the University of Tübingen. These revealed a massive accumulation of complete and partial skeletons of *Plateosaurus.* These were described in considerable detail by Friedrich Freiherr von Huene, a palaeontologist from Tübingen.

As can be seen from the skeletal reconstruction which is taken from von Huene's work •

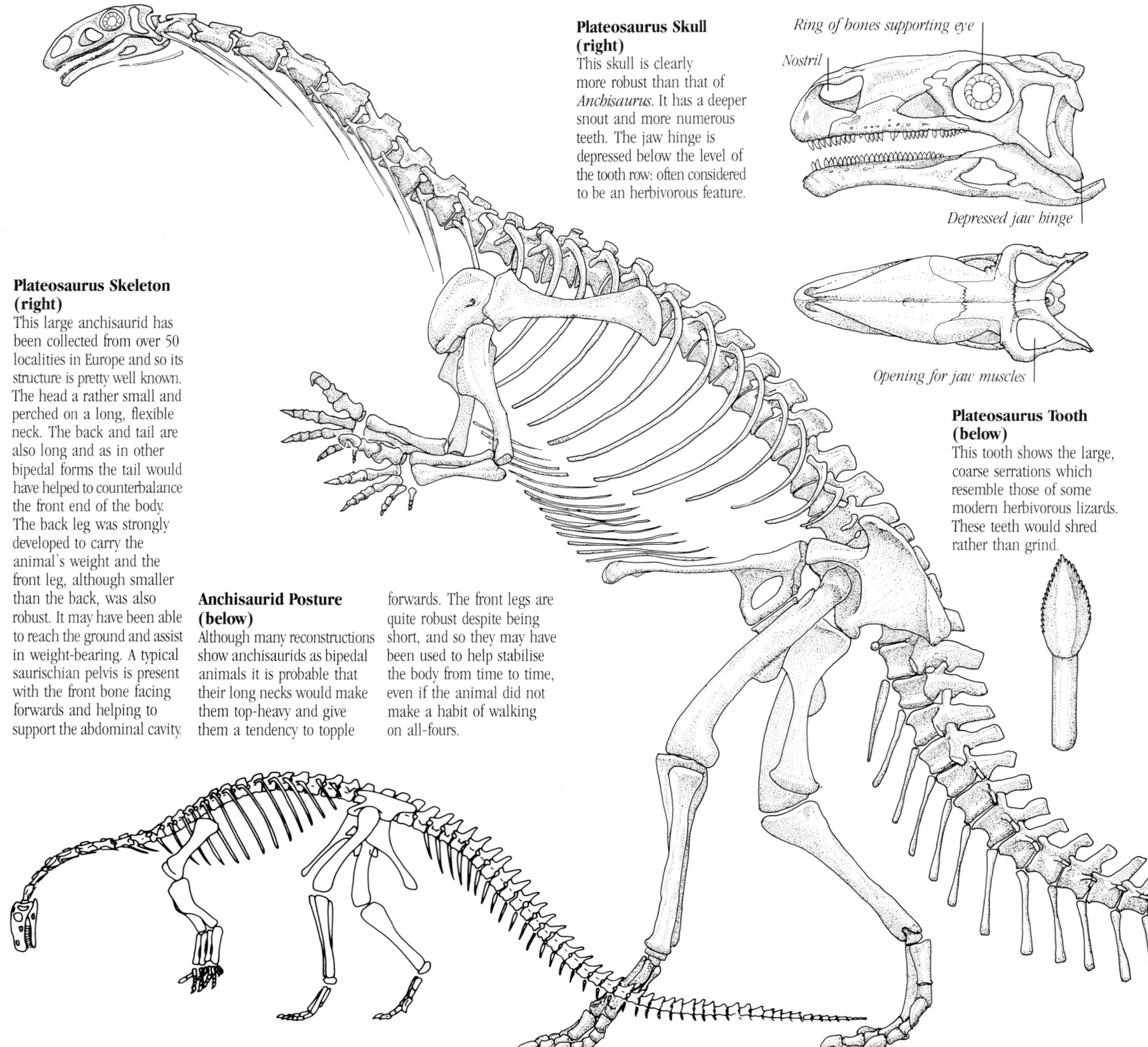


**Plateosaurus Skull (right)**
This skull is clearly more robust than that of *Anchisaurus.* It has a deeper snout and more numerous teeth. The jaw hinge is depressed below the level of the tooth row: often considered to be an herbivorous feature.

**Plateosaurus Skeleton (right)**
This large anchisaurid has been collected from over 50 localities in Europe and so its structure is pretty well known. The head a rather small and perched on a long, flexible neck. The back and tail are also long and as in other bipedal forms the tail would have helped to counterbalance the front end of the body. The back leg was strongly developed to carry the animal's weight and the front leg, although smaller than the back, was also robust. It may have been able to reach the ground and assist in weight-bearing. A typical saurischian pelvis is present with the front bone facing forwards and helping to support the abdominal cavity.

**Plateosaurus Tooth (below)**
This tooth shows the large, coarse serrations which resemble those of some modern herbivorous lizards. These teeth would shred rather than grind.

**Anchisaurid Posture (below)**
Although many reconstructions show anchisaurids as bipedal animals it is probable that their long necks would make them top-heavy and give them a tendency to topple forwards. The front legs are quite robust despite being short, and so they may have been used to help stabilise the body from time to time, even if the animal did not make a habit of walking on all-fours.

of 1926, *Plateosaurus* was larger and consequently more robustly constructed than *Anchisaurus,* although the general body proportions are remarkably similar. The skull is somewhat more heavily built, with a deeper snout region; the teeth are also more numerous. Also deserving of comment is the position of the jaw joint in *Plateosaurus;* this is sited *below* the level of the teeth, while in *Anchisaurus* the jaw joint is on practically the *same* level as the teeth. The teeth of *Plateosaurus* have coarse serrations running down the edges of the crown, as do the teeth of almost all other prosauropods.

The remainder of the skeleton is very similar to that of *Anchisaurus.* The natural pose of these anchisaurid prosauropods has been the subject of some disagreement in the past. In the 1890s O. C. Marsh produced the restoration of *Anchisaurus* seen below. The body in this pose does seem rather unbalanced; the tail looks to be too small effectively to counterbalance the front part of the body in this position. However, the arm and hand do not seem to be designed for walking upon. In particular the fingers are relatively slender and have narrow claws which would have enabled them to be used for grasping objects. A very similar posture was used by von Huene in his 1926 reconstruction of *Plateosaurus.* Peter Galton proposed a somewhat different posture for all prosauropods (shown in the drawing at bottom left) after reviewing the anatomy of the hand and the general body proportions of prosauropods. As was mentioned above, the relatively long neck and trunk of these animals does not give them a perfect balance at the hips; there is a strong tendency for the body to pitch forward on to all-fours. The arms and shoulders are quite long and robustly constructed, so that their use as weight-bearing legs would not have been prohibited; and on careful investigation the hands were found to be quite sophisticated in the range of movements that they could make. Not only could the fingers be flexed to grasp objects, but the fingers could also be *hyper-extended* (bent backwards) so that the fingers of digits II, III and IV could rest on the ground like the toes of a foot. The enlarged claw on the first finger was probably held clear of the ground in order to protect it from damage.

## Anchisaurid Biology

The way of life and probable diet of prosauropods has generated a lot of discussion in the past. Opinions as to the primary food of prosauropods have ranged from purely meat (regarding them as 'scavenger-predators'), to an omnivorous or mixed diet of plant and animal tissues, to one that is purely of plants.

The main problem here has been one of simple intepretation based on the characteristics of the teeth combined with the general body shape and head size. For example, prosauropod teeth are serrated; serrations are

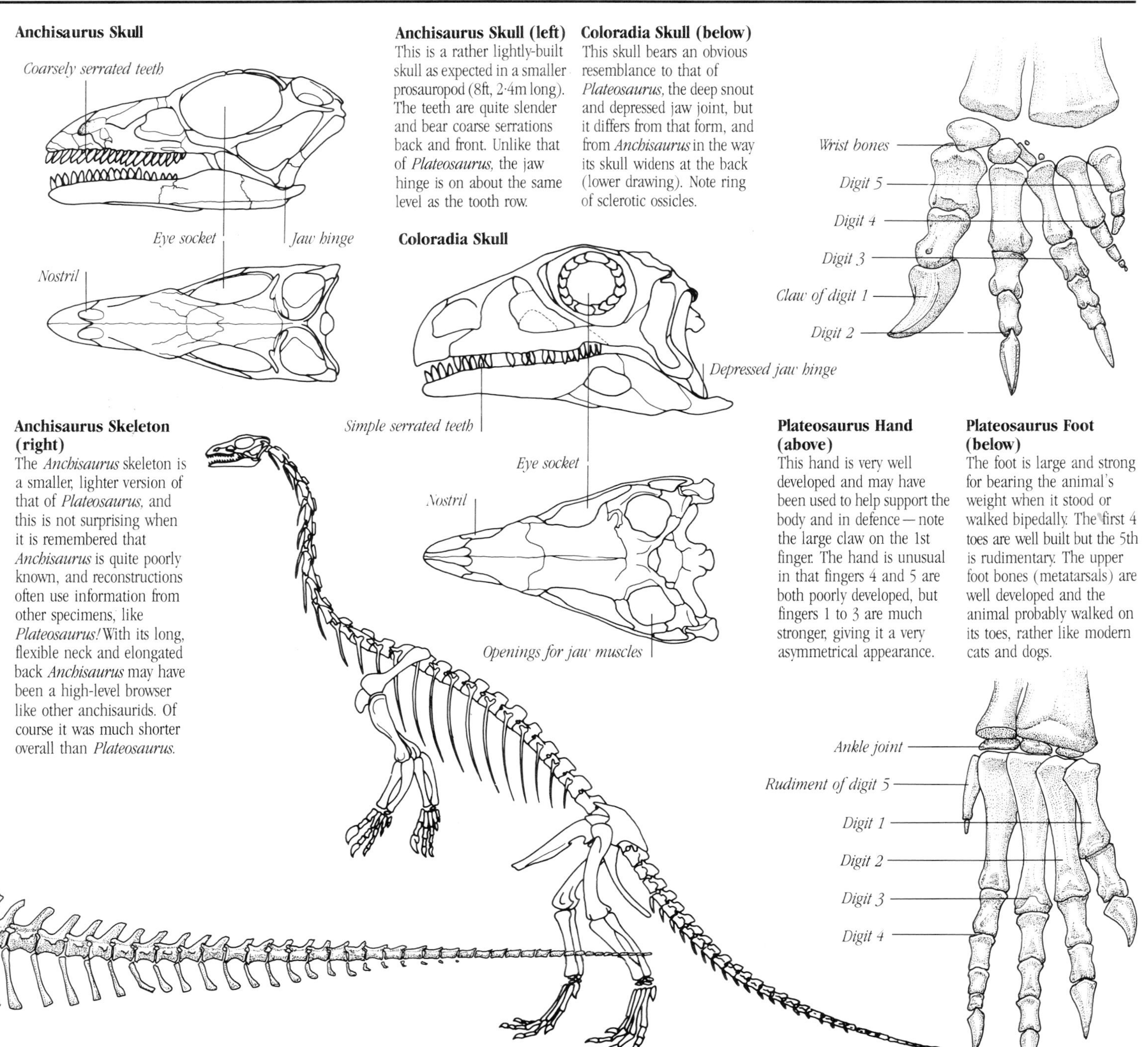


**Anchisaurus Skull (left)** This is a rather lightly-built skull as expected in a smaller prosauropod (8ft, 2·4m long). The teeth are quite slender and bear coarse serrations back and front. Unlike that of *Plateosaurus,* the jaw hinge is on about the same level as the tooth row.

**Coloradia Skull (below)** This skull bears an obvious resemblance to that of *Plateosaurus,* the deep snout and depressed jaw joint, but it differs from that form, and from *Anchisaurus* in the way its skull widens at the back (lower drawing). Note ring of sclerotic ossicles.

**Anchisaurus Skeleton (right)** The *Anchisaurus* skeleton is a smaller, lighter version of that of *Plateosaurus,* and this is not surprising when it is remembered that *Anchisaurus* is quite poorly known, and reconstructions often use information from other specimens, like *Plateosaurus!* With its long, flexible neck and elongated back *Anchisaurus* may have been a high-level browser like other anchisaurids. Of course it was much shorter overall than *Plateosaurus.*

**Plateosaurus Hand (above)** This hand is very well developed and may have been used to help support the body and in defence—note the large claw on the 1st finger. The hand is unusual in that fingers 4 and 5 are both poorly developed, but fingers 1 to 3 are much stronger, giving it a very asymmetrical appearance.

**Plateosaurus Foot (below)** The foot is large and strong for bearing the animal's weight when it stood or walked bipedally. The first 4 toes are well built but the 5th is rudimentary. The upper foot bones (metatarsals) are well developed and the animal probably walked on its toes, rather like modern cats and dogs.

also found on theropod teeth; theropods were carnivores. Therefore, the argument runs, prosauropods are likely to have been carnivorous as well. Add to this the small size of the head and the quite large, cumbersome body, then the most reasonable interpretation would suggest that it could not have been a devastatingly aggressive predator like the large 'carnosaur'-type theropods, but may perhaps have scavenged its meat from abandoned carcasses, or caught smaller slower-moving animals.

Other research workers have proposed a mixed diet for prosauropods implying that from an evolutionary point of view they were a sort of intermediate type of dinosaur: neither wholly carnivorous like the theropods, nor wholly herbivorous like the sauropods. In this way the theropod-type teeth and the sauropod body proportions of these creatures makes some sort of sense.

The third explanation, and the one preferred here, is that they were completely herbivorous. Dr Peter Galton (Bridgeport) has recently reviewed the arguments concerned with the diets of prosauropods in response to a paper presented in 1981 by Dr Mike Cooper (Zimbabwe) in which the scavenger-predator hypothesis was proposed very strongly. Galton observed that the serrations on the teeth of prosauropods were not the same as those on the teeth of theropod dinosaurs; as noted earlier they are relatively large and coarse compared with those of theropods and, in fact, resemble those on the teeth of the herbivorous land iguanas living in South America today. Rather than showing adaptations for slicing meat therefore, these teeth seem well-suited for shredding up plant material. The curious low position of the jaw joint is also of some significance in this argument because this feature is also seen in the herbivorous ornithischian dinosaurs (and in a modified form in herbivores living today) and seems to be an adaptation which improves the effectiveness of the teeth along the jaw during jaw closure in the process of eating.

Another important piece of evidence relating to the diet of prosauropods is the observation by Dr John Attridge (University of London) that the prosauropod *Massospondylus* ('massive vertebra') had a gastric mill ('stomach stones'— gastroliths). These sizeable pebbles, which were probably lodged in the muscular walls of a 'gizzard' or an equivalent region of the stomach of these dinosaurs, could have provided an area where plant material would have been ground to a pulp; it could then be more easily digested. Gastric mills would have been important for herbivores such as these because, unlike modern herbivorous mammals and many ornithischian dinosaurs, prosauropod dinosaurs did not have the complicated teeth or jaws designed for chewing food. This is a distinct disadvantage for herbivores because most of the nutritious parts of the plants are locked inside the enzyme-resistant cellulose plant cell walls. In order to extract the nutritious parts from plant tissues, the plant cell walls have to be crushed and broken either by chewing (the usual method), or by the use of gastric mill-stones. Crushing and pulping of plant food allows the animal to absorb the plant cell tissues more easily, and also provides an opportunity for special cellulose-digesting bacteria which live in the gut of herbivores to break down the plant cellulose; this can also be directly or indirectly absorbed by the animal. (Incidentally the presence of a large, stone-laden stomach may also have upset its posture.)

As Dr Galton pointed out, with their long necks and legs the prosauropods were probably adept 'high browsing' dinosaurs and as such may well have been the first group of reptiles to evolve the ability to feed on relatively high vegetation. Until the appearance of the prosauropods, all herbivores had been squat, short-necked creatures that would have been incapable of reaching high foliage. So, not only were they the first herbivorous dinosaurs, they were also the first high browsers as well.

The preponderance of prosauropod fossils at some Triassic and Jurassic localities has prompted the suggestion that many, perhaps all, species lived in herds. In fact the local abundance of *Plateosaurus* at Trössingen prompted von Huene to speculate vividly upon the circumstances which led to the mass accumulation. He proposed that vast herds of such creatures may have wandered through the ancient highlands of southern Germany, and that rather like the wildbeest of Africa, they underwent seasonal migrations during the dry season in search of water. Trössingen represented to von Huene a place where a large herd had perished on just such a journey. In 1982 Dr David Weishampel (Miami) re-investigated the Trössingen *Plateosaurus* quarry and was able to demonstrate that rather than being the remains of a single vast herd, many of the *Plateosaurus* skeletons were buried over a considerable period of time. These probably represented the chance fossilisation of normal deaths of individuals of a very abundant dinosaur living in this area. However, hidden within this record there were also two 'spikes', that is narrow geological bands which seem to have unexpectedly high numbers of skeletons. Weishampel interpreted these 'spikes' as representing catastrophic deaths of large numbers of individuals. What the cause of these might have been is uncertain; one possibility is that they were animals caught in flash-floods rather than members of herds that died during seasonal droughts.

## The 'Mouse Reptile'

*Mussaurus patagonicus* ('mouse reptile from Patagonia') is a remarkable prosauropod-like dinosaur. Several incomplete skeletons and two small eggs of this type of dinosaur were found in late Triassic rocks from the Province of Santa Cruz in Patagonia, southern Argentina in the late 1970s. These remains were described by Dr José Bonaparte and Martin Vince and are most remarkable for their size. The best preserved skeleton of *Mussaurus* is so small that it sits comfortably in the palm of a man's hand! The total body length was approximately 8in (20cm) allowing for a reasonable length of tail. Bonaparte and Vince concluded that they must have discovered a nest with the hatchlings of a prosauropod dinosaur. Certainly, looking at the skeleton, the bones seem typical of a juvenile animal, and in the skull the eye socket is extremely large which is a very common juvenile feature (see *Psittacosaurus* page 129).

The discovery of *Mussaurus* is very interesting because it adds to the knowledge of juvenile dinosaurs, which are quite rare in the fossil record. Unfortunately it is not possible to be sure of the precise relationship of *Mussaurus* to other prosauropods because most of these are represented by adults, and at present we have no idea what adult *Mussaurus* may have looked like. It has been tentatively suggested that *Mussaurus* may be hatchlings of *Coloradia*, another newly-described prosauropod known from a skull and jaws found in this formation.

## Other Groups

Another major group of prosauropods may be the melanorosaurids ('black reptiles'). Unlike the anchisaurids, these prosauropods are larger and much more heavily built. The melanorosaurids are based upon animals such as *Melanorosaurus* which is an assortment of large limb bones from South Africa. These seem to indicate the existence of a large, heavily-built prosauropod which walked on all-fours rather like the later sauropods (see pages 80 to 97). Another fairly well known form is *Riojasaurus* ('reptile of Rioja') from the late Triassic of Rioja, Argentina. *Riojasaurus* was a very large prosauropod up to 36ft (11m) long. At present it is known from postcranial remains which indicate a large and heavily-built prosauropod. The forelimbs are notably larger and more robust than those of anchisaurids which seems to suggest that it walked on all-fours all of the time. Unfortunately there is no cranial material known for any melanorosaurid, so whether they had typical anchisaurid-type skulls and teeth is unknown. The long slender neck of *Riojasaurus* does tend to suggest a relatively small skull.

Yunnanosaurids ('reptiles from Yunnan') are a special group of prosauropods devoted to a single species at present *(Yunnanosaurus huangi)* which was found in Yunnan Province, China, and described by Dr C. C. Young in 1942. Apparently smaller and less heavily-built than the melanorosaurids, the yunnanosaurids are

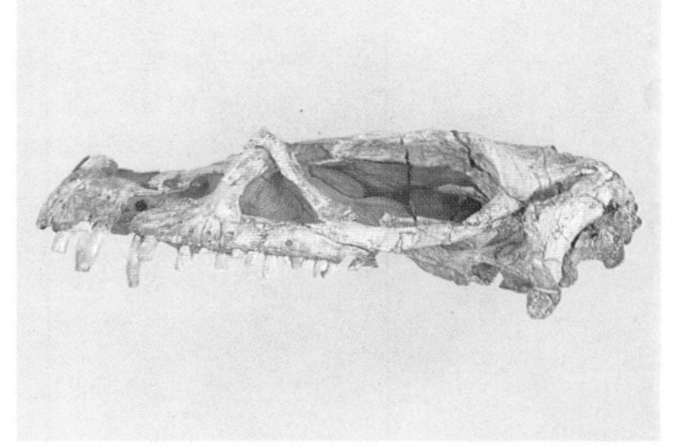

**Above:** A left lateral view of the skull of *Massospondylus carinatus* which was excavated at Blikana Mountain in the District of Herschel, Cape Province, South Africa. *Massospondylus* was one of the most widespread of the dinosaurs in this region in late Triassic/early Jurassic times (see Time Chart).

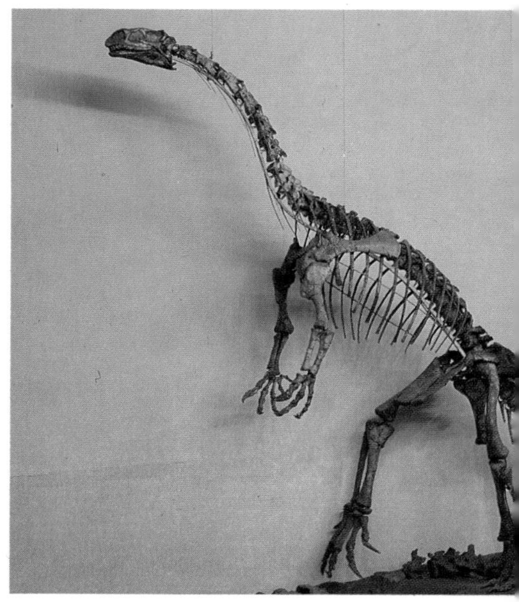

notable for one particular feature: the structure of their teeth. In his review of prosauropod diets Pêter Galton separated out *Yunnanosaurus* because it did not have the coarsely-serrated teeth typical of most prosauropods; its teeth were in fact reminiscent of those of true sauropods. They are cylindrical but somewhat flattened from side to side, presenting a somewhat chisel-like appearance. The tip of the tooth tends to be worn off at an angle forming quite a sharp cutting edge

*Yunnanosaurus* seems therefore to have developed a full set of truly sauropod-type teeth; they are in fact strikingly similar to those of the giant sauropod *Brachiosaurus* (see page 88) both in their shape and the way they are worn down. If only teeth had been found, they would almost certainly have been classified as belonging to an early sauropod dinosaur. However, the skeleton of *Yunnanosaurus* is quite typical of that of an anchisaurid prosauropod. This suggests that at least some of the prosauropods developed feeding techniques similar to those of the spectacularly successful sauropods of the late Jurassic.

It has been suggested that another *Plateosaurus*-like prosauropod from Yunnan Province, *Lufengosaurus* ('reptile from Lu-feng'), is in fact synonymous with *Yunnanosaurus*, but this is not the case.

## General Conclusions

The prosauropods were a very abundant and varied group of late Triassic and early Jurassic herbivorous dinosaurs. They seem to have evolved along several lines

(i) The anchisaurids seem for the most part to have been relatively agile bipedal and quadrupedal types capable of browsing on high foliage, using to advantage their long necks and hind legs. Their teeth were coarsely serrated and capable of shredding plant fibres reasonably effectively. A 'gastric mill' served further to pulp the otherwise indigestible plant tissues. Many of these herbivores may have been gregarious, living in herds in order to provide communal protection from some of the large predatory thecodontians of the late Triassic, such as *Saurosuchus* for instance, or large theropod dinosaurs (see *Dilophosaurus*, page 63) of the early Jurassic. The large claw on the hand may well have been used as a close-quarters defensive weapon.

(ii) The melanorosaurids may have represented an early attempt by prosauropods to use large size to become relatively invulnerable to predatory attack. Unfortunately these types are still rather poorly understood; for example it is not known whether they may even have developed sauropod-like teeth as did the third group, as mentioned below.

(iii) The yunnanosaurids retained the body form of the typical anchisaurid but developed a rather specialised dentition closely resembling that of the later sauropods.

**Below:** The Chinese prosauropod *Lufengosaurus huenei* broadly resembles *Plateosaurus*, and they were probably quite closely related. Its discovery in southern China bears witness to the wide geographical distribution of prosauropods in the late Triassic/early Jurassic.

**Right:** An extremely well preserved skull (now in the Humboldt Museum) of *Plateosaurus engelhardti* that was excavated from the Upper Triassic rocks of Halberstadt, Germany. The coarsely-serrated teeth seem well adapted to shredding plant material.

**Left:** Tübingen University's skeleton of *Plateosaurus* is restored in a bipedal pose, although recent research suggests that prosauropods may also have walked on all-fours. The long neck is an adaptation that would have allowed *Plateosaurus* to browse comfortably on high vegetation.

**Right:** The South African Museum's cast of the skeleton of *Massospondylus carinatus*. This dinosaur stood some 13ft (4m) tall, and the picture emphasises the generally small size of its head and jaws in relation to the overall body proportions. It is possible that its food was pulped by a gastric mill of stomach stones.

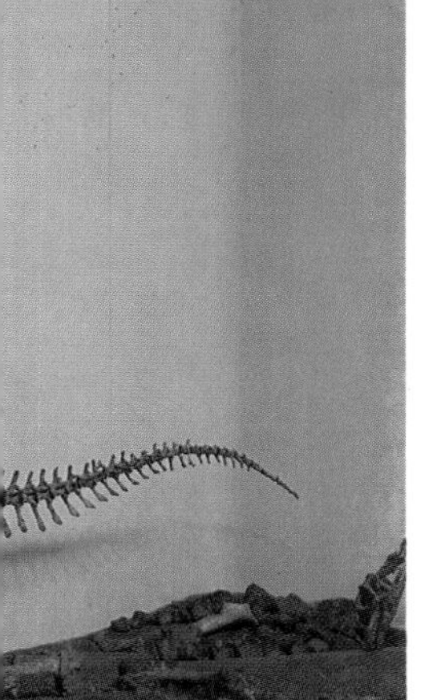

**PROSAUROPOD GENERA**

**Valid**
*Ammosaurus*
*Anchisaurus*
*Aristosaurus*
*Azendohsaurus (?)*
*Coloradia*
*Efraasia*
*Euskelosaurus*
*Lufengosaurus*
*Massospondylus*
*Melanorosaurus*
*Mussaurus*
(?= *Coloradia*)
*Plateosaurus*
*Riojasaurus*
*Sellosaurus*
*Sinosaurus (?)*
*Thecodontosaurus*
*Yunnanosaurus*

**Dubious**
*Aetonyx*
*Agrosaurus*
*Amphisaurus*
*Avalonia*
*Avalonianus*
*Basutodon*
*Clepsysaurus*
*Dimodosaurus*
*Dinosaurus*
*Dromicosaurus*
*Eucnemesaurus*
*Gresslyosaurus*
*Gryponyx*
*Gyposaurus*
*Hortalotarsus*
*Leptospondylus*
*Megadactylus*
*Nyasasaurus*
*Orosauravus*
*Orosaurus*
*Pachysauriscus*
*Pachysaurus*
*Pachyspondylus*
*Palaeosauriscus*
*Palaeosaurus*
*Picrodon*
*Thotobolosaurus*
*Yaleosaurus*
*Zanclodon*

# Diplodocids

**Apatosaurus (below right)**
An obviously large sauropod *Apatosaurus* weighed about 30 tonnes. The neck is relatively thick, and the head is small. *Apatosaurus* must have fed nearly continuously on low-lying vegetation around lakes, and on the leaves of tall trees. It snipped these off with its peg-like teeth and swallowed them whole. The plant material was ground up in the stomach, which probably contained a number of pebbles that *Apatosaurus* had swallowed for this purpose — so-called 'stomach stones' or gastroliths. Note the short, splayed, rather elephant-like toes.

The sauropods which are described in this section (pages 80-97) were undoubtedly the most spectacular of all dinosaurs. The very epitome of the popular image of the dinosaur, these were the long-necked and long-tailed giants of the Jurassic and Cretaceous Periods. They are often pictured wading in shallow lakes, feeding on a variety of water plants. However, as we shall see later, this view of them as giant amphibious creatures has been challenged in recent years.

The earliest sauropods known are of early Jurassic age (see *Vulcanodon,* page 92) and very probably arose from a stock of prosauropod-like animals in the late Triassic. As we saw in the previous section, both the melanorosaurids and the yunnanosaurids seem to show some sauropod-like features (either very large size or the shape of their teeth).

As is the case with many of the other saurischian groups, there are an enormous number of dinosaurs which have been named

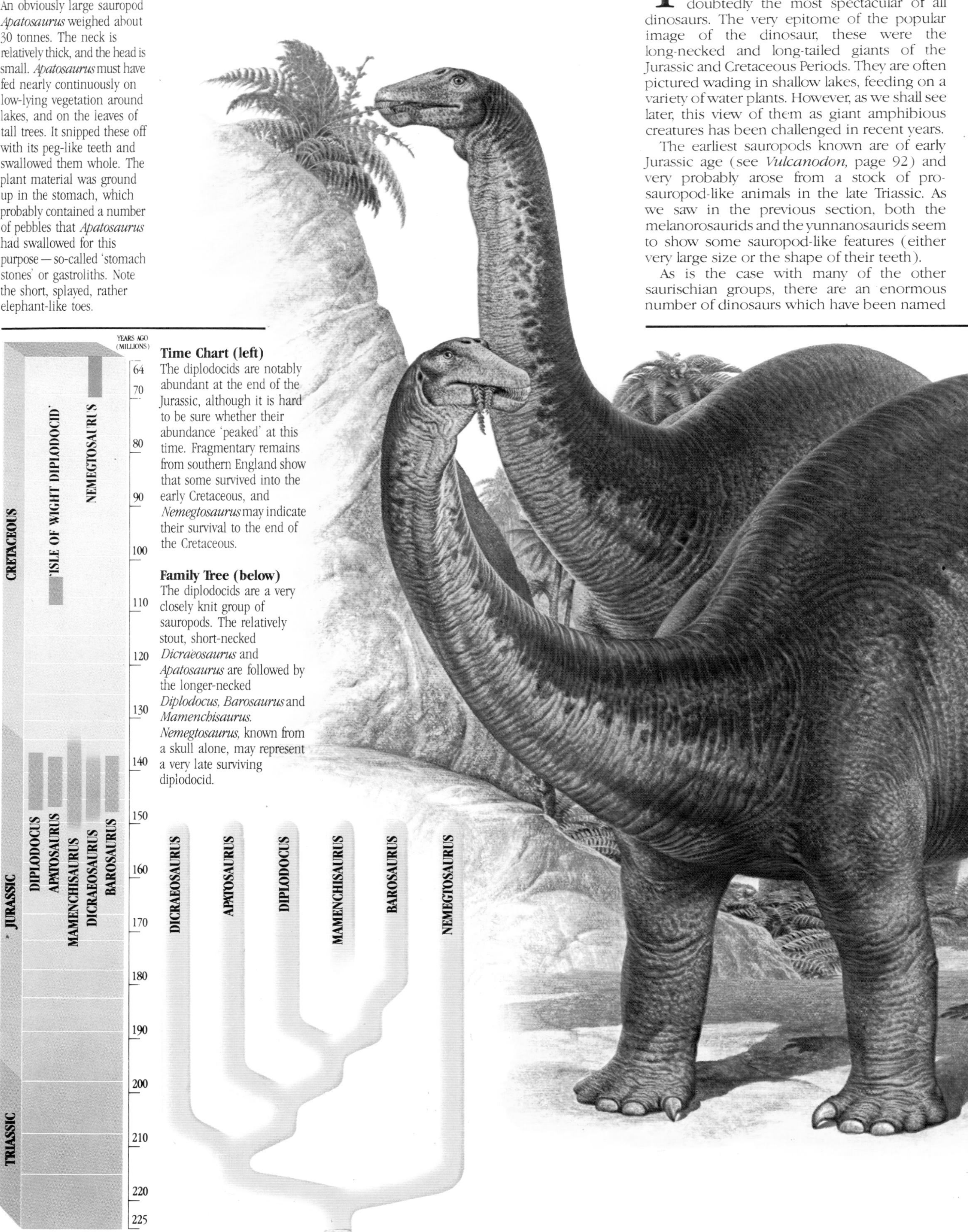


**Time Chart (left)**
The diplodocids are notably abundant at the end of the Jurassic, although it is hard to be sure whether their abundance 'peaked' at this time. Fragmentary remains from southern England show that some survived into the early Cretaceous, and *Nemegtosaurus* may indicate their survival to the end of the Cretaceous.

**Family Tree (below)**
The diplodocids are a very closely knit group of sauropods. The relatively stout, short-necked *Dicraeosaurus* and *Apatosaurus* are followed by the longer-necked *Diplodocus, Barosaurus* and *Mamenchisaurus. Nemegtosaurus,* known from a skull alone, may represent a very late surviving diplodocid.

on the basis of imperfect material and are consequently very hard to discuss in any meaningful way. I shall therefore restrict the coverage given to these sauropods to a survey of some of the better known and most distinctive types. A table of valid and dubious sauropod genera, which includes diplodocids, is given on page 97.

## The First Discoveries

Scientific study of *Apatosaurus* ('deceptive reptile') began in an extremely confused and confusing way in 1877. Much of this confusion has its origins in the rivalry between two palaeontologists: Othniel Marsh and Edward Drinker Cope. In the July of that year, O. C. Marsh described a large, incomplete section of hip bones found by Arthur Lakes near Morrison, Colorado; to this he gave the name *Titanosaurus montanus* only to discover that *Titanosaurus* ('giant reptile') had already been used for a sauropod from India. Later that year he coined the name *Atlantosaurus* ('Atlas reptile') for this material. In the same publication, Marsh also used the name *Apatosaurus ajax* for more hip and back bones found in another quarry in the Morrison area by Lakes. Incidentally this latter specimen was originally sent to Marsh's great rival, E. D. Cope, but Cope was obliged to send it to Marsh when he learned that Marsh had already bought the fossils from Lakes. Over the next few years more material of *Apatosaurus ajax*, and another larger skeleton named *Atlantosaurus immanis*, was recovered from the second quarry. This collection included fragments of a skull, which were later to prove to be of considerable importance. In 1879 two more of Marsh's collectors, W. H. Reed and E. G. Ashley, discovered two more sauropod skeletons at Como Bluff, Wyoming; these were from rocks of the same age as the previous find. One of these, an almost complete skeleton lacking only the skull, was described as *'Brontosaurus'* (=*Apatosaurus*) *excelsus* by Marsh in 1879, the other was named *B. amplus* (*Brontosaurus*: 'thunder reptile'). In 1883 Marsh produced the first ever reconstruction of any sauropod, based on his *'Brontosaurus' excelsus*, but unfortunately used several limb bones as well as the feet of *Camarasaurus* (page 87). As a result the animal was given rather graceful, slender forelimbs, as opposed to the much more stout, robust limbs that it actually had. *Camarasaurus*, or *'Morosaurus'* as it was then known, was also used as the model for the neck which was given 12 neck vertebrae, instead of the 15 that we now know there to be. Marsh was also unaware that *'Brontosaurus'* had a long whip-like end to its tail comprising more than 80 vertebrae, almost twice the number found in the tail of *Camarasaurus*.

Because of the confusion generated by Marsh in distinguishing between his *'Brontosaurus'* and the *Camarasaurus* skeleton, he also reconstructed *'Brontosaurus'* with a

**Diplodocus (below)**
Although a close relative of *Apatosaurus*, *Diplodocus* was lighter in build, weighing only 10-11 tonnes, even though it was longer (88·5ft, 27m). The neck was longer, and the tail was whip-like at the end. The limbs of diplodocids were pillar-like in order to support their great weight. Most of the toe-nails of the front foot were small hooves, except for the inner toes which bore long claws, possibly for self-defence. The drawing on page 97 shows this usage.

**Map (below)**
**1** *Antarctosaurus*
**2** *Apatosaurus*
**3** *Atlantosaurus*
**4** *Barosaurus*
**5** *Cetiosauriscus*
**6** *Dicraeosaurus*
**7** *Diplodocus*
**8** *Mamenchisaurus*
**9** *Nemegtosaurus*
**10** *Un-named diplodocid*

**Comparative Sizes (below)**
**1** *Apatosaurus:* l. 69ft (21m).
**2** *Diplodocus:* l. 88·5ft (27m).

*Camarasaurus*-type head based upon a partial skull recovered from another quarry at Como Bluff, and incidentally from geologically older rocks which had only yielded several sauropod skeletons, but none that could be identified as *Apatosaurus* (*'Brontosaurus'*).

Extensive collections of sauropod remains were recovered from south eastern Wyoming around the turn of the century, particularly at Como Bluff and Bone Cabin Quarry. These, however, were largely of disarticulated remains rather than well-preserved skeletons, and tended to add to the confusion rather than clarifying relationships between names and skeletal types. For example the hindlimbs of *Camarasaurus* (*'Morosaurus'*) and *Apatosaurus* (*'Brontosaurus'*) were regularly confused, as were the forelimbs of *Diplodocus* and *'Morosaurus'*.

One rather interesting consequence of this confusion can be seen in many museums around the world! Casts of a magnificent skeleton of *Diplodocus carnegiei* were sent to various museums around the world at the beginning of this century. In order to complete the skeleton in preparation for casting, a complete foot of *Camarasaurus* (*'Morosaurus'*) identified as *'Diplodocus'* by Henry Fairfield Osborn, was sent from the American Museum of Natural History to the Carnegie Museum. As a result many of the museums of the world have *Diplodocus* skeletons with front feet which are modelled on the hind feet of *Camarasaurus!*

Better-preserved material of *Apatosaurus* and careful work on the original material revealed that there were a number of inconsistencies in the early work on sauropods that had been undertaken by Marsh and others. As a result it was agreed that (i) *Apatosaurus* was the valid name for material described either as *'Atlantosaurus'* or *'Brontosaurus'*; (ii) *Camarasaurus* was the valid name for material also referred to as *'Morosaurus'*; and (iii) that there were more similarities between the skeletons of *Apatosaurus* and *Diplodocus* than there were between *Apatosaurus* and *Camarasaurus*.

The latter point is of some significance because despite this observation, until very recently (1975) the skeletons of *Apatosaurus* have always been restored with a *Camarasaurus*-like head, following Marsh's original drawings. This is slightly surprising, for in 1915 and 1924 W. J. Holland, a noted expert on the sauropods of North America, claimed that *Apatosaurus* very probably had a *Diplodocus*-type skull. He based his argument upon the overall similarities in their skeletons and the observation that a partial *Diplodocus*-like skull was discovered very close to two *Apatosaurus* skeletons recovered from Dinosaur National Monument (Utah). This claim seems to have been completely ignored by the scientific community until 1975 when the issue was re-examined by Dr Jack McIntosh (Wesleyan University), one of the leading experts on

**Diplodocus Skeleton (below)**
The skeleton of this form was considerably lighter than that of *Apatosaurus* although in other respects very similar. The very small head, long neck and long tail are hallmarks of the diplodocids. The rather slender neck is composed of 15 vertebrae, the back 10, and the tail about 70. Because of these proportions some workers suggest that *Diplodocus* had the body plan of a walking cantilever bridge! Both front and back legs (the pillars of the bridge) and their girdles were extremely strong to bear the animal's weight. Despite the large belly area, there is no evidence of gastralia.

**Diplodocid Skulls (right)**
These three skulls were found in very different places yet they all show basic diplodocid features. The eyes are far back in the head and the nostrils right on top of the skull. The snout is long and broad with a cluster of rather feeble-looking teeth at the front. *Nemegtosaurus* (near right, top) is from the late Cretaceous rocks of Mongolia. *Dicraeosaurus* (near right, bottom) was found in late Jurassic rocks of Tanzania. *Antarctosaurus* is from the Jurassic of Argentina, not Antarctica as its name suggests! It would seem that the jaw muscles of all these diplodocids were relatively feeble.

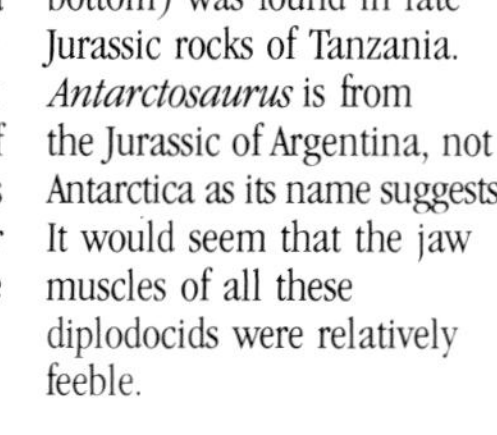

**Nemegtosaurus Skull**

Nostrils
Eye socket

**Dicraeosaurus Skull**

Nostrils
Eye socket

**Antarctosaurus Skull**

Eye socket
Nostrils
Peg-like teeth at front of jaw

Eye socket
Jaw joint

**Diplodocus Skull (left)**
Here the features of the diplodocids are seen clearly. In side view (top drawing) note the large eye-socket and fine pencil-like teeth at the front of the snout. In top view (lower drawing) you can see the unusual position of the nostrils.

**Diplodocus Hand (below)**
The hand is broad and rather short as expected in such a massive animal. It is possible that only the first finger bore a large curved claw, and that the other fingers were finished off with a blunt pad, probably of horn.

**Diplodocus Foot (below)**
Like the hand, the foot is short and broad with five rather stubby toes. Although the foot is often drawn with three clawed toes, at least one well-preserved specimen of *Diplodocus carnegiei* shows that only toes 1 and 2 bore claws.

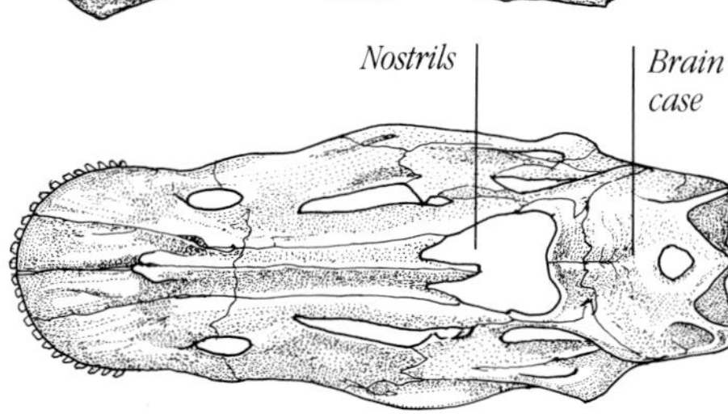


**Diplodocus Hand**

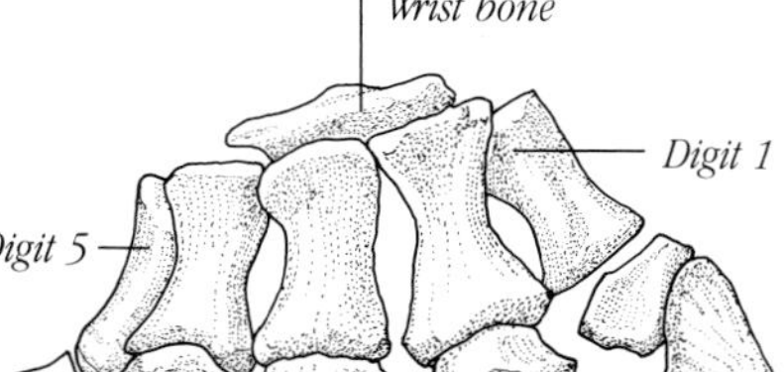


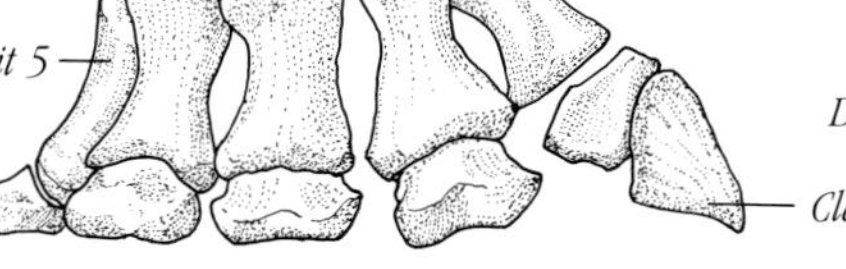


**Diplodocus Foot**

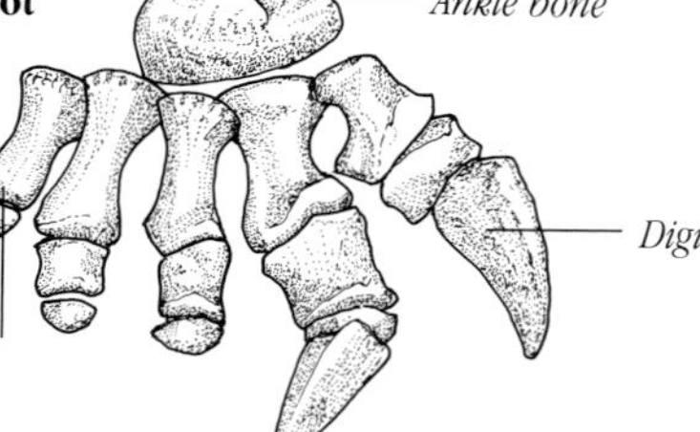

sauropod dinosaurs, and Dr David Berman (Carnegie Museum). They were able to demonstrate convincingly, that *Apatosaurus* probably possessed a skull that was virtually indistinguishable from that of *Diplodocus*. They were also responsible for bringing to light the reason for much of the confusion surrounding the early work on sauropods toward the end of the last century. In fact if Marsh had studied the skull fragments found in Colorado in the late 1870s, he could have avoided all this confusion.

## Dinosaur National Monument

In 1936 Charles Whitney Gilmore—one of the most productive and respected of research workers on dinosaurs in the early half of this century—described an almost complete skeleton of *Apatosaurus* (*A. louisae*, named in honour of the wife of Andrew Carnegie, the benefactor of the Carnegie Museum that is situated in Pittsburgh, Pennsylvania).

This particular skeleton was of considerable importance because of its key role in the establishment of Dinosaur National Monument. In 1909 Earl Douglass of the Carnegie Museum discovered the remains of the skeleton which was to become *A. louisae* which was weathering out on a sandstone ledge near Jensen on the Green River. Upon excavation, this specimen proved to be almost complete and while it was being dug out other specimens were discovered, one after another. Excavations led by the Carnegie Museum continued without a break until 1922, and the quarry was still far from exhausted of its fossils. In the early years permits for excavation were granted on an annual basis by the Department of the Interior. Finally the Carnegie Museum attempted to 'file a claim' for the site to prevent it from being exploited by unscrupulous collectors. This was refused on the grounds that fossil bones were not deemed to be minerals. However, this action provoked no less a person than President Woodrow Wilson on 4th October 1915 to set aside 80 acres in and around the quarry as an area to be preserved as an 'American Antiquity' and to be known as Dinosaur National Monument.

After the major excavations of the Carnegie Museum (1909-1922), further excavations were undertaken by the Smithsonian Institution (Washington D.C.) and the University of Utah to extract more skeletons before the exposure was enclosed in a huge permanent building. This remarkable site and Museum (opened in 1958) offers an almost unparalleled opportunity for visitors to visit a dinosaur excavation site 'in action'.

## Apatosaurus Described

The head of *Apatosaurus* is now thought to be like that of *Diplodocus* which is described below, in concordance with the views of Holland, McIntosh and Berman. The neck is

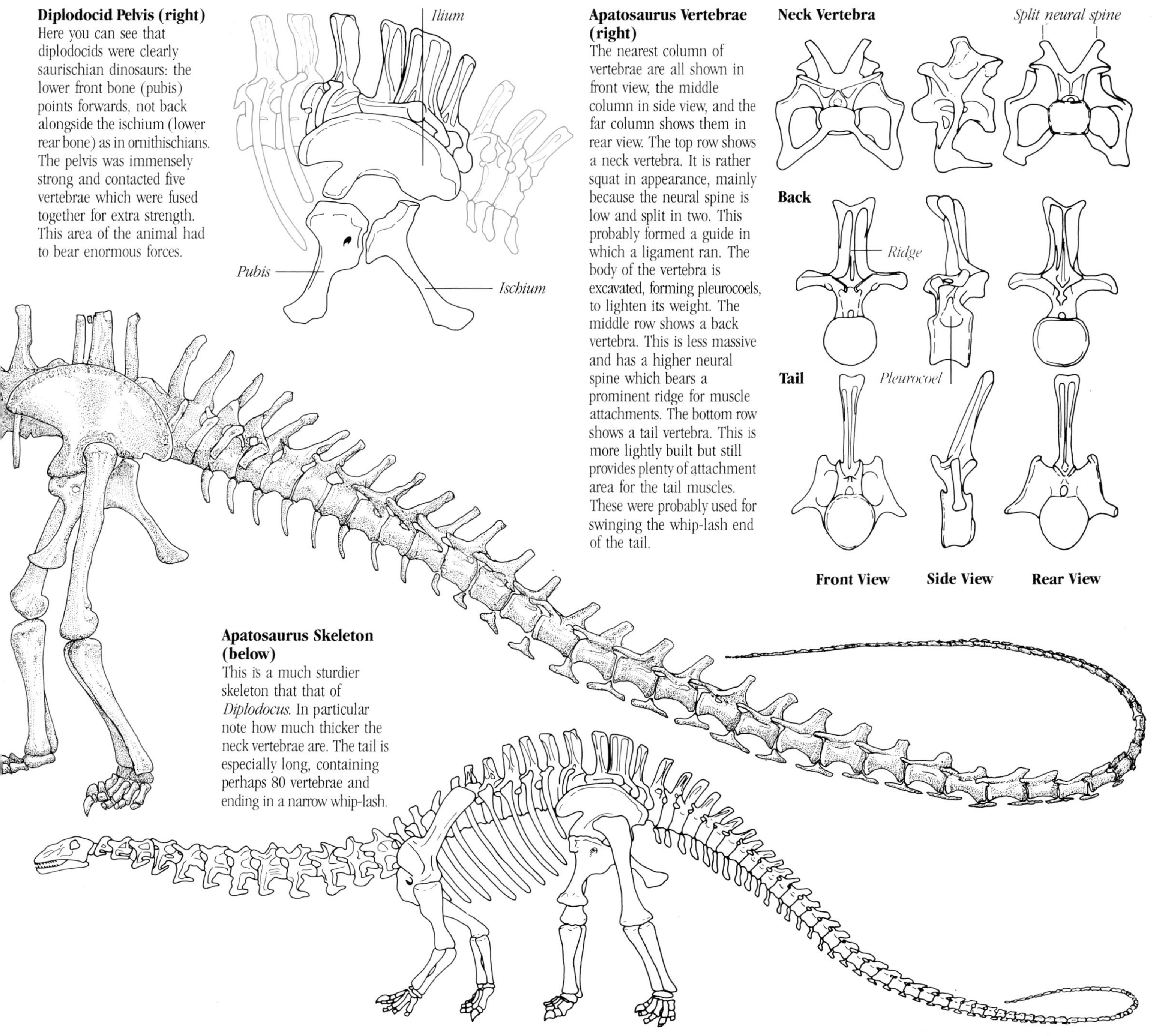


**Diplodocid Pelvis (right)**
Here you can see that diplodocids were clearly saurischian dinosaurs: the lower front bone (pubis) points forwards, not back alongside the ischium (lower rear bone) as in ornithischians. The pelvis was immensely strong and contacted five vertebrae which were fused together for extra strength. This area of the animal had to bear enormous forces.

**Apatosaurus Vertebrae (right)**
The nearest column of vertebrae are all shown in front view, the middle column in side view, and the far column shows them in rear view. The top row shows a neck vertebra. It is rather squat in appearance, mainly because the neural spine is low and split in two. This probably formed a guide in which a ligament ran. The body of the vertebra is excavated, forming pleurocoels, to lighten its weight. The middle row shows a back vertebra. This is less massive and has a higher neural spine which bears a prominent ridge for muscle attachments. The bottom row shows a tail vertebra. This is more lightly built but still provides plenty of attachment area for the tail muscles. These were probably used for swinging the whip-lash end of the tail.

**Apatosaurus Skeleton (below)**
This is a much sturdier skeleton that that of *Diplodocus*. In particular note how much thicker the neck vertebrae are. The tail is especially long, containing perhaps 80 vertebrae and ending in a narrow whip-lash.

rather thick, certainly by comparison with that of *Diplodocus*; it consists of 15 vertebrae to which the ribs—which no doubt anchored the powerful muscles which moved the neck—are firmly fused. The sides of the neck vertebrae and those of the back are deeply excavated to form cavities (pleurocoels—see also the theropods). As was the case with the larger theropods, these cavities undoubtedly served to lighten the bones of the back of the animal in order to reduce the total body weight of these gigantic creatures. The spines of the neck, although they seem in profile to be relatively short when compared with those of the back, are nevertheless connected to extremely powerful muscles and ligaments used for raising the neck. As in *Diplodocus*, the spines near the base of the neck are divided down the middle and probably provided a pulley-like guide for a massive ligament that ran along this groove.

The back vertebrae are less elaborately sculpted than the neck vertebrae, but have extremely tall spines which are prominently ridged and scarred for the attachment of powerful muscles. At the hips, five of the backbones are fused together to form a massive support for the pelvic bones in order to transmit the enormous weight of the body into the pillar-like legs. The tail is surprisingly long for a quadrupedal animal (82 vertebrae are known in one specimen), almost half of which consists of a very slender whip-lash.

Both fore and hindlimbs are massively built and pillar-like in order to support effectively the weight of the animal. The feet have relatively short toes which are splayed rather like those of an elephant. The fore feet, as in the majority of sauropods, have a single clawed inner toe, the other four ending in blunt pads. The hind foot has three claws, the outer two toes again presumably ending in blunt pads.

## Discovering Diplodocus

*Diplodocus* ('double beam'), another of the great and well-known sauropods from the late Jurassic of North America, was also initially described by O. C. Marsh. The first remains were found by Samuel Wendell Williston near the ranch of M. P. Felch not far from Canyon City, Colorado in 1877.

Williston managed to collect parts of a hind limb and numerous tail vertebrae. Marsh described these remains as *Diplodocus longus* in 1878. The name 'double beam' refers to the unusual form of the chevron bones which hang beneath the tail vertebrae; these are shaped like a pair of skids joined together at either end and were thought at the time to be unique to *Diplodocus*, though they have now been recognised in *Apatosaurus* and *Cetiosauriscus*. In subsequent years further fragmentary remains of sauropods, including *Diplodocus*, were recovered from Jurassic rocks in Colorado and Wyoming; however, it was not until 1899 that reasonable articulated skeletons were discovered, this time at Sheep Creek, Albany, County, Wyoming. Two partial skeletons were recovered which, together with the previously discovered remains, enabled John Bell Hatcher to provide a reasonably accurate reconstruction of the skeleton. This was modified in later years by further specimens described by W. J. Holland.

The skull of *Diplodocus* is surprisingly small for an animal of such large size. The snout is quite long and broad, and the teeth, which are narrow and pencil-like, are clustered closely together to form a fringe around the front of the mouth only. The eyes are situated quite far back on the side of the head and, rather curiously, the nostrils are located right on top of the head almost between the eyes, rather than in their usual position at the tip of the snout. The positioning of the eyes and nose gives a rather 'cramped' impression to the rear portion of the skull where the brain seems to have been relatively small, as were the jaw muscles. The joint between the head and neck suggests that the head was held at a distinct angle to the neck, rather than in-line with it.

As in *Apatosaurus*, there are 15 neck vertebrae; these, however, are somewhat longer, giving the neck a rather more slender appearance. The neck ribs are relatively short and fused to the vertebrae, while the vertebrae have extensive and complicated excavations in their sides to reduce their weight. The spines of the posterior neck vetebrae also have a V-shaped trough running down the centre which undoubtedly acted as a guide for a very powerful neck ligament.

Like *Apatosaurus* there are 10 back vertebrae with long, complexly-sculpted spines and deeply-excavated pleurocoels. In the tail slightly fewer, 73 or so, tail bones are known and again the posterior portion of the tail is developed into a thin whip-lash. At the base of the tail, the sides of the vertebrae have deep, vertical plates of bone; these may well provide areas for the insertion of massive muscles (*M. ilio-caudalis*) used for swinging the whip-lash end of the tail.

The ribs extending from the back of *Diplodocus* are very long and enclose a huge chest and belly cavity. Rather curiously there are no good records of these animals having bony gastralia (ribs lining the belly region) as are found extensively in prosauropods and theropods.

The shoulders and forelimbs are large and strong to carry the immense weight of these animals and provide areas for the attachment of powerful leg and shoulder muscles. The forelimb is pillar-like and ends in a rather short, broad foot. It would appear that only the inner toe of the foot bore a large curved claw, the remainder of the toes ending in blunt, possibly horny pads rather like the toes of elephants. This type of fore foot seems to have been common to almost all sauropods. However, owing to the confusion that prevailed concerning the identity of these sauropods at the end of the last century, *Diplodocus* and *Apatosaurus* are often illustrated with 3-clawed *Camarasaurus*-type feet!

The huge pelvis is firmly attached to the vertebral column by means of five fused vertebrae. As with the forelimb, the hindlimb is pillar-like, although it is slightly longer; as a result the back slopes down from the hips to the shoulders. The feet are again short, and five-toed. In one fine skeleton of *Diplodocus carnegiei*, the five-toed hind food is well preserved and appears to show that only *two* inner toes bore claws. However, as was the case with the fore foot, the reconstructions that have appeared in books and in dinosaur exhibitions persist in showing a foot bearing three claws which resembles that of both *Apatosaurus louisae* and *Camarasaurus lentus!*

## Sauropod 'Heels'

Notwithstanding the confusion over the type of feet that these sauropods possessed, the proportions of the toes do bear a remarkable resemblance to those of living elephants. In elephants, the feet are supported by a thick wedge of fibrous tissue which lies beneath the rear of the foot—rather like the heel of a modern shoe. As a result, the toes of elephants do not lie flat on the ground when they walk, but rest on the fibrous pad at an angle to the ground. By developing this wedge-heel arrangement, elephants have solved one of the 'problems' which we face when walking. Our toes lie flat along the ground and the ankle joint with the lower leg is a right-angle one. As a result, every time we take a step we have to lift our heel off the ground so that the weight of our bodies is supported on the ball of the foot. When we walk we therefore tend to bob up and down with each stride. This is in fact quite tiring, although we do not consciously realise this. It is one reason why shoes with moderate heels, which save some of the energy we would have used to lift the body up and down, are so comfortable. Elephants (being considerably heavier than humans) face this problem as well: they are heavy and therefore need broad, flat feet to bear their weight. However, they would tire very quickly if they rested the entire length of their toes on the ground when they walked, and 'bobbed' in the way that we do. They therefore have developed 'built-in' heels to save energy. Sauropods must have done the same sort of thing. The broad stubby toes were undoubtedly supported behind by a thick wedge of tissue which acted as a 'heel'.

Drs David Berman and Jack McIntosh, who have done a great deal of work on the sauropod dinosaurs in recent years, have concluded that of the great variety of sauropods that have been described, at least a few share characteristics in common with those seen in *Diplodocus*

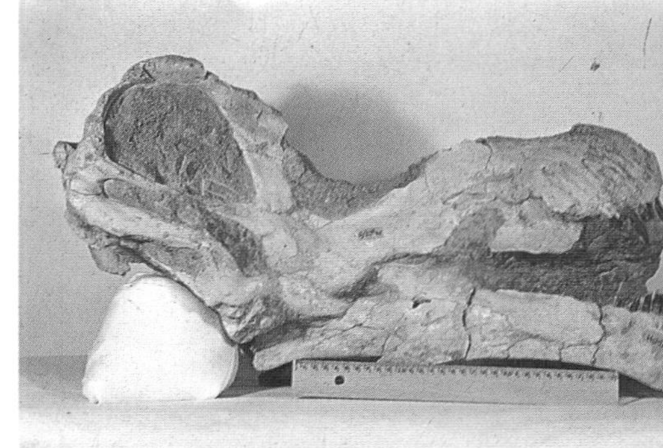

**Above:** The skull of *Nemegtosaurus mongoliensis* which was found at Altan Ula in the Gobi Desert during the 1965 Polish-Mongolian Expedition. It comes from late Cretaceous rocks, which is significant because most other diplodocids are known from the strata of late Jurassic formations. This may indicate that they survived throughout much of the age of the dinosaurs.

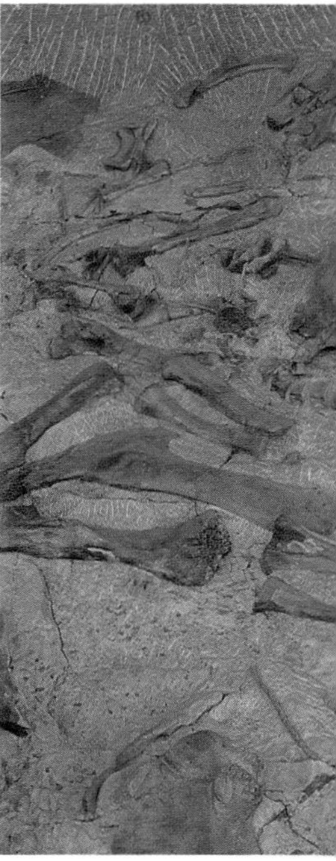

**Right:** The Dinosaur National Monument Quarry is one of the world's largest deposits of Jurassic fossils. The sediments containing the fossils are steeply inclined so that as they are exposed by the team of preparators they form a natural mural which can be studied by visitors. These scattered bones are principally of *Apatosaurus*.

and *Apatosaurus*. These include the shape of the head and teeth, peculiar skid-like chevron bones on the tail, a whip-lash tail and the relatively short front legs. These sauropods are referred to as diplodocids (members of the *Diplodocus* family) and include the following less well-known genera.

*Barosaurus* ('heavy reptile') was first described by O. C. Marsh in 1890. It comes from the late Jurassic of North America. It is a sauropod that is practically indistinguishable from *Diplodocus* except for the fact that it has very long neck vertebrae. It may even be a variant of *Diplodocus* rather than a different genus (see also table on page 97).

*Cetiosauriscus* ('whale-like reptile') is a genus named by Friedrich Freiherr von Huene in 1927 on the basis of a partial skeleton of a sauropod from the late Jurassic Oxford clay of Peterborough. Again it shows all the salient characters of other diplodocids (including the whip-lash tail and the skid-like chevrons). Another presently un-named diplodocid from the Isle of Wight (England) was also described by Dr Alan Charig (British Museum—Natural History) in 1980. So far this is only known from a characteristically skid-like chevron bone from the tail. However, it shows that diplodocids were also around in the early Cretaceous of England at least.

*Mamenchisaurus* ('Mamenchi reptile') from the late Jurassic of Sichuan Province, China was another very long-necked diplodocid, although it is not known from complete skeletons. Most of the skeletal reconstructions known appear to be composite skeletons. *Mamenchisaurus* possesses several dipodocid characteristics and is also cautiously referred to this group of dinosaurs.

*Dicraeosaurus* ('forked reptile') from the late Jurassic of Tendaguru (Tanzania) was described by Werner Janensch in 1929 on the basis of an almost complete skeleton. Again, although it differs in some details from other diplodocids, it clearly possesses the characteristically shaped head as well as the skid-like chevrons and whip-lash tail.

*Nemegtosaurus* ('reptile from Nemegtu') is currently only known from a skull found in the late Cretaceous rocks of the Nemegt basin of Mongolia. As can be seen from the drawing the skull is very similar to that of other diplodocids. If it was a diplodocid, then it shows that members of this group persisted until the very end of the Cretaceous Period.

*Antarctosaurus* ('Antarctic reptile') from the Jurassic of Argentina may also represent another imperfectly-known diplodocid. The skull certainly shows all the typical diplodocid features.

*Amphicoelias* ('paired cavities') from the late Jurassic of the Morrison area of Colorado was first described by Cope in 1887 on the basis of isolated vertebrae. These are considered to be 'diplodocid' by McIntosh and Berman but beyond that are not identifiable.

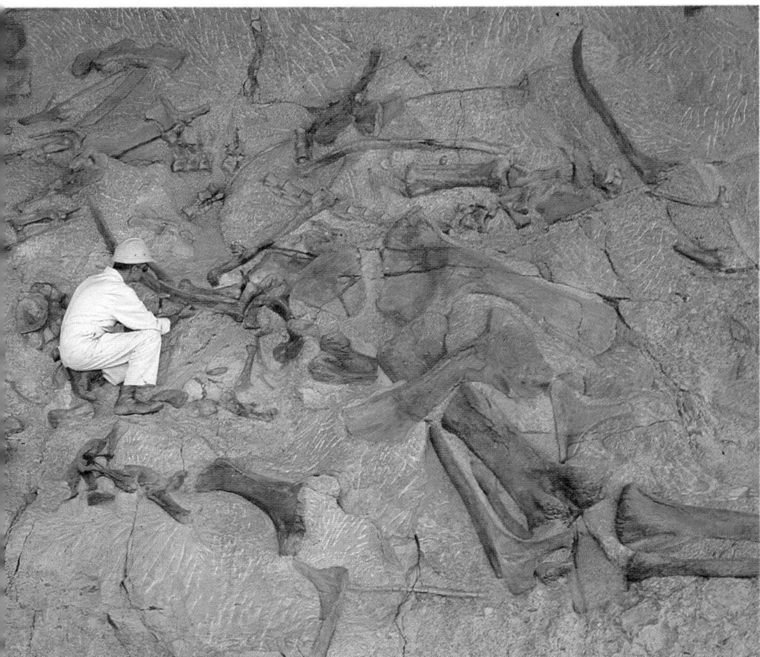

**Above:** Denver Museum's fine skeleton of *Diplodocus longus*. This specimen was excavated at Dinosaur National Monument and shipped to Denver in the matrix in 1936. The work of articulating the skeleton was directed by Philip Reinheimer. The overall length of this *Diplodocus* is 75·5ft (23m) and it stands 12·6ft (3·8m) high at the hips. Note the pleurocoels in the vertebrae.

**Below:** The extraordinarily long neck of *Mamenchisaurus* is evident in this view of the skeleton in Beijing. The neck accounts for 33ft (10m) of the creature's total body length of 72ft (22m).

# CAMARASAURIDS & BRACHIOSAURIDS

Another reasonably well known group of sauropod dinosaurs are the camarasaurids, based mainly upon *Camarasaurus* ('chambered reptile'). As we saw in the previous section, *Camarasaurus* which was first described by E. D. Cope in August 1877, was much confused with early discoveries of *Apatosaurus* and *Diplodocus*.

These dinosaurs all come from the same late Jurassic deposits of North America. E. D. Cope described *Camarasaurus supremus* on the basis of an imperfect series of vertebrae which were collected by O. W. Lucas from Canyon City, Colorado in 1877. In December of that year O. C. Marsh described more sauropod material (including an imperfect skull with major parts of a skeleton of an immature sauropod) as *Apatosaurus grandis*, and another partial skeleton of a more mature sauropod which he named *Apatosaurus ajax*; both of these specimens came from Como Bluff, Wyoming. In the following year more material from Como Bluff was described as *Morosaurus robustus* and *M. impar* by Marsh, while from Colorado Cope described *Caulodon leptoganus* and *C. diversidens*. Another genus *Uintasaurus douglassi* was described on the basis of a partial skeleton recovered from Dinosaur National Monument, Utah, by W. J. Holland, in 1924. When this material was subsequently reviewed by Dr Theodore E. White in 1958, all these species (apart from *Apatosaurus ajax*) were referred to Cope's genus *Camarasaurus*. The relationships of other possible members of the camarasaurid family are again difficult to pin down with any degree of certainty. A table of valid and dubious camarasaurid genera is included at the end of the section concerned with sauropods (pages 96-97).

## Camarasaurus Described

In 1925, shortly after Holland's description of *'Uintasaurus'* was published, Charles W. Gilmore described the beautifully preserved, almost complete skeleton of a young *Camarasaurus* that had been discovered by the Carnegie Museum excavations at Dinosaur National Monument, Utah. The skeleton was preserved almost completely intact, with just a few bones missing or lying slightly out of natural position. It must be supposed that the carcass of this animal was buried very rapidly beneath the shifting sand-bars of a deltaic area at the mouth of a large river; if not, the rotting carcass would surely have been scavenged by carnivores or have simply fallen to pieces and its bones been scattered as its flesh slowly rotted.Around the carcass, between the ribs in particular, was found a thin layer of carbon which probably represented remains of the skin of *Camarasaurus*. Unfortunately no details of the scaly surface of the skin were preserved in this layer.

The skull of this animal is very different in appearance from that of the diplodocids seen earlier. It is much deeper and the snout region

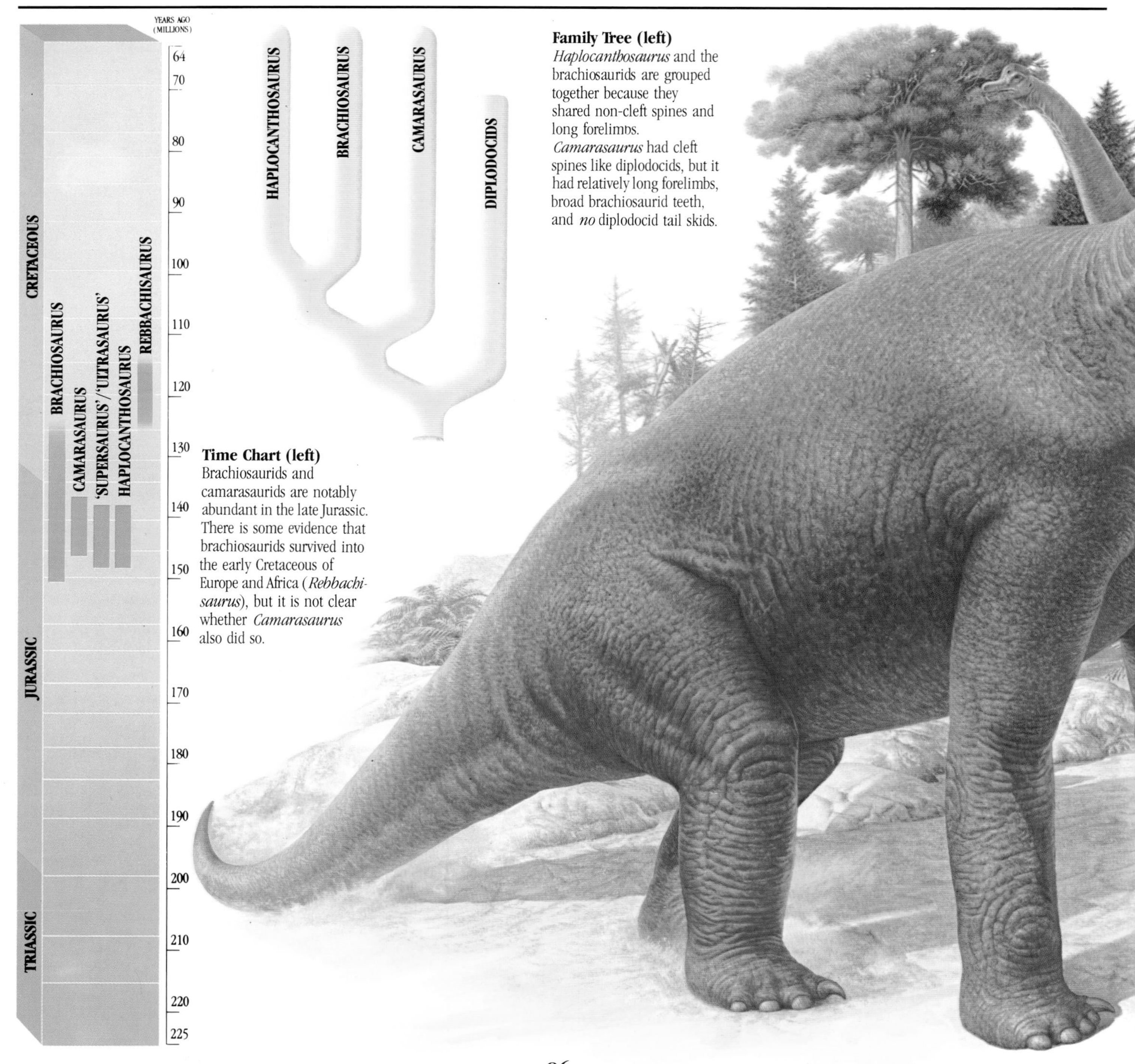


**Family Tree (left)**
*Haplocanthosaurus* and the brachiosaurids are grouped together because they shared non-cleft spines and long forelimbs. *Camarasaurus* had cleft spines like diplodocids, but it had relatively long forelimbs, broad brachiosaurid teeth, and *no* diplodocid tail skids.

**Time Chart (left)**
Brachiosaurids and camarasaurids are notably abundant in the late Jurassic. There is some evidence that brachiosaurids survived into the early Cretaceous of Europe and Africa (*Rebbachisaurus*), but it is not clear whether *Camarasaurus* also did so.

**Brachiosaurus (left)**
One of the most massive dinosaurs, *Brachiosaurus* was 74ft (22·5m) long, and it may have weighed as much as 77 tonnes. The most obvious feature of this animal is the great length of its neck, and also of its forelimbs which were longer than the hindlimbs — a very unusual characteristic of these dinosaurs. Both features seem to be adaptations for high browsing (there is an obvious analogy here with the giraffe), and it is probably correct to picture *Brachiosaurus* feeding from the tops of tall trees. The nostrils on top of the head are a puzzling feature.

is comparatively short. The jaws, which are heavier than those of *Diplodocus,* have larger, chisel-like teeth which are not only located at the tip of the jaws (like those of diplodocids), but are also spread along the sides of the jaws in a much more typical reptilian arrangement. The sides of the skull are also notable for the large window-like openings cut into their surfaces. The nostrils are positioned in front of the eyes (unlike diplodocids) and are quite enórmous. The eye itself must have been situated in an enormous cavity — far larger than the area that was actually occupied by the eyeball. Immediately behind the eye cavity there are openings in which the major jaw muscles were located. The only areas of the skull with any substantial thickness of bone are the rims of the jaws, where they support the large,long-rooted teeth and the smaller area at the rear of the skull which protected the brain.

Judging by the way the skull fits against the first of the neck vertebrae. the head was held at

**Map (right)**
1 *Brachiosaurus*
2 *Camarasaurus*
3 *Haplocanthosaurus*
4 *Rebbachisaurus*
5 *'Supersaurus'*
6 *'Ultrasaurus'*
7 *Zigongosaurus*

**Camarasaurus (below)**
This 59ft (18m) long sauropod is similar in general build to *Brachiosaurus,* but it is rather smaller. *Camarasaurus* had a short skull with a blunt snout. The nostrils are placed high on the head, just in front of the eyes, and it was once thought that this feature indicated that the sauropods lived underwater with just the tops of their heads showing. It has even been suggested that the high nostrils indicate that *Camarasaurus* had an elephant-like trunk! The body is held horizontally as the fore and hindlimbs are almost the same length.

**Comparative Sizes (right)**
**1** *Camarasaurus:* l. 59ft (18m).
**2** *Brachiosaurus:* l. 74ft (22·5m); h. 39ft (12m).

an angle to the neck as in diplodocids. The neck is somewhat shorter than that of *Apatosaurus* and *Diplodocus,* consisting of 12 vertebrae which are relatively short and compact. Unlike the diplodocids, the neck ribs are quite long and slender, and overlap one another quite considerably. The spines near the base of the neck, and at the front of the trunk are, as in other sauropods, deeply cleft to accommodate large ligaments which supported the neck. The 12 trunk vertebrae have relatively short, thick and heavily-scarred spines, and as in other sauropods the sides of the vertebrae are deeply excavated to form weight-saving pleurocoels. Unlike the neck ribs, those of the trunk are exceptionally long and stout, enclosing an enormous space for the chest and belly.

Five large back vertebrae are welded together in the hip region to support the massive pelvic bones which carry much of the weight of the animal. The tail is quite short compared with that of the diplodocids; there seem to have been 53 tail bones in the complete tail of the very well-preserved skeleton of *Camarasaurus* as distinct from the 82 of *Apatosaurus* and 73 of *Diplodocus.* The tail is also appreciably shorter because it lacks the thin whip-lash end so characteristic of the diplodocids.

The forelimb and hindlimb resemble those of other sauropods remarkably closely; the forelimb possessed one claw on its inner toe, while the hind foot bore claws on its three inner toes. One slightly unusual feature of *Camarasaurus'* limbs is their relative porportions. Whereas in diplodocids the humerus (upper foreleg bone) is only 2/3 the length of the femur (thigh bone),in *Camarasaurus* the humerus is very nearly eq̀ual to the femur in length (4/5 actually!). In the first reconstruction of *Camarasaurus* by H. F. Osborn and C.C. Mook in 1921, this observation so strongly affected their judgement that they restored the skeleton with shoulders that were higher than the hips. They had in fact exaggerated the natural pose of the animal by altering the position of the shoulder girdle. In 1925 Gilmore was able to correct Osborn and Mook's first attempt on the basis of the more-or-less complete Carnegie Museum skeleton of *Camarasaurus.* But even so the back of the animal has to be constructed practically horizontally, rather than sloping down toward the shoulders as is the case in diplodocids. This *trend* towards greater length of the forelimbs in some sauropods is taken to the extreme in brachiosaurids.

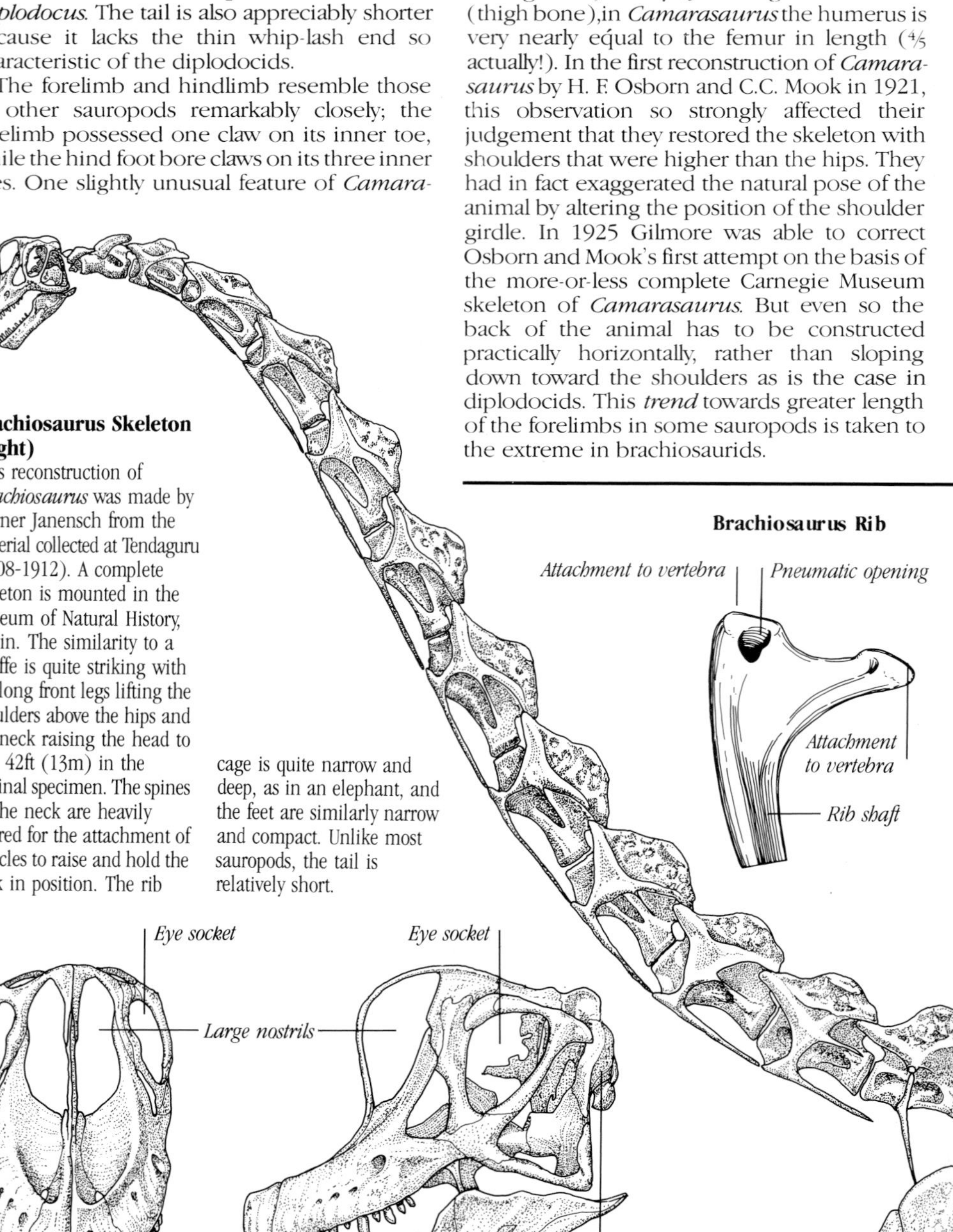


**Brachiosaurus Skeleton (right)**
This reconstruction of *Brachiosaurus* was made by Werner Janensch from the material collected at Tendaguru (1908-1912). A complete skeleton is mounted in the Museum of Natural History, Berlin. The similarity to a giraffe is quite striking with the long front legs lifting the shoulders above the hips and the neck raising the head to over 42ft (13m) in the original specimen. The spines on the neck are heavily scarred for the attachment of muscles to raise and hold the neck in position. The rib cage is quite narrow and deep, as in an elephant, and the feet are similarly narrow and compact. Unlike most sauropods, the tail is relatively short.

**Camarasaurus Skull (above)**
The skull of *Camarasaurus* is compact compared with that of diplodocids. The jaws are stout and support a closely packed array of chisel-like teeth. Above the level of the jaws the skull is high and spaciously designed. The large opening at the front of the skull is for extremely large nostrils. Immediately behind the nostril is the eye socket.

**Brachiosaurus Skull (right)**
In profile, this skull shows certain similarities to that of *Camarasaurus.* The jaws are stout and support large chisel-shaped teeth. The signs of heavy wear on these teeth suggest that these animals preferred abrasive plants. The unusual size of the nostrils may indicate either a powerful sense of smell, a resonating device or a cooling surface for the blood.

**Camarasaurus Skeleton (right)**
The skeletal reconstruction seen here is based on the work of Charles Gilmore. The proportions of the skeleton are notably different from the diplodocids. The skull is relatively large and deep, and is supported on a short neck which was evidently quite flexible. The ribs of the neck are long and slender and no doubt provided for the attachment of large muscles. The short neck means that the range of plants available to *Camarasaurus* must have been limited to the lower branches of trees and plants closer to ground level. As reconstructed here the shoulder region is at the same height as the hips and this is a reflection of the greater length of the forelimbs of *Camarasaurus.* In recent years it has been proposed that many sauropods were able to rear up on their hindlimbs in order to reach higher foliage. The large forelimbs and relatively short tail makes it seem unlikely that *Camarasaurus* could have done this.

## Brachiosaurus

*Brachiosaurus* ('arm reptile') takes its name from the prodigious length of its arms (forelegs) when compared with its hindlimbs. *Brachiosaurus* was first described by Elmer S. Riggs on the basis of a very incomplete skeleton that was discovered in 1900 at the Grand River Valley, Western Colorado. The original material,which was collected by the Field Museum of Chicago, consisted of various parts of the vertebral column, the pelvis, ribs,shoulder girdle and, most importantly from the point of view of diagnosis, the humerus and femur. Judging by the way the remains were preserved on site, it appeared that the original carcass of the animal probably settled into the sediment of a lake or river system in this area, but was disturbed somewhat later, perhaps by flood water, so that various parts of it were washed away as the carcass disintegrated, and so lost to us for ever.

The distinctive features of the bones of this large sauropod dinosaur were several. The vertebrae were large with the big pleurocoel cavities typical of all sauropod skeletons. Indeed these cavities were in some cases so large that the wall of bone down the middle of the vertebrae was practically paper thin, and was even broken through in some places. A striking feature of these vertebrae compared with those of most other sauropods is the absence of forked spines to accommodate a large neck ligament. The vertebrae also show rather complicated joints at the foot of the neural spines which served greatly to strengthen the joint between individual back vertebrae, and also provided them with an unexpected degree of flexibility. The pelvis is supported by five vertebrae, as in other sauropods. Unusually two tail bones,apparently coming from close to the hips, did not show any sign of pleurocoels. The dimensions of the humerus (80in, 204cm) and the femur (79·5in, 203cm) are, however, the most unusual among sauropods, in which the femur is always longer than the humerus, other than in this case. In fact so unusual was this feature that Riggs at first identified the humerus as a 'femur'. It was only after careful preparation and repair back in the laboratory that the true identity of these enormous bones emerged.

On the basis of this imperfect skeleton Riggs speculated upon the biology and habits of *Brachiosaurus* in an article in 1904. In this, he proposed that contrary to popular opinion of the time,the gigantic sauropods were probably not amphibious marsh dwellers, but were fully terrestrial animals comparable in most respects with animals such as the elephants of today. He based his argument upon the shape of the limbs and feet of these animals, rather narrow and deep chest, and the peculiar excavations and complexities of the vertebrae. The legs of large amphibious creatures such as hippos are relatively short and their feet are broad, the chest is barrel-shaped and their vertebrae

**Brachiosaurus Rib (left) and Sectioned Vertebrae (right)**
*Brachiosaurus* has many weight-saving features. The ribs in the chest region have a pneumatic opening near the top which leads to an air passage down the shaft of the rib. The cross section through a neck vertebra (top right) reveals the remarkable system of air spaces, while that of the back vertebra shows the extensive pleurocoels separated by a very thin sheet of bone (bony areas shown in red). The vertebra closely resembles an I-section girder.

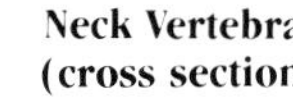


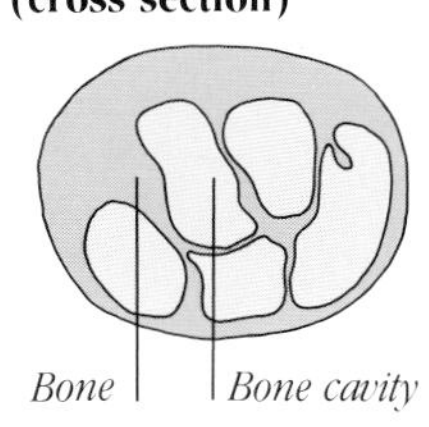


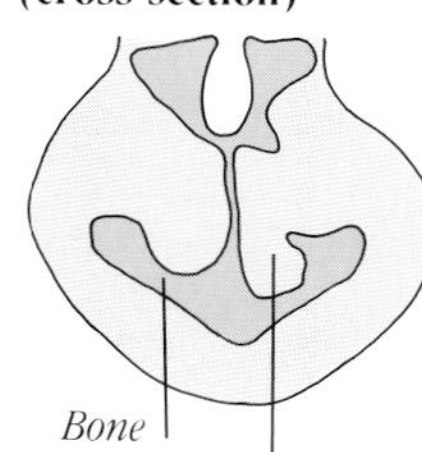


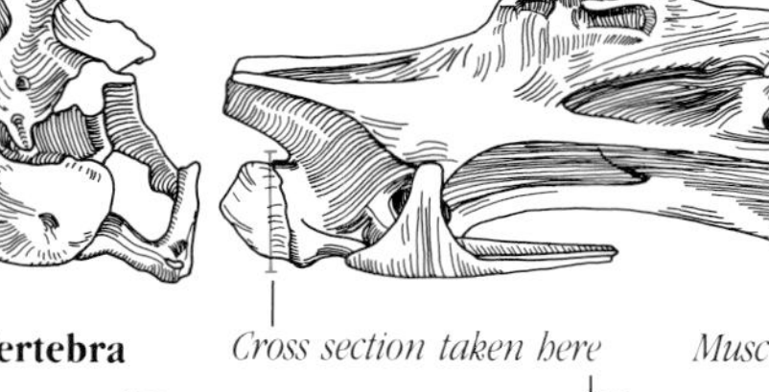


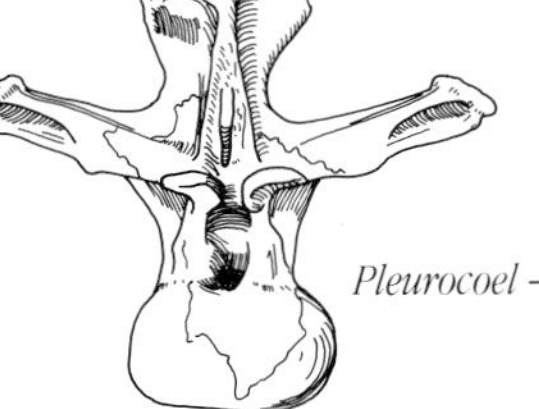


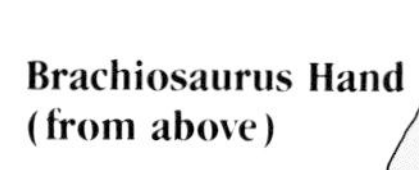

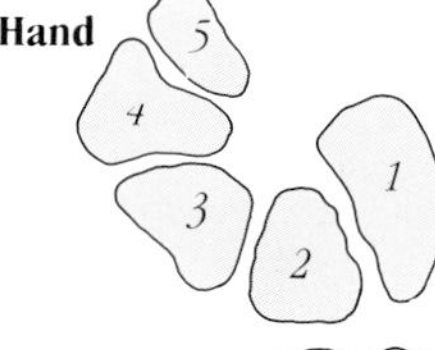


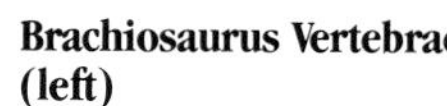

**Brachiosaurus Vertebrae (left)**
The neck vertebrae are long, narrow, elongated structures with a low spine on which muscles attached. The front end of the neck vertebra has a rounded surface that forms a strong and flexible joint against the cup-shaped depression on the rear of the vertebra in front of it. The back vertebrae are taller and squatter to withstand supporting the weight of this animal. The tall spine is scarred for the attachment of muscles; the large 'wings' projecting from its foot support the ends of the ribs. The red lines show where the cross sections are taken.

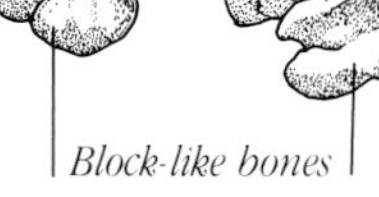


**Brachiosaurus Hand (left)**
This hand is remarkably specialised with very long metacarpals which are clustered closely together as can be seen in the top drawing. The toes (so far as they are known) have just one small bone on the end of each metacarpal except for the 1st toe which bears a small claw.

**Camarasaurus Foot (below)**
*Camarasaurus*' right foot has five short toes which are widely splayed to form a broad weight-bearing arrangement. The inner toe is larger and possesses a narrow curved claw which may have been used for self-defence. The foot of *Brachiosaurus* is only known from isolated bones.

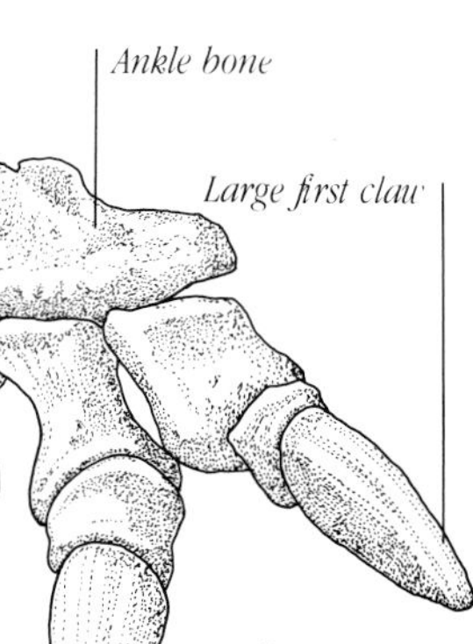


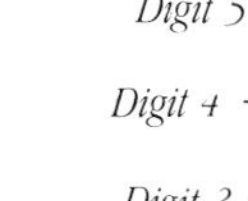

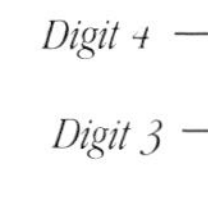

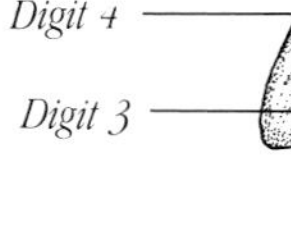

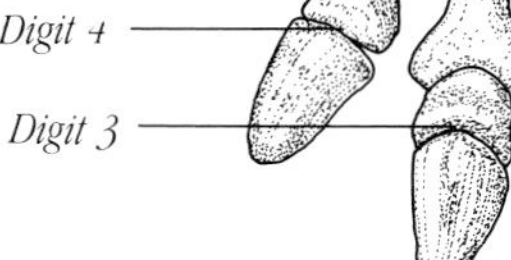

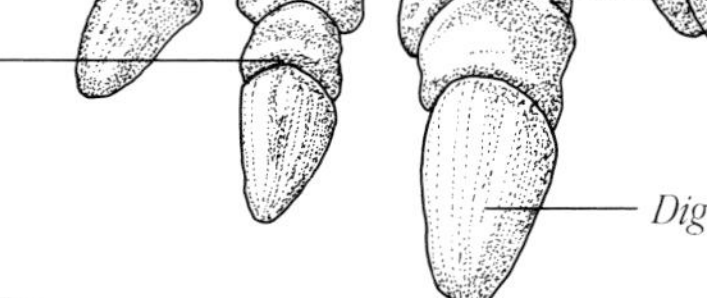

show none of the complexity seen in the giant sauropods. Riggs reasoned from these observations that sauropods were terrestrial rather than amphibious creatures. He even proposed that creatures such as *Diplodocus* and *Apatosaurus* were capable of rearing up on their hind legs, perhaps to browse on high foliage.

Bearing these characters in mind, Riggs suggested that *Brachiosaurus* was a peculiarly specialised sauropod with exceptionally long front legs, a strong yet flexible back and (he *guessed*) a relatively short tail. Riggs' conclusions have proved to be extremely far-sighted and accurate. Sadly, however, they were ignored by the majority of palaeontologists when they were first published, and it was not until the early 1970s that Riggs' comments were strongly supported by Robert T. Bakker (see later).

## Tendaguru and Brachiosaurus

Tendaguru is 40 miles (64km) inland from the east coast of Africa in Tanzania, which in 1907 was known as German East Africa. A series of very fortunate circumstances resulted in a very dramatic dinosaur discovery being made there – the African equivalent of Como Bluff or Dinosaur National Monument in the USA.

As recounted by Professor Edwin Colbert, in 1907 Herr W. B. Sattler, an engineering geologist prospecting for minerals in this largely uncharted part of the world, discovered weathered fragments of enormous fossil bones at Tendaguru. He reported these finds to the company he worked for. Very fortunately Professor Eberhard Fraas from Stuttgart, a noted authority on fossil reptiles, was in the colony at this time and was requested to visit the new site. Fraas established that the locality was incredibly rich in fossil vertebrates. He was able to collect several very fine fossil specimens and returned with them to Germany. These remains fired the interest of Dr W. Branca, then director of the Berlin Museum of Natural History, who determined to raise an expedition to collect the fossils from Tendaguru. In due course Drs Werner Janensch and Edwin Hennig of the Berlin Museum were put in charge of it.

The expedition, which lasted from 1908-1912, needed remarkable energy and co-ordination on the part of all participants and proved to be extremely expensive, both in terms of wages for the workers and in the necessary food and supplies. During the four year period over 250 tonnes of fossil bone were removed from the 4-5 square mile site at Tendaguru and carried on the heads and backs of native porters to the coastal port of Lindi for shipment to Berlin. This was obviously a colossal enterprise, but it was highly successful and it was matched by the dedication of the scientists in Berlin who put an enormous amount of effort into the preparation and study of the fossils.

The immense energy and skill that went into the Tendaguru Expedition was certainly rewarded handsomely. Among dinosaurian remains collected from Tendaguru which included *Kentrosaurus, Elaphrosaurus, Dicraeosaurus,* there was the skeleton of *Brachiosaurus.* Erected in the Natural History Museum (now in East Berlin) this must be the most impressive skeleton of any dinosaur in the world; it stands nearly 39ft (12m) tall, and the body is some 74ft (22·5m) long.

As Rigg surmised, *Brachiosaurus* is indeed an unusual sauropod. Its pose is totally unlike that of other sauropods because its back slopes upward from the hips to the shoulders, the forelimbs being considerably longer than the hindlimbs. The tail is quite short by the standard of diplodocid sauropods; and while the back vertebrae are massive and also deeply excavated by pleurocoels, the spines near the base of the neck and in the neck itself are not cleft to accommodate a large ligament. The neck vertebrae, of which there are 12 (as in *Camarasaurus*), are notably elongated; their sides are deeply excavated, the spines are relatively low and heavily scarred for muscle attachment, and the ribs are fused firmly to their sides.

The limbs and girdles which support this immense frame are stout and pillar-like. The forelimb ends in a rather narrow elephant-like five-toed foot which bears a single claw on its inner toe. The hindlimb is very similar to that of other sauropods, with the three inner toes of the foot bearing enlarged claws.

The head is similar in general shape and proportions to that of *Camarasaurus.* The jaws are quite sturdy and are lined with large, chisel-shaped teeth. Above the jaws the snout is quite flat and then rises in front of the eye region into enormously enlarged nostrils. Large recesses, which were apparently associated with the nostrils, extend forward on to the roof of the snout. There are also large cavities both in front and behind the eye, and the braincase is restricted to a relatively small area at the back of the skull.

## Other Brachiosaurids

In addition to the impressive remains of *Brachiosaurus* from North America and Africa, several other *Brachiosaurus*-like sauropods are known which constitute the brachiosaurid family.

*Haplocanthosaurus* ('single spined reptile') is based on two partial skeletons described by J. B. Hatcher in 1903. The remains were excavated from the Canyon City site in Colorado that was first exploited by M. P. Felch and O. C. Marsh in the 1870s. Although far from complete, the remains of the vertebrae are similar to those of *Brachiosaurus* and may perhaps justify placing this genus with other brachiosaurids.

*'Supersaurus',* a fragmentary skeleton discovered in 1972 by Jim Jensen in western Colorado, seems to have been even larger than *Brachiosaurus.* Estimates based on comparisons between the neck vertebrae and shoulder bones of these two dinosaurs suggest that *'Supersaurus'* may have stood 54ft (16·5m) tall with a body length of anywhere between 82-98ft (25-30m)! The name *'Supersaurus'* is used in quotation marks because it has not yet been scientifically described and named.

*'Ultrasaurus'* was found in 1979 in the same general area of Colorado as *'Supersaurus'* again by Jim Jensen, and it proved to be an even larger brachiosaurid. Still undescribed, the remains of this creature are rumoured to indicate an animal in excess of 98ft (30m) in length. Extrapolating from *Brachiosaurus,* which is estimated to have weighed anything up to 70 tonnes, *'Ultrasaurus'* may have tipped the scales at a staggering 130 tonnes.

*Rebbachisaurus* ('Rebbachi reptile') from Morocco and Tunisia and *Zigongosaurus* ('Zigong reptile') from Sichuan have also been referred to as brachiosaurids by some workers. Other brachiosaurid attributions are more dubious. *Astrodon* ('star tooth') based on spoon-shaped camarasaurid or brachiosaurid-type teeth, has been reported from Europe and North America over the past century but cannot be clearly allied to any particular group in isolation. *Pleurocoelus* ('side cavity'), based on cavernous vertebrae or isolated teeth, is again a

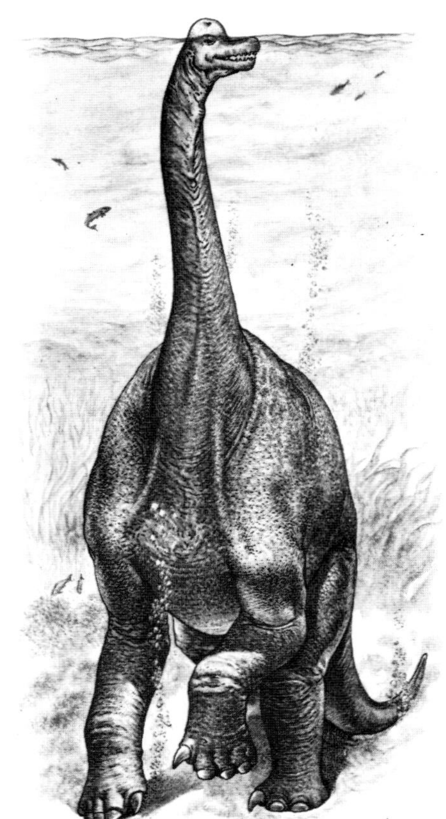

**The Underwater Dinosaur? (above)**
For some years it was thought that *Brachiosaurus* might have favoured an aquatic way of life, the nostrils on the top of its head acting as a snorkel. Recent analysis, however, indicates that *Brachiosaurus'* lungs would not have survived the water pressure that they would have experienced if this had been the case.

**Left:** *Camarasaurus lentus* in the Carnegie Museum of Natural History, Pittsburgh, Pennsylvania. The skeleton is in the position in which it was found.

practically meaningless genus. *Pelorosaurus* ('monster reptile'), based on a moderately large humerus from the Weald of Southern England, must be a very dubious brachiosaurid in the absence of any associated skeleton. Similarly, a large excavated vertebra from southern England referred to as *Ornithopsis* ('bird like'), originally likened to the vertebrae of birds and of flying reptiles such as pterosaurs, and similar vertebrae from Madagascar referred to as *'Bothriospondylus'* ('excavated vertebra') must both be considered dubious genera based on poor material.

## Probable Life-Style

*Brachiosaurus'* way of life has been the subject of much debate in recent years, as a result of which the long-forgotten views of Elmer Riggs have been unwittingly resurrected. For much of this century sauropods were thought to have been gigantic amphibious creatures that wallowed in swampy habitats. Several observations contributed to this view. Firstly, animals of this size and weight were not thought able to support themselves on land. Consequently they simply had to live in water where their bodies would have been buoyed up by displacement. Secondly, the position on the nostrils was widely interpreted as an adaptation for an aquatic way of life, allowing *Brachiosaurus* to breathe while almost completely submerged. Thirdly, their teeth were allegedly weak and only capable of cutting soft water plants.

Present-day opinions, however, all favour a land-living life-style for sauropods. This change of view was precipitated in 1971 by the publication of Robert T. Bakker's article which reassessed the evidence advanced in support of the amphibious way of life. Bakker showed that the pillar-like legs and relatively narrow feet, the deep, narrow rib cage, and the specially strengthened back were all features that were only consistent with land-living creatures. He argued that the long neck enabled these creatures to browse on high foliage rather like giraffes. Contrary to common belief, the teeth of *Camarasaurus* and *Brachiosaurus* do show evidence of having been quite heavily abraded, while many land animals have nostrils positioned near the top of the head (some aquatic ones do not for that matter!).

Further support for the terrestrial sauropod interpretation can be derived from the observation made by Professor Kenneth Kermack (London) in 1951 that if sauropods had lived in water they would have been unable to breathe! The water pressure at such depths, 33-39ft (10-12m) in the case of *Brachiosaurus*, would have collapsed its lungs, while the enormously high blood pressure would have caused heart failure. The deep-water snorkelling *Brachiosaurus*, so convincingly depicted by artists like Zdenek Burian and others, was thus utterly impossible.

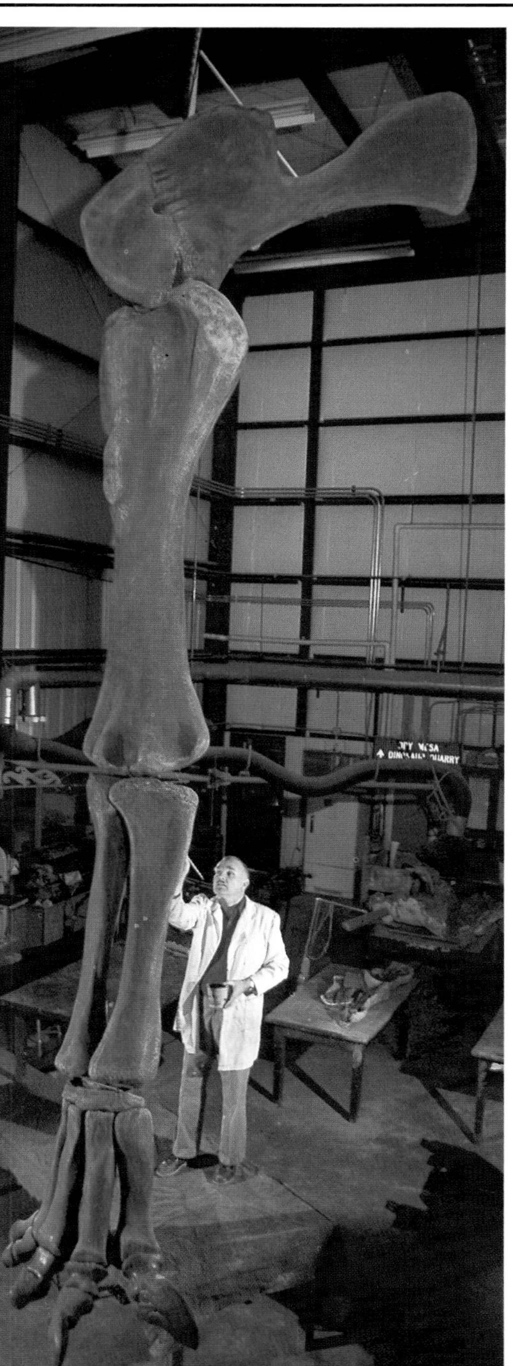

**Left:** James Jensen working on the front leg of the dinosaur popularly known as *'Ultrasaurus'*. In life this extraordinary creature may have been more than 98ft (30m) long, almost a third larger even than *Brachiosaurus*!

**Below:** This skeleton of *Brachiosaurus* in the Humboldt Museum, Berlin, is about 39ft (12m) tall. Discovered at Tendaguru in Tanzania, it is the largest mounted dinosaur skeleton in the world. Note the length of the forelimbs.

**Below:** James Jensen gives scale to the enormous scapula of *'Supersaurus'* that he found in the Dry Mesa Quarry, Colorado, in 1972. The can contains shellac with which the fossil is treated to preserve it after exposure to the air.

**Above:** The skull of a *Camarasaurus* being excavated by Tobe Wilkins, a preparator at the Dinosaur National Monument in Utah. This picture shows particularly well the long chisel-like teeth lining *Camarasaurus'* jaws.

# Miscellaneous Sauropods

In addition to the reasonably well represented and distinctive sauropods such as the diplodocids, camarasaurids and brachiosaurids described earlier, a large number of less well-known sauropods are known,whose fossil remains have been reported from practically every continent. Some of these will be discussed below, while many others are listed on page 97 as either 'valid' or 'dubious' genera, depending on how well-preserved the material is. In addition, several factors relating to the general biology or way of life of sauropods will be discussed.

*Opisthocoelicaudia* ('posterior cavity tail') is a recently described sauropod from Mongolia. The incomplete skeleton of *Opisthocoelicaudia* was discovered in 1965 during a Polish-Mongolian Expedition to the Gobi Desert. The carcass of the animal had evidently been buried before it had time to disintegrate; however neither the head nor the neck was recovered from the site. Magdalena Borsuk-Bialynicka, who described the skeleton in 1977, suggested that the carcass may have been attacked by carrion feeders (perhaps tyrannosaurids since *Opisthocoelicaudia* comes from rocks of late Cretaceous age). Some of the fossilised bones (femur and pelvis) apparently show some evidence of gnawing, so this may explain the absence of both the head and neck!

The skeleton of *Opisthocoelicaudia* is rather like that of most non-brachiosaurid sauropods in its general shape and proportions. The back vertebrae have well-developed pleurocoels and the ones near the neck have deeply-cleft spines to accommodate a large neck ligament (ligamentum nuchae). In addition, the individual spines of more posterior vertebrae have swollen and roughened sides and tops which indicate the areas of attachment of other powerful ligaments and muscles.In their general shape and proportions the back vertebrae most resemble those of *Camarasaurus*. Six vertebrae are fused together to form a sacrum for

**Vulcanodon (below)**
This restoration shows what we think the sauropods of the early Jurassic looked like; this is *Vulcanodon*, but *Barapasaurus* probably looked very similar. The animal is shown with a bulky body and pillar-like legs in accordance with the information that we have on these dinosaurs. In neither case is a skull known and so the head illustrated is of necessity somewhat conjectural. Teeth found near *Vulcanodon's* remains are those of a carnivore, but they probably belonged to a predator not *Vulcanodon*.

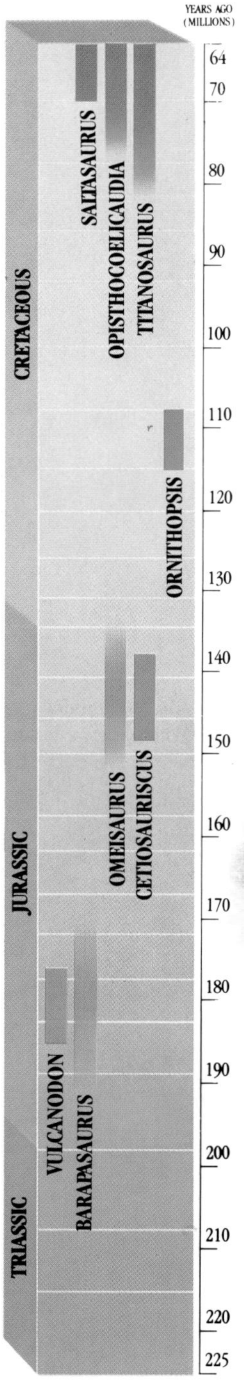

**Family Tree (below)**
This cladogram must be approached with caution, as it is very difficult to sort out the relations of this group of poorly known sauropods. *Barapasaurus* and *Vulcanodon* are separated from the others as they are distinct geologically and to some extent anatomically. *Opisthocoelicaudia* occupies its own branch because of its unusual tail vertebrae.

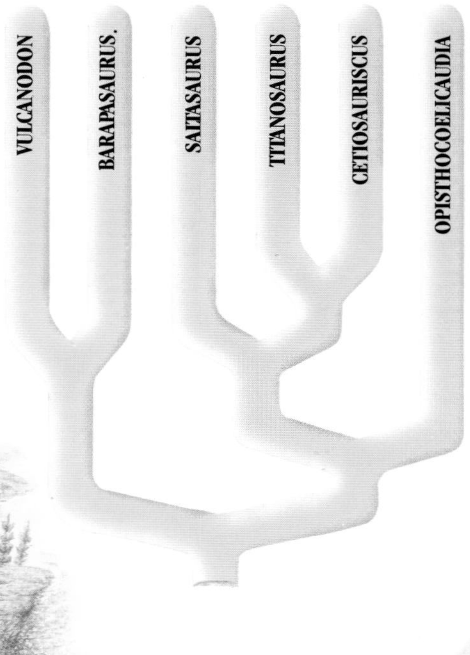

VULCANODON
BARAPASAURUS
SALTASAURUS
TITANOSAURUS
CETIOSAURISCUS
OPISTHOCOELICAUDIA

YEARS AGO (MILLIONS)
CRETACEOUS
JURASSIC
TRIASSIC
SALTASAURUS
OPISTHOCOELICAUDIA
TITANOSAURUS
ORNITHOPSIS
OMEISAURUS
CETIOSAURISCUS
VULCANODON
BARAPASAURUS
64 70 80 90 100 110 120 130 140 150 160 170 180 190 200 210 220 225

**Time Chart (left)**
*Barapasaurus* and *Vulcanodon* date from the earliest Jurassic and no doubt lived alongside some of the later prosauropods. Many and varied sauropods are known, albeit imperfectly, in the late Jurassic and again a considerable number are known in the Cretaceous Period. *Saltasaurus* and *Opisthocoelicaudia* are from the late Cretaceous.

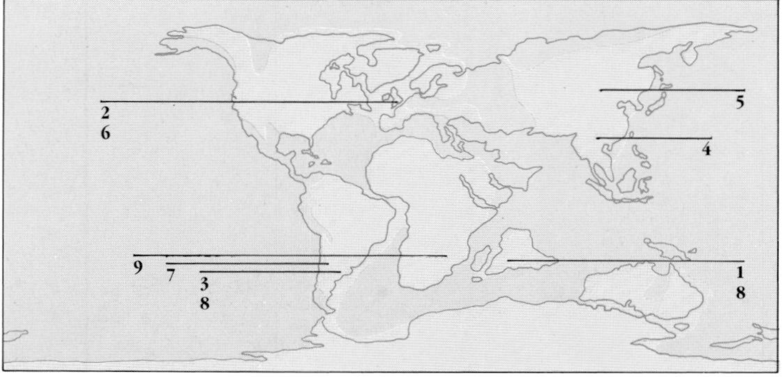


**Map (left)**
1 *Barapasaurus*
2 *Cetiosauriscus*
3 *Laplatasaurus*
4 *Omeisaurus*
5 *Opisthocoelicaudia*
6 *Ornithopsis*
7 *Saltasaurus*
8 *Titanosaurus*
9 *Vulcanodon*

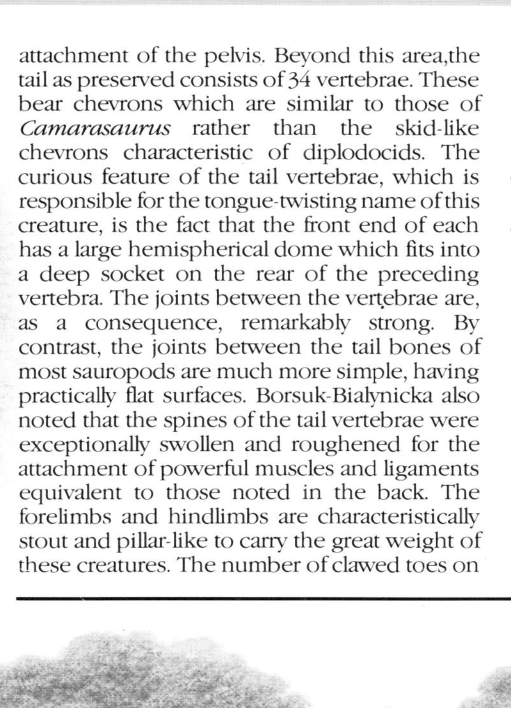

attachment of the pelvis. Beyond this area,the tail as preserved consists of 34 vertebrae. These bear chevrons which are similar to those of *Camarasaurus* rather than the skid-like chevrons characteristic of diplodocids. The curious feature of the tail vertebrae, which is responsible for the tongue-twisting name of this creature, is the fact that the front end of each has a large hemispherical dome which fits into a deep socket on the rear of the preceding vertebra. The joints between the vertebrae are, as a consequence, remarkably strong. By contrast, the joints between the tail bones of most sauropods are much more simple, having practically flat surfaces. Borsuk-Bialynicka also noted that the spines of the tail vertebrae were exceptionally swollen and roughened for the attachment of powerful muscles and ligaments equivalent to those noted in the back. The forelimbs and hindlimbs are characteristically stout and pillar-like to carry the great weight of these creatures. The number of clawed toes on the feet of this dinosaur are unknown at present. In terms of limb proportions, a factor that Jack McIntosh and David Berman consider of importance in at least some sauropods, the humerus is reported to be about three-quarters of the length of the femur. This falls mid-way between typical diplodocid and typical camarasaurid limb proportions.

## Biology and Probable Habits

The well-preserved nature of the limb and girdle bones of *Opisthocoelicaudia* allowed Borsuk-Bialynicka to attempt muscular restorations of both fore and hindlimbs. This showed that, unusually, there was little or no evidence for the massive and powerful muscles which run along the sides of the tail and insert upon the hindlimb (caudi-femoralis muscle). This is a muscle which almost always provides the main source of power for the stride in dinosaurs and most other reptiles. In *Opistho-*

**Opisthocoelicaudia (above)**
In its general body proportions *Opisthocoelicaudia* resembles *Camarasaurus* but it does have a number of peculiarities. The heavy pillar-like legs support a bulky body; the tail is held out straight and the shoulders are quite high. Unfortunately the head and neck are unknown; here we have speculatively given it a *Camarasaurus*-type, but it may have had a more slender-snouted *Nemegtosaurus*-type head. Until more material is found, this must remain a matter of conjecture.

**Saltasaurus (above)**
*Saltasaurus,* quite a recent discovery, is of great interest because it shows that some sauropods bore bony armour. Large round plates of bone are scattered across the hide and between them lie masses of small nodules. As shown the tail was flexible and could have supported the body when *Saltasaurus* reared on its back legs in its efforts to obtain food.

1 2 3

**Comparative Sizes (left)**
**1** *Opisthocoelicaudia:* 1. 39ft (12m)
**2** *Saltasaurus:* 1. 39ft (12m).
**3** *Vulcanodon:* 1. 21ft (6·5m)

*coelicaudia,* however, the posterior portion of the ilium (pelvic bone) in notably enlarged and roughened as if for the attachment of unusually powerful muscles; perhaps these were the main propulsive muscles instead? Quite why *Opisthocoelicaudia* should have had such an unusual arrangement of limb muscles is not immediately obvious.

The structure of the back vertebrae, particularly those close to the neck, led Borsuk-Bialynicka to suggest that the neck was not only flexible but that the vertebrae were relatively short, as they are in the neck of *Camarasaurus.* The evidence also pointed towards the back being held in an essentially horizontal position,or with perhaps a very slight downward slope from the shoulders to the hips.

The tail, which is shorter even than that of *Camarasaurus,* appears to have created the greatest problems of interpretation. Firstly, the tail bones when articulated naturally tend to rise slightly passing backwards from the hips, instead of falling toward the ground as in other sauropods. Secondly, the ball-and-socket joint between each tail vertebra is rare. Examples of some living reptiles with tail vertebrae of this type include a variety of fresh-water turtles; some of these are reported to use their tails as anchors to prevent themselves from being carried away in fast-flowing streams. Such a use in the case of *Opisthocoelicaudia* is plainly absurd. Other uses of this type of tail include its apparent function as a prop when on land. Borsuk-Bialynicka favoured this latter notion. The tail and rear legs were envisaged as a tripod arrangement which would allow these animals to rear up and reach higher branches for browsing. In fact she drew a parallel between *Opisthocoelicaudia* and the giant extinct ground-sloths (such as *Megatherium)* of South America. The latter seem to have been shuffling high browsers, which spent their time permanently balanced on their hind legs and tail, leaving their forelimbs free to grasp vegetation. A *permanent* tripodal posture was not suggested for *Opisthocoelicaudia,* merely that this was perhaps a favoured position for feeding.

## Sauropod Relations

Apart from the peculiarities in the tail, the greatest resemblance seems to lie with the *Camarasaurus*-like sauropods, and this possibility underlies the placing of it in the camarasaurid section of the table on page 97. If this is so, then it must be a very late representative of this predominantly late Jurassic group. However, the evidence so far is inconclusive, and so, while advancing this hypothesis, it seems sensible to adopt a cautious approach, and include the colour and skeletal restorations of *Opisthocoelicaudia* in this section of miscellaneous sauropods.

One outside possibility is that this skeleton belongs to the diplodocid sauropod *Nemegto-*

**Sauropod Armour (below)**
Recent work in Argentina has resulted in the discovery that some sauropods had bony armour plating. The first plates to be described are those of *Saltasaurus* and *Laplatasaurus,* and some are shown below. One type of plate with a low mid-line ridge has been referred to *Laplatasaurus;* the others are regarded as typical of *Saltasaurus.* These are variable in size and shape ranging from large, ridged plates (below middle) to the sheets of densely-packed, tiny nodular bones illustrated below right.

**Omeisaurus Skull (right)**
This skull is unusual when compared with those of other sauropods. It is wedge-shaped in side view and has typically sauropod struts of bone dividing large skull spaces. However, the nostrils are much nearer the front of the snout than in other sauropods. Though appearing to be toothless, there are sockets for at least 32 teeth in the upper jaw and 28-34 in the lower. The drawing is based on one included in Dong Zhiming's 1983 review of dinosaurs of south-central China.

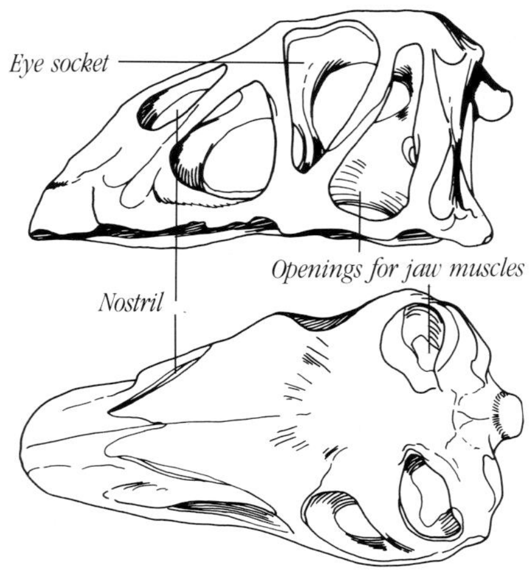

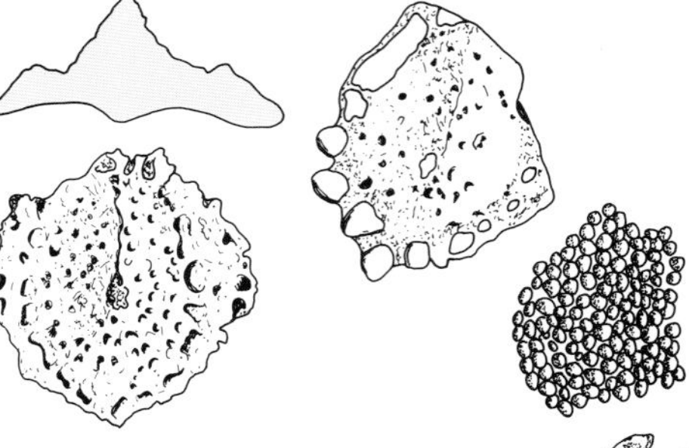


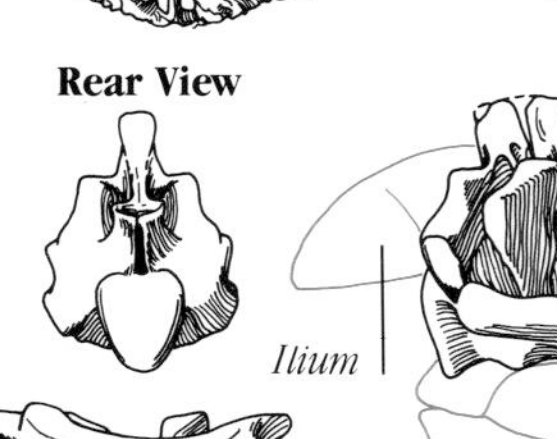


**Barapasaurus Sacrum and Pelvis (above)**
There are four vertebrae in the sacrum, all firmly fused together. On either side, the ribs are short, stout and welded together to form a sacral yoke. This attached firmly to the inner surface of the ilium.

**Ornithopsis Vertebra (below)**
Seen here in three views (rear, side and front), this vertebra is very similar to that of *Brachiosaurus,* and may indicate a relationship. The large weight-saving pleurocoels are particularly noticeable.

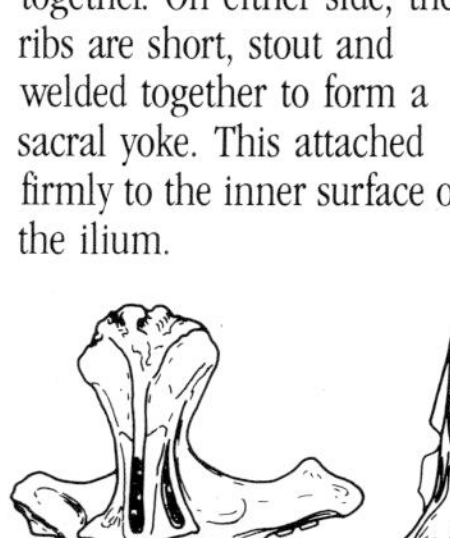

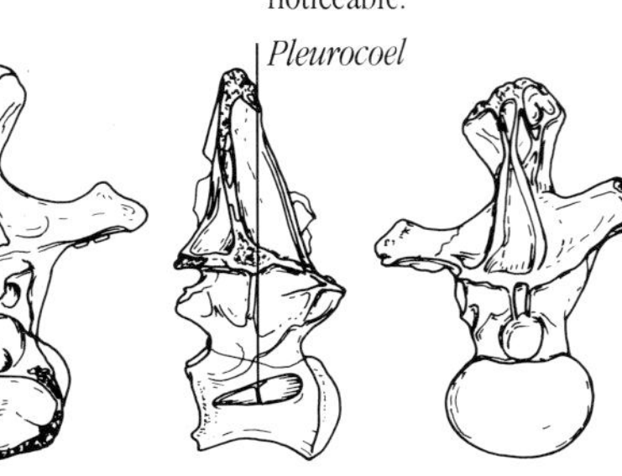


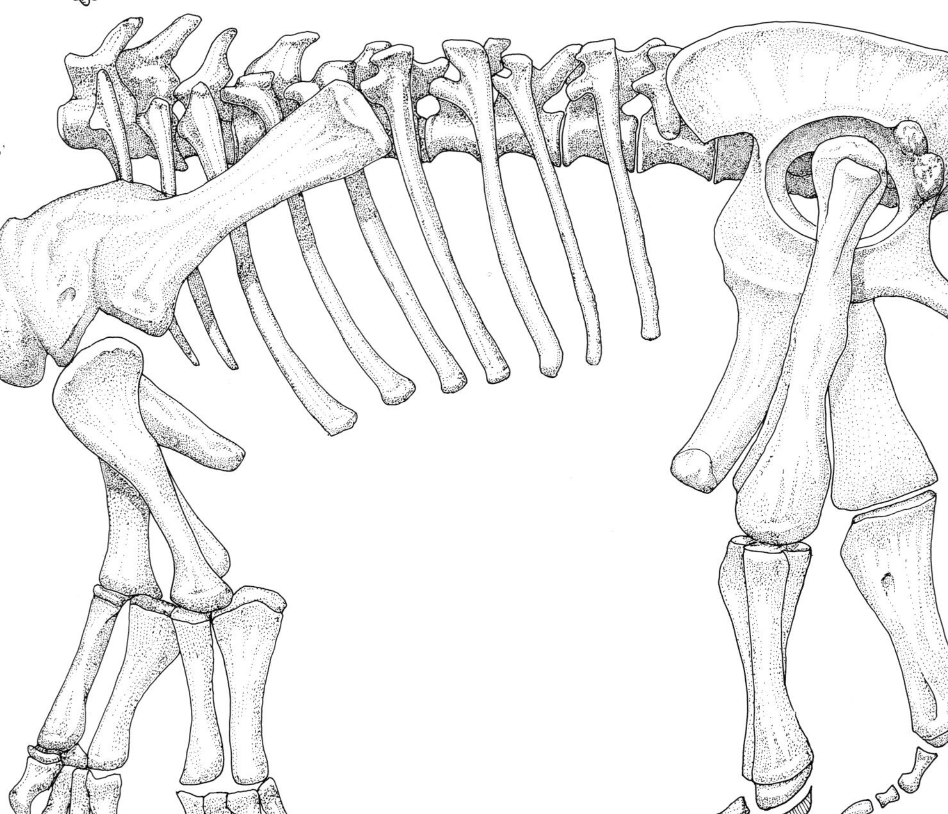

*saurus.* Both *Nemegtosaurus* and *Opisthocoelicaudia* are found in the same geological formation of the late Cretaceous. Since *Nemegtosaurus* is known only from a skull and *Opisthocoelicaudia* is known only from a headless skeleton, the temptation to place the head with the skeleton is great. However, I feel that the story of the head of *Apatosaurus* provides a salutary warning against taking anatomical short-cuts such as this. The fact that *Brachiosaurus, Camarasaurus, Diplodocus, Apatosaurus, Barosaurus* etc are all approximate contemporaries in the late Jurassic surely indicates that several distinct types of sauropod may well have lived together in the late Cretaceous.

Remains of an unusual sauropod *Saltasaurus* ('reptile from Salta Province') were first reported by José Bonaparte and Jaime Powell in 1980. They come from late Cretaceous rocks in north western Argentina and although incomplete provide unexpected evidence concerning the appearance of some sauropods. The remains of *Saltasaurus* appear to derive from several individuals, rather than an isolated skeleton. The general proportions and construction of the main skeletal elements (backbone and limbs) are typically sauropod-like. Points worthy of mention include spines in the neck and back region which are not cleft, tail vertebrae which are rather stout and have a reversed ball-and-socket arrangement, and chevrons which are not skid-like. However,of greatest interest was the discovery of two types of bony armour associated with these remains: fairly large, oval plates which were perhaps rather widely scattered in the skin; and a dense layer of smaller round or angular bony studs which were apparently widely spread across the back and sides of the animal.

This first clear record of armour-plating in sauropods may well prove to be an important one because it could lead to the re-identification of several supposed ankylosaur specimens elsewhere in the world. For example, *Titanosaurus* ('Titan reptile'),another sauropod from Argentina first described in 1893, was later redescribed in 1929 along with some fragments of bony armour found in the same area; these latter were referred to as an ankylosaur *Loricosaurus.* The supposed ankylosaur remains almost certainly belong to the sauropod *Titanosaurus.* There are also considerable similarities between *Titanosaurus* and *Saltasaurus,* although Bonaparte and Powell were not prepared to say that *Saltasaurus* and *Titanosaurus* belong to the same genus.

Described in 1972 by Mike Raath (Zimbabwe), *Vulcanodon* ('Volcano tooth') was found in early Jurassic rocks in Zimbabwe. It is of some importance because it may be one of the earliest sauropods to have been discovered to date. Unfortunately the skeleton, which was completely redescribed by Mike Cooper (Zimbabwe) in 1984, is far from complete. Cooper was able to demonstrate that *Vulcano-*

**Opisthocoelicaudia Skeleton (below)**
This reconstruction is based on the work of Magdalena Borsuk-Bialynicka. This dinosaur is currently only known from its headless skeleton so its relationships with other sauropods are not precisely known. It has an extremely unusual tail: the ball-and-socket joint between vertebrae works by means of a socket in the *rear* of each vertebra — unlike any other sauropod. As a result the joints between vertebrae are remarkably strong. Note the massive pelvic region.

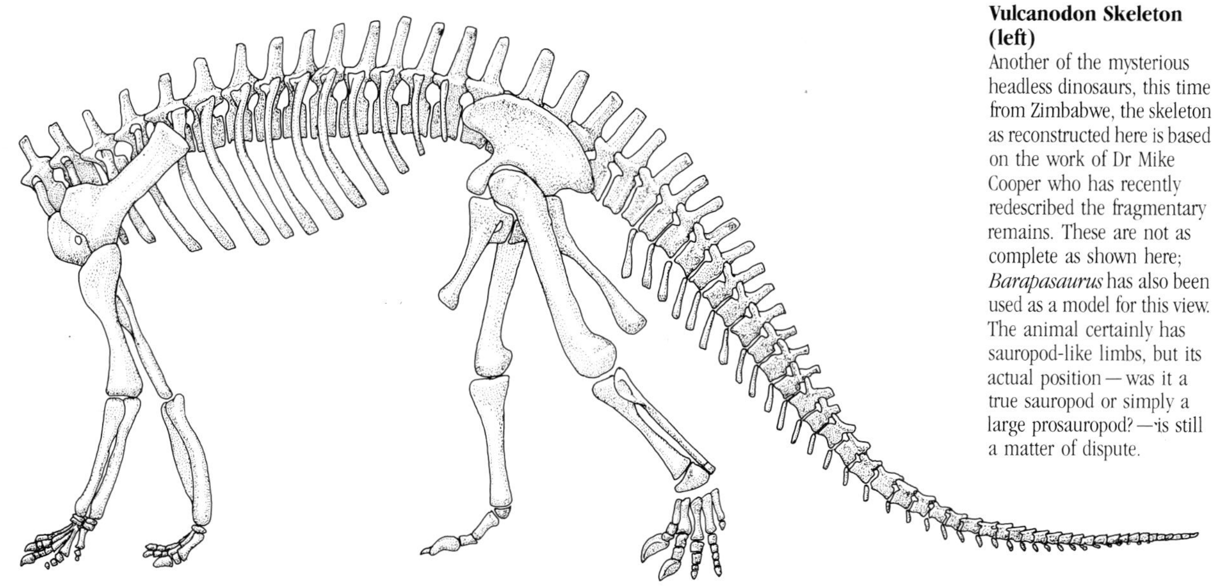

**Vulcanodon Skeleton (left)**
Another of the mysterious headless dinosaurs, this time from Zimbabwe, the skeleton as reconstructed here is based on the work of Dr Mike Cooper who has recently redescribed the fragmentary remains. These are not as complete as shown here; *Barapasaurus* has also been used as a model for this view. The animal certainly has sauropod-like limbs, but its actual position — was it a true sauropod or simply a large prosauropod? — is still a matter of dispute.

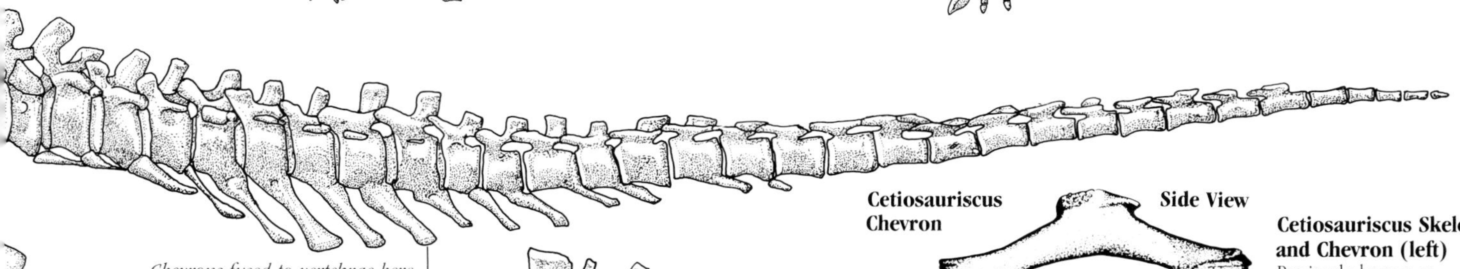

*Chevrons fused to vertebrae here*

**Cetiosauriscus Chevron**

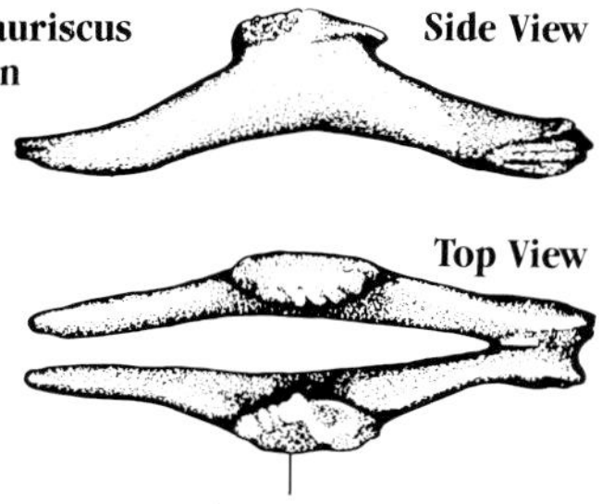

**Side View**

**Top View**

*Area of attachment to tail bone*

**Cetiosauriscus Shoulder and Forelimb**

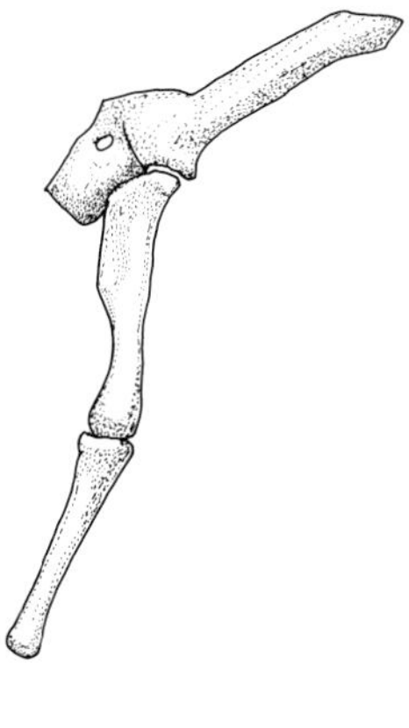

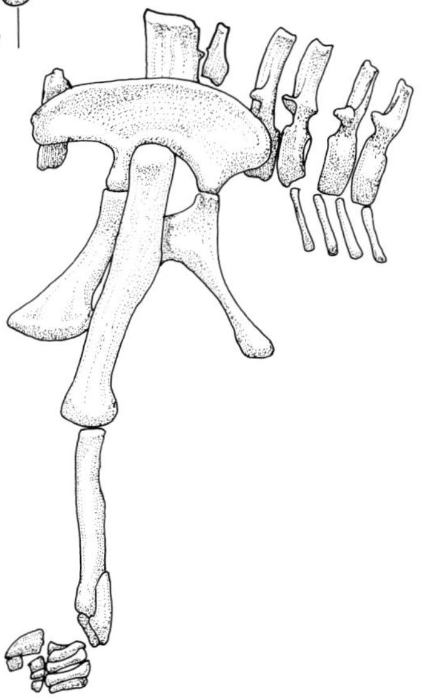

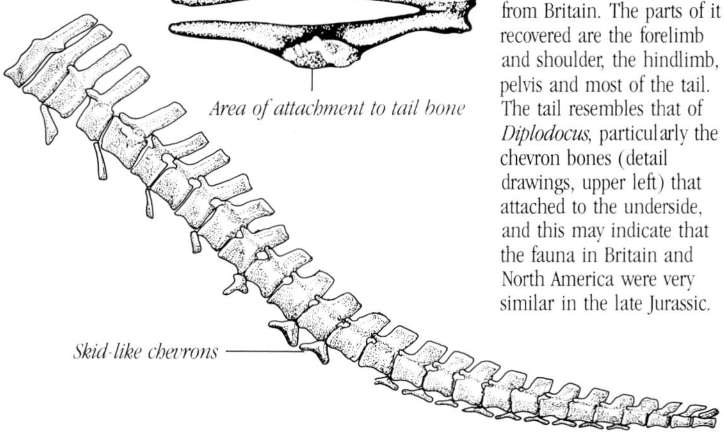

*Skid-like chevrons*

**Cetiosauriscus Skeleton and Chevron (left)**
Previously known as *Cetiosaurus,* this skeleton from the late Jurassic is one of the best sauropod skeletons from Britain. The parts of it recovered are the forelimb and shoulder, the hindlimb, pelvis and most of the tail. The tail resembles that of *Diplodocus,* particularly the chevron bones (detail drawings, upper left) that attached to the underside, and this may indicate that the fauna in Britain and North America were very similar in the late Jurassic.

*don* was a very large, quadrupedal saurischian dinosaur. It shows several prosauropod features, particularly in the hips, but he claimed that in other ways (particularly in subtle changes in the structure of the vertebrae), *Vulcanodon* was very much what might be expected of an early sauropod. Obviously Cooper's arguments are based primarily on shades of opinion rather than clear and unambiguous fact. Yet again, better preserved material may help to clear up the status of *Vulcanodon.*

*Barapasaurus* ('big reptile') is another sauropod from the early Jurassic, but this time of India. The remains of *Barapasaurus* which were apparently very abundant (300 fossils were recovered in 1961) indicated the presence of a *Diplodocus*-sized sauropod. At present *Barapasaurus* is not completely described by Dr S. L. Jain and colleagues (Calcutta), but from preliminary reports it would appear that it had typical sauropod limbs and girdles; and although cavernous excavations in the sides of the neck and back vertebrae are not developed fully, there are depressions in these areas indicating the beginnings of pleurocoels.

Unfortunately no skull material is known so far. Serrated-edge theropod-like teeth have been reported near the remains of both *Barapasaurus* and *Vulcanodon,* but rather than supposing that these teeth came from these dinosaurs, current opinion considers that they belonged to predatory dinosaurs that were feasting upon these remains.

## Possible Life-Style

In the 1830s when the first sauropod bones were collected in Oxfordshire and came into the possession of Dean William Buckland at Oxford University, they were identified as whale bones by Georges Cuvier. At the time Cuvier was the world's leading comparative anatomist and his views were widely respected. However, by the early 1840s Richard Owen had noticed that these remains, rather than being of whales (which are mammals), were more likely to have been those of whale-like reptiles—perhaps gigantic whale-sized crocodiles. He therefore coined the name *Cetiosaurus* ('whale-reptile') for these remains. A few years later (1848) more limb bones of *Cetiosaurus* were discovered; these looked remarkably like those of land-living dinosaurs that Owen had described, rather than whale-like reptiles. Finally in 1869 a fairly complete skeleton was discovered in the same area of Oxfordshire by Professor John Phillips (Buckland's successor); these showed clear dinosaur affinities. Despite the weight of this evidence, Owen was very reluctant to abandon the aquatic life-style that he proposed for his cetiosaurs. One of the main reasons for this was the absence of a well-preserved hip region in this creature (one of Owen's key dinosaur characteristics). It was T. H. Huxley who finally asserted that *Cetiosaurus* was a dinosaur in 1869.

Despite the long-held belief that sauropods were amphibious creatures, the majority of palaeontologists now support the idea that they were primarily terrestrial creatures similar to the elephants of today. Riggs and Bakker have provided powerful arguments in favour of this view based on the structure of the limbs and rib cage. In addition sauropods display several other structural characteristics of note.

(i) Pneumatic ducts and cavities. The large and extensive pleurocoels in the neck and back vertebrae have been mentioned previously, and such features undoubtedly served to lighten the skeleton as far as possible. This is clearly an adaptation associated with living on land where bodily support under the effects of gravity are critical in large animals. Large aquatic animals (e.g. whales) have vertebrae equally as large as sauropods but these show no developments of pleurocoels or comparable weight-saving devices because their body weight is buoyed up by displacement. The particularly large sauropods such as *Brachiosaurus* even go so far as to develop pneumatic openings into the ribs in order to save weight. It seems most likely that these so-called pneumatic spaces or openings were air-filled. Living birds (and extinct pterosaurs) which also need to save weight in their bodies in order to fly efficiently, have similar openings and excavations in their vertebrae and limb bones. These we know are filled with air by connections from their complicated lung/air-sac system; it seems likely that sauropods had a similar type of arrangement.

(ii) Energy-saving ligaments. Another fairly common feature among non-brachiosaurid sauropods is the development of cleft spines in the neck and back vertebrae.The cleft spines provide a deep trough in which probably lay a thick, rope-like ligament, roughly equivalent to the ligamentum nuchae of quadrupedal mammals, such as the horse. In horses this powerful ligament runs from the spines in the shoulder region along the back of the neck to insert on the rear edge of the skull. It effortlessly holds the head in its normal raised position. By this means the horse and many relatively heavy-headed quadrupeds save a great deal of muscular energy expenditure that would otherwise have to be used merely to hold the head in its normal position. In the case of sauropods it is not the head that is heavy, but rather the inordinately long neck. The massive neck ligament served therefore to hold the long, heavy neck of sauropods clear of the ground effortlessly. The neck ligament was also very probably connected via the tops of the back and hip spines to the tail vertebrae so that the neck and tail vertebrae tended to counter-balance one another. Such a system whereby the tail and neck were suspended against one another may have held the tail as well as the neck clear of the ground while on land, and may account for the rarity of tail-drag markings associated with sauropod footprint trackways.

Having gone to some lengths to 'prove' that sauropods were indeed terrestrial creatures, the reader must not suppose that I exclude sauropods from water altogether: just as elephants today wallow, so may have sauropods in the Mesozoic. Incontrovertible proof of this comes from some remarkable sauropod footprints unearthed by Roland T. Bird in the late 1930s in Texas. One remarkable series of footprints found in Bandera County shows a sauropod apparently walking on its front legs alone! No traces of its hindfeet are seen. Evidently the animal was floating in moderately deep water and moving along by kicking the bottom with its front feet. A little way along the track one large, clawed hindfoot was kicked down leaving its clear mark and the forefoot prints change direction: its back legs were obviously being used to steer the animal along!

Footprint trackways discovered by R. T. Bird and others have also provided an insight into other aspects of the biology of sauropods. Bird found other tracks in Bandera County which showed that more than 20 large sauropods had been moving together across an open area in the same direction; this evidence seems to indicate herding behaviour in these animals. Bob Bakker proposed that herding would have been a reasonable behaviour pattern for such creatures. While fully adult sauropods would undoubtedly have been almost immune to attack by even the largest of 'carnosaurs', juveniles may well have provided easy prey. Thus when moving to new feeding grounds, sauropods may well have clustered together in herds, with the vulnerable young individuals in the centre of the herd protected by the larger adult animals.

## Defence, Diet and Reproduction

In the case of diplodocids, the long, whip-lash tail very likely served as a weapon of defence against predatory 'carnosaurs'. In addition, most non-brachiosaurid sauropods could probably rear up onto their hind legs so that the massive forelimbs could be used as weapons. The curious feature of all sauropods is that they retain one enlarged, curved claw on the inner toe of the forefoot. The only obvious explanation for the persistence of this claw is an otherwise highly specialised elephantine foot is that it served as an important defensive weapon. Quite how brachiosaurids dealt with predators is uncertain; they had relatively short tails and were probably unable to rear on to their hind limbs. It is possible that like elephants today, brachiosaurids were so large that they were virtually invulnerable to attack.

The immense size of sauropods and their disproportionately small heads and simple teeth has prompted considerable speculation concerning their likely diet. In the days when sauropods were considered to be amphibious swamp dwellers, a diet of soft aquatic water weeds was popular; this seemed to fit well with the weak, pencil-like teeth of forms such as *Diplodocus.* Some early alternative suggestions arose from the belief that plant material could not have been sufficiently nutritious for animals of such immense bulk; thus they became variously fish eaters (piscivores) [Tornier] or oyster eaters (molluscivores) [Holland]. Neither of these latter proposals found much favour in subsequent years and most interpretations now suggest a diet of terrestrial plants. The argument about the weak teeth and jaws of sauropods has been partly deflected by the proposal that the

teeth served as rake-like devices in order to strip leaves or pine-needles from branches and twigs. Instead of chewing these items, they were simply swallowed and passed to a powerful muscular gizzard containing sharp, abrasive pebbles; these, rather than teeth, were used to pulp the tough plant tissues in readiness for digestion. The true stomachs of sauropods were probably like huge fermentation tanks in which vast quantities of plant matter were slowly broken down to release their nutrients—somewhat similar to the large complex stomach of cattle.

Two main types of teeth have been noted among sauropods, the narrow pencil-like teeth of diplodocids and the broader, spoon-like teeth of camarasaurids and brachiosaurids. These differences probably reflect different dietary preferences in these groups of sauropods; however at the moment the differences in tooth structure cannot be directly correlated with specific plant types.

With regard to reproductive behaviour, the enormous size of sauropods has frequently provoked the suggestion that these creatures, unlike the majority of reptiles, gave birth to live young. It seems inconceivable that a 30 or 40 tonne female sauropod could lay a clutch of eggs without crushing them. Nevertheless sauropod eggs are occasionally discovered. Aix-en-Provence (France) has produced numerous eggs attributed to the sauropod *Hypselosaurus* and in the Willow Creek Formation, Montana, from which hadrosaurid nests were recovered, Jack Horner also found some smaller sauropod-like eggs. The curious observation that Horner was able to make about both egg localities was that at least one sauropod seemed to be laying its eggs in batches of two in straight lines, presumably laying them while on the move! Perhaps this unusual technique avoided the almost inevitable prospect of crushing the eggs if full clutches were laid at a single nest site.

**Below:** Excavation at Altan Ula in the Gobi Desert in 1965 of *Opisthocoelicaudia skarzynskii.* Frustratingly neither the head nor neck of this sauropod were recovered from the site.

**Above:** The discovery of footprint trackways seems to indicate that, like elephants today, sauropods were herding animals. The fully grown adults probably protected the young.

**Fending off Predators (below)**
While the sheer size of an adult sauropod probably rendered it virtually immune from attack by carnivorous predators, it is possible that in the event of such an attack the large claw on the inner toe of each front foot could be used as a defensive weapon, the sauropod rearing onto its hind legs using its tail as a counterbalance.

### Diplodocid Genera

**Valid**
*Apatosaurus*
*Barosaurus*
*Cetiosauriscus*
*Dicraeosaurus*
*Diplodocus*
*Mamenchisaurus*
*Nemegtosaurus*

**Dubious**
*Amphicoelias*
*Atlantosaurus*
*Brontosaurus*
*(=Apatosaurus)*
*Elosaurus*
*(=Apatosaurus)*

### Brachiosaurid Genera

**Valid**
*Brachiosaurus*
*Pelorosaurus (?)*
*Rebbachisaurus*
*'Supersaurus'*
*'Ultrasaurus'*
*Zigongosaurus (?)*

**Dubious**
*Astrodon*
*Bothriospondylus*
*Dinodocus*
*'Hughenden sauropod'*

### Camarasaurid Genera

**Valid**
*Camarasaurus*
*Euhelopus*
*Opisthocoelicaudia (?)*
*Tienshanosaurus*

**Dubious**
*Asiatosaurus*
*Caulodon*
*Chiayüsaurus*
*(=Euhelopus)*
*Morosaurus*
*Uintasaurus*

### 'Cetiosaur' Genera

A poorly defined group of sauropods (mainly Jurassic): relatively short necks, no cleft spines, few pleurocoels.

**Valid**
*Austrosaurus*
*Cetiosaurus*
*(in part)*
*Haplocanthosaurus (?)*
*Patagosaurus*
*Rhoetosaurus*
*Volkheimeria*
*Zizhongosaurus (?)*

**Dubious**
*Amygdalodon*
*Chinshakiangosaurus*
*Cardiodon*
*Dystrophaeus*
*Shuosaurus*

### 'Titanosaur' Genera

A poorly defined, mainly Cretaceous group of sauropods: proportions similar to 'cetiosaurs', tail vertebrae have cupped front surface, possibly armoured.

**Valid**
*Antarctosaurus*
*Hypselosaurus*
*Laplatasaurus*
*Saltasaurus*
*Titanosaurus*

**Dubious**
*Aegyptosaurus*
*Aepisaurus*
*Alamosaurus*
*Algoasaurus*
*Argyrosaurus*
*Bothriospondylus*
*Campylodoniscus*
*Lametasaurus*
*Loricosaurus*
*(=Saltasaurus?)*
*Macrurosaurus*
*Microcoelus*

### Primitive Sauropod Genera

(early Jurassic forms)

**Valid**
*Barapasaurus*
*Shunosaurus*
*Vulcanodon (?)*

### Other Sauropods

This table lists names of other sauropods, mostly poorly preserved, whose names have figured in the scientific literature, but whose status is very dubious. Accurate classification is practically impossible

*Chondrosteosaurus*
*Chubutisaurus*
*Clasmodosaurus*
*Datousaurus*
*Dinodocus*
*Gigantosaurus*
*Hoplosaurus*
*Hypsibema*
*Ishyrosaurus*
*Mongolosaurus*
*Morinosaurus*
*Nanshiungosaurus*
*Neosodon*
*Ohmdenosaurus*
*Omeisaurus*
*(=Euhelopus?)*
*Oplosaurus*
*Ornithopsis*
*Parrosaurus*
*(=Hypsibema)*
*Pleurocoelus*
*Sanpasaurus*
*Succinodon*
(a mollusc!)
*Tapinosaurus*

# Fabrosaurids & Heterodontosaurids

As described earlier ornithischian dinosaurs are all herbivores and can be recognised by several peculiar features: (i) a bird-like pelvis — from which the group gets its name; (ii) a peculiar horn-covered predentary bone at the tip of the lower jaw; (iii) a trellis-like arrangement of long bony tendons along the backbone. There is also in most ornithischians a peculiar bone (palpebral) in the eye cavity. There are several distinct types of ornithischian dinosaur: ornithopods, ceratopians, pachycephalosaurs, stegosaurs and ankylosaurs.

## Ornithopod Dinosaurs

These are generally very abundant ornithischians found in rocks that date from the late Triassic until the very end of the Cretaceous. The early ones are typically small, agile creatures that run bipedally on their long back legs and have small front legs; later ones tend to be much larger although they are still mostly bipedal. The pachycephalosaurs ('bone-heads', pages 146-151) are often included with the ornithopods, but two Polish workers (Maryanska and Osmolska) consider them to be so unusual that they have separated them off from all other ornithopods.

The earliest ornithopod (possibly a heterodontosaurid) is claimed to be an animal named *Pisanosaurus* ('Pisano's reptile') from the late Triassic of Argentina. However, the very fragmentary remains of this animal do not make it clear even if it is an ornithischian, let alone an ornithopod, so we should perhaps note the existence of this fossil and hope that more material is discovered that will prove exactly what sort of animal this is.

Fabrosaurids have been known for a surprisingly long time. Well over a century ago, Sir Richard Owen described several small jaws and teeth which had been found in quarries in the Purbeck area of Dorset in southern England by an amateur collector of fossils, Samuel Beckles. These jaws were small and slender and the teeth had long, narrow roots and leaf-shaped crowns, with spiky edges. Owen supposed that these belonged to a small herbivorous lizard since they were so small and gave them the name *Echinodon becklesii* which literally means 'Beckles' spiky-tooth'.

Unfortunately no more remains of *Echinodon* have been found since Owen's first description. Another fragmentary piece of jaw with a few teeth was found much later (1964) in southern Africa. The teeth look remarkably like those of *Echinodon,* however this fossil came from rocks which were dated at the boundary between Upper Triassic and the Lower Jurassic, while those of *Echinodon* are from Upper Jurassic/Lower Cretaceous boundary. The African fossil was named *Fabrosaurus australis* ('Fabre's southern reptile') and eventually gave its name to the Family.

It was not until the early 1970s that anyone had any clear idea of the true appearance of

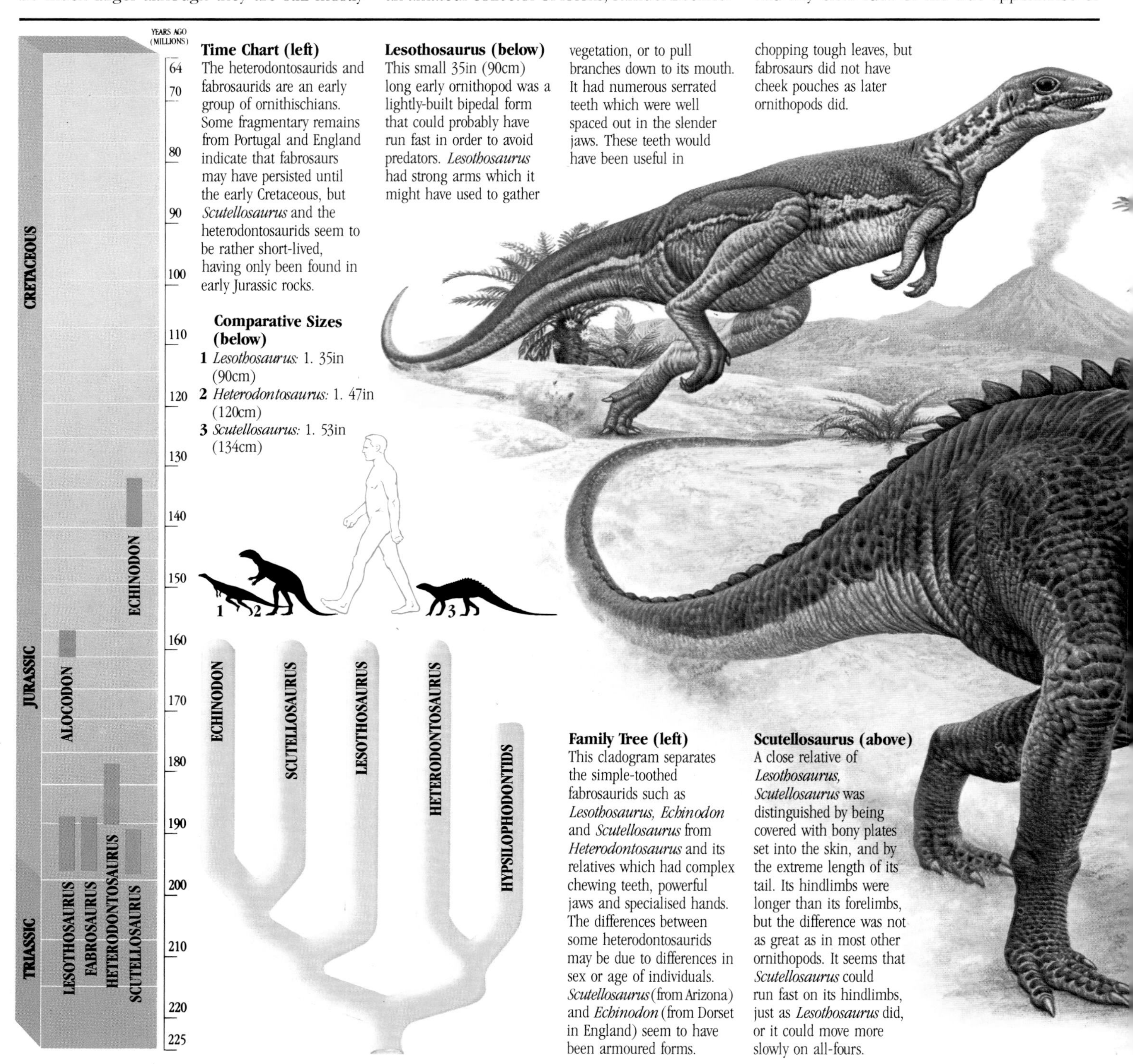


**Time Chart (left)**
The heterodontosaurids and fabrosaurids are an early group of ornithischians. Some fragmentary remains from Portugal and England indicate that fabrosaurs may have persisted until the early Cretaceous, but *Scutellosaurus* and the heterodontosaurids seem to be rather short-lived, having only been found in early Jurassic rocks.

**Comparative Sizes (below)**
1 *Lesothosaurus:* l. 35in (90cm)
2 *Heterodontosaurus:* l. 47in (120cm)
3 *Scutellosaurus:* l. 53in (134cm)

**Lesothosaurus (below)**
This small 35in (90cm) long early ornithopod was a lightly-built bipedal form that could probably have run fast in order to avoid predators. *Lesothosaurus* had strong arms which it might have used to gather vegetation, or to pull branches down to its mouth. It had numerous serrated teeth which were well spaced out in the slender jaws. These teeth would have been useful in chopping tough leaves, but fabrosaurs did not have cheek pouches as later ornithopods did.

**Family Tree (left)**
This cladogram separates the simple-toothed fabrosaurids such as *Lesothosaurus, Echinodon* and *Scutellosaurus* from *Heterodontosaurus* and its relatives which had complex chewing teeth, powerful jaws and specialised hands. The differences between some heterodontosaurids may be due to differences in sex or age of individuals. *Scutellosaurus* (from Arizona) and *Echinodon* (from Dorset in England) seem to have been armoured forms.

**Scutellosaurus (above)**
A close relative of *Lesothosaurus, Scutellosaurus* was distinguished by being covered with bony plates set into the skin, and by the extreme length of its tail. Its hindlimbs were longer than its forelimbs, but the difference was not as great as in most other ornithopods. It seems that *Scutellosaurus* could run fast on its hindlimbs, just as *Lesothosaurus* did, or it could move more slowly on all-fours.

either *Echinodon* or *Fabrosaurus*. It had been recognised that Owen had been wrong about *Echinodon* being a lizard. Its teeth had long roots which were borne in deep sockets in the jaw bones; this feature made it an archosaur rather than an ancient lizard and, more specifically, the leaf-shaped and spiky-edged crown to the tooth was typical of those seen in ornithischian dinosaurs. New information about these mysterious fabrosaurids came from an expedition to southern Africa organised by Professor Kermack of University College, London. Among the many fossils collected during the expedition, were the remains of the partial skeleton of a small animal which came from the Upper Triassic 'Red Beds' of Lesotho. Preparation of this fossil revealed the true appearance of a fabrosaurid. Being of the same geological age as the original *Fabrosaurus* and having teeth which seemed virtually identical, this new animal was also named *Fabrosaurus australis* when it was finally described in detail

**Heterodontosaurus (left)**
As the name suggests ('mixed tooth reptile'), *Heterodontosaurus* is distinguished by its differentiated teeth. That is, unlike most other dinosaurs, we can recognise three quite distinctive kinds of teeth in each jaw: sharp cutting teeth at the front, fangs just behind these, and broad ridged teeth in the cheek region. *Heterodontosaurus* fed on tough vegetation which it nipped of with its 'incisors', punctured with its 'canines', and ground up with its cheek teeth.

**Map (below)**
**1** *Abrictosaurus*
**2** *Alocodon*
**3** *Echinodon*
**4** *Fabrosaurus*
**5** *Geranosaurus*
**6** *Gongbusaurus*
**7** *Lanasaurus*
**8** *Lesothosaurus*
**9** *Nanosaurus*
**10** *Scutellosaurus*
**11** *Trimucrodon*

by Dr Tony Thulborn. However, since then this animal has undergone a name change! It is now claimed that the original material of *Fabrosaurus,* since it is only a small piece of jaw with a few teeth, cannot be closely compared to the newer skeleton so it is impossible to know exactly how similar these animals really were. To be safe, the new skeleton was renamed *Lesothosaurus australis.* (Indeed, if you look back in some older dinosaur books, you may well find this dinosaur illustrated and described as *Fabrosaurus*).

*Lesothosaurus* is the best example of a fabrosaurid dinosaur known to date and in fact establishes a very common body shape for all later ornithopod dinosaurs. *Lesothosaurus* was a small (about 35in, 90cm from head to tail), lightly-built animal with extremely slender, long hind legs and rather short forelimbs; its tail was long, and counterbalanced the front part of its body so that it could stand and run on its hind legs, leaving its hands free to perform other duties. Unfortunately, the hand of *Lesothosaurus* is not well-preserved; most probably it had five rather stubby little fingers ending in small claws which would have been ideal all-purpose hands, a little like our own.

Looking at the skeleton in more detail (see below), the head is rather small and triangular in outline, with a very large eye cavity and large open spaces behind for the jaw muscles. There is also a fairly large opening in front of the eye which may have been for a salt gland. The snout is short and quite pointed, with a very slender lower jaw tipped by the horn-covered predentary bone, and the teeth are small, leaf-shaped and separate. This general shape and arrangement suggests that these animals were probably herbivorous, although they may have taken a little carrion or perhaps even insects on occasions. The horn-covered predentary bone at the front of the lower jaw would have formed a very effective device for chipping off pieces of foliage. In life, these animals may well have used their narrow snout and beak to feed on small succulent shoots of plants. They did not really chew up their food because their teeth and jaws were apparently not designed to do this; they simply broke the food into small pieces before swallowing it. (As we shall see later, some of the more advanced ornithopods chewed their food a great deal.) There are reptiles living today that have very similar teeth and jaws to those of *Lesothosaurus,* and they give us a clue to the way that it may have fed.

*Conolophus,* the land iguana of the Galapagos, has small, leaf-like teeth, slender jaws and a short snout. It feeds on plants, including cacti, and occasionally takes small animals. Like (we suppose) *Lesothosaurus,* the land iguana does not chew its food, but merely bites off small pieces which it then swallows. One result of not chewing up plant food is that most of the nutrients are locked inside the tough plant tissues and they therefore have to spend a very long time in the stomach and gut, being

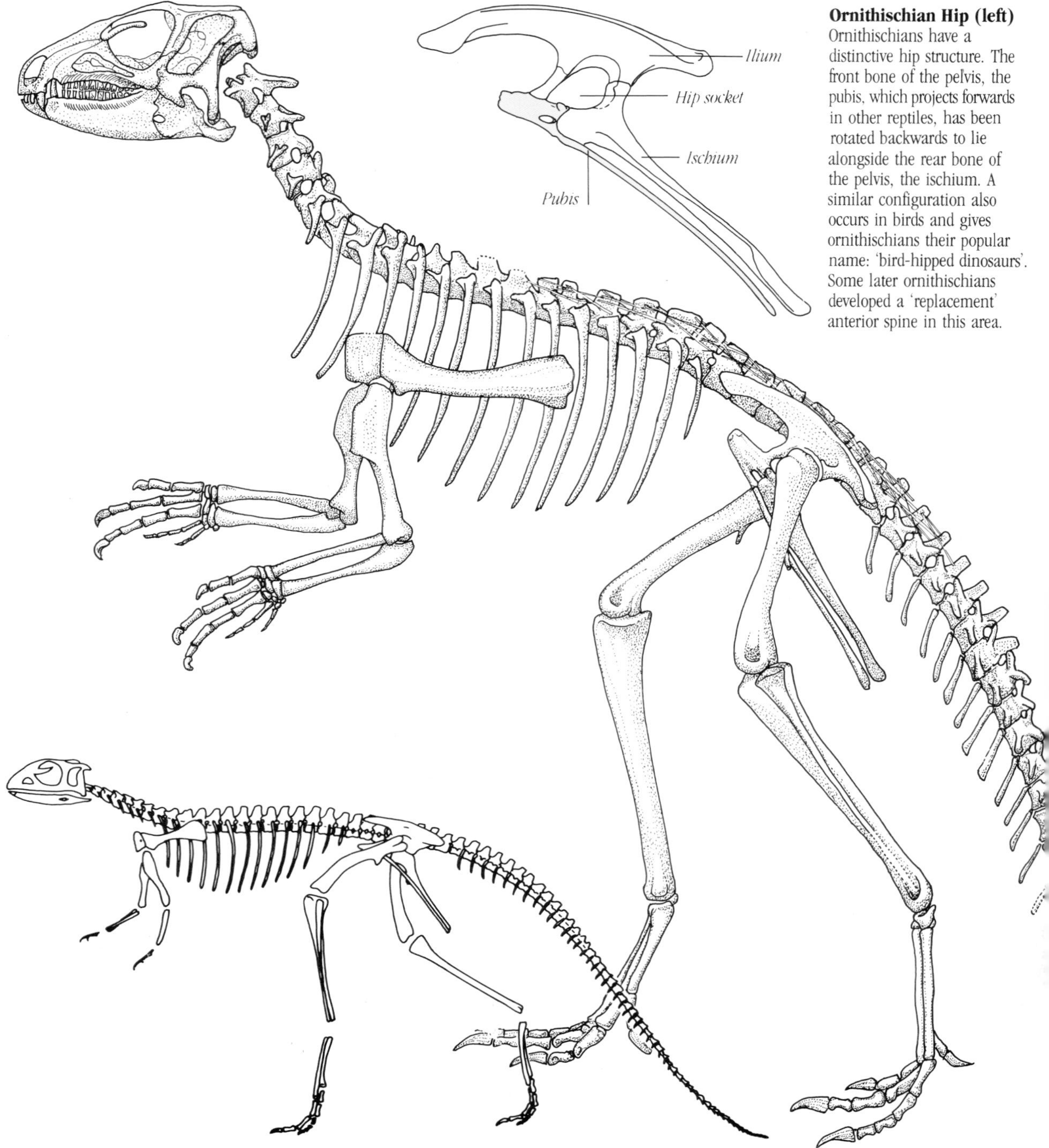


**Heterodontosaurus Skeleton (right)**
The reconstructed skeleton of *Heterodontosaurus* shows it to be a lightly-built, agile animal, typical of the early ornithopods. In particular notice how the foot bones (metatarsals) and lower leg bones are elongated relative to the upper leg bone (femur). This kind of long, slender hind leg is a sure sign of a fleet-footed runner which presumably relied on speed to escape from its predators. The long, tapering tail acted as a counterbalance for the front half of the body and was probably held out almost horizontally above the ground when the animal ran. The front limbs are very robust compared with those of *Lesothosaurus* and in particular the fingers and wrist bones are well-developed. Also visible are the bony rods lying along the backbone, which are characteristic of bipedal ornithischians; they were present in order to stiffen the back, hips and tail.

**Lesothosaurus Skeleton (right)**
This animal is another typical early ornithopod but it does not show the specialisations of a robust front leg and fused lower hind leg bones seen in *Heterodontosaurus.* In that form the front leg may have been used for digging or in defending itself or possibly even in tearing down vegetation. In both forms the neck is long and flexible, perhaps useful for getting the head into vegetation to pick off shoots or buds, or for keeping an eye out for predators. The long tail is typically ornithopod.

**Ornithischian Hip (left)**
Ornithischians have a distinctive hip structure. The front bone of the pelvis, the pubis, which projects forwards in other reptiles, has been rotated backwards to lie alongside the rear bone of the pelvis, the ischium. A similar configuration also occurs in birds and gives ornithischians their popular name: 'bird-hipped dinosaurs'. Some later ornithischians developed a 'replacement' anterior spine in this area.

fermented and digested. Both of these animals have quite a large belly. The iguana is very stout bodied and has a large belly slung between its front and back legs while *Lesothosaurus'* belly is situated between its legs underneath the hips so that it can maintain its balance and run unhindered on its hind legs. This point is important because while *Lesothosaurus* may well have fed like *Conolophus*, that is about as far as the comparison goes. *Conolophus* is a very sluggish reptile, in many respects it does not need to be anything else, after all its food does not need to be chased and it has no natural predators (apart from Man) to escape from. *Lesothosaurus* however, relied upon its speed and agility to survive in the world of the late Triassic.

Looking at the remainder of the skeleton, we see a pattern common to all later ornithopods. The neck is quite long, slender and was presumably very flexible. The back, hips and tail were stiffened and supported by narrow, bony tendons and the tail was long in order to balance the body over the hips. The forelimbs are quite short compared to the hindlimbs and have a small grasping hand. The hind legs of this animal are very long with the skin and toes being particularly elongate. These proportions are typical of fast running animals, such as antelopes and gazelles living today. We therefore suspect that fabrosaurids were an improbable mixture: iguana-like in feeding habits, and yet the equivalent of small gazelle-like creatures of the late Triassic and early Jurassic periods. Indeed, unprotected as it was by either bony armour or defensive weapons such as large teeth or claws, *Lesothosaurus* would have relied heavily upon its great turn of speed and agility to avoid being caught by the large and fearsome thecodontians and the smaller and equally agile theropod dinosaurs that inhabitated their world. One could easily imagine these animals living a life very similar to that of gazelles in the African bush, nervously picking off shoots and leaves from low shrubs and constantly on the lookout for predators.

Another rather unusual fabrosaurid, *Scutellosaurus* ('bony-plate reptile'), was discovered and described only very recently by Professor Edwin Colbert. Discovered in Arizona, but from rocks of an age similar to those in which *Lesothosaurus* and *Fabrosaurus* were found, this animal is peculiar because it has very well-preserved bony plates (or scutes) rather like those found on the back of a crocodile. Perhaps what we are seeing here is an alternative strategy for survival to that of *Lesothosarus*. *Scutellosaurus* is armour-plated as well as being moderately fleet of foot, judging by its limb proportions, and could be thought of as balancing two alternative ways of surviving predation: one technique would be to be extensively armour-plated—this makes an animal both heavier and slower and therefore more easily caught, but its armour would make it unpalatable (the armadillo uses just this type of

**Heterodontosaurus Hand (below)**
This is particularly well-made for a bipedal dinosaur. The individual finger bones are long and slender, and bear well-developed claws. The smallest finger does not seem to be quite so off-set as in some ornithischians, so the hand appears more symmetrical. The wrist bones are small and numerous, suggesting flexibility. *Heterodontosaurus* was probably able to manipulate vegetation quite adeptly.

**Heterodontosaurus Foot (below right)**
The foot bones are long and slender, reflecting that the animal possessing them was both a runner, and small and light—the foot did not have to be specially strengthened to bear the animal's weight. Notice how the smallest toe is reversed relative to the others. This may have given the foot extra surface area for bearing the animal's weight. The metatarsal bones are particularly elongated.

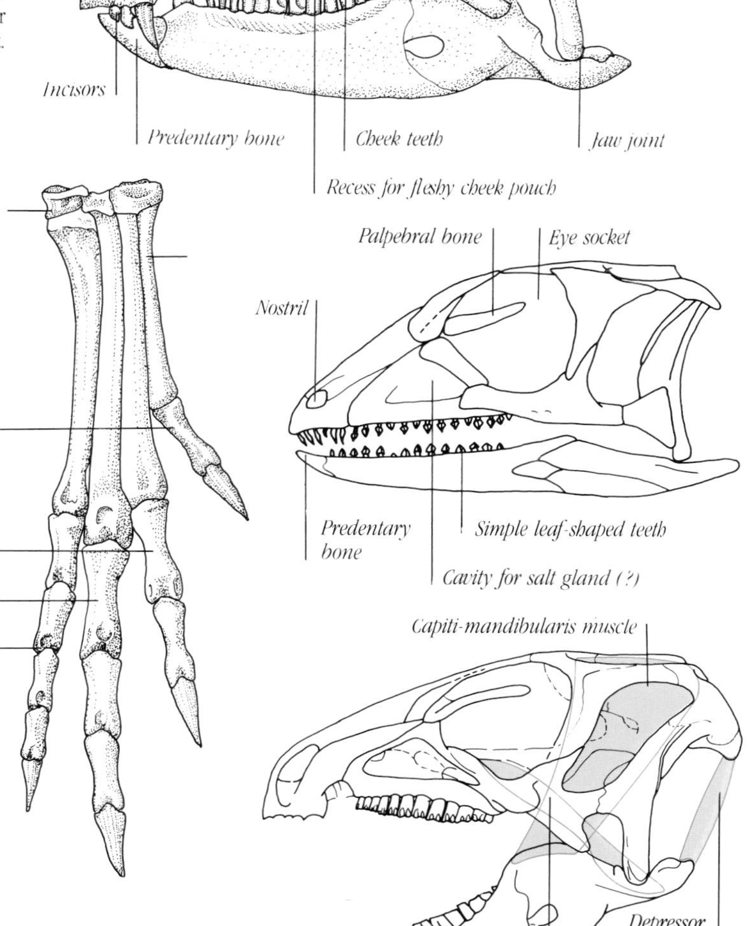


**Heterodontosaurus Skull (left)**
In this form the teeth may have chewed up food, rather than simply cropping it. There are various theories about how the chewing action was produced: it might have been caused by back and forwards movement of the lower jaw, but perhaps more likely, the lower jaw might have rotated relative to the upper jaw as it closed. The large tusks are probably a male characteristic.

**Lesothosaurus Skull (left)**
The cheek teeth here are much more slender and leaf-like, used perhaps for shredding food, but not chewing it. This form may have had a salt-gland and if so this could indicate that the animal lived in an arid environment, needing to conserve its body water. Doing this leads to a build-up of body salts which must be disposed of by the salt-gland. Note how the small teeth are separated.

**Tuskless Heterodontosaurus Skull (left)**
The lack of tusks in this specimen may indicate that it is a female of a tusked *Heterodontosaurus* since in other respects it is almost identical (compare with skull shown at top left). If this is so then it shows that even if the tusks were used in feeding, they were also used as a sexual signal—distinguishing males from females. The muscles shown on the skull are responsible for closing the jaw and also for producing the forces which cause the chewing action of the jaw.

technique). Alternatively, the less armour an animal carries, the greater its agility and speed and the better its chances of avoiding capture altogether, but if it is captured it is completely unprotected. *Scutellosaurus* seems almost caught in the act of balancing these strategies.

In addition to the quite well-preserved skeletons of *Lesothosaurus* and *Scutellosaurus*, there are several other fabrosaurids known: *Echinodon*, represented by a few jaws and teeth from the late Jurassic of southern Britain; *Fabrosaurus*, a single broken jaw with some teeth from the late Triassic of southern Africa; *Nanosaurus* ('dwarf reptile'), an incomplete jaw and some skeletal fragments from the later Jurassic, Colorado, North America; *Alocodon* ('wing tooth') and *Trimucrodon* ('three-pointed tooth'), some tooth fragments from the Jurassic of Portugal; and *Gongbusaurus* ('reptile from Gongbu') from the Jurassic of China; *Azendohsaurus* ('reptile from Azendoh'), another jaw fragment from Morocco may even be prosauropod.

## Heterodontosaurids

Heterodontosaurids are only known from the late Triassic and earliest Jurassic of southern Africa and North America. As was the case in the fabrosaurids, the earliest known heterodontosaurid fossil (described in 1911) was a jaw fragment with several teeth embedded in it. It came from southern Africa; this was named *Geranosaurus* ('crane reptile'). Somewhat later, another jaw was discovered, but this time was thought to belong to a mammal-like reptile and was named *Lycorhinus angustidens* ('wolf snout with sharp teeth'). It has a large pointed caniniform, or stabbing, tooth, at the front of the jaw and behind it a row of heavily worn cheek teeth. This specimen lay unrecognised as a dinosaur until 1962 when yet another new dinosaur from southern Africa was described and named *Heterodontosaurus* ('mixed-tooth reptile'). This too was discovered by an expedition from Britain organised this time by Dr Alan Charig of the British Museum (Natural History), and Dr John Attridge and Dr Barry Cox of the University of London. The animal, which has only recently be described, is apparently the same size and the same in general shape as the fabrosaurids above. However, there are, if we look a little closer, several striking differences.

The head is quite similar in shape to that of *Lesothosaurus*, but the teeth are notably different. At the front of the lower jaw there is a familiar horn-covered predentary, and immediately behind this there is a very large tusk-like tooth — like the one seen in *Lycorhinus* — and then a row of chisel-edged cheek teeth. The same arrangement is found in the upper jaw except that in front of the big tusk there are two small spiky teeth and then a gap at the front end of the snout which was probably covered by a horny pad to match the one on the predentary.

The remainder of the skeleton is similarly built to that of *Lesothosaurus* except that the hands are particularly large and strong with sharp claws, and the bones of the lower leg are welded together, a rather unusual feature which does not seem to occur in many other dinosaurs.

So what we seem to have are small, agile, bipedal ornithopod dinosaurs with several rather special features that distinguish them from their contemporaries, the fabrosaurids. They had special chisel-like cheek teeth behind the tusks; these were used to chew up food very finely, not at all like the simple feeding technique that was used by *Lesothosaurus*; and, associated with the chewing teeth, they probably possessed fleshy cheeks so that the food did not fall out of their mouths while they were chewing. The large tusks may also have had a defensive function. Large stabbing teeth are usually found in carnivores such as the big cats, where they are used for killing. In animals such as these heterodontosaurids which are herbivores, big tusks are usually used as defensive weapons and/or as feeding aids. Wild pigs and warthogs, for example, have teeth that are used both for digging and for defence. In some instances, such tusks can become long and very curly in males and are then used as social signals to establish a dominance hierarchy and to attract mates. The same sort of functions have been proposed for these teeth in heterodontosaurids.

In addition to *Heterodontosaurus*, there are several other heterodontosaurids: *Geranosaurus* and *Lycorhinus*, small pieces of jaw from the late Triassic of southern Africa; *Abrictosaurus* ('wide-awake reptile'), a moderately well-preserved skull which does not possess the large tusks seen in *Heterodontosaurus* (although in all other respects it is rather similar) again from the late Triassic of southern Africa; and *Lanasaurus* ('woolly reptile'), an upper jaw with some teeth, which appears to be distinct from other heterodontosaurids.

Such a variety of heterodontosaurids living at approximately the same time and in the same part of the world seems a little improbable; this seems particularly true when the different types are based largely upon tooth characters. Teeth are known to vary in shape tremendously within a single species of reptile, and even during the life of a single animal! One interesting possibility that has been suggested is that *Abrictosaurus* (the skull without the large tusks) may be a female, while *Heterodontosaurus* (with the tusks) is a male of the same species. Unfortunately, we cannot 'prove' in the strict sense whether one is a male and the other female, but it is certainly a possibility.

The general picture then of heterodontosaurids is that they are fleet-footed, agile bipeds, similar to the fabrosaurids that lived at the same time. However, unlike the fabrosaurids, they were able to chew a much greater variety of plant food much more efficiently using special cheek teeth and fleshy cheeks to hold the food

**Left:** The skull of a *Conolophus* (land iguana) killed by dogs on the Galapagos Islands. The similarity between its small, leaf-shaped teeth and those of fabrosaurids is immediately apparent. This suggests that their feeding habits were probably also similar.

**Below:** A detail of a 19th Century lithograph showing the teeth and fragments of jaw of the fabrosaurid *Echinodon becklesii* which were found in Dorset by Samuel Beckles. Compare the narrow roots and leaf-shaped crowns with those of the contemporary land iguana, *Conolophus* (left).

**Above:** A male African warthog displaying his huge tusks. It is tempting to draw a parallel between these animals and heterodontosaurids which also possessed large tusk-like teeth which were presumably used for defensive purposes and also for social display.

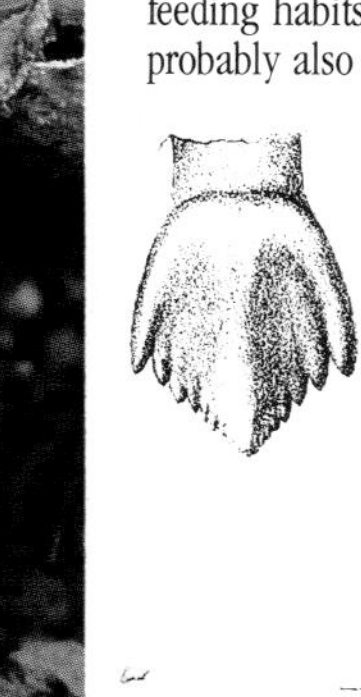

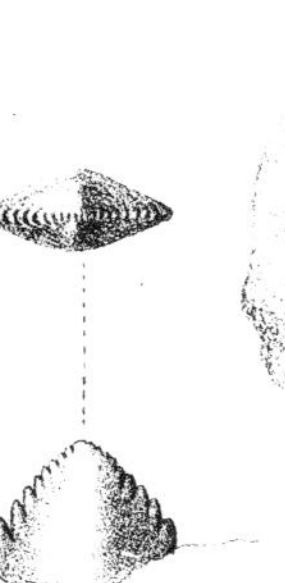

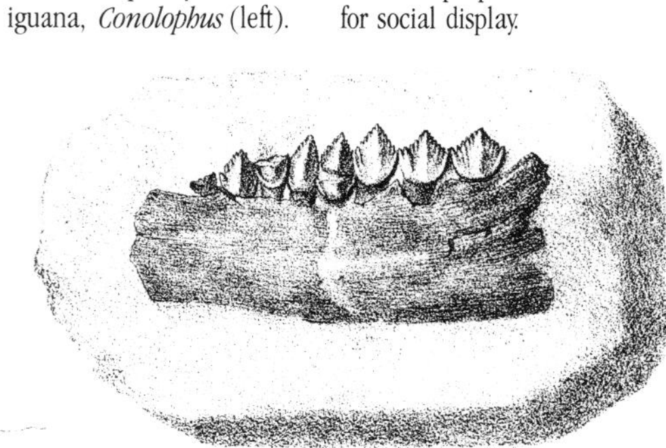

in the mouth; they also had large tusks for use both in defence against predators and perhaps for social display, especially if, as has been suggested, tusks were confined to males only; their hands were also surprisingly large and powerful and may have been used for digging as well as in defence.

### Aestivation Controversy

One interesting controversy that has broken out recently concerns the biology and way of life of fabrosaurid and heterodontosaurid dinosaurs. In 1978, Dr Tony Thulborn devoted a long article to the possibility that in the late Triassic and early Jurassic of southern Africa, there was an annual dry season during which both fabrosaurids and heterodontosaurids lay dormant or *aestivated*. The evidence for this suggestion came from a number of areas.

First of all, the so-called 'Red Beds' – the rocks of the Stormberg Series of southern Africa – are characteristically red in colour. The red colour is interpreted as indicating generally warm climatic conditions which were marked by alternating wet and dry seasons. Thus, if the interpretation is correct, then there will be times of the year (the dry season) when the vegetation will be in short supply during which both groups of ornithopods might have aestivated.

Secondly, Thulborn has found remains of fabrosaurids in a fossil assemblage which includes jaw bones bearing sharp and practically unworn teeth, together with others which were apparently discarded and heavily worn. He explains this occurrence by proposing that these individuals continued to grow and replace their teeth while they were aestivating. Fortunately, for us at least, in this instance the individuals perished while aestivating thereby preserving this unique record of their life-style.

Thirdly, Thulborn noted that the heterodontosaurids seem to have most unusual grinding cheek teeth. He was unable to find any evidence of tooth replacement in the family and also noted that the cheek teeth were worn in such a way that the wear facets on each tooth form a single flat cutting surface in each jaw. Thulborn claimed that the flat cutting surface could only have been produced if the lower jaw of heterodontosaurids moved forward and backward when they chewed their food, rather than in a more typical up and down movement. This in itself is not unreasonable because several living animals (notably rodents and elephants) also chew their food by moving the lower jaw backward and forward. However, he went on to develop his argument as follows. If these animals used this kind of chewing mechanism, then they cannot conform to the normal reptilian pattern of continual tooth replacement because if teeth periodically fall out and are replaced, then the whole chewing action would be disrupted: the jaws would in effect keep jamming. Therefore heterodontosaurids would seem to be unable to replace their teeth so long as they continued to feed. In addition to this, the degree of wear on the teeth seen in several heterodontosaurids is very severe, which implies that these animals fed on very abrasive plant food.

To Thulborn's mind, the heterodontosaurids are presented theoretically with a dilemma; they cannot continually replace their cheek teeth because it would impair their ability to feed, and yet they feed on abrasive food material which necessitates tooth replacement at least periodically. Again, the solution to their dilemma is found in aestivation. The teeth are worn down during each wet season and then replaced, *en masse*, during a short dry season while these animals lay dormant. The new set of teeth would be worn down rapidly to produce a smooth cutting blade once these animals re-emerged in the next wet season.

All in all, these proposals seem convincing and rather neatly and elegantly link environmental, geological and anatomical factors together to gain an insight into the life-style of these animals. However, elegant though this explanation may be, there are dissenting voices. Jim Hopson from Chicago has re-studied much of the heterodontosaurid material. He has demonstrated that these animals show definite evidence of tooth replacement, although it does seem to slow down in older individuals; also he argues that heterodontosaurids do not show fore and aft grinding movement of the lower jaw, but chewed in typical reptile fashion by simply opening and closing the jaws. By demonstrating these two points, Hopson has removed Thulborn's main arguments for proposing that heterodontosaurids replace their teeth completely once a year during a period of aestivation. This, of course, still leaves the evidence of the fabrosaurid assemblage of two individuals caught in the act of aestivating, but even this has been doubted as a reliable record because the presence of a saurischian tooth with the others suggests that the 'assemblage' might in fact be a chance accumulation of fossils.

Therefore, a very familiar story has emerged of the fossil record affording us a small glimpse of the world and behaviour of dinosaurs. But as always, the glimpse is a fleeting one and potentially misleading. If you are not careful it can lead to a quite erroneous view of the world of dinosaurs, or at least to one that is not justified by the evidence. Here, for example, it is still quite conceivable that seasonal climates prevailed in the late Triassic and early Jurassic and that some of the dinosaurs aestivated in the dry season – one simply cannot prove it!

**Self Defence (above)** The fabrosaurids and heterodontosaurids seem to show a full range of strategies for survival against predators. *Lesothosaurus* was very swift and agile and would flee; *Scutellosaurus* was moderately fleet of foot but also partly armoured; *Heterodontosaurus* was speedy, but agressive in defence when cornered.

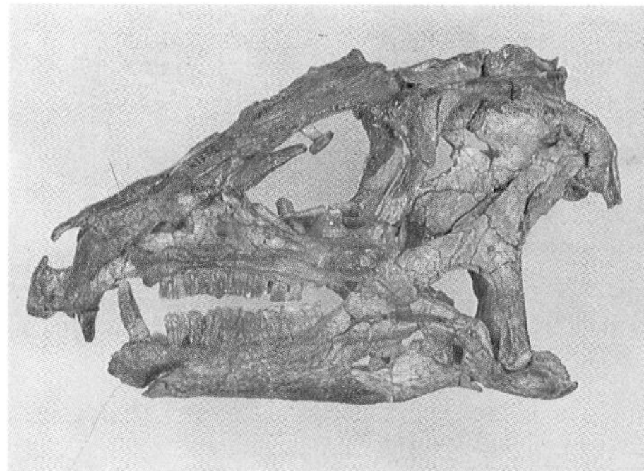

**Left:** A lateral view of the skull of *Heterodontosaurus tucki* which was excavated from the northern slopes of Krommespruit Mountain in South Africa. Note tusk-like tooth and cheek teeth.

**Below:** This skeleton of *Heterodontosaurus* provides us with a fine view of the dinosaur's strong, clawed hands and the fused bones of its lower leg.

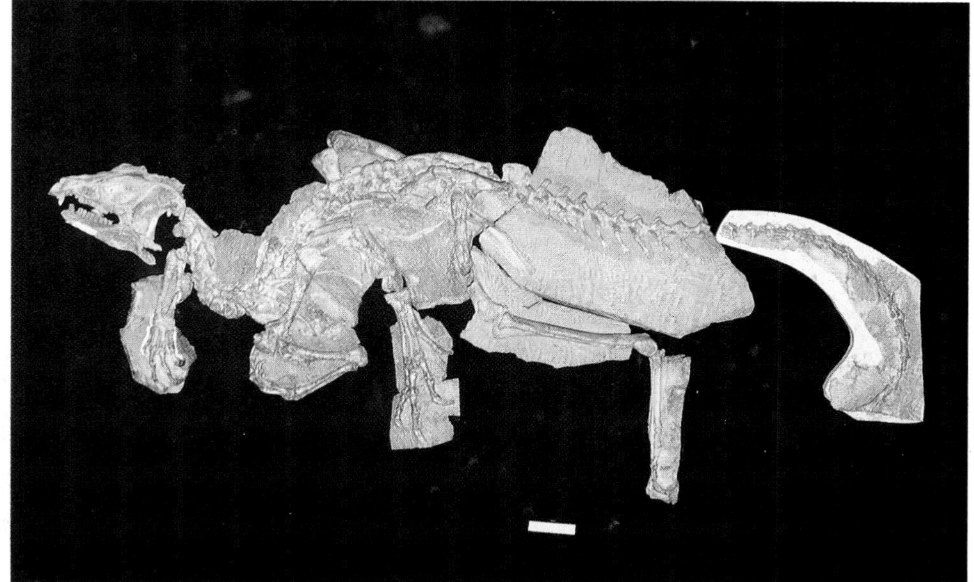

# HYPSILOPHODONTIDS

The hypsilophodontids are a family of small-to-medium sized (6·6-16·5ft, 2·5m in length) ornithopod dinosaurs. In outward appearance at least, they are not unlike the fabrosaurids described earlier. However, unlike the fabrosaurids, which seem to have been most abundant at the earliest stages of the history of the ornithischians—in the latest Triassic and early Jurassic—the hypsilophodontids first make their appearance in Middle Jurassic times (see time chart below). The first remains are rather scrappy, consisting of tooth fragments and pieces of limb bones from Oxfordshire. Indeed they are so poor that they are simply referred to as 'hypsilophodontid', by which we mean that although the material belonged to a hypsilophodontid dinosaur, it is not well enough preserved to give it a proper scientific name.

Shortly after this, in the Upper Jurassic, several much better preserved hypsilophodontids are known. In particular, *Dryosaurus* ('oak reptile') from North America and *Dysalotosaurus* ('lost wood reptile') from Tanzania in East Africa. These two dinosaurs have recently been very carefully compared bone-by-bone and are now considered by some workers to be so similar that they have been given the same name: *Dryosaurus,* the North American form being called *Dryosaurus altus* and the East African form *Dryosaurus lettowvorbecki* after the German General, von Lettow-Vorbeck. In addition to these two species, there is another quite well preserved but unfortunately incomplete skeleton which has been named *Othnielia* (after Othniel Charles Marsh).

In the Cretaceous Period various types of hypsilophodontids have been found. Lower Cretaceous forms include *Hypsilophodon* ('high-ridged tooth') from the Isle of Wight, England, represented by several excellent skeletons, also *Valdosaurus* ('reptile from the Wealden'), a very fragmentary species from southern England; *Zephyrosaurus* ('west wind reptile'), a partial

YEARS AGO (MILLIONS): 64, 70, 80, 90, 100, 110, 120, 130, 140, 150, 160, 170, 180, 190, 200, 210, 220, 225

TRIASSIC · JURASSIC · CRETACEOUS

DRYOSAURUS · HYPSILOPHODON · VALDOSAURUS · DYSALOTOSAURUS · TENONTOSAURUS · ZEPHYROSAURUS · OTHNIELIA · FULGUROTHERIUM · THESCELOSAURUS · PARKSOSAURUS

**Time Chart (left)**
Hypsilophodontids are found fairly widely in the fossil record. The earliest of the remains date from the late Jurassic, and they persist as small to medium-sized forms right up to the late Cretaceous. The largest of these types, *Tenontosaurus* of the early Cretaceous of North America, bore a considerable resemblance to the contemporaneous large iguanodontids.

**Dryosaurus (right)**
A large hypsilophodontid, 10-13ft (3-4m) long, *Dryosaurus* had long powerful hind legs, and strong arms, each with five fingers. Its tail was stiff, and it could have been used for balance when the animal ran. *Dryosaurus* had sharp ridged cheek teeth, but there were no teeth at the front of the jaw. It probably nipped vegetation off with its bony 'beak' and then chopped the leaves and shoots with its cheek teeth. *Dryosaurus* was a wide-ranging dinosaur: its remains have been found in North America and East Africa, and it could probably migrate long distances.

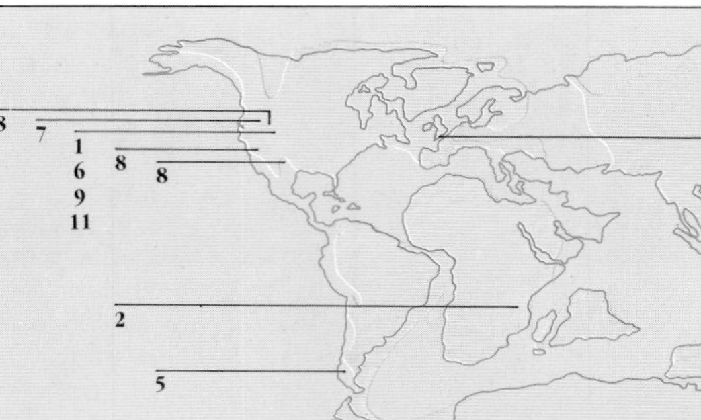


**Map (left)**
1 *Dryosaurus*
2 *Dysalotosaurus*
3 *Fulgurotherium*
4 *Hypsilophodon*
5 *Loncosaurus*
6 *Othnielia*
7 *Parksosaurus*
8 *Tenontosaurus*
9 *Thescelosaurus*
10 *Valdosaurus*
11 *Zephyrosaurus*

**Tenontosaurus (below)**
This was a much larger animal than its relative *Hypsilophodon;* it is estimated that it weighed up to 1 tonne. It has been classified as an iguanodontid, but it shows the same specialisations of the teeth as do other hypsilophodontids. *Tenontosaurus* was a strongly-built ornithopod and it had a massive powerful tail which might have been used at times to defend itself from packs of predatory *Deinonychus.*

skull from Montana; and the larger and heavier *Tenontosaurus* ('sinew reptile') represented by many skeletons from various areas in North America. Finally, in the Upper Cretaceous, there are two imperfectly known types: *Parksosaurus* ('Parks' reptile'), an incomplete skull and *Thescelosaurus* ('beautiful reptile') known from several part skeletons and skulls.

From their first appearance in the Middle Jurassic until their extinction at the end of the Cretaceous, the hypsilophodontids appear to have changed very little. In particular, *Othnielia* of the Upper Jurassic is remarkably similar to *Hypsilophodon* of the Lower Cretaceous, which is in turn very like *Thescelosaurus* of the late Cretaceous. It seems as though these animals evolved a particularly successful structure (and way of life) and simply retained that design to the end. The only obviously abberrant form would seem to be *Tenontosaurus* which is simply a hypsilophodontid grown rather large so that it resembles a small iguanodontid.

The geographic distribution of the hypsilophodontids seems to show a fairly easily understood pattern. Undoubtedly these animals were present in middle Jurassic times, perhaps even a little earlier—after all it is exeedingly unlikely that we would find the very first member of this or any other family in the fossil record. Anyway, at this time there were land links to all the continents, except perhaps eastern Asia, so that early representatives could have spread almost worldwide. The presence of *Dryosaurus* in both North America and East Africa demonstrates the likelihood of such widespread dispersal. In fact, we might predict that hypsilophodontids will eventually be found in Upper Jurassic rocks in South America, Australasia and India. In the Cretaceous, intercontinental seaways divided the land masses leading to the evolution in isolation, of distinctive hypsilophodontids on each continent: *Tenontosaurus, Parksosaurus* and *Thescelosaurus* in North America; *Hypsilophodon*

**Hypsilophodon (left)**
One of the best known and most successful of the small ornithopods, *Hypsilophodon* was a comparatively small dinosaur. It had short arms, each with five fingers, and long legs, each with four toes. *Hypsilophodon* was probably an agile and fleet-footed creature, and it may have used its long stiff tail as a stabiliser when running. It was once thought that *Hypsilophodon* lived in trees, but there is little evidence for this.

**Family Tree (right)**
*Hypsilophodon* is very like *Thescelosaurus* and *Zephyrosaurus. Tenontosaurus* seems to be larger relative of *Hypsilophodon,* while *Dryosaurus* and *Valdosaurus* are medium-sized forms that show certain similarities to the iguanodontids.

**Comparative Sizes (left)**
1 *Hypsilophodon:* 1. 6·6ft (2m).
2 *Dryosaurus:* 1. 10-13ft (3-4m).
3 *Tenontosaurus:* 15-21·3ft (4·5-6·5m).

and *Valdosaurus* in Europe. There are also new reports of two fragmentary Cretaceous hypsilophodontids from Australia (*Fulgurotherium,* 'Lightning Ridge beast') and South America (*Loncosaurus,* 'Lonco reptile') which, if confirmed, would support the prediction about the near worldwide dispersal.

So, having suggested that the hypsilophodontids had apparently hit upon a successful design as a reason for their not having changed very much in appearance, the obvious question is: what are the hypsilophodontids and how do they differ from their predecessors, the fabrosaurids?

For the most part, the skeletons of hypsilophodontids do not differ very much from that of fabrosaurids. They both are small, lightly-built, bipedal animals with long, slender, four-toed hindlimbs and quite short forelimbs with stubby, five-fingered hands. The real difference is only apparent when we look carefully at the head, and the jaws and teeth in particular. The skull of *Lesothosaurus* (a fabrosaurid) is small, light and roughly triangular in shape, as is that of *Hypsilophodon.* However, whereas the teeth of *Lesothosaurus* are separate and leaf-shaped and set in slender jaws, *Hypsilophodon* has broader, chisel-like teeth that lock together with their neighbours to form a continuous sharp cutting edge. The jaws are also quite massive and there is a cheek pouch alongside the teeth on each side of the head to store food while it is being chewed.

What we have, in effect, is a much more efficient chewing machine. The hypsilophodontids evolved more sophisticated teeth and jaws with cheek pouches to chew up plant food more efficiently and so extract more nutrients than the fabrosaurids could ever do. Thus, although these two groups look very similar, there is a world of difference between them in one vitally important respect: the design of their jaws. It seems quite likely that the hypsilophodontids rapidly replaced the majority of fabrosaurids in the small agile herbivore niche from mid-Jurassic times, with the few remaining fabrosaurids surviving as perhaps specialist feeders on young plants shoots.

## Hypsilophodon Described

Although there are many hypsilophodontids, we shall look in detail only at *Hypsilophodon,* because it is the best preserved and described. The first remains of any hypsilophodontid to be discovered were found in a slab of sandstone from the south-west coast of the Isle of Wight, England, in 1849. The remains, which consisted of a partial skeleton, were first described by Gideon Mantell, and later by Sir Richard Owen, as those of a young *Iguanodon.* By 1868, several other skeletons had been recovered from the same locality by the Reverend William Fox, a noted amateur collector of fossils. The new material displayed several characteristics not previously seen in *Iguanodon* and prompted

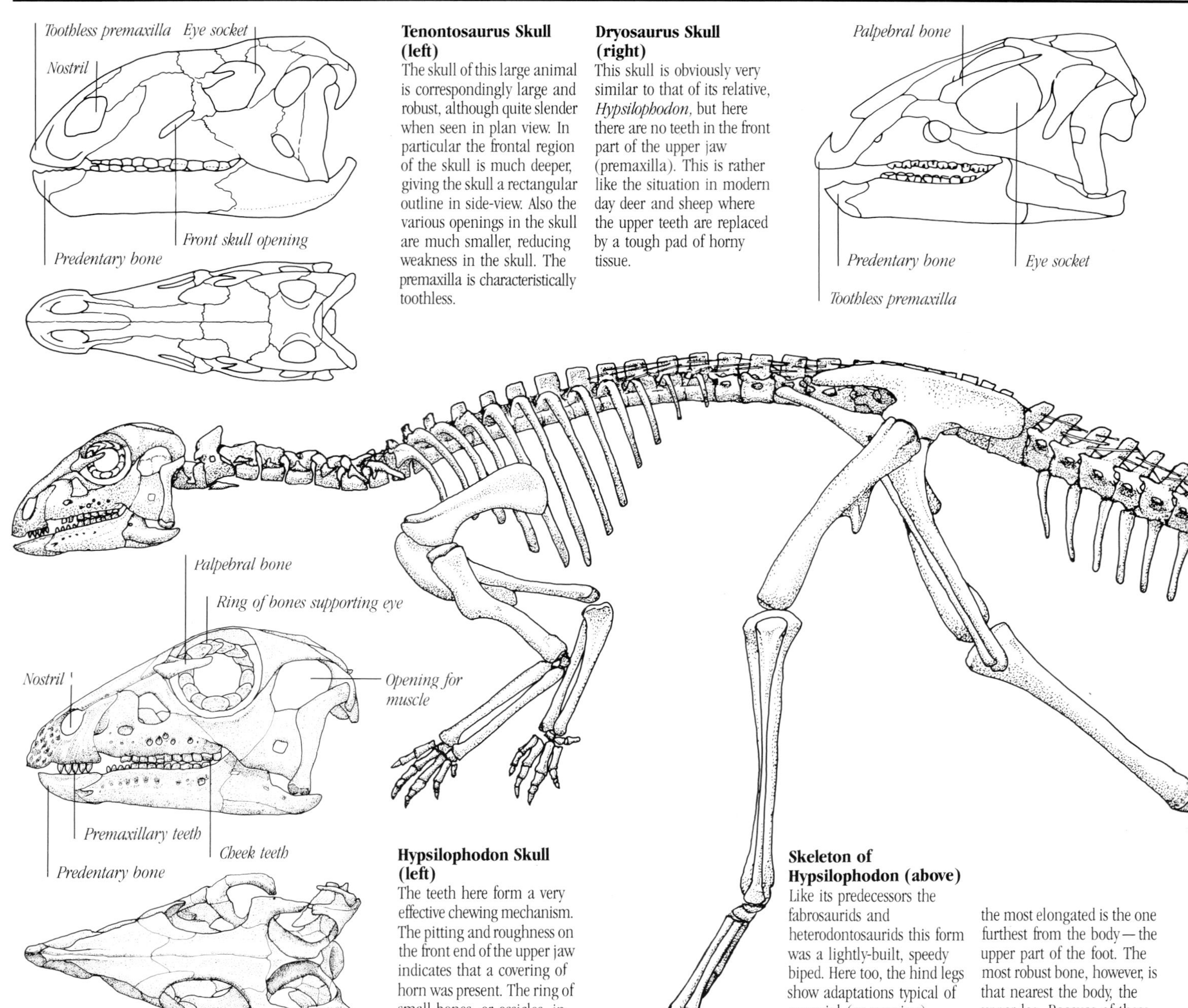


**Tenontosaurus Skull (left)**
The skull of this large animal is correspondingly large and robust, although quite slender when seen in plan view. In particular the frontal region of the skull is much deeper, giving the skull a rectangular outline in side-view. Also the various openings in the skull are much smaller, reducing weakness in the skull. The premaxilla is characteristically toothless.

**Dryosaurus Skull (right)**
This skull is obviously very similar to that of its relative, *Hypsilophodon,* but here there are no teeth in the front part of the upper jaw (premaxilla). This is rather like the situation in modern day deer and sheep where the upper teeth are replaced by a tough pad of horny tissue.

**Hypsilophodon Skull (left)**
The teeth here form a very effective chewing mechanism. The pitting and roughness on the front end of the upper jaw indicates that a covering of horn was present. The ring of small bones, or ossicles, in the eye is often found in reptiles and may be part of the focussing mechanism for sharp eyesight.

**Skeleton of Hypsilophodon (above)**
Like its predecessors the fabrosaurids and heterodontosaurids this form was a lightly-built, speedy biped. Here too, the hind legs show adaptations typical of cursorial (or running) animals. All segments of the leg (upper, lower, ankle, foot) are elongated, but the segment which is relatively the most elongated is the one furthest from the body—the upper part of the foot. The most robust bone, however, is that nearest the body, the upper leg. Because of these features the leg acts like a pendulum which has a long length but a small 'bob'. Such a pendulum has a short

Owen to propose that the animal represented a new species, *Iguanodon foxii*. However, it was Thomas Henry Huxley who first recognised that this dinosaur was totally unlike *Iguanodon*. Among the many differences, Huxley was struck by the shape of the teeth, which were smaller, narrower and more sharply pointed than those of *Iguanodon*. These prompted Huxley to re-name the dinosaur *Hypsilophodon foxii* ('Fox's high-ridged tooth').

In order to understand the anatomy of this animal more closely, let us look at one particular suggestion that was made about the way of life of this curious little dinosaur. In 1882 James Hulke completed the first description of *Hypsilophodon* and concluded that this dinosaur was adapted to climb on rocks and trees because it had long fingers and toes. From this observation, it was accepted as established fact that *Hypsilophodon* was an arboreal dinosaur (i.e. it lived in trees) and that this perhaps represented the primitive type of life-style of ornithopod dinosaurs. Many life-like restorations made earlier in this century show *Hypsilophodon* perched, bird-like, on the branch of a tree (see overleaf).

In addition to Hulke's original comments, numerous other 'facts' were used to support the proposal that *Hypsilophodon* was a tree-dweller and comparable to the tree-kangaroo, *Dendrolagus*, of Australasia. The list of anatomical characteristics is quite impressive: (i) the first toe of the foot was supposed to be reversed so that it could grip on to branches; (ii) the claws on the hindfoot were strongly arched and sharp so that movement on the ground would have been difficult; (iii) the bones of the forearm were bowed like those of the tree-kangaroo; (iv) the great range of movement that was possible at the shoulder; (v) the hindlimb muscles were so arranged that the animal could not run fast, but were well suited to climbing and balancing; and (vi) the tail was rigid and so served as a balancing aid.

Peter Galton reviewed these statements critically in order to find out whether it was possible to confirm that *Hypsilophodon* was arboreal. Let us go through the points one by one to see how convincing they are.

(i) The authenticity of the idea of a grasping toe on the foot depends on whether the first toe of the foot pointed backwards, as it does in a bird's foot, to grip a branch. As can be seen in the drawing overleaf, the first toe does *seem* to be reversed but it is rather short compared to that of a bird and, more importantly, looking back at the original fossil, it can be seen that the claw on the end of the toe has been reversed by the artist! In life the first toe of *Hypsilophodon* pointed in the same direction as all the other toes, and therefore could not be used to grip on to branches.

(ii) The curved claws on the hind feet are not in fact strongly arched and would certainly not have prevented this animal from walking and running on the ground.

**Hip Muscles (right)**
Here we see how the bulk of the leg-moving muscles are concentrated on the upper leg and pelvis. This position helps to concentrate the weight of the leg away from its lower end, helping it to swing faster during the stride. The limb can move the body in two main ways: the upper leg can be pulled backwards and if the foot is firmly anchored on the ground this will result in the body being forced forwards; the knee and ankle joints can be extended and as the leg straightens the body is forced forwards. The functions of these muscles are indicated by the annotations.

*Pulls leg back (Pubo-ischio-femoralis internus)*
*Pulls leg up (Ilio-femoralis)*
*Pulls leg back (Caudi-femoralis brevis)*
*Pulls leg up (Ilio-tibialis)*
*Pulls leg in (Adductor femoris)*
*Pulls leg back (Caudi-femoralis longus)*
*Extends the lower leg (Femoro-tibialis)*

**Hypsilophodon Hand**

*Radius*
*Ulna*
*Digit 5*
*Wrist bones*
*Digit 4*
*Digit 1*
*Digit 2*
*Digit 3*

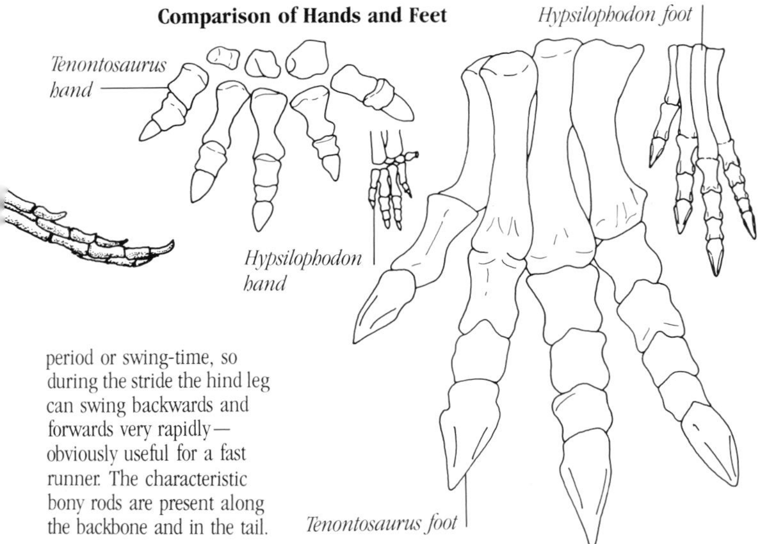


period or swing-time, so during the stride the hind leg can swing backwards and forwards very rapidly—obviously useful for a fast runner. The characteristic bony rods are present along the backbone and in the tail.

**Hypsilophodon and Tenontosaurus Hands and Feet (left and right)**
The foot of *Hypsilophodon* is typical of a fast-running creature, the upper foot bones being noticeably elongated. The toes are equipped with quite sharp claws. The hand is somewhat stubbier, and the stout claws may have been used for tearing of scratching. The drawings (left) compare the hands and feet of *Tenontosaurus* and *Hypsilophodon;* while the relative dimensions vary considerably, they are basically very similar in design, suggesting close relationship.

**Hypsilophodon Foot**

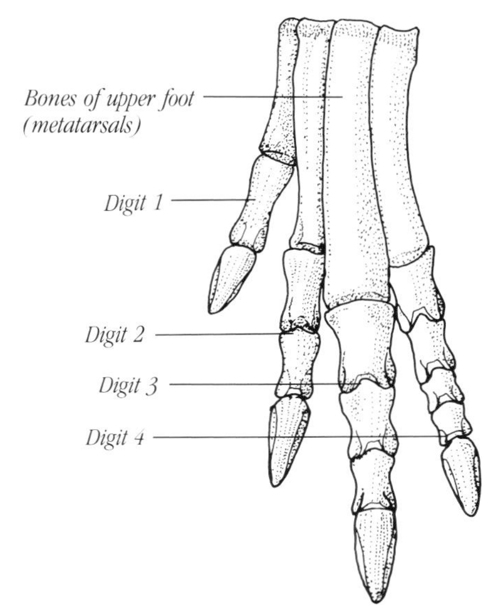

(iii and iv) The forearm bones are not particularly strongly bowed compared with other dinosaurs, indeed they are less strongly bowed than those of *Iguanodon* and nobody believes that *Iguanodon* lived in trees! Similarly, point (iv) about the greater range of movement possible at the shoulder does not hold up to detailed comparison with other dinosaurs.

(v) The arrangement of muscles in the hindlimb of *Hypsilophodon* is unlikely to have hindered movement; in fact they are arranged in such a way that the legs could be moved very quickly.

(vi) The rigid tail of *Hypsilophodon* is due to the fact that its end is sheathed in bony tendons (rather similar to the arrangement seen in *Deinonychus*, page 59). Such a stiff tail would have been most useful as a stabiliser during fast running and in rapid changes of direction, rather than for tree-dwelling where it may even have got in the way. Quite often tree-dwelling animals have long, flexible, prehensile tails to aid climbing and grip.

Peter Galton concluded that there was no good evidence for *Hypsilophodon* being arboreal and in fact presented rather convincing evidence that it was a very fleet-footed ornithopod. Comparing the proportions of the limbs in known fast-running animals alive today (horses, gazelles and antelopes), it was found that *Hypsilophodon* had limb proportions typical of very fast-running animals, such as some of the smaller antelopes.

## Family Members

Looking briefly at other hypsilophodontids, *Tenontosaurus* was a much larger animal (c. 15ft, 4·5m in length) that lived in North America at about the time that *Hypsilophodon* lived in Europe. As should be expected, its limbs are much more heavily built than those of *Hypsilophodon* to support its greater body weight. It has a sheath of tendons encasing the end of its tail, but unlike *Hypsilophodon* it appears to have walked on all four legs, although it probably ran on its back legs alone, with its great long tail stuck straight out to counterbalance the heavy chest and belly. Linked to the greater size of *Tenontosaurus*, the head is large and deeper to permit a more considerable intake of food and provide room for powerful jaw muscles.

*Tenontosaurus* remains have been found in the same quarries as *Deinonychus*. Unfortunately, *Tenontosaurus* relied on its large size to deter predators, coupled with its ability to run away at speed, since it had no defensive weapons. Neither of these ploys was likely to have been very successful against sophisticated and fast-moving predators such as *Deinonychus*.

*Dryosaurus* and *Dysalotosaurus* of the late Jurassic are very similar to *Hypsilophodon* in size and shape, although there are consistent differences in their anatomy. For example, there are no teeth at the front of the upper jaw in *Dryosaurus* and *Dysalotosaurus*, while there are five in *Hypsilophodon;* also the arrangement of the bones of the hips is rather different, and there are only three toes on the hindfoot while *Hypsilophodon* has four.

One intriguing observation that has been made relates to the similarity between *Dryosaurus* from western North America and *Dysalotosaurus* from Tanzania. As noted above, it has been proposed that these forms are so similar that they should both be named *Dryosaurus*. This has prompted one author to speculate that Africa and North America were linked by a land route in the late Jurassic so that animals could move from one area to the other unhindered. Geographical maps that reconstruct that period, however, seem to indicate that seaways separated America from Africa at this time. Perhaps there is not great problem here though. In middle to late Jurassic times the northern and southern continents were linked, so that their faunas were undoubtedly very similar. By late Jurassic times, the faunas were only recently separated so there had been relatively little time for evolutionary divergence in the faunas to come about. This is reflected in the fact that although one or two similar genera are found in western North America and Tanzania: *Drysosaurus*, *Brachiosaurus* (see page 86), and (doubtfully) *Ceratosaurus* (page 62) and *Allosaurus* (page 62), they are still

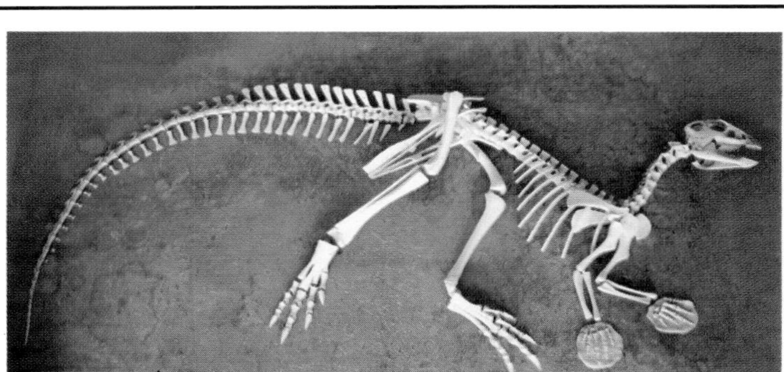

**Right:** This reconstruction of *Hypsilophodon foxii* is based on skeletal material held in the Sandown Museum, Isle of Wight. It is made of polyester resin reinforced with fibreglass, and was built under the supervision of Stephen Hutt. It is about 4·6ft (1·4m) in length and thus probably represents an immature individual, rather than a fully-grown specimen.

**Right:** The graceful lines and agile build of a typical hypsilophodontid are well displayed in this skeleton of *Dryosaurus altus* that is in the Carnegie Museum of Natural History in Pittsburgh. The relative dimensions of fore and hindlimbs are readily apparent, as is the absence of teeth from the front of its upper jaw. *Dryosaurus* is very similar to the East African form *Dysalotosaurus*.

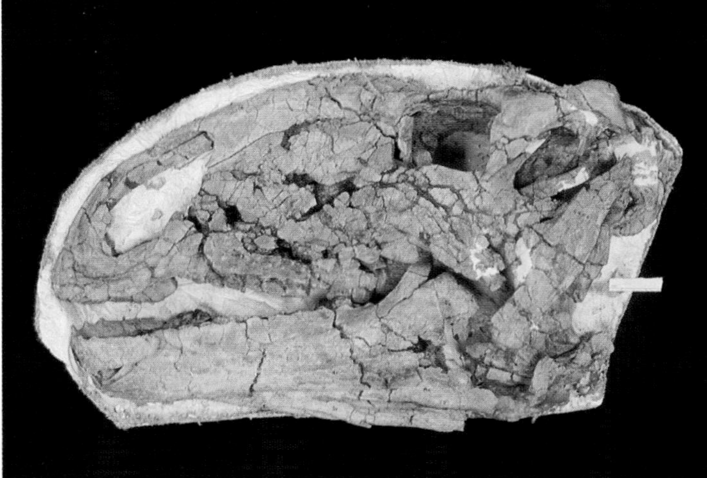

**Above:** This shattered skull of *Tenontosaurus* still semi-encased in its plaster jacket shows how much work often has to be put in to the task of reconstructing a dinosaur. *Tenontosaurus* has a fairly deep skull with plenty of room for the attachment of large jaw muscles. Though similar in size and shape to a small iguanodontid, it seems to be more closely related to the smaller *Hypsilophodon*.

different enough to be called separate species. Also other groups, for example, the stegosaurs, other sauropods and 'coelurosaurs' are represented by quite distinctive genera indicating that some of the dinosaurs are not common to both continents, thereby supporting the idea of a seaway separating these two areas. As always, a balanced view, weighing all the facts *pro* and *contra,* is necessary to any interpretation.

## Life-Style

Returning to *Hypsilophodon,* about twenty-three partial or complete skeletons have been discovered on the Isle of Wight; all of these have come from a small area of the cliffs, the so-called '*Hypsilophodon* bed' from which virtually nothing else has been discovered. Many of the skeletons are beautifully preserved with all the bones in position, and several skeletons are practically touching. Why there should be such a rich concentration of these small dinosaurs in one place is a mystery. One suggestion is that the animals preserved there represent part of a small herd that became trapped and perished in inter-tidal quick-sand. This is certainly a novel explanation, but it does have some merit. We would normally expect that the process leading to the fossilisation of any animal is quite a long and chancy one. The animal dies or is killed; its remains are left to rot and may be scavenged so that bits are lost before it is either finally destroyed, or buried in sediments, or washed into a river. Thus we should normally expect only very incomplete or fragmentary remains to be preserved. The *Hypsilophodon* bed, however, reveals complete and beautifully preserved skeletons; they must have been buried very rapidly at the time of death, allowing no time for scavenging or dipersal through rotting. Burial in quick-sand is certainly one way in which this could have happened.

So, what sort of a picture can we build up of hypsilophodontid dinosaurs and their possible way of life? The typical hypsilophodontids were small, agile and extremely fleet-footed creatures of the Jurassic and Cretaceous Periods. In this, however, they did not differ greatly from either of their predecessors of the late Triassic and early Jurassic, the fabrosaurids and heterodontosaurids. However, although the fabrosaurids survived until the end of the Jurassic so far as we can tell, they were never very abundant once the hypsilophodontids appeared. The heterodontosaurids fared even worse; they do not seem to have survived beyond the earliest part of the Jurassic Period.

The explanation for this evolutionary change advanced in the section on fabrosaurids compared the way in which these animals chewed plant food. Fabrosaurids have rather simple, well-separated teeth and slender jaws well suited to chipping off pieces of foliage or soft shoots and swallowing them directly, while hypsilophodontids have teeth which overlap one another to form a long cutting blade, have much heavier jaws, more powerful jaw muscles *and* cheeks. With this rather complicated arrangement, these animals could mince up tough plants by repetitively chewing them up and the food would not be lost from the sides of the mouth each time they chewed because of the presence of retentive fleshy cheeks.

From an evolutionary point of view, the hypsilophodontids can be seen to be more advanced than the fabrosaurids in terms of the efficiency with which they chewed plant food, and perhaps it was this development that allowed them to replace the fabrosaurids as the dominant small-to-medium size plant eaters in the fossil record. This argument seems convincing enough, but it does have its flaws because it does not take account of the other important group of early ornithopods, the heterodontosaurids. As we have seen, these were small, agile, fleet-footed creatures of the late Triassic and earliest Jurassic. However, like hypsilophodontids, these animals also had a blade-like arrangement of teeth in the jaws, heavy jaws and jaw muscles, and cheeks. So the question remains: why did the heterodontosaurids die out so early in the Jurassic when they appear to have had such an efficient mechanism for chewing food? The simple answer is that we do not know! One possibility is that heterodontosaurids evolved their special jaws and teeth to deal with a very particular type of plant growing in the late Triassic and that this plant died out early in the Jurassic Period. Such an explanation is very unsatisfactory because it can never be proved or disproved. It is biologically plausible because it is known that certain animals do have a very specific food preference, i.e. pandas only eat bamboo, and koala bears only eat some varieties of eucalyptus leaf. In both cases, if the plants died, so would the animals because they are unable to change their diet. However, this observation does not mean that heterodontosaurids necessarily had such precise dietary requirements.

I hope that this problem emphasizes how careful one has to be when formulating a particular theory to explain an observation. When dealing with living animals it is usually possible to test a theory by direct experimentation. When considering the fossil record, it is very easy to propose all manner of theories to explain a particular observation, but these theories are impossible to test in any practical way. If any preference is made, then it is usually based on a judicious mixture of personal experience, biological plausibility and the application of plain commonsense.

**Left:** The nearest parallels to the hypsilophodontids in the natural world today would appear to be very speedy and agile runners such as this Thomson's Gazelle. Comparison of the dimensions of their bones shows that the proportions of the limb bones of hypsilophodontids are very similar to those of fleet-footed antelopes, and thus their behaviour may also be similar.

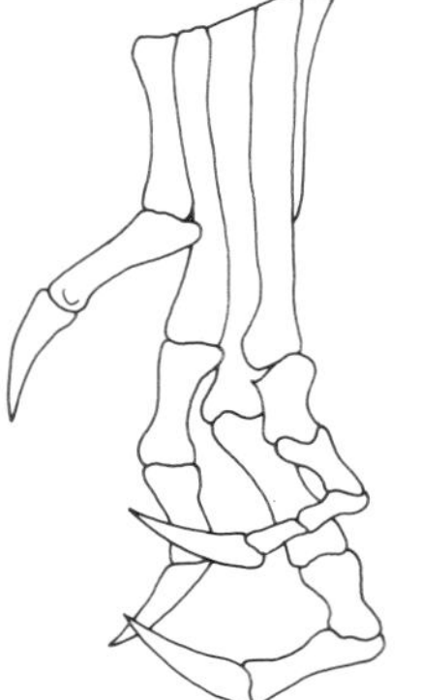

**The Tree-Dweller (left and below)**
The drawing (left) is based on Othenio Abel's 1912 illustration of the foot of *Hypsilophodon.* The reversed first toe was thought to be evidence that it was a tree-dweller and prompted restorations like Neave Parker's (below). In fact Abel had misinterpreted the data: *Hypsilophodon's* first toe pointed in the same direction as the others.

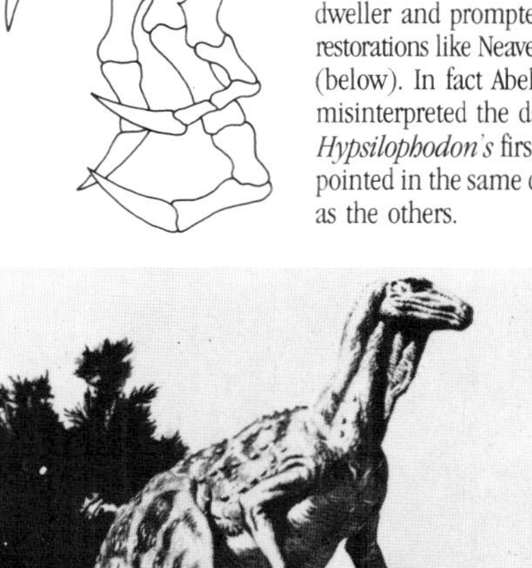

# IGUANODONTIDS

Iguanodontids are ornithopod dinosaurs of medium-to-large size (16·5-33ft, 5-10m long) which range in time from the late Jurassic to the end of the Cretaceous Period. They appear to have co-existed quite happily with the hypsilophodontids in the late Jurassic and early Cretaceous, but the appearance of the most advanced ornithopods, the hadrosaurids, resulted in a marked decline in the abundance and diversity of the iguanodontids. In fact they all but go extinct everywhere in the world except in Western Europe where, for some reason (perhaps geographic isolation), the hadrosaurids never seem to have become firmly established.

A general comparison with the hypsilophodontids shows that these are all rather large, clumsy animals with massive hindlimbs and broad feet to support their heavy bodies and quite large shoulders and forelimbs; the fingers of the hand show modification such that the claws are broad and flattened and rather hoof-like, as if they were used predominantly for walking rather than for grasping objects, as seemed to be the case in most hypsilophodontids. Many of these features are simply size-related characteristics, as can be appreciated if we look back and compare them with the only really large hypsilophodontid, *Tenontosaurus*. However, that is not to imply that iguanodontids are really just overgrown hypsilophodontids. There are a number of characteristic features of the iguanodontids, particularly in the structure of their skulls, teeth, forelimbs and hips, that set them apart as a distinct group and support the idea that they form a family of their own.

The illustrations below show clearly that iguanodontids retain the basic ornithopod characteristics: the body is counterbalanced by the tail and they walk on their hindlegs. It should be noted though that they are also perfectly capable of walking or resting on 'all-fours'—notice the large, blunt, hoof-like

**Muttaburrasaurus (below)**
This animal was about 23ft (7m) long and the skeleton shows affinities with *Camptosaurus* and *Iguanodon*, although it is not very well preserved. *Muttaburrasaurus* is very important because dinosaurs from Australia are still poorly known, and the new find extends our knowledge of the palaeogeographic distribution of iguanodontids which are otherwise mainly known from the northern hemisphere. *Muttaburrasaurus* had a low broad head, with a heavy bony lump above the snout, and it has been suggested that its teeth could have been used for chopping plants or meat. This idea has yet to be confirmed.

**Time Chart (left)**
Like the hypsilophodontids, the iguanodontids seem to arise in the late Jurassic with such forms as *Camptosaurus* in North America and Europe. These medium-sized ornithopods were fairly abundant in the early Cretaceous of Europe, Asia, Africa and Australia, but in the late Cretaceous were limited to just Europe and possibly Africa.

**Camptosaurus (right)**
This ornithopod is known from a number of skeletons, and these include both juvenile and adult specimens ranging in length from 4-23ft (1·2-7m). *Camptosaurus* is the earliest iguanodontid that is known from skeletons. It is more primitive than the typical Cretaceous iguanodontids in being smaller, in having four toes on the foot (*Iguanodon* had three) and in lacking a fully developed spiked thumb. Like other iguanodontids, *Camptosaurus* had small hooves on both its fingers and toes, and this suggests that it often walked on all-fours.

**Comparative Sizes (right)**
1 *Camptosaurus*: l. 16·5-23ft (5-7m)
2 *Ouranosaurus*: l. 23ft (7m).
3 *Muttaburrasaurus*: l. 23ft (7m).
4 *Iguanodon*: l. 33ft (10m)

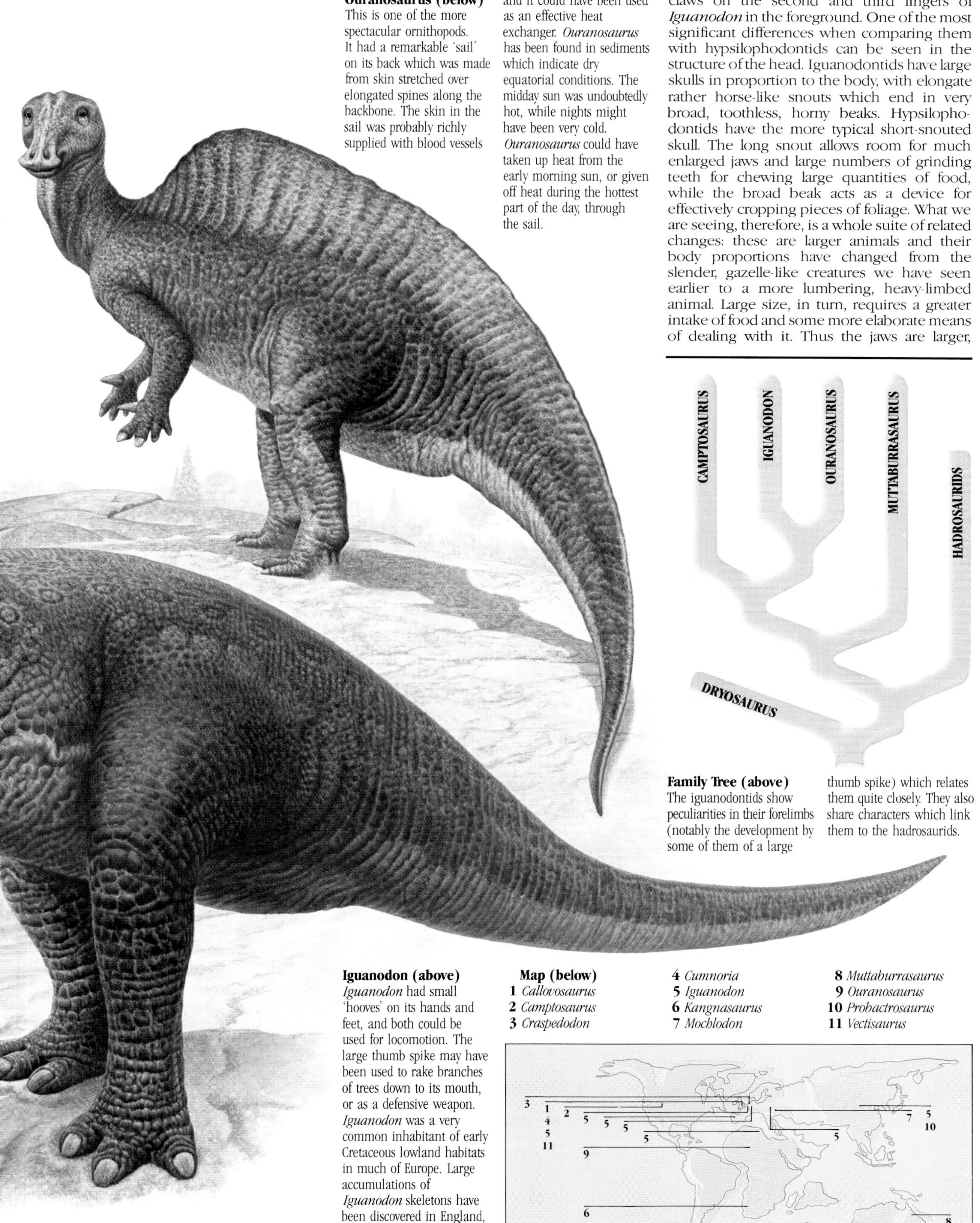


**Ouranosaurus (below)**
This is one of the more spectacular ornithopods. It had a remarkable 'sail' on its back which was made from skin stretched over elongated spines along the backbone. The skin in the sail was probably richly supplied with blood vessels and it could have been used as an effective heat exchanger. *Ouranosaurus* has been found in sediments which indicate dry equatorial conditions. The midday sun was undoubtedly hot, while nights might have been very cold. *Ouranosaurus* could have taken up heat from the early morning sun, or given off heat during the hottest part of the day, through the sail.

claws on the second and third fingers of *Iguanodon* in the foreground. One of the most significant differences when comparing them with hypsilophodontids can be seen in the structure of the head. Iguanodontids have large skulls in proportion to the body, with elongate rather horse-like snouts which end in very broad, toothless, horny beaks. Hypsilophodontids have the more typical short-snouted skull. The long snout allows room for much enlarged jaws and large numbers of grinding teeth for chewing large quantities of food, while the broad beak acts as a device for effectively cropping pieces of foliage. What we are seeing, therefore, is a whole suite of related changes: these are larger animals and their body proportions have changed from the slender, gazelle-like creatures we have seen earlier to a more lumbering, heavy-limbed animal. Large size, in turn, requires a greater intake of food and some more elaborate means of dealing with it. Thus the jaws are larger,

**Family Tree (above)**
The iguanodontids show peculiarities in their forelimbs (notably the development by some of them of a large thumb spike) which relates them quite closely. They also share characters which link them to the hadrosaurids.

**Iguanodon (above)**
*Iguanodon* had small 'hooves' on its hands and feet, and both could be used for locomotion. The large thumb spike may have been used to rake branches of trees down to its mouth, or as a defensive weapon. *Iguanodon* was a very common inhabitant of early Cretaceous lowland habitats in much of Europe. Large accumulations of *Iguanodon* skeletons have been discovered in England, Belgium and West Germany; these may indicate that *Iguanodon* lived in herds.

**Map (below)**
**1** *Callovosaurus*
**2** *Camptosaurus*
**3** *Craspedodon*
**4** *Cumnoria*
**5** *Iguanodon*
**6** *Kangnasaurus*
**7** *Mochlodon*
**8** *Muttaburrasaurus*
**9** *Ouranosaurus*
**10** *Probactrosaurus*
**11** *Vectisaurus*

creating the long snout, and the horny beak is broader to collect more food with each bite. Having found a modern equivalent of the fabrosaurids and hypsilophodontids among the small gazelles and antelopes of today, perhaps the most appropriate comparison for the iguanodontids would be with the larger type of equid (i.e. horses), which are large-bodied and have strong legs and large, long-snouted skulls.

Turning back to look at the evolutionary history of the iguanodontids, we find that the earliest fossils come from the late Jurassic of North America and Western Europe. The earliest remains so far reported are of an animal named *Callovosaurus* ('Callovian reptile') from the late Jurassic of Northampton, England, which consists of a femur. The assignment of this specimen, which is crushed in the middle,must be uncertain for it could easily belong to a *Dryosaurus*-like animal as it is quite slender, unlike typical iguanodontids.

Apart from *Callovosaurus,* the earliest iguanodontids belong to the genus *Camptosaurus* ('flexible reptile') which is known from several skeletons discovered in 1879 in the late Jurassic of Wyoming, North America; these animals seem to range in size from about 16·5-23ft (5-7m) in length. As was the case with the two hypsilophodontid dinosaurs named *Dryosaurus* and *Dysalotosaurus,* there is another genus named *Cumnoria* which was also discovered in 1879 in late Jurassic rocks at Cumnor, near Oxford in England. This has recently been redescribed by Dr Peter Galton and Philip Powell and renamed *Camptosaurus* since it is virtually identical with the North American species. As in the case of *Dryosaurus* and *Dysalotosaurus,* the similarity between these dinosaurs from North America and Europe testifies to a land connection between these two areas well into the late Jurassic.

In early Cretaceous times a variety of iguanodontids appear in various parts of the world. *Iguanodon* ('iguana tooth') which has given its name to the family, is found abundantly right across western Europe, from Spain, Portugal and Britain in the West, to the Urals in the East. Other well-preserved genera are *Ouranosaurus* ('brave reptile') which was discovered quite recently (1965) in Niger, West Africa. Although very like *Iguanodon* in most respects, *Ouranosaurus* has a very distinctive head and extraordinarily high spines on its back. *Muttaburrasaurus* ('reptile from Muttaburra') is another newly discovered iguanodontid from Queensland, Australia. Although not as well preserved as some of the other iguanodontids, this form does appear to have an extraordinary bump on its nose, which is reminiscent of that seen in the hadrosaurid *Kritosaurus* (page 117). There are several other rather fragmentary remains that have been described including *Probactrosaurus* ('before the Bactrian reptile') from Mongolia (which may in fact be *Iguanodon* judged by what is so

**Skull Comparison (below)**
The skulls of these iguanodontids show considerable differences, despite all being large compared to the body, having long snouts, and ending in a broad, toothless beak. The *Iguanodon* skull has a generalised structure but that of *Camptosaurus* is lower at the back and has a comparatively narrower snout. The skull of *Muttaburrasaurus* is the most peculiar, with a remarkable bump above and behind its nostrils. We do not know what this was for but it may have been implicated in sexual recognition. The Mongolian form, *Iguanodon orientalis,* has a similar protruberance. These three forms represent a wide distribution for iguanodontids, coming from Europe, North America and Australia respectively.

**Jaw Muscles (below)**
The jaw muscles of *Ouranosaurus* are large and powerful as expected in a large ornithopod. Muscle 1 arises from a large opening in the skull and it has a firm insertion on to a projection of the lower jaw (coronoid process). This insertion increases the moment arm of the muscle, a measure of the force which it can produce.

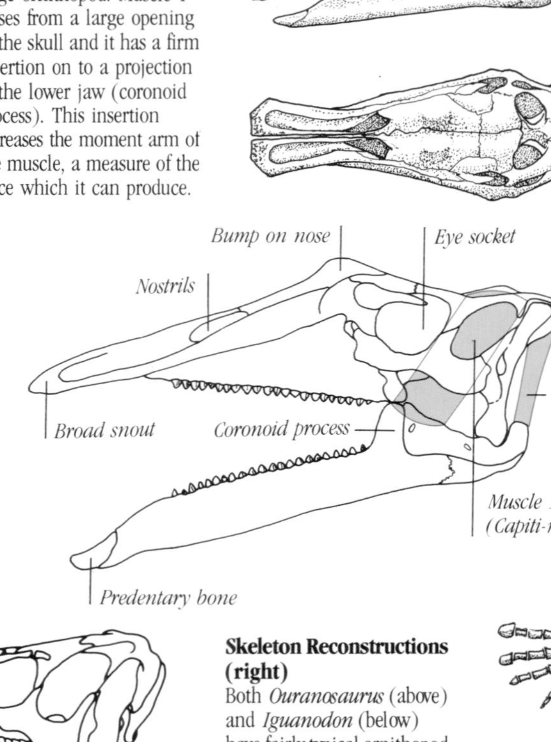


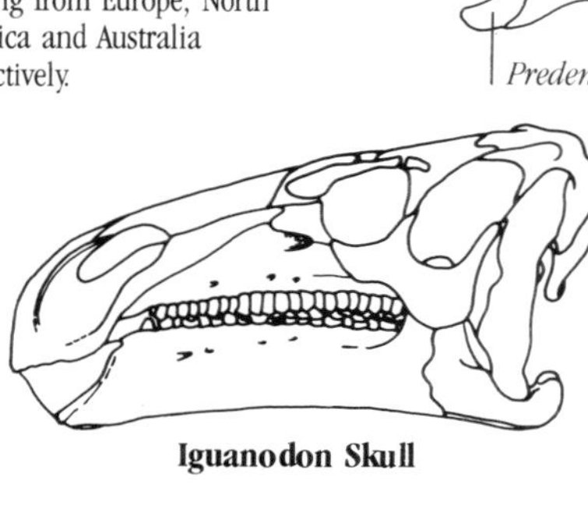

**Iguanodon Skull**

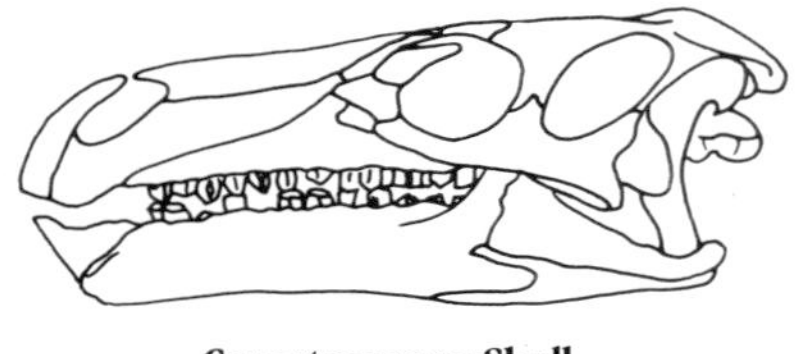

**Camptosaurus Skull**

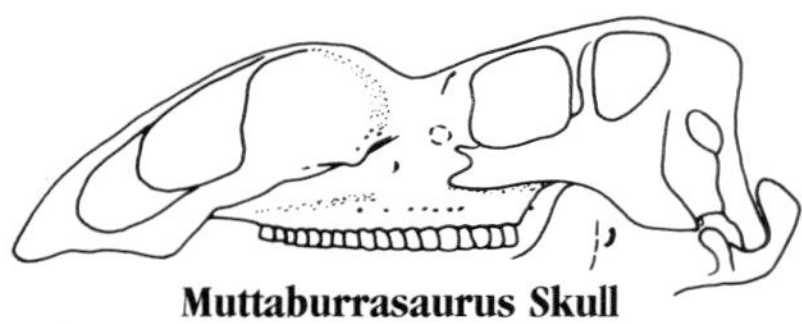

**Muttaburrasaurus Skull**

**Skeleton Reconstructions (right)**
Both *Ouranosaurus* (above) and *Iguanodon* (below) have fairly typical ornithopod skeletons. They are both bipedal, with the front legs reduced in size, but *Ouranosaurus* differs from the basic ornithopod plan in its large vertebral spines. They are both large animals, powerfully built compared with some ornithopods, and with particularly strong front legs. These may have been used in walking or resting on all-fours, rather like modern day kangaroos. This use of the front legs is quite different from that seen in the earlier ornithopods, and in fact iguanodontids are much more robust, less agile animals all round.

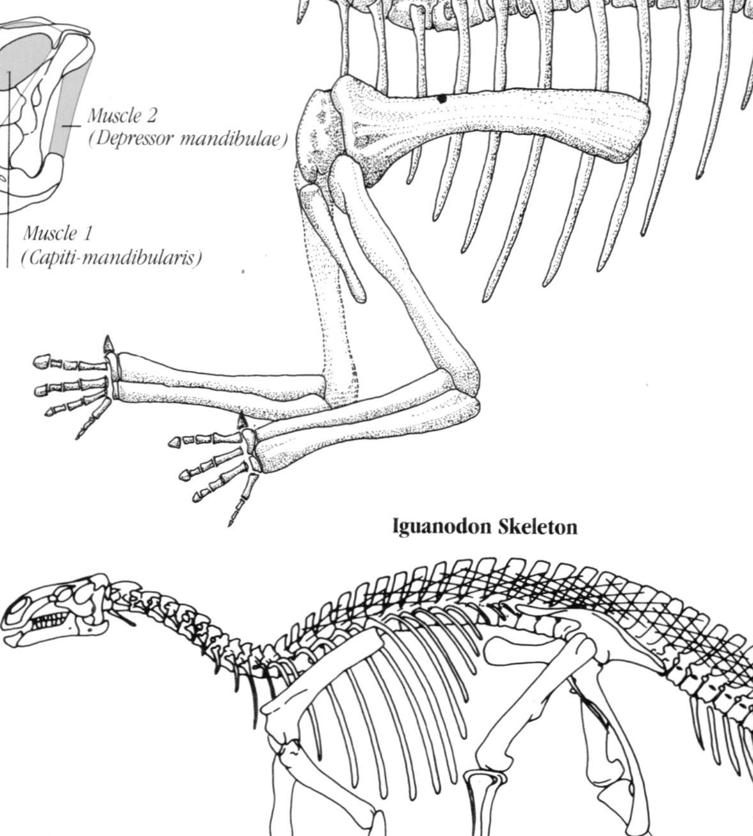

**Ouranosaurus Skeleton**

**Iguanodon Skeleton**

far known); *Vectisaurus* ('Isle of Wight reptile') from the Isle of Wight, which is definitely just *Iguanodon; Anoplosaurus* ('unarmoured reptile') from England, a very fragmentary skeleton; and *Kangnasaurus* ('Kangna's reptile') from a tooth and femur from Southern Africa that may be an iguanodontid.

The late Cretaceous seems to show a marked decline in the abundance and diversity of iguanodontids worldwide. The only record that these forms survived at all is some teeth from the late Cretaceous of Western Europe that have been named *Craspedodon* ('edge tooth'), and several incomplete skeletons of a small iguanodontid named *Mochlodon* ('bar tooth') from Rumania.

The evolution of the iguanodontids seems to tie in quite well with their biogeography. They first appear in the fossil record in the late Jurassic, and probably evolved sometime around the middle Jurassic at which time they would have been able to disperse practically worldwide, since the continents were then in contact. This is supported, partly at least, by the fact that *Camptosaurus* is found in western North America and Europe in the late Jurassic. In the early Cretaceous, seaways had begun to separate the various continents so that each was able to evolve its own distinct iguanodontid. Except, that is, for East Asia which may have received neither hypsilophodontid nor iguanodontid dinosaurs because of a sea barrier in the Jurassic. Thus the various continents show an interesting variety and abundance of iguanodontids: *Iguanodon* (Europe), *Ouranosaurus* (Africa), *Muttaburrasaurus* (Australia) and perhaps even *Kangnasaurus* (Southern Africa). However, the dispersal and evolution of iguanodontids seems to have been rapidly curtailed by the appearance of hadrosaurids in the late Cretaceous. After this time they seem to have become confined to just western Europe, where few hadrosaurids are found.

While the fortunes of the iguanodontids seem to have been adversely affected by the appearance of the hadrosaurids, they do not seem to have been so affected by the hypsilophodontids, which first appear at about the same time in the fossil record. This difference may indicate that the hypsilophodontids did not *compete,* in an ecological sense, with iguanodontids, whereas the hadrosaurids did. This means that the hypsilophodontids probably did not feed on the same sorts of plants, or generally live in the same sort of way, as did iguanodontids. This would seem reasonable because the two groups are not only very different in size, but their jaws and teeth are different. Probably they were able to co-exist quite happily. By contrast, the hadrosaurids exhibit the same body size range as the iguanodontids and their jaws and teeth are quite similar; the only real difference seems to be that the hadrosaurids have a more efficient arrangement for food grinding. The

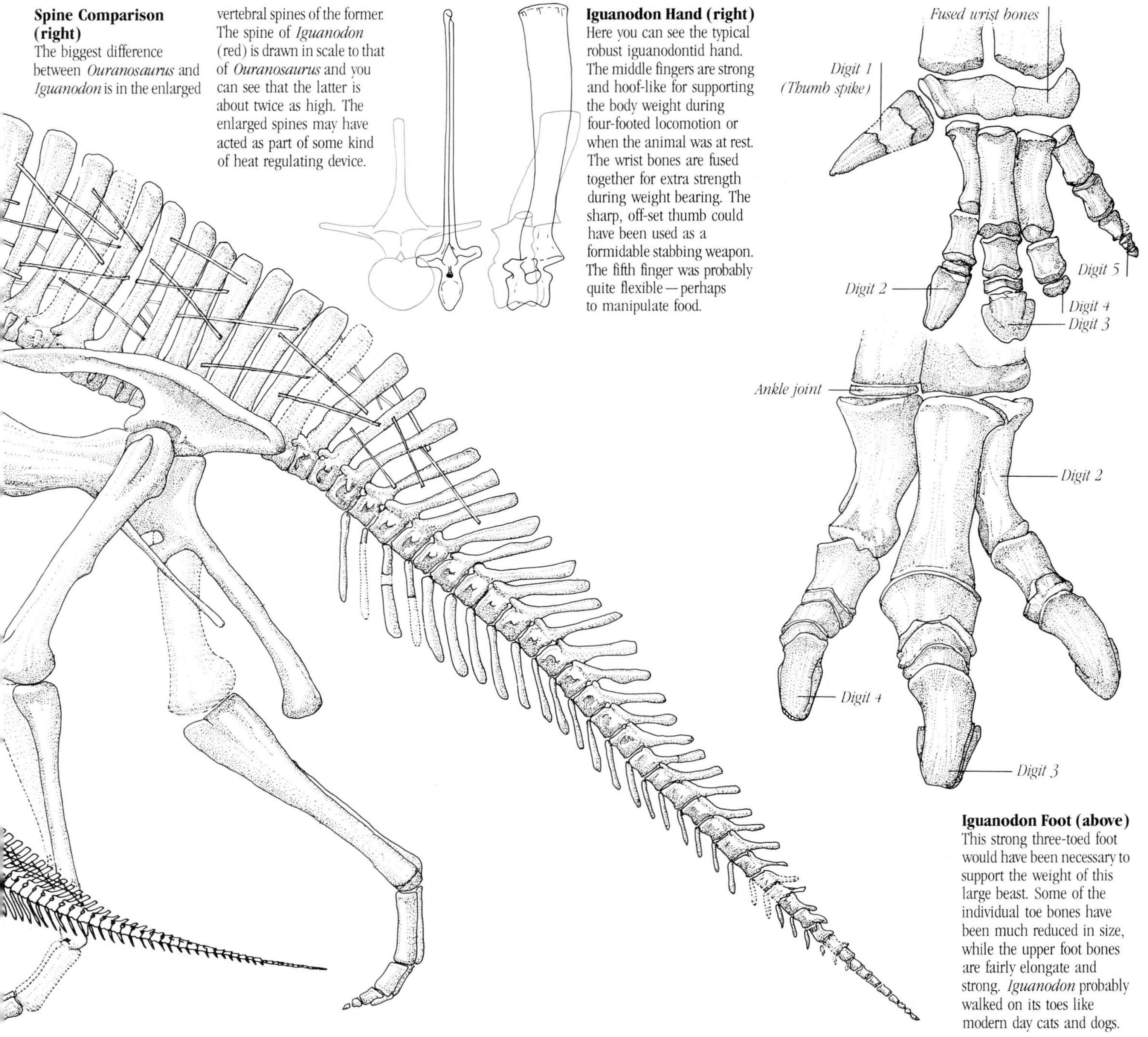


**Spine Comparison (right)**
The biggest difference between *Ouranosaurus* and *Iguanodon* is in the enlarged vertebral spines of the former. The spine of *Iguanodon* (red) is drawn in scale to that of *Ouranosaurus* and you can see that the latter is about twice as high. The enlarged spines may have acted as part of some kind of heat regulating device.

**Iguanodon Hand (right)**
Here you can see the typical robust iguanodontid hand. The middle fingers are strong and hoof-like for supporting the body weight during four-footed locomotion or when the animal was at rest. The wrist bones are fused together for extra strength during weight bearing. The sharp, off-set thumb could have been used as a formidable stabbing weapon. The fifth finger was probably quite flexible—perhaps to manipulate food.

**Iguanodon Foot (above)**
This strong three-toed foot would have been necessary to support the weight of this large beast. Some of the individual toe bones have been much reduced in size, while the upper foot bones are fairly elongate and strong. *Iguanodon* probably walked on its toes like modern day cats and dogs.

suspicions then are that these two groups probably fed on similar sorts of food and had similar sorts of life-style. Rather than peacefully co-existing, it is highly probable that these two groups of animals were so similar that they actively competed for the same resources. In this case, the most advanced or behaviourally best adapted would be expected to survive, and the less efficient to perish.

## Ouranosaurus

We have already looked at *Iguanodon* in some considerable detail in Chapter 2, so here we shall consider *Ouranosaurus*, the rather bizarre ornithopod from Niger. An almost complete skeleton of *Ouranosaurus* was discovered in 1966 near Elrhaz in Niger (West Africa). This was carefully excavated by a team of palaeontologists from the National Museum of Natural History, Paris, France, led by Dr Philippe Taquet. The skeleton was prepared and finally described in detail in 1976 by Dr Taquet.

The head of *Ouranosaurus* is very large and long, and this is especially striking when it is compared with a typical hypsilophodontid skull. In particular, the jaws are very long and have many more large teeth, while the end of the snout is very broad, flattened and toothless; in life this would have been covered by a large horny beak. The nostrils, which are formed just above the beak, are also extremely large. Immediately behind the nostrils there are a pair of low, broad bumps. The significance of these bumps is a mystery. It seems unlikely that they would have been used for defensive purposes, the most likely explanation would seem to be that they were of some behavioural significance, perhaps to aid recognition of members of the same species, or members of the opposite sex. Another rather curious feature, found in nearly all ornithischians, is the palpebral bone, which juts out across the cavity for the eye. Precisely why this should be where it is, and what it does there, is a total mystery. Behind the eye, there are large openings at the back of the skull through which passed the jaw muscles; these must have been large and powerful because of the great size of the jaws that they had to move. Associated with this arrangement is the presence of a large bony projection that sticks upward towards the back end of the lower jaw. This projection, named the coronoid process, was the point at which most of the large jaw muscles attached. In fabrosaurids there is no coronoid process and even in heterodontosaurids it is quite small. However, in the large-jawed iguanodontids (and the hadrosaurids) the coronoid process is very large. The reason for this is that it not only provides a greater attachment area for the large jaw muscles, but also greatly improves the leverage of the muscles on the jaws so that they can close the jaws more powerfully, and therefore chew food more efficiently. Of course, this all relates to the problems of being a large animal and having to feed on large quantities of plant food.

The neck is of the usual ornithopod type, and is highly flexible. The back, hips and tail, however, have the most enormous spines which form a high, almost sail-like, ridge down the back of the animal. Yet again, this animal presents us with a mystery: what are they for? One suggestion is that the skin covering the 'sail' on its back was used rather like a solar panel. Blood in the skin could be warmed by the Sun's rays so that these animals might warm up their bodies quickly—perhaps after enduring a cold night. Equally, the sail could be used as a radiator to cool the animal down in the heat of the day, or after very strenuous activity. This sort of function has recently been proposed for the plates of *Stegosaurus* (page 152), where it is supported by a lot of additional evidence. In the case of *Ouranosaurus* it is not quite so clear-cut, although a heat-regulating function is quite possible. It is also interesting to note that the carnivorous dinosaur *Spinosaurus*, which appears to have lived at the same time and in the same area as *Ouranosaurus*, also had tall spines on its back. Presumably both dinosaurs grew spines for a similar reason, although the actual cause, whether physiological, behavioural or ecological, is not yet clear.

In most respects the forelimb of *Ouranosaurus* is very similar to that of *Iguanodon*. It is fairly long in comparison with the hindlimb and could have reached the ground quite easily. The claws on its second and third fingers are also very broad and hoof-like for use when walking or resting on 'all-fours'. In addition, the wrist bones are very large and welded together so that the weight of the body would not dislocate them when the hands were used for walking. As in *Iguanodon*, the hand is equipped with a very large thumb-spike that would have made a formidable defensive weapon against large predatory theropods. The fifth finger is quite long and flexible, and may well have been used for holding or plucking plant stems or twigs.

The hindlimb of *Ouranosaurus* is much more heavily built than that of *Hypsilophodon*. The individual bones are much more massive to support the great weight of the body, while the proportions of the bones are rather different. The femur (upper leg bone) is longer,

**Above:** This skeleton cast of *Iguanodon* in Frankfurt's Senckenberg Museum is seen in a more conventional bipedal posture. It illustrates the generally massive build of these creatures, and the special nature of the hands with their thumb spikes for defence against predators, and 'hoofed' digits.

**Left:** On display in the Palaeontological Institute of the Academy of Sciences in Moscow, this is *Probactrosaurus mongoliensis*. Although the skull is not completely known, the dinosaur seems very similar to—and may even be—*Iguanodon*. The pose is interesting; it suggests quadrupedal motion.

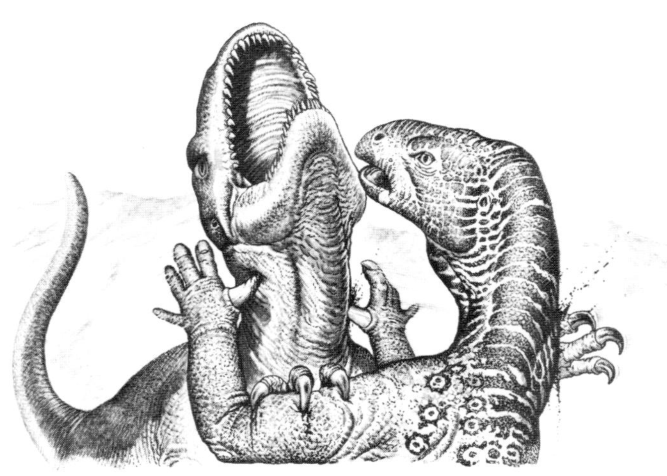

**Self Defence (below)**
A fully grown iguanodontid must have posed a formidable challenge to any potential predator. Here we see a 'carnosaur' being viciously stabbed by an *Iguanodon* using its thumb spike to good effect. At close quarters, *Iguanodon* was probably more than a match for most attackers.

while the tibia (lower leg) is shorter and the foot is much shorter, more compact and only has three toes. All these changes indicate that the legs were designed primarily to act as pillars, rather than to move the animal quickly as was the case with hypsilophodontids.

### Camptosaurus and Muttaburrasaurus

Of the other iguanodontids, *Camptosaurus* from North America and Europe is well described and resembles quite closely both *Iguanodon* and *Ouranosaurus*. The main differences are to be found in the head, hands, hips and feet. The head of *Camptosaurus* is long, but quite low when compared with *Iguanodon,* and it lacks *Ouranosaurus'* bumps on the nose and its very broad muzzle.

The backbone is much more ordinary and '*Iguanodon*-like' in its construction, with no tall spines. The forelimb differs slightly from that of *Iguanodon* in that the hand has a short spur-like first finger, rather than a distinct spike; also the claws on fingers two and three are more curved and less hoof-like. However, *Camptosaurus* does possess the large bony wrist to enable it to walk on all-fours.

As far as the hips are concerned, the pubis has a very long, narrow, posterior rod, which reaches the end of the ischium. In *Iguanodon* and *Ouranosaurus,* the posterior rod of the pubis only reaches about half-way down the ischium. Finally, its foot possesses four, well-developed toes, while there are only three in *Iguanodon* and *Ouranosaurus*.

*Muttaburrasaurus* is not known from such well-preserved material as the other iguanodontids mentioned above, but those features that have survived seem to share similarities with the iguanodontids, and in particular with *Camptosaurus*. However, unlike *Camptosaurus,* the head has a large bump between the nostrils at the front of the snout—different from the double bumps seen *behind* the nostrils in *Ouranosaurus*. Unfortunately, the hand is not completely known, so it is not certain that it possessed a large thumb-spike as did *Iguanodon* or *Ouranosaurus*. The illustration on page 110 shows it with a thumb spike, but this is speculative.

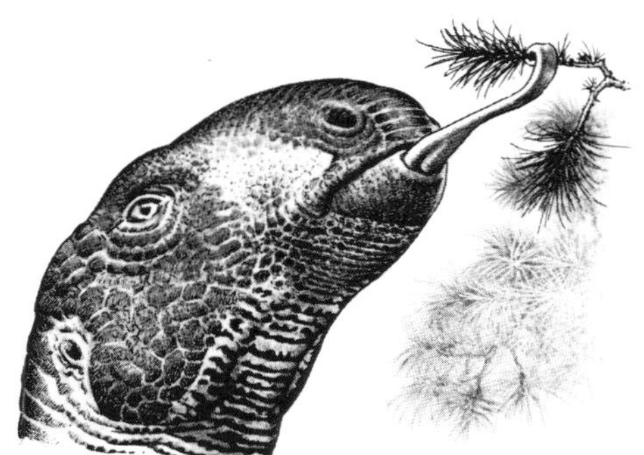

**Reptilian Giraffe? (above)** This drawing is based on Gerhard Heilmann's 1928 restoration that pictured *Iguanodon* with a prehensile tongue being used to gather foliage. Heilmann was influenced by Louis Dollo who had noticed an opening at the front of *Iguanodon's* lower jaw and surmised that its tongue could extend through it. In fact the hole was broken bone; there is no evidence to support Dollo's view.

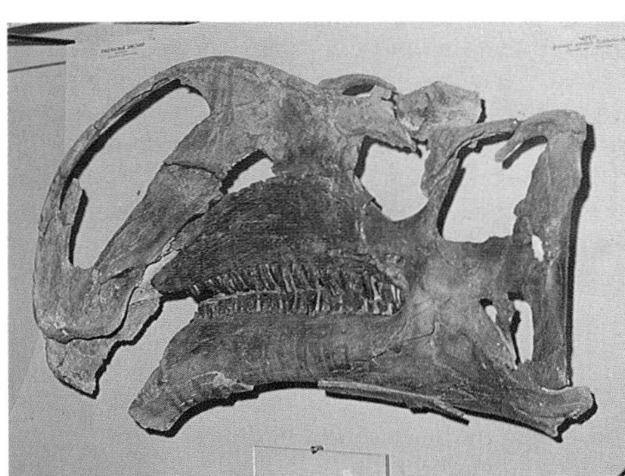

**Above:** This fine skull of *Iguanodon orientalis* from Mongolia is very similar to European *Iguanodon* except for its enormous bulbous 'nose'. This is a totally unexpected feature and of great scientific interest.

**Below:** The impressive skeleton of *Ouranosaurus nigeriensis* in the Museo Civico di Storia Naturale, Venice. The remarkable dorsal 'sail' may have acted like a solar panel for temperature regulation.

### Life-Style

Iguanodontids, therefore, would seem to represent the first group of large-bodied ornithopods to evolve. They show characteristic differences when compared to the hypsilophodontids (and fabrosaurids), changes which are largely explicable in terms of the greater size of these animals and the simple physical and biological changes that this entails. The sort of life that these particular creatures led is not too difficult to deduce. Their larger size rendered them slower and less agile than the previous groups and much more liable to attack from the large, megalosaur-type predators of the time: *Allosaurus, Ceratosaurus Altispinax, Spinosaurus* etc. Rather than being evasive, these dinosaurs seem to have used defensive weapons to repel predators. All of them (except perhaps *Muttaburrasaurus* for which evidence is not yet available) had a spur-like claw on the first finger of the hand which would have been a surprisingly effective weapon. All of the large predatory dinosaurs named above possess characteristically massive heads, perched on quite short but powerful necks and relatively short forelimbs. This means that in order to make an attack, these predators would have to lunge at their prey from close-quarters, bringing them into range of the iguanodontid's forelimb spur. At close-quarters the spur, swung with all the weight of the massive body behind it, could cause hideous injuries to the eyes, face or neck of the predator.

Large accumulations of skeletons of *Iguanodon* in Belgium and Germany, and tracks of footprints from England, provide circumstantial evidence of the social behaviour of this type of dinosaur. Large numbers of fossil skeletons suggest that they were very numerous and by implication quite successful for their time. Footprint trackways, particularly in southern England, seem to show several dinosaurs moving about in the same direction at the same time—perhaps as a herd. Herding, if it did take place, is another important method of gaining protection from predators (see also sauropod herding, page 97). Looking at *Iguanodon,* the largest fully grown individuals were 33ft (10m) or more in length and probably sufficiently large to be practically invulnerable to attack. The prime subjects for attack would undoubtedly have been old or infirm individuals or the smaller, less powerful, young ones. Herding allows animals to protect themselves, and particularly the more vulnerable individuals, by structuring the herd so that the young (and perhaps pregnant females) stay near the centre, while the larger adults (perhaps exclusively the males if they are the larger) patrol the edges as 'look-outs' in order to give the alarm and defend the herd from predators.

The remains of *Iguanodon* are frequently found in lowland, marshy or estuarine areas in Britain and Europe and it seems quite possible that these animals lived in herds in such areas, feeding on the rich vegetation that would be expected to grow in such conditions. The plants growing in these areas were probably primarily horsetails (*Equisetum*), ferns, cyads, bennettitaleans and various conifers; many of these, athough we do not know exactly which, would have formed the diet of these animals.

# HADROSAURIDS I

Hadrosaurids were the last group of ornithopods to evolve, appearing as they did in the middle of the Cretaceous Period. Despite their relatively short time of existence—they perished along with all other dinosaurs at the end of the Cretaceous Period (some 30 million years later)—hadrosaurids evolved spectacularly into a remarkable variety of types. As you will see by looking carefully at the variety of hadrosaurids illustrated in the following pages, the main differences between the many species are found in the shape of the heads of these creatures; the bodies of virtually all the hadrosaurids are remarkably similar. Indeed, hadrosaurid body shape is just the same as seen in the earlier iguanodontids apart from a few relatively minor changes. For example, hadrosaurids have no thumb at all and have slightly differently shaped hip-bones.

The first hadrosaur skeleton was described in 1858 by Joseph Leidy, an American palaeontologist. The remains were excavated by William Parker Foulke from a marl pit at Haddonfield, New Jersey. Apparently Foulke had heard that many large reptile bones, probably vertebrae, had been excavated from the pit about twenty years earlier, but these remains had been scattered and lost. So in 1858 Foulke re-located the pit, which had been filled in and was overgrown again, and re-excavated it in the hope of finding more of the same animal. At a depth of about 10 feet (3m) a pile of fossil bones was discovered including twenty-eight vertebrae, teeth and bones of the forelimb, hindlimb and pelvis; these remains were described by Leidy in 1858 and if complete would probably have resembled *Kritosaurus* ('chosen reptile') below. Leidy immediately recognized similarities between the shape of the teeth of this new animal (which he named *Hadrosaurus foulkii,* 'Foulke's big reptile') and the then known British dinosaur *Iguanodon.* However, as noted earlier, *Iguanodon* was at this time rather poorly known, having only

**Bactrosaurus (below)**
This is one of the earliest hadrosaurs. Although *Bactrosaurus* lacked a crest, it seems to be related to later 'lambeosaurine' hadrosaurs such as *Corythosaurus* and *Parasaurolophus* (see pages 122-123). Like all other hadrosaurs, *Bactrosaurus* had batteries of cheek teeth set well back in the mouth which could have ground up very tough plant material. *Bactrosaurus* was a fairly small hadrosaur, being only 20ft (6m) long.

**Time Chart (left)**
The uncrested hadrosaurine hadrosaurs are notably abundant in the very last part of the Cretaceous. Perhaps they were better able to cope with the harsher climate and vegetation than the crested lambeosaurine forms (see pages 122-127).

**Anatosaurus (below)**
This was a common hadrosaur, and it is one of the best known 'crestless' forms. It was a large animal, normally c. 33ft (10m) long, and weighing about 3 tonnes. The massive limbs and the broad 'duck bill' are very clear in this front view. *Anatosaurus* could have gathered up large amounts of vegetation in its broad mouth, and it had batteries of strong cheek teeth.

**Comparative Sizes (left)**
1 *Bactrosaurus:* l. 13-20ft (4-6m).
2 *Kritosaurus:* l. 30ft (9m)
3 *Anatosaurus:* l. 33-42ft (10-13m).
4 *Edmontosaurus:* l. 33-42ft (10-13m).

been described from fragmentary remains, and was believed to look rather like a giant reptilian rhinoceros. Leidy quickly recognized that although *Hadrosaurus* had teeth like those of *Iguanodon,* it did not look at all like a reptilian rhinoceros because its front legs were much shorter than its back ones. Indeed he suggested that the animal might have stood upright when feeding, rather like a kangaroo resting on its back legs and tail, dropping down on to 'all-fours' to creep along the ground in a rather toad-like manner.

So it was that Leidy was able to provide a much more accurate picture of the shape and proportions of ornithopod dinosaurs such as *Iguanodon* and *Hadrosaurus* from the fortunate discovery of a single incomplete skeleton—a feat that neither Mantell nor Owen had managed despite having studied remains of *Iguanodon* for nearly forty years. The discovery of complete skeletons of *Iguanodon* in 1878 finally proved the correctness of Leidy's views.

Another of the earliest hadrosaurids known is *Bactrosaurus* ('reptile from Bactria') from Mongolia pictured below; it comes from rocks dated at the early part of the Upper Cretaceous Period. In its general appearance this animal resembles iguanodontids very strongly. It does, however, show, in the structure of its teeth in particular, the development of a grinding battery. Unfortunately the fossilized remains so far discovered do not include its hands, so it is uncertain whether this dinosaur possessed an iguanodontid thumb-spike or whether it was like all other hadrosaurids and had only four fingers on its hand.

At least two types of early hadrosaurid are known from Mongolia, the other is known as *Gilmoreosaurus* (named after Charles Witney Gilmore, the palaeontologist who first described this fossil in the 1930s). As with *Bactrosaurus, Gilmoreosaurus* is not at all well preserved so that its detailed anatomy is very unclear. After these early first appearances, hadrosaurids seem to

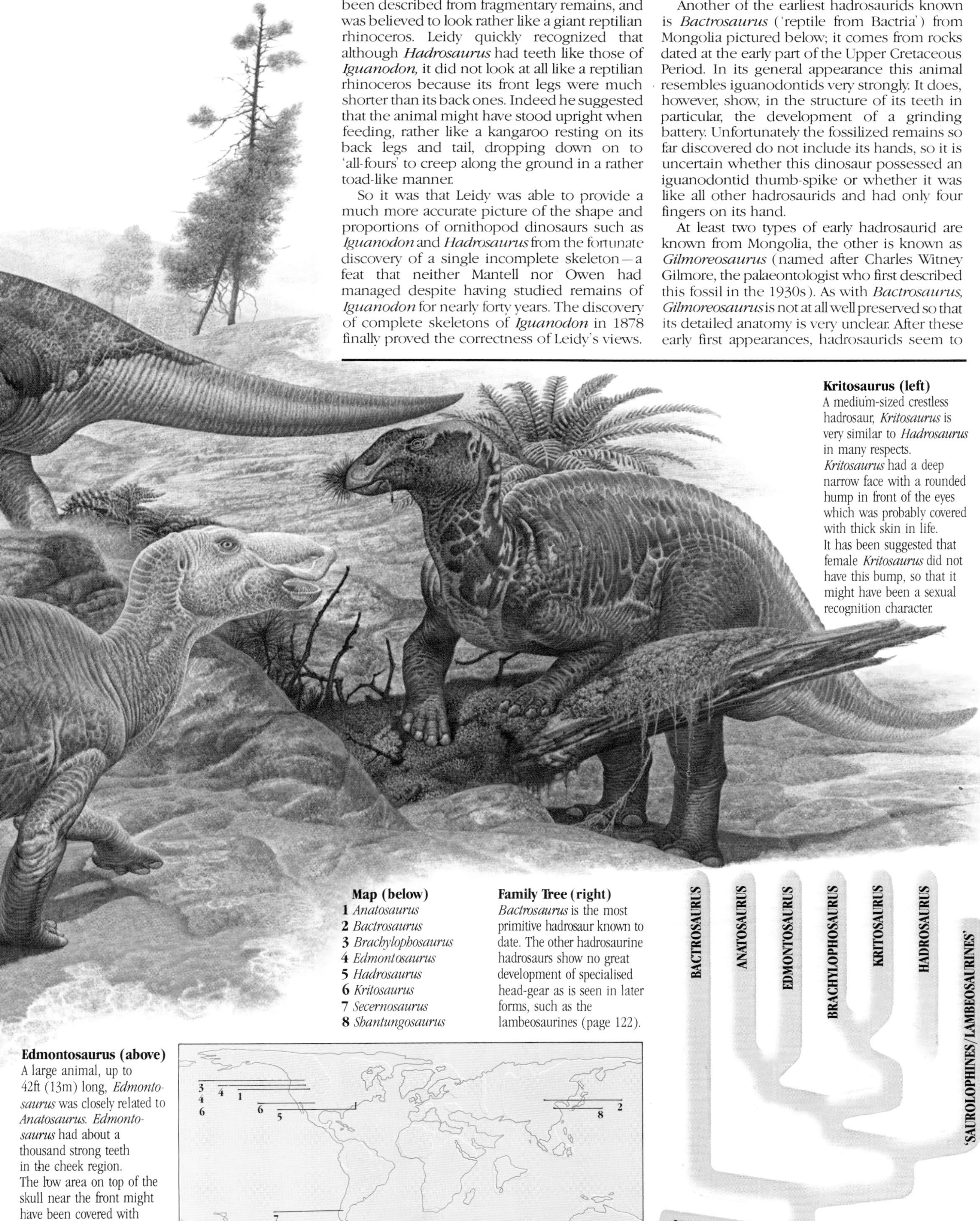


**Kritosaurus (left)**
A medium-sized crestless hadrosaur, *Kritosaurus* is very similar to *Hadrosaurus* in many respects. *Kritosaurus* had a deep narrow face with a rounded hump in front of the eyes which was probably covered with thick skin in life. It has been suggested that female *Kritosaurus* did not have this bump, so that it might have been a sexual recognition character.

**Map (below)**
1 *Anatosaurus*
2 *Bactrosaurus*
3 *Brachylophosaurus*
4 *Edmontosaurus*
5 *Hadrosaurus*
6 *Kritosaurus*
7 *Secernosaurus*
8 *Shantungosaurus*

**Family Tree (right)**
*Bactrosaurus* is the most primitive hadrosaur known to date. The other hadrosaurine hadrosaurs show no great development of specialised head-gear as is seen in later forms, such as the lambeosaurines (page 122).

**Edmontosaurus (above)**
A large animal, up to 42ft (13m) long, *Edmontosaurus* was closely related to *Anatosaurus*. *Edmontosaurus* had about a thousand strong teeth in the cheek region. The low area on top of the skull near the front might have been covered with loose skin which could have been inflated to make a loud bellowing call.

have evolved very rapidly producing a considerable variety of different species (including *Anatosaurus*, 'duck reptile', and *Edmontosaurus*, 'reptile from Edmonton' seen here), which are found quite widely distributed.

## Hadrosaurid Life-Style

In addition to the perceptive comments that he made on the structure of hadrosaurids, Leidy also made several observations concerning the way of life of *Hadrosaurus* which deserve some consideration. He proposed that *Hadrosaurus* was probably an amphibious creature, living in and around water courses. Quite why he thought this is not clear from what he wrote; perhaps the notion that it crawled along like a giant toad, in combination with his observation that it had a rather deep, paddle-like tail convinced Leidy of this way of life. Whatever the reasons, his ideas were adopted wholeheartedly by later palaeontologists working on these animals. In 1883, Edward Drinker Cope went so far as to state that hadrosaurids had very weak, broad, horny beaks and small loosely attached teeth in their jaws which could only have been used for scooping up and chewing soft aquatic plants. Indeed he proposed that they probably habitually waded in deep water upon their long legs rather like gigantic flamingoes. Further evidence for the supposed aquatic or semi-aquatic way of life of hadrosaurids came from the discovery of 'mummified' remains of another hadrosaurid (*Anatosaurus*) in 1908 by C.H. and C.M. Sternberg. Both of these skeletons showed evidence of a mitten-like covering of skin over the hand giving it the form of a paddle. The evidence then would seem to be very persuasive in favour of Leidy's original proposal that *Hadrosaurus* was amphibious. Indeed many books on dinosaurs feature hadrosaurs wallowing in lakes or on the banks of rivers, chewing water plants. However, there is an argument that favours a way of life for hadrosaurids away from lakes and rivers. This is based on a careful analysis of the geological nature of the rocks in which hadrosaurids have been found, evidence from the plant fossils preserved with these dinosaurs and a detailed analysis of their anatomy.

(i) The geological evidence suggests that hadrosaurids in North America lived in areas that were coastal plains, close to sea-level with swamps and large meandering rivers. This fits well with the notion that they were amphibious creatures. However, it would also be a reflection of the environment in which the carcasses of these animals were deposited after they had died and been washed down into swampy or lake areas.

(ii) One of the main pieces of evidence concerning the environment in which hadrosaurs lived comes from the plants preserved with these dinosaurs. An analysis of these plant fossils has suggested that they grew in warm

**Hadrosaurid Teeth (below)**
Hadrosaurid jaws contain a formidable array of hundreds of teeth arranged in batteries on either side of both upper and lower jaws. These teeth acted like a rasping file and could deal with tough vegetation. The front end of the jaws was formed into a wide beak. The drawing below is a cross section through top and bottom jaws, showing how an up-and-down chewing action would cause the teeth to rub abrasively past one another and so crush the plant food. The drawing lower right is solely of the lower jaw. It clearly shows the tooth batteries.

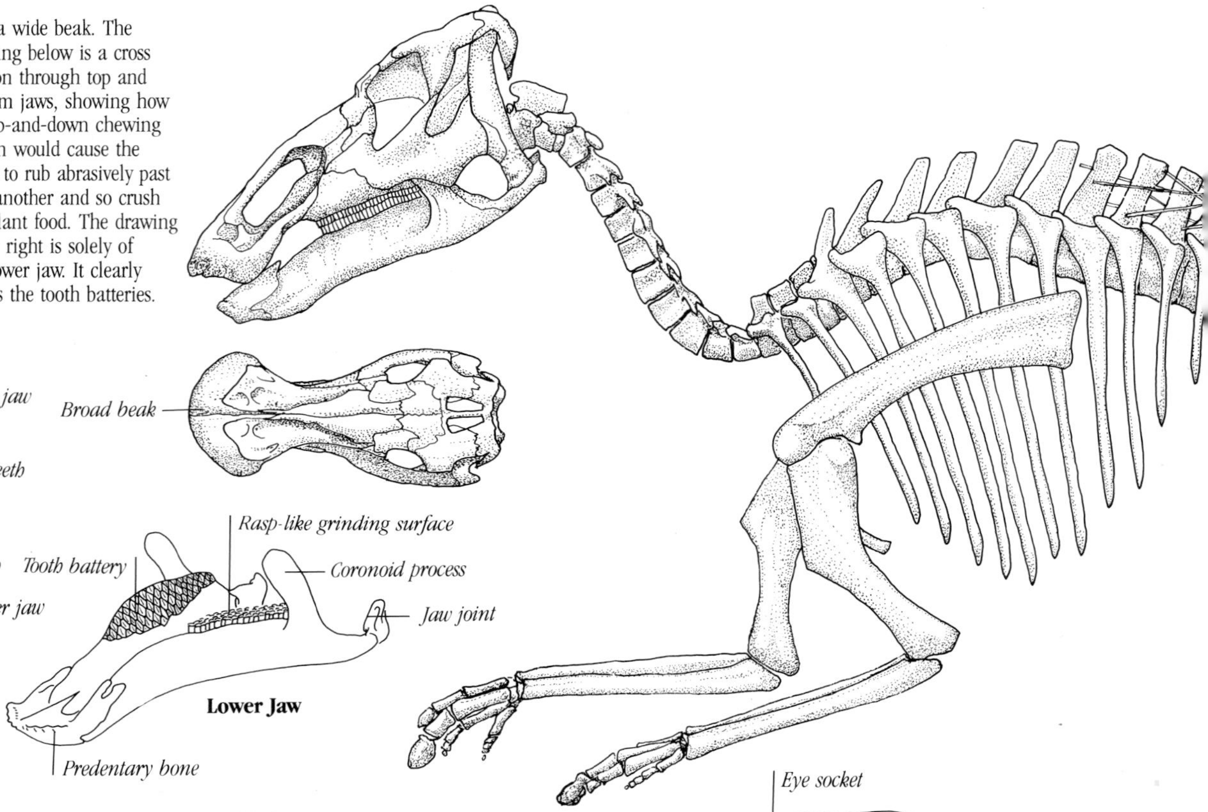

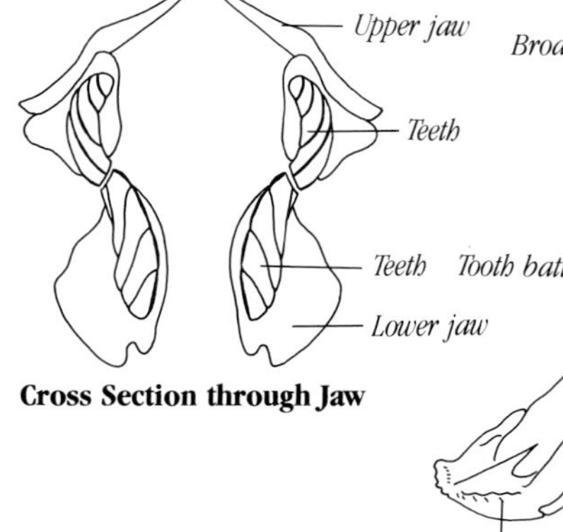

**Cross Section through Jaw**

Broad beak

Rasp-like grinding surface
Tooth battery
Coronoid process
Jaw joint
Predentary bone

**Lower Jaw**

**Hadrosaurid Skulls (right)**
The skulls drawn here and on page 125 show the tremendous variety in the hadrosaurid skull. The three forms here belong to the 'hadrosaurines'. These had large duck-like beaks but little development of the crest, as you can see if you compare the regions coloured red here, which delineate the area of the nasal passages, with those on page 125. The back of the skull in all forms does not change very much which is surprising when you consider what is happening at the front! Even the three crestless forms here show some variation in their snouts: *Bactrosaurus* is very generalised, rather like an iguanodontid, *Kritosaurus* has an unusual bump on its nose and *Anatosaurus* has an extremely long, broad snout, which gave rise to the description 'duck-billed'.

**Kritosaurus Skull**

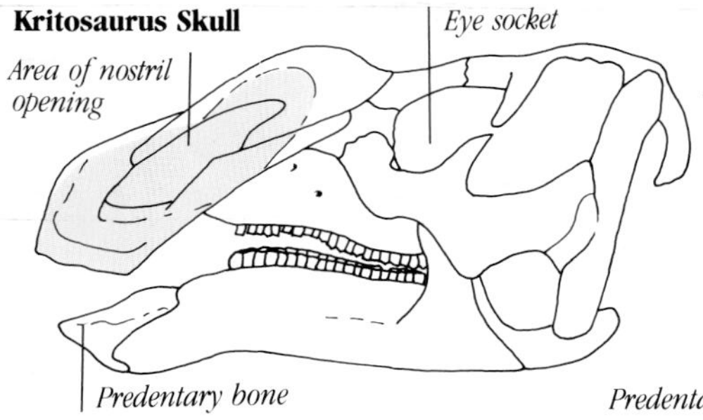

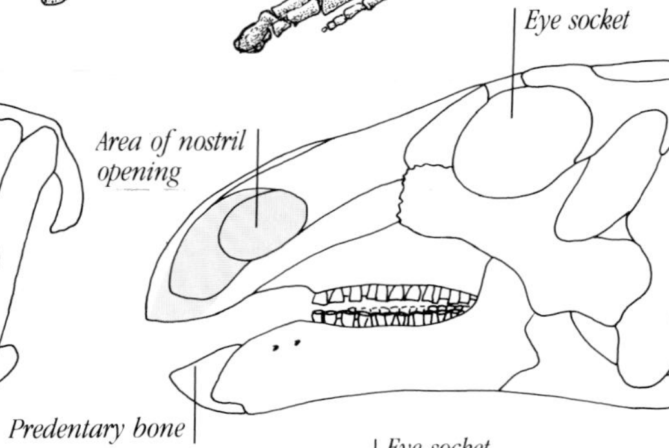

Area of nostril opening
Eye socket
Predentary bone

Area of nostril opening
Eye socket
Predentary bone

**Anatosaurus Skull**

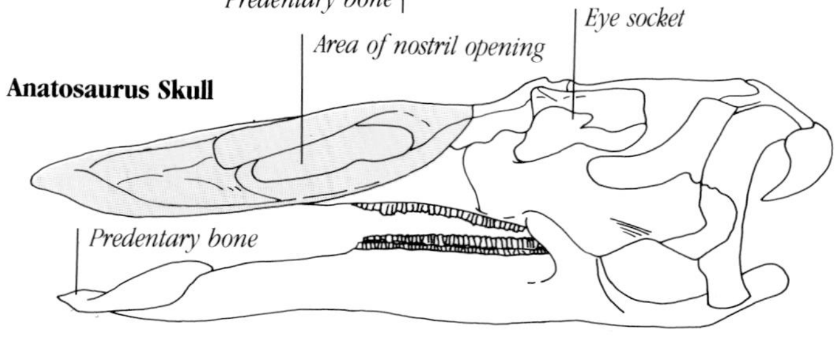

Area of nostril opening
Eye socket
Predentary bone

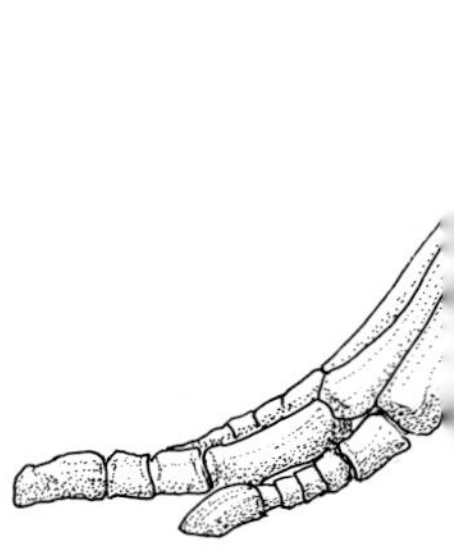

temperate or subtropical conditions in humid, lowland areas. The plants themselves, however, are represented by very *few* aquatic or marginal pond weeds but by abundant remains of lowland forest trees and shrubs: dominated by conifers, poplars, willows and oaks. Thus most plant food seems to have been on land.

(iii) The animals living (or rather preserved as fossils) with the hadrosaurids include hypsilophodontids, ankylosaurids, ceratopians, sauropods, tyrannosaurids, and other smaller theropods. Very few of these types of dinosaur have ever been thought of as being aquatic or amphibious — only the sauropods, but there is quite convincing evidence that these animals probably only ventured into water occasionally.

(iv) The anatomical evidence consists of two main lines of enquiry. Firstly, what their diet may have been? And secondly, are there any anatomical features that clearly demonstrate that these animals were either *exclusively* amphibious or terrestrial?

## Hadrosaurid Diets

Cope's claim that hadrosaurids had soft, weak, beaks and fragile teeth seems to have been mistaken, and probably reflected the poor state of the material that he had to work on at the time. The teeth of hadrosaurids are anything but weak (see below); they are in fact arranged in dental batteries, each with hundreds of teeth in each jaw. The teeth are cemented together by bony tissue and form a long grinding surface (rather like a rasp, a carpenter's coarse file) which could have been used to pound up tough plants, even woody twigs. The teeth of hadrosaurids do not therefore predispose them to feed upon soft, succulent aquatic plants. Similarly the horny beaks can hardly be regarded as weak either. The obvious comparison that has been drawn here is between hadrosaurid beaks and ducks' bills (hence the common name for these dinosaurs: 'duck-billed dinosaurs'). The implication is that hadrosaurids grovelled about in muddy ponds and streams for small shrimps and water weeds as do ducks today. However, the outward similarity between a duck's bill and the beak of a hadrosaur is contradicted by the lack of teeth in the duck's jaws compared with the massive tooth batteries of hadrosaurids. Also a duck-like existence does seem a little improbable for a 2-3 tonne hadrosaurid! A far better comparison, particularly with regard to the beak, would be with the turtles and tortoises which have sharp, horny beaks. Such a tough, sharp and continuously growing beak would have been well suited to nipping off twigs and stripping leaves from branches.

However, the most convincing piece of evidence of all was that provided by Kräusel who, in 1922, analysed the fossilized stomach contents of one of the hadrosaur 'mummies' (now preserved in the Senckenberg Museum, West Germany). This showed that its stomach contained conifer needles and twigs, seeds and

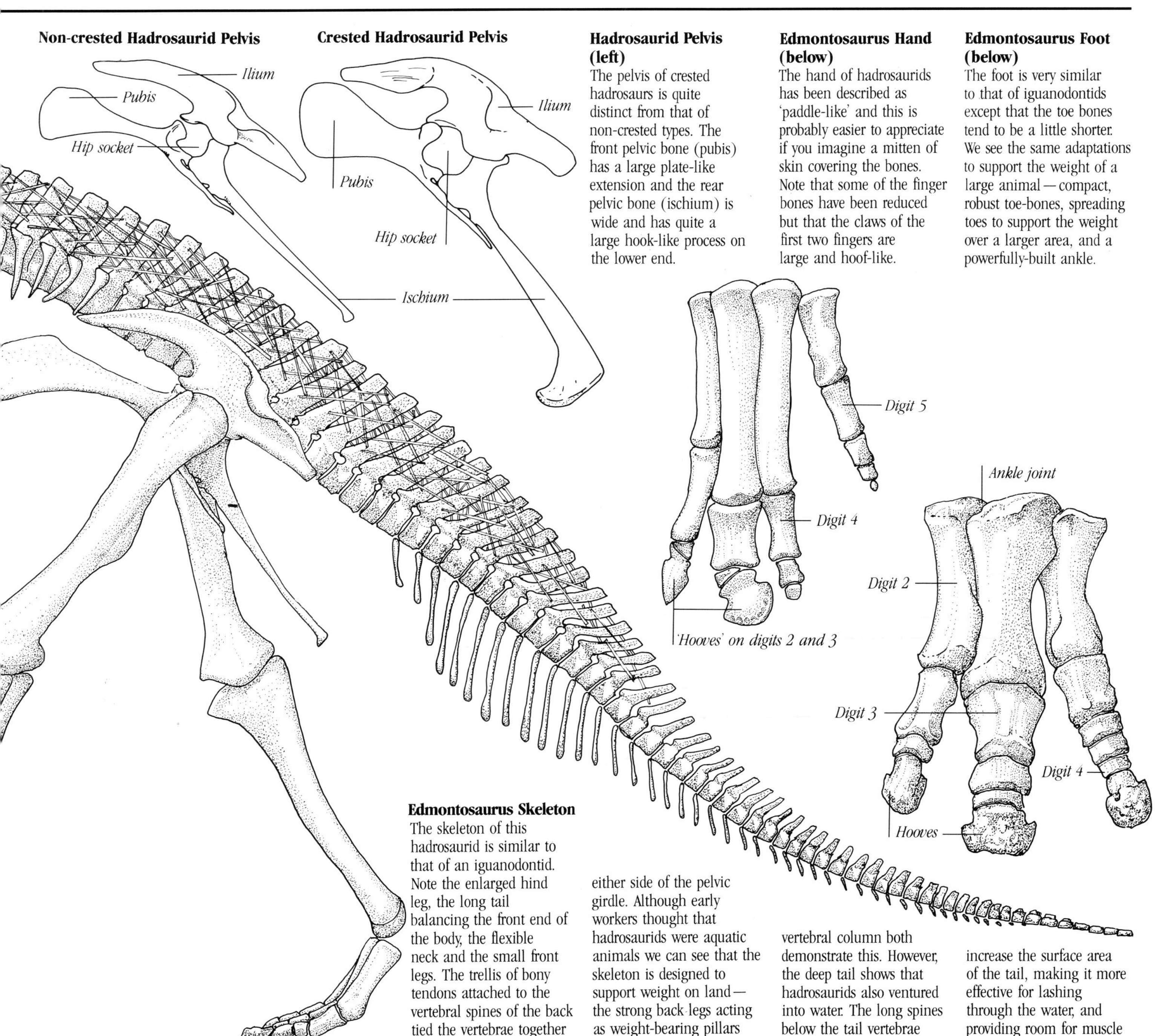


**Hadrosaurid Pelvis (left)**
The pelvis of crested hadrosaurs is quite distinct from that of non-crested types. The front pelvic bone (pubis) has a large plate-like extension and the rear pelvic bone (ischium) is wide and has quite a large hook-like process on the lower end.

**Edmontosaurus Hand (below)**
The hand of hadrosaurids has been described as 'paddle-like' and this is probably easier to appreciate if you imagine a mitten of skin covering the bones. Note that some of the finger bones have been reduced but that the claws of the first two fingers are large and hoof-like.

**Edmontosaurus Foot (below)**
The foot is very similar to that of iguanodontids except that the toe bones tend to be a little shorter. We see the same adaptations to support the weight of a large animal — compact, robust toe-bones, spreading toes to support the weight over a larger area, and a powerfully-built ankle.

**Edmontosaurus Skeleton**
The skeleton of this hadrosaurid is similar to that of an iguanodontid. Note the enlarged hind leg, the long tail balancing the front end of the body, the flexible neck and the small front legs. The trellis of bony tendons attached to the vertebral spines of the back tied the vertebrae together so that the body did not sag either side of the pelvic girdle. Although early workers thought that hadrosaurids were aquatic animals we can see that the skeleton is designed to support weight on land — the strong back legs acting as weight-bearing pillars and trellis-strengthened vertebral column both demonstrate this. However, the deep tail shows that hadrosaurids also ventured into water. The long spines below the tail vertebrae (haemal spines) would increase the surface area of the tail, making it more effective for lashing through the water, and providing room for muscle attachment.

other land plants. All of this evidence points to hadrosaurids having a diet of land plants rather than one exclusively of soft aquatic plants.

### Anatomical Features

The main anatomical evidence for the likely environment of hadrosaurids comes from the posture of the animal. The body is balanced at the hips, as in typical ornithopods, and the hindlimbs are long and arranged so that they act as pillars, so as to support the weight of the body most effectively. The foot is also arranged so that the three toes splay outward, forming a broad contact with the ground for good grip and balance. In addition, the ankle region is very powerfully built, presumably in order to prevent dislocation of this joint during walking and running. Another curious feature of hadrosaurids, and all other ornithopods as well, is the presence of a trellis-like arrangement of bony rods (ossified tendons or ligaments) found alongside the spines on the back, in front of, and behind the hip region of the animal (see below right). These rods most probably acted like hawsers supporting the backbone of the animal which would have naturally tended to sag on either side of the hips. Indeed we can turn to engineering for a comparable arrangement. The trellis-like arrangement of bony rods is precisely like that of the supporting struts of a balanced cantilever bridge. Thus we have another list of features that seem most readily explicable if these animals lived on land rather than in the water.

However, against this evidence, there is the undoubted paddle-like structure of the hand and the very deep tail. It has also been claimed that the extraordinary tubes and crests found on the heads of some hadrosaurids (pages 122-123) served as 'snorkels' for underwater breathing, as reserve 'air tanks', or as 'air-traps' to prevent water flooding the lungs. However, each of these suggestions is untenable. The 'snorkel' idea relied on the presence of holes in the tops of the crests—there were none; the 'air tank' idea is implausible because the crests could only have stored a minute amount of air; and the 'air-trap' idea simply would not work! The most likely function of the peculiar head-gear of hadrosaurids is discussed on pages 126-127.

### Drawing Conclusions

So, having looked at the various features that may have a bearing on the way of life of hadrosaurids, is there a satisfactory interpretation? Well, the answer seems to be yes, there is! Hadrosaurids were probably land living browsers, feeding on the abundant vegetation of the fertile lowland areas of North America, and elsewhere. Their bodies were clearly designed to cope with the problems of support and movement on land, and their jaws and teeth were well able to cope with the abundant woody plant material available at the time. This is confirmed by the discovery of fossilized stomach contents in one example. The presence of the deep tail and paddle-like hand indicates that these animals were certainly capable of swimming; however, they may not have swum ***habitually.*** One suggestion which seems quite plausible is that hadrosaurids may have retreated into deep water to escape from predators such as the large tyrannosaurids. Hadrosaurids had no notable defensive weapons; they had no large teeth, claws or spikes to fight with and had lost the large thumb-spike so characteristic of the earlier iguanodontids; they were also probably far too large and heavy-footed to be able to outrun predators, so that an ability to escape into deeper swamps may have been very useful.

### Feeding and Evolution

Having seen that hadrosaurids were capable of feeding on very tough plant food such as conifer needles and twigs, let us look in a little detail at precisely how they were able to do this. As has been seen earlier in the iguanodontids, these animals have rather long snouts and heavy jaws with many teeth, which in hadrosaurids are cemented together to form batteries. Chewing of tough plant fibres wears the teeth down to produce a flat grinding surface. Precisely how these animals moved their jaws while chewing has been studied in some detail.

At first it was thought that hadrosaurids were able to slide their lower jaw backwards and forwards to produce a grinding action on the food trapped between the teeth. This was supposed to be possible because the jaw hinge was quite loose to allow the jaw to slide, and because they had special muscles that were able to pull the jaw backwards and forwards. This model indicated that these animals chewed their food in the same way that rats and elephants do today. However, further detailed study of hadrosaurid teeth and jaws proved that their jaws could not have worked in this way. The arguments are quite detailed, but put very simply can be expressed in this way. The grinding ability of teeth depends on their roughness. The example of the carpenter's rasp is a very good one. Teeth can create this 'roughness' by being made of different materials (enamel which is very hard and covers your teeth, and dentine which is slightly softer). As teeth are worn down with use, they develop ridges of resistant enamel separated by grooves of softer dentine. In hadrosaurids the ridges of enamel are found arranged along the length of the jaw. If the jaws moved only backwards and

**Above:** A restoration of the skeleton of an infant *Maiasaura;* this specimen is about 3ft (1m) long, whereas an adult grew to about 29ft (9m) in length. The discovery of infants in a nesting colony suggests that *Maiasaura* actively cared for their young.

**Below:** Still encased in half its supporting field jacket of plaster of paris and burlap (sacking), this skull of *Edmontosaurus* is from the Belly River Formation of Alberta, Canada. It was excavated in the 1920s by Charles Sternberg junior, and is now in the British Museum (Natural History).

**Signalling Devices (left)** These drawings show how *Edmontosaurus* may have been equipped with an inflatable sac on its nose that it could use as a resonator to produce distinctive calls to attract or warn members of its group, rather in the manner that elephant seals do today.

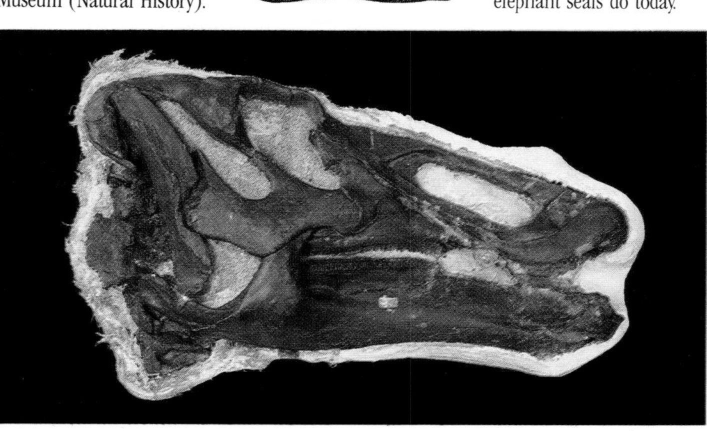

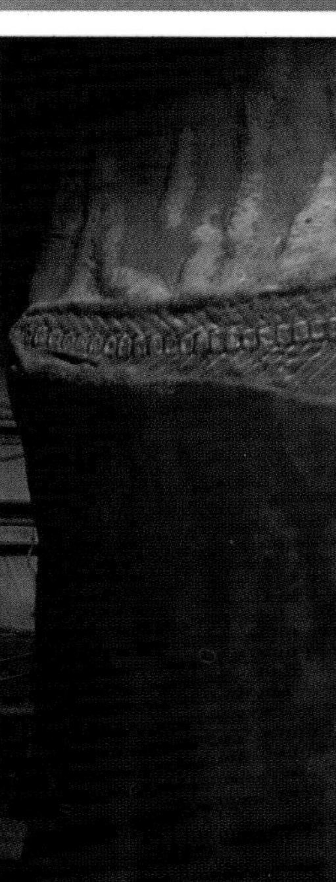

forwards the enamel ridges on the teeth in one jaw would wear against the softer dentine of the teeth in the other jaw, producing huge grooves; such grooves are *never* seen in hadrosaurid teeth. However, if the jaws move in the normal way up-and-down rather than backwards and forwards, the ridges of enamel in the jaws rub past one another, crushing and slicing the food trapped between them and also maintaining even wear across the grinding surface.

Very powerful jaw muscles and abrasive batteries of teeth seem to have been very important developments in later ornithopods, such as the iguanodontids and hadrosaurids, and in fact may be largely responsible for the dramatic evolution of these animals in the Cretaceous Period: both these groups becoming very abundant (hadrosaurid fossils are extremely common in late Cretaceous rocks in North America and Asia). It is possible that the increase in abundance of hadrosaurids (with their very efficient jaws) mirrors changes that took place in the type of plants living in the world during the Cretaceous Period. This time marks the arrival of the first flowering plants and the disappearance of more primitive plants such as the bennettitales and seed ferns, so that soon the plant kingdom was dominated by mainly flowering plants, coniferous trees and ferns. This changeover seems, perhaps by accident or maybe by design, to coincide with changing fortunes of the plant-eating dinosaurs. The earlier part of the reign of the dinosaurs (the Jurassic Period) was marked by an abundance of earlier plants and big sauropod dinosaurs, whereas the Cretaceous sees the decline of the earlier plants and the sauropods which presumably fed upon them and the rise to dominance of the flowering plants and the later ornithopods. Although it is practically impossible to prove, it is tempting to propose that the apparent success of the ornithopods was a reflection of their greater ability to feed upon the newly-evolved flowering plants.

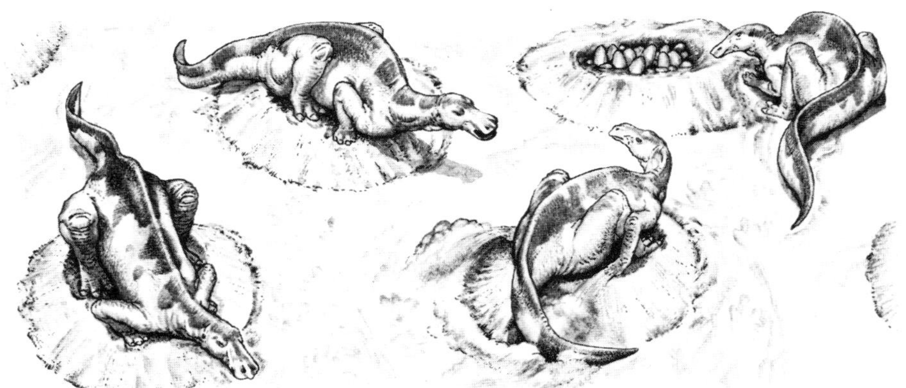

**Left:** Part of the upper jaw of a hadrosaur from the Oldman Formation of Alberta, Canada. Hadrosaurs were equipped with extensive batteries of teeth that enabled them to pound up thoroughly their food of tough plants and woody vegetation.

**Parental Care (above)** The work of Horner and Makela on the fossilized eggs, hatchlings, and infant *Maiasaura* found in Montana has provided us with a major insight into a dinosaur community. Evidently some hadrosaurs looked after their young in a nesting colony. Here we see a female digging out a nest (front right) while the central dinosaur adopts an aggressive posture to defend her territory. At the back, newly-laid eggs are being covered with sand by the mother reptile. The fourth *Maiasaura* sleeps on the nest.

**Below:** The Royal Ontario Museum's fine panel mount of the skeleton of *Hadrosaurus*, a dinosaur that could grow to a length of c. 30ft (9m). Note the rounded bump above the nostrils, and the mass of reinforcing bony rods along the spines of the back.

## Care of the Young

In 1978 a remarkable discovery was made in western Montana. The fossilized remains of fifteen baby *Maiasaura* ('good mother reptile') hadrosaurids were found in and around a mound-shaped structure. The presence of many fragments of eggshell and the fact that the dinosaurs were obviously young, being only 3 feet (1m) long, suggested that what had been discovered was a dinosaur nest. Apart from the very famous *Protoceratops* nests from Mongolia, very few dinosaur nests or hatchlings are known and it was generally supposed that dinosaurs tended to lay their eggs in inaccessible upland areas and were unlikely to survive as fossils.

This discovery, reported by John Horner and Robert Makela, not only provided evidence about the existence of nest sites for hadrosaurids but also gave some indication of family structure in these dinosaurs. The young dinosaurs found around the nest were seen to have well-worn teeth and were considerably larger than newly hatched individuals. This indicated that the young dinosaurs had stayed together for some time which implies a degree of parental care. Either food was brought to the nest-site by the adults, or the young went out of the nest in search of food and subsequently returned. If the latter was the case, then it seems unlikely that the young would have returned to the nest without parental supervision. Such care of the young is perhaps not as surprising as it at first seems because crocodiles, distant relatives of the dinosaurs, show considerable care of their young—for example, moving the hatchlings to 'nursery' pools and guarding them against predators until they are large enough to defend themselves.

Further excavation and exploration of the Montana nest site in following years has revealed another nest with even smaller hatchlings (approximately 20in, 50cm long) and another six unoccupied nests with lots of egg-shell fragments. The nests that have been discovered so far seem to indicate that these animals would return and rebuild their nests year after year, and that the nests are approximately 23ft (7m) apart (a distance equal to the length of an adult hadrosaurid). John Horner has concluded that what has been discovered is not just a few odd nest sites, but in fact a nesting colony of hadrosaurids. He suggests that hadrosaurids probably used colonial nest sites because such an arrangement may have provided protection against predators (because of the continual presence of adult hadrosaurids) and also that the young most probably stayed in the nests waiting for the parents to bring food to them. This arrangement would enable the young to grow very quickly, and may explain why two nests had large numbers of young preserved within. The instinct to stay in the nest would have been very strong, so that the accidental loss of parents, perhaps killed by predators or by some other agent, would have resulted in the young, devoid of parental protection, starving to death in the nest.

In addition to this hadrosaurid nesting colony, Horner has found other nests at a different site, which seem to be those of a small hypsilophodontid dinosaur. These remains show very clearly that these animals returned to the same nest year after year and also reveal the way in which their eggs were laid, with the pointed end directed into the soil so that the hatchling could emerge from the rounder top end of the egg.

Hadrosaurid fossils are known in western and eastern North America, Central and South America, Europe and Asia (Mongolia, China and Japan). This type of distribution pattern is now quite familiar (see the dromaeosaurids, pages 56-7), with these animals being distributed across most of the northern continents, but almost completely absent from the southern continents. The most likely reason for the northerly distribution of hadrosaurids would seem to be the relative position of the various continents at the time when they first evolved. In the mid-Cretaceous the southern continents, Gondwanaland (South America, Africa, India, Australia and Antarctica), were separated from the North (Laurasia) by a large sea composed of Tethys to the east and the beginnings of the Atlantic Ocean to the west. This sea barrier would have prevented the hadrosaurids from spreading from their probable northerly area of origin southward. The spread of hadrosaurids across the northern continents may have been partly impeded by a shallow seaway, the Turgai sea, which separated Europe and America on one side from Asia on the other, but this cannot have been a complete barrier to hadrosaurids, which could almost certainly swim (especially across a shallow sea), because they are found in both areas anyway. That the North-South barrier was not absolute is also proven by the recent discovery of hadrosaurids in South America (*Secernosaurus*, 'divided reptile' from Argentina). These hadrosaurids were probably able to migrate to South America across an island chain which then ran between the southernmost part of North America and the South American mainland. So far there are no reports of hadrosaurid dinosaurs elsewhere on Gondwana but fresh discoveries on, say, India or Australia might mean that we will have to re-think our ideas about the origin and evolution of hadrosaurids.

Towards the end of the Cretaceous Period the geographic situation was further complicated by the expansion of the Atlantic Ocean, the development of yet another seaway, the Western Interior Sea, which split North America into western and eastern regions and the establishment of a link between North America and Asia across the Bering Straits.

## Anatomical Observations

The hadrosaurids themselves are rather conservative ornithopods if we look at their skeletons. They continue the typical anatomical plan seen in the iguanodontids with relatively few changes. However, looking carefully at the two hadrosaurids that are illustrated as skeletons, it is possible to distinguish some subtle differences. *Edmontosaurus* is rather more lightly built than *Parasaurolophus* ('beside ridged reptile') and has lower spines along the backbone, while the bones of the pelvis have a strikingly different shape. The really obvious differences between the various species of

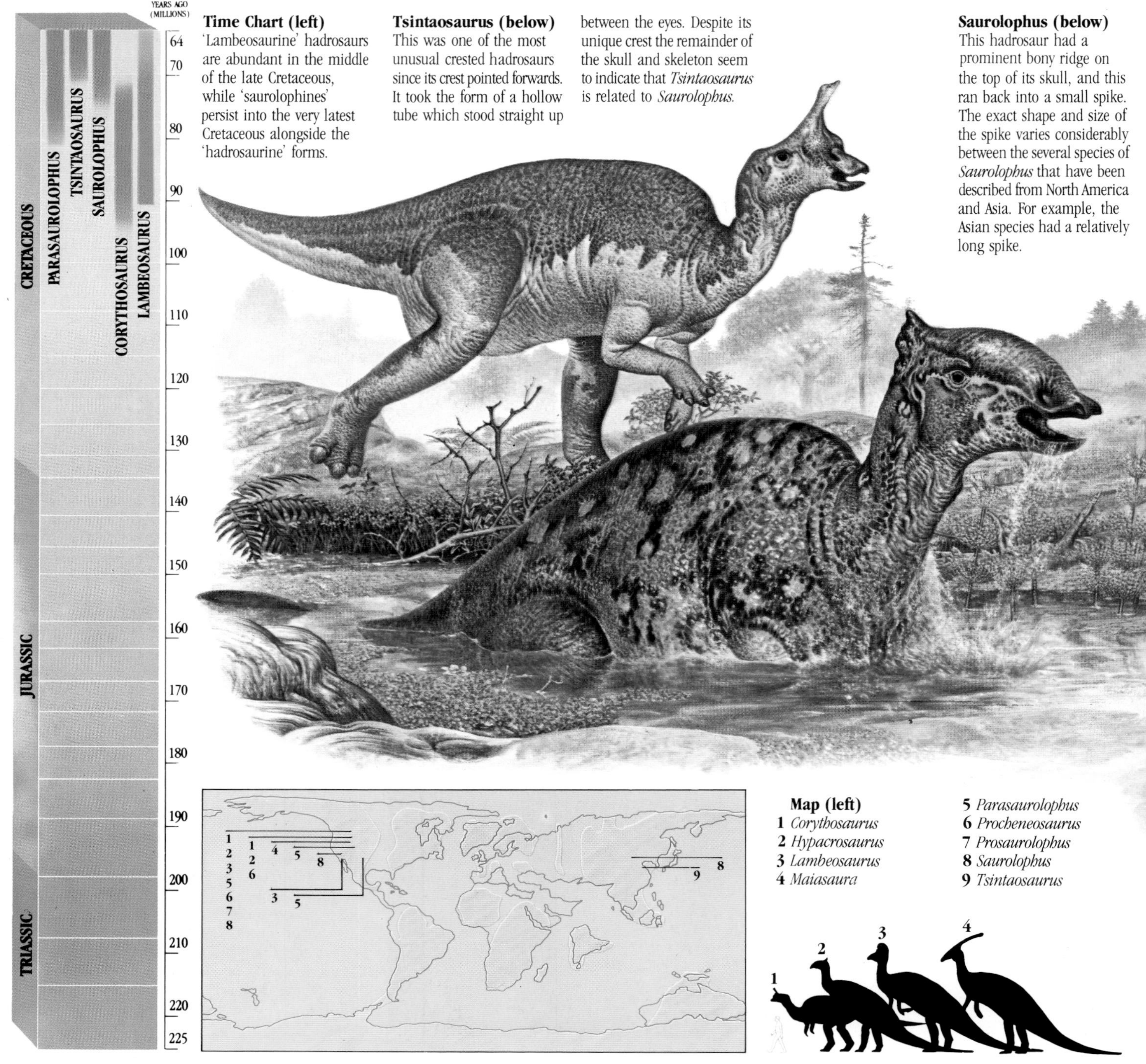


**Time Chart (left)**
'Lambeosaurine' hadrosaurs are abundant in the middle of the late Cretaceous, while 'saurolophines' persist into the very latest Cretaceous alongside the 'hadrosaurine' forms.

**Tsintaosaurus (below)**
This was one of the most unusual crested hadrosaurs since its crest pointed forwards. It took the form of a hollow tube which stood straight up between the eyes. Despite its unique crest the remainder of the skull and skeleton seem to indicate that *Tsintaosaurus* is related to *Saurolophus*.

**Saurolophus (below)**
This hadrosaur had a prominent bony ridge on the top of its skull, and this ran back into a small spike. The exact shape and size of the spike varies considerably between the several species of *Saurolophus* that have been described from North America and Asia. For example, the Asian species had a relatively long spike.

**Map (left)**
**1** *Corythosaurus*
**2** *Hypacrosaurus*
**3** *Lambeosaurus*
**4** *Maiasaura*
**5** *Parasaurolophus*
**6** *Procheneosaurus*
**7** *Prosaurolophus*
**8** *Saurolophus*
**9** *Tsintaosaurus*

hadrosaur, however, are to be found in their heads. Some hadrosaurs, such as *Edmontosaurus, Anatosaurus, Bactrosaurus* and *Kritosaurus*—so-called 'hadrosaurines'—have very broad, duck-like beaks, quite large nostrils but very little development of elaborate ridges or crests of bone on the head. At most there developed a low bump on the nose as in *Kritosaurus*. Other types of hadrosaurid, however, possess all manner of strange headgear. 'Saurolophines' such as *Saurolophus* ('ridged reptile'), *Maiasaura* ('good mother reptile'), and *Tsintaosaurus* ('reptile from Tsintao') show the development of a spine-like outgrowth from the top of the head. The spine of *Tsintaosaurus* is particularly odd because, unlike the others of this general type, the spine projects forward from the top of the head, just like the horn of the legendary unicorn. The other variety of hadrosaurids is the so-called 'lambeosaurines' which have much larger hollow or tubular crests or bone on their

**Parasaurolophus (right)**
This hadrosaur probably had the most striking crest of all. It was a long tube that extended back for a distance of up to 3·3ft (1m) behind the skull. Palaeontologists at first thought that *Parasaurolophus* used this as a snorkel, but this could not be so as there was no opening at the end of it.

**Corythosaurus (left)**
A well-known crested hadrosaur which was up to 33ft (10m) long, *Corythosaurus* had a crest which was shaped like a large dinner plate set up on end on top of the skull. Inside the crest there was a rather complex system of breathing tubes running from the nostrils at the tip of the snout to the back of the throat.

**Family Tree (below)**
The division here is into hadrosaurs with big tubular crests ('lambeosaurines') and those with a spike-like structure or excavated nasal region ('saurolophines').

**Comparative Sizes (left)**
**1** *Tsintaosaurus:* l. 23ft (7m)
**2** *Saurolophus:* l. 30-40ft (9-12m).
**3** *Corythosaurus:* l. 33ft (10m).
**4** *Parasaurolophus:* l. 33ft (10m).

heads—*Parasaurolophus* ('beside ridged reptile') and *Corythosaurus* ('Corinthian helmet reptile') are quite typical examples.

Before looking at other aspects of the biology of these animals, let us briefly examine the geographic distribution and relative evolutionary success of these different types of crested or crestless dinosaurs. The earliest known types of hadrosaurids seem to be the crestless 'hadrosaurines'; these are found on all continents and appear to rise in abundance until the very end of the Cretaceous. The 'saurolophines' seem never to have been particularly abundant at any time in their history in North America, apparently going extinct before the end of the Period, but they may have been more successful in Asia. Finally the 'lambeosaurines' (those hadrosaurids with large, hollow crests) seem to have been particularly abundant, outnumbering all other hadrosaurids in the middle part of the late Cretaceous of western North America but declining rapidly toward the end of the Period. Curiously, to date there are no reliable fossils of any 'lambeosaurines' from Asia.

The curious waxing and waning of these groups of hadrosaurid may simply be caused by biases of the collectors of fossils. However, if they are a reflection of the natural numbers of these animals, then they suggest some interesting questions. Why were the crested 'lambeosaurine' hadrosaurids so successful earlier than the flat-headed types? Why were the 'saurolophines' never particularly abundant in North America and why do 'lambeosaurines' appear not to have inhabited Asia? To attempt to answer these questions, we need to propose new theories. These theories can then be 'tested' by further investigation of the fossils in order to try to either 'prove' or 'disprove' them. In this way we hope gradually to get closer to the real explanation. For example it should be possible to find out, by renewed collecting, if the differences in the abundance of some of these dinosaurs was due to the biases of past collectors or whether apparent absences, such as the lack of definite 'lambeosaurines' in Asia, simply reflects the fact that people have not looked hard enough in the past.

## Hadrosaurid Crests

By far the most intriguing aspect of hadrosaurid anatomy is their crests: why do some have them and others not, and what was their purpose? As we shall see a little later, numerous theories have been put forward to explain the function of hadrosaurid crests. However, one of the first real discoveries in this area resulted from the work of Dr Peter Dodson of the University of Pennsylvania. Dr Dodson conducted a very detailed series of measurements in order to make an analysis of the shape of the heads of a large range of 'lambeosaurine' hadrosaurids. As a result of this work he was able to propose that many species of 'lambeosaurine' were in fact simply female, male

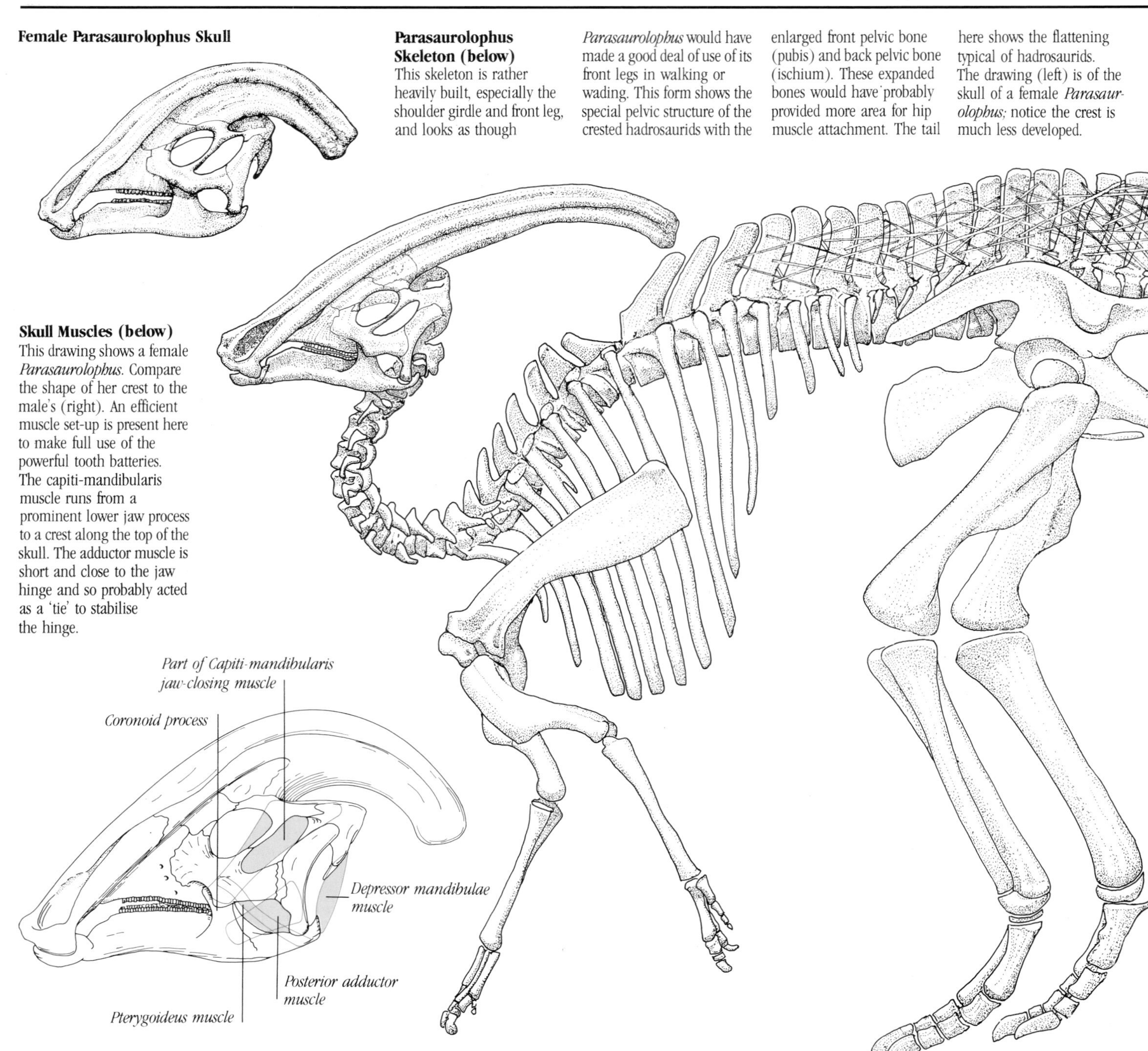


**Female Parasaurolophus Skull**

**Parasaurolophus Skeleton (below)**
This skeleton is rather heavily built, especially the shoulder girdle and front leg, and looks as though *Parasaurolophus* would have made a good deal of use of its front legs in walking or wading. This form shows the special pelvic structure of the crested hadrosaurids with the enlarged front pelvic bone (pubis) and back pelvic bone (ischium). These expanded bones would have probably provided more area for hip muscle attachment. The tail here shows the flattening typical of hadrosaurids. The drawing (left) is of the skull of a female *Parasaurolophus;* notice the crest is much less developed.

**Skull Muscles (below)**
This drawing shows a female *Parasaurolophus*. Compare the shape of her crest to the male's (right). An efficient muscle set-up is present here to make full use of the powerful tooth batteries. The capiti-mandibularis muscle runs from a prominent lower jaw process to a crest along the top of the skull. The adductor muscle is short and close to the jaw hinge and so probably acted as a 'tie' to stabilise the hinge.

or young individuals of a small number of species of hadrosaurid. For example, of the 'lambeosaurines' with helmet-shaped crests, *Corythosaurus casuarius* and *Corythosaurus intermedius* are now thought to be male and female respectively of the same species, while other species, known previously as *Procheneosaurus erectofrons,* and *Procheneosaurus cranibrevis* along with *Corythosaurus excavatus, Corythosaurus bicristatus* and *Corythosaurus brevicristatus* are all juveniles of the same species. This sort of very careful analysis is of vital importance to palaeontology because it greatly reduces the confusion that can be created by naming so many different fossil species. Almost at the stroke of a pen, Dodson has reduced the number of one type of 'lambeosaurine' in one area of North America from seven to one. In this same area of North America (The Old Man Formation of Alberta in Canada) Dodson has identified just two other 'lambeosaurines': *Lambeosaurus* ('Lambe's reptile') with a somewhat more full and pronounced helmet-like crest, and the tubular-crested *Parasaurolophus,* where previously there had been thirteen different species. From a simple biological viewpoint, it is far easier to imagine three species of ecologically distinct hadrosaurids living in approximately the same area at the same time, rather than thirteen distinct species of similar types of dinosaur.

Thus the crests have had one very useful function, in that they have given us a clue about growth stages in the life of hadrosaurids and the differences between males and females of the same species. However, this does not explain why some hadrosaurids had crests while others did not, nor what the crests were used for.

## The Function of Crests

The extraordinary variety of crest shape displayed by hadrosaurids has provoked a considerable number of theories relating to their probable function. Some of these are described and discussed below.

(i) Underwater feeding. The long, curved tubular crest of *Parasaurolophus* was thought to act as a snorkel so that the animal could breathe while feeding on submerged plants. It was supposed that the tip of the crest had a small hole, through which air could pass, as with a true snorkel. Unfortunately no such hole exists in any of the crests of *Parasaurolophus* so far discovered. Even if such a hole had existed, the snorkel explanation could not have been readily applied to other hadrosaurids, for example *Corythosaurus* whose crest was nothing like a snorkel.

An alternative to the snorkel theory was the proposal that the crests served as air-storage 'tanks', so that these animals could stay submerged for long periods while feeding. However, the amount of air that could have been stored in the crests was really very small, and is unlikely to have permitted crested

**Sections through Crests (below right)**
These drawings show the internal anatomy of the crests of three 'lambeosaurine' hadrosaurs: *Parasaurolophus cyrtocristatus, Lambeosaurus clavinitialis* and *Corythosaurus excavatus.* The areas marked in red are the nasal cavities. Many intriguing theories have been advanced concerning the function of these remarkable crests, ranging from snorkels for underwater feeding to foliage deflectors. The most probable explanation supposes that they were visual signals to allow members of individual species to recognise one another. In addition to this, it is likely that the tubular cavities inside the crests would serve as resonators, allowing these hadrosaurs to produce distinctive calls. 'Saurolophines' and 'hadrosaurines' could probably also make noises by inflating flaps of skin over their nostrils. Possibly these spaces also allowed for a greater area of sensitive skin and thus an improved sense of smell.

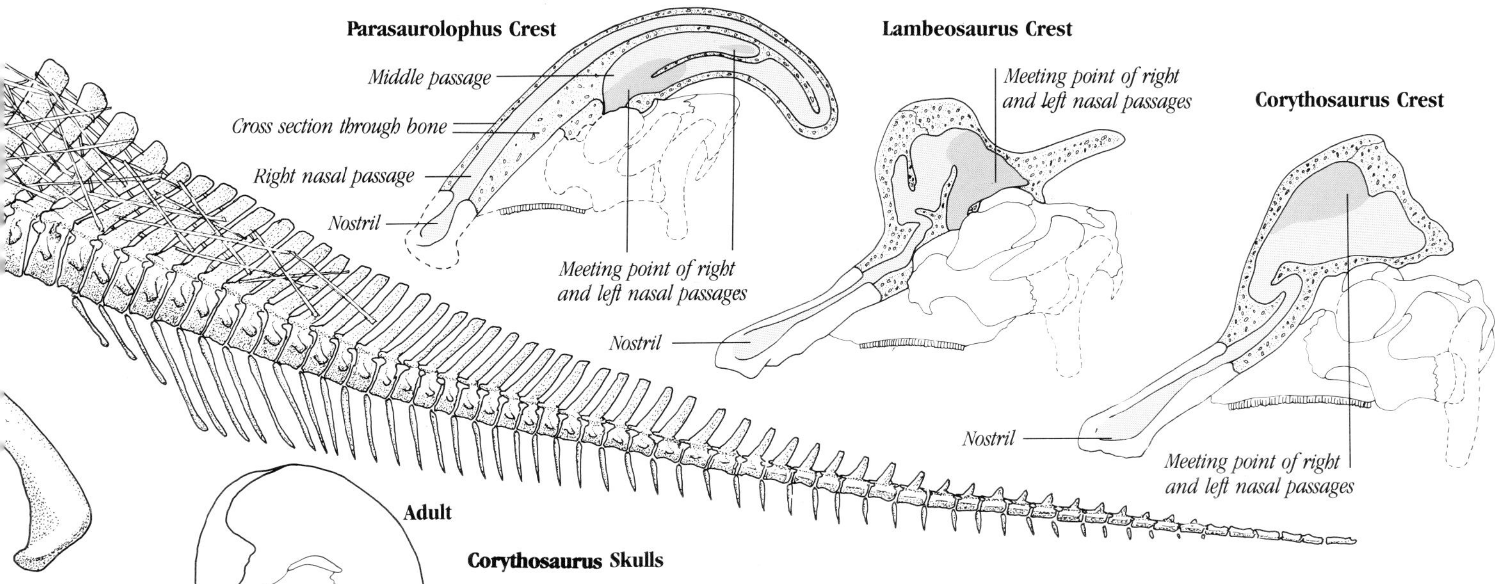

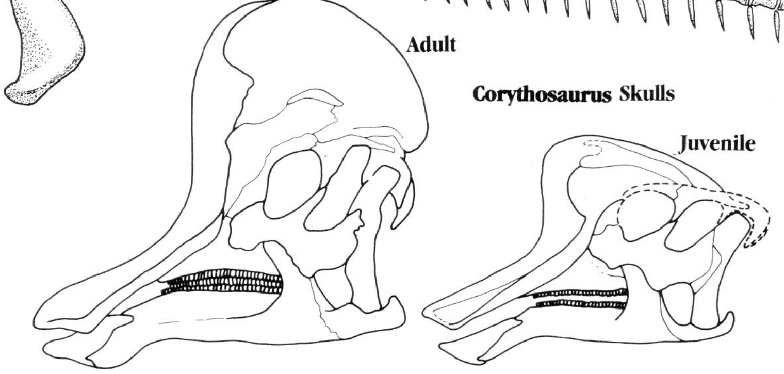

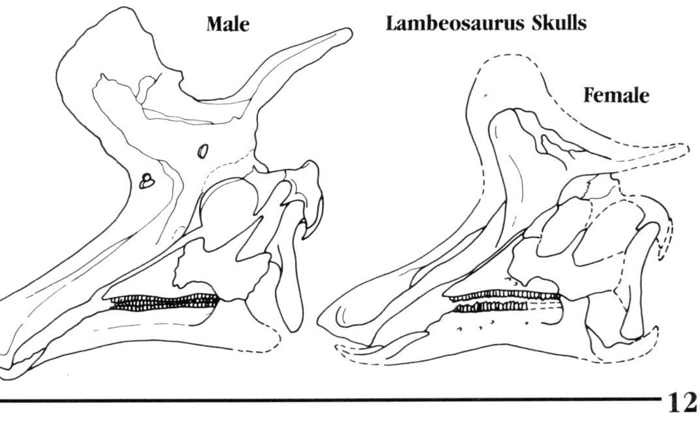

**Parasaurolophus Crest**

*Middle passage*
*Cross section through bone*
*Right nasal passage*
*Nostril*
*Meeting point of right and left nasal passages*

**Lambeosaurus Crest**

*Meeting point of right and left nasal passages*
*Nostril*

**Corythosaurus Crest**

*Nostril*
*Meeting point of right and left nasal passages*

**Corythosaurus Skulls**

Adult

Juvenile

**Lambeosaurus Skulls**

Male

Female

**Hadrosaurid Skulls (left and right)**
These skulls continue the series started on page 119. *Saurolophus* and *Prosaurolophus* belong to the 'saurolophine' group whose members had spine-like outgrowths on the top of the head. In *Prosaurolophus* this is not at all well developed. The other forms belong to the 'lambeosaurine' group which had a hollow or tubular outgrowth on the head. As a result of Peter Dodson's work, it is now thought that the many variations in crest size and shape were a reflection of sexual dimorphism i.e. males and females (and juveniles) of the same species probably had differently shaped crests.

**Prosaurolophus Skull**

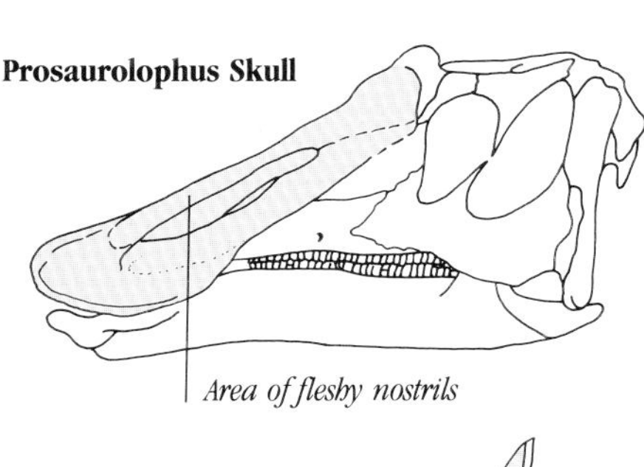


**Saurolophus Skull**

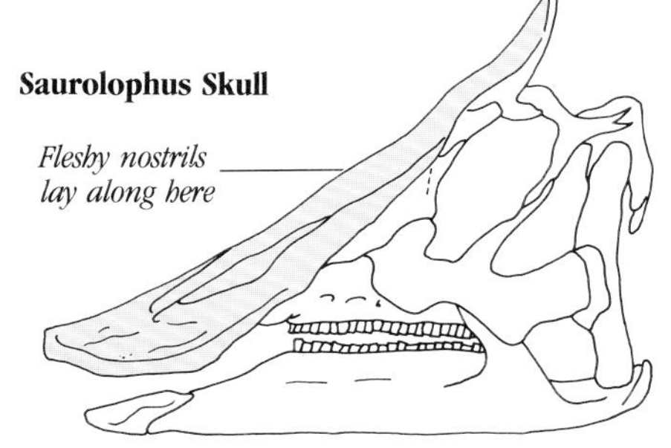

hadrosaurs to stay submerged for very much longer than their crestless counterparts. Nor does this theory readily explain why the crests should be so variable in shape.

The third proposal concerned with underwater feeding suggested that the loop in the air passages inside the crests acted as 'air-locks' to prevent water from flooding into the lungs when the head was underwater. In this case such an 'air-lock' just would not have worked in life, and in any case most aquatic animals have special muscular valves around their nostrils to stop water from rushing into their lungs. Therefore, most of these proposals seem improbable when considered in detail, which reinforces the earlier argument that hadrosaurids were not primarily aquatic plant feeders.

(ii) Salt glands. An alternative suggestion concerning the function of the cranial crests is that they were occupied by salt glands. Many living reptiles, especially those that feed on plants and those that live in the sea, have well developed salt glands in the cavity for the nose or the eye to regulate the salt balance in their bodies (the perpetual tears in the eyes of turtles on land are produced by these salt glands). It therefore seems reasonable to suppose that such large herbivorous reptiles also had well-developed salt glands. Whether the salt glands were housed in the large bony crests is at present not at all certain. Again the problem encountered in this explanation is, if they were to house salt glands alone, why are the crests so variable in shape, and how did the crestless hadrosaurs survive?

(iii) The sense of smell. Another proposal, somewhat similar to the last one, is that the tubular cavities inside the crests, which are continuous with the nostrils, may have provided space for a much enlarged sensory area which endowed these animals with a very acute sense of smell. This idea is quite appealing because it seems to fit in with the proposed life-styles of these animals. As defenceless, moderately mobile herbivores, it would have been extremely advantageous for them to have very acute senses of hearing, sight and smell to give them adequate warning of the approach of predators such as the large tyrannosaurids.

As with previous theories, there still remains the difficulty of explaining precisely why the crests of 'lambeosaurines' are so varied if they were simply providing more area for nasal lining, *and* why do some 'hadrosaurines' lack crests altogether and yet others ('saurolophines') have solid crests?

(iv) Foliage deflectors. One extremely novel suggestion concerning crest function in 'lambeosaurines' was made by Dr Andrew Milner of London University. Dr Milner's explanation relied upon an observation which he made on the skeleton of *Parasaurolophus*. He noticed that at the base of the neck, the spines show a peculiar flattened structure. A slight adjustment in the position of the neck in the preserved skeleton allows the extremely long tubular crest of this species to rest against this notch. The suggestion which was made was that if *Parasaurolophus* was indeed able to lock its crest onto this notch in its neck, then the smooth contours of the head and back would form an ideal deflector of low branches. Perhaps, therefore, some 'lambeosaurines' such as *Parasaurolophus* lived in quite heavily wooded areas and used the 'deflector' arrangement in order to crash through heavy foliage in order to escape from predators, without damaging their heads. As an extension of this idea, the elaborate crests of 'lambeosaurines' may have correlated with their living in quite dense forests, while the flat-headed forms lived in open areas where deflectors were not necessary. An interesting observation in this respect comes from the habits of the cassowary, a large flightless bird from the forested area of Northern Queensland, Australia. This curious bird has a large helmet-like crest on its head which very closely resembles the crest of *Corythosaurus*. When disturbed, this bird can run very quickly through dense undergrowth to escape. To do this, the cassowary lowers its head and deflects low branches with its helmet-clad head, neck and back.

Although this is a very interesting proposal there are a number of problems associated with it. At the moment it is impossible to tell whether 'lambeosaurines' were indeed confined to heavily forested areas. Also it is not possible in all cases to reconcile the crest shape of hadrosaurids with the proposed deflector function. An obvious example of the latter would be the long, slender, unicorn-like spike of *Tsintaosaurus* which would certainly not survive impacts against branches.

(v) Signalling devices. The last proposal we shall consider interprets the head structures of hadrosaurids as features that may reflect their behaviour. The crests are regarded as visual

**Left:** *Tsintaosaurus spinorhinus*, a 23ft (7m) tall 'saurolophine', in the Institute of Vertebrate Palaeontology, Beijing. This specimen is from late Cretaceous rocks of Laiyang County, Shandong Province,China. Its most distinctive feature is the unicorn-like, forwardly-pointing crest extending from the top of the skull.

**Below:** *Lambeosaurus lambei* being prepared for display at the Tyrrell Museum of Palaeontology in Alberta; the reason for the rather odd posture is that in the final exhibit it will be shown drinking water from a pool. Evidence from trackways, however, does suggest that large hadrosaurids were quadrupedal for much of the time.

**Beating A Retreat (left)**
Although the general consensus now is that hadrosaurids were not primarily aquatic animals, their characteristic deep tails and paddle-like hands is evidence that they were certainly capable of swimming. It is possible that when threatened by a tyrannosaurid predator they would retreat to the safety of deep water just as these *Parasaurolophus* are doing with some alacrity.

signal structures and as resonators for producing distinctive calls. Both of these functions would serve to help individual hadrosaurids recognize members of their own species, which would be especially useful in courtship and mating.

## Visual Signals

In order to support this proposal, Dr Jim Hopson of Chicago University made a series of predictions which should be confirmed if the above proposal is to be considered plausible. Firstly, hearing and sight would be expected to be acute in hadrosaurids. As expected, the eye socket is very large in these animals. Also there is fossil evidence of a bony ring of thin bones in the eye (the sclerotic ring) which seems to demonstrate that hadrosaurids did indeed have very good eyesight. Several hadrosaur skeletons have also been found with a very thin, delicate ear bone in position at the back of the skull, confirming that they had quite acute hearing.

Secondly, and this has a bearing on proposals (ii) and (iii), the shape of the crest should not necessarily closely follow the shape of the cavities within. That is to say that the external shape of the crest was more important than its internal structure, because it acted as a visual signal. This prediction is borne out by *Corythosaurus*, in which the internal passages are clearly not the same shape as the crest. In fact several of the cranial crests give the heads very distinctive shapes, as can be appreciated by looking at the colour drawings.

Thirdly, if the crests acted as visual signals, then they would be expected to be specific to each species, that is they should be visually very distinct, and males and females should be indentifiable. This prediction seems to be strongly supported by Dodson's work (see above) which shows that in the Old Man Formation there are three very distinct species of 'lambeosaurine': *Corythosaurus, Lambeosaurus* and *Parasaurolophus*, and that males and females of at least the first two species have been tentatively identified. Unfortunately only one individual of *Parasaurolophus* is known in this area at the present time so that no conclusion can yet be drawn about its status.

Fourthly, if several species are found in the same area then they should exhibit great differences in head shape. This would have prevented any confusion when animals were trying to meet members of the same species, at mating time for example. This prediction seems to be amply confirmed. Again in the Old Man Formation there are known to be at least six hadrosaurid species — the three very distinctive 'lambeosaurines' seen above, one 'saurolophine' (*Prosaurolophus*) and two species of 'hadrosaurine'. The latter are again quite distinctive as *Kritosaurus* and the unusual plate-headed *Brachylophosaurus* ('short ridged reptile'). By contrast, in other Formations such as the Lance or Hell Creek, although many hadrosaurid specimens are known, they are all of one type: the flat-headed species *Anatosaurus*.

The fifth and final prediction postulated that the crests should become much more prominent as time passed. This, however, is certainly not supported in the case of 'lambeosaurines', although there may be some evidence for a trend of increasing spike length in the crests of 'saurolophines'.

Thus Hopson's predictions generally seem to be fulfilled and the variable form of the crests in these dinosaurs seems to fit with the idea that they provided visual cues connected with social behaviour in these animals.

This idea has been further elaborated in order to explain likely behavioural differences between crestless and crested dinosaurs. Hopson proposed that a hadrosaurid like *Kritosaurus* probably used the hump on its nose as a crude weapon for fighting during male butting contests. In other flat-headed species such as *Brachylophosaurus*, the flat, shield-like roof to the head allowed these animals to indulge in head-to-head pushing contests of strength. However, in all the other hadrosaurids the 'combat' was ritualized; instead of physical fighting, the animals relied upon sight and sound displays. The 'lambeosaurines' and 'saurolophines' used their distinctive cranial crests as visual signals to establish a dominance hierarchy. In the 'lambeosaurines' this was probably accompanied by noisy honking or bellows. David Weishampel of Florida State University has demonstrated that the tubular crest of *Parasaurolophus* served as a resonator for producing distinctive calls, and has suggested that the helmet-crest *Corythosaurus* and *Lambeosaurus* were also able to produce distinctive sounds.

'Hadrosaurines' such as *Anatosaurus* and *Edmontosarus,* and 'saurolophines' such as *Saurolophus* and *Tsintaosaurus* probably possessed inflatable flaps of skin over their nostrils which may not only have served as resonators to produce loud snorts (perhaps rather like the roars produced by elephant seals which have very bulbous noses), but also have formed inflatable (perhaps highly coloured) display structures. Such visual signals play a prominent part in the lives of present day reptiles; many (for example *Anolis*) have highly colourful dewlaps that are used as flash signals for courtship and various other behaviours.

The most convincing explanation of the purpose of cranial crests seems to be that of Jim Hopson. It serves to explain all the crested or non-crested forms so far known. If he is right, the late Cretaceous must have been a colourful and noisy time in the Earth's history!

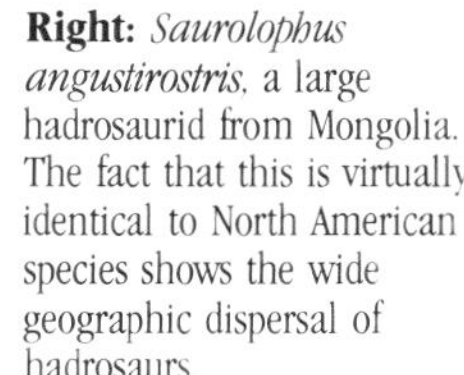

**Above:** A plaster cast of the skull of *Parasaurolophus walkeri*, a species from the Red Deer River area of Alberta. The great tubular crest of this creature could grow to a length of up to 6ft (1·8m).

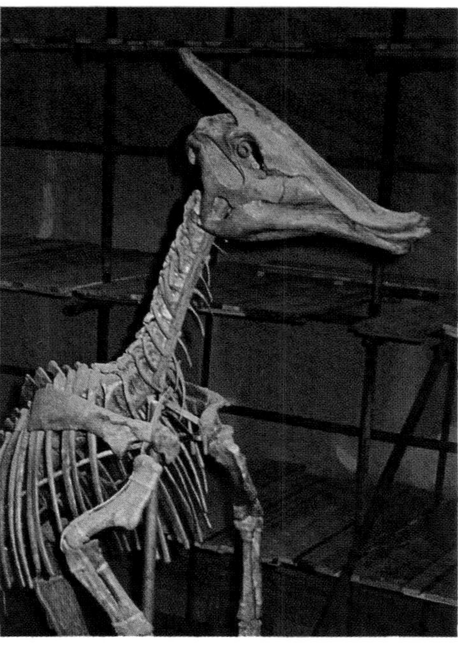

**Right:** *Saurolophus angustirostris*, a large hadrosaurid from Mongolia. The fact that this is virtually identical to North American species shows the wide geographic dispersal of hadrosaurs.

# PSITTACOSAURS & PROTOCERATOPIDS

The ceratopian ('horned-face') dinosaurs were a group whose history was confined to the latter part of the reign of the dinosaurs: the late Cretaceous. During this last 35 million years or so, however, these dinosaurs became particularly abundant. Some areas of North America have yielded literally hundreds of remains (including complete skeletons) of these dinosaurs; this must be a reflection of their great abundance in the world at this time.

The distinctive characteristics seen in most of the ceratopians are the facial horns, the distinctive parrot-like, hooked beak and the large frill, a bony ruff projecting from the back and sides of the head. The great majority of ceratopians were also quadrupedal and bear quite a strong resemblance to the living rhinoceroses of Africa and South East Asia. *Centrosaurus* ('sharp point reptile') (pages 134-137) and *Chasmosaurus* ('cleft reptile') (pages 140-143) are typical representatives of the ceratopian type of dinosaur. Illustrated below (and on the next four pages), however, are several rather less typical ceratopians.

*Psittacosaurus* ('parrot reptile') illustrated below does not really resemble the general description of ceratopian dinosaurs. The remains of *Psittacosaurus* were first discovered during an expedition to the Mongolian Peoples' Republic organized by the American Museum of Natural History between 1922 and 1925. During this expedition, two quite well preserved skeletons were discovered in the Oshih Formation (early Cretaceous) of Mongolia. These were first described as different animals and named *Psittacosaurus* and *Protiguanodon*. The fact that neither of the skeletons was complete, and both were not completely cleared of matrix, caused a certain amount of confusion; they are now both recognised as specimens of *Psittacosaurus*.

For many years *Psittacosaurus* was thought to be a member of the ornithopod group of dinosaurs (hence the name *Protiguanodon* coined for one skeleton) as a fairly close relative of *Hypsilophodon*. I think it should be fairly obvious why this was believed. Just like *Hypsilophodon* and its relatives, *Psittacosaurus* was a small (6·6ft, 2m long) bipedal, fairly lightly built creature, with a long tail counter-balancing its body over the hips; its front legs were also equipped with blunt-clawed hands which seem to have been 'multi-purpose', serving both to walk upon and to grasp foliage for feeding. The head, supported on the long flexible neck, was apparently unadorned by the horns or frills so characteristic of ceratopians generally. The key to the affinities of *Psittacosaurus*, however, does lie in the head—in the beak to be exact! As the name suggests, these animals had a sharp, narrow, parrot-like beak typical of all other ceratopians. More important than the shape of the beak was the fact that beneath the horn-covered part of the upper beak there is found a characteristic bone known as the rostral bone which is only found

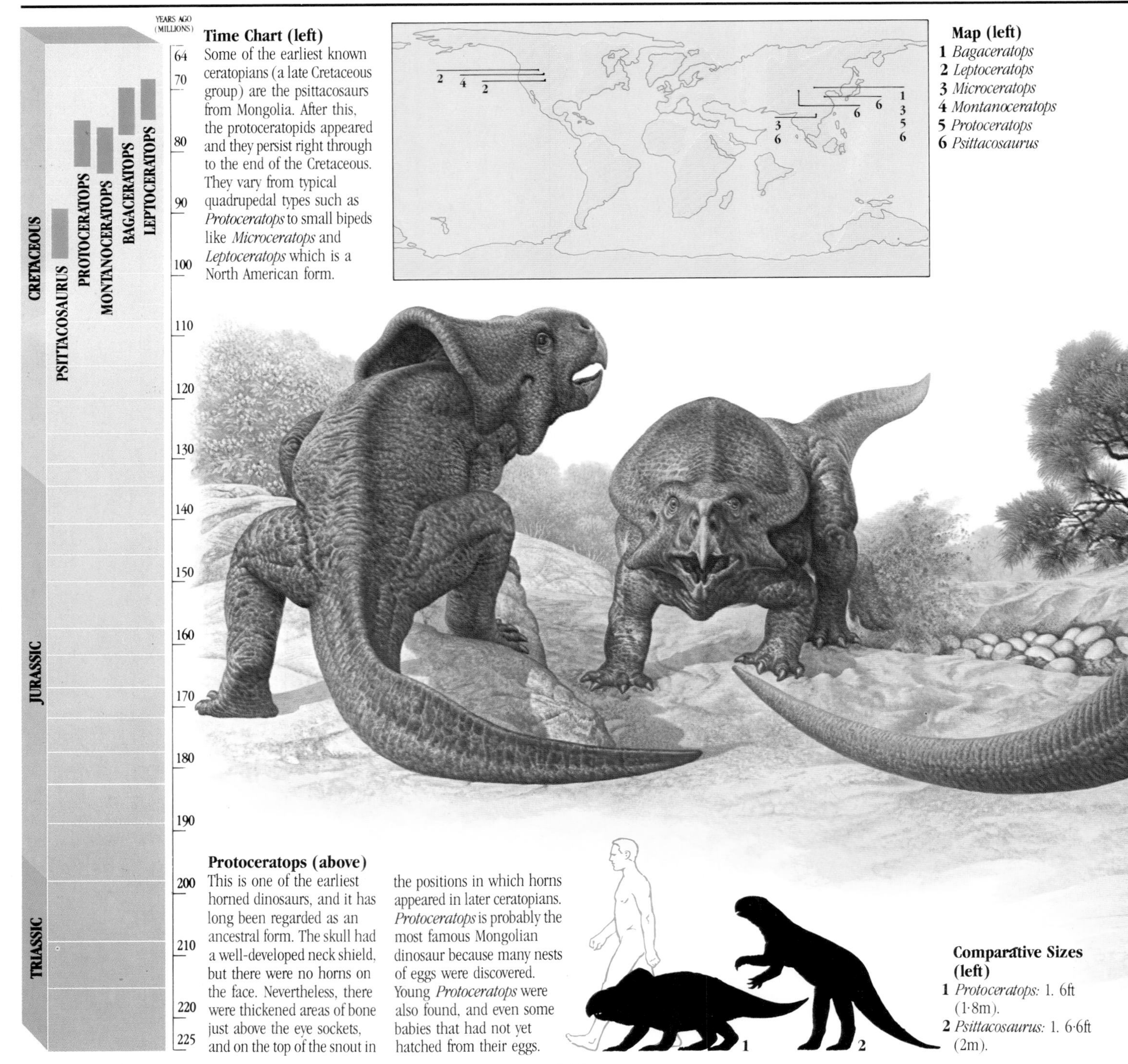


**Time Chart (left)**
Some of the earliest known ceratopians (a late Cretaceous group) are the psittacosaurs from Mongolia. After this, the protoceratopids appeared and they persist right through to the end of the Cretaceous. They vary from typical quadrupedal types such as *Protoceratops* to small bipeds like *Microceratops* and *Leptoceratops* which is a North American form.

**Map (left)**
**1** *Bagaceratops*
**2** *Leptoceratops*
**3** *Microceratops*
**4** *Montanoceratops*
**5** *Protoceratops*
**6** *Psittacosaurus*

**Protoceratops (above)**
This is one of the earliest horned dinosaurs, and it has long been regarded as an ancestral form. The skull had a well-developed neck shield, but there were no horns on the face. Nevertheless, there were thickened areas of bone just above the eye sockets, and on the top of the snout in the positions in which horns appeared in later ceratopians. *Protoceratops* is probably the most famous Mongolian dinosaur because many nests of eggs were discovered. Young *Protoceratops* were also found, and even some babies that had not yet hatched from their eggs.

**Comparative Sizes (left)**
**1** *Protoceratops:* l. 6ft (1·8m).
**2** *Psittacosaurus:* l. 6·6ft (2m).

in ceratopian dinosaurs. The remarkable overall similarity between *Psittacosaurus* and hypsilophodontids, and the fact that *Psittacosaurus* pre-dates all other ceratopians, seems to suggest quite strongly that ceratopians *evolved* from hypsilophodontid types of dinosaur. Precisely why ceratopians should have appeared when they did and why the peculiar rostral bone appeared in the upper beak is not at all clear. My best guess (and it is only a guess) would be that the rather subtle changes in the proportions of the skull, which follow on from the development of the parrot-like beak at the front of the mouth, may perhaps reflect one of two things: either a new type of plant had evolved which required this type of beak to crop it, or perhaps the parrot-beak was a new 'invention' that allowed the ceratopians to feed on plants which had previously been inedible to most dinosaurs. The appearance of the ceratopian dinosaurs coincides very roughly with the time of appearance of the first angiosperms—or

**Psittacosaurus (left)**
An important early ceratopian, *Psittacosaurus* was quite a small dinosaur, about 6·6ft (2m) long, and it has been considered particularly significant because it seems to show characteristics that are intermediate between the ornithopods and the ceratopians. The long hindlimbs, short forelimbs with grasping hands, and the powerful skull all seem to be ornithopod characters. However, *Psittacosaurus* has a curved parrot-like beak which is a ceratopian characteristic, although it lacks the neck frill that is seen in *Protoceratops.*

**Family Tree (right)**
The relations of early ceratopians have been studied by Paul Sereno (New York) and are shown here. *Psittacosaurus* is clearly the most primitive known ceratopian. *Leptoceratops* of the late Cretaceous seems to be a persistently primitive type while *Bagaceratops, Protoceratops* and *Montanoceratops* show a clear trend towards the characteristics of the larger quadrupedal ceratopids.

flowering plants—is this the key to the problem? At the moment we have no positive evidence of the true diet of ceratopians, so this suggestion can be neither supported nor denied.

In 1980 Walter Coombs Jnr reported that among the collections from the Asiatic expeditions of 1922-1925 in the American Museum of Natural History he had found some more *Psittacosaurus* material. This comprised the skull of one individual, and the skull with several parts of the skeleton of another individual. The remarkable thing about these specimens however was their size. The skulls of the two individuals were tiny: 1·6in (42mm) and 1·1in (28mm) long respectively. A simple size-for-size comparison between the original skeletons of *Psittacosaurus* and these tiny ones suggests that they could only have been about 16in (40cm) and 10in (25cm) in total length when complete. These are some of the smallest dinosaur remains so far discovered. Various features of these two specimens, such as the very large size of their eyes and the incomplete way in which the bones of the back are arranged, tell us that these were hatchling dinosaurs. Even at this tiny size, these young dinosaurs were evidently quite independent because their teeth show signs of wear which indicates that they were already feeding on abrasive plant food. Dr Coombs suggested that the minute size of these hatchlings and the fact that they already had worn teeth indicated that there was unlikely to be parental care of the young. Attempts to feed such small young, it was claimed, would most likely result in their being stepped on. However, this type of argument does not seem very convincing, because we already know that adult crocodiles (which are considerably larger than their hatchlings) show considerable parental care—even ferrying them to favoured nursery pools between their jaws. As was suggested in the case of the hadrosaurid *Maiasaura*, *Psittacosaurus* parents may well have brought plant food to the nest for the young hatchlings.

Since *Psittacosaurus* was a herbivore it probably relied upon its fleetness of foot to escape from predatory dinosaurs, in the same way that hypsilophodontids were able to. This strategy however would not have been available to another rather primitive early ceratopian dinosaur *Protoceratops* ('first horned-face').

## Protoceratops

While *Psittacosaurus* has so far only been discovered in Asia, *Protoceratops* and its close relatives (together known as protoceratopids) are known from the late Cretaceous of Asia and North America. Protoceratopids are typically small ceratopians (maximum length about 6·6ft, 2m) which have the characteristic parrot-like beak seen in *Psittacosaurus*, and also a well-developed bony frill which overhangs the neck. Although the areas over the eyes and the

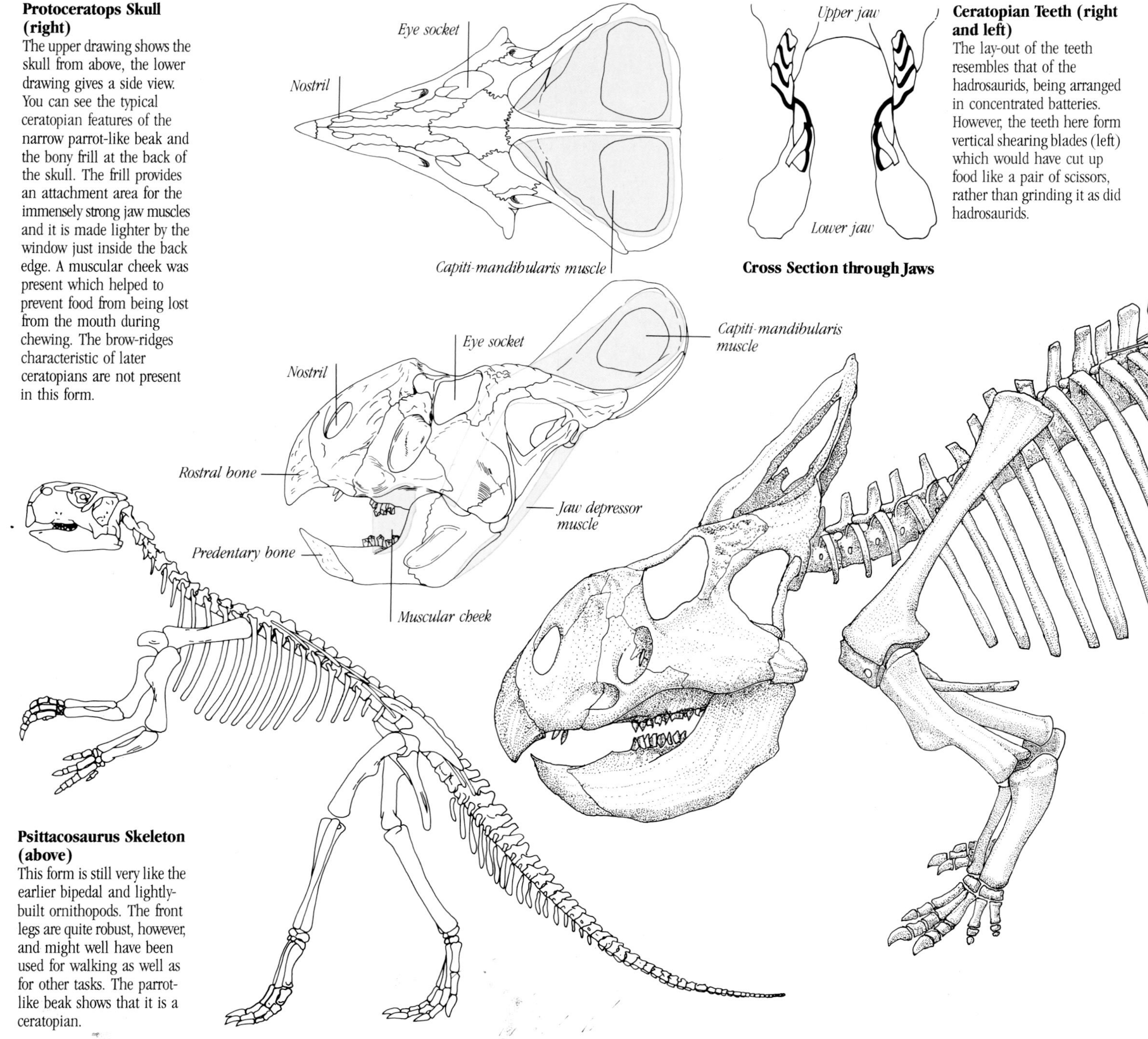


**Protoceratops Skull (right)**
The upper drawing shows the skull from above, the lower drawing gives a side view. You can see the typical ceratopian features of the narrow parrot-like beak and the bony frill at the back of the skull. The frill provides an attachment area for the immensely strong jaw muscles and it is made lighter by the window just inside the back edge. A muscular cheek was present which helped to prevent food from being lost from the mouth during chewing. The brow-ridges characteristic of later ceratopians are not present in this form.

**Ceratopian Teeth (right and left)**
The lay-out of the teeth resembles that of the hadrosaurids, being arranged in concentrated batteries. However, the teeth here form vertical shearing blades (left) which would have cut up food like a pair of scissors, rather than grinding it as did hadrosaurids.

**Psittacosaurus Skeleton (above)**
This form is still very like the earlier bipedal and lightly-built ornithopods. The front legs are quite robust, however, and might well have been used for walking as well as for other tasks. The parrot-like beak shows that it is a ceratopian.

snout tend to be rather raised and roughened there is no strong development of the brow or nose horns as there is in later ceratopians.

The first protoceratopid to be discovered was *Protoceratops*, another trophy of the expedition to Mongolia in the early 1920s. In fact, of all the new and dazzling fossil discoveries made in Mongolia during these expeditions, the discoveries of *Protoceratops* were the most renowned. This was because the remains found in the Djadochta Formation in the Gobi Desert included dozens of complete skulls and skeletons of individuals that ranged from newly emerged hatchlings right through the age-range to elderly specimens. In addition to this, the first nests of dinosaur eggs were discovered with these skeletons. Many of the nests were very well preserved, and showed clearly that the eggs had been laid in ring-shaped clutches in shallow depressions scooped out of the sand. The discovery of such a great abundance of skeletons of all ages and numerous nests suggests very strongly that this is another nesting site, like the hadrosaurid one described by Horner and Makela. It seems that at least towards the end of the Cretaceous some dinosaurs were notably gregarious creatures, indulging in a variety of group activities such as using colonial nesting sites. These patterns of behaviour are more reminiscent of the birds of today than most reptiles, and give us a rather different perspective on dinosaur life-styles.

Indeed the discovery of this rich collection of fossil skeletons of *Protoceratops* has provided another of those, unfortunately rare, occasions when palaeontologists have been able to look a little closer at the biology of these animals. Peter Dodson from the University of Pennsylvania carried out a very detailed analysis of the skulls of twenty-four of the best preserved *Protoceratops*. His method of analysis was to take a series of measurements of various parts of the skull. For example, the height of the nose, the diameter of the eye, the length and width of the frill, etc. Having done this, he was then able to analyse his results mathematically, in order to see whether there are certain parts of the skulls which could help him to distinguish between young individuals, males and females. In the sample that Dodson used, he was able to identify with certainty 7 adult females and 8 adult males using key measurements such as the height of the nose, the width of the frill and the total height of the skull. You can see the difference in skull shape between adult male and female skulls on page 133.

This study has also revealed something rather unexpected, which has repercussions upon long-held beliefs about the general function of the frill in ceratopians. For a long time it was thought that the purpose of the frill at the back of the skull was solely to provide a large area for attachment of powerful jaw muscles. As can be seen clearly in the drawing of the skull, the main jaw-closing muscles seem to have run forward and downward from an

**Tooth Battery**

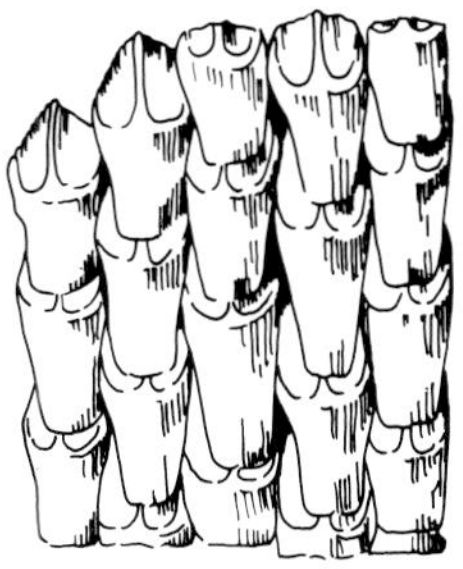

**Protoceratops Skeleton (below)**

The *Protoceratops* skeleton has changed quite a lot from the basic ornithopod plan, producing an animal which probably moved much more slowly. *Protoceratops* moved around on all-fours and the front legs are nearly the same length as the hind legs, although, as in most land vertebrates, the hind leg is still much the bigger. This probably has something to do with it being the source of power during locomotion, whereas the fore leg acts much more as a shock absorber as the body is forced forwards. Even though the front leg now supports the front of the body, there are still trellis-like bones spanning the vertebrae, helping to prevent the body sagging. The long tail and rotated pubic bones, typical of all ornithischians, are seen here too. The feet and hands are well built and the fingers and toes rather splayed out, helping to support the weight of this fairly bulky animal on land. The head is quite low.

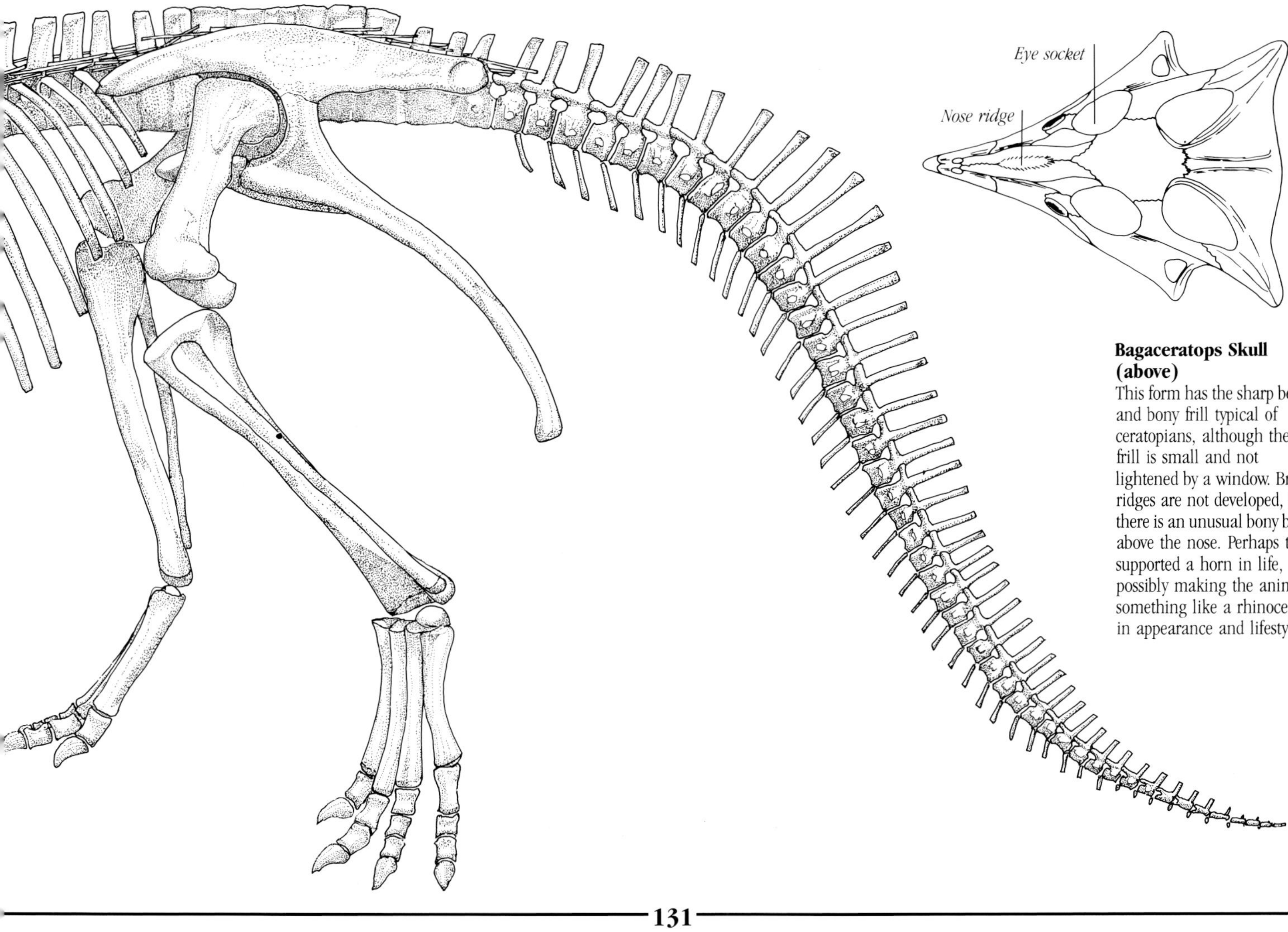

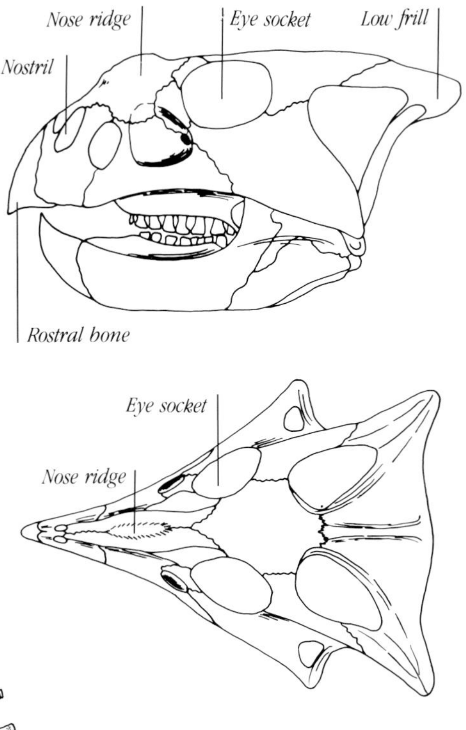

Nose ridge
Eye socket
Low frill
Nostril
Rostral bone

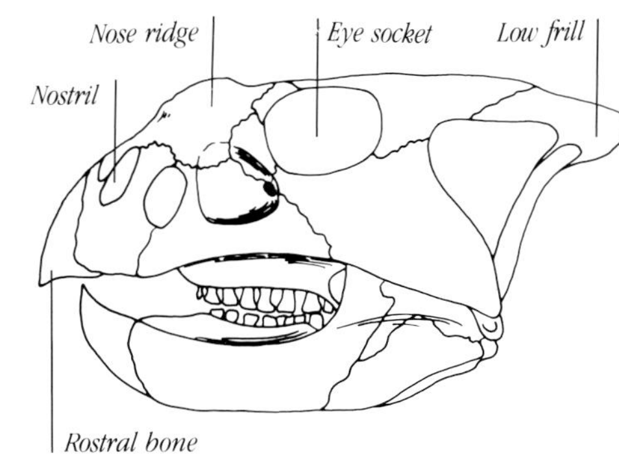


**Bagaceratops Skull (above)**

This form has the sharp beak and bony frill typical of ceratopians, although the frill is small and not lightened by a window. Brow ridges are not developed, but there is an unusual bony boss above the nose. Perhaps this supported a horn in life, possibly making the animal something like a rhinoceros in appearance and lifestyle.

area of attachment around the margins of the frill. The edge of the frill is thickened to withstand the stresses and strains of muscular attachment. The area immediately in front of the back edge of the frill has a large, window-like opening on either side, which at first sight seems rather strange if large muscles are attached to the frill. However, the muscle would almost certainly have only been firmly attached to the edges of the frill and the edges of the 'windows', and in fact these 'extra' edges make the attachment stronger rather than weaker. There is another advantage to these openings in the frill which is slightly more obvious: they make the head and frill lighter and more easy to carry than it would be if it were a solid sheet of bone.

To return to these jaw muscles, they run forward and downward from the edge of the frill into long, slit-shaped holes on either side of the back of the skull. From here they run straight downward to attach to the raised bone on the lower jaw behind the teeth. The large bulk of such a muscle — far greater than that of any of the plant eaters we have seen so far, even those such as the hadrosaurids with their grinding batteries of teeth — is most impressive, and suggests that ceratopians had an immensely powerful bite. The strong jaw muscles also make sense when we look at the teeth of ceratopians which are rather similar to those of the hadrosaurids; at least insofar as there are many replacement teeth stacked together to form a *tooth battery.* However, one notable difference is the fact that instead of forming sloping wear surfaces as they do in hadrosaurids, ceratopians' teeth form vertical shearing blades — just like an enormous pair of scissors. They must have chewed their food rather differently than did the hadrosaurids. Hadrosaurids seem to have used their teeth and jaws like grindstones to pulverise plants. Ceratopians with their scissor-like tooth blades would presumably have chopped their food into short, uncrushed lengths of twig or leaf. Like most other ornithischians, ceratopians seem to have had muscular or fleshy cheeks which would have prevented the food from spilling out of the sides of the mouth when they were slicing it up. The implications of this method of chewing are interesting because plant foods are very difficult to digest. One of the best ways to prepare food for digestion is to chew it throroughly in the mouth so that it is completely broken up. If ceratopians only sliced up their food into short lengths, then they may have had either to keep the food in the stomach for a very long time so that it could be fermented; or perhaps have used stomach stones to pound up the tough plant tissues. Either that or ceratopians were feeding on very juicy, succulent, nutritious plants which needed only to be chopped into neat lengths to release all their goodness. Once again we seem to be stumped for a convincing answer!

To return to the issue of the function of the bony frills in *Protoceratops:* while it is not, I think, seriously doubted that the frill served as a site for jaw-muscle attachment, nevertheless Dr Dodson was able to show, through his careful study of the shape of the frill in *Protoceratops,* that its shape was not in all circumstances controlled by the need for powerful jaw muscles. After all if this had been the only requirement then both males and females would surely have had exactly the same shaped frills — which they do not! There is more discussion of ceratopian frill shape and function on pages 144-145.

## Other Protoceratopids

Other protoceratopid dinosaurs known to date all show a general similarity in size and shape to *Protoceratops. Leptoceratops* ('slender horned face') is a rare type from the very late Cretaceous of Alberta and Wyoming. By comparison with *Protoceratops, Leptoceratops* is smaller and more lightly built, and may well have been at least partially bipedal; its hindlimb was long and well-suited to running, while its forelegs were quite short and had small, grasping-type hands. The head of this animal was also less elaborate than *Protoceratops.* There was no high nose-ridge, the face sloped down quite steeply toward the snout. The frill at the back of the skull was also very little developed, with none of the window-like openings seen in

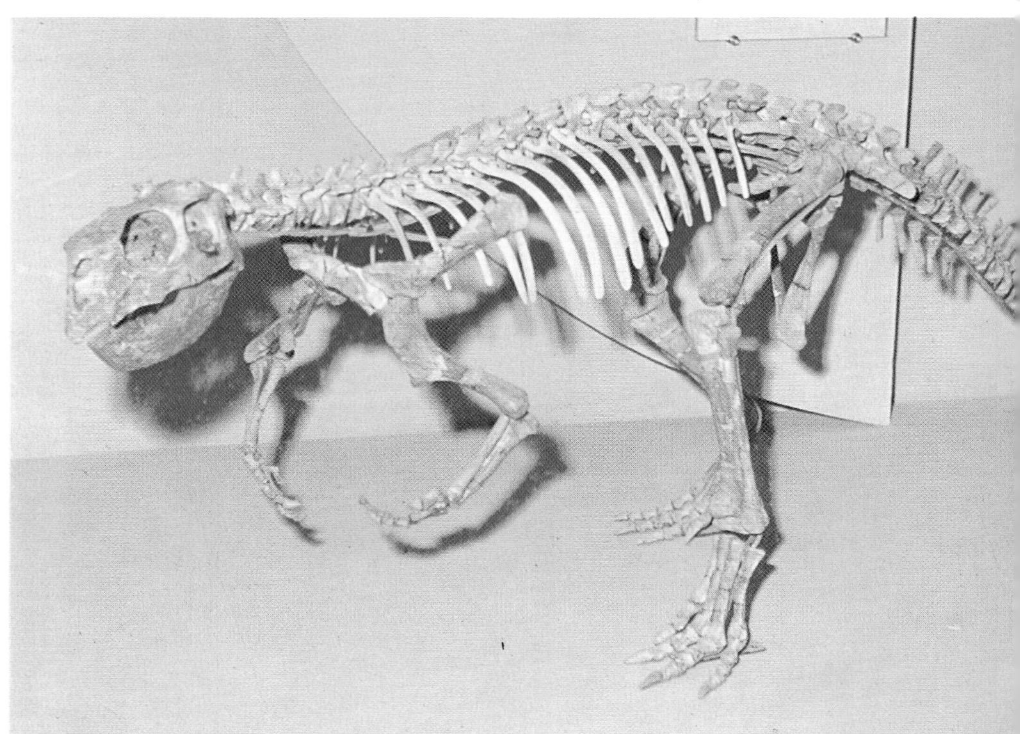

**Above:** This skeleton of *Psittacosaurus mongoliensis* illustrates the generally light build of this bipedal dinosaur, the clawed hands, and the distinctive parrot-like beak from which it derives its name. This specimen is in the Moscow Academy of Sciences' Palaeontological Institute.

**Left:** *Protoceratops* is known from the Late Cretaceous of both Asia and North America. This is a North American specimen on display in the Field Museum of Natural History, Chicago. The quadrupedal posture seems more typically 'ceratopian', as does the well-developed bony frill above the animal's neck. The pelvic structure is shown well here.

*Protoceratops*. In fact if it were not for its very late time of appearance in the fossil record, *Leptoceratops* would be very much the sort of creature that might have been expected to have evolved from *Psittacosaurus*.

*Montanoceratops* ('horned-face from Montana') was another North American protoceratopid. From Montana, as its name indicates, this creature was similar in size and shape to the Mongolian *Protoceratops*. The main difference lies in its possession of a quite prominent nose-horn. Otherwise, the very close resemblance between these two forms is striking, and suggests that they may have been quite close relatives.

More material of protoceratopids has recently been collected from Mongolia during joint Polish-Mongolian expeditions in the early 1970s. This includes the moderately well-preserved remains of *Microceratops* ('tiny-horned-face'). The parts of it that are known indicate that its skull had a better developed frill than *Leptoceratops*. The remainder of the skeleton is very slender and light with the very long hind limbs and slender feet of a fast runner. Rather unusually, for an animal that ran on its hindlegs, its front legs were also quite long. Quite why this was so is not certain.

Finally there is *Bagaceratops* ('small horned-face') a recently (1975) described protoceratopid from the Khermeen Tsav formation of Mongolia. So far this new species is only known from several skulls. These range in size from 1·5-10in (4-25cm) in length. The skull on page 131 is 6in (15cm) long and shows the main characteristics of this new type. The frill is solid and only slightly developed, although it is somewhat larger in the biggest skulls. As is the case in *Montanoceratops*, there is quite a well developed horn on the nose, which gives *Bagaceratops* a rather similar appearance. It will be interesting to see, when new and more complete skeletons of *Bagaceratops* are eventually discovered, whether or not these apparent similarities indicate any relationship between these two types of dinosaur.

Looked at together, the psittacosaurids and protoceratopids seem to represent an interesting intermediate step in the evolutionary line that led to the large and very powerful horned dinosaurs that appear in the late Cretaceous. Psittacosaurids retain many of the features of ornithopod dinosaurs such as the hysilophodontids as well as the very beginnings of the ceratopian features: notably the parrot-like beak. The protoceratopids in many ways seem to continue this 'trend'; some of them became essentially slower-moving, four-footed animals with well developed bony frills and the first rudiments of horns: very much smaller versions of the later ceratopids. Others, such as *Microceratops* and possibly *Leptoceratops*, seem to have persisted with the more active lifestyle of the psittacosaurids. These latter, however, seem never to have become as successful as the larger four-footed forms.

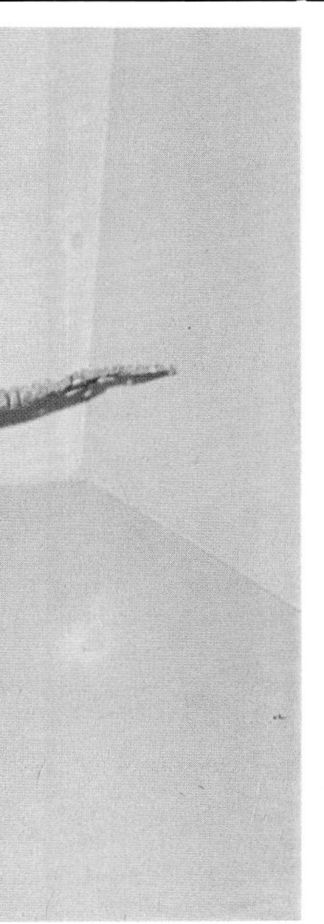

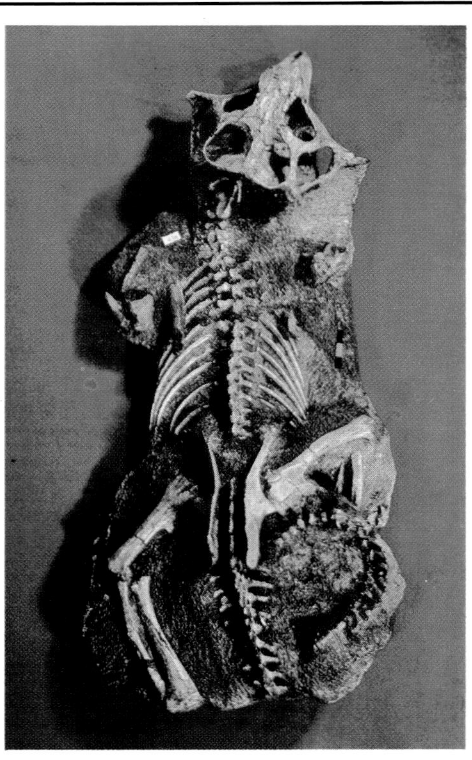

**Left:** A dorsal view of *Psittacosaurus sinensis*, a Chinese fossil from Shandong Province, now in the IVPP, Beijing. The length of the hind legs is particularly evident, an indication that this dinosaur may have resembled *Hypsilophodon* in its speed and agility.

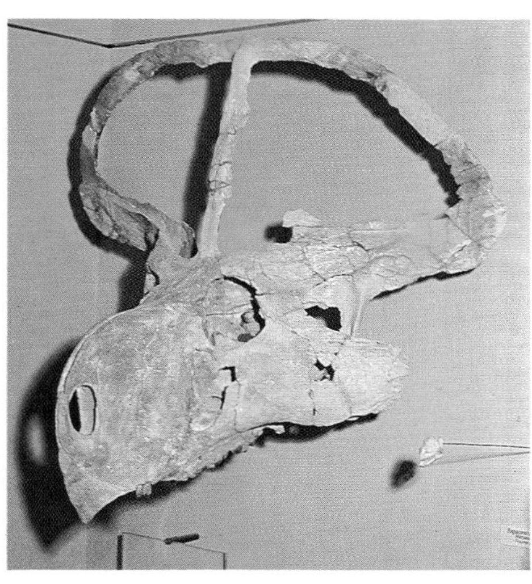

**Right:** The size of the frill suggests that this skull is that of an adult male *Protoceratops andrewsi*. The tiny skull to its right is that of a small *Bagaceratops rozhdestvensky*. This Mongolian form has a small horn on its nose, rather like *Montanoceratops*.

**Below:** This cast of a nest of *Protoceratops* eggs is in the British Museum (Natural History). It seems that female *Protoceratops* would lay their clutches of eggs in concentric rings in hollowed-out depressions in the ground, much as we see here.

**Sexual Dimorphism (below)**
These drawings are based on the work of Dr Peter Dodson who has carefully analysed the skulls of several *Protoceratops* discovered at the same site. His research has shown that adult males (lower drawing) have more erect frills and a more prominently humped snout than females. These differences may be related to social and sexual behaviour — the larger the frill, the more sexually attractive the male might appear to the female.

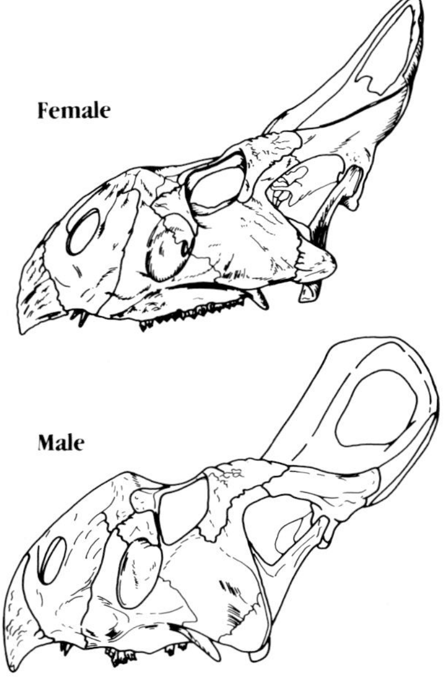

# Ceratopids I

The larger and more typical ceratopian or horned dinosaurs were first found in North America in 1855 by Ferdinand Hayden during a geological reconnaissance of the Upper Missouri, around the mouth of the Judith River in Montana. Among the rather broken and fragmentary remains collected were found several characteristically double-rooted teeth which were later to be referred to the genus *Monoclonius* ('single horn'). As was the case with *Hadrosaurus*, Joseph Leidy also described these first remains. Following these very early reports no other significant discoveries of ceratopids were made until 1872. This time, remains were discovered on the Union Pacific Railroad at Black Buttes Station about 50 miles from Green River in Wyoming. Again, and rather typically, the remains of this dinosaur, named *Agathaumas* ('marvellous') by Edward Drinker Cope, were very incomplete. They included backbones, leg bones and other scraps, but nothing which gave any clear clue as

**Styracosaurus (right)**
This interesting ceratopid had one of the most remarkable neck-frills. The frill was surrounded with the usual nodules of bone at the sides, but these became progressively longer round the back. The six most posterior pieces of bone were very long pointed spines that must have formed a very prominent visual display to threaten rivals or attract mates. The horn on its nose was, no doubt, a formidable weapon.

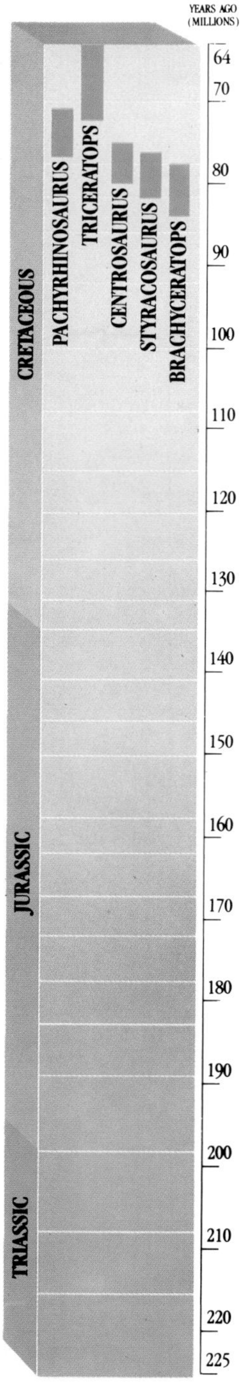

**Time Chart (left)**
The ceratopids were a very successful group in the late Cretaceous. The short-frilled forms were particularly abundant in the Red Deer River area of Alberta, which is of middle Upper Cretaceous age.

**Triceratops (right)**
The best known horned dinosaur, *Triceratops* was one of the largest members of the group. It might weigh up to 5·4 tonnes and reach a length of 30ft (9m). The neck frill was short, and rimmed by bony lumps. There were three sharp horns on the face, one on the snout, and one above each eye. The bony horn cores measure 3ft (90cm) long. so that they must have been considerably longer in life with the addition of the horn covering.

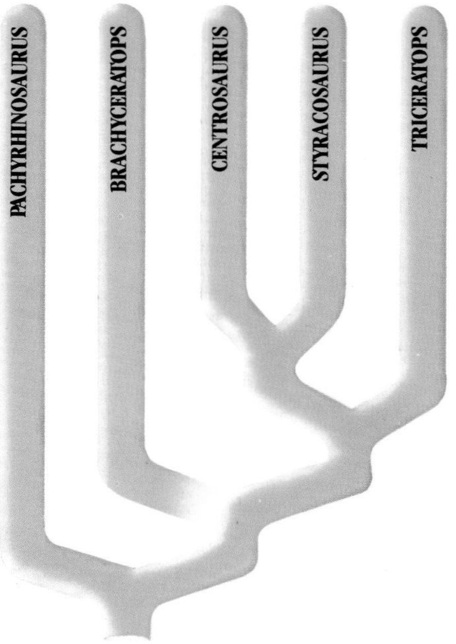

**Family Tree (left)**
The relations of the so-called short-frilled ceratopids are not clear. Each is so distinct that kinship is not at all obvious. *Centrosaurus* and *Styracosaurus* show some similarities: both have large nasal horns and elaborate frill margins. Where *Pachyrhinosaurus* fits is uncertain, and there is some doubt about the position of *Triceratops* as a short-frilled type at all.

**Comparative Sizes (below)**
**1** *Styracosaurus:* l. 18ft (5·5m).
**2** *Centrosaurus:* l. 20ft (6m).
**3** *Triceratops:* l. 29·5ft (9m).

to the real identity of these dinosaurs. Indeed, although Cope and his assistants managed to collect quite a lot of remains (which we can now recognize as belonging to ceratopids) from Colorado, Alberta and Montana, none of these was well enough preserved to add anything new. The solution to this mystery came about through the activities of Cope's great rival, Othniel Charles Marsh—although Marsh himself was somewhat confused by the first remains that he was shown. These were a pair of very large bony horn cores which had been discovered in 1887 by George L. Cannon in Green Mountain Creek, near Denver, Colorado. Marsh initially thought that these remains, which were sent to him by a government geologist, belonged to an extinct buffalo. In fact he even named these bones *Bison alticornis* ('high-horned buffalo'), and suggested that it had only comparatively recently become extinct: Marsh was wrong! This specimen later became known as *Triceratops alticornis* ('high-horned three-horned face'). In 1888 John Bell Hatcher, another early dinosaur collector who subsequently became a world authority on these and other dinosaurs, was shown a massive horn core by a ranch owner in Niobrara County, Wyoming. This new specimen was shown to Marsh who immediately sent Hatcher back to Niobrara County to look for the remainder of the animal. Quite remarkably, this is exactly what Hatcher did with some style, returning in the following year with a skull weighing over 1 tonne. This was identified as the type *Triceratops horridus* ('terrifying three-horned-face'). Between 1889 and 1892, Hatcher collected dinosaurs continuously from this Niobrara County locality, discovering more than thirty complete or partial skulls and skeletons of ceratopian dinosaurs. All of these remains were sent to Marsh and are now either in the collections of or on display in the Peabody Museum,Yale University or at the United States National Museum, Washington D.C. Following the frantic activity of the years of the Cope and Marsh rivalry, ceratopids continued to be discovered in North America. Between 1909 and 1916 some equally remarkable dinosaur collections were made along the Red Deer River in Canada. The collectors responsible for this were Barnum Brown and the Sternberg family, Charles Hazelius Sternberg and his sons, Charles, George and Levi. This all began in 1908, when a ranchman, John Wagner, showed Brown a rich deposit of dinosaur bones on the Red Deer River. Because the river was broad and slow-flowing, Brown decided that the best way to explore and collect was by boat. To do this, Brown and his assistants built a broad raft. Upon this they pitched a tent and stored their equipment for the expedition. They travelled slowly down river, stopping at likely places and setting off to explore and collect inland. At the end of the season when the weather became too cold to continue work, the raft was hauled

**Map (above)**
**1** *Agathaumas*
**2** *Brachyceratops*
**3** *Centrosaurus*
**4** *Diceratops*
**5** *Monoclonius*
**6** *Pachyrhinosaurus*
**7** *Styracosaurus*
**8** *Triceratops*

**Centrosaurus (left)**
This medium-sized ceratopid had a single horn on its snout, and small spines round the back of its neck frill. There were two horns on the posterior edge of the frill that pointed forwards. *Centrosaurus* had strong limbs and its feet were equipped with small hooves, rather like those of a rhinoceros. There is evidence that *Centrosaurus*, and other ceratopids, lived in herds of several dozen animals, and it is likely that they defended themselves communally, as do many living herbivores. The young animals and females might have remained in the middle, while the males formed a ring, facing outwards.

out and the materials stored until the next season. In this way large numbers of dinosaurs: ceratopids, hadrosaurs, and carnosaurs were discovered, many of which are to be found on display not only in North America, but in several museums around the world.

The next chapter in the story of the discovery of the ceratopian dinosaurs starts in the 1920s and continues, with interruptions, through to the present day. It centres on Asia, rather than North America. In the early 1920s there was considerable interest among scientists in North America in the fossils of Central Asia, because a prevailing theory of the time suggested that man's ancestors may be found there. With this in mind, a large expedition was mounted by the American Museum of Natural History in collaboration with the Mongolian government. Between 1922 and 1925 a series of expeditions was organized to map out the land and collect fossils from various parts of Mongolia. The results of this series of expeditions were spectacular. The second and third years of the expedition saw the systematic collection of not the ancestors of man, but dinosaurs of many types, and small early mammals. Most of these were completely new to science. Of the dinosaurs, the most notable were the remains of *Protoceratops* which are described in the section preceding this. More than one hundred specimens were collected, many of complete animals. Not only that, but they also showed a complete age range, from tiny hatchlings up to fully grown adults. Perhaps one of the most famous discoveries of all was the collection of eggs and nest-sites of these animals. At the time this was the first ever discovery of a nest of dinosaur eggs (see also *Maiasaura* page 121). In addition to *Protoceratops*, other dinosaurs were discovered including *Pinacosaurus* (a large ankylosaur, page 165), as well as the small carnivorous dinosaurs *Oviraptor* (page 45), *Saurornithoides* (page 55), *Velociraptor* (page 56) and remains of a *Tarbosaurus* (page 72).

Further expeditions went to Mongolia shortly after the Second World War, this time from Russia, and collected many more dinosaurs. Much more recently there have been a series of jointly organized Polish-Mongolian expeditions to the Gobi Desert in the 1960s and 1970s which have also proved to be very successful. Interest has also been renewed in North America by the discovery of a spectacular new dinosaur locality in Alberta, which has so far revealed hundreds of remains of the ceratopian dinosaur *Centrosaurus* ('sharp point reptile'). These have been carefully collected during several field-seasons in recent years by a team of palaeontologists and voluntary helpers from the new Tyrrell Museum of Palaeontology at Drumheller in Alberta. Thus ceratopids are still attracting considerable interest and attention.

The larger and more spectacular ceratopid dinosaurs illustrated on these pages are both numerous and varied in appearance. However, they do share a considerable number of

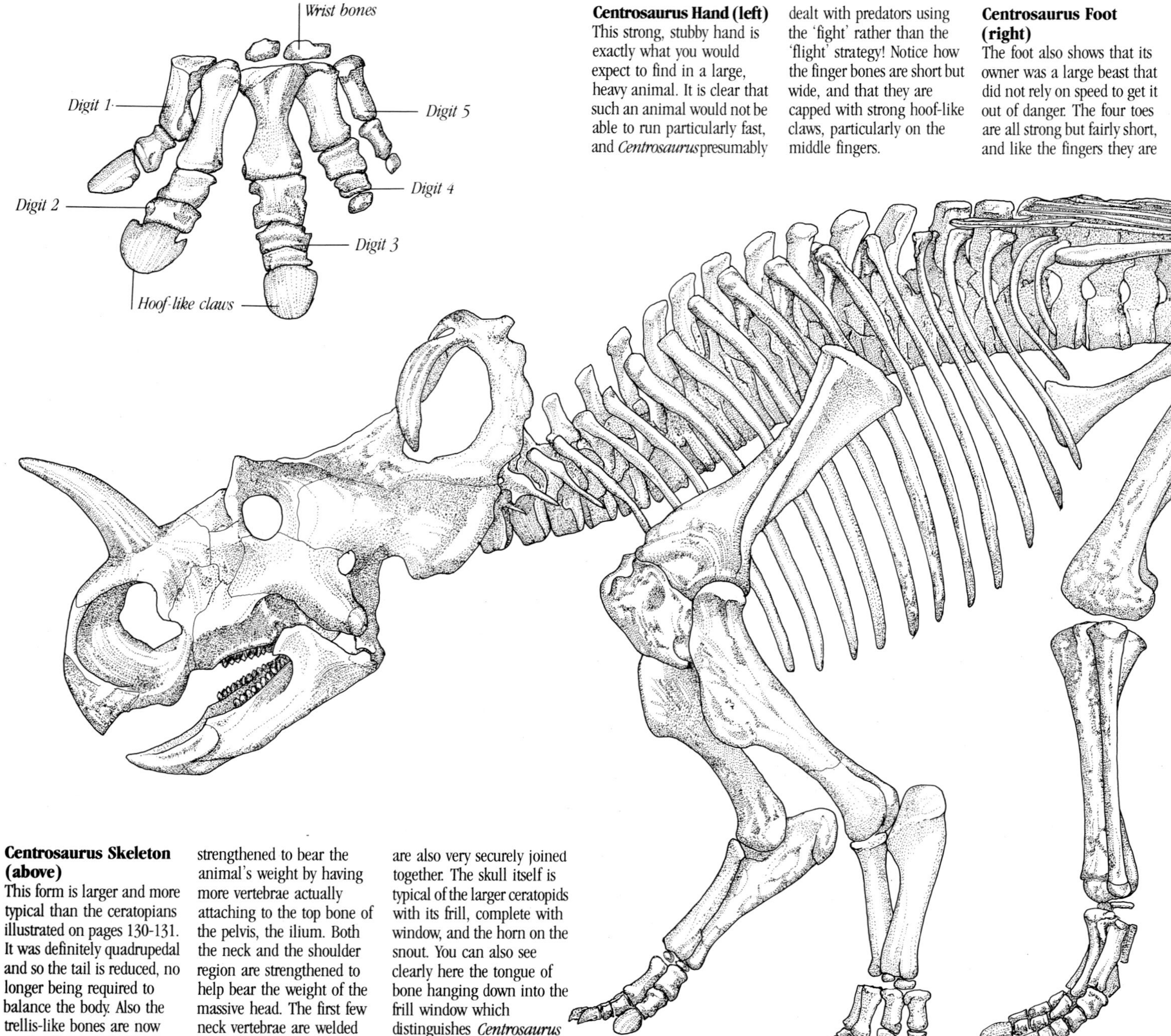


**Centrosaurus Hand (left)**
This strong, stubby hand is exactly what you would expect to find in a large, heavy animal. It is clear that such an animal would not be able to run particularly fast, and *Centrosaurus* presumably dealt with predators using the 'fight' rather than the 'flight' strategy! Notice how the finger bones are short but wide, and that they are capped with strong hoof-like claws, particularly on the middle fingers.

**Centrosaurus Foot (right)**
The foot also shows that its owner was a large beast that did not rely on speed to get it out of danger. The four toes are all strong but fairly short, and like the fingers they are

**Centrosaurus Skeleton (above)**
This form is larger and more typical than the ceratopians illustrated on pages 130-131. It was definitely quadrupedal and so the tail is reduced, no longer being required to balance the body. Also the trellis-like bones are now confined just to the hip region. This has been strengthened to bear the animal's weight by having more vertebrae actually attaching to the top bone of the pelvis, the ilium. Both the neck and the shoulder region are strengthened to help bear the weight of the massive head. The first few neck vertebrae are welded together, and the two principal bones of the shoulder girdle are also very securely joined together. The skull itself is typical of the larger ceratopids with its frill, complete with window, and the horn on the snout. You can also see clearly here the tongue of bone hanging down into the frill window which distinguishes *Centrosaurus* from other ceratopids in this group.

features in common. They are all large, four-footed creatures with tails that were relatively short because they were no longer used as a counterbalance as in *Psittacosaurus.* The back legs are stout, pillar-like and considerably longer than the front legs. In fact the extreme difference in length between front and back legs seems to provide strong support for the idea that the large ceratopids *evolved* from originally bipedal ancestors not unlike *Psittacosaurus* or *Microceratops.* The forelimbs may be short, but they are very powerfully built with large crests of bone for the attachment of strong muscles. The muscles of the forelimb of these ceratopids can be reconstructed in quite some detail. This is because the shoulder and arm muscles were so powerful that they left distinctive patterns of large roughened areas and ridges on the shoulder and arm bones. By using modern animals for comparison it is possible to decide the arrangement of these muscles with a fair degree of confidence.

The need for such strong front legs is fairly obvious. These animals must have had extremely heavy heads, so that the front legs would have had to bear considerable weight, even when they were standing still. Add to this the fact that these animals swung their heads around to browse on plants, and also used them for fighting, and we can conclude that the power and strength of the front legs must have been quite remarkable.

## Ceratopid Characteristics

The heads of all these ceratopids are considerably larger in proportion to body size than is the case in the protoceratopids. And here at last are developed the full set of ceratopid features, the sharp beak, large neck-frill and large horns. Some idea of the great weight of the head in the dinosaurs can be gained by looking at the structure of the neck vertebrae. The first three vertebrae immediately behind the head are fused together into a solid piece of bone. All ceratopids (and some protoceratopids) show this type of modification which was undoubtedly a means of strengthening the top of the neck in order to be able to bear the great weight of the head.

The ceratopids chosen for illustration on pages 134-135 and 140-141 have been deliberately separated into two groups: short-frilled and long-frilled ceratopids respectively. *Centrosaurus* (sometimes referred to as *Monoclonius* instead), *Styracosaurus* ('spiked reptile') and *Triceratops* have been selected as representatives of the short-frilled type of ceratopid, although there are at least two other well known species: *Pachyrhinosaurus* ('thick-nosed reptile') and *Brachyceratops* ('short horned-face'). The skeleton of each of these animals is practically indistinguishable in general shape, and the *Centrosaurus* skeleton that we see illustrated is quite typical. A comparison with *Triceratops* for example would simply show that

splayed out to provide a greater surface area over which to take the animal's considerable weight. As the posture of the main skeleton indicates, this form probably walked up on its toes, rather than on its whole foot.

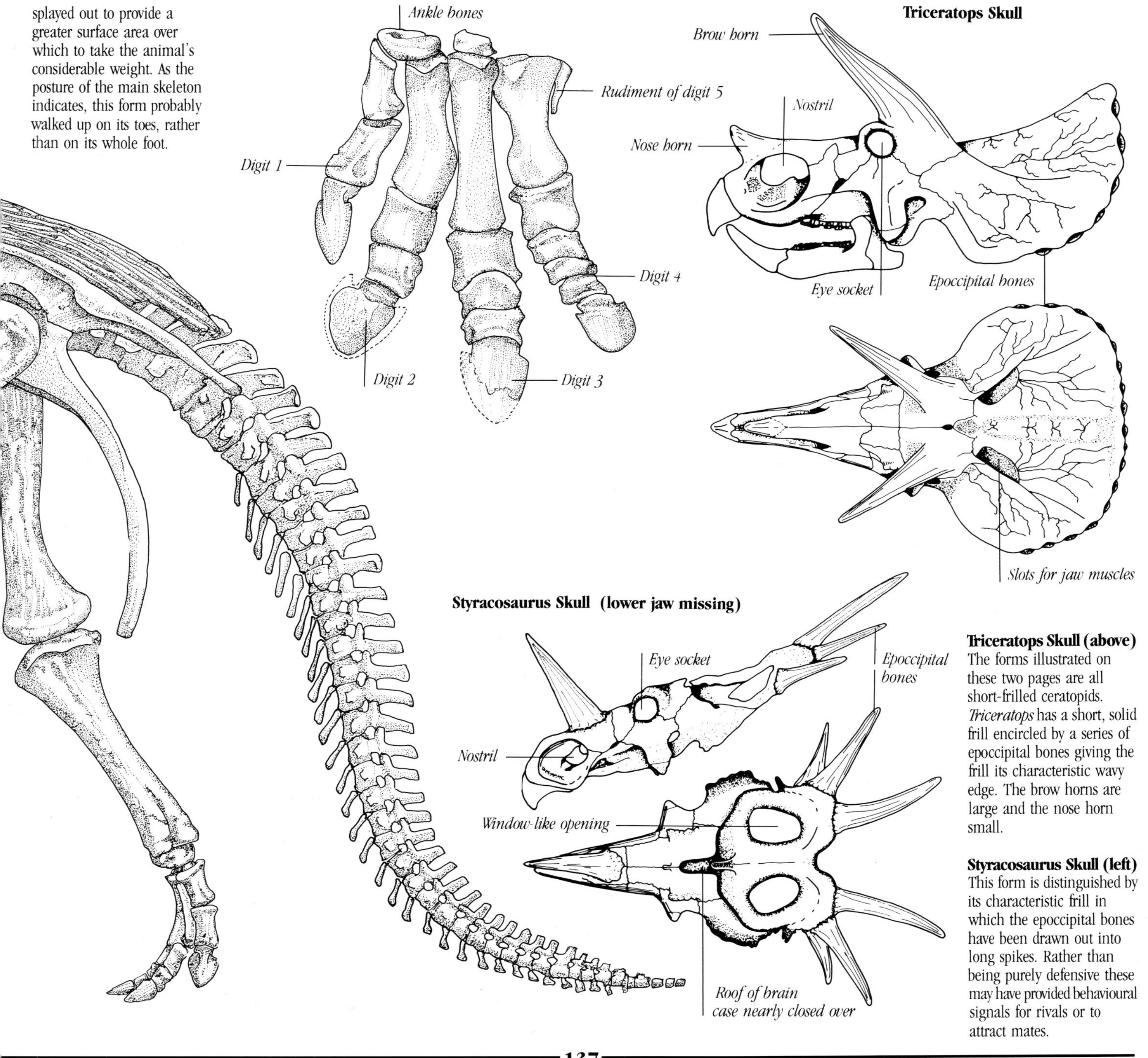


**Triceratops Skull (above)**
The forms illustrated on these two pages are all short-frilled ceratopids. *Triceratops* has a short, solid frill encircled by a series of epoccipital bones giving the frill its characteristic wavy edge. The brow horns are large and the nose horn small.

**Styracosaurus Skull (left)**
This form is distinguished by its characteristic frill in which the epoccipital bones have been drawn out into long spikes. Rather than being purely defensive these may have provided behavioural signals for rivals or to attract mates.

the *Triceratops* skeleton was more stoutly built than *Centrosaurus*, but this was simply a reflection of the fact that *Triceratops* was a larger and heavier animal. All the really obvious differences between these species are to be found in the skull.

## Centrosaurus Described

*Centrosaurus* remains are found almost exclusively in the Red Deer River area of Alberta where it seems to have been remarkably abundant. It is known from several complete skeletons and detailed skin impressions. Despite this, there remains to this day much confusion about the name that should be applied to this dinosaur. Some describe it as *Monoclonius*, while others refer to it as *Centrosaurus*. The problem has arisen because of the very fragmentary nature of the early ceratopian material. The name *Monoclonius* was coined by Cope in 1876 for some broken fragments of a crest, and a few pieces of skeleton discovered in Montana (as described earlier). None of this material can be used for defining this type of dinosaur, or for comparing anything else with it, so the use of the name *Monoclonius* to describe any other dinosaur material could only be a matter of shrewd guesswork rather than strictly scientific comparison. *Centrosaurus* by contrast was described by Lawrence Lambe in 1904 and was based on another frill of a ceratopid this time from the Red Deer River. This admittedly fragmentary specimen does, however, have one crucial character present, and that is the rather curious tongue-shaped pieces of bone which point downward into the window-like openings of the frill. These do not appear in any other known ceratopid to date; so, imperfect though Lambe's specimen is, that piece of frill clearly characterises *Centrosaurus* and must take precedence. *Monoclonius*, interesting though it is from an historical point of view, has sadly to be looked upon as a dubiously named dinosaur.

*Centrosaurus*, in addition to possessing the unique tongue-shaped bones on its frill, has a very prominent nasal horn giving it quite a strong resemblance to a rhinoceros. There are also small eyebrow horns but these are very poorly developed compared to the nose horn. Most of the characters of the skull are similar to those seen in protoceratopids such as *Protoceratops* (pages 136-137). There is a pronounced parrot-like, toothless beak at the tip of the jaws, and the teeth, which are set in from the sides of the jaws to allow room for cheeks, form powerful cutting blades. The jaws of these larger ceratopids are better developed than the protoceratopids and have longer cutting blades with more teeth. The jaws are also operated by very powerful muscles which run down from the frill (as we saw in *Protoceratops*) but which this time attach to a large bar of bone that sticks up from the back end of the lower jaw. This process, termed the coronoid process (also seen in iguanodontids and hadrosaurids) provides extra leverage for the jaw-closing muscles.

Two other features in the skull not found in the protoceratopids are the so-called *epoccipital* bones and a secondary skull roof. Epoccipitals are small, rounded lumps of bone found around the edge of the frill, giving it an irregular wavy margin. In the case of *Centrosaurus* the epoccipitals are not very strongly developed. Precisely what their function was is not at all certain. Most likely, these lumps were decorative, and covered in life by horny layers of skin. Such horny edging may have helped with individual recognition, thereby acting as signalling structures, rather than as a spiky defensive edge to deter predators.

The secondary skull roof can be seen most clearly in the top views of the skulls. In the area of the roof of the skull, just in front of the frill and between the raised ridges over the eyes, there is found a deep U-shaped notch. This notch represents the ingrown edges of the top of the skull roof which have grown up and over the original roof of the braincase. This rather complicated arrangement of bones probably reflects the changes that have taken place in ceratopian skulls when compared with more ordinary ornithischian dinosaur skulls, such as those of hypsilophodontids. Not only has the enormous frill been added to the back, but horns have been added to the nose and eyes, the skull has become much narrower and deeper, and huge muscles now operate the jaws. Some reinforcement of the skull would have been inevitable, and the adding of a second skull roof between and behind the eyes was probably essential in holding the skull together.

Looking at the remainder of the skeleton, the progressive trend toward a fully four-footed way of life, seen earlier in the protoceratopids, is now complete. The tail, which was still quite long and very deep in *Protoceratops* can now be seen to be quite short and slender, with only its tip resting on the ground, obviously of no use for counterbalancing the body. The peculiar bony rods, which ran along much of the length of the back and tail in most ornithischians and acted to stiffen the backbone so that it could be held fairly straight without sagging, are now simply concentrated across the spines immediately above the hip area. The connection between the backbone and hips is very greatly strengthened by increasing the number of vertebrae attaching to the pelvic bones from about 4-6, as seen in most dinosaurs, to about 10. The back legs are large and powerful with broad, hooved, four-toed feet. The rib cage is very large and deep and against this was slung the massive shoulders and forelimbs. As was noted with the protoceratopids, the bipedal ancestry of the ceratopids is very clearly shown in the obvious disparity between the lengths of the front and back legs.

The great size and weight of the head of *Centrosaurus* has produced several inevitable changes in the rest of the skeleton. As was noted with the protoceratopids, several of the neck vertebrae have become welded together, presumably to prevent dislocation of these bones when the head was being shaken or used more violently, such as when defending itself against predatory dinosaurs. The shoulders and forelimbs also show evidence of great strengthening, in order to carry the heavy head. The two main shoulder bones are large and very tightly knitted together, thereby improving their strength for carrying weight and also their ability to anchor large and powerful shoulder muscles. That the shoulder muscles were powerful is indicated by large bony crests and ridges on the surface of both the shoulder and forelimb. As shown in the drawing on page 143, several of these muscles can be restored in their probable positions in life. The front feet are broad (five-toed), the inner ones with well developed hooves.

The powerful front legs and broad feet gave these animals great strength. This was not only simply to support the very heavy head, while walking, running or feeding; it would also have been necessary for fending off predators. The most likely predators of these dinosaurs were the giant tyrannosaurids of the late Cretaceous. When faced by the threat of a hunting tyrannosaurid, *Centrosaurus* probably had several options. It seems likely that *Centrosaurus* was a gregarious animal, in which case the largest and most powerful bull males may have defended the herd in groups. Armed with such formidable nose horns, these animals were very likely more than a match for any tyrannosaurid. However, herding animals do not remain packed tightly together all of the time; they have to spread out to find suitable food. Sneak attacks on isolated feeding animals may have been a good strategy for tyrannosaurids hunting such formidable creatures. The outcome of such attacks would depend upon numerous complicated factors: the respective ages of predator and prey, their agility, acceleration and top running speed, and many others beside. On occasion, tyrannosaurids must have cornered *Centrosaurus*. However, even when cornered by a full-sized *Tyrannosaurus*, *Centrosaurus* would have still been a considerable opponent. A tyrannosaurid would need to make its first bite a killing one, because its attacking lunge would leave it open to being severely gored by the nasal horn. When crouching low by spreading its front legs apart, *Centrosaurus* would be an elusive and dangerous target.

## Other Species

*Triceratops* must be one of the best known of all dinosaurs; it has come to be known to the world at large through the labours of John Bell

**Above:** The most distinctive feature of this skull of *Pachyrhinosaurus*, a Tyrrell Museum of Palaeontology specimen, is the rough bony pad that extends along the upper surface of the snout region. Only two skulls of this dinosaur have been so far discovered.

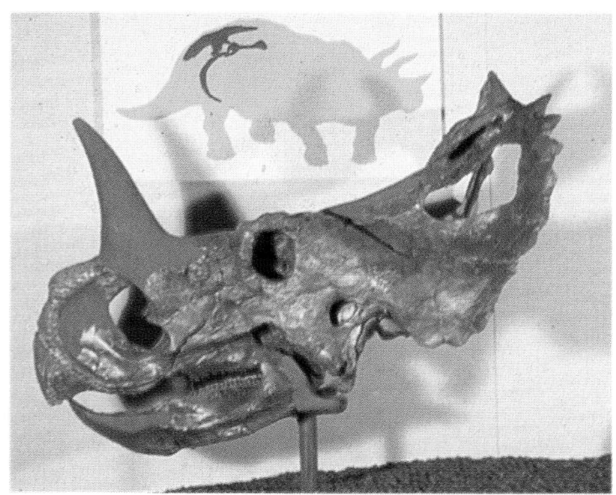

**Above:** This skull on display in the National Museum of Natural History, Washington D.C., is identified as *Monoclonius flexus*. As can be seen, the skull is incomplete and many areas, including the nose horn, have had to be reconstructed in the laboratory.

Hatcher in Niobrara County, Wyoming. From this area Hatcher recovered thirty-two ceratopian skulls, almost all of them belonging to the genus *Triceratops*. There are 10 species of *Triceratops* currently recognized from these collections. These are distinguished by their size and general proportions, but it does seem very unlikely that there were in fact 10 distinct species living within a relatively short time period. More likely is the prospect that this number would be reduced if we were able to establish with some confidence young individuals, the normal range of variations within any single species population of *Triceratops*, and the differences between males and females. A study of the type done by Peter Dodson on *Protoceratops* may be one way of resolving this problem.

Nevertheless, all *Triceratops* share a number of common features. They have relatively short, but solid frills (there are no window-like openings as in *Centrosaurus*, and indeed most other ceratopids). Around the fringe of the frill is an even row of conical epoccipital bones. In contrast to *Centrosaurus*, the eyebrow horns are very large and the nasal horn tends to be somewhat shorter. In fact the length of the nose horn may vary from individual to individual. The snout of *Triceratops* is also lower and longer than that of *Centrosaurus*. However, apart from these differences, the remainder of the skeleton is very similar in these two animals. Some *Triceratops* species were enormous. The head alone of *Triceratops horridus* ('horrible three-horned face') was 6·6ft (2m) long and the whole animal was probably 29·5ft (9m) long (even though its tail was very short). It may have weighed as much as 6 tonnes. More information about *Triceratops* is to be found in the following section: Ceratopids II.

*Styracosaurus* from the Belly River of Alberta has a rather extraordinary skull; it is long and low with a very prominent nose-horn like that of *Centrosaurus*. At first sight this seems to be a long frilled ceratopid. However, if you look closely, the frill is actually short with large windows in it—just like *Centrosaurus*. However the epoccipitals, which are small nubbins in *Centrosaurus*, are developed into great long spikes which stick out backward. The visual effect of the spikes on the edge of the frill is quite striking and will be discussed later. Unfortunately all that is known of *Styracosaurus* is this extraordinary skull and a few other smaller skull fragments.

*Pachyrhinosaurus* from Alberta is another extraordinary ceratopid which has similar skull proportions to *Centrosaurus*. However, instead of a horn core on its nose, there is a broad, thick, rough plate of bone. Two skulls of this species have been discovered to date. The extraordinary roughness and irregularity of the nose-pad in these specimens tempts the suggestion that this might be a *pathological* feature developed after fracturing of an original horn core.

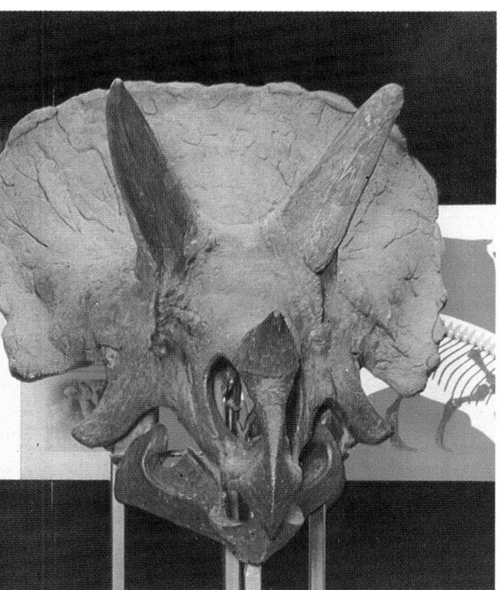

**Left:** This photograph graphically illustrates the massive size and robust construction of the skull of *Triceratops*. The eyebrow horns are noticeably larger than the nose horn, and the frill, which lacks window-like openings, is edged with an array of small epoccipital bones.

**On The Attack (above)** An aggressive 5-tonne adult *Triceratops* charges a full-grown tyrannosaurid predator. The combination of its long facial horns and powerful build would have made it a formidable opponent for even the largest 'carnosaur'.

**Below:** The Smithsonian Institution's skeleton of *Triceratops prorsus*, the smallest species of *Triceratops*. The head is very large in proportion to the body, while the tail, no longer needed as a counter-balance as it was for bipedal ornithopods, has grown correspondingly shorter and just touches the ground.

**Below:** This charging rhino invites comparison with *Centrosaurus*; were scenes like this enacted in late Cretaceous times?

# CERATOPIDS II

The other major group of ceratopids comprises the long-frilled types considered here. The examples illustrated below and overleaf (*Chasmosaurus* 'ravine reptile', *Torosaurus* 'bull reptile', *Pentaceratops* 'five-horned face', *Anchiceratops* 'close-horned face') are all absolutely typical of this type of dinosaur. The body of these animals is practically identical to that of the short-frilled forms described earlier: they are, without exception, large lumbering quadrupedal dinosaurs.

The skulls of these creatures are even more bizarre than those of their short-frilled cousins. The general pattern seen in all these dinosaurs is for the frill to be greatly lengthened and somewhat lower than the short-frilled types, when seen in profile. As a result, the frill seems to have lain like a shield over the shoulder region of the animal, completely covering its neck. This would seem to suggest that their frills had some sort of defensive function, perhaps protecting the neck against the attacks of predators. In fact, as we shall see later, this is now considered to be an extremely unlikely function indeed. In addition to the variations in the proportions of the frill, the faces of these ceratopids are somewhat different from those of the short-frilled forms. Typically, they are not as deep, being long and low with a tapering muzzle. The arrangement of horns is also rather different. Whereas in the short-frilled forms (especially *Centrosaurus* and *Styracosaurus*) the nose horn is very long and pointed, the long-frilled types have very short, blunt nose horns, while the brow horns, which tend to be short in the short-frills, are long and pointed.

The best known long-frilled ceratopids are *Chasmosaurus, Pentaceratops, Torosaurus, Anchiceratops* and *Arrhinoceratops* ('no nose-horned face'), all of which come from the late Cretaceous of western North America. A few rather dubious types such as *Eoceratops* are also known, but these are discussed at the end of this section.

*Chasmosaurus* is known from several well-preserved skulls and skeletons which were discovered, along the Red Deer River in Alberta, by Lawrence Lambe and the Sternberg family. The skull of this ceratopid is very long and low. Its frill is large and has thick edges, which are fringed by low, rounded epoccipitals (lumps of bone edging the frill) which get progressively larger and more pointed toward each of the posterior corners of the frill. When viewed from above, the enormous size of the frill's window-like openings is very noticeable. Its back edge is formed by quite a thin bar of bone supported by a thin spar of bone projecting backward from the middle of the head. Presumably all the strength of the frill lay in the thick bones lying along either side of it. The enormous size of the openings immediately casts doubt on the idea that it was used as a defensive shield. The space between the thickened edges of the frill is scooped out on either side of the ridge which runs down its

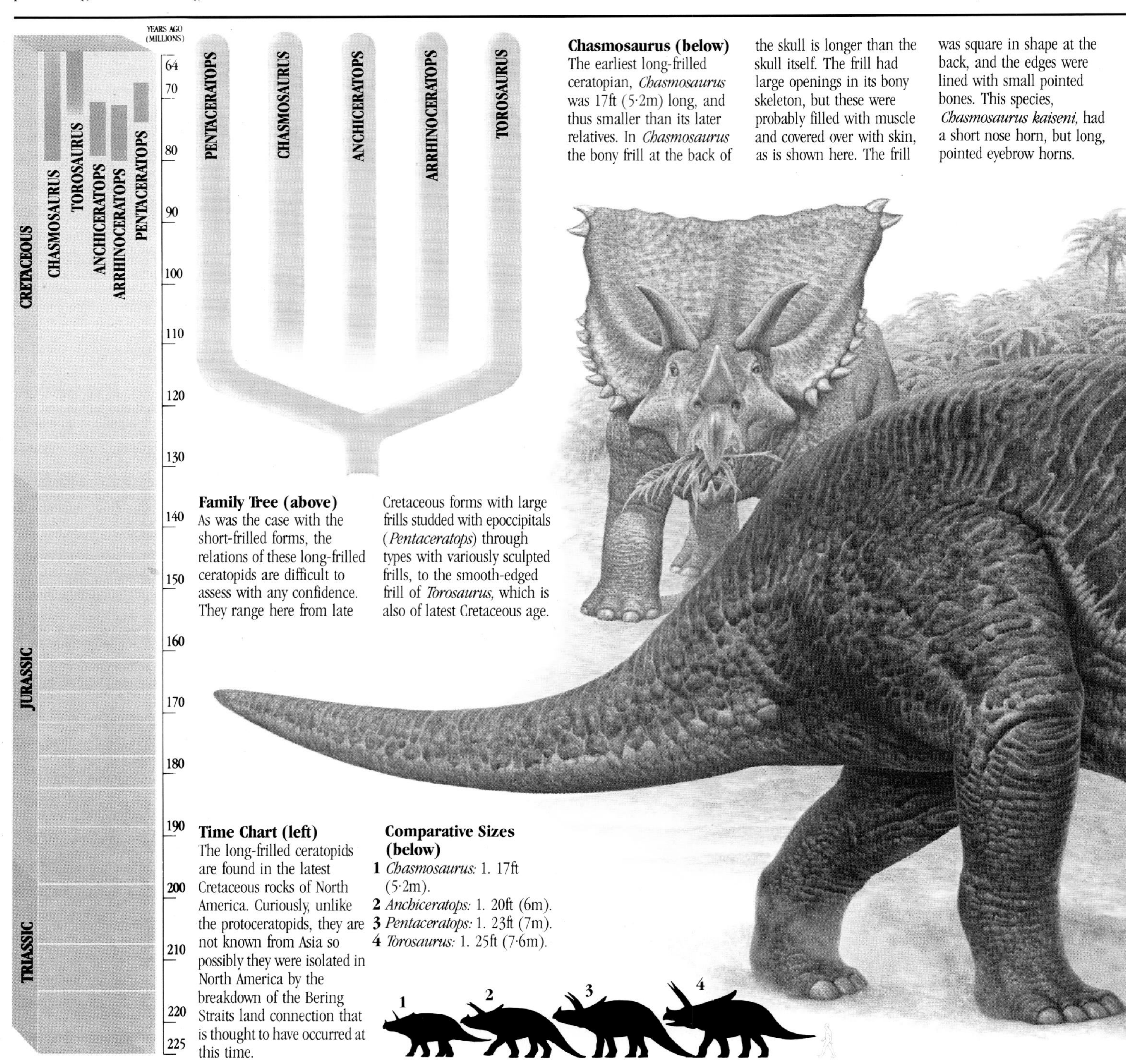


**Chasmosaurus (below)**
The earliest long-frilled ceratopian, *Chasmosaurus* was 17ft (5·2m) long, and thus smaller than its later relatives. In *Chasmosaurus* the bony frill at the back of the skull is longer than the skull itself. The frill had large openings in its bony skeleton, but these were probably filled with muscle and covered over with skin, as is shown here. The frill was square in shape at the back, and the edges were lined with small pointed bones. This species, *Chasmosaurus kaiseni,* had a short nose horn, but long, pointed eyebrow horns.

**Family Tree (above)**
As was the case with the short-frilled forms, the relations of these long-frilled ceratopids are difficult to assess with any confidence. They range here from late Cretaceous forms with large frills studded with epoccipitals (*Pentaceratops*) through types with variously sculpted frills, to the smooth-edged frill of *Torosaurus,* which is also of latest Cretaceous age.

**Time Chart (left)**
The long-frilled ceratopids are found in the latest Cretaceous rocks of North America. Curiously, unlike the protoceratopids, they are not known from Asia so possibly they were isolated in North America by the breakdown of the Bering Straits land connection that is thought to have occurred at this time.

**Comparative Sizes (below)**
1 *Chasmosaurus:* 1. 17ft (5·2m).
2 *Anchiceratops:* 1. 20ft (6m).
3 *Pentaceratops:* 1. 23ft (7m).
4 *Torosaurus:* 1. 25ft (7·6m).

middle. These two trough-shaped depressions almost certainly contained the enlarged jaw-closing muscles of these dinosaurs which plunge deep into spaces in the head just behind the eye, before attaching to the lower jaw. This arrangement is like that seen in *Protoceratops*, but on a much larger scale.

As well as the frill, the face deserves mention. It was stated earlier that most long-frilled ceratopids have long, pointed eyebrow horns and short blunt nose horns. *Chasmosaurus* already shows a variation on that theme: the eyebrow horns of the individual illustrated overleaf are really quite short and blunt, as is the nose horn. This combination of horn sizes characterizes a particular species of *Chasmosaurus—Chasmosaurus belli*. Another species, known as *Chasmosaurus kaiseni*, is also known from the Red Deer River. In most respects, the skulls of these two species are similar. The horns, however, differ strikingly: *Chasmosaurus kaiseni* has very long, pointed eyebrow horns

**Pentaceratops (below)**
As its name suggests ('five-horned face'), *Pentaceratops* was supposed to have five horns, two more than is usual in ceratopids.
The additional 'horns' are in fact pointed cheek bones which are found in the skulls of nearly all ceratopians. The bony frill was massive, and the border was set with pointed bony nodules which were both decorative and an added defence against predators that might have tried to sink their teeth into the fleshy neck area.

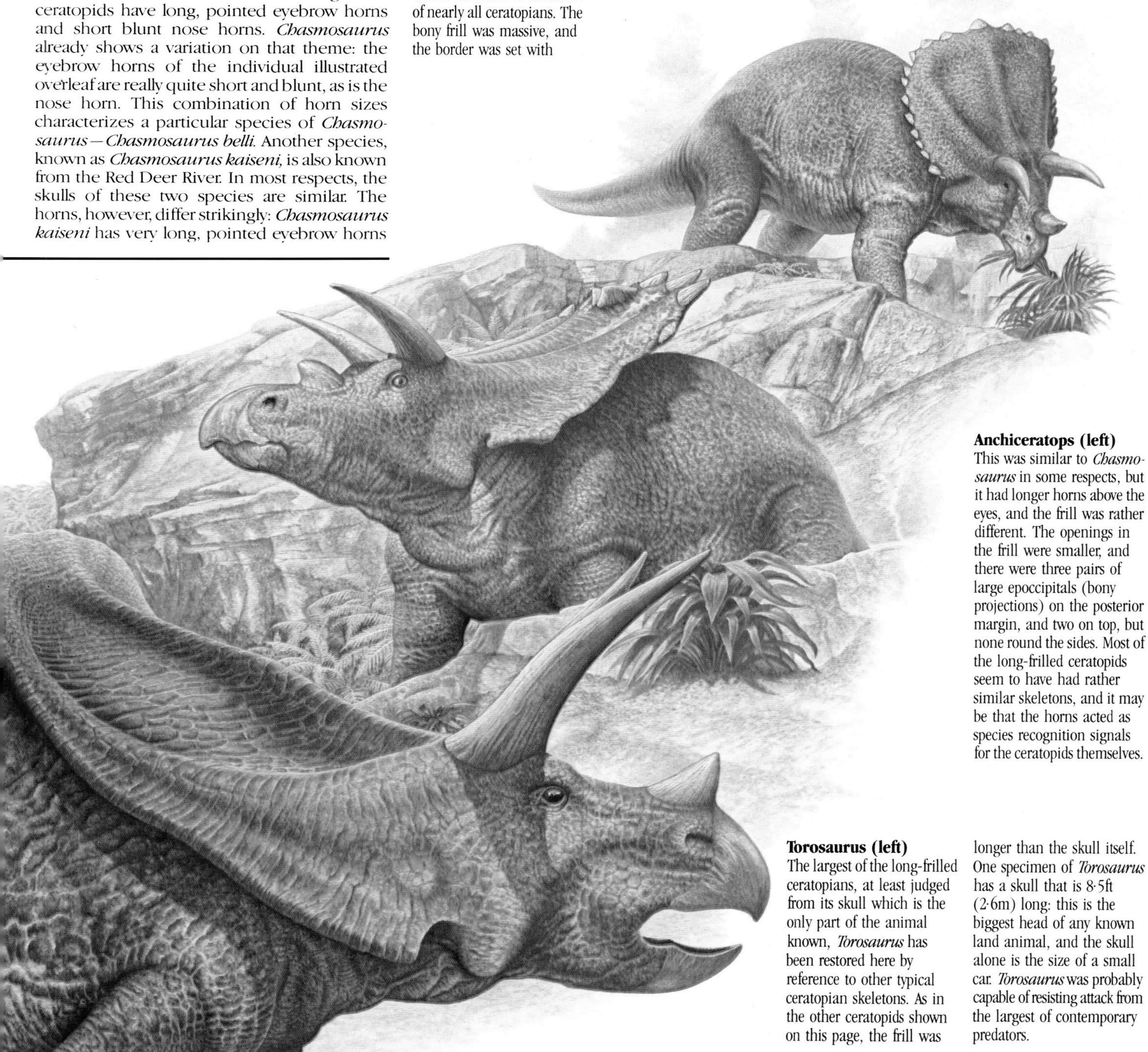

**Anchiceratops (left)**
This was similar to *Chasmosaurus* in some respects, but it had longer horns above the eyes, and the frill was rather different. The openings in the frill were smaller, and there were three pairs of large epoccipitals (bony projections) on the posterior margin, and two on top, but none round the sides. Most of the long-frilled ceratopids seem to have had rather similar skeletons, and it may be that the horns acted as species recognition signals for the ceratopids themselves.

**Torosaurus (left)**
The largest of the long-frilled ceratopians, at least judged from its skull which is the only part of the animal known, *Torosaurus* has been restored here by reference to other typical ceratopian skeletons. As in the other ceratopids shown on this page, the frill was longer than the skull itself. One specimen of *Torosaurus* has a skull that is 8·5ft (2·6m) long: this is the biggest head of any known land animal, and the skull alone is the size of a small car. *Torosaurus* was probably capable of resisting attack from the largest of contemporary predators.

**Map (right)**
**1** *Anchiceratops*
**2** *Arrhinoceratops*
**3** *Chasmosaurus*
**4** *Eoceratops*
**5** *Pentaceratops*
**6** *Torosaurus*

(see colour illustration). The discovery of two such similar dinosaurs in the same geological deposit seems to point quite strongly to the possibility that the difference in brow horn size may in fact be an indicator of their sexes. We saw earlier in the case of *Protoceratops* how the shape of the nose and frill was associated with the sex of individuals. It seems equally possible that *Chasmosaurus kaiseni* (with the large brown horns) was a male individual, while the short-horned species, *C. belli,* may well have been the female. Unfortunately a detailed analysis to identify sexual characteristics in *Chasmosaurus* is not possible, because there are simply not enough skulls known to get sufficient scientific data for such an exercise.

*Anchiceratops* lived a little later in the Cretaceous Period than *Chasmosaurus* although it was also discovered on the Red Deer River. *Anchiceratops* is fairly similar to *Chasmosaurus kaiseni* as regards the shape of its skull; it has quite a long face, a short nose horn and long pointed brow horns. The frill, however, is distinctive. The window-like openings are much smaller than in *Chasmosaurus* and three pairs of large, triangular epoccipitals are found along the back edge of the frill. There are also two epoccipitals which project forward from the middle of the back edge of the frill; these are smaller than, but vaguely reminiscent of, the curious tongue-shaped bones which project into the frill openings of *Centrosaurus.* Apart from this, these two genera are very similar.

*Arrhinoceratops* was a contemporary of *Anchiceratops;* both were found in the same area of the Red Deer River. The name of this ceratopid—'no nose-horned face'—is particularly inappropriate because *Arrhinoceratops* does indeed have a nose horn. The peculiar name for this animal arose because William Parks, who first described this dinosaur in 1925, claimed that its skull did not have a *true* nose horn. There was clearly a 'lump' on the nose where a horn should be, but Parks believed that it should be clearly visible as a *separate* bone, rather than just a thickening of the bones covering the nose area of the animal. This type of interpretation is now regarded as improbable since horns of this type would tend to weld themselves to the nose bones, and it is impossible to tell whether the bone was ever separate or not. However, despite the fact that Parks' name is inappropriate, the rules which govern the names given to animals make it impossible to change the name retrospectively.

*Arrhinoceratops* has large, pointed brow horns and the frill is quite large and broad, with two moderate-sized openings like those of *Anchiceratops.* The margins of its frill are wavy because of an even fringe of low, rounded epoccipitals. In many respects *Arrhinoceratops* resembles *Triceratops* very closely, the only obvious difference being the absence of openings in *Triceratops*' frill.

*Pentaceratops* was first described in 1923 by Henry Fairfield Osborn. The name was

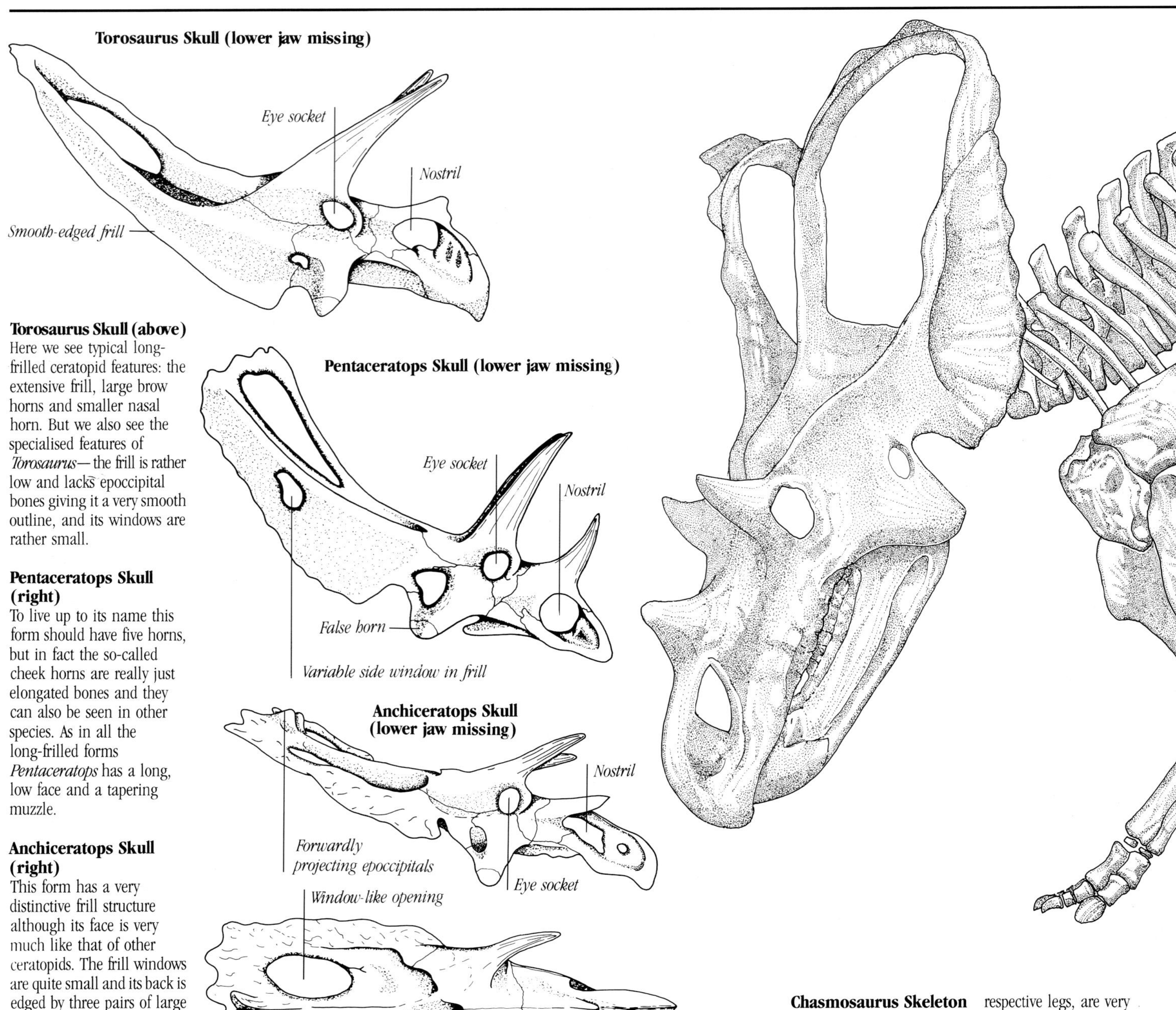


**Torosaurus Skull (above)**
Here we see typical long-frilled ceratopid features: the extensive frill, large brow horns and smaller nasal horn. But we also see the specialised features of *Torosaurus*—the frill is rather low and lacks epoccipital bones giving it a very smooth outline, and its windows are rather small.

**Pentaceratops Skull (right)**
To live up to its name this form should have five horns, but in fact the so-called cheek horns are really just elongated bones and they can also be seen in other species. As in all the long-frilled forms *Pentaceratops* has a long, low face and a tapering muzzle.

**Anchiceratops Skull (right)**
This form has a very distinctive frill structure although its face is very much like that of other ceratopids. The frill windows are quite small and its back is edged by three pairs of large epoccipitals. Two of these bones also project forwards from the back edge of the skull. The eyebrow horns are very long and pointed.

**Chasmosaurus Skeleton (above)**
This skeleton is typical of a large, lumbering reptile. Both the hip and shoulder girdles, as well as their respective legs, are very solidly built—designed for weight-bearing, not speed The vertebrae are also very large and strong, especially in the neck and back regions.

suggested to Osborn by William Diller Matthew to recognize the fact that in addition to the usual three horns of the head, this new specimen had two others formed by the long pointed cheek bones beneath and behind the eye (see illustration). In fact, as was the case in *Arrhinoceratops,* the name *Pentaceratops* turned out to be rather fanciful. These cheek bones are not particularly horn-like in some specimens and other ceratopids have equally large cheek bones. Nevertheless, we are again stuck with this rather misleading name.

All the remains of *Pentaceratops* come from the San Juan Basin of New Mexico, and are of a very large-frilled ceratopid. The brow horns are very long and pointed, the nose horn is of moderate size. The frill has many low triangular epoccipitals which run along its margins. The openings in the frill are large and rather like those of *Chasmosaurus.*

*Torosaurus* was, along with *Triceratops,* one of the last of the dinosaurs, appearing in the latest part of the Cretaceous Period. *Torosaurus* is known only from the character of its skull; none of the remainder of the skeleton has so far been identified. The skull, however, is quite remarkable. The genus is represented by two species, *Torosaurus gladius* and *Torosaurus latus,* both of which were first described by O. C. Marsh from material collected by Hatcher in Niobrara County, Wyoming.

Both of these species are represented by single skulls, each of which is incomplete. *Torosaurus latus* had a skull that was probably almost 8ft (2·4m) long when complete. Unfortunately the muzzle of the skull is not preserved, so it is not possible to give an exact measure of the length of the skull or the shape of the snout.

The arrangement of horns on the skull is similar to that seen in *Arrhinoceratops,* with a rather short nose horn and long pointed brow horns. The frill, however, is distinctive; it is very long and low, with very smooth edges exhibiting no sign of the epoccipitals seen in all other ceratopids. The frill also has moderately sized circular openings, unlike most other ceratopids. The smooth contours and smoothness of the frill contrast quite strongly with the features of the only other very late ceratopian genus *Triceratops,* which has a scalloped edge to its frill and no openings at all.

The inner surface of parts of the frill in this specimen of *Torosaurus* has proved to be of some interest because it reveals signs of a bone disease. This frill was examined in the 1930s by Dr Roy L. Moodie, a noted expert on bone disorders. The bone had a series of irregular holes and dimples in its surface. Dr Moodie's comments were rather surprising, because he showed that these lesions were identical to some found in the skeletons of prehistoric Indians. He diagnosed this disease as *Multiple Myeloma,* or perhaps the dinosaur equivalent of this disease, the pockmarking having been caused by the growth of small cancerous

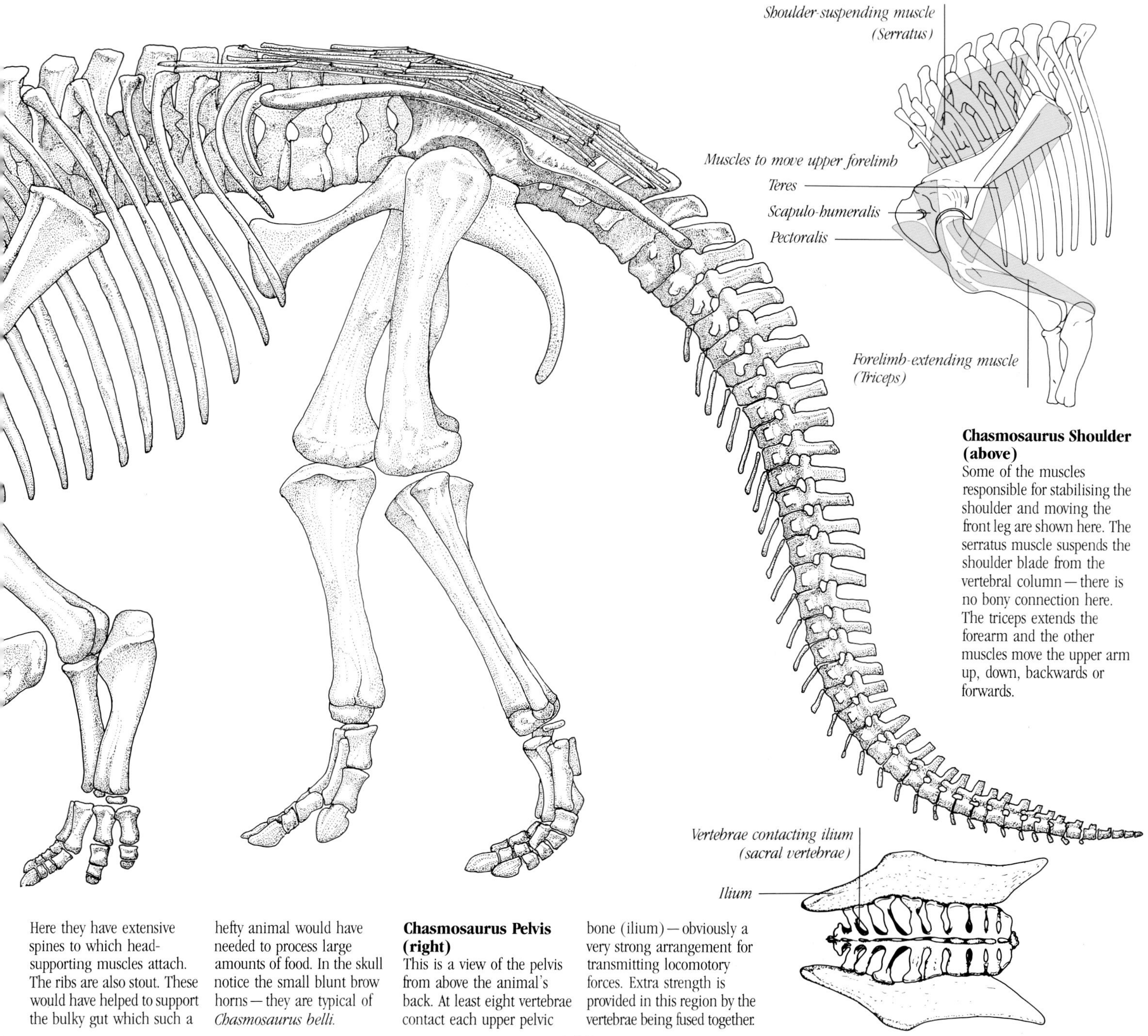


**Chasmosaurus Shoulder (above)**
Some of the muscles responsible for stabilising the shoulder and moving the front leg are shown here. The serratus muscle suspends the shoulder blade from the vertebral column — there is no bony connection here. The triceps extends the forearm and the other muscles move the upper arm up, down, backwards or forwards.

Here they have extensive spines to which head-supporting muscles attach. The ribs are also stout. These would have helped to support the bulky gut which such a hefty animal would have needed to process large amounts of food. In the skull notice the small blunt brow horns — they are typical of *Chasmosaurus belli.*

**Chasmosaurus Pelvis (right)**
This is a view of the pelvis from above the animal's back. At least eight vertebrae contact each upper pelvic bone (ilium) — obviously a very strong arrangement for transmitting locomotory forces. Extra strength is provided in this region by the vertebrae being fused together.

tumours within the bone. This is rather a chilling example of just how long cancers, in this case bone-cancer, have been around.

The other species of *Torosaurus*, *T. gladius*, is represented by another incomplete skull which may have reached a total length of 8·5ft (2·6m); this is the largest skull known of any land-living animal. The skull differs slightly in its general shape from that of *T. latus* in, for example, the position of the brow horns, the shape of the eye, and the angle of the frill. Again, whether these differences really justify the placing of these specimens in different species is an open question. It seems quite probable that both of these individuals belong to the same species and represent normal variations in shape due to age or sex differences. As we have seen before, however, such proposals are very difficult to prove scientifically.

## Frill Classification

The division of the ceratopids into long-frilled and short-frilled types that we have used here is rather an arbitrary one, but it serves as a convenient way of dividing up a very varied group of animals into two more manageable groups. By doing this, we can learn about them more easily. However, there is built into this division the assumption that all the short-frilled ceratopids are more closely related to one another than to the long-frilled types, and *vice versa*. This assumption may or may not be true, and indeed there is still much debate about the significance of this division.

As an example of the problems that can be created by this kind of classification, let us look at the position of *Triceratops*— the best known of all ceratopids. *Triceratops* was described with the other short-frilled ceratopids on pages 134-139. However, although *Triceratops* does indeed have a relatively short frill, it does not share some of the other characteristics normally seen in the short-frilled forms. In particular, it has long pointed brow horns and a short nose horn: a combination typical of the long-frilled types that have just been described. The question then arises: is *Triceratops* really a long-frilled type of ceratopid with an unusually short frill, or is it a short-frilled type that is mimicking the horn arrangement usually found in long-frilled types? Or, even more importantly perhaps, does *Triceratops* prove that dividing the ceratopids into long- and short-frilled types is a complete waste of time?

One solution to the 'problem' of *Triceratops* was provided by Charles M. Sternberg. He decided that instead of looking at the overall length of the frill, it was more useful to study the individual bones from which it was made. Using this method he was able to divide the ceratopids into so-called 'long-squamosaled' and 'short-squamosaled' forms. (The *squamosal* is the bone that forms each side of the frill.) By doing this, Sternberg was able to include *Triceratops* with all the other 'long-frilled' forms described above, which may perhaps seem more satisfactory to our tidy minds. However, neat though this solution might seem to us, it is very difficult to be sure that what we have arrived at is a 'better' or more natural arrangement of these animals, rather than one that merely satisfies our sense of order.

## Ceratopian Miscellany

In addition to the many well known ceratopids that we have looked at over the last few pages, there are several others whose names are also familiar to many, but are in fact very poorly known indeed. *Monoclonius* ('single shoot') is one obvious example; it was first described by Joseph Leidy in 1856 on the basis of a single tooth which had the characteristically double-fanged root found in all ceratopids. Several species of this genus were described in the 1870s on very poor, fragmentary material. As a result little is known about this genus, apart from the fact that it is a ceratopid from the Judith River in Montana. Despite this, *Monoclonius* is frequently illustrated in books about dinosaurs, creating the misleading impression that it is a very well-known form indeed.

*Agathaumas sylvestris*, a ceratopid from the Green River of Wyoming, was described by E. D. Cope. Again this was based on poor material: several bones from the back, hips and legs. None of these are of any use in characterizing a new type of ceratopid. *Ceratops* ('horned face') was an alternative name provided by O. C. Marsh for *'Bison alticornis'* which finally became known as *Triceratops alticornis*, along with several other totally useless fragments.

*Diceratops* based on a partial skull from Niobrara County was originally supposed to differ from *Triceratops* from the same area because it lacked a nose horn (hence the name *Diceratops*, or 'two-horned face'). In fact the degree of development of the nose horn tends to vary quite a lot in *Triceratops*. It seems very probable that *Diceratops* is just a variant of the normal *Triceratops* and should be included in the latter genus.

*Eoceratops* ('dawn horned face') comes from the Red Deer River, Alberta and consists of a partial skull of another ceratopid. It was a young individual with long brow horns and a short nose horn, and a relatively short frill without any obvious epoccipitals. The two other well-known ceratopids found in this area are *Centrosaurus* and *Chasmosaurus*, but the skull of *Eoceratops* does not resemble that of *Centrosaurus* at all closely. Neither does it seem to resemble that of

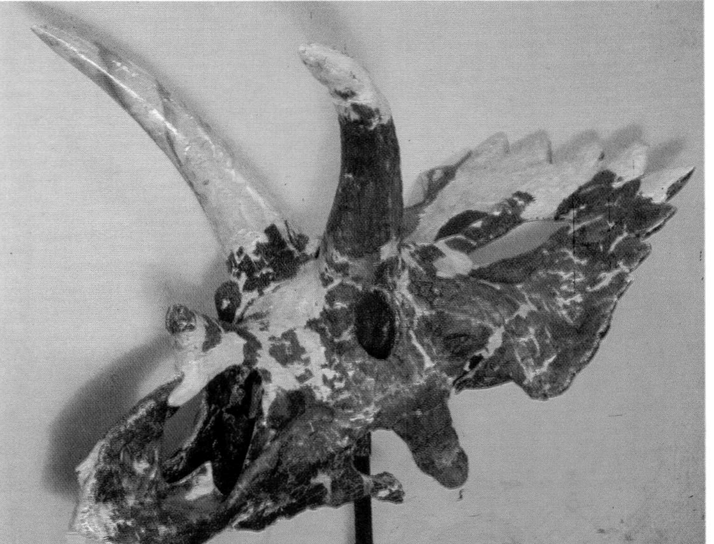

**Left:** Despite its name, *Arrhinoceratops* ('no nose horn') does have a small nose horn as this Tyrrell Museum skull confirms. Note the typically low tapering muzzle, the long pointed brow horns, the fairly small openings in the frill, and the even fringe of epoccipitals around the posterior edge of the frill.

**Right:** It would seem that a natural parallel can be drawn between the behaviour of rutting stags and the likely behaviour of long-frilled ceratopids. Frills may have been used for display, while males might lock horns in trials of strength to attract mates.

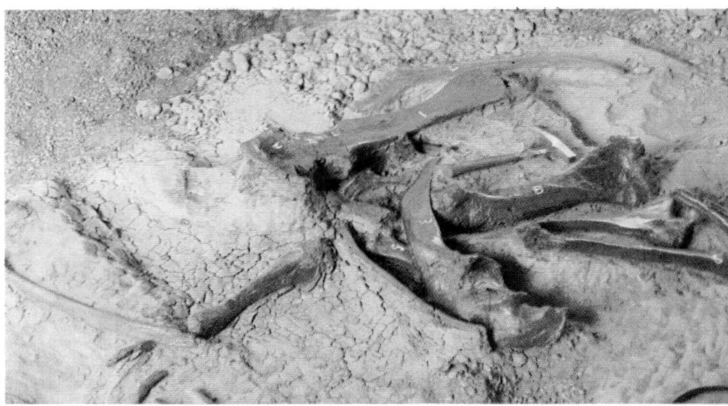

**Right:** The ceratopids are known almost exclusively from the Cretaceous rocks of north west America. Here the bones of a juvenile ceratopid are excavated from Dinosaur Provincial Park, Alberta, Canada.

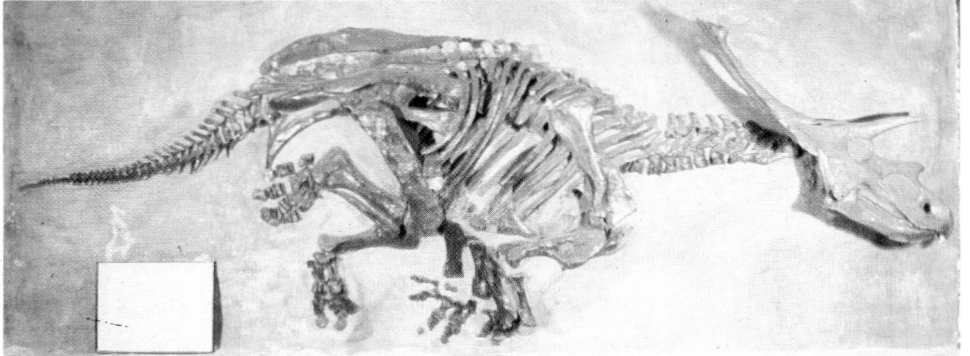

**Below:** The body plan of *Anchiceratops* resembles that of the short-frilled ceratopids; distinguishing features are to be found in the skull, particularly in the form of the frill.

*Chasmosaurus*, since the frill is relatively short and there are no epoccipitals—hence the alternative name. However, the fact that it was a juvenile specimen may explain the differences. It is very probable that the frill of young *Chasmosaurus* was rather shorter than that of a fully-grown specimen (young *Protoceratops* show this characteristic), and the lack of epoccipitals may well be a result of their not being firmly attached to the frill in young individuals. I therefore suspect that *Eoceratops* is a young *Chasmosaurus* rather than a new type of ceratopid.

## Ceratopian Behaviour

The great variety of ceratopian head shape has puzzled palaeontologists for a long time. Professor Edwin Colbert, a noted authority on dinosaurs, suggested that the development of a bewildering array of horns was essentially a random phenomenon. Each group of ceratopids had independently developed its own pattern of horns and frill shapes as a common type of solution to a single problem, i.e. resisting predatory dinosaurs. He used for comparison the variety of horns displayed by African antelopes as evidence of a similar type of phenomenon.

Recent work, however, has suggested that the chief function of the horns of antelopes, and many of the larger, hoofed mammals of today, is to establish a form of social order among these animals, and for the maintenance of territories, especially between male animals (cf. the rutting of deer). The variety of horn and antler shapes, therefore, reflects special display functions allied to fighting behaviour, rather than simply serving to deter predators. Behaviour patterns tend to vary a great deal among living hoofed mammals, but they can nevertheless be divided into several fairly distinctive types. Small-horned types tend to swing their heads sideways at the flanks of opponents, and to show them off in side-on visual displays. Larger-horned types tend to use their horns either for head-to-head ramming (this is particularly well known in sheep and goats) or, alternatively like deer they can lock horns and have a complicated pushing-and-wrestling type of test of strength. Some animals, such as the recently extinct giant Irish Elk, had an enormous spread of antlers which was probably used in simple postural movements to display their antlers to the best advantage; these antlers were far too large and heavy to have been used for fighting.

The frills of ceratopids have also given rise to much speculation about their probable function, and the factors governing their variable shapes. Professor Ostrom suggested that the frill developed its shape in order to increase the effectiveness of the jaw-closing muscles which were attached to it. Unfortunately this does not seem to be the case in all examples when they are analysed mechanically. There are also ceratopids, such as *Styracosaurus*, with elaborate spikes around the frill edge which were clearly nothing whatever to do with jaw-closing muscles.

Jim Farlow and Peter Dodson reviewed the structure and function of ceratopian frills and horns in 1975. They concluded that the combination of variable horn arrangement and frill shape were most likely explained as having behavioural functions. Looking at the various types of ceratopian dinosaur they proposed the following:

(i) *Protoceratopids* probably behaved like small-horned antelopes. The low nasal horn may have been used to deliver sideways blows to the flanks of opponents. The moderately large frill may have also been used as a visual display signal; the larger the frill, the more dominant the animal in its social group. Most of the protoceratopids would have used similar sorts of behavioural strategies.

(ii) *Short-frilled ceratopids* tend to have large unpaired nose horns and their behaviour has been compared to that of rhinoceroses. The large nose horns would have been formidable weapons if used for fighting. To avoid the likelihood of severe injury resulting from combat, these animals probably relied heavily upon bluff displays and evasive manoeuvring. It is even possible that the short-frilled ceratopids were rather solitary animals, thereby reducing the need for combat in defence of their own territories.

*Styracosaurus* is unusual among the short-frilled ceratopids in its possession of long spikes on its frill margin. These probably formed a striking visual display when the head was waved about. Such development may have reduced the probability of combat between individuals and consequent severe injury. *Pachyrhinosaurus*, yet another unusual short-frilled ceratopid, may well have indulged in head-to-head pushing contests.

*Triceratops*, the problematic short-frilled form, has large eyebrow horns and more closely resembles the long-frilled ceratopids in this respect. It seems quite probable that *Triceratops* locked horns in pushing-and-twisting contests between individuals. The solid neck frill may well have acted as a shield to deflect the horns of opponents, and to protect the neck and shoulder muscles if either they slipped or failed to lock horns in such a contest of strength.

(iii) *Long-frilled ceratopids* would, by virtue of the great length of the frill, have been able to produce an impressive frontal threat display simply by nodding the head forward and swinging it from side to side. Such displays (as in *Styracosaurus*) may have reduced the need for direct combat between individuals. However, when combat did occur, then the brow horns may have locked together in pushing-and-wrestling contests.

The pose of the front legs in these ceratopids was probably quite variable. The front legs could be held directly beneath the body like pillars as in the colour illustrations, or alternatively held slightly apart with the feet more widely spaced. In the latter position these animals would be very stable and they may well have adopted this posture in combat.

All in all, the ceratopids are not only some of the most bizarre-looking of all known dinosaurs, but also the most interesting, allowing us many revealing insights into their possible way of life.

**Above:** *Torosaurus* is known only from skulls. However, these are huge, some measuring over 8ft (2·4m) in length, the largest recovered of any land-living animal. Note the relatively smooth edge to, and circular openings in the frill of this skull that is on display in the Peabody Museum.

**Defensive Circle (right)** Apart from their display function, ceratopian horns were also probably very powerful defensive weapons. Evidence of herding behaviour indicates that ceratopids may have formed defensive circles in order to protect their young as these *Chasmosaurus* are doing.

# PACHYCEPHALOSAURS

Pachycephalosaurs ('thick headed reptiles') are a relatively rare and puzzling group of dinosaurs which lived toward the end of the Cretaceous Period. The history of their discovery is unusual. The first possible pachycephalosaur remains to be discovered consist of a single tooth from the Judith River Beds of Montana, which was found by Ferdinand Hayden. It was flattened and slightly curved and had serrations along its edges. This tooth was described by Joseph Leidy in 1856 and named *Troödon formosus (Troödon:* 'wounding tooth'). Leidy suggested that the tooth may have belonged to a large monitor lizard or some other extinct meat-eating reptile.

Little more material of this enigmatic reptile was discovered until just after the turn of the century. In 1902 Lawrence Lambe reported more similar *Troödon*-type teeth from the Belly River of Alberta, and in 1905 John Bell Hatcher described some more teeth from Wyoming. Hatcher was the first to propose that *Troödon* teeth may have belonged to a dinosaur rather than to a large lizard. The fact that *Troödon* was only recognized as a series of teeth proved extremely unsatisfactory and confusing as we shall see.

At the same time that Lambe described the Belly River *Troödon* teeth (1902), he described two skull fragments, also from the Belly River Formation of Alberta, to which he gave the name *Stegoceras* ('horny roof'). The skull fragments were unusually thick and were at first thought, not unreasonably, to be from a ceratopian dinosaur. A little later Hatcher recognized that the fragments were from the back part of the skull, and were so different from any other known dinosaur that *Stegoceras* should be placed in an entirely new family. With the discovery of more fragments in later years Lambe was able to redescribe the skulls found in 1902 with more confidence, and he proposed that *Stegoceras* was a distant relative of the stegosaurids (pages 152-157).

Things became a little clearer in 1924 when Charles Gilmore was able to describe a skull and partial skeleton of a new dinosaur discovered on the Red Deer River in 1920 by George Sternberg. The material, although incomplete, gave a much clearer idea of the nature of the animals previously named *Troödon* and *Stegoceras;* the teeth near the front of the upper jaw were very similar to *Troödon,* while the head showed the great thickening of the skull roof which had caused such problems in the description of *Stegoceras.* Gilmore was able for the first time to describe the likely appearance of these creatures. And, incomplete though this specimen is, it is still today one of the few specimens which comprises more than just a skull. Gilmore named it *Troödon validus* because he claimed that the teeth were identical to *Troödon* described by Leidy. Most palaeontologists regard this as dubious practice, because using teeth alone for comparisons is extremely hazardous. In most reptiles teeth are

**Time Chart (left)**
Pachycephalosaurs have a solely Cretaceous time span. They may have originated in the latter half of the early Cretaceous (*Yaverlandia*), but by the late Cretaceous they were fairly widespread in North America and Asia. The discovery of *Majungatholus* also points to a southerly distribution.

**Family Tree (below)**
Pachycephalosaurs have been divided into high-domed (pachycephalosaurid) and low-domed (homalocephalid) forms. The differences probably reflect different behaviour patterns (head butting vs pushing). *Stygimoloch* may represent yet another group which had highly decorated skulls like modern deer. *Yaverlandia* may be an early pachycephalosaur but it is only known from a tiny fragment of skull.

**Homalocephale (below)**
This pachycephalosaur is remarkable since parts of its skeleton are known in addition to the skull. *Homalocephale,* as its name ('even head') suggests, had a flat head, and it lacked the massively thickened cranial roof that most of its relatives had. Nevertheless, *Homalocephale* did have a thickened skull roof lined with nodules of bone at the sides. The hip bones of *Homalocephale* are very wide, and it has been suggested that it gave birth to live young rather than laying eggs in typical dinosaurian fashion.

**Comparative Sizes (left)**
1 *Stegoceras:* l. 6·5ft (2m)
2 *Homalocephale:* l. 10ft (3m).
3 *Pachycephalosaurus:* l. 26ft (8m).

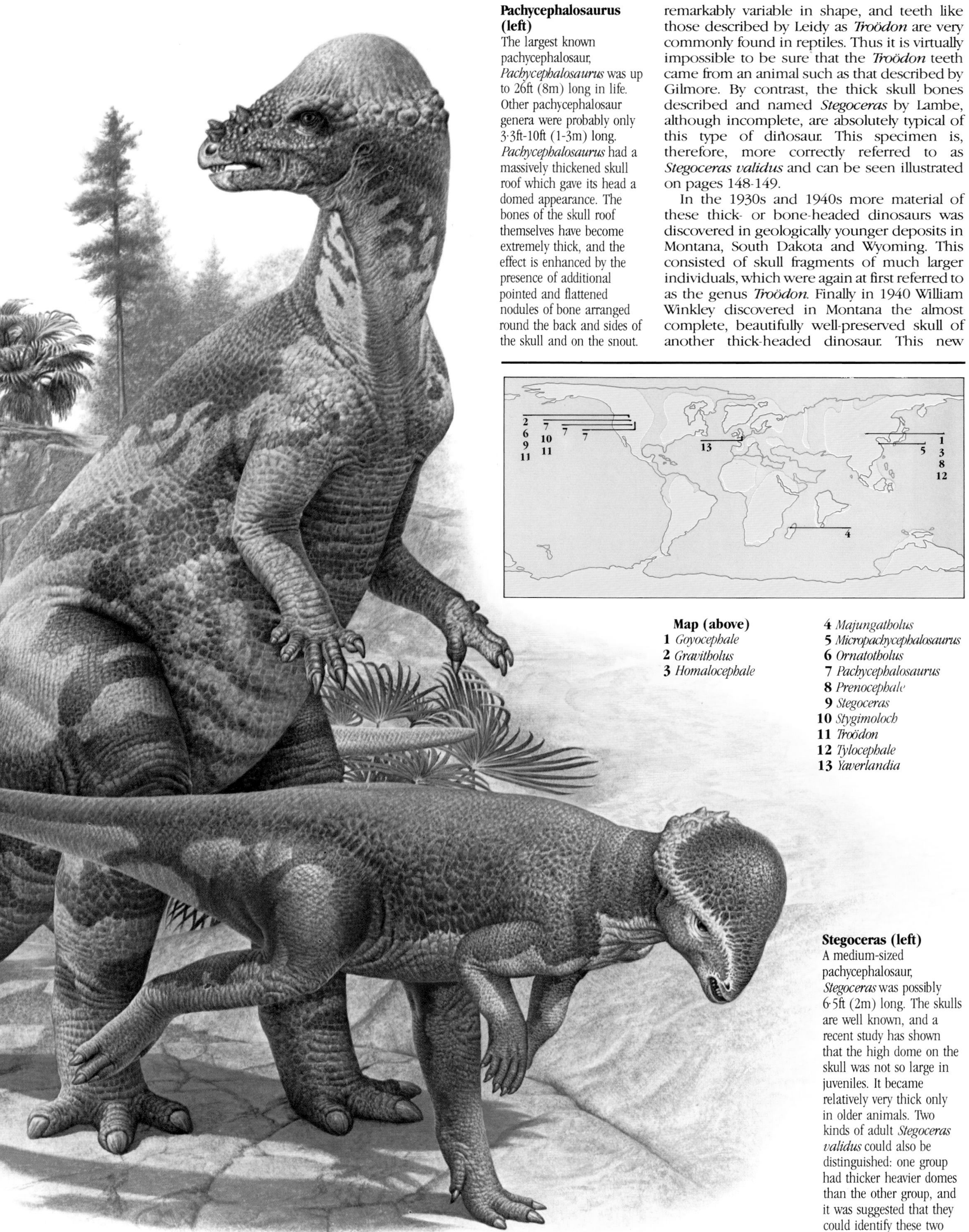


**Pachycephalosaurus (left)**
The largest known pachycephalosaur, *Pachycephalosaurus* was up to 26ft (8m) long in life. Other pachycephalosaur genera were probably only 3·3ft-10ft (1-3m) long. *Pachycephalosaurus* had a massively thickened skull roof which gave its head a domed appearance. The bones of the skull roof themselves have become extremely thick, and the effect is enhanced by the presence of additional pointed and flattened nodules of bone arranged round the back and sides of the skull and on the snout.

remarkably variable in shape, and teeth like those described by Leidy as *Troödon* are very commonly found in reptiles. Thus it is virtually impossible to be sure that the *Troödon* teeth came from an animal such as that described by Gilmore. By contrast, the thick skull bones described and named *Stegoceras* by Lambe, although incomplete, are absolutely typical of this type of dinosaur. This specimen is, therefore, more correctly referred to as *Stegoceras validus* and can be seen illustrated on pages 148-149.

In the 1930s and 1940s more material of these thick- or bone-headed dinosaurs was discovered in geologically younger deposits in Montana, South Dakota and Wyoming. This consisted of skull fragments of much larger individuals, which were again at first referred to as the genus *Troödon*. Finally in 1940 William Winkley discovered in Montana the almost complete, beautifully well-preserved skull of another thick-headed dinosaur. This new

**Map (above)**
**1** *Goyocephale*
**2** *Gravitholus*
**3** *Homalocephale*
**4** *Majungatholus*
**5** *Micropachycephalosaurus*
**6** *Ornatotholus*
**7** *Pachycephalosaurus*
**8** *Prenocephale*
**9** *Stegoceras*
**10** *Stygimoloch*
**11** *Troödon*
**12** *Tylocephale*
**13** *Yaverlandia*

**Stegoceras (left)**
A medium-sized pachycephalosaur, *Stegoceras* was possibly 6·5ft (2m) long. The skulls are well known, and a recent study has shown that the high dome on the skull was not so large in juveniles. It became relatively very thick only in older animals. Two kinds of adult *Stegoceras validus* could also be distinguished: one group had thicker heavier domes than the other group, and it was suggested that they could identify these two groups as males and females.

specimen was so obviously different from *Stegoceras ('Troödon')* that it was given a different generic name, *Pachycephalosaurus* ('thick-headed reptile'). The large size of the skull of this creature indicated that it probably had a body length of about 26ft (8m). Unfortunately although several skulls in varying states of completeness are known, there is very little skeletal information, so any body restorations are based largely upon guesswork and comparison with the little that is known about *Stegoceras*. Until *Pachycephalosaurus* was discovered, *Stegoceras* and its allies were known as Troödontids. However, since *Troödon* is a dubious name (based only on non-diagnostic teeth) a new family name was chosen by Sternberg in 1945: the Pachycephalosauridae. This name has stuck with us to the present day and, although the status of the family is now a matter of some scientific dispute as will be explained later, it remains a particularly descriptive term for these dinosaurs.

## Further Discoveries

Since those early days a considerable number of remains of pachycephalosaurs have been discovered from many parts of the world. In addition to *Stegoceras* and *Pachycephalosaurus,* there are several rather imperfectly known North American pachycephalosaurs. *Stygimoloch* ('river of Hades [Hell Creek] devil') from the Hell Creek Formation of Montana is presently known from parts of the rear end of the skull. These are notable for the development of large, elaborate horn cores. In life these must have formed clusters of horns on either side of the domed skull roof. *Gravitholus* ('heavy-dome') is known from Alberta and consists of part of a very large, heavy dome which may in fact belong to *Pachycephalosaurus*. *Ornatotholus* ('ornate dome'), from the Red Deer River, Alberta, was first thought to be another species of *Stegoceras* which was characterized by having a rather low-domed skull. Originally named *Stegoceras browni,* it has been proposed as a female of *Stegoceras validus*. However, Dr Peter Galton and Dr Hans-Dieter Sues have proposed that it is sufficiently different to merit the new name.

An apparently very primitive pachycephalosaur has been identified from the early Cretaceous of the Isle of Wight, southern England. It consists of a small fragment of the skull roof of an animal named *Yaverlandia* ('from Yaverland Point'). The outer surface has two low, rounded bulges. Peter Galton has identified this as a very primitive pachycephalosaur which had only developed a slight thickening of its skull roof. By comparing this small fragment of the skull with that of *Hypsilophodon,* Galton has been able to suggest that pachycephalosaurs may have evolved from small bipedal ornithopods similar to *Hypsilophodon*. No other clear pachycephalosaur remains have been recovered from Europe. However, central and eastern Asia

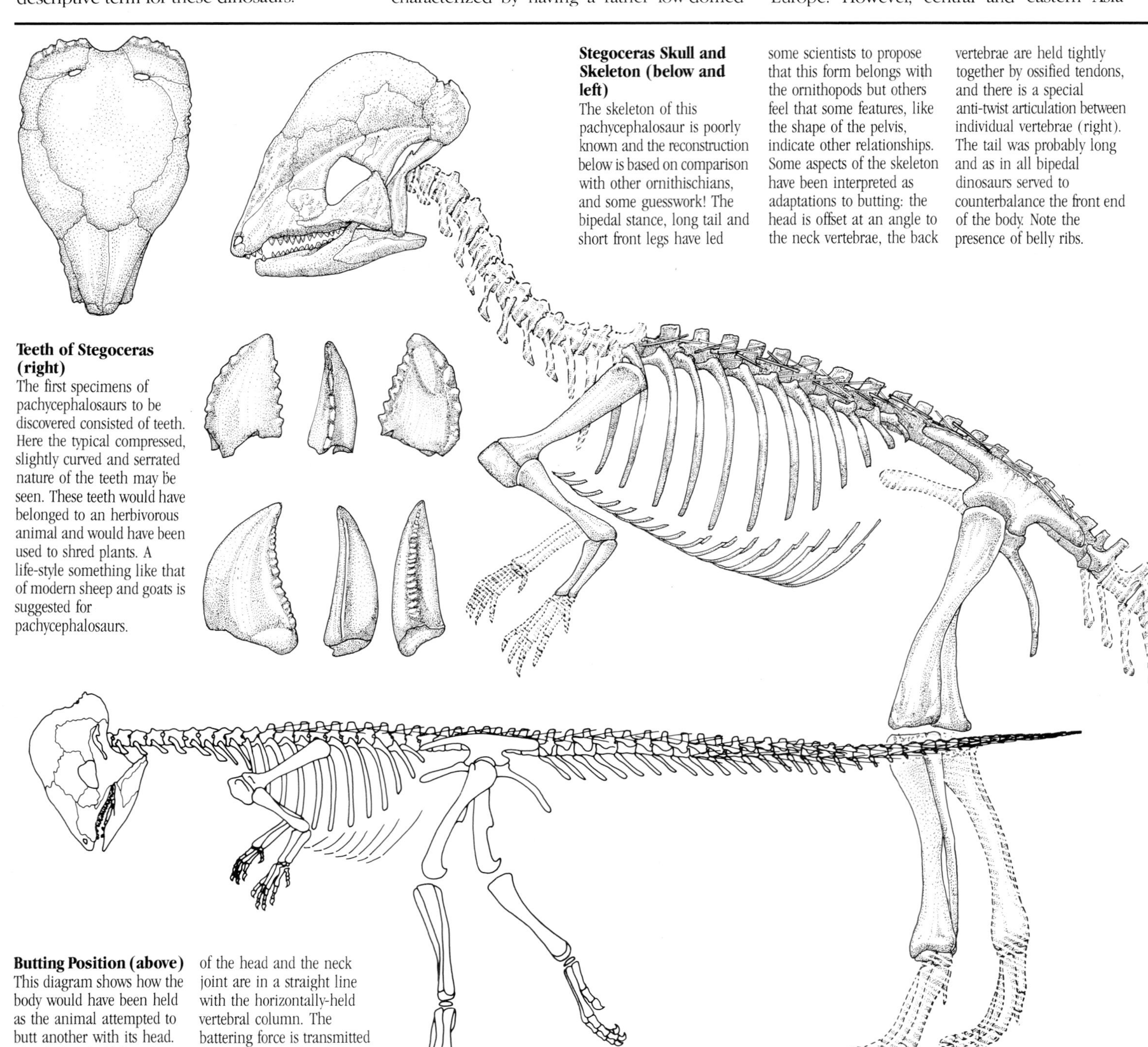

**Stegoceras Skull and Skeleton (below and left)**
The skeleton of this pachycephalosaur is poorly known and the reconstruction below is based on comparison with other ornithischians, and some guesswork! The bipedal stance, long tail and short front legs have led some scientists to propose that this form belongs with the ornithopods but others feel that some features, like the shape of the pelvis, indicate other relationships. Some aspects of the skeleton have been interpreted as adaptations to butting: the head is offset at an angle to the neck vertebrae, the back vertebrae are held tightly together by ossified tendons, and there is a special anti-twist articulation between individual vertebrae (right). The tail was probably long and as in all bipedal dinosaurs served to counterbalance the front end of the body. Note the presence of belly ribs.

**Teeth of Stegoceras (right)**
The first specimens of pachycephalosaurs to be discovered consisted of teeth. Here the typical compressed, slightly curved and serrated nature of the teeth may be seen. These teeth would have belonged to an herbivorous animal and would have been used to shred plants. A life-style something like that of modern sheep and goats is suggested for pachycephalosaurs.

**Butting Position (above)**
This diagram shows how the body would have been held as the animal attempted to butt another with its head. The skull is held face-down, so that the ramming surface of the head and the neck joint are in a straight line with the horizontally-held vertebral column. The battering force is transmitted through the skull and absorbed by the backbone.

(Mongolia and China) have produced several completely new types of pachycephalosaur in recent years. In Mongolia at least four have been identified: *Prenocephale, Tylocephale, Homalocephale* and *Goyocephale.*

*Prenocephale* ('sloping head') consists of an exceptionally well-preserved skull which bears a very strong resemblance to *Stegoceras.* The main difference is that *Prenocephale* has many rows of small bony knobs ornamenting the sides of the face and dome. *Tylocephale* ('swollen head') is rather similar in shape, although the skull is missing much of the snout and part of the dome. *Homalocephale* ('even head') does not have the high dome seen in the previous two Mongolian types, although like *Prenocephale* there are small rows of bony knobs about the sides of the face. *Goyocephale* ('decorated head') is another of these flat-headed pachycephalosaurs which is known from both partial skull and skeletal remains including much of the tail, the fore and hind limbs. Unlike *Homalocephale,* which has a fairly flat, smooth skull roof, that of *Goyocephale* is rough and pitted rather like that of *Ornatotholus* of North America. *Goyocephale* also has a pair of large stabbing teeth in the upper and lower jaw.

China has two pachycephalosaurs to date: *Wannanosaurus* ('reptile from Wannan') and *Micropachycephalosaurus* ('tiny thick-headed reptile'). Both of these are flat-headed types of pachycephalosaur.

Finally and quite surprisingly a pachycephalosaur has also been reported from Madagascar: *Majungatholus* ('dome from Majunga'). So far this is only known from a fragment of a domed skull. Until *Majungatholus* was discovered the geographical distribution of pachycephalosaurs was quite typical of dinosaurs that seem to have arisen in middle to late Cretaceous times. As with the ceratopids, hadrosaurids, and dromaeosaurids, they were apparently restricted to the northern hemisphere and further restricted within that hemisphere to western North America and Asia. Early in the Cretaceous Period, primitive pachycephalosaurs such as *Yaverlandia* (provided that Galton has correctly interpreted this tiny skull fragment) were probably widely distributed but relatively rare animals in northern continents. Later in the Cretaceous, with the division of the northern lands by seaways separating western North America and Asia from Europe, the later and more sophisticated pachycephalosaurs were confined to Asia and North America. Quite why they did not persist in Europe is not clear (unless *Yaverlandia,* the only European pachycephalosaur, has been misidentified). The presence of *Majungatholus* in Madagascar is, however, somewhat unexpected.

## The Madagascar Fauna

Fossil remains from the late Cretaceous of Madagascar are unfortunately of rather poor

**Pelvis and Vertebrae of Homalocephale (right)**
The pelvis (bottom drawing) has a long, low ilium which contacts at least six, and possibly eight vertebrae (drawing 2nd from bottom). This would be an extremely strong arrangement perhaps involved in transmitting the head-butting force to the ground via the back leg. The vertebrae shown here in the top two drawings are from the back region. The complete rib is not drawn but it would have been long and robust. The joints between the vertebrae are ridged and would have been very important in stabilising the backbone as it was held horizontal during battering. The rib of the tail vertebra (3rd drawing) was smaller and more delicate.

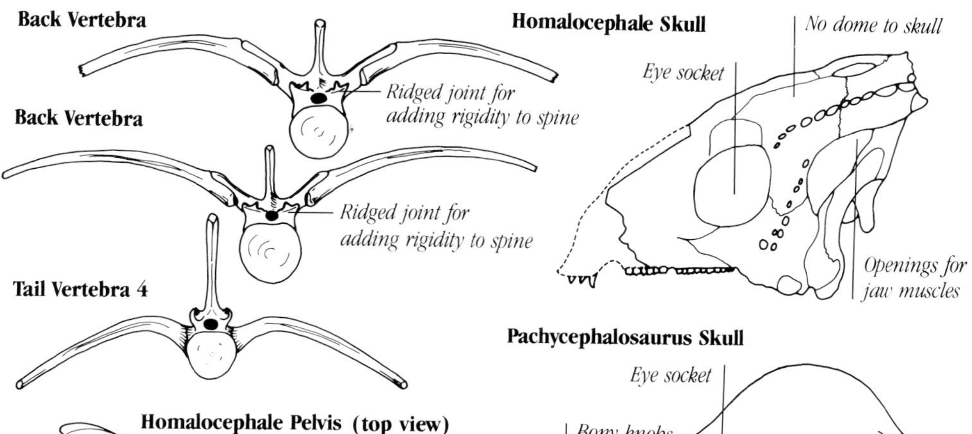


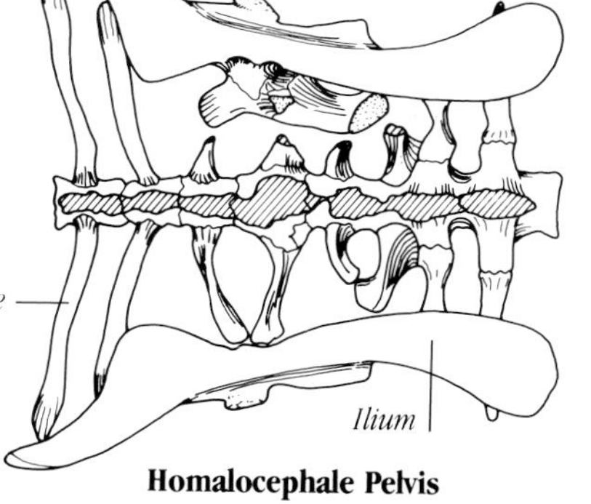


**Homalocephale Pelvis**

Ilium

Hip socket

Pubis

Forward prong of ischium

Ischium

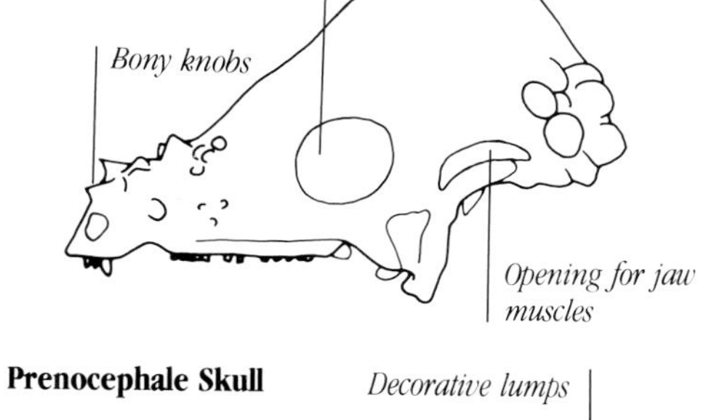


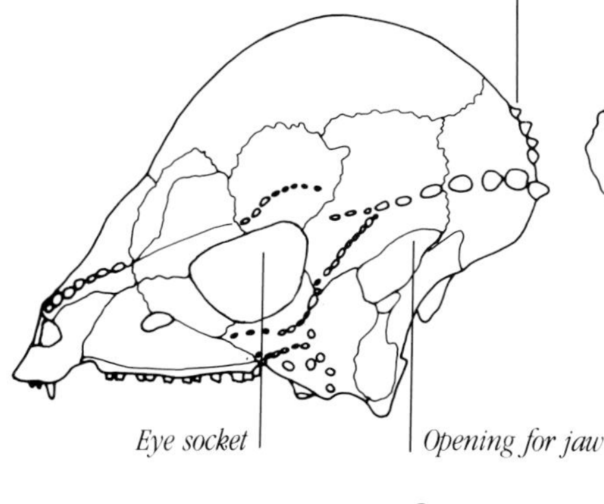


**Pachycephalosaur Skulls (left)**
These skulls show some of the variation which existed within the pachycephalosaurs. *Prenocephale* (bottom skull) is similar to *Stegoceras* but has a high-domed skull and rows of small bones along the sides and back of the head. *Homalocephale* (top skull) also has rows of small bones but lacks the doming of the skull. *Pachycephalosaurus* (middle skull) is another high-domed form, and while it does not have the rows of small bones like *Prenocephale* it does have very distinctive bony spikes on its snout and knobs on the back of its head! The variation in skull shape (high or low-domed) affords us one way of categorising these dinosaurs.

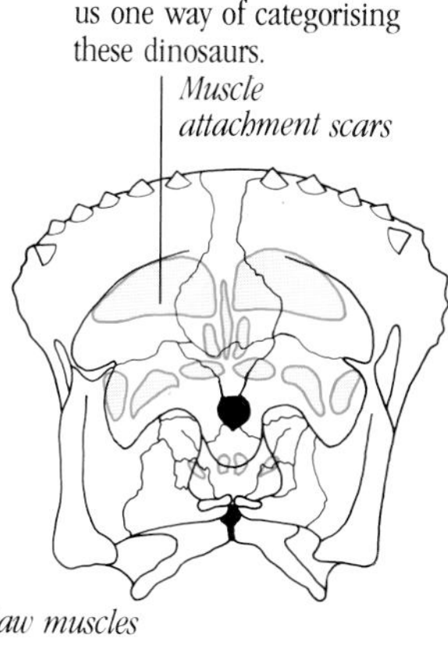


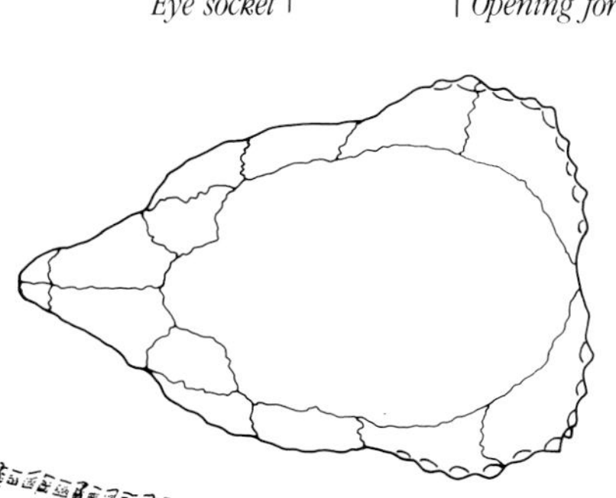

**Back view of Prenocephale Skull (above)**
This view shows the positions of certain muscle scars. Most of the muscles would be responsible for attaching the powerful head to the neck. The nuchal ligaments, running from the back of the head to the neck vertebrae, were particularly important in supporting the head.

quality. Nevertheless those that have been found are of interest because they provide information on the likely land connections in the world at this time. Along with *Majungatholus* were also found the remains of a large sauropod dinosaur named *Titanosaurus madagascarensis.* This bears some similarities to *Saltasaurus,* the armoured South American sauropod. More bony armour of this type has also been reported from India. *Majungasaurus,* a medium-sized theropod is unfortunately too fragmentary for any fruitful comparisons to be drawn with theropods from elsewhere.

The fossil evidence then seems to point to land connections between South America, Africa-Madagascar and India in the late Cretaceous. In addition, we know that hadrosaurids, sauropods, and tyrannosaurids, as well as pachycephalosaur dinosaurs of similar types, are found in both the northern and southern continents in late Cretaceous times. Precisely how this distribution occurred is difficult to assess. There seem to be two alternative interpretations: either these families of dinosaur migrated across narrow seaways separating the northern and southern continents (perhaps between North and South America, which were very close) or alternatively, these dinosaurs were widely spread across both northern and southern continents *before* the continents divided. A really good record of fossils from the southern continents might help to decide which of the alternatives is correct, but this is not available at present.

## Relationships

Because bone-head remains are so scarce, and even when found are usually just skulls or skull fragments, it has proved very difficult to decide how they relate to other dinosaurs generally. They are clearly ornithischians because they have the tell-tale horn-covered predentary beak in the lower jaw. However, their skulls are so highly modified by the great dome of bone that they show no overwhelming similarities to any of the other ornithischian groups.

The great thickening of the skull roof gives them a passing resemblance to the ankylosaurids. However, the similarity is more apparent than real because the thickening of the skull in ankylosaurids is created by the plastering of new bone on to the skull while in pachycephalosaurids it is the actual bones of the skull roof that become thicker.

In 1974 Doctors Teresa Maryanska and Halska Osmolska from Warsaw, Poland reviewed the pachycephalosaurs lately discovered in Mongolia and noted that pachycephalosaurs had an extraordinary pelvis, vaguely similar to that of ankylosaurids. On the basis of this and several other characteristics, they proposed that the pachycephalosaurs should be raised to the same level of importance as the ornithopods, stegosaurs, ceratopians and ankylosaurs, and categorized as a major group of ornithischians. This view is not accepted by all palaeontologists. For example, Dr Peter Galton prefers to consider them as rather unusual ornithopods. As noted earlier, he proposes that they evolved from hypsilophodontid-type ornithopods via forms such as the early Cretaceous *Yaverlandia.* The position of the pachycephalosaurs is very much an open question at present. Within the pachycephalosaur group, Maryanska and Osmolska have suggested that they may, perhaps, have been divided into low-domed and high-domed types: *Stegoceras, Pachycephalosaurus, Gravitholus, Tylocephale, Prenocephale, Stygimoloch* and *Majungatholus* being high-domed 'pachycephalosaurids'; while *Homalocephale, Goyocephale, Ornatotholus, Yaverlandia,* and *Micropachycephalosaurus* were low-domed 'homalocephalids'. Much more work needs to be done on these dinosaurs, and new and better material needs to be found, before any of these issues can be clarified.

## Head-to-Head Butting

From quite an early date the enormously thickened dome of bone on the skulls of pachycephalosaurs has attracted attention and comment. It was not, however, until 1955 that Professor Edwin Colbert suggested a functional explanation of this feature; he proposed that it may have served as a protective zone for the head if it were used as a battering ram. This proposal was not elaborated upon by Professor Colbert at the time, but it has served as a spur to several palaeontologists in recent years, notably Dr Peter Galton (Bridgeport) and Dr Hans-Dieter Sues (Montreal).

Peter Galton agreed with Professor Colbert's proposal concerning the function of the thick skull roof in pachycephalosaurs and went on to discuss it further. He noted that like most ornithopods, the pachycephalosaur's backbone may well have been held horizontally—balanced at the hips. In addition, the head of these animals, instead of being held in-line with the bones of the neck, is offset from it at a sharp angle. So, the 'natural' position of the head would seem to be such that it pointed nose-downward while these animals walked or ran. Obviously there was no need for them to walk in this 'nose-down' position all of the time, because the neck was flexible and could be bent upward sharply so that the head could be held in a more normal raised position. However, the arrangement of the neck-head joint, which is unlike all other dinosaurs, does

**Above:** A cast of the skull of *Pachycephalosaurus* from the British Museum (Natural History) collection. Note the round bony knobs on the back of the skull, and the more pointed bony projections on the snout.

**Below:** This skull cast of *Stegoceras*—also from the BM (NH)—makes an interesting comparison with that of *Pachycephalosaurus* (above). The high bony dome (*Stegoceras:* 'horny roof') to the skull is present in both specimens, but *Stegoceras* lacks the profusion of knobbly projections, while its face is shorter and deeper. *Stegoceras* is known from the Belly River Formation of Alberta, Canada.

**Above:** Looking almost as if it had been sculpted from the rock, the skull of *Prenocephale* is excavated from the late Cretaceous sandstone at Nemegt in the Gobi Desert, Mongolia during the 1970 Polish-Mongolian Palaeontological Expedition. *Prenocephale* is a high-domed pachycephalosaurid; the frill of bony studs at the back of the skull is clearly visible.

allow the dome to be held forward in a 'battering' position. When you add to this the fact that the backbones fit together in an especially stiffened arrangement, and that in addition to the ossified tendons of the back, the joints between individual bones of the back have special grooved surfaces to stop them from twisting too much, then the design of these animals certainly does seem to fit in with the idea that they were able to use the head as a battering device.

The obvious question that has to be asked is why did they do this? Galton proposed that pachycephalosaurs did not just employ head-down charging to fend off predatory dinosaurs, but also used it as a part of their social life! He drew what seems to be a very appropriate comparison between pachycephalosaurs and living sheep and goats. These animals, especially the males, have large horns and are well known for their propensity to fight among themselves by head-to-head butting or ramming—even females tend to butt one another though they do not have well-developed horns. In these animals, the butting behaviour is a part of a way of creating an ordered society. Especially among the males, the horns serve as visual signals of dominance: the larger the horns, the more dominant the male. However, when competing males have very similar-sized horns, then head butting is resorted to as a test of strength or endurance.

Mountain sheep have very large horns which help to absorb the initial shock of head-to-head butting; they also have special air-spaces at the front of their heads which serve to dull the shock that the brain would otherwise receive. Pachycephalosaurs differ from sheep and goats in the structure of their heads. Firstly, they do not have well-developed horns. There are small lumps and ridges around the dome on the skull roof of most pachycephalosaurs (especially *Stygimoloch* which has quite long spikes) but these are clearly ornamental rather than functional. Secondly, there are no special air-spaces in the skull roof of pachycephalosaurs: the skull dome is solid bone right through to the brain cavity. These differences suggest that the impacts of head butting were carried straight through the skull roof across the brain cavity—giving it quite a severe shock—and then into the specially strengthened backbone. The brains of these dinosaurs were, fortunately for pachycephalosaurs, much smaller than those found in sheep and goats, and quite probably there were spaces around the brain itself which cushioned it from too severe a shock.

Dr Sues further elaborated on the mechanism of head butting in pachycephalosaurs by showing that the arrangement of bone in the skulls of these animals was ideally suited to transmitting shocks through the dome, around the sides of the head and then into the backbone. He was able to do this by using a photoelastic analysis of thin sections of the skull. He also noted that special ligaments running from the neck to the back of the head (nuchal ligaments) were very large and powerful, and helped to absorb a great deal of the shock of head clashes.

## Life-Style

Pachycephalosaurs may well have lived rather like sheep and goats do today: in small groups in upland areas. Their social life was dependent upon the use of the head as a means of signalling the status of individuals. In most cases the visual signal would have been sufficient. However, when similarly-sized individuals met, the seniority of each would have to be decided by head-to-head pushing or butting contests. The low-domed 'homalocephalids' probably used head-to-head pushing contests rather than violent head-banging struggles because their skulls were not very strongly built The high-domed forms undoubtedly indulged in violent head-butting contests. *Stygimoloch,* unusual among the high-domed pachycephalosaurids, may not have indulged in head butting at all, relying instead upon the visual effect of the tall bony spikes around its domed head to establish its place in the social hierarchy.

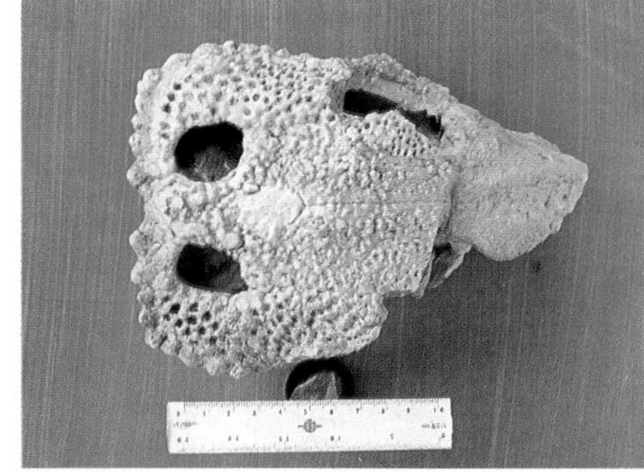

**Head Butting (left)** Here we see two pachycephalosaurs indulging in the sort of violent head-butting contest for which their extraordinary skulls made them uniquely qualified. It is thought that such behaviour was a way of establishing a social hierarchy, allowing males in particular to achieve dominance over one another within the group.

**Above:** A dorsal view of the skull of *Homalocephale calathocercos,* another of the pachycephalosaurs discovered at Nemegt in the Gobi Desert, this time by the 1965 Polish-Mongolian Expedition. The skull of *Homalocephale,* a flat-headed type, is noticeably less heavily armoured; the two openings at the back are for the attachment of the jaw muscles.

# STEGOSAURIDS

The stegosaurids are a group of quite large, four-footed ornithischians that are characterized by their possession of a double row of tall spines which run down their backs. By far the best known of these dinosaurs is *Stegosaurus* (see below), several very fine specimens of which were discovered in North America toward the end of the last century.

The first stegosaurid remains to be described were those of an incomplete skeleton found in England and illustrated by Richard Owen in 1875. These remains were originally described as *Omosaurus armatus* (later renamed *Dacentrurus* 'pointed tail'). It was recognized as an armour-plated dinosaur, because among the remains were found large shield-like plates of bone. These early reports were, however, eclipsed by the discoveries made in North America in the late 1870s by teams of excavators in two quarries: one known as 'Quarry 13' in Albany County, Wyoming, the other as 'Quarry 1' in Fremont County, Colorado.

Quarry 13 was discovered in 1879 and was worked by a team of excavators led by William H. Reed, under the supervision of Othniel Marsh, between 1879 and 1882, and later with interruptions until 1887. This quarry produced the largest concentration of *Stegosaurus* ('roofed reptile') remains discovered to date. Quarry 1 was discovered in 1876 by M. P. Felch and his family. News of this discovery reached Marsh through newspaper reports. The following year Marsh sent Samuel Wendell Williston (later to become an eminent palaeontologist in his own right) to investigate the reported discovery. This quarry was worked for several years by Williston and although it did not produce as many stegosaurid remains as the Albany County Quarry, nevertheless it did produce a very fine, practically complete, skeleton of *Stegosaurus stenops*. Between 1877 and 1897 Marsh published numerous scientific articles describing parts of these new dinosaurs. Since the time of Owen and Marsh, several other stegosaurids have been discovered which indicate that they were reasonably widely spread across the world.

Apart from *Stegosaurus* from North America, stegosaurids are also known from Europe: *Lexovisaurus* ('Lexovi reptile'), *Dacentrurus* and *Craterosaurus* ('bowl reptile'); Africa: *Kentrosaurus* ('prickly reptile') and *Paranthodon* ('beside Anthodon'); India: *Dravidosaurus* ('reptile from south India'); and China: *Huayangosaurus* ('Huayang reptile'), *Chialingosaurus* ('Chialing reptile'), *Wuerhosaurus* ('Wuerho reptile') and *Tuojiangosaurus* ('Tuojiang reptile'). The earliest stegosaurid remains identified so far are some odd plates and bones from the middle Jurassic of England, and the latest come from the late Cretaceous of India.

## Stegosaur Distribution

The distribution of stegosaurids in time and space reveals an interesting pattern. The earliest

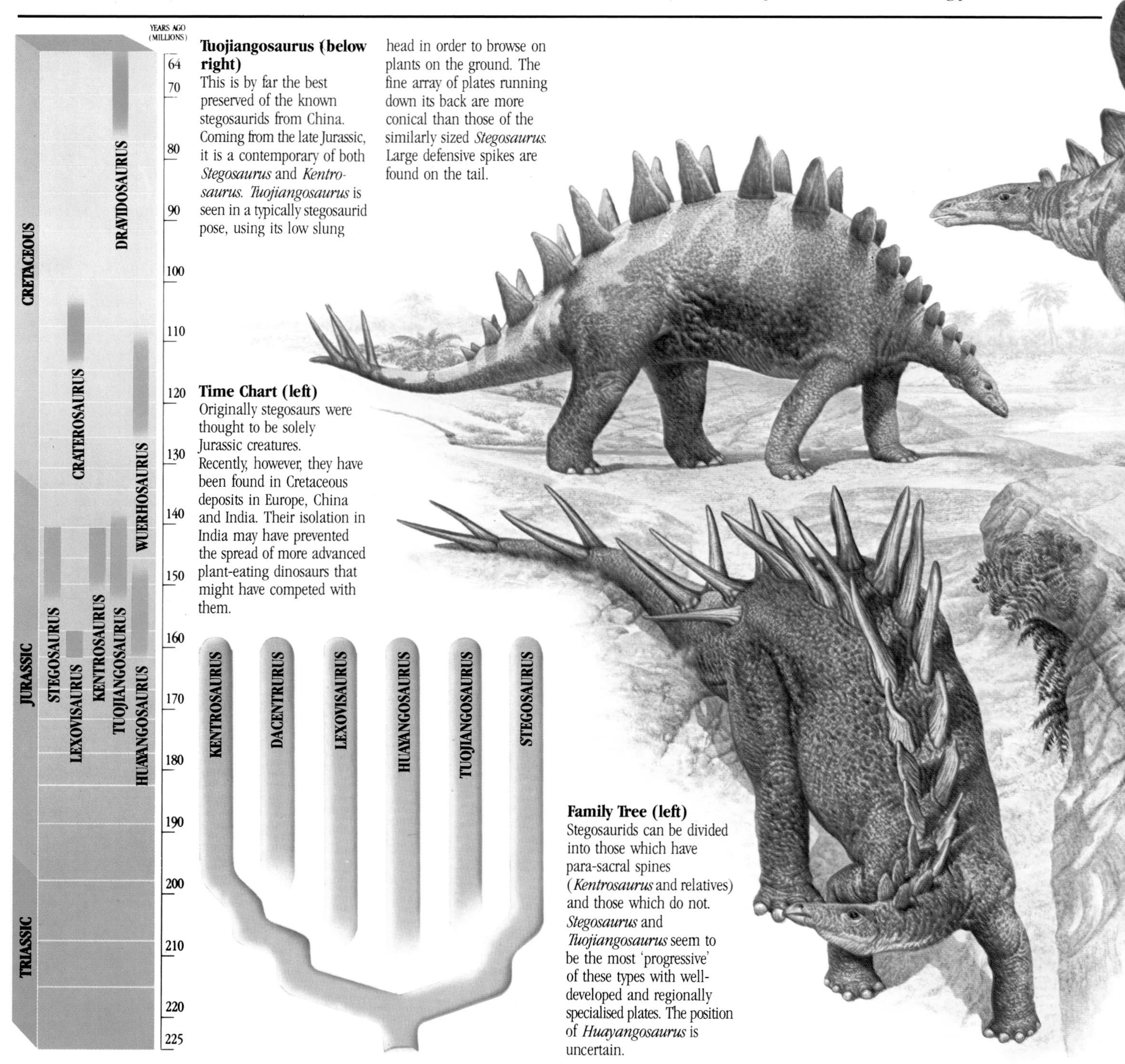


**Tuojiangosaurus (below right)**
This is by far the best preserved of the known stegosaurids from China. Coming from the late Jurassic, it is a contemporary of both *Stegosaurus* and *Kentrosaurus*. *Tuojiangosaurus* is seen in a typically stegosaurid pose, using its low slung head in order to browse on plants on the ground. The fine array of plates running down its back are more conical than those of the similarly sized *Stegosaurus*. Large defensive spikes are found on the tail.

**Time Chart (left)**
Originally stegosaurs were thought to be solely Jurassic creatures. Recently, however, they have been found in Cretaceous deposits in Europe, China and India. Their isolation in India may have prevented the spread of more advanced plant-eating dinosaurs that might have competed with them.

**Family Tree (left)**
Stegosaurids can be divided into those which have para-sacral spines (*Kentrosaurus* and relatives) and those which do not. *Stegosaurus* and *Tuojiangosaurus* seem to be the most 'progressive' of these types with well-developed and regionally specialised plates. The position of *Huayangosaurus* is uncertain.

stegosaurid remains are of the rather poorly known *Lexovisaurus* from the middle Jurassic of Oxfordshire (England). Shortly after this, in the late Jurassic, stegosaurids are found in North America, Africa and China as well as Europe. Looking at the map of the world at this time, the discovery of stegosaurids in North America, Africa and Europe seems quite reasonable, because these continents had all been in contact with one another up to this time, so we would expect their dinosaur faunas to be rather similar. However, the Chinese stegosaurids are not so readily explained. Eastern Asia seems to have been separated from the rest of the world by quite large seaways for much of the reign of the dinosaurs. In fact, it seems that it was not until quite late in the Cretaceous Period that a substantial link was established between western North America and eastern Asia. The most likely explanation for the Chinese stegosaurids is that they must have spread there quite early on in the Jurassic

**Stegosaurus (left)**
This North American form is by far the best known of the stegosaurids. Several fine skeletons have been recovered but this has not led to complete agreement about its appearance in life. The main areas of disagreement relate to the arrangement of the plates and the pose of the forelimbs: were they bent or straight? As can be seen, we have adopted a straight-legged pose and an array of upright plates staggered alternately along the back. They were probably used as heat transfer surfaces, while the sharp tail spikes were for defence.

**Comparative Sizes (right)**
**1** *Stegosaurus:* l. 20-24·6ft (6-7·5m).
**2** *Tuojiangosaurus:* l. 20ft (6m).
**3** *Kentrosaurus:* l. 8·2ft (2·5m).

**Kentrosaurus (left)**
The pattern of spikes in *Kentrosaurus*, one of the smaller stegosaurids, so far known only from Tendaguru in Tanzania, is very distinctive. Those near the front of the body are flat and plate-like. However, by the middle of the back they have changed into narrow spines which continue to the end of the tail. In addition there is another pair of spines which point diagonally backwards from their attachment to the pelvis. Clearly these spines are primarily defensive in nature, and were intended to deter larger predators which risked impalement upon them. Whether *Kentrosaurus* could rush backwards at predators in the way that porcupines can do today is uncertain. The tail spines certainly look defensive in nature.

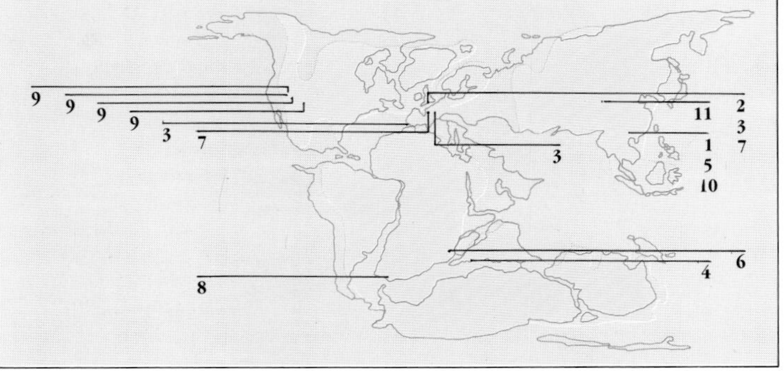


**Map (left)**
**1** *Chialingosaurus*
**2** *Craterosaurus*
**3** *Dacentrurus*
**4** *Dravidosaurus*
**5** *Huayangosaurus*
**6** *Kentrosaurus*
**7** *Lexovisaurus*
**8** *Paranthodon*
**9** *Stegosaurus*
**10** *Tuojiangosaurus*
**11** *Wuerhosaurus*

by means of some sort of short-lived land connection between Europe and Asia. The sauropods of the Jurassic seem to show a similar pattern of movement. The late Jurassic was probably the most successful time for the stegosaurids, because in the Cretaceous they are far less abundant and widespread. Stegosaurids seem to go extinct in North America at the end of the Jurassic; no Cretaceous stegosaurid remains have ever been discovered in this area. Fragmentary remains of stegosaurids are, however, known from the early Cretaceous of Europe *(Craterosaurus),* Africa *(Paranthodon)* and China *(Wuerhosaurus).* By the late Cretaceous stegosaurids seem to be absent from all the continents except for India where *Dravidosaurus* seems to persist to the end of the Cretaceous Period.

The precise reason for this rather unusual distribution pattern is not easy to explain, and any explanation given here could be radically upset by any new discovery of stegosaurids. However, the most reasonable interpretation that could be made is as follows: stegosaurids probably first evolved in the early to middle Jurassic Period and were able, because of the arrangement of the continents, to spread to most, if not all, the major continents. Thus, by the late Jurassic they were both diverse and widespread. The dawn of the Cretaceous Period marked a time of dramatic decline for most stegosaurids. The absence of stegosaurids in North America is very significant, because so much intensive collecting of Cretaceous dinosaurs has been done there that it seems inevitable that if stegosaurids had been around, some fossils would have been found by now. In all the other continents stegosaurids are found with much less frequency than during their heyday in the Jurassic, and by the mid-Cretaceous they seem to be extinct everywhere except India.

The survival of stegosaurids in India is interesting, because from the middle of the Cretaceous onward, India was isolated from the rest of the world. Right up until the early part of the Cretaceous, India nestled against the southern end of Africa and presumably shared its fauna of dinosaurs with those of Africa. Once India began to drift away from Africa, then its fauna became isolated and it may perhaps have acted as a haven for, amongst others, the stegosaurids which elsewhere went extinct.

The cause of the widespread waning and extinction of stegosaurids in the Cretaceous has often been suggested to be the appearance of the ankylosaurs (pages 160-169). The ankylosaurs certainly show a pattern of emergence, diversification and extinction which seems to complement that of the stegosaurids. In the Jurassic ankylosaurs were scarce and not very widely distributed; they gradually increased in number and type in the early Cretaceous, reaching a peak in late Cretaceous times, before the final Cretaceous extinctions. It is certainly tempting to suggest that the rise of

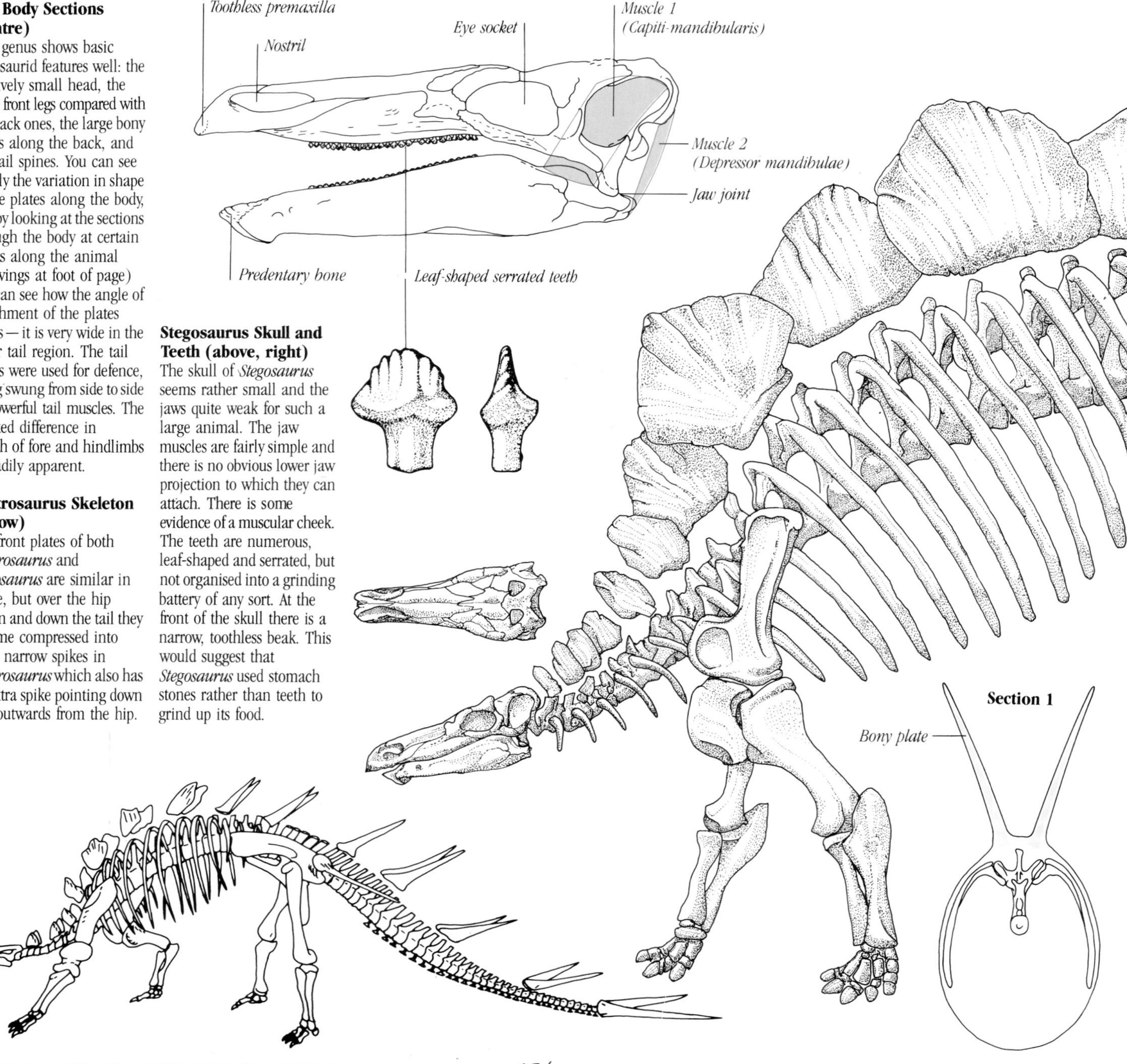


**Stegosaurus Skeleton and Body Sections (centre)**
This genus shows basic stegosaurid features well: the relatively small head, the short front legs compared with the back ones, the large bony plates along the back, and the tail spines. You can see clearly the variation in shape of the plates along the body, and by looking at the sections through the body at certain points along the animal (drawings at foot of page) you can see how the angle of attachment of the plates varies — it is very wide in the lower tail region. The tail spikes were used for defence, being swung from side to side by powerful tail muscles. The marked difference in length of fore and hindlimbs is readily apparent.

**Kentrosaurus Skeleton (below)**
The front plates of both *Kentrosaurus* and *Stegosaurus* are similar in shape, but over the hip region and down the tail they become compressed into long, narrow spikes in *Kentrosaurus* which also has an extra spike pointing down and outwards from the hip.

**Stegosaurus Skull and Teeth (above, right)**
The skull of *Stegosaurus* seems rather small and the jaws quite weak for such a large animal. The jaw muscles are fairly simple and there is no obvious lower jaw projection to which they can attach. There is some evidence of a muscular cheek. The teeth are numerous, leaf-shaped and serrated, but not organised into a grinding battery of any sort. At the front of the skull there is a narrow, toothless beak. This would suggest that *Stegosaurus* used stomach stones rather than teeth to grind up its food.

the ankylosaurs is associated in some way with the decline of the stegosaurids. The intriguing fact is that ankylosaurs are not found in India at all. Perhaps stegosaurids were able to survive in India because, through freakish geological conditions, India became isolated from the rest of the world in the early Cretaceous just at the time when the ankylosaurs were diversifying. One can only hope that new discoveries will confirm whether this explanation is anywhere near to the truth, or else disprove it.

## Stegosaurid Anatomy

*Stegosaurus* gets its name – 'roofed reptile' – from the large bony plates found along its back; these were long thought to form some sort of protective shield ('roof') over the back of this animal. Apart from *Kentrosaurus* and *Tuojiangosaurus* which are both known from quite reasonable skeletons, *Stegosaurus* is the only other really well known stegosaurid, most of the remainder are known from fragmentary pieces of skeleton alone. *Stegosaurus,* because it is well-preserved and well-described, will serve excellently as an example of this type of dinosaur.

The head of *Stegosaurus* is rather low and slender for such a large animal, with a narrow, toothless, horn-covered beak at the tip of its snout. Behind the beak the teeth are quite numerous, but are not arranged into a special cutting battery. Therefore it seems that the stegosaurids were not capable of grinding up plant food in their mouths in the way that some ornithopods and ceratopids could. The jaw muscles were also, so far as we can tell, quite simple, without the special mechanical devices for improving the efficiency of the jaw-closing muscles such as are seen in ceratopids. Despite this, the great size of these animals suggests that they had to consume large quantities of plant food to sustain themselves. It seems most likely that these ornithischians used feeding techniques like those employed by the prosauropods and sauropods. They probably used their jaws to chop up crudely large quantities of plant food and then swallowed this quickly, passing it to a very large stomach where it was left slowly to ferment. Stomach stones may also have been used to help pulverize some of the tougher plant tissues.

The remainder of the body of *Stegosaurus* is striking in a number of ways, when compared with previous ornithischians. The plates found in two rows down the back of the animal are unique to stegosaurids, though they do tend to vary a bit in shape between different genera (compare skeleton drawings of *Stegosaurus* and *Kentrosaurus*).

In *Stegosaurus* the plates are quite small and flat, with irregular edges in the region immediately behind the head, becoming progressively taller and broader across the back. The largest plates of all are found just behind

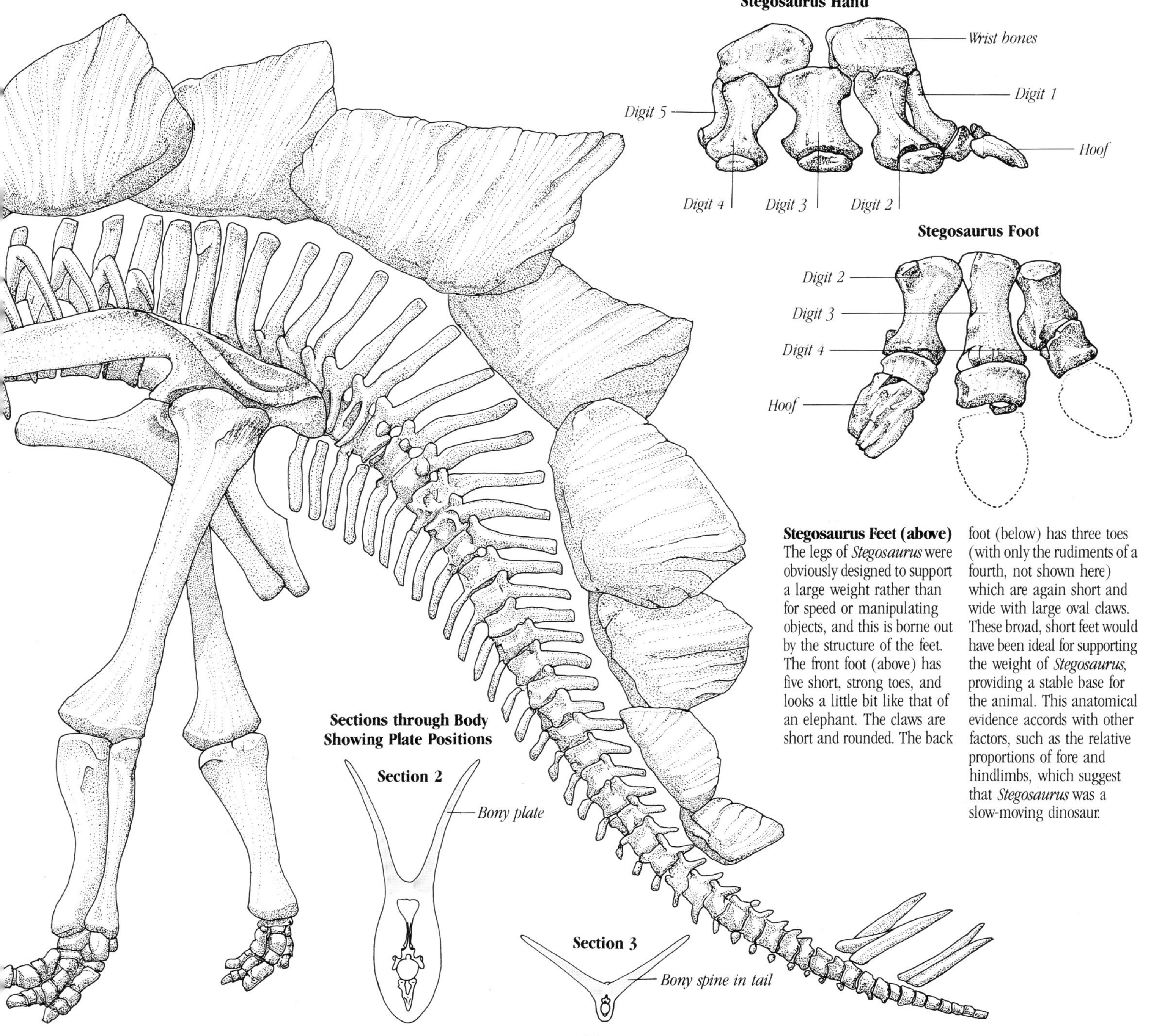


**Stegosaurus Feet (above)** The legs of *Stegosaurus* were obviously designed to support a large weight rather than for speed or manipulating objects, and this is borne out by the structure of the feet. The front foot (above) has five short, strong toes, and looks a little bit like that of an elephant. The claws are short and rounded. The back foot (below) has three toes (with only the rudiments of a fourth, not shown here) which are again short and wide with large oval claws. These broad, short feet would have been ideal for supporting the weight of *Stegosaurus,* providing a stable base for the animal. This anatomical evidence accords with other factors, such as the relative proportions of fore and hindlimbs, which suggest that *Stegosaurus* was a slow-moving dinosaur.

the hip region. Beyond this there seem to be a few smaller plates (six pairs) before the end of the tail. The end of the tail also possesses bony plates but these are shaped as two pairs of long, thin pointed spikes. The precise arrangement of these bony plates along the back has been the subject of some debate over the years. Marsh, when he first described the skeleton in 1891, assumed that they formed a single line which ran right down the middle of the back of the animal with four pairs of spines on the tail. This was later disputed by other authorities, who suggested various alternative arrangements. In 1901 Lucas proposed that the plates were arranged in a double row of pairs of plates on either side of the backbone. A little later Lucas restored these in a staggered series of alternating pairs with only two pairs of tail spines – the pattern we illustrate. Restorations since the early part of this century have tended to vary between these alternative arrangements.

The source of this disagreement is the very well preserved skeleton of *Stegosaurus* in the Smithsonian Institution in Washington, D.C. A drawing of this skeleton as it was originally discovered is included below. As can be seen, the large bone plates are shown in a definite alternating pattern along the back of the skeleton. The question then arises: are these plates really in their natural arrangement? Lucas believed that they were, but Richard Lull and others claimed that the plates may have simply slipped past one another as the flesh of the carcass rotted during burial in lake sediments. These two viewpoints seem quite irreconcilable; however, as can be seen from the colour restoration and the skeletal drawings, the alternating arrangement of the plates is favoured here. Despite the fact that reptiles typically possess paired rows of armour, the reason for preferring the alternating pattern stems from the work of Jim Farlow and his associates on the probable biological significance of stegosaurid plates. This is discussed in greater detail at the end of this section.

In addition to these large and obvious bony plates, *Stegosaurus* also has quite a well developed layer of bony knobs and bumps over other parts of its body. Again some of these can be seen in the drawing of the skeleton as it was found; these small bones were found in clusters around the throat area and were very probably widely spread in the skin all over this animal.

Another noteworthy feature of *Stegosaurus* is the remarkable difference in length between the fore and hindlimbs, a difference which is even more pronounced than that seen in the ceratopids. The forelimb is stout and powerful to support the weight of the animal, and the feet are broad, with five stubby toes, clearly designed for walking upon rather than grasping. The hindlimb is considerably longer than the forelimb and is designed to be a pillar-like support for these slow-moving animals. This is particularly obvious if the proportions of the bones of the hind leg are compared with those of a fast runner such as *Hypsilophodon* (pages 106-107). The fast runner has a short thigh, a longer shin and slender, long toes; *Stegosaurus'* legs show the exact opposite of these proportions, with a long thigh, short shin and broad, short-toed feet.

Another feature of *Stegosaurus* is the almost legendary small size of the brain of this animal. One of the skulls of *Stegosaurus* was sufficiently well preserved for O. C. Marsh to be able to obtain a cast of the cavity in which the brain lay. This showed that the brain must have been very small, perhaps the smallest of any dinosaur. For an animal that grew to a length of 20ft (6m), and may have weighed 1·5 tonnes or more, to possess a brain that could have weighed no more than 2·5-2·8oz (70-80 grams) seems extraordinary. This observation more than any

**Above:** A *Stegosaurus* back plate is treated with a protective fluid at Dinosaur National Monument, Utah. As can be seen, the surface of the plate is finely grooved, a texture that suggests the presence of many blood vessels.

**Below:** This drawing shows the disposition of the skeleton of *Stegosaurus stenops* as it was found. The plates seem to lie in an alternating pattern but arguments persist as to whether this was how they were arranged in life.

**Above:** Excavated at Garden Park, Fremont County, Colorado in 1937, this is the Denver Museum's skeleton of *Stegosaurus stenops*. The comparative lengths of fore and hindlimbs are clearly illustrated in this photograph.

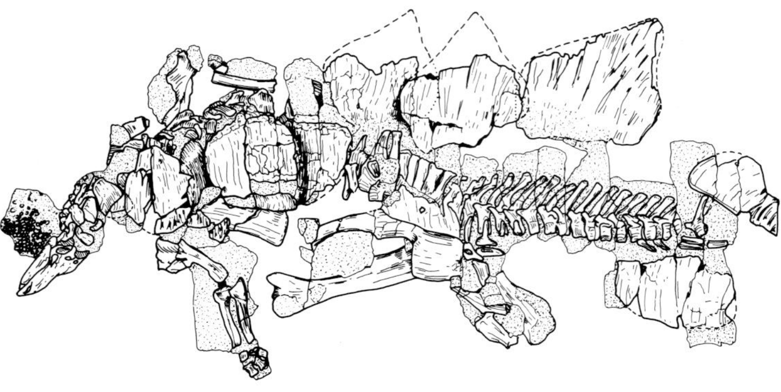

other must be responsible for the persistent and very widely held belief that all dinosaurs were dull and extremely stupid animals. Quite why *Stegosaurus* should possess such a small brain is not obvious. Many dinosaurs have quite respectably sized brains, particularly the carnivorous theropods. All we seem to be able to say at the moment is that the brain of *Stegosaurus,* although it was small, was evidently large enough for its needs! Associated with the very small brain of this animal is the fact that the spinal cord in the region of the hips was enormously enlarged. Again casts were made of this area which seemed to show that this part of the spine was over 20 times the size of the brain. This gave rise to the belief, again still widely held, that dinosaurs had a second brain in their tail.

This rather curious enlargement of the spinal cord almost certainly does *not* form a second brain. The enlargement of the spine at the hips probably marks the area where all the nerves of the back legs and tail met, forming a large relay station for messages or signals on their way to and from the brain. In addition to this, most land animals seem to store fat around this area of the spinal cord.

Apart from *Stegosaurus,* there are several other reasonably well-known stegosaurids. *Kentrosaurus* is a much smaller stegosaurid, reaching a length of about 8·2ft (2·5m), from the late Jurassic of Tanzania. Many remains of *Kentrosaurus* were found in East Africa between 1909 and 1912. Unfortunately the great majority of these fossils, which were preserved at the Humboldt Museum in Berlin, cannot now be found, and it seems likely that they were lost during World War II.

In comparison with *Stegosaurus, Kentrosaurus* has a clearly different plate and spine pattern. The anterior plates are like those of *Stegosaurus* being quite narrow and flattened, and these become slightly larger and more triangular towards the rear of the animal. However, instead of resembling the huge triangular plates above the hips of *Stegosaurus,* those of *Kentrosaurus* become taller and narrower and continue down the length of the tail as pairs of long, very sharp spines. In addition to this double row of spines there is another pair of 'para-sacral' spines attached to the hips on either side, which point obliquely downward and backward. The little that is known of the head of *Kentrosaurus* indicates a shape rather similar to that of *Stegosaurus.*

*Tuojiangosaurus* is the only other well-preserved stegosaurid. It comes from Zhucheng County, south-Central China and the remains indicate a *Stegosaurus*-sized animal with somewhat narrower spines over the hips and no para-sacral spines.

The other stegosaurids so far mentioned are based upon material which, though obviously stegosaurian (i.e. body plates or skulls and teeth), are not complete enough to provide details of their overall body shape and general characteristics. We can say, though, that *Lexovisaurus* and *Dacentrurus* appear to have possessed para-sacral spines like those of *Kentrosaurus. Huayangosaurus* is another very interesting stegosaurid which is only known so far from a complete skull. This skull is much more deep and square than that of *Stegosaurus;* it is also unusual because it still retains teeth at the front of the upper jaw which are not found in *Stegosaurus. Huayangosaurus* seems, therefore, to be a very primitive stegosaurid indeed, and if the remainder of its skeleton were to be discovered, it might well provide clues to the relationships of stegosaurids to the other ornithischian dinosaurs.

**Above:** *Kentrosaurus* in the Humboldt Museum, East Berlin. The shapes of its dorsal plates are very different from those of *Stegosaurus.* Note also the backwardly-pointing para-sacral spines on the hips.

**Left:** One of the Chinese stegosaurids, this is *Tuojiangosaurus multispinus* on display in Beipei Museum. The discovery of stegosaurids in China is significant as it implies that although we think that Europe and Asia were separated by sea for most of the age of the dinosaurs, some brief land connection may have allowed them to spread into Asia during the late Jurassic period.

**Body Armour (above)**
It has been suggested that the plates on *Stegosaurus'* back actually fulfilled the role of armour plating, protecting these slow-moving creatures from predators. In fact, as the drawing shows, even if the plates had lain flat on its back (which is improbable physiologically), the belly and flanks of *Stegosaurus* would still have been vulnerable to attack.

## Stegosaurid Life-Style

Since they are so unusual when compared with most other dinosaurs, stegosaurid remains provide us with a considerable number of clues as to their way of life. The structure of their legs indicates that they were rather slow, lumbering creatures. The low position of the head was probably well suited to a habit of browsing on ferns, cycads and other low ground cover, rather than higher up in the trees where the ornithopods and sauropods presumably fed. The rather feeble jaws and teeth simply served as cutting devices and the plants (once swallowed) were probably stored for several days in a very large stomach which acted as a fermenting tank.

As slow-moving herbivores, these stegosaurids must have been preyed upon by the large carnosaurs of the time: *Allosaurus* and *Ceratosaurus.* In the past it was assumed by many palaeontologists that since stegosaurids were unable to run to escape such predators, they must have used some defensive tactics. The rows of huge plates and spines were regarded as a defensive armour, either like that of a porcupine with the upright plates acting as deterrents, or that they were armour plated like armadillos. Some scientists have proposed that the large plates of *Stegosaurus* lay flat against the sides of its body as a protective shield.

Looking at the skeleton of *Stegosaurus,* neither of these proposals seems particularly convincing. Most of the plates across the back are broad and not particularly sharp, hardly the equivalent of the sharp quills of a porcupine. On the other hand, if the plates were indeed laid flat, then they would scarcely form a complete bony covering to the flanks of the animal—great areas of belly and neck would still be very vulnerable.

In fact a recent (1977) suggestion by Jim Farlow and colleagues is that the large plates were nothing at all to do with protection against predators. The proposal was that the plates of *Stegosaurus* acted both as radiators and solar-panels for regulating the body temperature of the animal. The first clue that this might be the case was provided by some of the very earliest descriptions of these plates. It was noted that they were covered with lots of fine grooves which are usually associated with numerous small blood vessels running across the surface of the plates: hardly what you would expect of bony armour plating! When Farlow cut a thin section across one of these plates the result was quite unexpected. Instead of the expected solid bone, the plate was found to be a honeycomb of spaces. This implied that the plates of *Stegosaurus* were very richly supplied with blood, and raised the obvious question, what was all this blood doing in these plates? The answer seems now quite obvious: like most living reptiles *Stegosaurus* was using its blood rather like the water in the central-heating system of a house to regulate its body temperature.

Farlow tested this answer by looking at the shape of the *Stegosaurus* plates and their performance in a wind-tunnel. It appeared that the plates were the ideal shape for dissipating heat in a breeze, and so cooling these animals. However, they may also have been used like solar panels to absorb heat from the Sun to warm the animal should it become chilled. No doubt *Stegosaurus* was able to regulate precisely the amount of blood passing into its plates, and so exercise fine control over its body temperature. This explanation seems particularly convincing, and may have a bearing on the arrangement of the plates down the back of *Stegosaurus.* If the plates were used as radiators or solar-panels, then the staggered pattern is the one that would have provided the most efficient arrangement. *Stegosaurus'* actual defence against predators would undoubtedly have been the spike-bearing tail. The large, sharp double pair of bone spikes on the end of the tail could have inflicted severe injury on an attacking theropod.

The other stegosaurids such as *Kentrosaurus* do not have such broad, high plates across the back as *Stegosaurus.* Presumably these forms were much more porcupine-like, with their rump, hips and tail protected by long, sharp spikes. However, these forms do tend to possess broader, flatter plates near the shoulders and on the neck which may have served as a slightly less sophisticated temperature regulation arrangement.

Until the discovery of *Heterodontosaurus* in 1962 (page 102), *Scelidosaurus* ('limb-reptile') was the earliest known ornithiscian dinosaur. It was first referred to by Richard Owen in 1859 who described remains recovered from early Jurassic rocks of Charmouth (Dorset) in southern England. Owen went on to describe and illustrate an assortment of bones under the name *Scelidosaurus* in 1861. A little later, in 1863, Owen described an almost complete skeleton of this animal. This latter skeleton forms the basis for the flesh reconstruction below. Fragmentary remains of another possible scelidosaurid—*Lusitanosaurus* ('Lusitania reptile')—have also been found in Portugal.

It has since been shown by Barney Newman that the odd bones that were described by Owen in 1861 were in fact a mixture of theropod *(Megalosaurus)* and ornithopod bones. Technically the name *Scelidosaurus* should apply to these bones alone, rather than the complete skeleton described in 1863, but this would clearly be absurd, and Barney Newman proposed that the rules governing the use of fossils' names should be suspended in this case so that the skeleton could 'adopt' the name *Scelidosaurus*. This is yet another example of the complicated tangles scientists can get into through naming fossil species on inadequate material.

## Scelidosaurus Described

*Scelidosaurus* grew to at least 13ft (4m) in length and is now known not only from the original skeleton, but also from a very small partial skeleton found in a nodule of rock earlier this century, and some imperfect fragments discovered in 1980. And very recently (1985) a group of amateur collectors, Simon Barnsley, David Costain and Peter Langham, discovered and excavated a very exciting new skeleton from Charmouth. As a result of all these discoveries, *Scelidosaurus* is now a reasonably well understood dinosaur. As with the stegosaurs (seen earlier) and the ankylosaurs (to follow), *Scelidosaurus* had many bony plates embedded in its skin; these did not form the high, thin plates seen in stegosaurs, but more closely resemble the low, bony studs seen on the backs of most ankylosaurs.

The skull of *Scelidosaurus* is deeper and shorter than that of *Stegosaurus,* and not so heavily armoured as that of a typical ankylosaur. However, as with ankylosaurs, there is evidence of extra bony tissue being welded on to the surface of the skull and the sides of the lower jaw. The teeth are simple and leaf-shaped, extending right down towards the tip of the snout so that the horny beak, if it was present, must have been extremely small.

The skeleton of *Scelidosaurus* is quite heavily built, with pillar-like hind legs and broad four-toed feet. The form of the front legs is a bit of a mystery since none is presently known. An upper arm bone preserved with the newly discovered skeleton is quite large and heavily built; this suggests that *Scelidosaurus* was a quadruped, rather than a biped—as reconstructed here. The tail, however, is long judged by the standard of most ornithischians and may have at least partly counterbalanced the front part of the animal. As a result, most of the weight was probably carried by the hind legs.

The bony armour of *Scelidosaurus* appears to have formed a broad covering across the back and sides of the animal, judging by the way that the bony plates are found scattered along the back and across the ribs of the skeleton. Immediately behind the head, the bony plates on either side are arranged in clusters of three, a

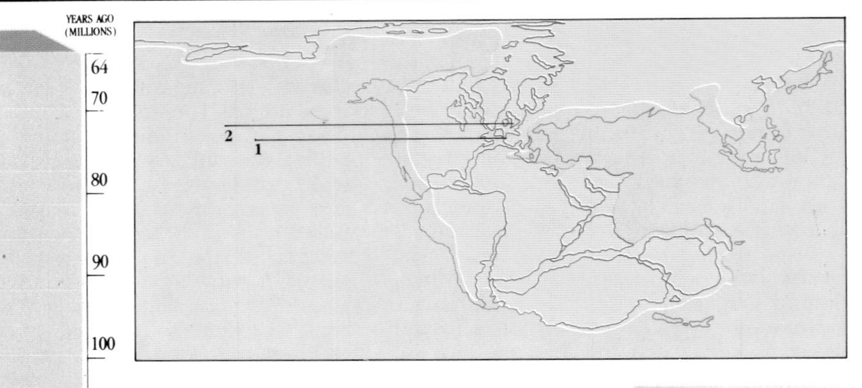


**Map**
**1** *Lusitanosaurus*
**2** *Scelidosaurus*

**Time Chart (left)**
*Scelidosaurus* is known from the early part of the Jurassic and is therefore one of the earliest ornithischian dinosaurs, and so very important in terms of the evolution of the Ornithischia as a whole. *Lusitanosaurus* may be another similar early armoured dinosaur.

**Right:** This specimen is part of the new find made by Barnsley, Costain and Langham and is extremely interesting because it shows, for the first time, the structure of the front end of *Scelidosaurus'* upper jaw. Six small, conical teeth can be seen. This part of the skull is missing from the very fine British Museum specimen—see above right. Behind is an array of leaf-shaped cheek teeth.

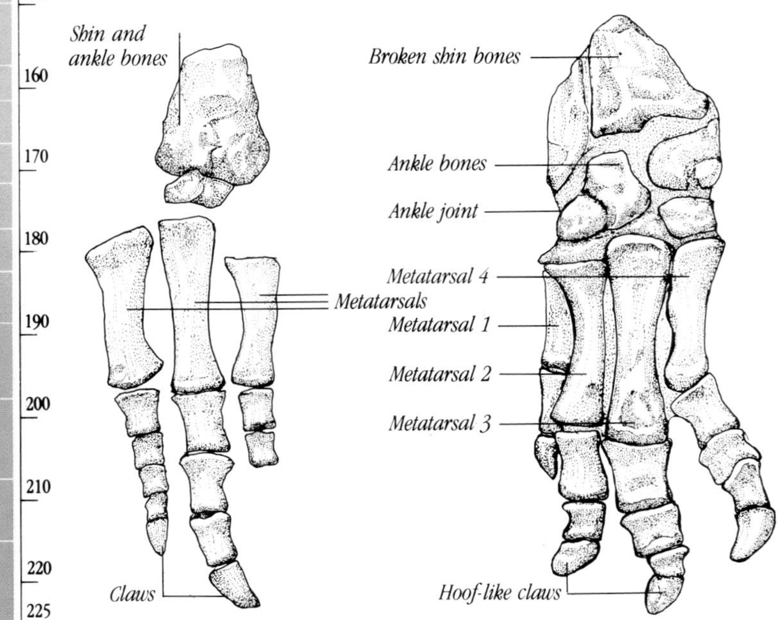


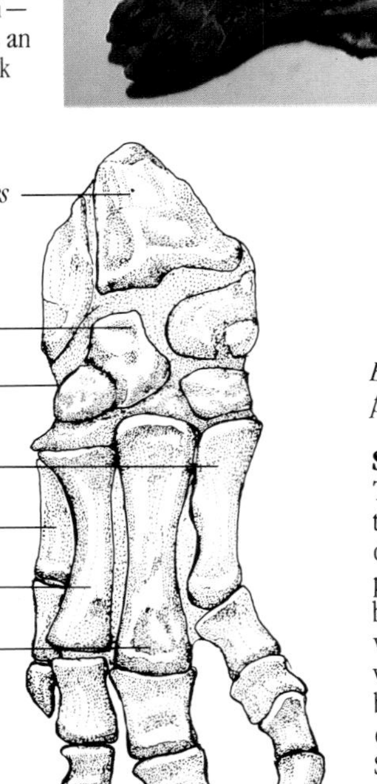


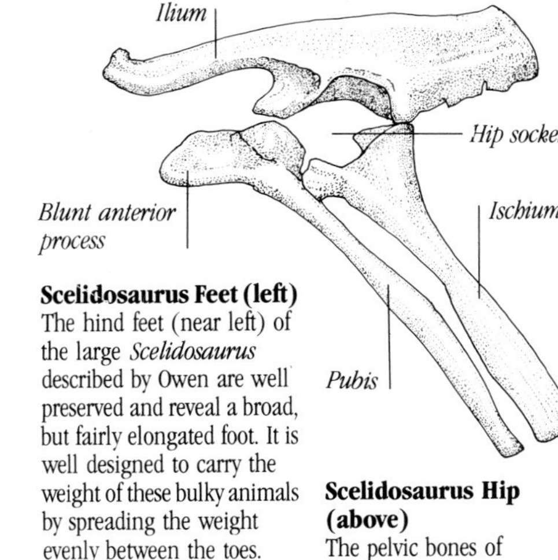


**Scelidosaurus Feet (left)**
The hind feet (near left) of the large *Scelidosaurus* described by Owen are well preserved and reveal a broad, but fairly elongated foot. It is well designed to carry the weight of these bulky animals by spreading the weight evenly between the toes. So far the new Charmouth specimen has not revealed a complete foot; the best pieces found to date are shown (far left).

**Scelidosaurus Hip (above)**
The pelvic bones of *Scelidosaurus* show very clearly the typical ornithischian pattern of bones, with pubis lying against the ischium.

curious pattern not seen anywhere else in the skeleton as can be appreciated by looking at the colour restoration below.

The rocks in which *Scelidosaurus* has been found are ones deposited at the bottom of a sea (rather than a lake or river). Indeed nearly all the other fossils found in these rocks are of sea-dwelling creatures such as ichthyosaurs and plesiosaurs. It is unusual to find the remains of land-living creatures on the sea-floor, and the only explanation would seem to be that carcasses of *Scelidosaurus* were occasionally washed down a nearby river into the sea before they sank and were buried by sediment, after which the process of fossilisation began.

The rocks in which it was buried, therefore, give us no clue to the way of life of *Scelidosaurus*. Most probably it was a fairly slow-moving plant eater which relied upon its armoured skin to protect it from the large theropods of the time. It is always possible that *Scelidosaurus* was capable of short bursts of speed to evade the larger theropods. The long tail, which might have counterbalanced the front of the body, may have permitted them to run for short distances on the hind legs alone.

## Probable Relatives

The reason for dealing with *Scelidosaurus* on its own is because at the present time palaeontologists are undecided about its closest relatives. Some claim that they are the stegosaurs, while others suggest ankylosaur relationships, and yet others propose that it is an early ornithopod. This state of affairs has arisen for two main reasons. Firstly a detailed description of *Scelidosaurus* has never been published. This is now in the process of being rectified. For the past decade a team of people led by Ron Croucher in the laboratories of the British Museum (Natural History) have been carefully preparing in acid the large skeleton, described by Owen in 1863. The rock in which this skeleton was embedded has now been completely cleared away so that a full description can begin. The second problem is an evolutionary one. Being one of the early ornithischians, *Scelidosaurus* is primitive in many of its characters. Therefore, it does not have all the features associated with one particular ornithischian group. For example its feet, legs and tail are rather similar in shape to many ornithopods. Equally it has body armour like that of many ankylosaurs as well as a skull and hips reminiscent of stegosaurs. So, where does *Scelidosaurus* fit? My feeling is that of all the ornithischians currently known, the ankylosaurs seem to be its closest relatives. This *opinion* is based on three features: the development of extensive body armour, the arrangement of its teeth, and the fact that there is evidence of extra bone being welded onto the roof of the skull and the jaws; all of these features are found in ankylosaurs. Only time will tell whether this opinion is correct!

**Scelidosaurus Skeleton (right)**
For many years the large *Scelidosaurus* skeleton described by Richard Owen was on display in the BM (NH), looking like this. In recent years a team of laboratory preparators have carefully prepared this entire skeleton in acid baths in order to dissolve away the limestone. This difficult task is almost complete now and should result in *Scelidosaurus* being one of the best known of all early ornithischians.

**Below:** The upper arm bone or humerus of *Scelidosaurus* has again been seen for the first time in the new specimen from Charmouth. As might have been expected in such a robustly constructed creature, it is a short powerful bone.

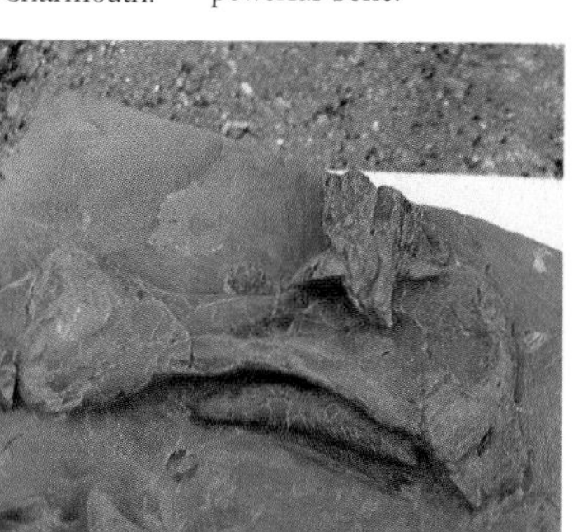

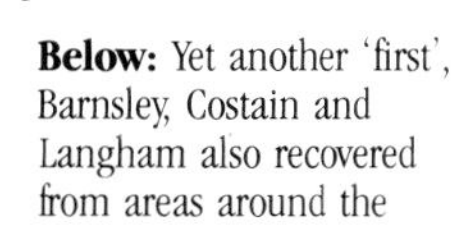

**Below:** Yet another 'first', Barnsley, Costain and Langham also recovered from areas around the skeleton some fine skin impressions which show a mosaic of small, rounded scales embedded in the skin surface.

**Scelidosaurus (below)**
This restoration is based upon illustrations prepared for Dr Alan Charig at the BM (NH). The back is studded with low conical bones and just behind the head these are modified into peculiar tricorn arrays perhaps for extra protection. The long tail may have counterbalanced the front of the body.

**Size (below)**
*Scelidosaurus*: l. 13ft (4m).

# NODOSAURIDS

The other major group of armoured dinosaurs and the last of the major groups of dinosaurs that we shall be looking at are the ankylosaurs ('fused or joined-together reptiles'). Ankylosaurs are known from Jurassic and Cretaceous rocks worldwide. The unusual name refers to the fact that the bones in the skin of these animals tend to be fused together into great shield-like pieces of armour plating. In fact, this armour plating was so extensive that large slabs of bone were even welded onto the head, giving them quite a grotesque appearance. These were the tanks of the dinosaur era.

The ankylosaurs as a whole have a long and rather chequered history. Until quite recently they were very poorly understood. Fortunately, however, Dr Walter Preston Coombs Jr (Amherst) has completely restudied many of the known ankylosaurs and cleared away much confusion. And Dr Teresa Maryanska (Warsaw) has described several completely new ankylosaurs from Mongolia.

In general, ankylosaurs are medium sized (6·5-26·2ft, 2-8m long) heavily built, quadrupedal ornithischian dinosaurs; they all tend to have low, broad, heavily armoured heads. Their bodies are low and broad, the legs being short and powerful rather than long and graceful. Their backs and legs also tend to be covered in various patterns of bony plates and studs or spikes. The tail tends to be relatively short and in some cases bears a very large bony club.

Dr Coombs has been able to show that the ankylosaurs can be divided into two quite distinct families: the nodosaurids ('nodular reptiles') and the ankylosaurids. The differences between these two families are many, but one of the most obvious is the presence or absence of a tail club.

## Nodosaurid Ankylosaurs

The first nodosaurid to be discovered was *Hylaeosaurus* ('woodland reptile') which was found in 1833 in the Tilgate Forest area of Sussex in southern England. The fossil remains of *Hylaeosaurus* consisted of the front half of the skeleton embedded in a large piece of stone. This fossil was first described by Gideon Mantell and somewhat later by Richard Owen and, along with *Megalosaurus* and *Iguanodon*, was one of the founder members of Owen's *Dinosauria*. This fossil, which is now in the British Museum (Natural History) has, unfortunately, never been prepared out of the stone in which it is embedded. Nevertheless, the parts which are exposed seem to show an animal with rows of large, curved plates running down its back. Few other remains of *Hylaeosaurus* have been discovered to date, so that not a great deal is known about either its appearance or its relations with other ankylosaurs.

Another early British nodosaurid is *Polacanthus* ('many-spikes') which was discovered in 1865 by the Rev. William Fox. The skeleton, which consisted of the hind part of the animal

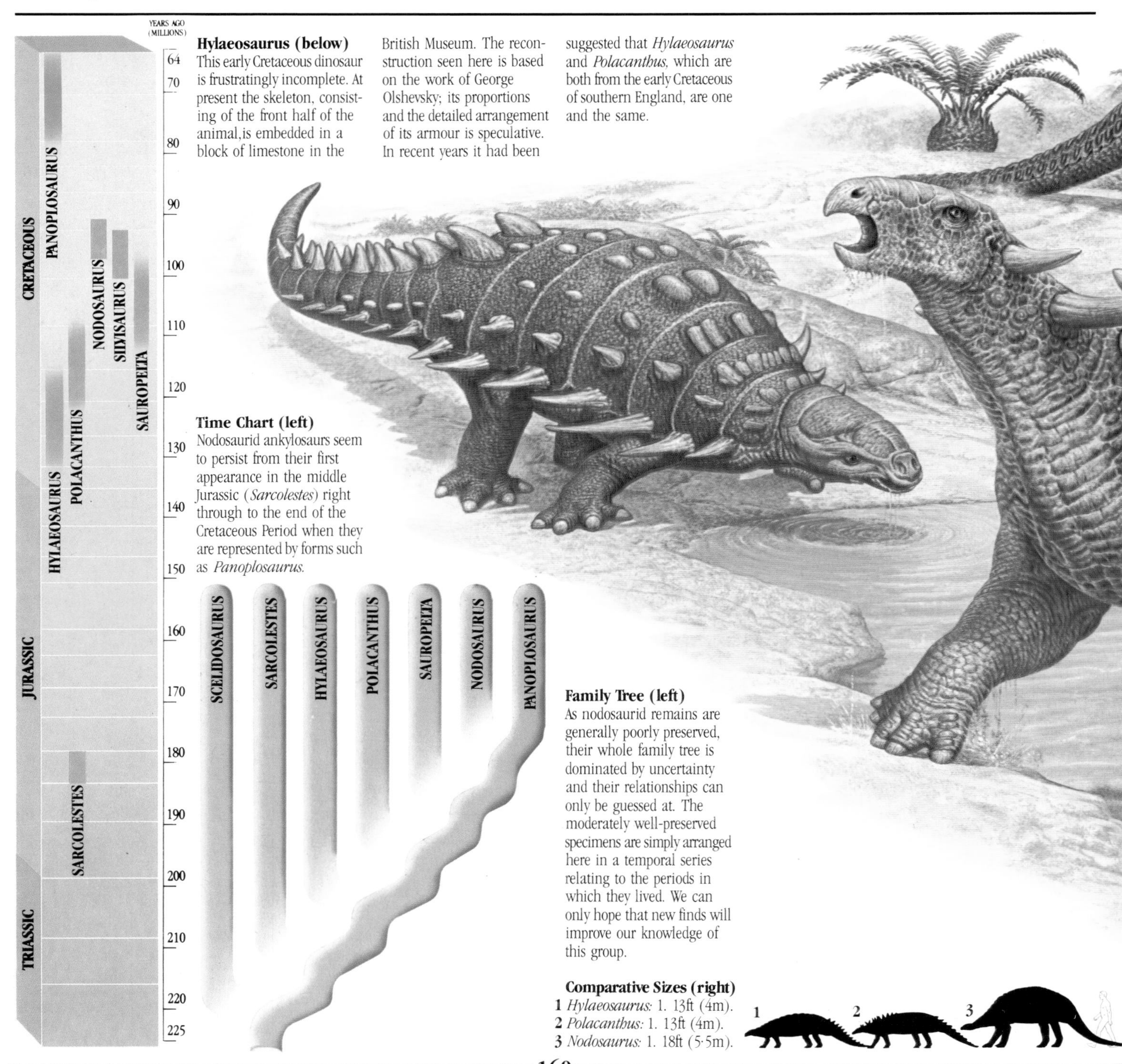


**Hylaeosaurus (below)** This early Cretaceous dinosaur is frustratingly incomplete. At present the skeleton, consisting of the front half of the animal,is embedded in a block of limestone in the British Museum. The reconstruction seen here is based on the work of George Olshevsky; its proportions and the detailed arrangement of its armour is speculative. In recent years it had been suggested that *Hylaeosaurus* and *Polacanthus*, which are both from the early Cretaceous of southern England, are one and the same.

**Time Chart (left)** Nodosaurid ankylosaurs seem to persist from their first appearance in the middle Jurassic (*Sarcolestes*) right through to the end of the Cretaceous Period when they are represented by forms such as *Panoplosaurus*.

**Family Tree (left)** As nodosaurid remains are generally poorly preserved, their whole family tree is dominated by uncertainty and their relationships can only be guessed at. The moderately well-preserved specimens are simply arranged here in a temporal series relating to the periods in which they lived. We can only hope that new finds will improve our knowledge of this group.

**Comparative Sizes (right)**
1 *Hylaeosaurus*: l. 13ft (4m).
2 *Polacanthus*: l. 13ft (4m).
3 *Nodosaurus*: l. 18ft (5·5m).

**Nodosaurus (below)**
From what is known of the skeleton, the armour is the most distinctive feature of *Nodosaurus*. It seems to have consisted of broad bands of alternately large and small rounded nodules (hence its name). It is possible that the margins of the armour were fringed with tall spines as seems to have been the case with *Hylaeosaurus* and *Polacanthus*. The head of this colour reconstruction is conjectural, based upon that of *Panoplosaurus*, as no head was found with the skeleton in Albany County, Wyoming.

including many spines, various back and tail vertebrae, the hips and hind legs, had evidently weathered out of the cliffs on the coast of the Isle of Wight. It seems quite likely that much of the skeleton was present originally but that, once exposed by a cliff fall, much was lost by being washed out to sea. The frustrating thing about this specimen is that although it must have lived at about the same time as *Hylaeosaurus*, the parts of both skeletons do not overlap (one being the front half, the other the back half). It is therefore impossible to compare the two skeletons directly to *prove* that they belonged either to the same or to different animals. Quite recently (1979) Mr William T. Blows, an amateur collector of fossils who is continuing the tradition of collecting dinosaurs from the Isle of Wight established by the Rev. Fox, discovered some more *Polacanthus* material. Again this is far from complete, but it does include some very nice pieces of its armour-plated hide, and various bones from the back of the animal. Some of these latter may help to solve the problem of the *Polacanthus-Hylaeosaurus* relationship. However, this awaits preparation of the original *Hylaeosaurus* skeleton.

The story of frustration revealed in the *Polacanthus-Hylaeosaurus* issue is by now a familiar one. The fossil remains are not well enough preserved to give precise information about these interesting animals, and indeed this problem applies very strongly to nearly all ankylosaurs. In some geological formations ankylosaur-type bony plates can be very abundant, but these always seem to be isolated bones, presumably scattered from rotting carcasses. Very few nodosaurids are known at all well, and many of the reconstructions of these animals seen in books are based on little more than guesswork. Bearing this fact in mind, we shall simply look at a few details of the anatomy of some of the better known members of nodosaurid group.

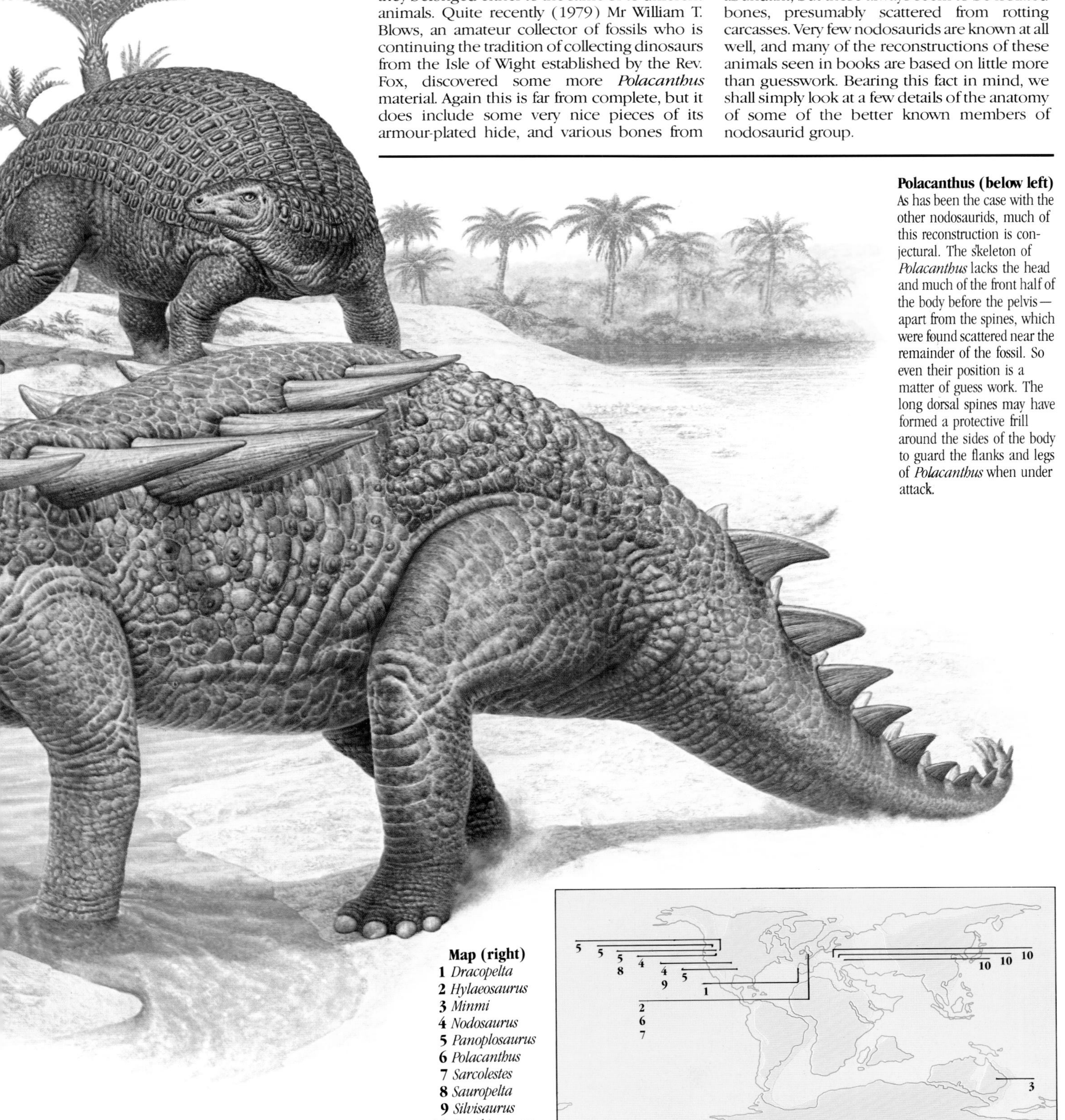

**Polacanthus (below left)**
As has been the case with the other nodosaurids, much of this reconstruction is conjectural. The skeleton of *Polacanthus* lacks the head and much of the front half of the body before the pelvis—apart from the spines, which were found scattered near the remainder of the fossil. So even their position is a matter of guess work. The long dorsal spines may have formed a protective frill around the sides of the body to guard the flanks and legs of *Polacanthus* when under attack.

**Map (right)**
**1** *Dracopelta*
**2** *Hylaeosaurus*
**3** *Minmi*
**4** *Nodosaurus*
**5** *Panoplosaurus*
**6** *Polacanthus*
**7** *Sarcolestes*
**8** *Sauropelta*
**9** *Silvisaurus*
**10** *Struthiosaurus*

*Nodosaurus* ('nodular [lumpy] reptile') was first mentioned by Marsh in 1889, but was only described in some detail in 1921 by Richard Lull on the basis of partial remains of the skeleton. *Nodosaurus* remains come from the late Cretaceous of Wyoming and Kansas. *Nodosaurus* gives us a fair idea of how most nodosaurids must have looked. The skeleton is about 18ft (5·5m) long and the whole of its upper surface is studded with bony plates forming a very thick and heavy protective coat. The pattern of armour plating seen in *Nodosaurus* consists of regular bands of larger and smaller bony plates. This would have undoubtedly conferred upon this animal both considerable strength and a certain amount of flexibility. The hind legs are pillar-like in order to support the heavy body, and the feet are naturally short and broad. The pelvis is rather a different shape to that of other ornithischians because the ilium at the top of the hip is greatly enlarged and overhangs the legs, while the lower hip bones (pubis and ischium) are very much reduced. Large leg muscles attached to the underside of the ilium, while its upper surface was covered by extensive armour-plating. The front legs of *Nodosaurus* are not very well preserved but were undoubtedly, as shown here, short and powerfully built to support the great weight of the body. The shoulders were similarly very strong and in many cases clearly scarred by powerful muscles.

The skull of *Nodosaurus* is unfortunately not known to date; however, that of another late Cretaceous North American nodosaurid, *Panoplosaurus* ('fully plated reptile'), is very well preserved (see right). The skull of all known nodosaurids seems to resemble that of *Panoplosaurus*. Unlike the ankylosaurids (pages 164-169) the nodosaurid skull is rather narrow with a more pointed snout, and lacks the horn-like projections from the rear corners of the skull. There is also an opening on the side of the skull behind the eye, which is not seen in ankylosaurids. The teeth are quite simple, leaf-shaped and rather similar to those of stegosaurs. Indeed although the jaws are massive, they are not specially modified for grinding in the way that the jaws and teeth of ceratopids and hadrosaurids were. The front of both upper and lower jaws ends in a toothless, horn-covered beak.

*Silvisaurus* ('forest reptile') is another nodosaurid which was described by Theodore Eaton Jr. in 1960. It consisted of a skull and partial skeleton collected from Ottawa county, Kansas and is dated at early Cretaceous. Measuring about 8ft (2·5m) in length, this small armoured dinosaur is slightly unusual in that it has 8 or 9 small pointed teeth near the front of its upper jaw — the area covered by a horny beak in most other ankylosaurs. This does not mean that *Silvisaurus* had no horny beak at all, merely that the upper beak was quite small and situated right at the tip of the upper jaw.

*Sauropelta* ('shielded reptile') is another early Cretaceous nodosaurid described by Professor John Ostrom in 1970. Again the material of this animal is far from complete, even though abundant remains have been recovered in recent years. One specimen of *Sauropelta* includes a very well-preserved tail which clearly tapers toward the tip and lacks the club characteristic of ankylosaurids. The body armour is also quite well preserved in several specimens and seems to show transverse rows of alternating large low bony studs and smaller pebbly armour. Towards the sides of the animal the larger studs seem to be taller and spike-like, and probably formed a fringe of defensive spikes protecting the sides of the animal from attack by predators.

In addition to these admittedly poorly known animals there are several other even less well known nodosaurids. *Struthiosaurus* ('ostrich reptile') is known from the latest Cretaceous of southern Europe (France, Hungary, Austria) and especially from localities in an area originally known as Transylvania in Rumania. These remains are particularly interesting because all the dinosaurs from this area (including a sauropod, a hadrosaurid and an iguanodontid) are *dwarf* species. *Struthiosaurus* is the smallest of all known nodosaurids, measuring no more than 6·5ft (2m) in length. Why all these dinosaurs should be so small is a mystery. One explanation is that they lived on small islands, whereon there has been shown to be a surprisingly common tendency toward miniaturization. Several Mediterranean islands

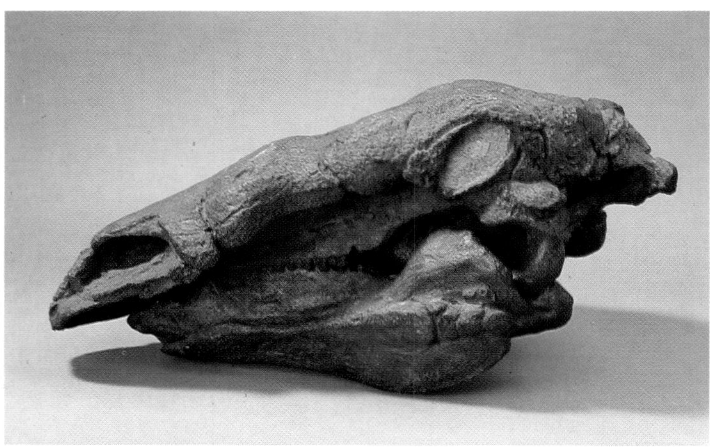

**Left:** The massive construction of the nodosaurid skull is plainly seen in this picture of *Panoplosaurus*. Large slabs of bone are plastered all over the skull.

**Panoplosaurus Skull (right)**
From above (near right) the details of the armour plating are clear; the grooves show where the slabs of bone join. From below one can see the toothless beak on the snout, the teeth, the internal nostrils and the braincase behind.

**Nodosaurus Skeleton (right)**
It is a sad fact that nodosaurids are very poorly known at present. This reconstruction of *Nodosaurus textilis* is based on Richard Swann Lull's work, and has been given additional material from other nodosaurids. The specimen is badly preserved and so the skull is 'borrowed' from *Panoplosaurus*, while the shoulders are those of *Sauropelta*. The armour plating is distinctive, consisting of bands of rounded nodules. It is not known whether this animal had a fringe of longer spikes, as other nodosaurids did.

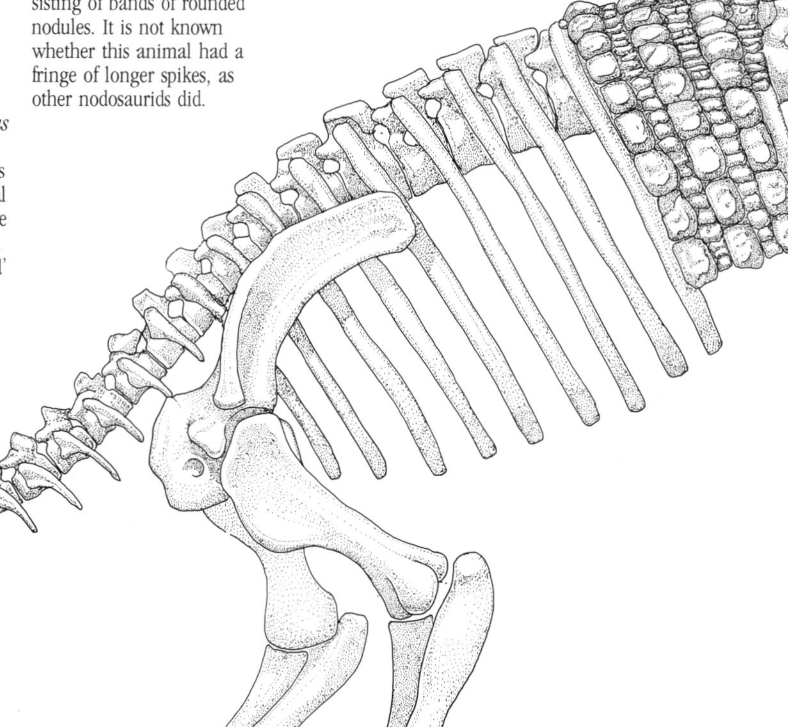

'Pseudo-acromion process'
Shoulder blade
Shoulder joint

**Nodosaur Shoulder Blade (above)**
This shoulder blade belongs to *Sauropelta* and is typical of the type seen in nodosaurids. Its most outstanding feature, and one in which it differs from that of ankylosaurids, is the large pseudo-acromion process which overhangs the shoulder joint and which may have improved the mechanical advantage of some of the shoulder muscles. It is possible that this allowed nodosaurids to crouch against the ground for protection against predators, relying on their armour to withstand any attack (see also drawing of nodosaurid defensive strategy on page 168).

are known to have had miniature elephants and even today Madagascar still has a fauna which includes a dwarf hippopotamus. So perhaps these dinosaurs were island dwellers as well.

Other important but very poorly known nodosaurids include *Minmi* (named after Minmi Crossing where it was found), the first Australian ankylosaur which was discovered in early Cretaceous rocks near Roma, Queensland. *Minmi* is only known from a small portion of the back and parts of a foot. *Dracopelta* ('armoured dragon') is a small late Jurassic nodosaurid from Portugal. This new species described by Galton in 1980 is known from part of a rib cage with several types of armour plate preserved in position. *Sarcolestes* ('flesh robber'), mistakenly identified as a meat-eating dinosaur, comes from the middle Jurassic of Cambridgeshire. It consists only of an incomplete piece of jaw which seems to be typically ankylosaurian in that it has a large piece of armour-plating welded to its outer surface. This is the earliest record of a nodosaurid from anywhere in the world. *Priodontognathus* ('saw-toothed jaw') of uncertain age may be a fragment of ankylosaur jaw from England, and *Cryptodraco* ('hidden dragon') is an ankylosaurian thigh bone from the late Jurassic of Cambridgeshire.

Apart from these interesting but very fragmentary records of nodosaurid ankylosaurs, there are many other commonly named nodosaurids which are unfortunately very dubious indeed. These include *Acanthopholis* ('thorn bearer'), *Brachypodosaurus* ('short-footed reptile'), *Hoplitosaurus* ('hoplite reptile'), *Polacanthoides* ('like many spikes'), *Onychosaurus* ('crawling reptile'), *Palaeoscincus* ('ancient skink') and *Priconodon* ('saw cone-shaped tooth'). All of these are based on fossil specimens that are inadequate for scientific comparison with other species and should therefore be considered as 'nomina dubia' or dubious names.

Many other names have been proposed for nodosaurids but these have proved to be incorrect. For example *Struthiosaurus* has, over the years, been given the following names, all of which are incorrect: *Cretaeomus, Danubiosaurus, Danubriosaurus, Hoplosaurus, Leipsanosaurus, Lepanosaurus, Pleuropeltis, Pleuropeltus, Rhodanosaurus.* This is not the only example of a variety of names applying to a single fossil genus. In this case it very forcefully makes the point that the original material of *Struthiosaurus* was extremely poorly understood. As a result, each time more ankylosaur material was discovered in southern Europe it was given a new name because it could not be compared adequately with the original. Obviously this sort of phenomenon can bedevil scientific research on groups such as this because it can take such an inordinate length of time to track down all these different names and undertake the necessary work to prove that they are incorrect.

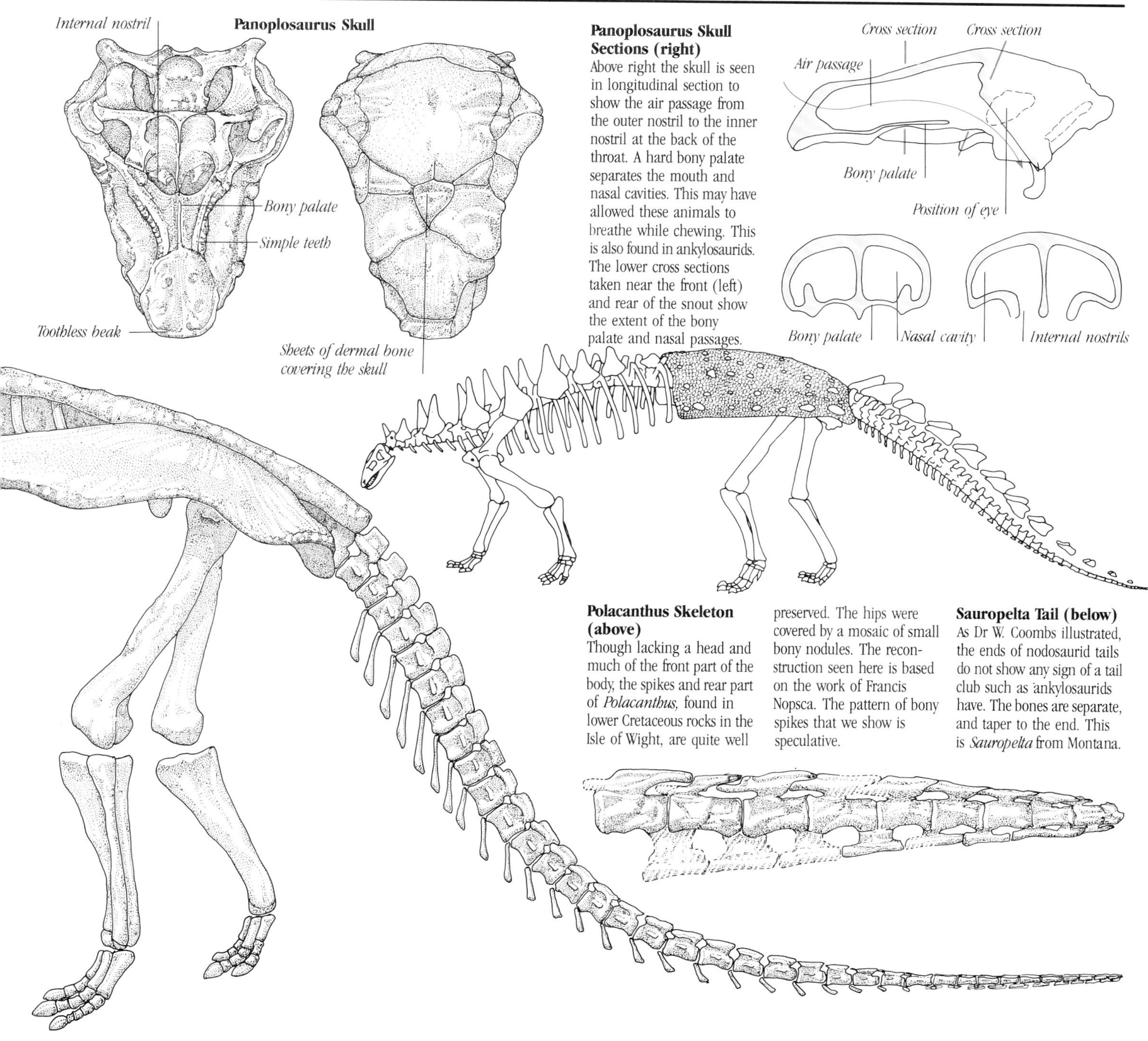


**Panoplosaurus Skull**

**Panoplosaurus Skull Sections (right)**
Above right the skull is seen in longitudinal section to show the air passage from the outer nostril to the inner nostril at the back of the throat. A hard bony palate separates the mouth and nasal cavities. This may have allowed these animals to breathe while chewing. This is also found in ankylosaurids. The lower cross sections taken near the front (left) and rear of the snout show the extent of the bony palate and nasal passages.

**Polacanthus Skeleton (above)**
Though lacking a head and much of the front part of the body, the spikes and rear part of *Polacanthus,* found in lower Cretaceous rocks in the Isle of Wight, are quite well preserved. The hips were covered by a mosaic of small bony nodules. The reconstruction seen here is based on the work of Francis Nopsca. The pattern of bony spikes that we show is speculative.

**Sauropelta Tail (below)**
As Dr W. Coombs illustrated, the ends of nodosaurid tails do not show any sign of a tail club such as ankylosaurids have. The bones are separate, and taper to the end. This is *Sauropelta* from Montana.

# ANKYLOSAURIDS

The second group of ankylosaurs known as ankylosaurids are described in this section. Ankylosaurids may be distinguished from the nodosaurid ankylosaurs in a number of ways. Ankylosaurids have broad, armoured heads which are about as wide as they are long. Large triangular horns are found at the rear corners of the skull, and the sides of the head are completely closed in by bone. The bony armour-plating covering the body tends to have very few tall spines and the tail is highly modified to form a heavy bony club.

While nodosaurids are found in rocks which vary in age between the middle Jurassic and the late Cretaceous, the ankylosaurids appear to be restricted in time to the Cretaceous. Ankylosaurids also appear to have been much less widespread geographically, having been recovered with certainty only from western North America and eastern Asia (Mongolia and China). As was the case with nodosaurids, remains of ankylosaurid-type dinosaurs are quite abundant. Unfortunately, these remains tend to be isolated pieces of armour-plating or other skeletal fragments, which cannot be identified with any great confidence. This abundance of poor material has therefore tended to generate many invalid or extremely dubious names. Again we have to be grateful to Dr Walter Coombs Jr and Dr Teresa Maryanska for their detailed work which has, over the last decade, helped to clarify what, until recently, has been a very confusing group of dinosaurs.

In order to discuss some of the main features of ankylosaurids, we shall look at what is known of the dinosaur illustrated in the foreground below: *Euoplocephalus* ('true plated head').

## Euoplocephalus Described

The first remains of the animal later to be known as *Euoplocephalus* were recovered from the Red Deer River of Alberta in 1902; they consisted of a partial head and incomplete skeleton. Lawrence Lambe created the name *Stereocephalus* ('twin-head') for this skeleton. Unfortunately this particular name had already been used for an insect! So Lambe changed it to *Euoplocephalus* in 1910. Other remains of armoured dinosaurs were found in the same general area in subsequent years. Some of these remains were named *Dyoplosaurus* ('doubly armoured reptile'), others were named *Scolosaurus* ('thorn-reptile') and *Anodontosaurus* ('toothless reptile'). Coombs eventually realized, after studying these separate species carefully, that they were all parts of the same type of animal and renamed them all *Euoplocephalus*.

All of this material, which includes skulls, several partial skeletons and fairly complete armour, provides enough information for a reasonably accurate picture of *Euoplocephalus* to be drawn. The reconstructions seen here are based on the work of Dr Kenneth Carpenter (Boulder, Colorado). In common with all the

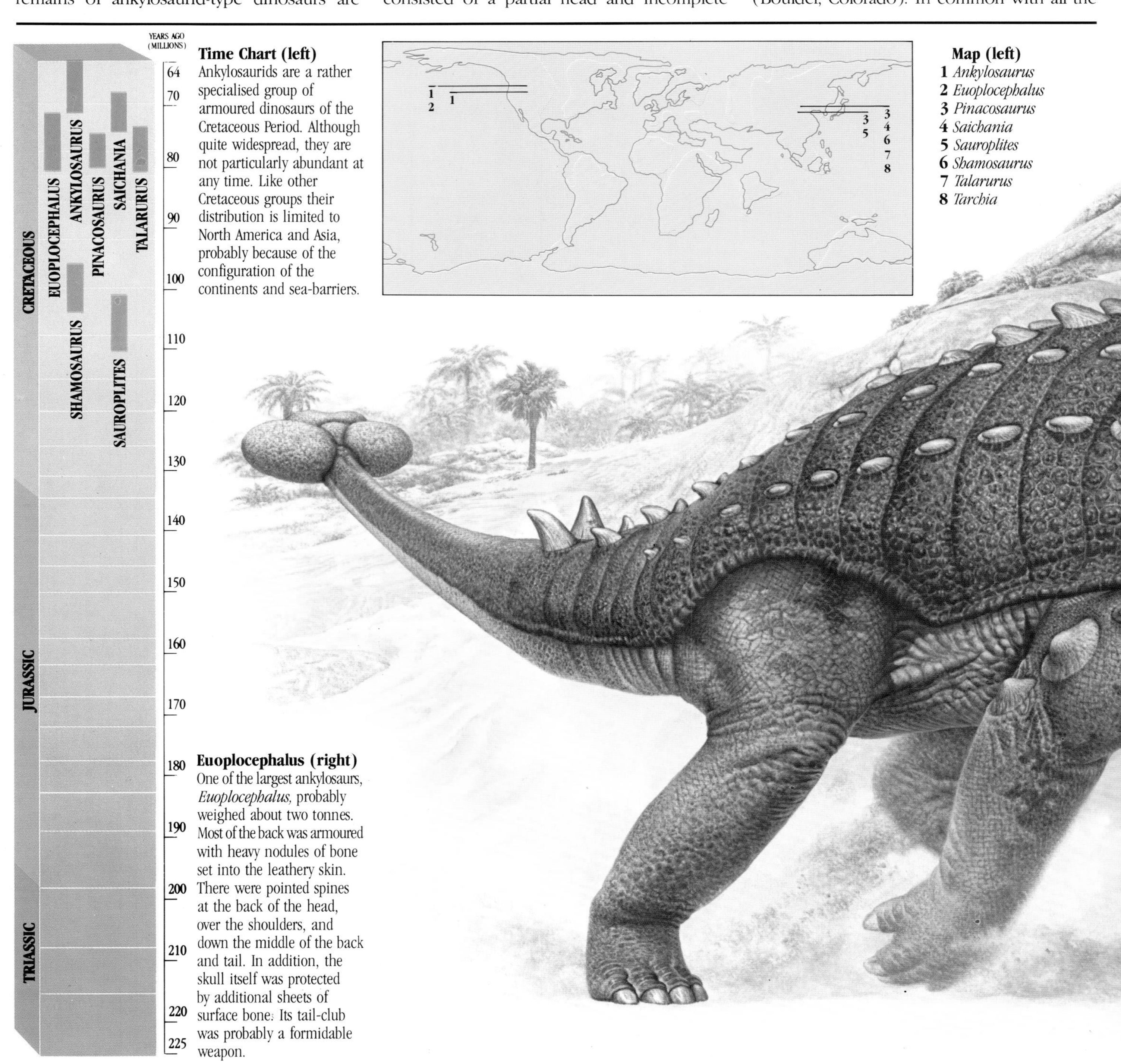


**Time Chart (left)**
Ankylosaurids are a rather specialised group of armoured dinosaurs of the Cretaceous Period. Although quite widespread, they are not particularly abundant at any time. Like other Cretaceous groups their distribution is limited to North America and Asia, probably because of the configuration of the continents and sea-barriers.

**Map (left)**
1 *Ankylosaurus*
2 *Euoplocephalus*
3 *Pinacosaurus*
4 *Saichania*
5 *Sauroplites*
6 *Shamosaurus*
7 *Talarurus*
8 *Tarchia*

**Euoplocephalus (right)**
One of the largest ankylosaurs, *Euoplocephalus*, probably weighed about two tonnes. Most of the back was armoured with heavy nodules of bone set into the leathery skin. There were pointed spines at the back of the head, over the shoulders, and down the middle of the back and tail. In addition, the skull itself was protected by additional sheets of surface bone. Its tail-club was probably a formidable weapon.

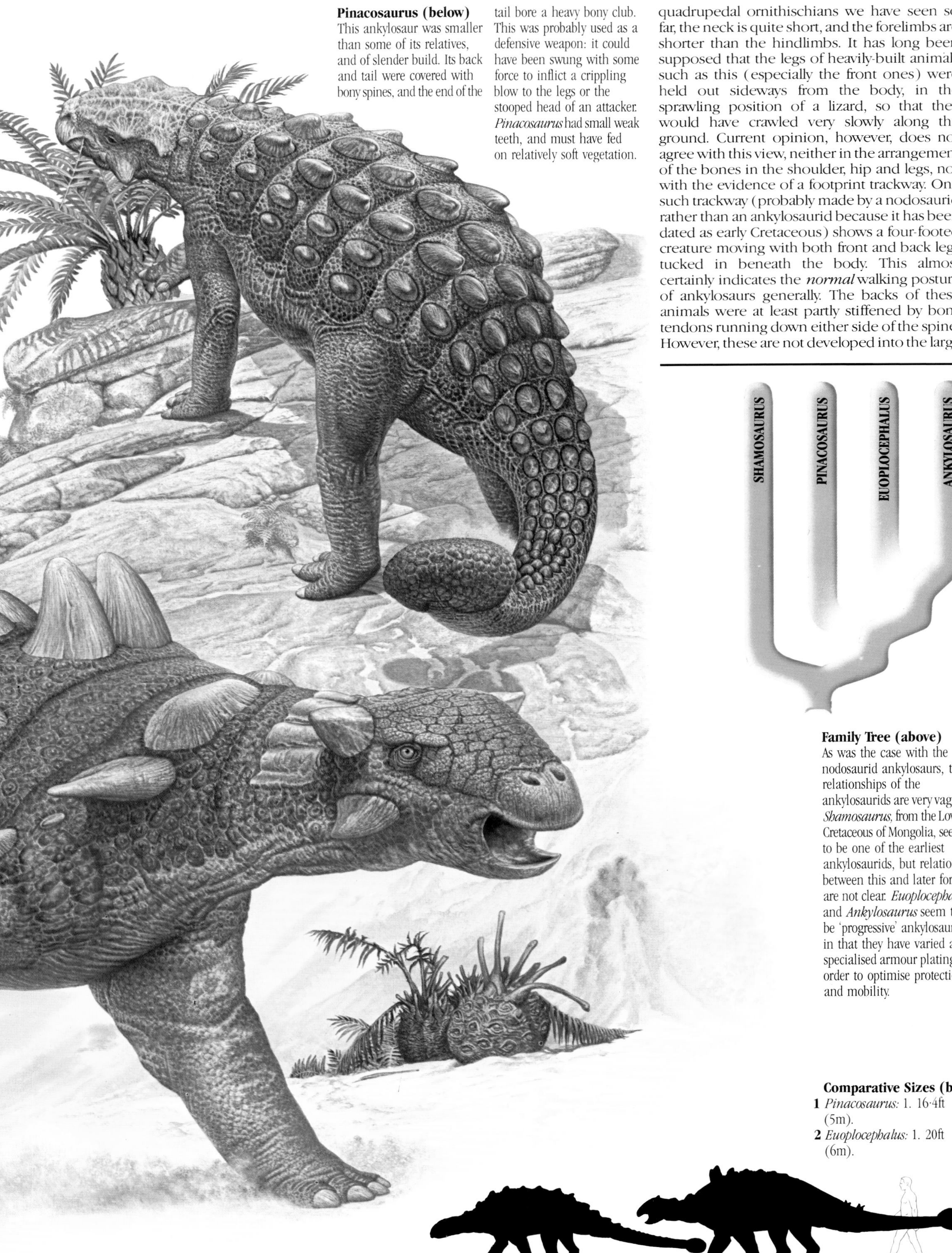


**Pinacosaurus (below)**
This ankylosaur was smaller than some of its relatives, and of slender build. Its back and tail were covered with bony spines, and the end of the tail bore a heavy bony club. This was probably used as a defensive weapon: it could have been swung with some force to inflict a crippling blow to the legs or the stooped head of an attacker. *Pinacosaurus* had small weak teeth, and must have fed on relatively soft vegetation.

quadrupedal ornithischians we have seen so far, the neck is quite short, and the forelimbs are shorter than the hindlimbs. It has long been supposed that the legs of heavily-built animals such as this (especially the front ones) were held out sideways from the body, in the sprawling position of a lizard, so that they would have crawled very slowly along the ground. Current opinion, however, does not agree with this view, neither in the arrangement of the bones in the shoulder, hip and legs, nor with the evidence of a footprint trackway. One such trackway (probably made by a nodosaurid rather than an ankylosaurid because it has been dated as early Cretaceous) shows a four-footed creature moving with both front and back legs tucked in beneath the body. This almost certainly indicates the *normal* walking posture of ankylosaurs generally. The backs of these animals were at least partly stiffened by bony tendons running down either side of the spine. However, these are not developed into the large

**Family Tree (above)**
As was the case with the nodosaurid ankylosaurs, the relationships of the ankylosaurids are very vague. *Shamosaurus,* from the Lower Cretaceous of Mongolia, seems to be one of the earliest ankylosaurids, but relations between this and later forms are not clear. *Euoplocephalus* and *Ankylosaurus* seem to be 'progressive' ankylosaurids in that they have varied and specialised armour plating in order to optimise protection and mobility.

**Comparative Sizes (below)**
**1** *Pinacosaurus:* 1. 16·4ft (5m).
**2** *Euoplocephalus:* 1. 20ft (6m).

lattice-like arrangements seen across the hips of hadrosaurids (pages 118-119 and 124-125), but appear much more sporadically in this area. The region where they are best developed is toward the end of the tail—near the tail-club. These tendons probably served two purposes in life. Firstly, they provided firm anchorage for the tail-swinging muscles; secondly, they stiffened the end of the tail in order to prevent 'whip-lash' effects from damaging the bones near the tail-club. The main part of the tail had no ossified tendons and could therefore be swung freely from side to side.

The dominant characteristic of this animal is, however, the bony armour-plating. The ground plan for the arrangement of the armour lies in the skin, practically all of which is embedded with small, bony studs. On the back and tail the studded skin is divided up into bands of much larger bony plates of various shapes running across the body. Over the neck there are two bands, the first appears to consist of two large, slightly ridged plates, followed by a second ring with a whorl of very large, oblique blunt spikes. These are arranged so as to give not only protection, but also a great deal of flexibility to the neck. Behind this area, the back is covered by four bands of armour studded with rows of large but quite low, keeled plates. Across the hips there are three further bands which are covered by a mosaic of disc-shaped studs. The front part of the tail is also banded, with four rows of keeled spikes which get progressively smaller, except for the middle two spikes on the last band. Beyond this region the tail lacks the bands of bone, but is studded with small bony nodules. The shoulders, arms and thighs were probably also covered with variously sized bony plates, but their arrangement is not at all well understood.

What we have then is a large animal (20ft, 6m or more in length) weighing something like two tonnes. Rather than being an enormous, very slow-moving creature somewhat like a gigantic tortoise, it is here pictured as a surprisingly agile animal, perhaps more like a modern rhinoceros which, although it is large and heavy, is by no means slow-moving.

The degree to which ankylosaurids were armoured is quite remarkable, as can be appreciated by looking at the skulls of *Euoplocephalus, Pinacosaurus* and *Saichania.* Large slabs of bone are plastered all over the exposed surfaces of the skull and jaws forming an almost impregnable covering; these must have given them almost complete immunity to attacks by the large theropods of the time. Two rather exceptional skulls of *Euoplocephalus* in the American Museum of Natural History show that these dinosaurs even went so far as to develop bony eyelids! Both of these skulls are preserved with curved bony plates inside the eye socket which undoubtedly closed rather like steel shutters to protect the delicate eye from the talons of theropods. Although such bony eyelids have only been found in *Euoplocephalus*

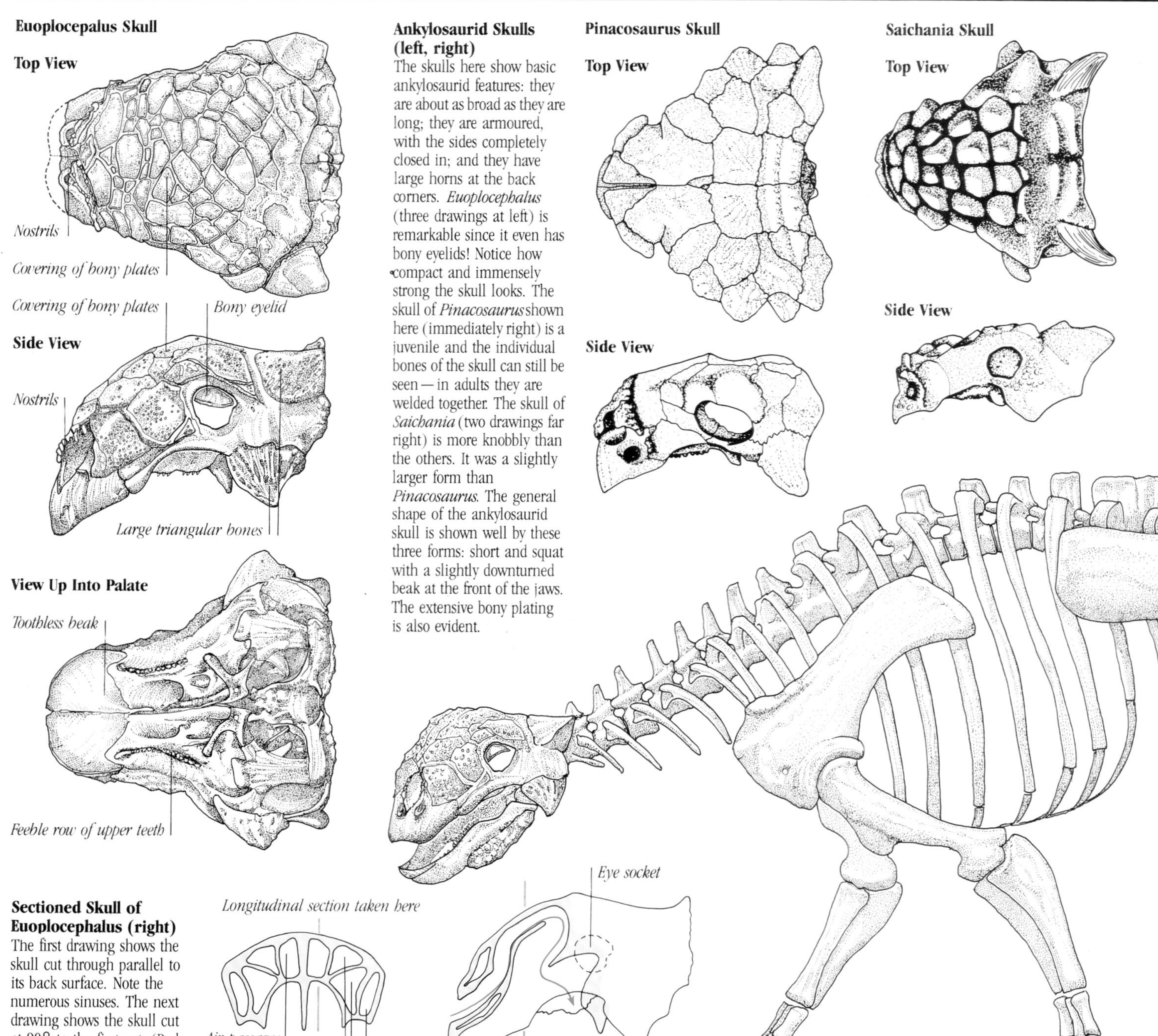


**Ankylosaurid Skulls (left, right)**
The skulls here show basic ankylosaurid features: they are about as broad as they are long; they are armoured, with the sides completely closed in; and they have large horns at the back corners. *Euoplocephalus* (three drawings at left) is remarkable since it even has bony eyelids! Notice how compact and immensely strong the skull looks. The skull of *Pinacosaurus* shown here (immediately right) is a juvenile and the individual bones of the skull can still be seen—in adults they are welded together. The skull of *Saichania* (two drawings far right) is more knobbly than the others. It was a slightly larger form than *Pinacosaurus.* The general shape of the ankylosaurid skull is shown well by these three forms: short and squat with a slightly downturned beak at the front of the jaws. The extensive bony plating is also evident.

**Sectioned Skull of Euoplocephalus (right)**
The first drawing shows the skull cut through parallel to its back surface. Note the numerous sinuses. The next drawing shows the skull cut at 90° to the first cut. (Red shows respiratory passages).

to date, it seems quite likely that other ankylosaurids possessed them.

## Nasal Passages

Nodosaurid nasal passages are relatively simple paired tubes which run from the nostrils directly to the back of the throat. By contrast ankylosaurid nasal tubes follow an S-shaped course through the head and on either side of these there are additional passages (sinuses). These elaborate sinuses may have had several purposes in life. Similar sorts of complicated passages in the heads of hadrosaurids have been interpreted as allowing for an improved sense of smell, or for making characteristic noises. Teresa Maryanska believes that they served to filter, warm and moisten the air which these animals breathed. In *Pinacosaurus* ('plank reptile') and *Saichania* ('beautiful') skulls recovered from Mongolia, Maryanska has discovered thin curved bones within the nasa passages which look strikingly similar to the turbinal or scroll bones found in the noses of mammals. These bones are covered by membranes which filter, warm and moisten the air we breathe, so that a similar function in ankylosaurids does seem reasonable.

With regard to the structure of the ankylosaurid brain, we are fortunate that an endocranial cast of *Euoplocephalus* has been illustrated and described by Dr Coombs. This seems to show a fairly typical reptile brain cavity. The only unusual characteristic is the large, divergent pair of olfactory stalks which run towards the complex nasal passages. The relatively small size of the parts of the brain concerned with co-ordination and general activity compared with some other dinosaurs, such as ornithopods, tends to confirm the notion that these animals were slower-moving than their agile, bipedal contemporaries.

Because ankylosaurs were large and heavy animals, their leg muscles were of necessity extremely powerful. One fortunate result of this for the palaeontologist is that the muscles have left remarkably clear scars on the areas where they were originally attached to the bones. Walter Coombs was able to analyse these muscle scars and used them to build up a detailed picture of the arrangement of muscles in the hips and shoulders of ankylosaurs. Some of the muscles are indicated in the diagrams below. There is, of course, no way in which we can be *absolutely* certain about the muscular arrangement proposed here. However, by comparing the *known* arrangement of muscles in the shoulders and hips of crocodiles with the pattern of muscle scars in ankylosaurs, we believe that we can get fairly close to the original pattern. The general impression gained from the arrangement and likely size of the muscles of both fore and hindlimbs is that they were designed to generate great power and moved the limbs quite slowly. Some of the muscles show interesting arrangements.

**Shoulder and Hip Muscles (right)**
Although the muscles are labelled here with just one function, this is merely their primary function. Usually muscles exert quite a complex force. For example, the coracobrachialis pulls forwards, but also inwards and upwards. Ankylosaurids needed powerful leg muscles to support and move their rather large, heavy bodies. Notice the bulky muscles arising from the back of the hip region. In most reptiles these pull the leg back, but here they are also responsible for swinging the tail, a very important part of the ankylosaurid defensive armoury.

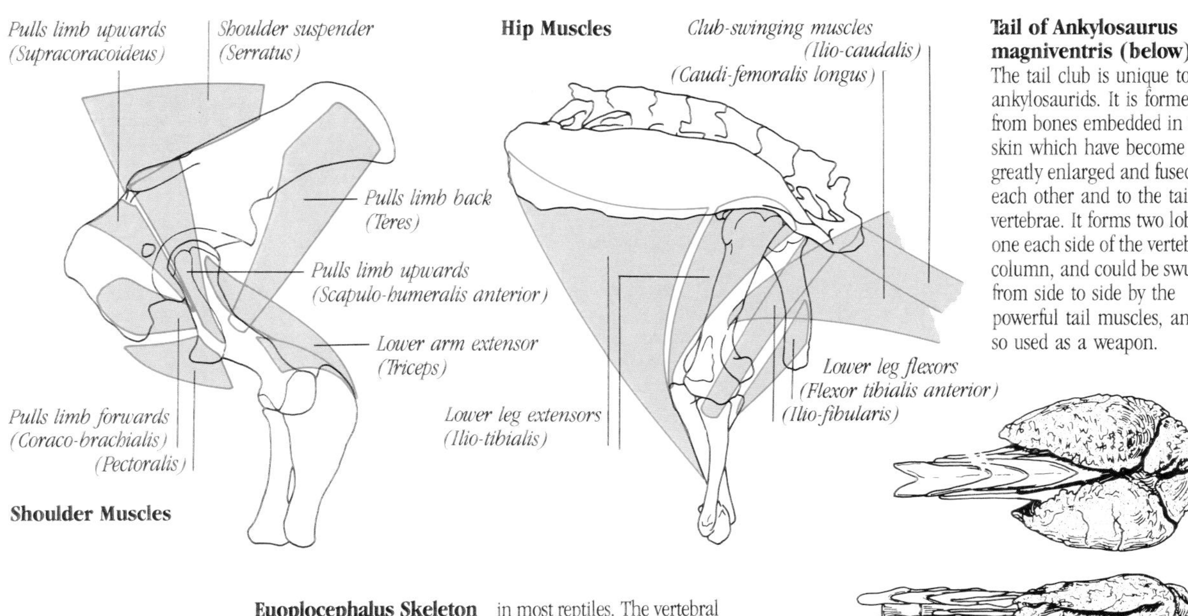


**Tail of Ankylosaurus magniventris (below)**
The tail club is unique to ankylosaurids. It is formed from bones embedded in the skin which have become greatly enlarged and fused to each other and to the tail vertebrae. It forms two lobes, one each side of the vertebral column, and could be swung from side to side by the powerful tail muscles, and so used as a weapon.

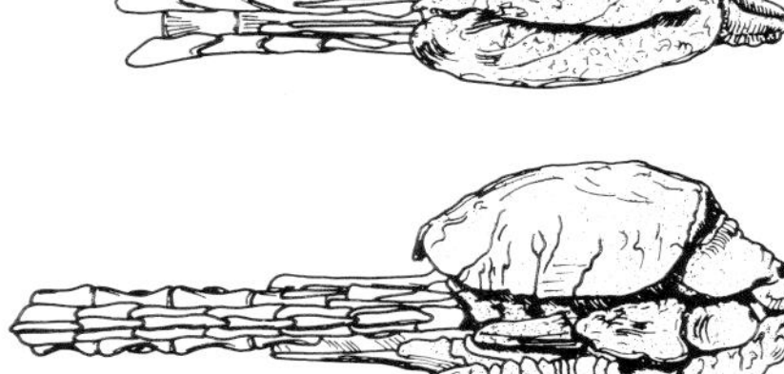

**Euoplocephalus Skeleton (below)**
In this ankylosaurid skeleton you can see the characteristic armoured head with its toothless beak, the shortish neck, the strongly-built legs and the tail club. The legs are tucked in, underneath the body, more like the situation in mammals than in most reptiles. The vertebral spines in the hip region are welded together, giving extra attachment area for hip muscles, and also extra strength to transmit the powerful locomotory thrust of the leg. The relative size of the tail club can be fully appreciated in the plan view (bottom).

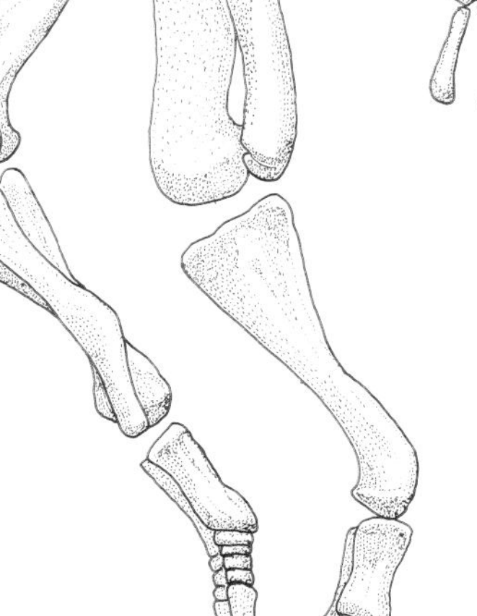

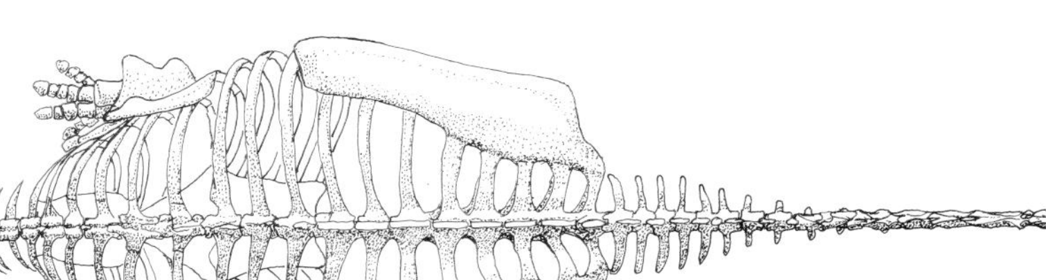

In the case of ankylosaurid hindlimb there are a cluster of muscles which run from the tail up towards the pelvis and hindlimb. In most ornithischian dinosaurs (see *Hypsilophodon* page 106-107) these were solely concerned with moving the hind leg powerfully backwards. While this would no doubt have been one function of these muscles in ankylosaurids, there was undoubtedly another function which was to provide the power to swing the heavy tail-club. Some of these muscles ran the length of the tail (M. caudi-femoralis longus) and attached to the ossified tendons clustered around the tail-club.

## Defensive Strategies

Both ankylosaurids and nodosaurids lived at times when theropods were many and varied in type. The differences between these two types of armoured dinosaur suggest that they used different tactics to avoid or resist predators.

(i) Armour-plating. First (and most obviously) the well-developed bony armour plating would have acted as a deterrent to all but the largest and most powerful of the theropods. There are, however, a few differences in the pattern of the bony armour in the two groups. The ankylosaurids, as we have just seen with *Euoplocephalus,* have armour plating which is divided into bands which are studded with variably-sized bony plates. Only the front end of the tail seems to be plated. This arrangement confers not only protection, but gives these animals a surprising degree of flexibility of movement, and of course a free-swinging tail-club. Nodosaurids, at least on the evidence of *Sauropelta* for which there is a reasonably well-preserved skin, have a much more extensive armour; this is not so clearly divided into flexible bands and seems to extend to the end of the tail. The large, protective bony studs are very numerous and tend to develop into long, pointed spikes forming a fringe along the sides of the animal. *Panoplosaurus* (=*Palaeoscincus*) seem to show the same sort of arrangement. Other nodosaurids, such as the earlier form *Polacanthus,* do not have well-preserved skins to show the clear arrangement of its armour. Nevertheless, these did bear numerous large, sharply pointed spikes embedded in the skin either along the back and tail, or around the sides of the animal.

The heads of both nodosaurids and ankylosaurids are extensively plated by bone, but whether nodosaurids possessed bony eyelids like those of *Euoplocephalus* is not known.

(ii) Defensive weapons. Nodosaurids possess no obvious defensive weapons unless, like porcupines today, they were able to run backwards at their predators and attempt to wound or impale them on their spikes. This strategy does not seem very likely because the spikes of nodosaurids are not really comparable with the very long, sharp, detachable quills of porcupines.

Ankylosaurids by contrast possessed the unique tail-club. Several of the bones embedded in the skin at the end of the tail are greatly enlarged and have become fused to one another, and to the last few tail bones, to form a very heavy club. The rear half of the tail is not apparently heavily-armoured so that the long muscles of the tail, which are anchored to the hips and legs, were capable of swinging the club from side to side. The size and weight of an ankylosaurid club can be appreciated from the drawings on page 167.

The tail-club is an unusual weapon among dinosaurs (or any other animal groups for that matter!). The spike-adorned tail of *Stegosaurus* is perhaps the nearest equivalent. The club, however, would have been an extremely useful weapon. The likely predators of ankylosaurids would have been the tyrannosaurid theropods, all of which were extremely large, bipedal predators with very small forelimbs. The way in which a tyrannosaurid would have attempted to deal with an ankylosaurid would have been to try to overturn one. Once on its back, the ankylosaur would probably be unable to right itself, and the predator would be able to gorge itself on the relatively poorly-protected belly of the unfortunate creature. However, to do any of this, the tyrannosaurid would have to get close to the ankylosaurid in order to be able to use its hind legs, and perhaps its jaws, to catch one side of the animal and flip it over. Ankylosaurids were probably quite mobile creatures, and no doubt would have avoided the lunges of a tyrannosaurid quite skilfully. In addition, the ankylosaurid would attempt to position itself so that it could swing its club at the legs of its assailant. One telling blow from an ankylosaurid club could have been fatal to a tyrannosaurid. Standing as they did on two legs, these heavy creatures would have been relatively unstable, and if caught on the ankles by a scything blow could well have been sent crashing to the ground with the risk of breaking their legs or pelvis. Any such injury would have been fatal to a 4-5 tonne tyrannosaurid, because it would have been unable to rise from the ground, and would undoubtedly have been devoured by other tyrannosaurids in turn.

To sum up, it would seem that both groups of ankylosaurs were well able to withstand attacks from large theropods. The ankylosaurids were no doubt both fairly agile, with heavy but flexible body armour, and they possessed a very effective defensive weapon—the heavy tail-club. The nodosaurids by contrast seem to have been rather more heavily-armoured and did not possess the tail-club as a defensive weapon. Presumably their strategy for survival was simply to 'weather the storm', relying on their heavier and more complete armour to protect them against predators, much as tortoises do today. This passive means of defence may in fact provide an alternative explanation for the peculiar structure of their shoulder muscles which might have allowed them to *retract* the front legs very powerfully (more so than ankylosaurids). Perhaps when attacked by predators, nodosaurids dug their claws into the ground and retracted their legs, thereby anchoring themselves to the ground. By doing this they would have been able to resist attempts by large theropods to turn them onto their backs. Also, by pulling themselves closer to the ground, the long spikes which form a fringe along the sides of the body would have created a spiky apron to protect the legs and sides of the creature under attack.

All in all, the ankylosaurs seem to be a most remarkable group of dinosaurs. Only one other group of animals comes close to them in general appearance, and these are the extinct South American glyptodonts—extinct relatives of the armadillos. These animals had bony shields covering their heads and backs, and a tail covered in rings of bone. Some glyptodonts such as *Doedicurus* had a mace-like spiky club which resembles the ankylosaurid club, and probably served the same sort of defensive function. Glyptodonts lived long after the reign of the dinosaurs, during the late Pleistocene Epoch (a mere 500,000 years ago), but they had to contend with equally fierce predators, such as the marsupial sabre-toothed cats *(Thylacosmilus).* The spiky club was presumably a very effective defensive weapon at close-quarters.

## Ankylosaurid Genera

Apart from *Euoplocephalus,* which has been looked at in some detail, there are several other reasonably well-established ankylosaurids, but only two are known from North Amerca. *Ankylosaurus* ('fused reptile'), the only other North American form, was one of the largest ankylosaurids known, growing up to 33ft (10m) long. The remains of this species have been recovered from Alberta and Montana.

Several genera are known from eastern Asia. *Pinacosaurus* ('plank reptile'), also incorrectly referred to as *Syrmosaurus, Ninghsiasaurus* and *Virminicaudus,* was first described by Charles Gilmore from material collected in the Gobi Desert during the American Museum-Mongolian expedition. A newly discovered skull of a young *Pinacosaurus* is a rare example in which the bones which normally form a solid covering to the skull have not yet firmly attached themselves, so that the pattern of true

**Defensive Strategies (above and left)**
These drawings illustrate the different ways in which ankylosaurs may have defended themselves against predators. *Hylaeosaurus,* a nodosaurid, adopts a passive defence, clutching the ground with its strong limbs and relying on its body armour and fringe of spikes to deter the attacker. The ankylosaurid *Euoplocephalus,* however, is more active in its self defence, swinging its big tail-club in order to topple and so disable the tyrannosaurid.

skull bones is revealed for the first time. This may prove to be of great help when trying to discover the relationships of ankylosaurs to other ornithischians. Reaching a maximum body length of 16·4ft (5m), *Pinacosaurus* was a relatively slender-built ankylosaurid.

*Saichania* ('beautiful') consists of the skull and much of the front part of the skeleton of a 23ft (7m) long ankylosaurid from Mongolia. First described in 1977 by Dr Maryanska, it has a broad, knobbly skull (see illustration). As preserved, the armour reveals many different types of plates, including spiked half-rings around the neck, and low backwardly-pointing spikes across the back similar to those of *Pinacosaurus*.

*Talarurus* ('basket-tail') is a 16-23ft (5-7m) long ankylosaurid from Bayn Shireh in southern Mongolia. At present this is not fully described but comprises skull and skeleton remains in the Palaeontological Institute of the Academy of Sciences, Moscow (see below).

*Tarchia* ('brain'), from the Barun Goyot formation of Mongolia, is known from an incomplete skull. The skull, which is about the same size as that of *Saichania* has a much larger braincase: hence the name!

*Shamosaurus* ('Gobi reptile') was described in 1983 from material collected from the early Cretaceous of Mongolia. This and the poorly-known *Sauroplites* ('hoplite reptile') are the earliest ankylosaurids known. The skull, the only part so far described, is typically ankylosaurid, being low, broad and having bony horns at the posterior corners.

Many genera of ankylosaurid are rather dubiously established. For example *Amtosaurus* ('Amtgay reptile') from Bayn Shireh in Mongolia may well be the same as *Talarurus* from the same area. While *Heishanosaurus* '('Heishan reptile'), *Peishanosaurus* ('Peishan reptile'), *Lametasaurus* ('Lameta reptile') and *Stegosaurides (Stegosauroides)* ('Stegosaur form') are all very dubiously established types.

When we consider the geographical distribution of ankylosaurids, it is clear that good species are known only from western North America and eastern Asia. Only two late Cretaceous species are definitely known in North America, *Euoplocephalus* and *Ankylosaurus*, while at least six species are established in Asia ranging from the early Cretaceous right through to the end. This distribution pattern suggests that ankylosaurids originated in Asia during the early Cretaceous and were able to migrate into western North America, perhaps via the Bering Straits, in the late Cretaceous. This certainly accords with the distribution of tyrannosaurids and 'saurolophine' hadrosaurids in the late Cretaceous. The nature of this late Cretaceous link is peculiar, because the ceratopids, a very diverse group in the late Cretaceous of North America, never managed to spread back across the Bering Straits into Asia, as one might expect in the light of the distribution of other dinosaurs.

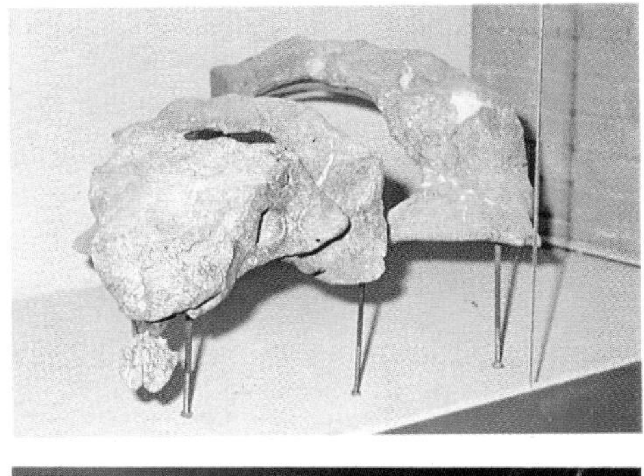

**Right:** Parts of the skull and body armour of the Mongolian ankylosaur *Shamosaurus scutatus*. The general shape of the skull and the bony projections jutting out from it are typically ankylosaurian.

**Left:** The BM (NH) specimen of *Scolosaurus* (=*Euoplocephalus*) *cutleri* which is from the Belly River Formation at Red Deer River, Alberta. We are looking down on the back of the fossil, which lacks its skull, and the nature of the bony armour bands studded with plates, embedded in its skin are clear to see.

**Left:** The skull and partial skeleton of *Saichania* are gradually exposed during excavations at Khulsan in the Gobi Desert undertaken by the 1971 Polish-Mongolian Palaeontological Expedition. The skull (right) is covered with knobbly studs, while a multitude of triangular spikes can be made out around the neck and back. *Saichania's* forelimbs were also found to be fairly well preserved.

**Above:** Another Mongolian ankylosaurid: *Talarurus plicatospinus*. This is a very well preserved skeleton, and this view nicely shows the rather squat posture and broad hippo-like chest typical of ankylosaurs. The body was evidently covered in bony nodules, but there is no evidence of any tall, *Euoplocephalus*-like spikes projecting from the back or tail of this animal. Note the heavily armoured head.

This chapter will deal with several controversial issues which involve the dinosaurs, namely their origins, their physiological status (were they 'warm-blooded' or not?), the ancestry of birds, and finally that perennial problem, why did the dinosaurs go extinct at the end of the Cretaceous Period?

## Dinosaur Origins

The question of the origin of dinosaurs is one that has puzzled palaeontologists for many years. The issue we shall be addressing here is not so much one of *which* particular group of archosaurs evolved into dinosaurs, although that is important in itself, but rather *why* did dinosaurs appear in late Triassic times and then prove so successful for the next 140 million years. This is particularly relevant because, as we have seen earlier, true mammals had also evolved in the late Triassic.

Looking at the animals inhabiting the world today, it must seem obvious that the mammals are a very important group indeed. They are found in all habitats from polar ice caps to tropical rainforests, hot deserts to arctic tundra, in the sea, up trees, in the air and burrowing underground. Compared with the reptiles which are only found in any great numbers in the tropics, they are obviously very successful animals. The question that poses itself then is this: if mammals are so much more successful than reptiles in the present day, why were they not so successful in the Mesozoic Era? Several attempts have been made to answer this question, some of these are examined below.

## Dinosaur Posture

One of the most prominent theories attempting to explain dinosaur success in the Triassic has been put forward by Dr Alan Charig (London). Its principal claim is that the success of dinosaurs is related to their ability to walk with erect limbs.

As was explained earlier, dinosaurs can be distinguished from other archosaur reptiles by changes that have taken place at the hip, knee and ankle; these enable their legs to be tucked directly beneath the body to act not only as pillar-like supports but also to provide a longer stride and more effective walking and running abilities. According to Dr Charig the circumstances that led to this change in posture can be traced back to large semi-aquatic archosaurs (proterosuchians) of the late Permian or early Triassic. These large, swamp-dwelling creatures are supposed to have developed large, paddling hind legs which were, in later archosaurs of the Triassic Period,used as powerful hindlimbs on land. Whatever the actual reason, the archosaurs of the early and middle Triassic were characterised by their carnivorous way of life and an ability to assume a more erect posture, as seen in living crocodiles. The best comparison may perhaps be with the late Permian carnivorous therapsids such as *Lycaenops* with their 'dual' or 'variable gait' limbs.

Some middle Triassic archosaurs of this type (such as *Ticinosuchus*) were quite large creatures (10-13ft, 3-4m long) and were probably the top carnivores of the time. The large skulls with dagger-like teeth and the relatively efficient running abilities of these archosaurs are supposed to have endowed them with superior predatory abilities compared with the contemporary carnivorous cynodonts. As a result of competition between the carnivorous archosaurs and cynodonts, the cynodonts rapidly declined in middle to late Triassic times leaving the archosaurs as dominant carnivores. By late Triassic times the improvements in limb posture which had begun in the earlier Triassic in these variably-gaited archosaurs finally resulted in the evolution of true dinosaurs.

It is argued that becaue of their superior running and walking abilities, the early carnivorous dinosaurs of the late Triassic proved to be excessively efficient at preying upon the surviving herbivorous cynodonts and dicynodonts. As a consequence, in the early part of the late Triassic the first dinosaurs had caused the extinction of all the herbivorous mammal-like reptiles and a few other aberrant groups of herbivorous reptiles (e.g. rhynchosaurs and aëtosaurs). Under the circumstances, there would have been intense competition between the various carnivorous dinosaurs of the late Triassic because of the general absence of herbivores to prey upon. There must, therefore, have been very strong evolutionary 'pressure' in favour of some early dinosaurs becoming herbivorous in order to capitalise on the vegetation that was not being consumed by other vertebrates, and simultaneously to provide a more balanced fauna of herbivores and carnivores.

Indeed that is what is seen in the latest Triassic with the appearance of a variety of herbivorous dinosaurs: the relatively large-bodied prosauropod saurischians and the smaller, fleet-footed fabrosaurid and heterodontosaurid ornithischians.

Thus the faunal succession of mammal-like reptiles to dinosaurs in the late Triassic is interpreted as an inevitable consequence of progressive improvements in the limb posture. The 'variable-gaited' carnivorous archosaurs causing first the extinction of the carnivorous cynodonts, then the herbivorous cynodonts with the consequent rise of carnivorous erect-gaited archosaurs (dinosaurs!) and the subsequent evolution of herbivorous dinosaurs to fill the niches vacated by the herbivorous cynodonts and dicynodonts.

Elegant though this argument undoubtedly is, there are one or two disquieting aspects to it. First, if mammal-like reptiles had already evolved a variable-gait walking technique in the late Permian, why was its apparent re-invention by archosaurs in the Triassic Period so devastatingly effective. The cynodonts were in possession of just as effective, if not more effective, walking and running techniques as

**Dinosaur Posture (left)** This restoration of *Diplodocus* is based on the work of Hay and Tornier who believed it had a sprawling posture. As we see, this is totally unrealistic. In fact dinosaurs were able to walk with fully-erect limbs.

**Changing Fortunes (below)** This time chart logs the relative abundances of (red) the synapsid, or mammal-like, reptiles and their descendants, the mammals, and (grey) archosaurs and their descendants, the birds. The synapsids flourished in the Permian and Triassic, but in the late Triassic were replaced by the dinosaurs which dominated the Earth in the Jurassic and Cretaceous. Following the Cretaceous extinction of the dinosaurs, the relative abundance of mammals and birds rose very dramatically.

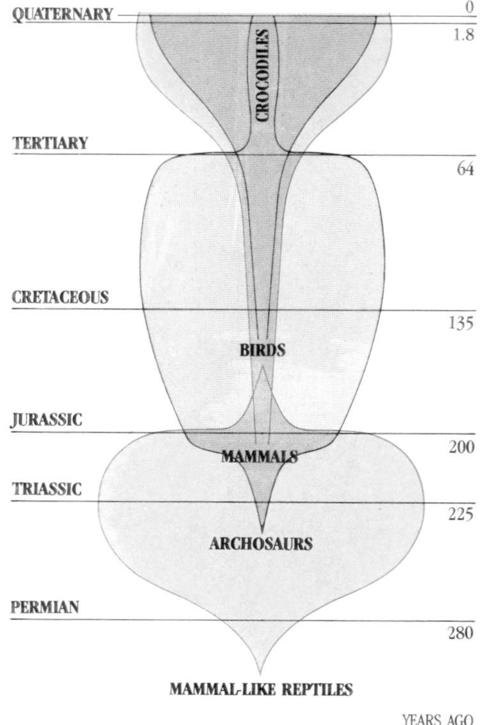

**Right:** One major issue that has been raised in relation to the success of the dinosaurs in the late Triassic concerns the nature of the climate. The presence of 'Red Bed' rocks, similar to these in Australia, has been used to support the idea that it was very arid then.

the contemporary archosaurs. Secondly the account of the origin of herbivorous dinosaurs seems rather improbable. The likelihood of carnivores causing the extinction of their prey animals runs counter to current ecological theory. Predator numbers follow prey abundance very closely under normal conditions, so that the extinction of its prey would be followed by extinction of the predator.

## Climatic Change

Another model which has been used to explain the rise of the dinosaurs is based on an interpretation of the climatic conditions which prevailed in the late Triassic.

This theory has had several advocates, notably Dr Pamela Robinson (London), and it stems from the fact that many of the late Triassic rocks are characteristically red in colour. This has been widely interpreted as indicating that seasonal, hot and arid conditions prevailed. The red coloration of the rocks is due to their being literally 'rusty'. If it is true that the late Triassic was a time of hot dry conditions, then considerations can be given to the type of animals that could best survive then.

Comparing reptiles and mammals it can be seen that reptiles are on the whole very economical types of animals, well suited to dry, desert environments. Reptile skin is scaly and impervious to water so they do not tend to dry out in the Sun; they also lose very little water in their urine; they do not generate their own body heat, so they do not need to eat a great deal of food simply to generate heat. Reptiles seem well designed to live in areas where there is little water, little food and plenty of heat (desert conditions). Mammals on the other hand find it unexpectedly hard to tolerate these conditions. All mammals sweat to keep cool and in hot deserts are constantly losing water through their skin; they also lose rather a lot of water in their urine (certainly by comparison with reptiles); and they require a constant source of food to fuel the internal heat production system. In general mammals find hot deserts particularly stressful because of the high temperatures, lack of water and general unavailability of food.

Perhaps then, if we are looking for a cause for the rise of the dinosaurs instead of the mammals at the end of the Triassic we need look no further than this. Widespread desert conditions would have favoured a reptilian type of creature because of its generally economical life-style. Once the dinosaur-type reptiles were firmly established on land, the mammals had no opportunity to replace them.

Again this solution is both simple and elegant. The only real dispute tends to revolve around the evidence for a world-wide desert-type climate in the Triassic and the true significance of 'Red Bed' rocks. It is claimed by some that 'Red Bed' type rocks are being deposited today in areas that have high seasonal temperature *and* high rainfall. Obviously these issues will need to be settled before this explanation can become widely accepted.

## Opportunistic Dinosaurs

In the last few years a rather different type of theory has been proposed by Dr Mike Benton (Belfast). This theory claims that rather than invoking some element of competition between mammals and dinosaurs, perhaps dinosaurs were simply given the opportunity to evolve in the late Triassic because some unknown factor had caused the extinction of the previously abundant groups.

**Right:** This is a skin impression from the hadrosaurid *Edmontosaurus*. All reptiles have scaly skin, a feature that is of great advantage to them in hot, dry desert conditions because very little water is lost through it.

**Below:** If the climatic change theory is correct, then perhaps this photograph provides us with a vivid impression of the harsh arid conditions that prevailed in the late Triassic, which may have allowed dinosaurs to succeed mammal-like reptiles (synapsids).

**Above:** A display of the sauropod *Diplodocus* and the ornithopod *Iguanodon*. The pressure required to pump blood to *Diplodocus*' brain when its head was raised would have been enormous. Is this evidence that dinosaurs had fully divided hearts like endothermic mammals?

Detailed analysis of fossil finds from rocks in the Triassic seems to reveal a pattern of extinctions towards the end of the Triassic among many reptile groups (mammal-like reptiles, rhynchosaurs, various archosaurs). It would seem from this record of events that the dinosaurs simply evolved into the spaces left by all the forms that had gone extinct and that therefore a chance event (whatever caused these extinctions) may have given the dinosaurs the chance that they had been waiting for.

This seems to be yet another highly plausible explanation of the rise of the dinosaurs. Obviously this interpretation is heavily dependent upon the accuracy of the recorded fossils from the late Triassic and will probably stand or fall on this evidence over the next few years.

**Above:** This skeleton of *Daspletosaurus* in Ottawa shows clearly several attributes of theropod dinosaurs that have been linked to endothermy: an erect gait, bipedality, and the generally active 'air' of the creature.

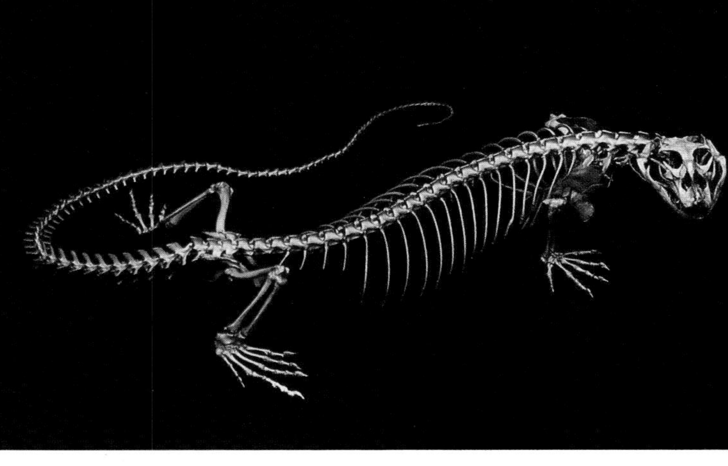

**Right:** The sprawling posture of today's reptiles, such as this varanid lizard, is radically different from that of the dinosaurs. Some have interpreted this variance as evidence in favour of endothermy (warm-bloodedness) in dinosaurs.

## Dinosaurs and 'Warm Blood'

The fourth and final theory to explain dinosaur success in the Triassic has had one notable advocate in recent years, Dr Bob Bakker. This theory has its roots in the general observation that was made at the beginning of the chapter about the timing of the origin of mammals and dinosaurs *and* the self-evident superiority of mammals in the present-day.

The argument is quite simple and can be stated as follows: mammals are superior to reptiles today, the reason for this superiority is that they are 'warm-blooded'—to be more accurate the term is *endothermic* ('internal heat')—as a consequence of which they are more active and intelligent animals than living reptiles. Since mammals and dinosaurs evolved at practically the same time, the endothermic mammals should have prevailed. For the dinosaurs to have radiated at the expense of the mammals, dinosaurs must have been as 'competitive' as mammals and therefore *must* have been endothermic or 'warm-blooded'. The argument is basically sound and the logic impeccable, but as the debate over the past decade has shown, the case for endothermy in dinosaurs is far from proven.

The body temperature of dinosaurs (something that can never be actually established) has become a major palaeontological issue in the last decade. Dr Bob Bakker has single-mindedly and virtually single-handedly pursued his belief that dinosaurs were endothermic for more than a decade and really whether he is right or wrong (much current opinion seems to be against his views), his contributions to our appreciation of the biology of both dinosaurs and living reptiles and mammals have been of enormous value.

As explained in the previous section, the crux of Bakker's argument comes from the simple observation that mammals and dinosaurs appear to have evolved at about the same time in the late Triassic. Bearing in mind that living (endothermic) mammals are almost completely dominant over the (ectothermic) reptiles, the interpretation that can be put on the events of the late Triassic is that dinosaurs must have been as efficient as the mammals, and they must have been endothermic. Taking this argument as a reasonable working hypothesis Bakker then set about garnering evidence from the fossil remains of dinosaurs in an attempt to 'prove' that they were endothermic.

**Dinosaur posture** Dinosaurs are, as we have seen, characterised by a fully erect gait; the legs are drawn underneath the body and appear to have operated very effectively on land. Dinosaurian reptiles differ from living reptiles because living reptiles display a primitive sprawling posture, with the legs held out to the sides of the body. Looking at our present-day animals, the only ones with limb postures resembling those of dinosaurs are the mammals and birds—both of which are endothermic. The proposition that Bakker made was that only animals with an endothermic physiology are capable of walking with an erect gait; therefore dinosaurs must have been endotherms.

The basic argument has been built upon in two ways. Professor Ostrom modified the reasoning and proposed that rather than simply an erect gait, it was the ability to walk bipedally (as many dinosaurs did, some mammals and all birds do) that was a crucial feature linked to endothermy. Another posturally-related proposition was based on the height of the head above the heart. An upright posture also coincides with an elevated head and neck in all dinosaurs. Taking an extreme example, the

**Heart Systems (below)** In the toad, deoxygenated blood from the body (blue) returns to the heart where it is mixed (mauve) with oxygenated blood (red) from the lungs. This rather 'leaky' system works for the ectothermic toad. In the case of the reptile, blood in the heart is not mixed to the same extent, although a pressure-sensitive valve allows blood to mix in some conditions. In endothermic mammals, birds, (and perhaps dinosaurs?), the heart is fully divided: no mixing can occur. This is the most efficient circulatory system.

**Toad** (undivided heart)

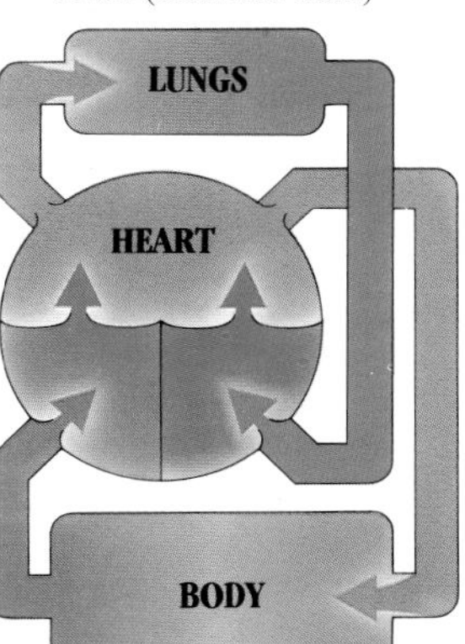


**Reptile** (semi-divided heart)

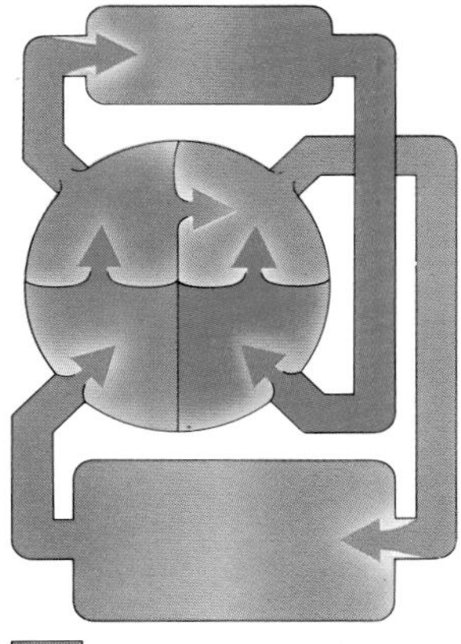

**Endotherm** (fully divided heart)

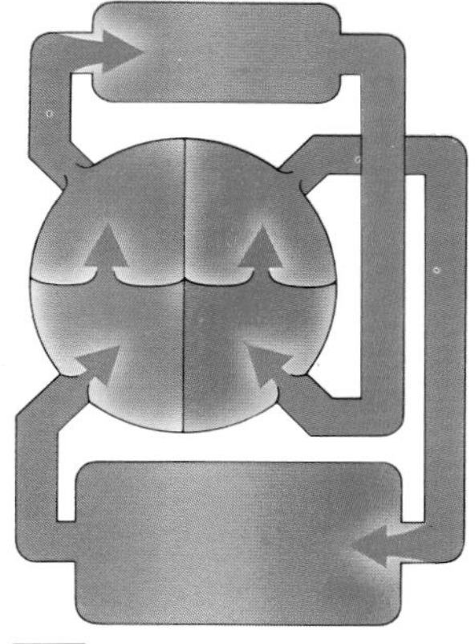

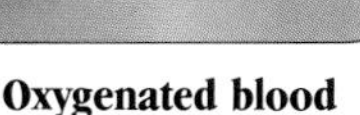

**Oxygenated blood** **Deoxygenated blood** **Mixed blood**

dinosaur *Brachiosaurus*: if we consider the action of the heart which has to pump blood all the way up its neck to its brain, we realise that it would have to generate very high blood pressure to raise the blood that distance. However, if, like all modern reptiles, the heart was not fully divided into a lung circulation and a body-and-head circuit, then the high pressure in the body-and-head circuit would cause massive bleeding in the thin blood vessels of the lungs. *Brachiosaurus* must therefore have had a fully divided heart, so that the blood pressure in the lung circuit could be lower than that in the body-and-head circuit. Again only the endothermic mammals and birds today have a fully divided heart; since dinosaurs also had a divided heart, they may have been endothermic.

This group of arguments seems positive and compelling evidence of endothermy in dinosaurs. They have been countered, however, by the following comments: just because dinosaurs have an erect posture it does not necessarily follow that they were endothermic; an erect posture may have been a design feature which simply allowed dinosaurs to grow large (large animals with sprawling legs are a physical impossibility!); also what about the humble chamaeleon, this is a living ectotherm with an erect gait!

**Activity levels** Linked to the previous point about the posture, we can go on to consider the way in which dinosaurs may have moved. The arguments have concentrated on the small agile types of dinosaur (particularly theropods and ornithopods). Taking *Deinonychus* as an example, we have seen that it was a remarkably specialised predator. Not only could it run fast (judging by its limb proportions) but it had a special balancing tail and had a large offensive claw on its hind foot; the latter would have obliged *Deinonychus* to leap at its prey or slash at it while standing on one foot.

What we have then is an extremely sophisticated type of dinosaur able to do a whole range of things that we would not normally associate with the usual scope of activity of a living ectothermic lizard or crocodile. The high activity levels implied in the life-style of *Deinonychus* are more compatible with the high activity levels seen in living endotherms.

Again this is a very compelling argument. Ultimately it depends upon the assumption that high activity levels can only be sustained by endotherms. As we shall see later this may not be true.

**Below:** This is a cast of the brain cavity of *Triceratops*. Although it may be hard to appreciate, the brain is not only quite large by reptile standards, but it is also quite complicated in structure, which indicates that these animals were not un-intelligent.

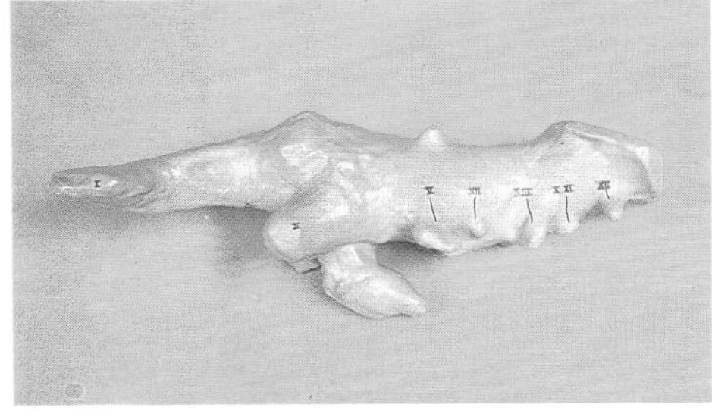

**Brain-size and behaviour** Mammals and birds both possess large brains and exhibit a great deal of what we might call 'intelligent' activity. Ectothermic reptiles have relatively smaller brains and are not renowned for their intellectual prowess. There would appear to be an important link between endothermy and brain size amongst vertebrates. Large brains are highly complex structures which need constant supplies of food, oxygen *and* an even temperature in order to function properly. The endothermic regime of mammals and birds supplies these requirements and can therefore maintain a large brain. Reptiles with their ectothermic regime can supply food and oxygen moderately efficiently (though the levels do tend to vary slightly), but their body temperature does tend to vary in a normal 24 hour cycle; they therefore seem unable to support a large brain.

At first sight this seems to counter the argument for endothermy in dinosaurs very effectively; dinosaurs are notorious for their lack of brain power. However, all is not lost! Dr Jim Hopson (Chicago) has estimated brain size in a whole range of dinosaurs and by comparing ratios of brain size to body size has revealed that most dinosaurs have at least typical reptilian-sized brains. More interesting still, however, is his observation that among the theropods, *Stenonychosaurus* (page 54) had a brain equivalent in size to that of some living birds and mammals. Indeed among the dinosaurs, the theropods and ornithopods seem to have been of above average reptile brain-size. Thus at least a few dinosaurs did have large and presumably complex brains more like those of living animals and birds.

This argument about 'intelligence' in dinosaurs has been extended into the field of behaviour as well. As we have already seen, dinosaurs have left various clues about their behaviour: nesting activities, care of their young, herding, visual and auditory recognition systems etc. It has been proposed on the basis of this 'evidence' that dinosaurs had very complex behaviour patterns more comparable to those of mammals and birds than to reptiles. This type of argument, however, seems based more on ignorance of reptile behaviour than sound logic. As we saw a little earlier, crocodiles are capable of extremely complex behaviour. Dinosaur behaviour therefore may well fall within the normal range of reptile behaviour.

**Latitudinal spread of dinosaurs** The report of dinosaur remains from the Yukon area of North America and footprints from Spitzbergen has also been used as evidence of endothermy in dinosaurs. The argument supposes that in order to survive in such high latitudes (near the Arctic Circle) dinosaurs must have been able to generate body heat internally. Ectothermic reptiles are incapable of surviving at such high latitudes because they cannot use the Sun to warm their bodies sufficiently.

This argument was countered by Professor Ostrom who pointed out that in the Mesozoic the latitudinal bands of climate were very different from those that exist today. The plants that were contemporaries of the dinosaurs in these high latitudes were of sub-tropical type. Thus, even at high latitudes the climate was warm and mild in Mesozoic times. Such distributional patterns cannot therefore be used to support arguments concerning the physiology of dinosaurs in either direction.

**Predator/prey relationships** One of the most novel of Bakker's arguments in favour of endothermy in dinosaurs depended on being able to take censuses of communities of animals from the fossil record. Again his idea was simple and quite elegant. Endothermic and ectothermic animals require different amounts of food in order to survive – what we might term their 'running costs'. Endothermic mammals and birds have high running costs because much of the food that they eat (80 per cent or more) is simply burned up (in a chemical sense) to produce body heat. Ectothermic reptiles need to take in far less food than endotherms because very little of it is used to generate heat. A working approximation is that an ectotherm needs about 10 per cent (or less) of the food requirements of an endotherm.

Bakker used this basic observation to make the following prediction. Since a balance is usually found in nature between the number of predator and prey animals, surely if we take a census of the fossil record, then the actual ratio of fossil predator to prey animals may indicate the physiology of these creatures. The results of his survey seem to support his claim. Looking first at ancient fossil 'communities' of ectothermic amphibians and reptiles, he noted that predator and prey were about equally represented. Dinosaur 'communities' seemed to show small numbers of predators and large numbers of prey. Finally looking at (endothermic) Tertiary mammal 'communities' he found again small numbers of predators balanced by large numbers of prey.

The similarity in pattern of predators to prey in dinosaur and early mammal 'communities' was striking, and prompts the suggestion that community structure among dinosaurs resembled that of mammals and therefore that predatory dinosaurs (at least) were endothermic.

This very novel approach has been challenged by several workers, notably Dr Alan Charig (London) who has pointed out that there are enormous difficulties and many suppositions that have to be made when estimating numbers of fossils in Bakker's alleged 'communities'. Other workers have also begun to assess predator/prey ratios in modern ectothermic communities and curiously seem to find that ectothermic predators make up only 10 per cent or so of the potential prey population – the sort of figure that would have been expected of an endothermic predator. The picture, therefore, is yet again far from clear. The repercussions of Bakker's novel idea have nevertheless posed many problems even for scientists working on living groups.

**Bone structure (histology)** For a long time evidence from the internal structure of the bones of dinosaurs and other animals has strongly favoured the notion that dinosaurs were endothermic. Looked at simply the case seems very clear-cut. If we compare thin, polished sections of bone from a lizard, a dinosaur and a mammal then we are immediately struck by the great similarity between dinosaur and mammal bone. The highly vascularised bone of endothermic mammals seems virtually identical to that of dinosaurs. This similarity is linked with the high activity levels and endothermic status of mammals and by implication of dinosaurs as well.

However various scientists, particularly Dr Armand de Ricqlès (Paris) and Dr Robin Reid (Belfast), have begun to look in detail at the structure of bone and the factors that govern its appearance under the microscope. It now appears that highly vascular bone is found in many reptiles while poorly vascular bone is found in small birds and mammals; highly vascular bone is of two types, one type is formed very quickly and is associated with fast-growing animals, the other type of vascular bone is specially designed to help bones to carry heavy loads.

So yet again the categories are less clear-cut than was first thought. The type of bone found in dinosaurs is that which would have allowed them to grow very quickly (as would be expected of an animal that had to grow to the size of an adult dinosaur) and also would have made the bones well able to carry heavy loads

**Right:** This crocodile can consume enough food at one time to last it for several days before it is driven by hunger to pursue its next victim. A similar-sized meal might last an endothermic lion a matter of hours rather than days.

**Below:** A superb display of dinosaur predator and dinosaur prey in Fort Worth Museum, Texas. Having successfully brought down this *Camptosaurus*, how long would the ensuing meal have satisfied a large 'carnosaur' like *Allosaurus?*

**Predator/Prey Ratios (left)**
One lion (an endotherm) consumes on average about the same as 10 crocodiles (ectotherms) i.e. ten times more than a similar-sized crocodile. Thus to be in natural balance, endotherms need to have prey that are ten times more numerous than those needed by ectothermic predators. High predator to prey ratios among dinosaurs seemed to confirm Robert Bakker's ideas that they were indeed endotherms. However, further work has led to doubts being voiced about his conclusions.

(a natural prerequisite of most dinosaur bones!). The evidence for dinosaurs being endothermic on the basis of bone structure is therefore not very strong.

**Birds and dinosaurs** Finally there is the claim that birds (which are endothermic) evolved from dinosaurs. If this claim is correct, then dinosaurs, at least those close to the ancestry of birds, may have been endothermic as well.

**Conclusions** Convincing though the arguments for 'warm-blooded' dinosaurs appeared at first we have seen that there is doubt about most of them.

The present view of most palaeontologists involved in this subject is roughly as follows:

i) Dinosaurs lived at a time of very mild climatic conditions, with no strong seasons and high average temperatures.

ii) Dinosaurs were mostly very big animals. Being big has its advantages because large animals lose and gain heat only very slowly compared with small ones.

iii) Dinosaurs may well have had a fully divided heart which would have made them capable of high activity levels.

Taking these three main factors into account, dinosaurs may well have been ectothermic reptiles (which meant they did not have to eat enormous quantities of food) which were able to keep the temperature of their bodies constant and warm by being very large and living in a warm mild climate. Given these conditions and a fully divided heart, they could have been warm-bodied, highly active creatures (like mammals and birds today) without any of the costs associated with being an endotherm. Perhaps this combination of features was a key to their success in the Mesozoic Era.

## Dinosaurs and Birds

The proposition that birds and reptiles are fairly closely related has not really been seriously disputed in the past. The presence of scales on the legs of birds and the fact that both birds and reptiles lay shelled eggs seems ample proof of some distant evolutionary ancestor. The more precise question of which of the various reptile groups currently recognised is closest to the ancestry of birds has, however, exercised many biologists' minds.

The issue of bird origins came to the forefront of biological and evolutionary thinking in 1861 with the discovery of the fossilised skeleton of a bird-like creature in a limestone quarry near Solnhofen (southern Germany). The limestones were of late Jurassic age and were of a peculiarly fine-grained high quality stone that was used in printing processes. As a consequence not only were the bones of the skeleton very finely preserved but also impressions of the original feathers of this early bird had been left around the skeleton.

The skeleton was named *Archaeopteryx lithographica* ('ancient wing from lithographic limestone') by Hermann von Meyer and the specimen was eventually acquired from Dr Karl Häberlein, its discoverer, by the British Museum (Natural History). In 1877 another skeleton in an even better state of preservation (it included a well preserved skull most of which was missing from the first skeleton) was obtained in the same general area by Ernst Häberlein (Karl Häberlein's son). This was subsequently sold to the Berlin Museum of Natural History. No more material of *Archaeopteryx* was recorded until 1956 when another headless specimen was discovered. Since that time another two specimens have turned up in collections, having lain unrecognised for some time. One of these, some fragments of leg and wing bone, was thought to belong to a pterosaur until in 1970 Professor Ostrom noticed the feather impressions around them. Finally, a fifth specimen was identified: another very well-preserved skeleton which had been discovered in 1951 but which had been thought to be another skeleton of *Compsognathus* until it was recognised as *Archaeopteryx* in 1973.

## Archaeopteryx Described

The impression of feathers provides an immediate clue to the relationships of *Archaeopteryx* because, notwithstanding Kurzanov's dubious claims regarding *Avimimus*, birds are the only vertebrates known to possess feathers.

**Left:** This is the London specimen of *Archaeopteryx lithographica* which is kept in the British Museum (Natural History). Since it was first discovered in 1861, it has been surrounded by controversy. In 1985 some scientists, including Sir Fred Hoyle, wrongly expressed doubts about the authenticity of the feather impressions, claiming they were printed on the specimen as an elaborate hoax.

**Above:** Discovered in 1951, the Eichstätt *Archaeopteryx* shows no obvious feather impressions. It was labelled as *Compsognathus*, a small 'coelurosaur', until 1973, when it was recognised and described by Dr Peter Wellnhofer. It is a fine specimen, and it emphasises the point that *Archaeopteryx* and small coelurosaurian dinosaurs are very alike, and so by implication may be closely related.

**Euparkeria Skull**

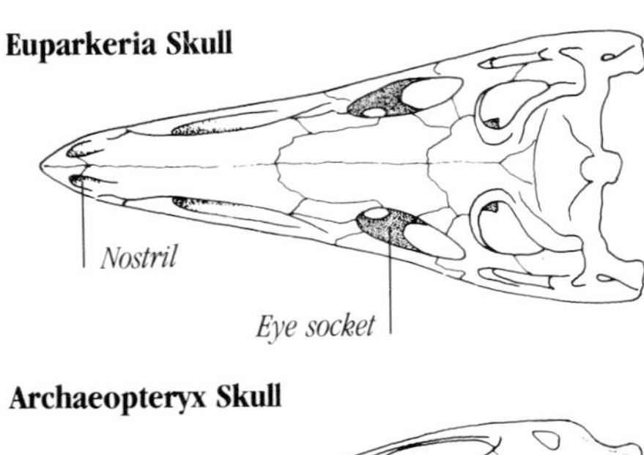


**Archaeopteryx Skull**

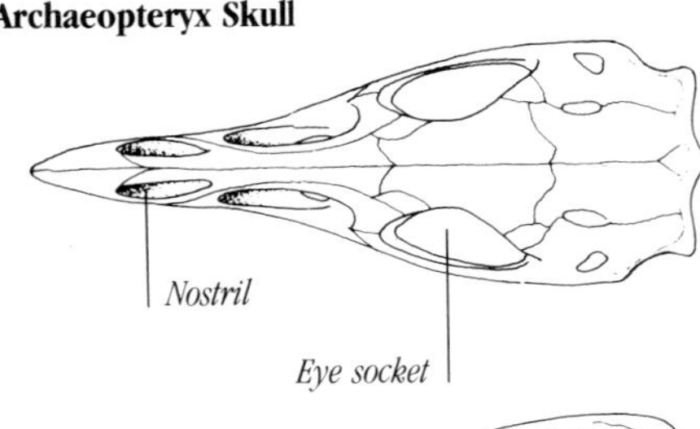


**Pigeon Skull**

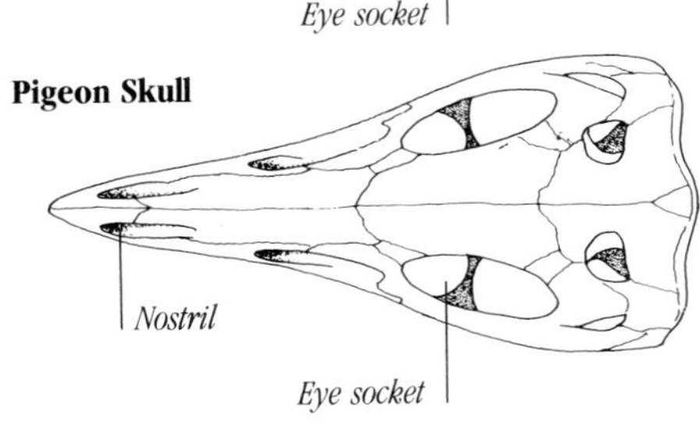


So *Archaeopteryx* is an early bird, but one with some rather unusual features.

The head has a fairly long narrow snout. However, while superficially bird-like, the jaws are in fact lined with small, sharply pointed teeth. All modern birds by contrast lack teeth and have horny beaks or bills instead. The eye of *Archaeopteryx* is large, as is the brain; both of these are bird-like features – although it should perhaps be mentioned that small theropod dinosaurs share these features as well! The neck is slender and swan-like, while the back is somewhat long and more flexible than that of typical birds. Also the attachment between the hips and backbone is not nearly as extensive as it is in birds. The tail is long and bony, like that of a typical reptile and quite unlike that of birds in which the tail is reduced to a small fleshy stump: the 'Parson's Nose'.

The 'wings' of *Archaeopteryx* are not quite the same as those of birds because they still have three separate, *clawed* fingers. The shoulders do however have a distinctly bird-like 'wishbone' or furcula which is supposed to represent the fused collar bones (clavicles) of primitive reptiles. The hips seem bird-like in that the configuration of bones seems to show that the pubis lay parallel to the ischium as it did in the primitive ornithischian dinosaurs, although there is some dispute about this. The legs and feet are also slim and generally bird-like with a reversed (though rather short) first toe on the foot. One other feature notably lacking in *Archaeopteryx* and found in the other flying forms (birds *and* pterosaurs) is the presence of air ducts running into the long bones to give them added lightness.

Given all these features, what do they tell us about *Archaeopteryx*'s nearest relatives? The pointed teeth in the jaws, the claws on its hand, and the long bony tail, all signify reptilian forebears, but the question is, which *particular* reptile group is closest.

In the late 1860s and early 1870s the British palaeontologist Thoms Henry Huxley was an ardent advocate of a dinosaur relationship with birds. At the time, dinosaurs as a group were still rather poorly understood but Huxley had noted many similarities between the hips and legs of dinosaurs and birds. However, as the new dinosaur discoveries from the American mid-West came rolling in during the 1870s and 1880s these relationships became less clear as the bewildering variety of dinosaurs started to emerge.

The whole issue of bird origins was comprehensively summarised by Gerhard Heilmann in a book on the subject which was published in 1926. In this book Heilmann dealt at length with all the anatomical factors that seemed to have any relevance to bird origins, including the anatomy and embryology of

**Comparative Skulls (above)**
From above, the skulls of *Euparkeria*, *Archaeopteryx*, and *Columba* (the pigeon) look fairly similar. This tends to lend support to Heilmann's contention that birds have evolved from thecodontian archosaurs (*Euparkeria*) rather than 'coelurosaur'-type dinosaurs. This is, however, rather misleading because the skull of *Euparkeria* is very different in side view.

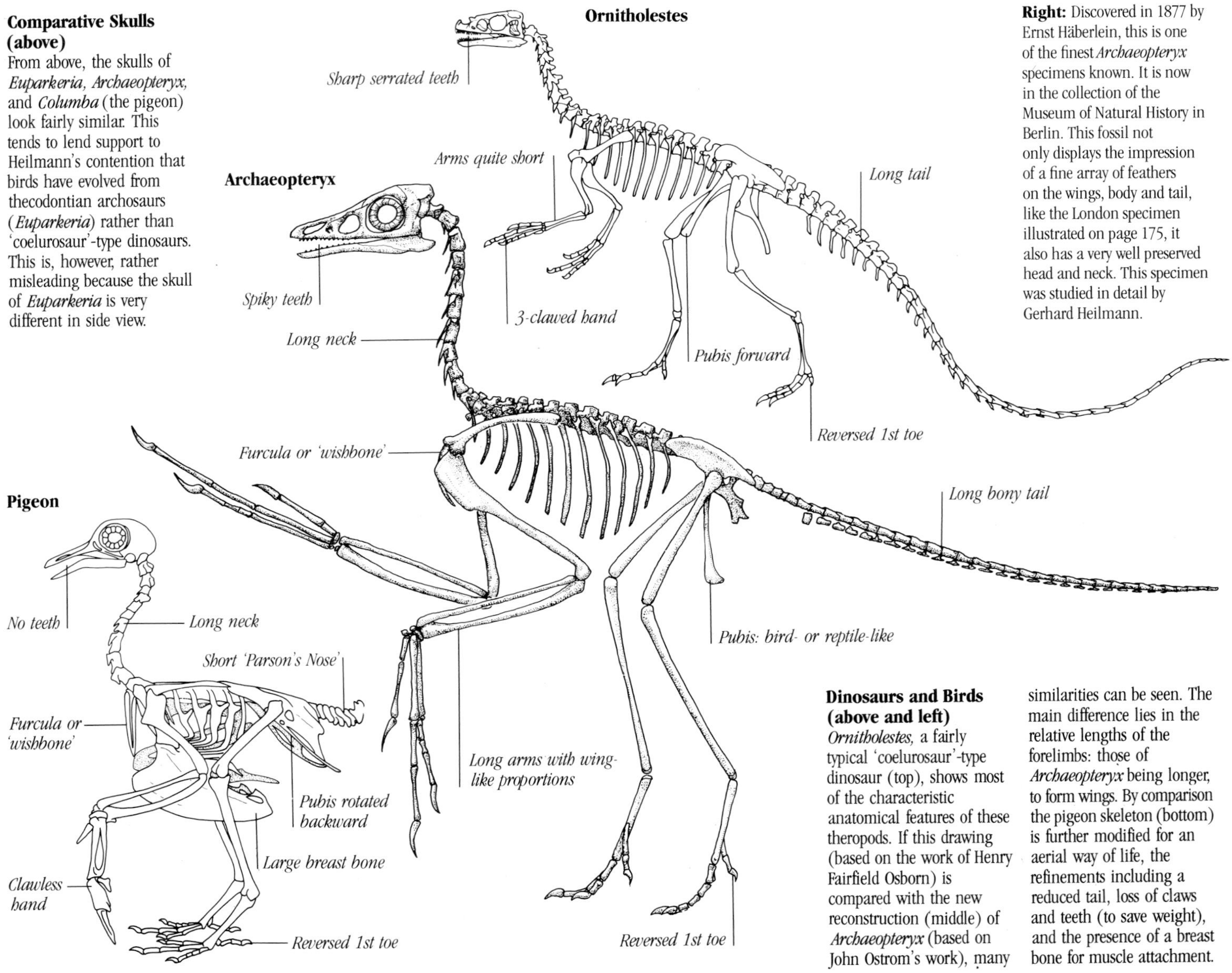

**Right:** Discovered in 1877 by Ernst Häberlein, this is one of the finest *Archaeopteryx* specimens known. It is now in the collection of the Museum of Natural History in Berlin. This fossil not only displays the impression of a fine array of feathers on the wings, body and tail, like the London specimen illustrated on page 175, it also has a very well preserved head and neck. This specimen was studied in detail by Gerhard Heilmann.

**Dinosaurs and Birds (above and left)**
*Ornitholestes*, a fairly typical 'coelurosaur'-type dinosaur (top), shows most of the characteristic anatomical features of these theropods. If this drawing (based on the work of Henry Fairfield Osborn) is compared with the new reconstruction (middle) of *Archaeopteryx* (based on John Ostrom's work), many similarities can be seen. The main difference lies in the relative lengths of the forelimbs: those of *Archaeopteryx* being longer, to form wings. By comparison the pigeon skeleton (bottom) is further modified for an aerial way of life, the refinements including a reduced tail, loss of claws and teeth (to save weight), and the presence of a breast bone for muscle attachment.

modern birds and reptiles, the anatomy of *Archaeopteryx*, and the anatomy of a whole range of fossil reptiles. The outcome of this masterly review of the problem was as follows. Of all the reptile groups that can be considered as the ancestors of birds, the most likely candidates were archosaurs; within this category the 'coelurosaurs' among the saurischian dinosaurs were by far the best candidates. Unfortunately, as Heilmann pointed out, dinosaurs did not possess collar bones (clavicles) in their shoulders, so a 'coelurosaur' ancestry for birds was out of the question. After all, how could a bird with a well-developed wishbone (formed from the fused clavicles) ever have evolved from an animal that did not have such a bone? Caught by this one irreconcilable problem Heilmann therefore proposed that the resemblance between 'coelurosaurs' and birds was a result of evolutionary convergence, and thus proposed that birds must have evolved from more primitive archosaurs such as those found in early and middle Triassic rocks. He postulated that a group of these reptiles may have taken to the habit of living in trees where they became small agile creatures in which feathers may have first evolved as parachuting devices either to break their fall or allow them to glide from tree to tree, thereby providing the first stage which resulted in the origin of feathers, flight and birds.

Heilmann's review was so thorough and authoritative that it was not seriously questioned until the early 1970s when three alternative proposals appeared in fairly quick succession.

**1970: ornithischians and birds** In 1970 Peter Galton proposed that the 'bird-hipped' (ornithischian) dinosaurs were the closest relatives of birds. Galton was in fact reviving a rather old idea that had been dismissed by Heilmann in 1926. His argument, if looked at carefully, was rather evasive because he had to admit that all known ornithischian dinosaurs were far too specialised to have given rise to birds. So he was forced to propose that birds arose from an unknown archosaur of middle Triassic age which possessed a bird-like pelvis. So far no such creature has been found, and Peter Galton now admits he was wrong.

**1972: crocodiles and birds** In 1972 Dr Alick Walker (Newcastle) proposed that modern birds share several features in common with a Triassic crocodile-like archosaur named *Sphenosuchus*. The detailed similarities were rather complex ones relating to the arrangement of the skull bones, as well as more general ones concerning the structure of the shoulders, forelimbs and ankle of embryo birds and crocodiles.

Walker's proposals were essentially that birds evolved from a primitive, lightly-built, crocodile-like group of archosaurs some of which took to tree-climbing, essentially as Heilmann had proposed, while others became amphibious and developed into true crocodiles.

One curious aspect of Walker's work is that little account was taken of the structure of *Archaeopteryx* which must surely receive some attention when bird origins are discussed. Interesting and provocative though Alick Walker's ideas are, it seems that he too has begun to recant in favour of the third and last proposal.

**1973: theropods and birds** In 1973 Professor John Ostrom revived the idea of a 'coelurosaur' ancestry for birds. A careful anatomical review of *Archaeopteryx* revealed that it shared over 20 features in common with 'coelurosaur'-type dinosaurs. The major problem of the lack of a 'collar-bone' or clavicle in theropods was shown not to be a problem at all, because several theropods did in fact possess clavicles (see page 47). In any case some embryological evidence suggests that the 'wishbone' is not equivalent to 'collar bones' at all.

Some of Ostrom's most telling points in favour of a theropod ancestry for *Archaeopteryx* and therefore of birds can be summarised as follows. First, he claimed that the hips of *Archaeopteryx* were not bird-like at all but rather were crushed into the bird-like arrangement during fossilisation; in life, therefore, they may have closely resembled the arrangement seen in theropod dinosaurs. Secondly, the forelimbs of theropods and *Archaeopteryx* are remarkably similar down to the minutest detail and thirdly, the hindlimbs and feet of *Archaeopteryx* are also very similar to those of theropods. In the light of Ostrom's long list of similarities, the question arises: could all these detailed similarities have arisen through convergent evolution? The answer would seem to be a resounding no!

This is not to say that the debate is now closed. Dr Sam Tarsitano and Dr Max Hecht are recent ardent advocates of Heilmann's original proposals of a more distant Triassic archosaur ancestor of birds. They claim to have found major faults with Ostrom's original work. Also several embryologists claim that the three fingers of the modified hand of living birds could not possibly have evolved from the three fingers of the theropod hand because the hand of birds is composed of the 2nd, 3rd and 4th fingers while in theropods the fingers are the 1st, 2nd and 3rd ones! Quite where this leaves *Archaeopteryx*, which also appears to have a theropod-like hand of fingers 1, 2 and 3, is a matter of some embarrassment—does it mean that *Archaeopteryx* was merely a feathered dinosaur and not related to birds at all?

Obviously the debate over the origins of birds is far from over even though a strong consensus of opinion now favours a theropod/ 'coelurosaur' ancestry.

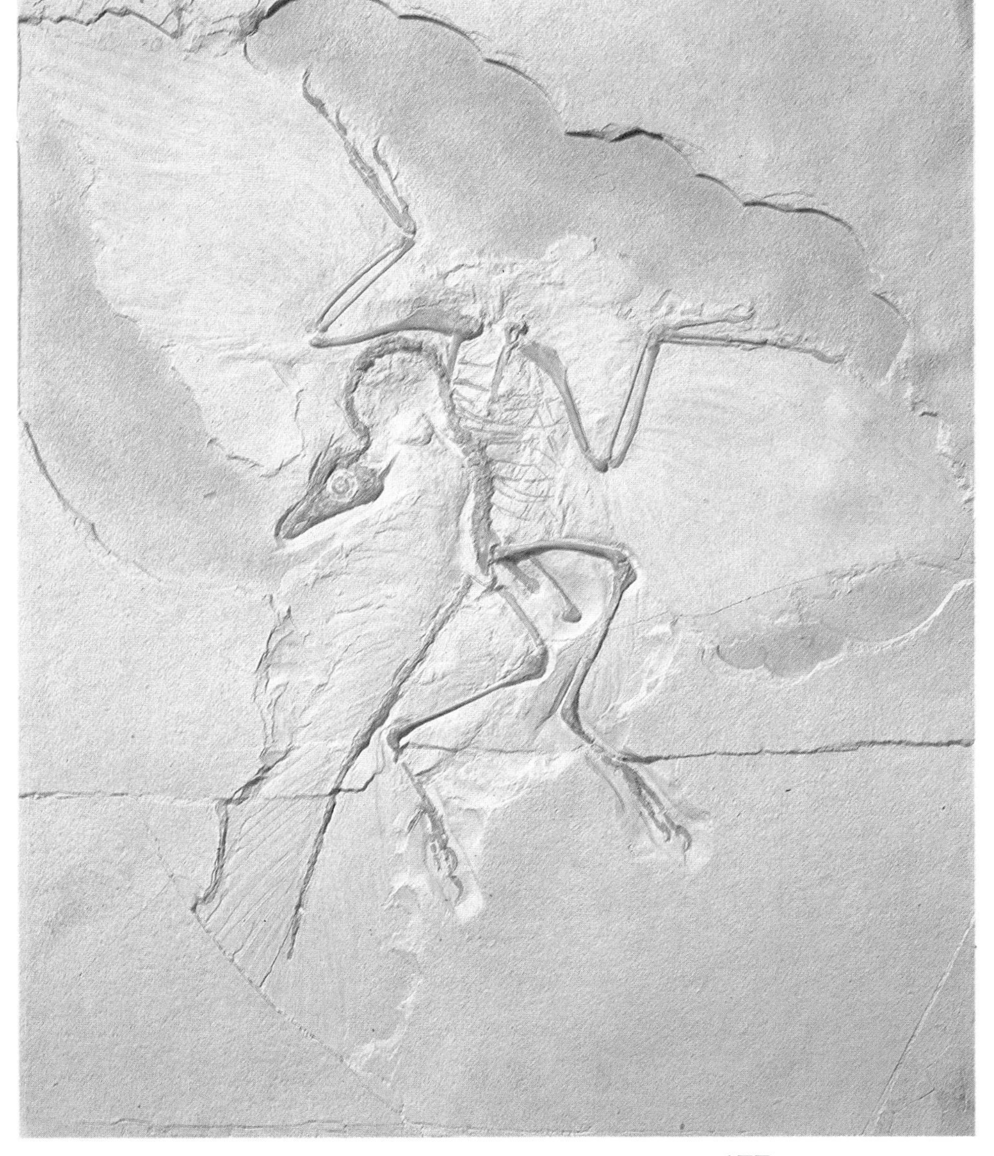

## The Origin of Flight

Almost as contentious an issue as the origin of birds, the origin of flight has also aroused much attention. There are in essence two main schools of thought: flight either evolved in fast-running ground animals or from gliding tree-dwellers.

**Flying from the ground** Leading advocates of this theory have been S.W. Williston (1879), F.B. Nopsca (1907) and J.H. Ostrom (1974). The general notion is that bird ancestors were, like 'coelurosaurs', fast-running creatures. The development of wings is therefore seen as a means of adding propulsion (in Nopsca's and Williston's interpretation). This idea is not regarded with great enthusiasm by most palaeontologists because the 'proto-

**Below:** The origin of flight in birds, and vertebrates in general, is a matter of some dispute. From an energetic point of view, it is far easier for an animal to begin flying by parachuting or gliding, as Stephen Winkworth's model of *Pteranodon* here illustrates.

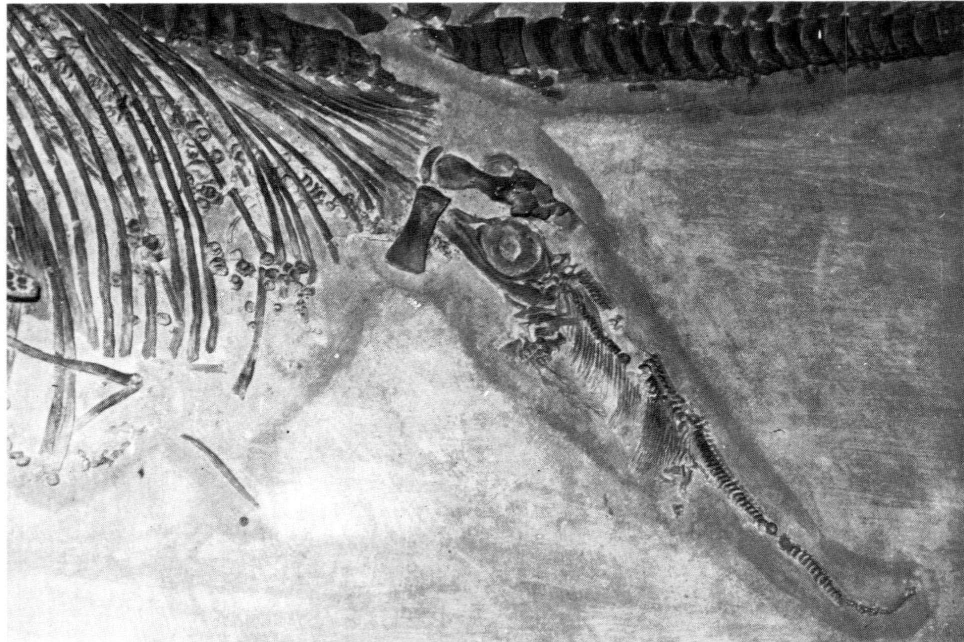

wings' would create either a lot of drag or lift, neither of which will help the animal run any more quickly.

John Ostrom's idea provides a novel twist to these earlier ideas in that he imagines *Archaeopteryx* as, at best, a very poor flier. Feeding on flying insects, he imagines that its feathered arms ('wings') were used as traps to help catch insects; these arms, he argues, allowed *Archaeopteryx* to make short fluttering jumps upwards to help it catch insects, thereby providing the first step toward active flapping flight.

**Gliding from trees** By far the most popular theory of the origin of flight is that proposed by Heilmann. Flight is seen as developing in stages from the efforts of tree-dwelling 'proto-birds' which used feathered limbs to break their fall and/or glide from tree to tree. Such gliding adaptations (using skin, ribs etc.) are seen in a host of tree-dwelling vertebrates living today – from frogs, to snakes and lizards, squirrels and monkeys. The advantages of gliding are great in that they save the time and energy that would have to be expended going down one tree and then up the next. The move from gliding to powered flight is then a relatively minor matter of modifying muscles and joints in order to flap the wings.

Although this issue is difficult to resolve with any degree of certainty, I favour Heilmann's interpretation. There are certain bio-mechanical problems associated with fast ground-running with wings outspread: as lift is generated so traction with the ground would be lessened. It seems more feasible that gliding from trees allowed intermittent flying patterns to be developed, and a gradual modification of gliding surfaces into wings to be achieved.

## Extinction of the Dinosaurs

The last and perhaps most controversial issue to concern dinosaurs relates to their eventual downfall. For an enormously long period of time, slightly in excess of 140 million years – from the end of the Triassic until the close of the Cretaceous Period – dinosaurs of one sort or another dominated the terrestrial environments of the world. At the same time other groups of reptiles dominated the two other physical environments, air and water. In the sea the dominant predators appear to have been the sleek ichthyosaurs and remarkable plesiosaurs, and to a lesser extent crocodiles and mosasaurs. In the air the pterosaurs seem to have been dominant for the early part of the Mesozoic, but in the Cretaceous their radiation may have been limited by the appearance of newly-evolved birds. Then, apparently quite suddenly, the dinosaurs went extinct 64 million years ago at the end of the Cretaceous Period. The extinction of the dinosaurs at this time has, quite unfairly, been the primary focus of attention for a large number of scientists, as well as the public at large. This is perhaps understandable, the dinosaurs were large and extremely interesting forms of life and have provoked a great deal of public interest in fossil animals as a whole. However, their prominent position has provoked a great number of theories which have attempted to explain the extinction of dinosaurs *alone*. An example of this type of thinking is one theory that was put forward quite seriously by a palaeontologist many years ago, which proposed that the small Mesozoic mammals took to the habit of eating dinosaurs' eggs. The end result of this change of diet was the over-predation of eggs leading to the extinction of the dinosaurs.

A few moments reflection are probably all that are needed to come to a decision about this particular theory. In the first place, it is exceedingly improbable that the change to an egg-eating diet by mammals should have caused the extinction of *all* dinosaur species; after all we cannot even be sure they all laid eggs! Secondly, many egg-eating species are known today but these show no sign whatever of causing the extinction of their prey; indeed it is biological 'common-sense' not to cause the extinction of the organisms that you feed upon otherwise you will surely hasten your own end!

Notwithstanding these immediate and obvious objections to such a theory, one much more important observation can be made which renders it a complete non-starter. At the end of the Cretaceous Period, it was not simply the ornithischian and saurischian dinosaurs that went extinct, but also pterosaurs, mosasaurs, plesiosaurs, and ichthyosaurs among the vertebrate animals, as well as ammonites and calcareous (chalky) plankton. The end of the Cretaceous marked the time of what is called a mass-extinction, that is to say the extinction of not just one or two species, but a whole range of near and distantly related forms. As we have seen from the fossil record of dinosaurs alone which we have traced in some detail in this book, extinction is the eventual fate of all species. Indeed, no matter how optimistic we might feel at the present, even our human species is almost certainly destined for extinction in the end. Thus we would expect to find species originating, diversifying and finally becoming extinct throughout the fossil record. For the most part that is indeed the pattern that seems to emerge. However, at apparently irregular intervals, notably the Permian-Triassic and the Cretaceous-Tertiary boundaries, mass-extinctions appear to have occurred. Such events would not have been predicted from what we know of the process of evolution. The simultaneous extinction of a whole range of species, both closely and distantly related, implies that some common cause or event must have been responsible. The possibility

**Above:** Frozen in time, this remarkable fossil shows the moment of birth of a baby ichthyosaur, tail first, from its mother. It is a graphic illustration that not all reptiles lay eggs, which in turn rebuts the argument that egg-eating mammals were the cause of the mass-extinction at the end of the Cretaceous Period.

**Below:** This ammonite is just one example of a vast array of marine animals that went extinct at the close of the Cretaceous Period. While it is all very well to try to explain the extinction of the land-living dinosaurs in isolation, such explanations more often than not founder when they have to account for ammonite extinctions.

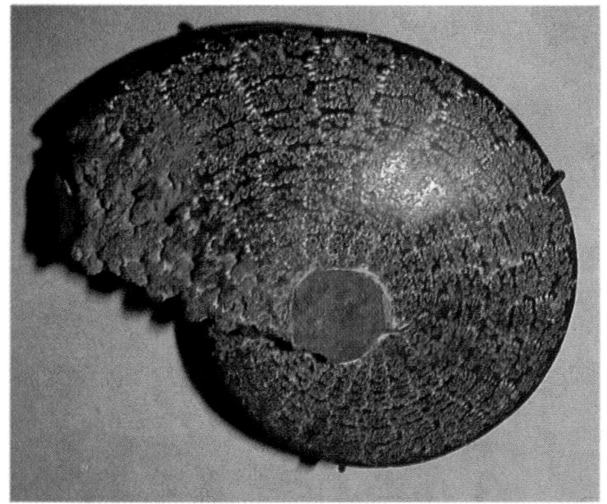

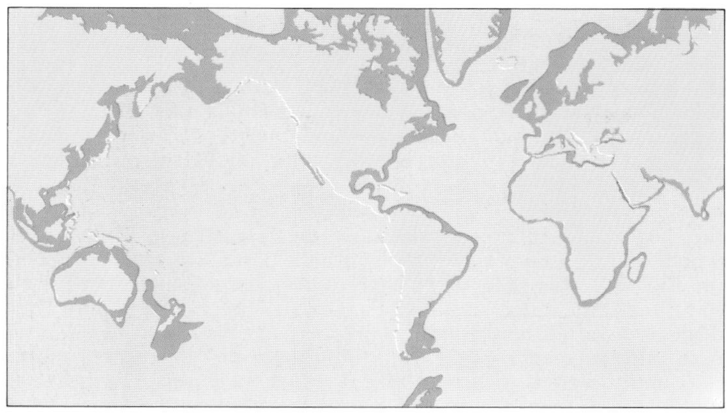

**Continental Shelves (left and below left)**
The continental shelves (dark brown) reveal the real extent of the continents below sea level. The links that exist today between North America and Asia, and the countries of Northern Europe, can be clearly seen. The section through a continental margin (below left) shows the relation between a continental shelf and other major submarine features. These areas are densely populated by marine organisms. A large drop in sea level as a result of the formation of the super-continent of Pangaea, such as that proposed in the Permo-Triassic, would have had catastrophic effects on the animals living on the continental shelf, and may explain the mass-extinction.

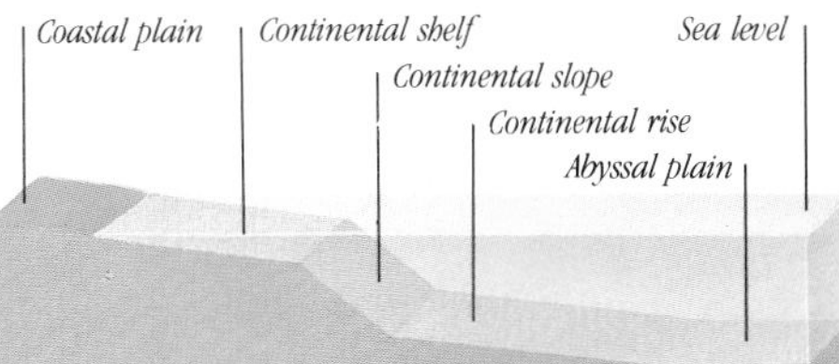


**Below:** The excavation of a plesiosaur skeleton of Jurassic age at Fletton near Peterborough in England. Plesiosaurs lasted until the end of the Cretaceous. The cause of their extinction, like that of the dinosaurs, remains unexplained.

that all the species went extinct purely coincidentally seems too remote for most scientists to give it serious consideration. Therefore, returning briefly to our first dinosaur extinction theory, the likelihood that egg-eating mammals caused the extinction of ammonites, chalky plankton, ichythyosaurs (which bore live young!) etc. cannot be entertained seriously.

I have dwelt on the egg-eating mammal theory not because it is particularly contemptible, but rather because it serves as an excellent example of a whole range of theories which have been advanced simply to explain the extinction of the dinosaurs at the end of the Cretaceous. No consideration is given to the other animals that went extinct simultaneously.

## Mass-Extinctions

Two mass-extinctions were mentioned above. Both of these 'events' are particularly prominent in the fossil record: one at the end of the Permian Period and the other at the end of the Cretaceous Period. Although the former 'event' precedes the era of the dinosaurs, it has aroused a great deal of interest and deserves some consideration here, because it can be compared with the events of the late Cretaceous.

**Permo-Triassic extinctions** The fossil record of marine animals shows a remarkable mass-extinction at the end of the Permian as a result of which up to 70 per cent of all known groups went extinct. This is a more dramatic but less heavily publicised mass-extinction that the one that involved the dinosaurs. Evidence of the dramatic marine mass-extinction has prompted many explanations. One of the most popular theories at present is based upon our knowledge of plate tectonics ('continental drift', see also pages 15-17).

Coincident with the mass-extinction event, the various continents of the late Palaeozoic world, which had up till then been separate and drifting across the oceans, seem to have drifted towards one another. In the late Permian the continents appear to have fused together to form one gigantic supercontinent named Pangaea. The potential effects of the formation of Pangaea upon the ecosystems of the Earth may hold the key to the mass-extinction phenomenon at this time. It has been suggested that the formation of Pangaea would have dramatically changed the conditions for marine organisms in a number of ways.

First, at least 50 per cent of the area of the continental shelf surrounding each of the continents would have been 'lost' where the continents actually joined together. This would restrict the area available for marine species to exist and presumably also the total number capable of living in this sea.

Secondly, the joining together of continental shelves would have reduced species diversity because there would be competition between previously isolated species and only the most vigorous would survive. Thus in the end fewer species would be more widely spread.

Thirdly, the joining together of the continents may have caused a temporary halt in sea-floor spreading activity at the mid-oceanic ridges and marginal continental trenches (subduction zones). As a result the huge ocean ridges may have collapsed back into the Earth's crust. If this happened then there would have been an enormous increase in the capacity of the oceans causing a large drop in the sea-level. Some estimates have proposed that the sea-level may have dropped by over 200 feet—perilously close to the top of the continental shelf. Since most of the marine organisms tend to live in or on the continental shelves the effect of a drop in sea-level of this magnitude may have been catastrophic.

What we have therefore is a single unified explanation for the mass-extinctions at the end of the Permian. All can be seen as a natural consequence of the chance formation of Pangaea as a result of continental movements. The evidence from the marine fauna is also backed up by evidence from the terrestrial fauna. Here, although extinctions are not nearly so marked, the diversity of species drops noticeably as animals originally confined to one continent find that they are able to spread almost world-wide at the expense of others (e.g. the dicynodont *Lystrosaurus* has been found in India, Antarctica, South Africa and Central Asia in early Triassic times). The geophysical and fossil evidence therefore seems to be in remarkable accord with this theory to explain the mass-extinction.

## Cretaceous-Tertiary Extinctions

If we exclude from consideration those theories which explain the extinctions at the end of the Cretaceous Period in terms of the dinosaurs alone, we are left with just two main theories which attempt to explain the mass-extinction: a 'cosmic' theory and a climatic change theory.

**Cosmic explanation** A long-standing theory to explain the Cretaceous extinctions has been one which favours some sort of global cosmic influence. One of the favourites in this category has been the possibility of a star exploding in a nearby constellation and forming a supernova. The effects of this supernova would be to bathe the Earth's surface in deadly cosmic rays which could have caused the widespread extinctions. This has always run into the problem of explaining how the deadly cosmic rays killed some groups but left others, such as the birds, mammals, crocodiles and turtles, to survive apparently unscathed. Secondly there do not appear from astrophysical observations to be many good candidates within nearby constellations of the remnants of stars that may have caused such a supernova at this time.

Such cosmic theorising, however, has had an unexpected boost in recent years as a result of the work of Luis Alvarez, his son Walter Alvarez and colleagues in California. While carrying out routine sampling of sediments from the late Cretaceous of Gubbio (Italy) they discovered unexpectedly high levels of a rare element named iridium. Iridium is a heavy metal which is not normally found in large amounts in the Earth's crust. What iridium there is on Earth is concentrated in the molten core. It would have sunk there at the time of the formation of the Earth 4,500 million years ago when the Earth was still molten rock. One potential source of iridium, however, is extra-terrestrial: from meteorites, asteroids and comets.

The iridium 'spike' or anomaly was explained by Alvarez and his team as evidence of a truly massive meteorite impact at the end of the Cretaceous Period. Examination of clays of late Cretaceous age from elsewhere in the world turned up similar iridium 'spikes' confirming the widespread nature of the iridium-rich layer.

Scientists attempting to account for this phenomenon theorised that the iridium may have been introduced into these sediments as dust. This dust could have been created by the impact of a massive (6-9 mile, 10-15km wide) meteorite with the Earth. Such a collision would have caused a massive explosion as the meteorite scorched its way through the atmosphere and then impacted the Earth's crust. The meteorite would have vaporised on impact and an enormous cloud of dust and steam would have risen into the atmosphere. The resulting cloud of steam and dust is held to be the main cause of the extinctions. It is proposed that if the cloud shrouded the Earth for an appreciable length of time, several weeks or even months so the predictions go, then the biological effects would have been dramatic. Shrouding the Earth in dust and water vapour would cut out the light from the Sun which is essential for plant growth on land and at sea (phyto-plankton). These are the organisms at the bottom of th food pyramid upon which life on Earth is almost totally dependent. If the Earth was shrouded for an appreciable length of time then the damage to ecosystems on land and in the sea would have been profound. Most of the animals near the top of the pyramid, the great carnivores and herbivores of the time, would go extinct. In fact the creatures best able to survive in the short term may well have been the smaller opportunistic scavenging types of animals: mammals, lizards and snakes, crocodiles, rather than the larger, more specialised types.

Thus, as in the case of the Permo-Triassic extinctions, the meteorite impact theory also has the benefit of linking a chance event with natural and understandable biological repercussions. A large body of scientists now endorse this particular theory very strongly although there is still much discussion about its finer aspects.

Much debate has centred on the nature of the extra-terrestrial bombardment that the Earth is thought to have experienced, and the celestial mechanism that may have set it off. Rather than being the result of a meteor impact, some scientists argue that the iridium anomaly might have been caused by a rain of comets that, judging by the stratigraphic evidence, is believed to strike the Earth every 26 million years or so. Such comets might be 'shaken out' of the Oort Cloud — a vast field of comets that orbits the Sun at a distance of about 9 million million miles — by the action of some cosmic agency. There are three major theories of how this might come about.

The first envisages that the Sun is part of a binary star system i.e. it has a (so far undiscovered) companion star circling it in a highly elliptical orbit, which periodically exerts gravitational influence on the Oort Cloud, causing comets to be hurled towards the inner Solar System. The second theory ascribes this gravitational influence to the presence of a tenth planet (Planet X, also undiscovered to date) which may be orbiting the Sun in a sharply inclined orbit which is constantly changing as a result of the gravitational influences of the other planets, and which may thus intersect the cometary disc only at very long intervals. Such a planet might also account for observed anomalies in the orbit of Neptune.

The third explanation takes as its starting point the nature of the Solar System's orbit around the centre of our galaxy. The Milky Way galaxy is shaped rather like a disc with a bulbous centre; the Sun and the planets slowly orbit this centre and in doing so bob up and down through the plane of the galaxy rather like riders on a merry-go-round. It has been postulated that the passage through the denser dust clouds in the galactic plane might be the cause of comets being hurled out of their normal orbits.

All these theories have their ardent proponents, and also their vociferous critics who can find fault with the astrophysical assumptions underlying them. However, in contrast to the 'cosmic school' there are several palaeontologists who favour a less dramatic explanation of the end of the Mesozoic Era.

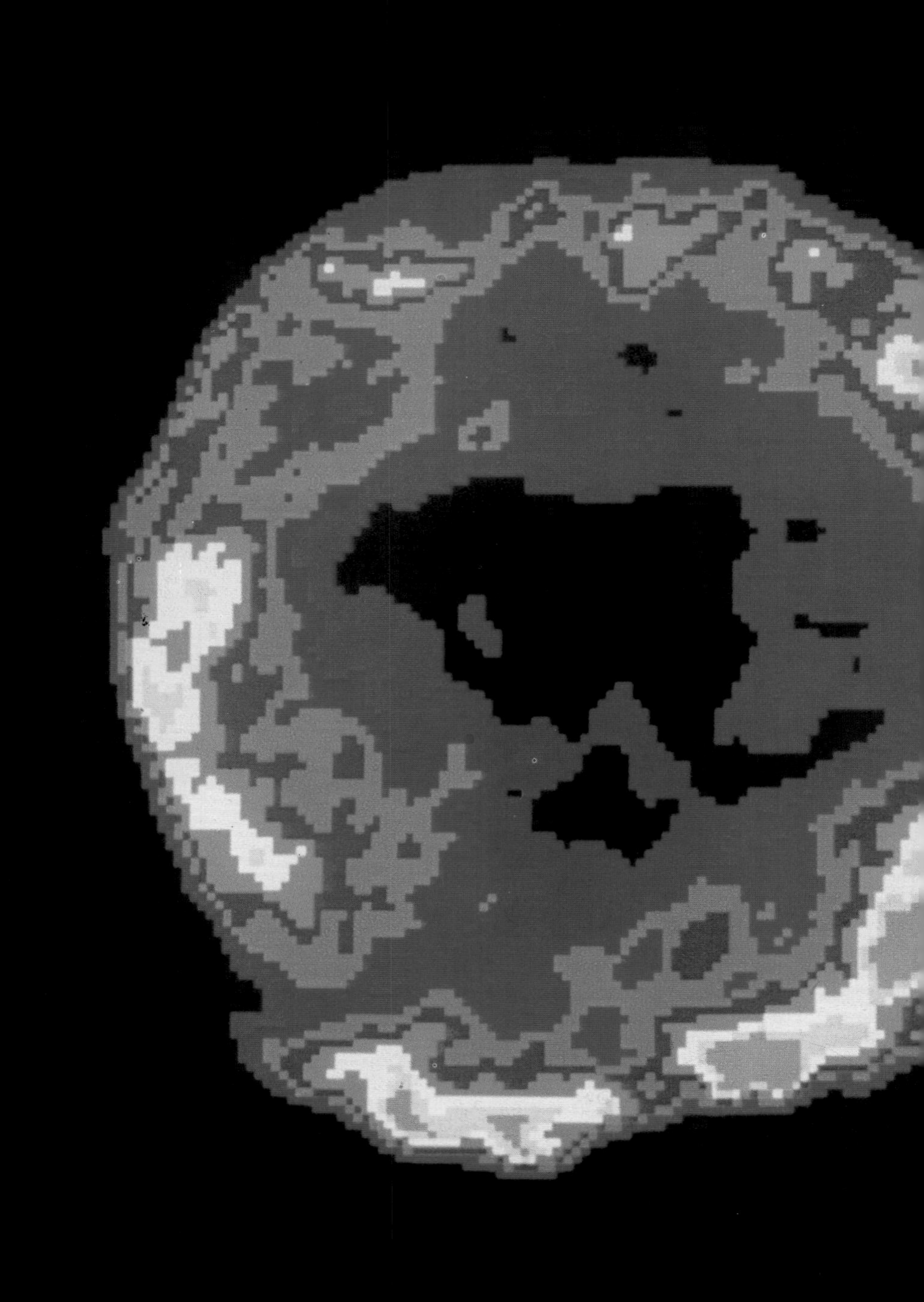

**Climatic change theory** This theory has had several advocates, notably Leigh Van Valen and Robert Sloan, in the last decade. Their contention is that the events of the late Cretaceous were not quick and dramatic, as proponents of the cosmic theories believe, but were the culmination of changes in climate that had begun in the early part of the late Cretaceous.

Careful analysis of geological sections from North America has revealed, according to Van Valen and Sloan, a marked but gradual change in plant and animal types. About 5 to 10 million years from the end of the Cretaceous Period the vegetation was very lush with abundant tropical and sub-tropical species of plants; these conditions supported a rich and varied dinosaur fauna. However, towards the close of the Cretaceous the flora changed markedly to one dominated by cool, temperate woodland plants; the dinosaurs became fewer in variety and various small mammals were more conspicuous elements in the fauna.

The implication is that the climate deteriorated towards the end of the Cretaceous Period. The consequent change in plant types supported less varied dinosaur types while the cooler conditions favoured the insulated endothermic mammals rather than the uninsulated ectothermic dinosaurs. The story that seems to be emerging from these studies is thus one of slower, climatically induced change.

What may the cause of this climatic change have been? One possible cause may be, yet again, continental drift. In the late Cretaceous, continental movement had separated all the major continents. Indeed, all the sea-floor spreading activity may have resulted in appreciably raised sea-levels (exactly the reverse of the late Permian!) resulting in shallow seas dividing, for example, west from east North America, Asia from Europe and subdividing Africa. The effect of all these separate continental areas may have been to alter ocean currents, wind patterns and consequently climatic patterns from the prevailing mild conditions of the Jurassic and Cretaceous to the cooler, more seasonal, conditions which seem to mark the late Cretaceous.

## Drawing Conclusions

Could climatic changes induced by continental drift explain the late Cretaceous extinctions? While they might explain terrestrial extinctions, the marine extinctions are not so readily understood. The idea is that lower global temperatures affected the plankton. Many types of plankton are notoriously temperature sensitive; perhaps this was the reason for the extinction among chalky plankton. If such was the case, then climatic changes may have indeed induced extinctions in the sea because plankton forms the base of the food pyramid upon which plesiosaurs, mosasaurs and ammonites may have depended.

In the final analysis, neither of these theories is entirely satisfactory. Were the late Cretaceous extinctions almost instantaneous or more gradual? Could the iridium 'spike' have been caused by volcanic activity associated with great tectonic activity in the late Cretaceous? Could the marine extinctions really have been caused by climatic changes as proposed above?

At the moment a great deal of work is being undertaken by scientists to try to find answers to these and many other questions. For example efforts are being made to try to correlate geological sections from various areas, particularly in North America, to see whether or not they show *exactly* similar timings of the Cretaceous extinctions. This is extremely difficult (perhaps it will prove impossible) work, but if a clear answer emerges it will surely bring us very close to the answer to this perplexing 64 million year old question.

**Above:** This photograph shows the team of explorers who discovered the Hoba West meteorite in 1920. The largest meteorite discovered to date, this would be dwarfed by the one that is supposed by some authorities to have caused the end of the dinosaurs and other Mesozoic organisms.

**Left:** Tycho's Supernova. This striking picture is a radio-telescope image of the remnants of a supernova which occurred in 1572 AD. The ring-like structure represents the radio emission from the supernova blast wave. Remnants of a stellar explosion of this type which occurred 64 million years ago would be needed to link such an event to the extinctions at the end of the Cretaceous.

**Right:** Comet Ikeya-Seki, vivid in the night sky. One theory favours comet showers resulting from disturbances in the Oort Cloud as the agent of periodic extinctions on the Earth.

# GEOGRAPHY OF FINDS

To give some impression of how widespread dinosaur discoveries are, a map of the world has been provided with many of the dinosaur localities marked. Many of these sites have already been described earlier in the book, under the various sections devoted to the individual groups of dinosaurs.

The overwhelming impression that is gained from studying the map is that dinosaur fossils are remarkably widespread. Almost all of the continents (excluding Antarctica) have produced dinosaur remains. Even Antarctica no doubt contains fossil dinosaurs, the obvious problem, however, is that the rocks of the appropriate age are mostly covered by ice-sheets. The fact that the early Triassic *Lystrosaurus* (a mammal-like reptile) has been discovered here shows that Antarctica has not always been an inhospitable ice-bound continent as it is today.

A map of discoveries of dinosaurs made in the middle of the last century would have looked very different from the one we see here. At that time, dinosaur remains were only known from Europe (England and Germany) and North America, as a result of the pioneering work of Gideon Mantell in Britain, Hermann von Meyer in Gemany and Ferdinand Vandiveer Hayden in Montana, North America. From these rather modest beginnings the rate of dinosaur discoveries increased dramatically in the second half of the nineteenth century. Most of the finds were centred on North America.

## North America

The first important discovery around the 1850s was that Hayden found several dinosaur localities both in western and eastern North America. Then, in the late 1870s, further dramatic discoveries in Wyoming and Colorado attracted the attention of the two rival palaeontologists, Othniel Charles Marsh and Edward Drinker Cope. The feverish activities of these two scientists, and perhaps more importantly their hired teams of explorers and excavators, resulted in the discovery of dinosaurs right across the continent from New England in the east to Utah and Colorado in the west. North America has been an extremely fine hunting ground for dinosaurs. Not only have some localities proved to be particularly rich in dinosaur remains—notably those in Wyoming, Colorado, Montana and Alberta—but they have also revealed dinosaurs from all three periods of the Mesozoic. Triassic and early Jurassic dinosaurs have been recovered from Arizona and Connecticut in particular. In fact very recently (1985) Robert Long reported the discovery of a new, extremely early dinosaur from the Painted Desert of Arizona. This may be one of the earliest dinosaurs found to date, but as yet it has not been fully prepared or described. Jurassic, and particularly late Jurassic, rocks are those of Utah, Colorado and Wyoming where some of the most spectacular discoveries have been made. Cretaceous finds are largely from the late Cretaceous of States such as Montana, Alberta and New Mexico. Early Cretaceous discoveries are less abundant on the whole, although significant finds have been made in southern Montana and South Dakota.

## South America

In the latter half of the nineteenth century dinosaurs were also discovered in South America. Interest in fossils had been stimulated by the work of Georges Cuvier and Richard Owen who were both able to describe fossil material of giant extinct mammals brought back by early explorers of that continent—notably one Charles Darwin during the voyage of the *Beagle*. Most dinosaur discoveries have been made in southern Brazil and Argentina where Mesozoic rocks are quite widespread. While much of the early work revolved around chance discoveries, careful and systematic collection in the last few years by teams led by José Bonaparte have begun to discover very important, well-preserved remains.

## Europe

Western Europe has a long tradition of dinosaur discovery and excavation, but, despite this, its collections have been largely outshone by the more dramatic discoveries elsewhere in the world. Some of the best Triassic deposits are in Germany where the famous *Plateosaurus* quarries of Halberstadt and Trössingen were excavated earlier this century. Jurassic rocks, although quite widespread, have never produced really good fossil skeletons. The best are from the quarries of central-western Britain; the ones that have produced the partial remains of creatures such as *Megalosaurus, Eustreptospondylus* and *Cetiosauriscus,* but never the wonderful, fully articulated, huge dinosaur skeletons found in North America or China. The late Jurassic lagoon deposits of southern Germany have, however, yielded the beautifully preserved small skeletons of *Archaeopteryx* and *Compsognathus*.

Early Cretaceous rocks have been a little more generous, yielding many skeletons of *Iguanodon* in southern England, Belgium, Germany and Spain in particular. Little else is well preserved. Later Cretaceous rocks are also frustratingly poor. Some well-preserved remains are known from Rumania (Transylvania) and the dinosaur egg locality of southern France (Aix-en-Provence), but most remains are fragmentary and poor.

## Central Asia

Until the early 1920s and the American Museum Central Asiatic Expeditions, virtually nothing was known of the fossil remains of this area. The Central Asiatic Expedition revealed rich dinosaur-bearing rocks in Mongolia which were subsequently explored by Russian and Polish Expeditions in the 1940s and more recent decades. Finds from this area, particularly in the late Cretaceous of the Gobi Desert, have proved as interesting and exciting as those from North America at the turn of the century. Notable among them are the discoveries of *Tarbosaurus, Saurolophus,* various ankylosaurs, pachycephalosaurs and a host of small theropods and large sauropods.

## China

China has extensive Triassic, Jurassic and Cretaceous exposures that have begun to yield enormous numbers of dinosaurs in recent years. Early chance discoveries in north-eastern China (*Mandschurosaurus*) at the turn of the century were followed by systematic excavations by Chinese palaeontologists in the 1930s and 1940s and the discovery of *Lufengosaurus* from the Triassic. This was followed by work in

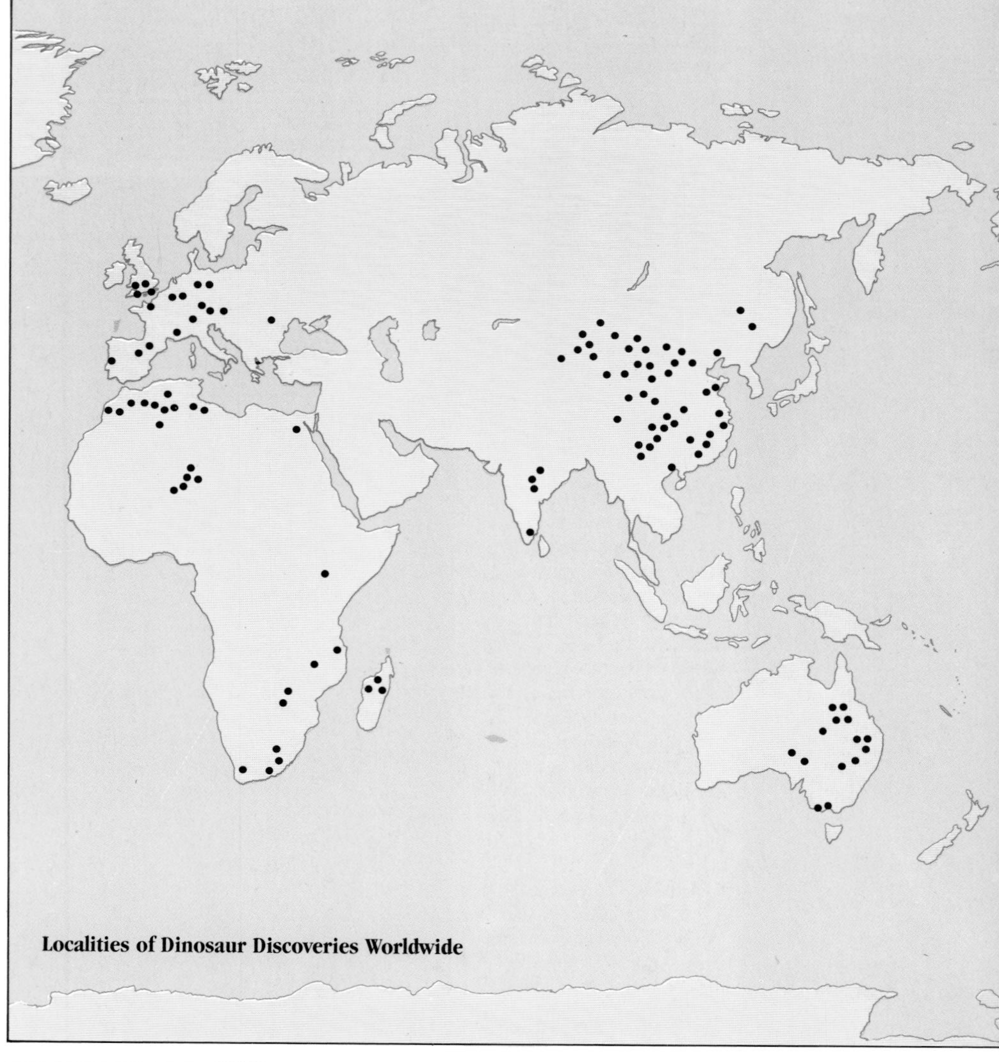

Localities of Dinosaur Discoveries Worldwide

Cretaceous and Jurassic exposures, which has produced some quite spectacular finds, notably those from Sichuan Province.

## Australia and India

Again, discoveries of dinosaurs date back to the early part of this century. Most remains have so far been frustratingly poor, but it seems to be only a matter of time before rich dinosaur-bearing localities are discovered. Recent Australian finds include *Austrosaurus, Muttaburrasaurus* and *Fulgurotherium.*

First reports of dinosaurs in India date back to the latter half of the nineteenth century (notably the sauropod *Titanosaurus*). More recently the Kota area of central India has revealed abundant remains of the early Jurassic dinosaur *Barapasaurus.* The interesting late Cretaceous stegosaur *Dravidosaurus* was found in southern India.

## Africa

Finds of dinosaurs in Africa are quite widespread: ranging from the Triassic and early Jurassic exposures in southern Africa that have produced prosauropods such as *Massospondylus* and *Anchisaurus* and the ornithopods *Lesothosaurus* and *Heterodontosaurus;* through the late Jurassic deposits of Tanzania that have revealed forms such as *Brachiosaurus, Dicraeosaurus* and *Kentrosaurus;* to the Cretaceous deposits of the central Sahara, Niger and Morocco that have yielded large sauropods, *Ouranosaurus* and the peculiar *Spinosaurus.*

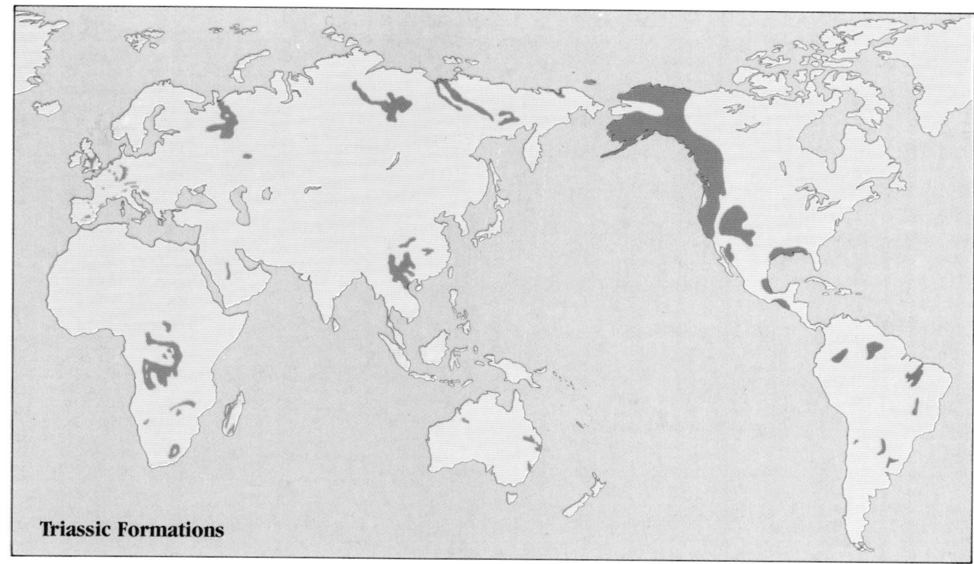


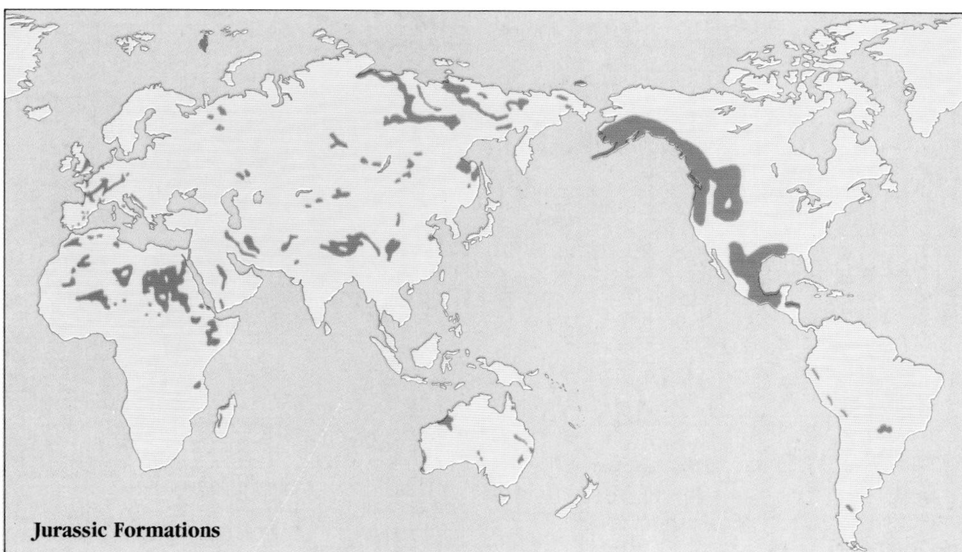


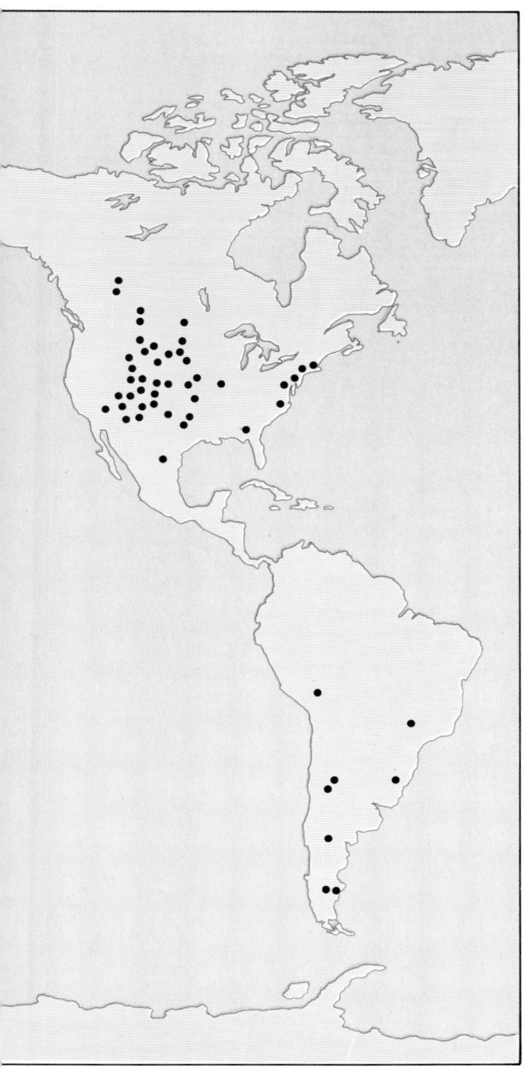

**Left:** This map shows many of the important localities worldwide where dinosaur discoveries have been made. It is at once obvious how widespread was the dispersal of the dinosaurs on land. New expeditions will no doubt extend the picture even further.

**Top:** This map shows those exposures of Triassic rocks that are currently charted. Important finds from this Period include *Coelophysis* (USA), *Plateosaurus* (West Germany), *Anchisaurus* (South Africa) and Robert Long's new dinosaur from the Arizona desert.

**Above:** Notable among the finds from Jurassic rocks are many of the large sauropods, the small theropod *Compsognathus* from South Germany, and two very early ornithischians, *Scelidosaurus* (England) and *Heterodontosaurus* (South Africa).

**Below:** Fossils finds in Cretaceous rocks are many; they include numerous ceratopians from Canada and North America, an abundance of hadrosaurids and iguanodontids, and most of the recent spectacular discoveries from Mongolia and China.

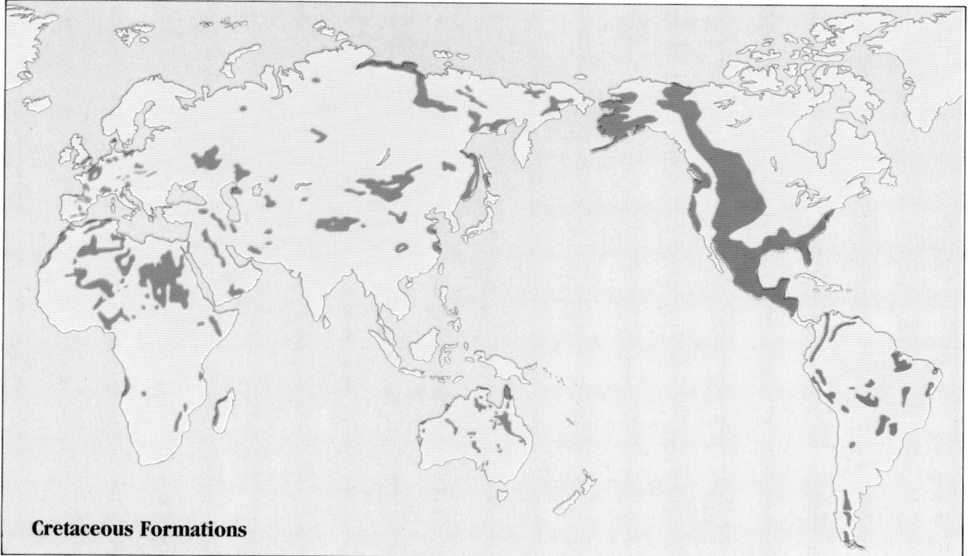

The purpose of this listing is to show the major institutions where dinosaur skeletons, casts, or fossil remains are on display around the world, and to indicate the most important specimens that particular collections hold. Wherever possible, full postal addresses have been included. This list is obviously not exhaustive, and the editor would welcome correspondence from the curators of any museums that have been inadvertently left out, or, where appropriate, information to update the listing of specimens on display. The list is split into four broad continental groups: Africa, the Americas, Asia and Australia, and Europe.

## AFRICA

### Morocco

**The Museum of Earth Sciences**
Rabat
*Cetiosaurus*
*Rebbachisaurus*

### Niger

**Musée National du Niger**
B.P. No 248,
Niamey
*Ouranosaurus*

### South Africa

**Bernard Price Institute of Palaeontology**
University of Witwatersrand,
Jan Smuts Avenue,
Johannesburg 2001
*Melanorosaurus*

**South African Museum**
PO Box 61,
Cape Town,
South Africa 8000
*Anchisaurus*
*Heterodontosaurus*
*Massospondylus*
*Melanorosaurus*

### Zimbabwe

**National Museum of Zimbabwe**
Harare
*Syntarsus*
*Vulcanodon*

## THE AMERICAS

### Argentina

**Museo Argentino de Ciencias Naturales**
Av. Angel Gallardo 470,
1405 Buenos Aires
*Antarctosaurus*
*Mussaurus*
*Noasaurus*
*Riojasaurus*
*Saltasaurus*
*Titanosaurus*

**Museum of La Plata University**
La Plata
*Centrosaurus*
*Diplodocus*

### Brazil

**Museu Nacional**
20942 Quinto da Boa Vista,
São Cristovao,
Rio de Janeiro 20940
Various sauropods

### Canada

**Dinosaur Provincial Park**
Patricia,
Alberta
Excavation in progress

**National Museum of Natural Sciences**
Ottawa,
Ontario KA1 OM8
*Anchiceratops*
*Daspletosaurus*
*Dromiceiomimus*
*Leptoceratops*
*Panoplosaurus*
*Styracosaurus*
*Triceratops*
Various hadrosaurids

**Provincial Museum of Alberta**
12845 102 Avenue,
Edmonton,
Alberta T5N OM6
*Ankylosaurus* model
*Corythosaurus* model
*Lambeosaurus*
*Struthiomimus* model

**Redpath Museum**
McGill University,
859 Sherbrook Street West,
Quebec H3A 2K6
*Majungatholus*
*Saurornithoides*
*Zephyrosaurus*

**Royal Ontario Museum**
Toronto,
Ontario M5S 2C6
*Albertosaurus*
*Allosaurus*
*Camptosaurus*
*Chasmosaurus*
*Corythosaurus*
*Edmontosaurus*
*Hadrosaurus*
*Lambeosaurus*
*Ornithomimus*
*Parasaurolophus*
*Prosaurolophus*

**Tyrrell Museum of Palaeontology**
PO Box 7500,
Drumheller,
Alberta
*Albertosaurus*
*Centrosaurus*
*Coelophysis*
*Corythosaurus*
*Dromaeosaurus*
*Hadrosaurus*
*Hypacrosaurus*
*Lambeosaurus*
*Ornitholestes*
*Saurornitholestes*
*Tyrannosaurus*

**Zoological Gardens**
Calgary,
Alberta
Outdoor display of models

### Mexico

**Natural History Museum**
Mexico City
*Diplodocus* cast

### United States of America

**Academy of Natural Sciences**
19th & The Parkway,
Logan Square,
Philadelphia,
Pennsylvania 19103
A new display is under construction; exhibits will include:
*Brachyceratops*
*Corythosaurus*
*Deinonychus*
*Hadrosaurus*
*'Supersaurus'* leg
*Tenontosaurus*

**American Museum of Natural History**
Central Park West/79th St,
New York,
New York 10024
*Albertosaurus*
*Allosaurus*
*Anatosaurus*
*Apatosaurus*
*Camptosaurus*
*Coelophysis*
*Corythosaurus*
*Lambeosaurus*
*Montanoceratops*
*Monoclonius*
*Ornitholestes*
*Panoplosaurus*
*Plateosaurus*
*Protoceratops*
*Psittacosaurus*
*Saurolophus*
*Stegosaurus*
*Styracosaurus*
*Triceratops*
*Tyrannosaurus*

**Amherst College**
Pratt Museum,
Amherst,
Massachusetts 01002
*Anchisaurus*

**Buffalo Museum of Science**
Buffalo,
New York
*Allosaurus*
*Psittacosaurus*
*Triceratops*

**Carnegie Museum of Natural History**
4400 Forbes Avenue,
Pittsburgh,
Pennsylvania 15213
*Allosaurus*
*Apatosaurus*
*Camarasaurus*
*Camptosaurus*
*Corythosaurus*
*Diplodocus*
*Dryosaurus*
*Protoceratops*
*Stegosaurus*
*Tyrannosaurus*

**Denver Museum of Natural History**
City Park,
Denver,
Colorado 80205
*Anatosaurus*
*Diplodocus*
*Stegosaurus*
*Tyrannosaurus*

**Cleveland Museum of Natural History**
Wade Oval,
University Circle,
Cleveland,
Ohio 44106
*Haplocanthosaurus*

**Dinosaur National Monument**
PO Box 128,
Jensen,
Utah 84035
A vast quarry site where excavation is still in progress. Dinosaurs found here include:
*Allosaurus*
*Apatosaurus*
*Camarasaurus*
*Camptosaurus*
*Ceratosaurus*
*Dryosaurus*
*Stegosaurus*

**Earth Sciences Museum**
Brigham Young University,
Provo,
Utah 84602
*'Supersaurus'*
*'Ultrasaurus'*

**Field Museum of Natural History**
Roosevelt Road at Lake Shore Drive,
Chicago,
Illinois 60605
*Albertosaurus*
*Apatosaurus*
*Diplodocus*
*Lambeosaurus*
*Protoceratops*

**Forth Worth Museum of Science**
1501 Montgomery Street,
Forth Worth,
Texas 76107
*Allosaurus*
*Camptosaurus*

**Above:** The spacious main hall of the British Museum (Natural History) provides a magnificent setting for the Museum's permanent exhibition: ***Dinosaurs and their living relatives.*** In the foreground we see a cast of the skeleton of the 85ft (26m) long sauropod *Diplodocus*; behind that is a cast of the skeleton of *Triceratops*. Normally this hall is thronging with adults and children—living (and noisy!) proof of the enduring fascination of dinosaurs.

**Houston Museum of Natural Science**
Houston,
Texas
*Diplodocus*

**Los Angeles County Museum**
900 Exposition Boulevard,
Los Angeles,
California 90007
*Allosaurus*
*Camptosaurus*
*Corythosaurus*
*Dilophosaurus*
*Edmontosaurus*
*Parasaurolophus*
*Tyrannosaurus*

**Museum of Comparative Zoology**
Harvard University,
Cambridge,
Massachusetts 02138
*Heterodontosaurus*
*Plateosaurus*
*Scutellosaurus*
*Staurikosaurus*

**Museum of Northern Arizona**
Box 720,
Flagstaff,
Arizona 86001
*Coelophysis*
*Scutellosaurus*

**Museum of Palaeontology**
University of California,
Berkeley,
California 94720
*Dilophosaurus*

**Museum of the Rockies**
Montana State University,
Bozeman,
Montana 59715
*Maiasaura*

**National Museum of Natural History**
Smithsonian Institution,
Washington D.C. 20560
*Albertosaurus*
*Allosaurus*
*Brachyceratops*
*Camarasaurus*
*Camptosaurus*
*Diplodocus*
*Edmontosaurus*
*Stegosaurus*
*Thescelosaurus*
*Triceratops*

**Peabody Museum of Natural History**
Yale University,
170 Whitney Avenue,
PO Box 6666,
New Haven,
Connecticut 06511
*Apatosaurus*
*Camarasaurus*
*Camptosaurus*
*Claosaurus*
*Deinonychus*
*Monoclonius*
*Stegosaurus*
*Torosaurus*

**University of Michigan Exhibit Museum**
Alexander G. Ruthven Museums,
1109 Geddes Avenue,
Ann Arbor,
Michigan 48109
*Allosaurus*
*Anatosaurus*
*Stegosaurus*

**University of Wyoming**
Geological Museum,
Box 3254,
Laramie,
Wyoming 82071
*Anatosaurus*
*Anchiceratops*
*Apatosaurus*
*Tyrannosaurus*

**Utah Museum of Natural History**
University of Utah,
Salt Lake City,
Utah 84112
*Allosaurus*
*Barosaurus*
*Camptosaurus*
*Stegosaurus*

## ASIA AND AUSTRALIA

### Australia

**Australian Museum**
PO Box A285,
Sidney,
New South Wales 2000
*Dilophosaurus*

**Queensland Museum**
Gregory Terrace,
Fortitude Valley,
Queensland 4006
*Muttaburrasaurus*
*Rhoetosaurus*

### China

**Beipei Museum**
Beipei,
Sichuan Province
*Omeisaurus*
*Tuojiangosaurus*
*Yangchuanosaurus*

**Institute of Vertebrate Palaeontology and Palaeoanthropology**
PO Box 643,
Beijing
*Lufengosaurus*
*Mamenchisaurus*
*Psittacosaurus*
*Shantungosaurus*
*Tsintaosaurus*
*Yangchuanosaurus*

### India

**Geology Studies Unit**
Indian Statistical Institute,
Calcutta
*Barapasaurus*
*Lametasaurus*

### Japan

**National Science Museum**
Tokyo
Permanent display includes
*Nipponosaurus*

### Mongolia

**Mongolian Academy of Sciences**
Geological Institute,
Ulan Bator
*Bactrosaurus*
*Nemegtosaurus*
*Opisthocoelicaudia*
*Oviraptor*
*Protoceratops*
*Psittacosaurus*
*Saurornithoides*
*Tarbosaurus*

## EUROPE

### Austria

**Natural History Museum**
Vienna
*Ouranosaurus*
*Struthiosaurus*

### Belgium

**Bernissart Museum**
Bernissart,
Hainaut
*Iguanodon*

**Institut Royal des Sciences Naturelles de Belgique**
Rue Vautier 29,
B-1040 Brussels
*Craspedodon*
*Iguanodon* from Bernissart
*'Megalosaurus'*
*Orthomerus*

### Federal Republic of Germany

**Bavarian State Collection for Palaeontology and Historical Geology**
Richard-Wagner-Strasse 10/2,
8000 Munich 2
*Compsognathus*

**Geological and Palaeontological Institute**
University of Münster,
Pferdegasse 3,
D4400 Münster
*Iguanodon*

**Institute and Museum of Geology and Palaeontology**
University of Tübingen,
Sigwartstrasse 10
7400 Tübingen 1
*Coelophysis*
*Hypsilophodon*
*Kentrosaurus*
*Plateosaurus*

**Senckenberg Nature Museum**
Forschungsinstitut Senckenberg,
Senckenberganlage 25,
6000 Frankfurt 1
*Anatosaurus*
*Diplodocus*
*Iguanodon*
*Plateosaurus*
*Protoceratops*
*Triceratops*
*Tyrannosaurus*

**State Museum for Natural History**
Arsenalplatz 3,
D7140 Ludwigsburg 1
*Plateosaurus*

### France

**National Museum of Natural History**
Institute of Palaeontology,
8 rue Buffon,
F-75005 Paris
*Compsognathus*
*Diplodocus*
*Iguanodon*
*Ouranosaurus*
*Protoceratops*
*Tarbosaurus*
*Triceratops*

### German Democratic Republic

**Natural History Museum**
Humboldt University,
Unter den Linden 6,
108 Berlin
*Archaeopteryx*
*Brachiosaurus*
*Dicraeosaurus*
*Dryosaurus*
*Elaphrosaurus*
*Kentrosaurus*

### Italy

**Museo Civico di Storia Naturale di Venezia**
S. Croce 1730,
30125 Venice
*Ouranosaurus*

### Poland

**Dinosaur Park**
Chorzow,
Silesia
Models of Mongolian dinosaurs including:
*Saichania*
*Saurolophus*
*Tarbosaurus*

**Institute of Palaeobiology**
Al Zwirki I Wigury 93,
02-089 Warsaw
Many specimens from the Polish-Mongolian expeditions are studied here including:
*Deinocheirus*
*Gallimimus*
*Homalocephale*
*Nemegtosaurus*
*Pinacosaurus*
*Protoceratops*
*Opisthocoelicaudia*
*Saichania*
*Tarbosaurus*
*Velociraptor*

### Sweden

**Palaeontological Museum**
Uppsala University,
PO Box 256,
751 05 Uppsala
*Euhelopus*

### United Kingdom

**Birmingham Museum**
Dept of Natural History
Chamberlain Square,
Birmingham B3 3DH
*Allosaurus*
*Triceratops*

**British Museum (Natural History)**
Cromwell Road,
London SW7 5BD
*Diplodocus*
*Euoplocephalus*
*Gallimimus*
*Hypsilophodon*
*Iguanodon*
*Protoceratops* eggs
*Triceratops*
Specimens held in store include:
*Brachiosaurus*
*Cetiosauriscus*
*Dacentrurus*
*Hylaeosaurus*
*'Megalosaurus'*
*Mochlodon*
*Polacanthus*
*Proceratosaurus*
*Scelidosaurus*
*Struthiosaurus*
*Titanosaurus*

**Crystal Palace Park**
Sydenham,
London SE20
Display of Waterhouse Hawkins' 19th Century dinosaur models

**The Dinosaur Museum**
Icen Way,
Dorchester,
Dorset DT1 1EW
*Hypsilophodon*
*Iguanodon*
*Stegosaurus* model
*Tyrannosaurus* model

**Hunterian Museum**
The University,
Glasgow G12 8QQ
*Iguanodon* footprints
*Triceratops*

**The Leicestershire Museums**
96 New Walk,
Leicester LE1 6TD
New sauropod: ?*Cetiosaurus*

**Museum of Isle of Wight Geology**
Sandown Library,
High Street,
Sandown,
Isle of Wight PO36 8AF
*Hypsilophodon*
*Iguanodon*
*Yaverlandia*

**Royal Scottish Museum**
Chambers Street,
Edinburgh EH1 1JF
*Allosaurus*
*Triceratops*
Footprint trackway

**Sedgwick Museum**
Cambridge University,
Downing Street,
Cambridge CB2 3EQ
*Iguanodon*

**University Museum**
Parks Road,
Oxford OX1 3PW
*Camptosaurus*
*Cetiosaurus*
*Dacentrurus*
*Eustreptospondylus*
*Iguanodon*
*Megalosaurus*
*Metriacanthosaurus*

### USSR

**Central Geological and Prospecting Museum**
Leningrad
*Diplodocus*
*Mandschurosaurus*

**Palaeontological Institute**
Academy of Sciences,
Profsoyuznaya 113,
Moscow 117321
*Avimimus*
*Bactrosaurus*
*Bagaceratops*
*Iguanodon orientalis*
*Probactrosaurus*
*Procheneosaurus*
*Protoceratops*
*Psittacosaurus*
*Saurolophus*
*Talarurus*
*Tarbosaurus*

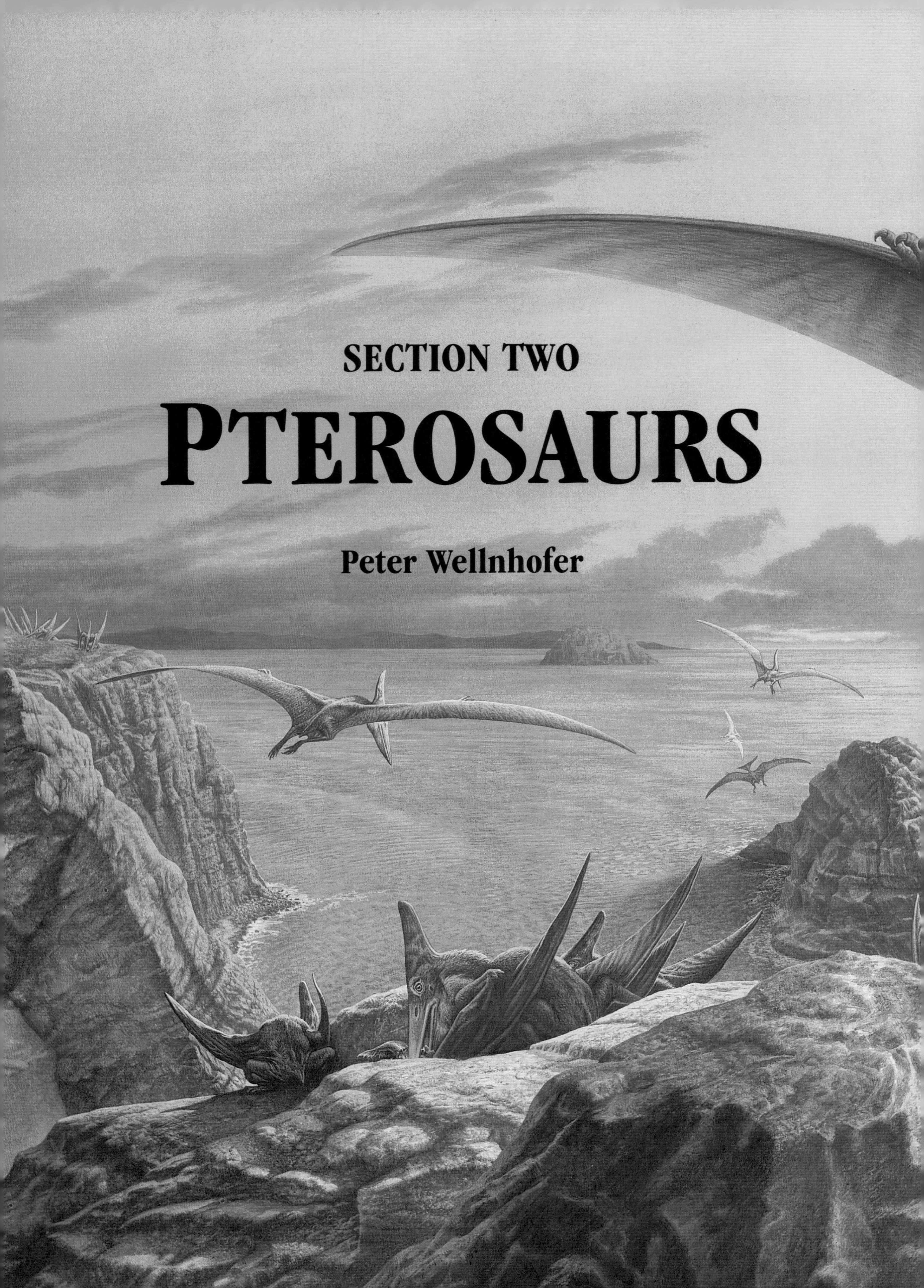

SECTION TWO

# PTEROSAURS

Peter Wellnhofer

# Introduction to Pterosaurs

In the early years of this century, four English explorers, led by the famous London zoologist Professor George Edward Challenger, discovered living primeval creatures in a faraway corner of South America, creatures which had hitherto been believed to have become extinct at least from the Mesozoic. On an inaccessible plateau, completely cut off from the outside world, Professor Challenger, his colleague Professor Summerlee, traveller and sportsman Lord John Roxton and Ed Malone, reporter on the *Daily Gazette*, also met living pterosaurs from the Jurassic. Malone's reports provide a clear record of the adventures and dangers faced by the members of the expedition.

Malone describes their first encounter with a pterosaur like this: '. . . we saw, at the distance of a mile or so, something which appeared to be a huge grey bird flap slowly up from the ground and skim smoothly off, flying very low and straight, until it was lost among the tree-ferns.' On the same evening they were to make even closer acquaintance with a pterosaur: this is the only thing it could possibly have been. The men were sitting around the camp fire roasting an aguti, a small pig-like animal, that Lord Roxton had killed for their supper. But let Ed Malone tell us himself: 'The night was moonless, but there were some stars, and one could see for a little distance across the plain. Well, suddenly out of the darkness, out of the night, there swooped something with a swish like an aeroplane. The whole group of us were covered for an instant by a canopy of leathery wings, and I had a momentary vision of a long, snake-like neck, a fierce, red greedy eye, and a great snapping beak, filled, to my amazement, with little gleaming teeth. The next instant it was gone – and so was our dinner. A huge black shadow, twenty feet across, skimmed up into the air; for an instant the monster's wings blotted out the stars, and then it vanished over the brow of the cliffs above us.'

Finally the expedition succeeded in capturing a living creature and bringing it back to London in a big crate. Professor Challenger reported on his discovery of living pterosaurs at a meeting of the Royal Zoological Society. The meeting was not prepared to believe him; the professor gave a sign and a large, rectangular crate was brought on to the platform. He pushed back the lid, and a moment later an indescribably loathsome creature appeared with a scratching, rattling sound, unfolded two leathery wings to a span of ten feet and rose into the air to circle slowly under the ceiling of Queen's Hall, in which the meeting was taking place. Everyone was staring at this display as if transfixed, when suddenly Professor Challenger yelled: 'The window! For Heaven's sake close the window!' But it was too late. The next second the creature reached the opening, forced its body through it and disappeared.

**Above:** 'The next instant it was gone -- and so was our dinner.' Zdeněk Burian's illustration of a scene in Conan Doyle's *The Lost World* when Professor Challenger's party of explorers meet a living pterosaur on a mountain plateau in South America.

The last record of the London *pterodactyl*, as it was later called, is found in the log of the *Friesland*, a postal steamer of the Holland-America Line. This contains an entry saying that next morning at 9 o'clock, ten miles off Start Point, a strange creature, 'something between a flying goat and a monstrous bat', flew past at enormous speed in a south-westerly direction. Its homing instinct had certainly set it on the right course. It probably never reached its goal, so this last living pterosaur perished somewhere out in the wastes of the Atlantic.

**Below:** The last glimpse of the London pterodactyl as observed by the crew of the Dutch-American steamer, S.S. *Friesland*. This reconstruction of a scene from *The Lost World* is again by Zdeněk Burian.

The reader will certainly have noticed that this story is far too good to be true. Its author, Sir Arthur Conan Doyle, creator of the legendary Sherlock Holmes, published it in 1912 under the title *The Lost World*.[9] It is remarkable in two respects.

Firstly, Conan Doyle describes the appearance, way of life and behaviour of animals that disappeared from the face of the earth 65 million years ago. Thus no human being can ever have seen them alive; all we have are fossils, remains of the creatures that have been turned to stone. Conan Doyle does not describe these strange primeval creatures as a scholar, but as an imaginative writer, but thoroughly convincingly and realistically.

Secondly, Conan Doyle has his prehistoric pterosaurs survive on a high plateau somewhere in South America, more precisely in the Amazon region, thus in Brazil. It is quite amazing that in 1970, that is to say 60 years after Conan Doyle wrote the story, fossilized pterosaur bones actually were found on an extensive high plateau in north-eastern Brazil, the Araripe plateau. The Brazilian geologist Llellewyn Price described the find and called the species *Araripesaurus castilhoi*.[10] Pterosaur fossils from the Araripe plateau have continued to appear, representing several different genera, some with wing spans of up to 20ft (6m). Some of them actually must have looked as Conan Doyle described them: '. . . with a long, snake-like neck, a great snapping beak, filled with little, gleaming teeth'. The Araripe plateau in north-eastern Brazil became one of the most important sources of Cretaceous pterosaurs, documenting the highly diverse development of this group of animals about 100 million years ago.

In fact the first discoveries of pterosaur fossils were made as early as the 18th century, at the time when people started to collect natural objects and display them in natural history collections. Thus the first pterosaur find, a small fossil on a slab of Solnhofen lithographic limestone from Eichstätt in Bavaria, appeared in the natural history collection of the Palatine prince, Karl Theodor, in Mannheim. The supervisor of this collection, Cosimo Alessandro Collini, probably noticed that this was an unusual fossil skeleton, but was undecided in his interpretation of what sort of a creature it was. It was not until 1801 that the great Parisian anatomist Georges Cuvier recognized that it was a reptile that could fly. It was neither a bat nor a bird, as others thought, but a hitherto entirely unknown type of creature that he called *Pterodactylus* (=flight finger), because the wing membrane was stretched over a single, albeit very long, digit.

Genuine scientific research on pterosaurs began with Cuvier. The small *Pterodactylus* from Eichstätt was followed by many other finds, not only in Solnhofen lithographic limestone, which also provided the famous primeval bird *Archaeopteryx*, but from many other

9 Conan Doyle, A., 1912. *The Lost World.* A new edition of this fascinating book was published in paperback by Puffin Books and Penguin Books in 1981.

10 Price, L.I., 1971. *A Presença de Pterosauria no Cretáceo Inferior da Chapada do Araripe, Brasil.* Anais Academia Brasiliana de Ciencias, 43 (suppl.): 352-461.

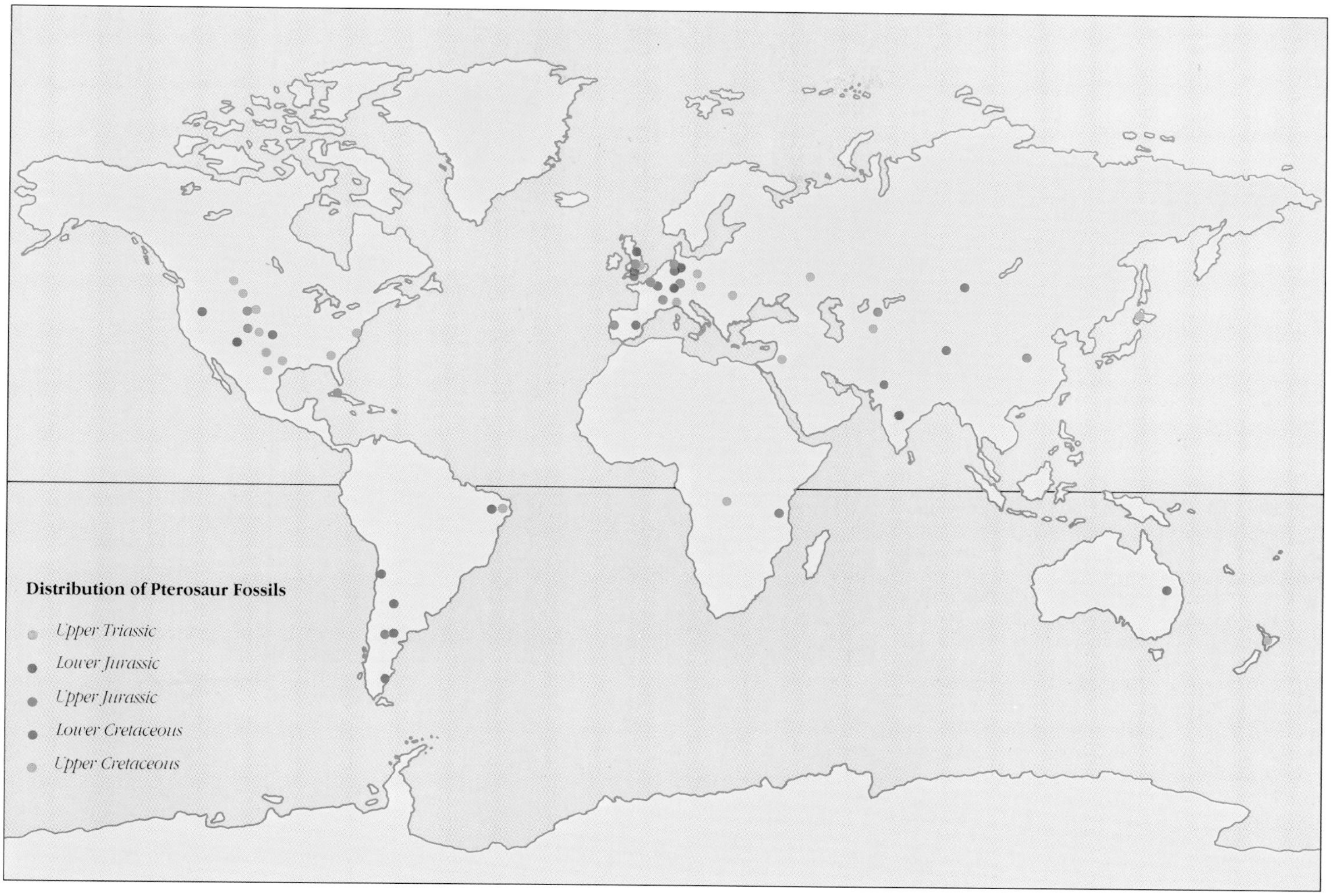

**Distribution of Pterosaur Fossils**

- *Upper Triassic*
- *Lower Jurassic*
- *Upper Jurassic*
- *Lower Cretaceous*
- *Upper Cretaceous*

**Above:** The distribution of fossil finds indicates that pterosaurs once lived on all continents except Antarctica. Only sedimentary rocks of the Mesozoic era are likely to yield pterosaur fossils. This fact is reflected by the distributional pattern shown here, which also reflects the accessibility of the available fossil sites around the globe.

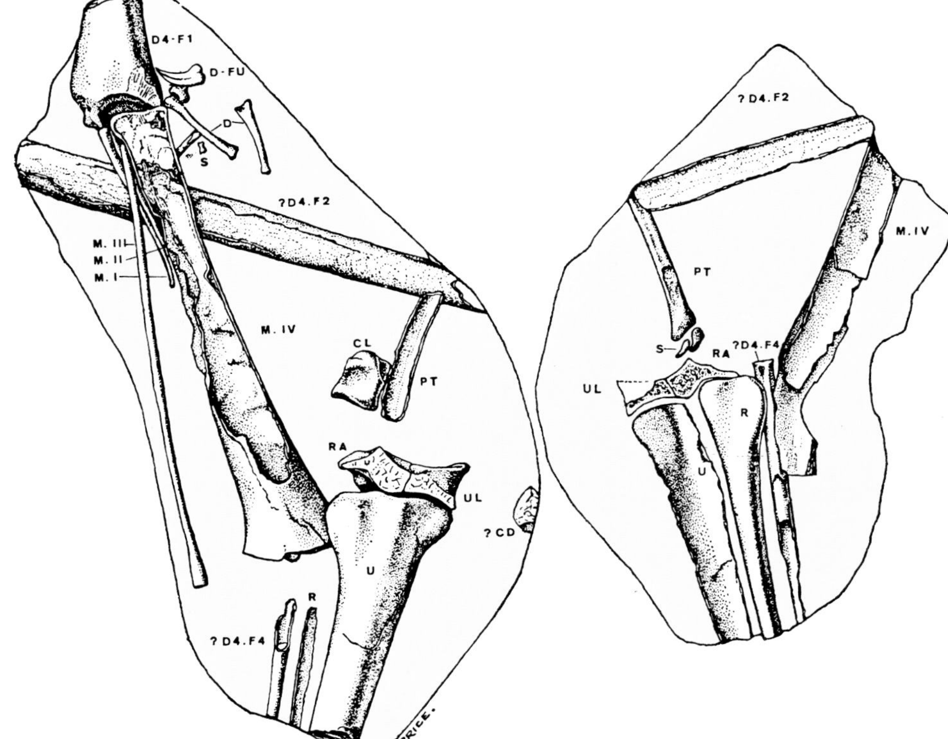


**Below:** Fossil wing bones of a pterosaur discovered in a split nodule from the Lower Cretaceous Santana Formation of the Araripe Plateau in north-eastern Brazil. This specimen, named as *Araripesaurus castilboi*, was the first scientific record of pterosaurs from this area of South America, where, prophetically, Conan Doyle set *The Lost World*.

geological formations as well, from the late Triassic (220 million years ago) to the late Cretaceous (65 million years ago).

They appeared in an extraordinary variety of forms, ultimately distributed world-wide. Pterosaurs lived on all continents with the exception of the Antarctic, and included genera from the size of a sparrow up to the largest flying creatures of all time, with a wing span of 39ft (12m). Despite the wide range of different forms, pterosaurs maintained their special characteristics to the end: a unique wing structure and extreme lightness of skeleton.

Scientific research has not been at a standstill since Cuvier. Generations of palaeontologists and zoologists since that time have tried to find out what sort of creatures pterosaurs were, what they looked like, where and how they lived, how they moved, how they flew, fed and reproduced themselves, what their flight membranes and body covering were like, whether they were warm-blooded or not, how they evolved and developed phylogenetically, what role they played in the prehistoric animal world and finally why they became extinct 65 million years ago, without successors, leaving birds to take over domination of the air.

Scientific research on these and many other questions is in full swing. It will probably never reach an ultimate conclusion, as new fossil finds are always being made, and also because human curiosity, the driving force in any field of science, will never be extinguished. Thus attempts have recently been made to reconstruct the aerodynamics of the pterosaur wing using mathematical and physical methods, and to test the results by building flying models.

Today pterosaurs can be considered as one of the most thoroughly investigated groups of fossil reptiles. Interesting answers have been provided to many of the questions. Others could only be answered by making assumptions, as documentation available to palaeontologists in fossil form is by its very nature incomplete. Unfortunately we are not in the position of Conan Doyle's Professor Challenger, and able to observe living pterosaurs. However, if we allow our imaginations to be inspired and stimulated by Conan Doyle, this and our scientifically based knowledge unite to convince us of their fascination.

### Fossilization

It is the palaeontologist's task to draw conclusions from fossils about life in prehistoric times. The word fossil comes from the Latin verb *fodere*, to dig, and originally meant anything that had been dug up, or discovered in the ground. Today, by fossils we understand remains of organisms, but also traces of creatures' activities. As a rule fossils are found in older deposits from the Earth's past, usually in sedimentary rocks, and consist of the hard parts of the creature that survived decay. A close connection with geology is thus of fundamental importance to palaeontology. Fossils are not only biological, but also historical documents of the development of life on Earth. Thus as far as zoology and botany are concerned, fields of research concerned with the modern world of plants and animals, this represents an enormous broadening of our knowledge of life forms, as plants and animals of earlier ages, now long since extinct, can be included. Today palaeontology has an overview of the development of organized life on the higher level over a period of almost 600 million years.

But along with this broader knowledge of the formal variety of life in general there is also

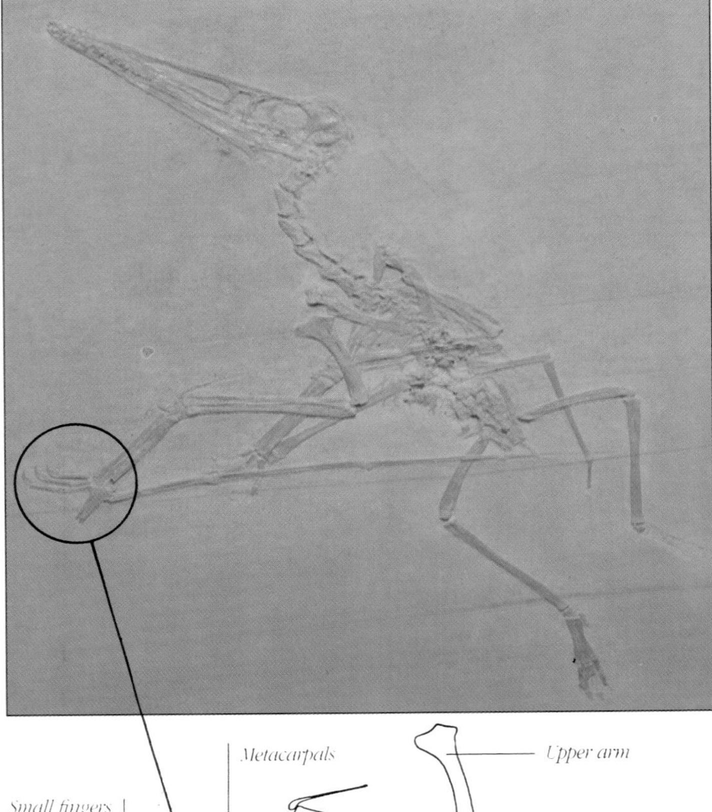

**Left:** This *Pterodactylus* from the Solnhofen lithographic limestone of Bavaria has a broken wing finger (see also the close-up photograph of the fracture below). This accident probably happened while the creature was alive, and as a result it would not have been able to spread its wing membrane which relied upon the extension of the wing finger for its proper functioning. With one wing hanging limp, flight would have been impossible and the search for food severely impaired. It is quite likely that this individual starved to death, and its corpse was then washed into the lagoon where the process of fossilization began. The drawing below shows in detail the arm and hand bones, and the broken finger, which is circled in the photograph above.

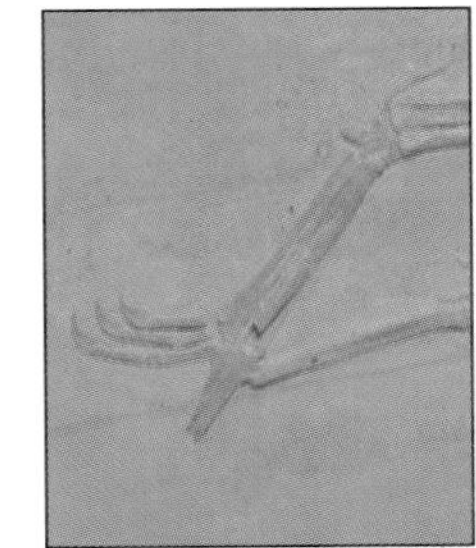

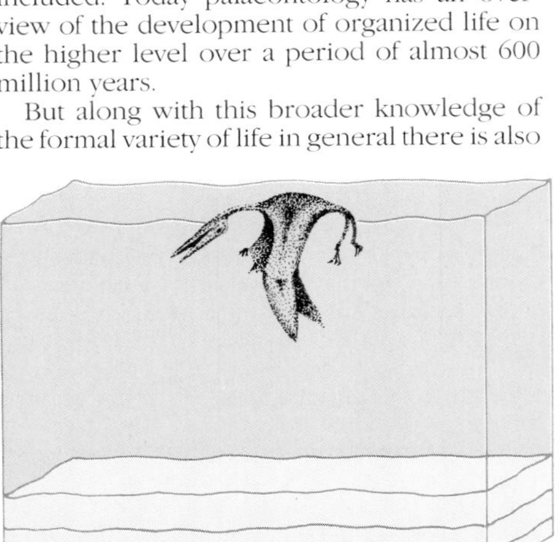

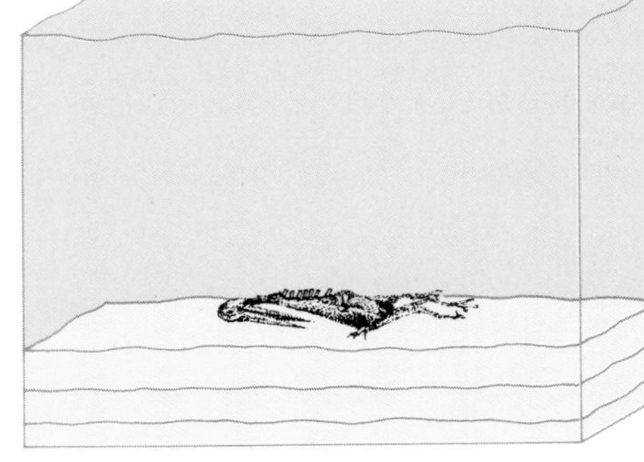

**Fossilization (above and below)**
This sequence of drawings shows the first of the stages by which a dead pterosaur may have been turned into a fossil. In the first drawing the carcass is seen floating in the sea. After some time it sinks to the sea floor where it is embedded in soft mud. At this stage the soft parts, muscles, skin and connective tissue decay completely, and water currents may disturb and eventually dislocate parts of the skeleton.

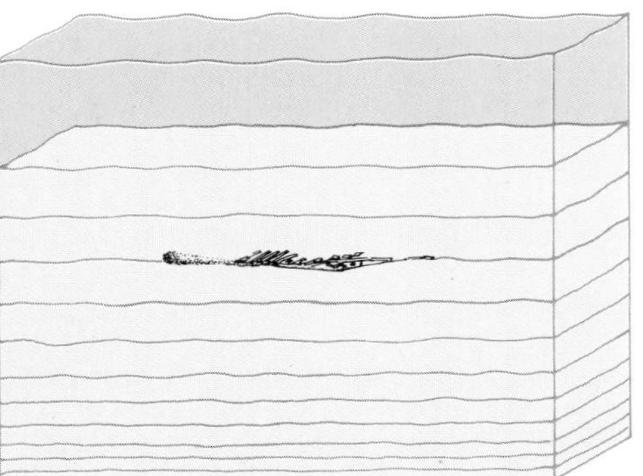

Steady sedimentation will enclose and preserve the bones, and, as the overburden increases, also compress the skeletal remains. In the course of compaction, dehydration, and mineralisation the sediment is transformed into hard rock, for example flaggy limestone, and the pterosaur bones will be petrified, i.e. fossilized (middle drawing above). Finally, if the quarryman is lucky enough, he will find the fossil pterosaur on a slab of limestone.

an associated loss of information. A palaeontologist cannot experiment like a zoologist. Direct research into physiological processes is not available to him. Only in rare cases can he make statements about soft parts, body covering and colouring. This is a result of the fossilization process itself.

After death a living organism usually breaks down into inorganic substances, and no trace of it remains. Thus fossilization represents an exception to the general rule, and several factors have to be present simultaneously to make the process possible. This is particularly true of pterosaurs, which have very lightly constructed and fragile skeletons. One of the most important prerequisites was that the pterosaur corpses had to be quickly covered up and protected from exposure to the air, so that natural processes of decomposition were checked. As pterosaurs were land creatures, they are likely to have died on land in most cases, and so only had a chance of becoming fossils if their bodies were washed into a river or lake, or if they fell into a sand bank or sank into mud.

By far the most frequent pterosaur finds are made in marine strata, that is to say in rocks which originated in prehistoric marine deposits. Most of the known species of pterosaur probably lived near the coast and fed on fish or other aquatic organisms. The cause of their death was probably natural only in the rarest cases, in other words they did not often die of old age. Pterosaurs found as fossils could have died of disease, parasites, poisoning or wounds. Many were probably themselves prey to larger predatory saurians, and were eaten. It is quite conceivable that flight membrane injuries left them unable to fly, and were thus life threatening. Pterosaur fossils have been found in Solnhofen limestone in Bavaria with the first wing phalanx broken. That can only have happened while the creature was alive. These pterosaurs had thus, for whatever reason, had an accident or been attacked, and broken the flight digit that spread the flight membrane. This meant that one wing hung limp, and the creatures could no longer fly in search of food. They had to starve.

In many cases we can assume that pterosaurs were forced into water in a tropical storm and drowned, or were carried from the mainland by rivers into the sea near the coast. In both cases the corpse sank to the sea bed after drifting for a longer or shorter period, then was finally covered in mud and subsequent sedimentation of increasingly massive strata. In the course of this, soft parts, muscles, skin and connective tissue decomposed.

Water and oxygen cause decay. If there is no oxygen, putrefaction sets in. In rare cases soft parts also survived as fossils: their decomposition was delayed, meaning that they could be infiltrated by mineral substances during the fossilization process. This preserves a detailed image of parts of the body not usually capable of fossilization. In the case of some pterosaurs we are therefore familiar with imprints of flight membranes, of webs between the long toes, of a throat pouch, of respiratory tubes and of the outline of the body.

Evidence of a hair-like body covering caused a sensation. Sometimes it is in the form of an imprint, or hair has even been preserved itself in some cases.[11] In general, fossil pterosaur skeletons have only come down to us incomplete or as fragments. The smaller a pterosaur was, the greater its chance of being completely

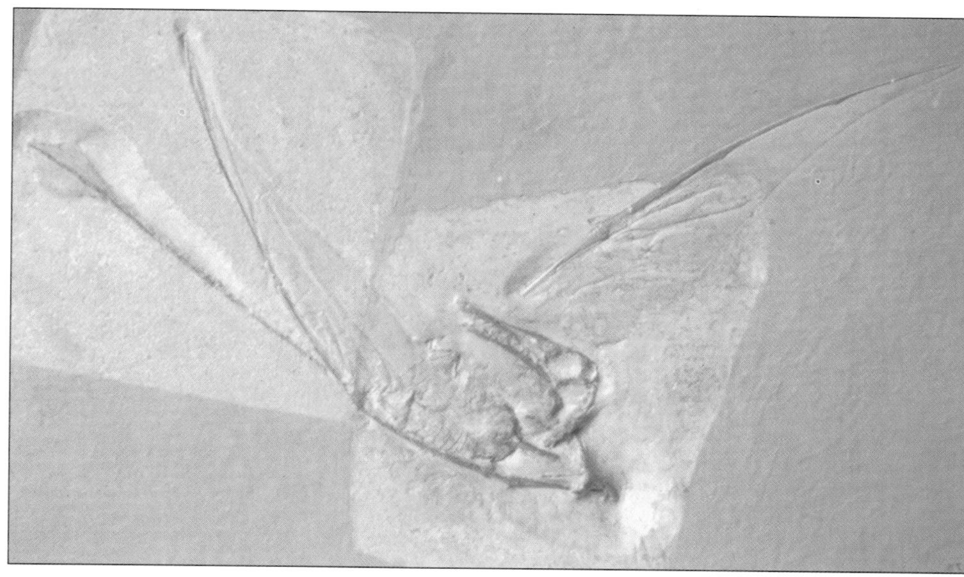

**Below:** The skeleton of this juvenile *Pterodactylus antiquus* from Solnhofen is completely preserved. Its undisturbed position shows that the carcass was quickly embedded in the sediment together with its soft parts. However, wing membranes, muscles, skin and tendons have decayed later, leaving no trace.

**Above:** This *Rhamphorhynchus* from Solnhofen still shows the impressions of wing membranes preserved in much detail, as well as the imprint of a terminal vane on the tail. The fossil documentation of soft parts like these requires very favourable conditions, and a fine grained sediment.

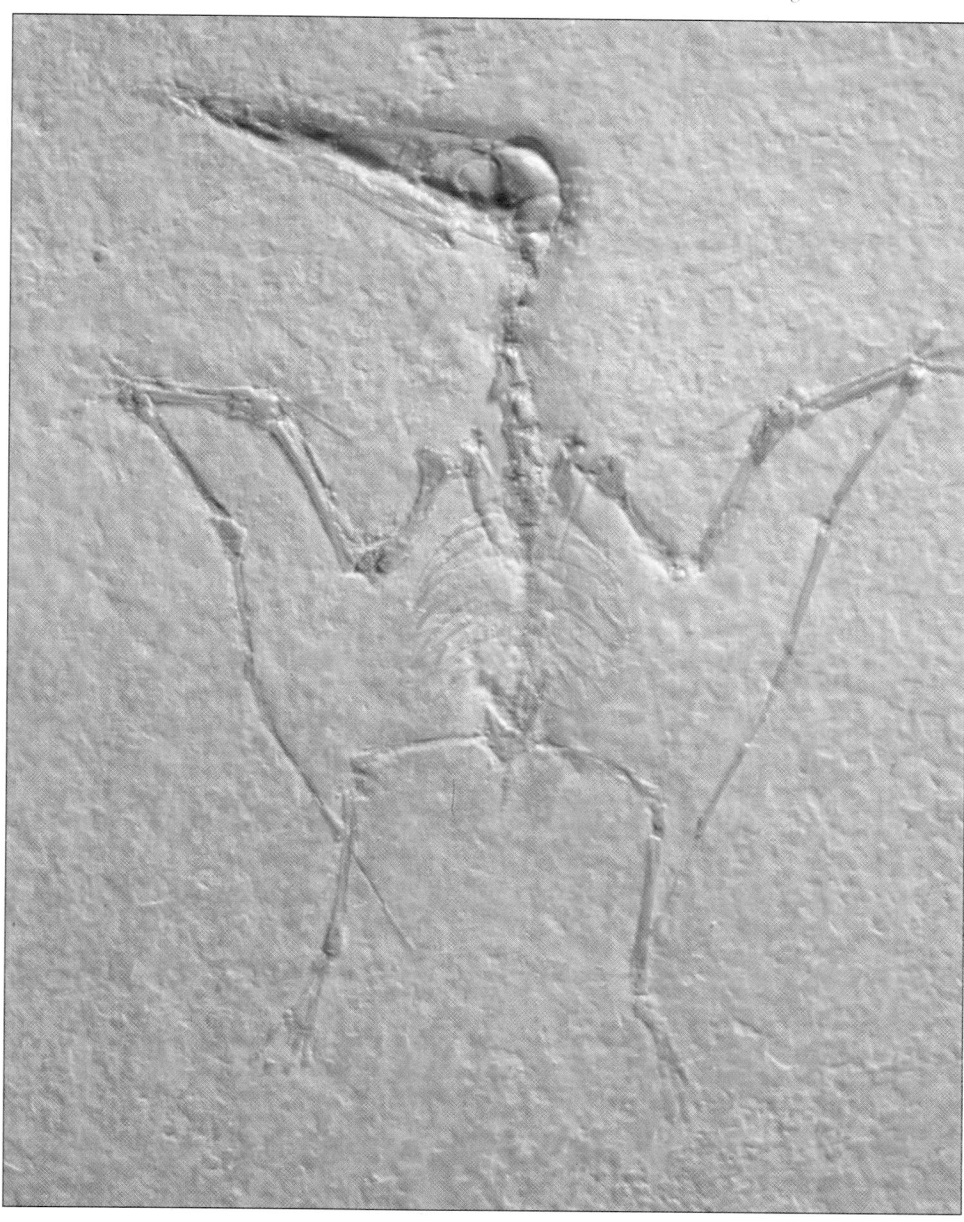

11 Sharov, A.G., op. cit. (8).

fossilized. If the size of the body was greater than that of a pigeon or a seagull, we generally only find incomplete skeletal remains or individual parts of the skeleton, like isolated skulls, wing bones, leg bones, pelvises or shoulder blades. The reason for this is that pterosaur corpses, rather like the corpses of birds, drift around in the water for a long time.[12] Their bodies were light, their bones hollow, and partially filled with air. The heavy parts, above all the head, wings and hind legs of the dead pterosaur hung down and were the first items to be detached from the body after decomposition of the soft parts. They sank to the sea bed and were embedded individually. The other parts of the body followed, until the whole skeleton was spread over a large area of the sea floor.

In the case of complete skeletons one frequently observes that the pterosaur's neck is bent back, and is often drawn backwards so strongly that the skull is above the pelvis. This position also occurs in modern bird corpses, especially when they have dried out on land to become a 'mummy'. This is caused by contraction of the muscles of the neck, which draws the neck backwards. This might mean that fossilized pterosaur skeletons with heads bent back belonged to creatures that died on land and dried out there, thus becoming mummified. They must then have been washed in this condition by a river into the sea or a lake.

However, this bending back of the neck could also be explained by the fact that a decrease in tension of the neck muscles after death caused elastic ligaments between the neural spines of the cervical vertebrae to draw the neck back automatically. One also observes

12 Schäfer, W., 1962. *Aktuo-Paläontologie nach Studien in der Nordsee*. Frankfurt am Main. Schäfer investigated post-mortem history of seabirds in detail. His findings can also be applied to pterosaurs.

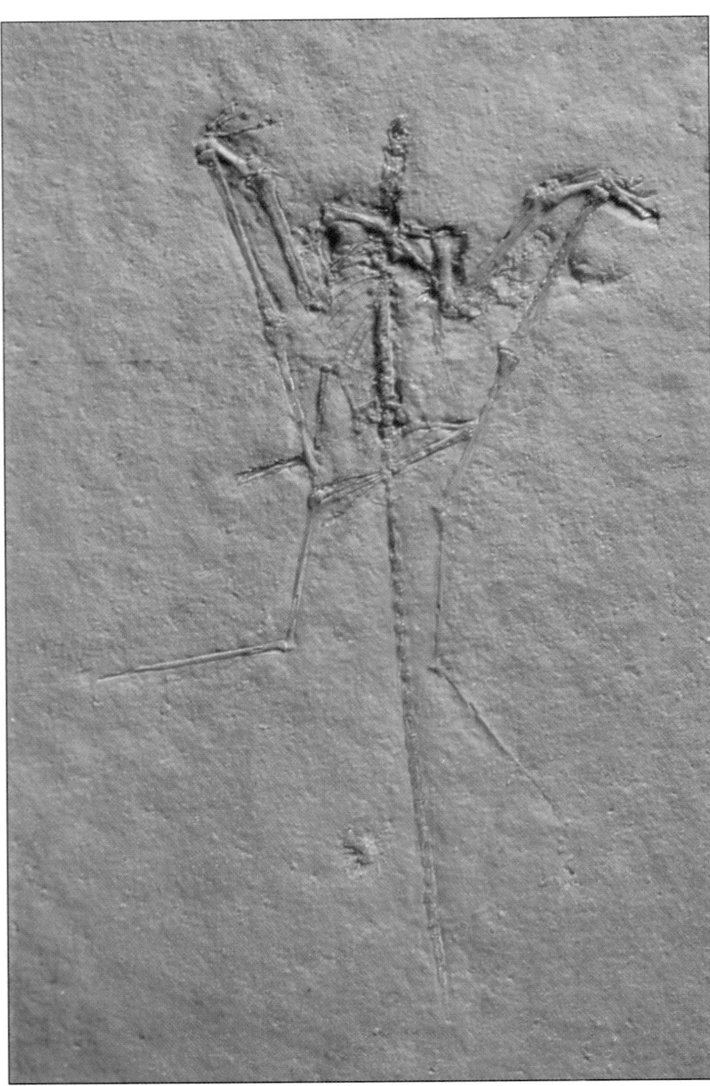

**Left:** This *Rhamphorhynchus longicaudus* presumably lost its head when its carcass was floating in the waters of the Solnhofen lagoon. If a dead pterosaur drifted around on the surface of the water for a long period of time, it must have been quite usual for parts of the carcass to disintegrate and eventually get lost. The skull would normally become detached first, and then the wings and legs. In this specimen, only the skull is missing; the rest of the skeleton has remained intact.

**Below and below right:** This skeleton of *Pterodactylus elegans* from the Solnhofen limestone of Bavaria is seen with its head and neck strongly bent backward. Such a posture is commonly observed in fossil pterosaurs, and is caused by the pull of ligaments between the neck vertebrae after the tension of the musculature has ceased to operate after the animal has died. This peculiar bending of the neck can also be seen in fossil and extant birds, especially when the carcass has been mummified on dry land. Such an example is shown in the drawing of the Common Tern (p.193).

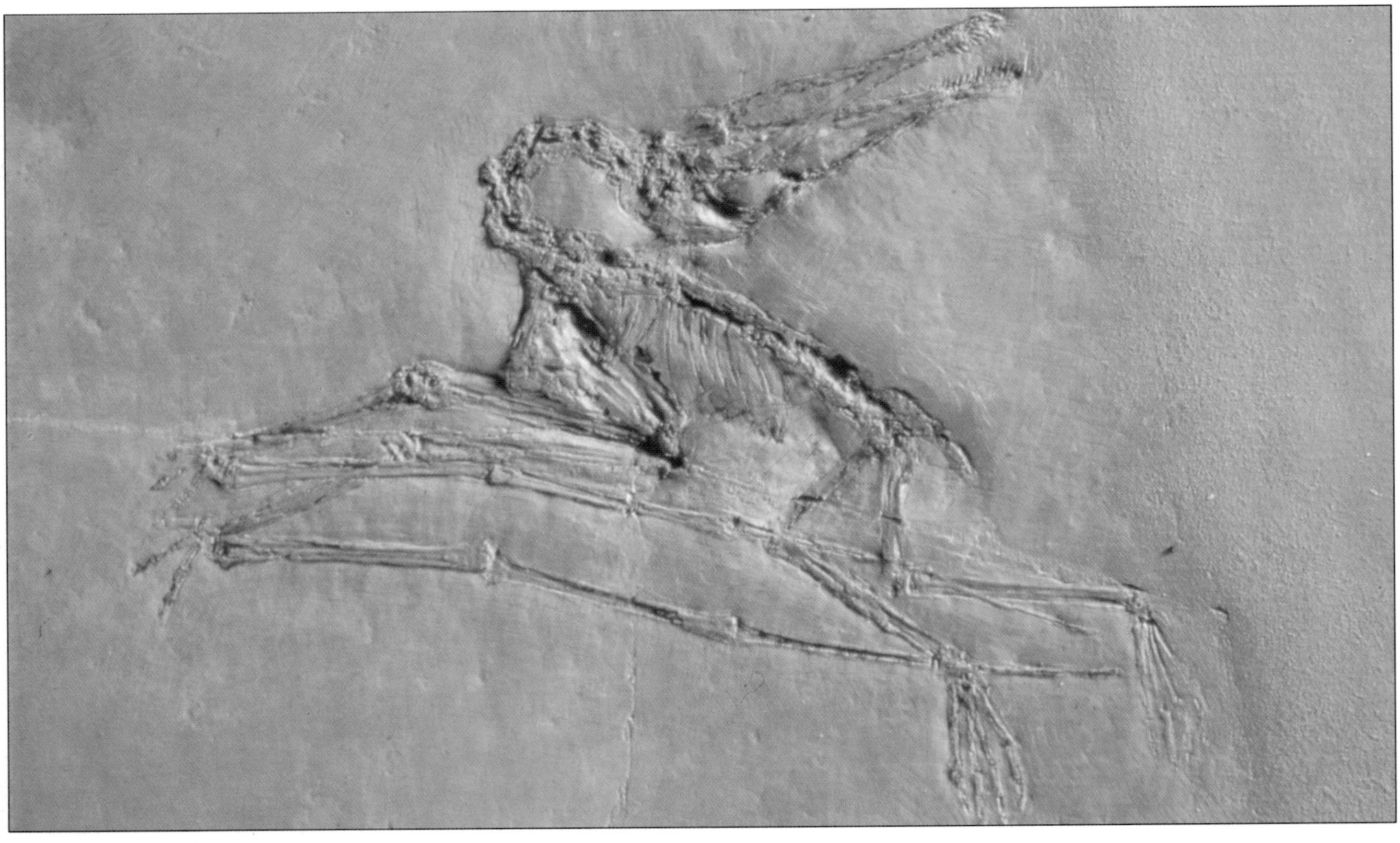

this in many birds who sleep with their heads turned back into their feathers. They do not need any muscular activity to do this, it is enough to relax the neck muscles so that the interspinal ligaments can exert a backward pull.

If the skeletal remains finally sank to the bottom of a lake or sea, they could possibly still have been disarticulated by currents and gradually covered and completely embedded by continuing sedimentation. The skeleton was crushed by pressure from the layers of sediment, which at first contained a lot of water, then gradually became more and more compacted and heavy. In the course of further compacting petrifaction, or mineralization, gradually occurred, and this also affected the bones of the skeleton.

The bones were impregnated with circulating mineral solutions. This explains why fossil bones and teeth generally consist of inorganic, mineral substances rather than organic ones, and thus are 'petrified'. In this way the internal structure of the bones is often preserved, often down to very fine details.

The kind of mineralization that occurs is dependent on the surrounding milieu. Limestone is formed from limy marine ooze, of the kind that occurs in the Upper Jurassic lagoon of Solnhofen. Fossil bones then consist of calcite or calcium carbonate ($CaCo_3$). Sandy deposits turn into sandstone; the bones are then usually silicified, that means they consist of very hard quartz-like silicic acid ($SiO_2$). Clayey ooze becomes shale or slate. Here too bones can occur in calcified form.

A special form of fossil preservation is that in calcareous nodules or concretions. Famous examples are fish fossils from the Santana formation in Brazil.[13] Concretions are concentrated accumulations of materials that were originally evenly distributed. They can form as a result of the presence of decomposing organic substances. Pterosaur bones are preserved three-dimensionally in the concretions of the Santana formation; these fossils are not compressed and fragmented, as is usually the case. Often complete wings, vertebral columns and whole skulls are found in a concretion, and in rare cases remains of wing membranes as well. The concretion surrounds the fossils and protects them at the same time. Thus extremely thin-walled and hollow pterosaur bones are protected from the distorting pressure of the rocks above them. However, a fossil enclosed in a solid limestone concretion is extremely difficult to prepare and requires a great deal of patience, skill and experience from the preparator concerned.

Fossilization is only possible in sedimentary rock. In magmatic rock, formed from red-hot molten magma in the depths of the earth's crust or from volcanic lava, no fossils can survive. Thus when looking for fossils we can happily ignore rocks like granite or basalt. We restrict ourselves to strata formed at some point in the history of the Earth as sedimentary rocks, whether on land or at sea. In the case of pterosaurs these were mainly deposits formed in lakes and seas.

Also with respect to pterosaurs we must always be aware that only a small percentage of all organisms has survived in fossil form, probably well below 1 per cent.[14] Thus a large proportion of individual finds of a species or genus shows that on many occasions we are dealing with random finds and owe our knowledge of them merely to collector's luck. Primarily there is little chance of fossilization in areas affected by erosion, in uplands in other words, as most remains are carried away and destroyed.

Thus in the case of pterosaurs we have to reckon with enormous gaps in the fossil record, especially for forms that inhabited higher inland areas. A group of animals that lived on Earth for as long as birds have today, in other words at least 150 million years, must have occupied as many habitats as modern birds. We know that pterosaurs lived all over the world. It can hardly be assumed that they lived exclusively near to coasts and shores, where their fossils have been found in sedimentary lowland areas. Additionally one must take into consideration that only very small sections of the sedimentary rocks in which pterosaur fossils potentially could occur are on the surface of the Earth today. To a large extent they were eroded in the course of the history of the Earth or are concealed under more recent deposits.

However, although we only know a small proportion of the pterosaurs that once lived on Earth, it is astonishing how much information we nevertheless have about them. Indeed, they

**Above:** By contrast with the previous specimens, this *Rhamphorhynchus* skeleton has been disarticulated, and some elements may have already been lost when it sank to the sea bed. There, water currents scattered the bones before they were embedded.

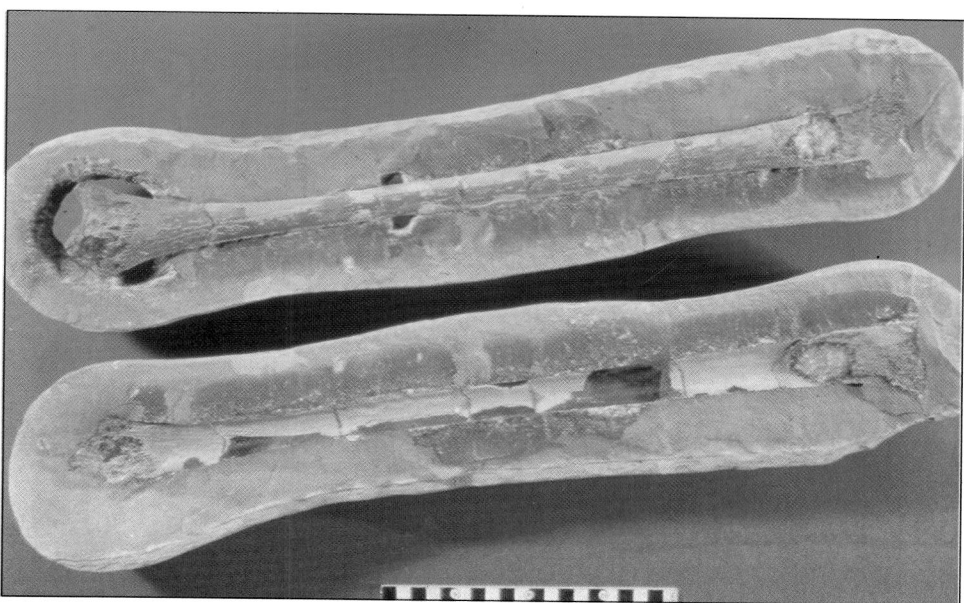

**Below:** The famous fossil concretions of the Santana formation in Brazil contain mostly fishes, but rarely also skeletal remains of pterosaurs. Here the first wing phalanx of a large pterosaur, *Araripesaurus dehmi*, is preserved three-dimensionally.

13 Martill, D.M., 1988. *Preservation of Fish in the Cretaceous Santana Formation of Brazil.* Palaeontology, 31 (1): 1-18.

14 The number of plant and animal species to have lived since the Cambrian, i.e. in the last 590 million years, is estimated at about one thousand million. Some even suggest 1·6 thousand million fossil species. Of these about 130,000 are described. An estimated 4·5 million plant and animal species live on the Earth today. (E. Kuhn-Schnyder, 1977. *Die Geschichte des Lebens auf der Erde.* Mitteilungen der Naturforschenden Gesellschaft des Kantons Solothurn, 27.)

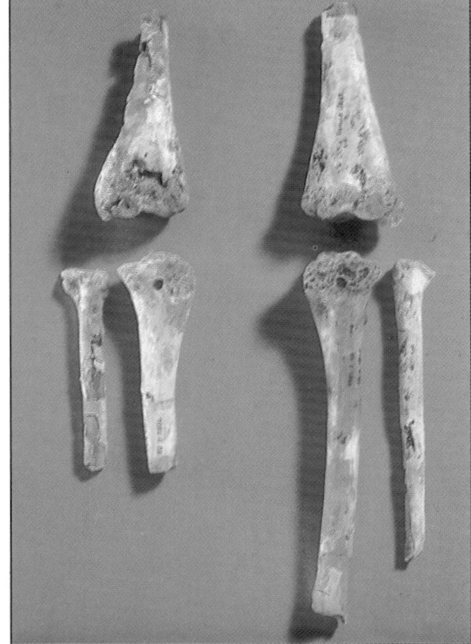

**Left:** Since Roman times the Solnhofen quarries in Bavaria have been worked by hand to excavate the bright yellow limestone for tiles, steps, and latterly printing stones. Careful removal of the slabs often reveals fossils here.

**Above:** Bones preserved in calcareous nodules at the Santana formation on the Araripe plateau are not compressed and so may be preserved three-dimensionally. Careful preparation has revealed these pterosaur wing bones.

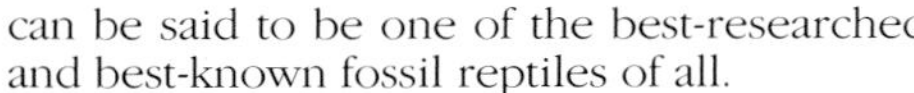

can be said to be one of the best-researched and best-known fossil reptiles of all.

## Excavation and Preparation

It is not really possible to look specifically for pterosaur fossils. They are far too rare for that. Even in the well-known sites where finds have been made, like Solnhofen in Bavaria, on the Araripe Plateau in Brazil or in the Kansas Chalk, pterosaurs are always rare and valued finds. The relatively high number of specimens from these sites is due to intensive quarrying and tireless collecting over a long period.

Pterosaur bones are extremely light in structure. The long bones are hollow like those of birds, and have extremely thin walls. The vertebrae of larger species also have cavities. The skull is often only a structure of bands surrounding large openings and apertures. This means that skeletal bones of a pterosaur were often very fragile, and were damaged or rubbed away by coarser sediments like sand and gravel. And indeed we only find pterosaurs in fine-grained sediments like limestone, shale and marl, or in calcareous concretions, but very rarely in coarse sandstones. Here the delicate, fragile bones scarcely had a chance of fossilizing.

If the remains of a skeleton are discovered on a stratum of rock, the first thing to be attempted is carefully to loosen the rock containing the fossil from the stratum in which it is set without breaking or losing bones. Also it is essential that care is taken that all the parts of the fossil are completely excavated. It has frequently occurred that hours have to be spent looking for a missing piece of stone that was mistakenly thrown away, but still contained parts of the fossil. Usually fossil remains are enclosed in rock and thus protected. Remains of skeletons can then only be recognized by irregular protrusions on the surface of the rock or from cross-sections of bones on the edges of the rock.

If the fossilized bones are brittle and crumbly, then they have to be fixed and hardened on site. Shellac or thin artificial resin lacquers are used for hardening them. To guarantee safe transport to the laboratory, protective plaster bandages may be used or a plaster jacket, and possibly polyurethane foam as well, may have to be wrapped around the fossil remains. It is advisable to sketch or photograph the position of the skeletal remains beforehand. It is often sensible to take a compass bearing in order to determine the distribution of the fossils. This is important if the position of the fossils was affected by water currents: their position can be used to work out the direction of the current and thus the likely position of further fossil remains.

After discovering and excavating fossils, the next task is to preserve the remains, i.e. remove them from the rock, which is usually hard, by suitable methods, and uncover them. This is done both with the traditional tools of hammers and chisels of various sizes and degrees of fineness, and nowadays often with the aid of

**Left:** Quarry 'Mina Pedra Branca' at the Araripe plateau in Brazil. The quarry is operated for the gypsum at the bottom of the wall; above it is a section of the early Cretaceous Santana formation.

electrically driven vibrating needles, with an air abrasive or in suitable cases with various acids (acetic acid or formic acid), which eat away the rock.[15] This work requires expert knowledge, a craftsman's art and above all patience and instinctive skill. This preparation is the work of a team of experts without whose technical assistance palaeontology as a science would not be possible.

X-ray technology has often proved a valuable aid for reliable preparation work.[16] An X-ray of a suitable fossil will show up all the details of a skeleton, even if it is still enclosed in rock itself. The preparator can use X-ray photography as an aid to uncovering the bones of a pterosaur skeleton, which are often very small and delicate.

Thus the palaeontologist's working methods are often based on the morphology, shape and form of the hard parts of a skeleton that may be preserved in fossil form. Fortunately under particularly favourable conditions the structure of soft parts has also survived, usually as an imprint of the body skin or the flight membrane. With the aid of ultra-violet light, organic fossil remains can be made visible against the inorganic surface of the rock. Organic substances fluoresce in yellow-green light, so that (for example) soft parts, horn beaks or horn claws, become visible. Even the shape of the brain is known in the case of some pterosaurs, for example if fine ooze was forced into the empty brain case of the skull and the ooze petrified along with the skull. A natural endocast produced in this way is a faithful copy of the brain, as it is possible to work on the assumption that the pterosaur brain filled the entire brain cavity, as is the case with birds.

## Dating the Fossils

When we work on pterosaur fossils, we know that we have before us the fossilized remains of living animals that really did exist in the mists of time. They were creatures of flesh and blood, subject to the same biological life principles as we are. Palaeontology as the study of the living world of the geological past is, however, not just a biological, but also an historical discipline. It does not only investigate animal and plant organisms in previous ages, but also follows the changes they underwent in the course of time, that is to say their development or evolution. This is only possible if fossil finds can be dated.

Fossils are generally found in geological bodies, usually in sedimentary deposits. Thus palaeontology's connection with geology is just as important as its connection with biology.

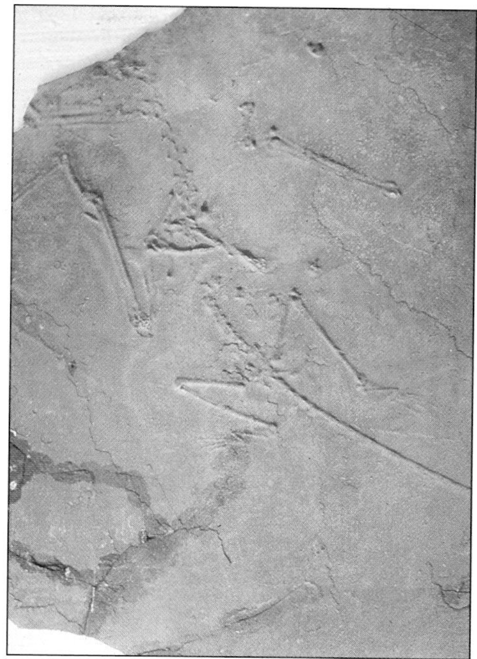

**Above:** The weak outlines of bone in this thin slab of shale indicate a pterosaur skeleton within. The X-ray photograph (below) reveals the complete skeleton of *Dorygnathus*, and guides the preparator in his efforts to uncover the bones.

**Above right:** Sometimes the brain cavity of fossil vertebrates was filled with sediment resulting in an endocast of the brain case which duplicates the size and shape of the brain itself. This is *Parapsicephalus*, a Liassic pterosaur.

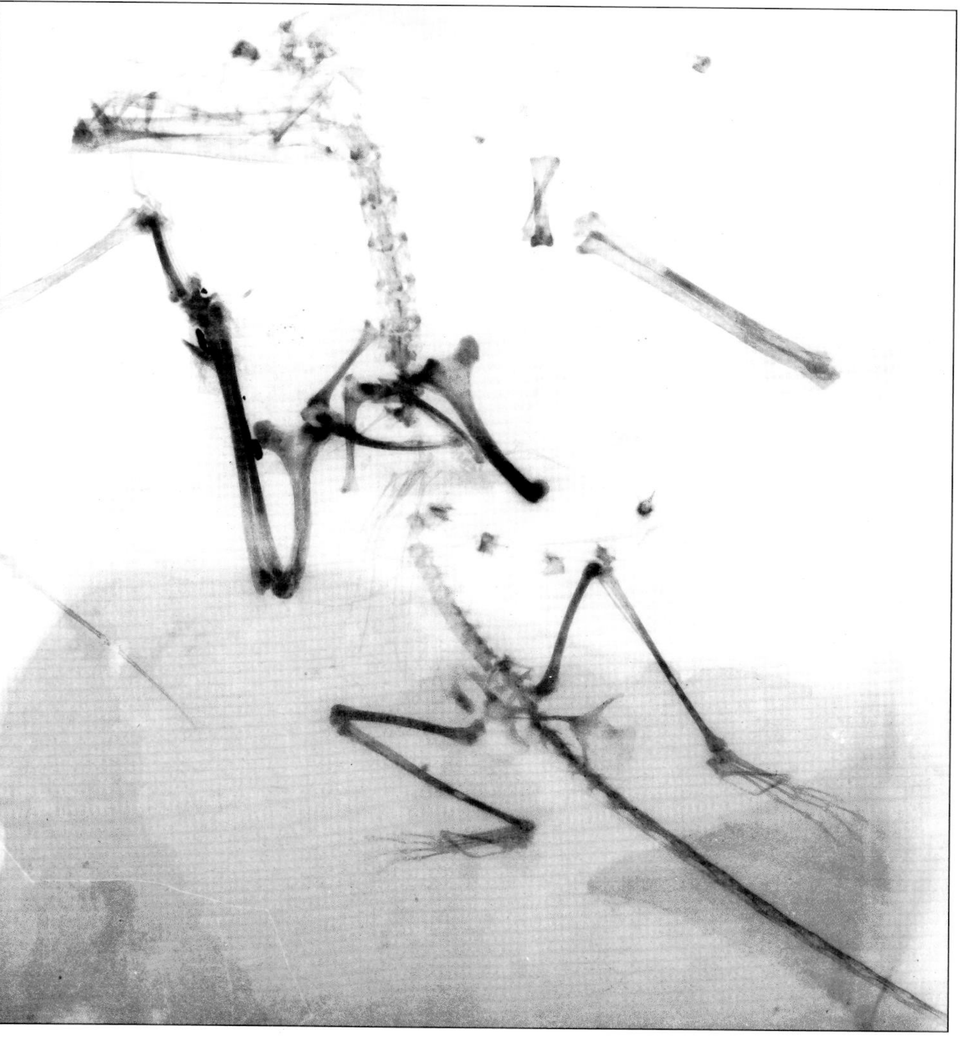

15 Acid preparation is particularly successful if the matrix surrounding the fossil is limestone, which dissolves in acid (usually acetic or formic acid). The most suitable fossils are those which are silicified in limestone, as silicon dioxide ($SiO_2$) is not attacked by the preparation acids. This procedure was used very successfully for the preparation of fish and pterosaurs from Solnhofen limestone and the limestone concretions of the Brazilian Santana formation. Usually 10 per cent acetic acid is used ($CH_3COOH$), but 8-10 per cent formic acid (CHCOOH) is better. The concretion is left in the acid for 6-30 hours, and is then treated with water and neutralized with soda lye. The bones thus released from the rock are dried, then coated with diluted polystyrol adhesive or paraffin. They are then put back in the acid. This process is repeated for as long as is necessary to free the remains of the skeleton from the rock adhering to them. This can take several weeks.

16 Fossils were X-rayed soon after the discovery of X-rays by Wilhelm C. Röntgen in 1896. The best results are achieved with thin fossil slabs in which there is a high contrasting density between the fossil and the surrounding rock, as for example in the case of pyritic fossils in slate slabs. Pioneers in the field of X-ray investigation of fossils were the Bonn physicist Walter M. Lehmann and the Erlangen physical chemist and palaeontologist Wilhelm Stürmer.

On the question of the age of fossils therefore, geological methods have to be applied. This produces the concept of relative geological time, which works with *relative* determination of the age of rocks and the fossils they contain. Beyond this geology has, by various physical methods, also established *absolute* dating by year numbers, refining and extending it down to the present day.

### Relative Dating

Long before it was possible to calculate the absolute age of rocks using radioactive isotopes, a system of relative dating was used. This is based on the so-called *stratigraphic principle*, first established by the Danish doctor Nicolaus Steno in 1669. This simply means that when sedimetary rocks are formed the upper strata are bound to be more recent than the ones underneath them, as they were deposited at a later date. In an undisturbed sequence of rocks, known to geologists as a *profile*, there is thus an age sequence from bottom to top, from the older rocks to the more recent ones.

This essentially obvious regularity became extraordinarily important for palaeontology and historical geology. At a very early stage, particularly in England, France and Germany, scholars began to classify rocks according to their relative position and age, to divide them into geological epochs and formations and to give them names. Geological periods like *Cambrian* or *Devonian* are named after landscapes in Wales and South-West England, the *Permian* after a Russian province, and the *Jurassic* after the Jura range in Switzerland. *Ordovician* and *Silurian* are derived from the names of Celtic tribes which once lived in Wales. *Carboniferous* denotes the presence of coal, and Carboniferous deposits throughout the world contain a great deal of coal. The *Cretaceous* is associated with chalk via the Latin. This leaves the *Triassic*, the trinity, because of its three subdivisions, *Bundsandstein*, *Muschelkalk* and *Keuper*, and *Tertiary*[17] and *Quaternary*, the third and fourth systems. At first only four *systems* were identified.

Later the six older periods, Cambrian, Ordovician, Silurian, Devonian, Carboniferous and Permian were grouped together and classified as the Palaeozoic ('ancient life') era, the middle three, Triassic, Jurassic and Cretaceous were termed the Mesozoic ('middle life') era and the two latest, the Tertiary and Quaternary, became the Cenozoic ('recent life') era. The period before the Palaeozoic is called the Pre-Cambrian.

This geological history without dates was principally worked out from fossils, from the point around 1800 when the English engineer William Smith[18] observed in the course of canal-building in the Midlands that fossils of animals and plants do not occur randomly in rock, but that each stratum contained characteristic fossils distinct from those above and below. Strata that occur at various, often widely separated points, must be of the same age if they contain the same fossils. Later, when observations were refined, it was recognized that many species of fossilized flora or fauna remain the same over several strata, but that others only occur at a particular level. This led to the conclusion that some species must have had longer and others shorter existences. It was the short-lived species that were of greatest significance for the establishment of relative geological age. If at the same time they were widely distributed, they could be used as time markers and for dating and correlating strata that were a considerable distance apart. These are then known as *index fossils*.

Now that it was possible to use the terms *older* and *younger* in geological terms, it was noticed that only simpler, more 'primitive' organisms occurred in the older strata, and more complicated, more 'progressive' organisms in the younger strata, but never the other way round. This can only lead to the conclusion that a development, an *evolution* of life took place in the course of geological history, which in the last resort led from unicellular organisms to man. Thus the relative age of species preserved as fossils in rock can be determined from their evolutionary level. This *biostratigraphy* is very refined today. It uses various plant and animal groups as index fossils. The smallest unit of time in this system is the *biozone*, which is determined by the lifespan of an index fossil species. Its beginning is marked by the first and its end by the last appearance of the index species.

Unfortunately it is not possible to make such refined zone classifications for pterosaurs. Finds are far too rare for this, and they obviously do not develop as quickly as the ammonites, for example. These marine, squid-like molluscs with spiral shells are outstanding index fossils, especially in the Jurassic and Cretaceous. But if we apply a somewhat coarser time-grid, it is perfectly possible to make state-

17 The name Tertiary is derived from Montes tertiarii, a concept introduced by the Italian geologist Giovanni Arduino in 1759 for deposits at the foothills of the Alps in northern Italy. At that time the older strata were called Montes primarii (pre-Cambrian and Palaeozoic) and Montes secundarii (Mesozoic). The name Quaternary (the fourth age) was introduced by the French geologist Jules Desnoyers in 1829 to cover the post-Tertiary period.

18 William Smith (1769-1839), English geologist and engineer, established stratigraphy, the science of the age sequence of rock strata, in 1816-1819. *Strata identified by organized fossils.* 4 parts.

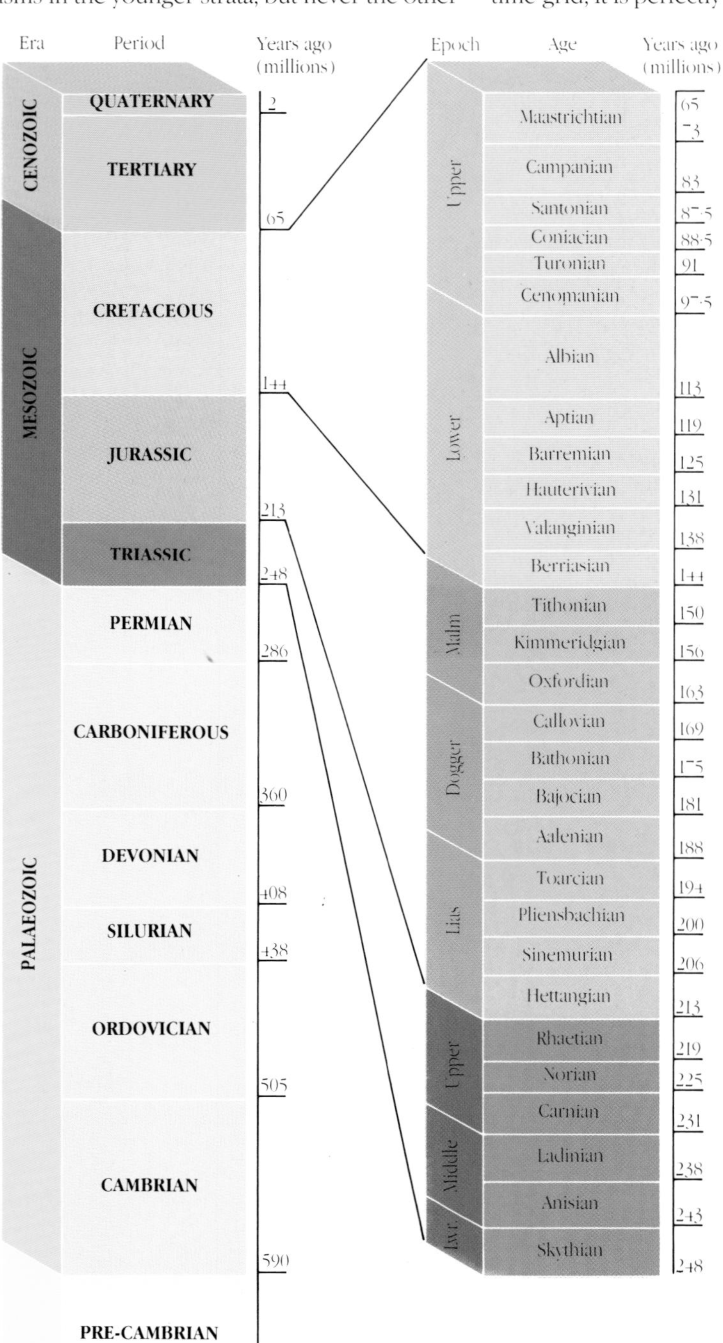


**The Mesozoic Era (left)**
This diagram shows how geologists and palaeontologists classify rocks according to their relative position and age, and so can construct a stratigraphic sequence which is basically a step-by-step history of the Earth's formation. The major divisions are called eras, and shown here are the Palaeozoic era (590-248 million years ago), the Mesozoic era (248-65 million years ago) and the Cenozoic era (65 million years ago to the present day). The time before the Palaeozoic is called the Pre-Cambrian. These eras are then divided into smaller units called periods, as can be seen from the main diagram (far left). In this book we are concerned with the Mesozoic, which was the age of the pterosaurs. This era has been pulled out in detail (near left) to enable the reader to see the further sub-divisions which scientists recognise during this span of time. The three Mesozoic periods — Triassic, Jurassic and Cretaceous — are split into epochs, and each epoch in turn encompasses a number of ages which, refined with absolute dates, form a relatively exact calendar of Mesozoic life history.

**Relative Dating (right)**
This geological profile shows different sedimentary rocks deposited at different times. The lower the position of the rock in the profile, the earlier it was deposited and hence the older are the fossils it contains.

Above: Fossil preparation is a delicate art. Here the preparator uses a hammer and fine chisel to chip away the rock containing the skull of a large pterosaur from the Santana formation of Brazil. For fine details a binocular microscope is also a necessary tool.

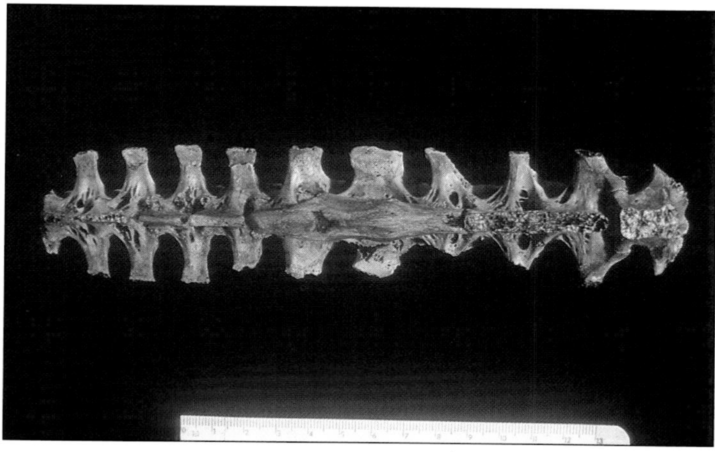

Right: If the chemical conditions of the rock and fossil are right, acid preparation can be applied. These vertebrae were treated with acetic acid.

ments about age, as indeed it is for other fossil reptiles as well. We know for example that short-tailed pterosaurs, the Pterodactyloidea, first appear in the Upper Jurassic, but not in any older strata. On the other hand long-tailed pterosaurs (Rhamphorhynchoidea) only occur until the Upper Jurassic, and not at all in the Cretaceous. Thus if remains of long-tailed pterosaurs are found, then the Cretaceous can confidently be excluded from our dating estimates. Equally a short-tailed pterosaur can never occur in Triassic deposits, but is typical of the Upper Jurassic or Cretaceous. In most cases more precise relative dating is possible by identifying accompanying fauna in the same deposit and from the geological situation.

## Absolute Dating

Measured by the standards of human age, the age of the Earth, today thought to be about five thousand million years, is not conceivable to us. And yet the enormously long periods in which the Earth and life upon it have developed are the daily bread of palaeontologists and geologists. These periods are part of the reality of the world, just as the gigantic distances to the stars and galaxies in space, which astronomers no longer measure by earthly standards, in miles, but only in light-years. A light-year is the distance travelled by light at a speed of 186,000 miles per second (300,000 km/sec) in a year. That is over 6·2 million million miles (10 million million km).

As the notion of a light-year contains a time component, it is possible at least in our minds to make a connection with the history of the Earth. We receive light from distant stars that was emitted millions of years ago in some cases. We do not even know whether these light sources far out in space still exist today or have already been extinguished. On the other hand for example a hypothetical observer in a group of galaxies in the Coma Berenices constellation between Virgo and the Great Bear looking at the Earth today through an enormously powerful telescope, could see living pterosaurs and dinosaurs. The light from the Earth would have taken from the Cretaceous until today to arrive.

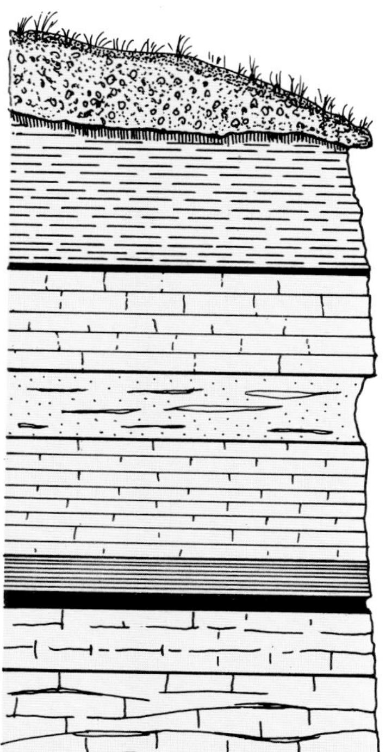

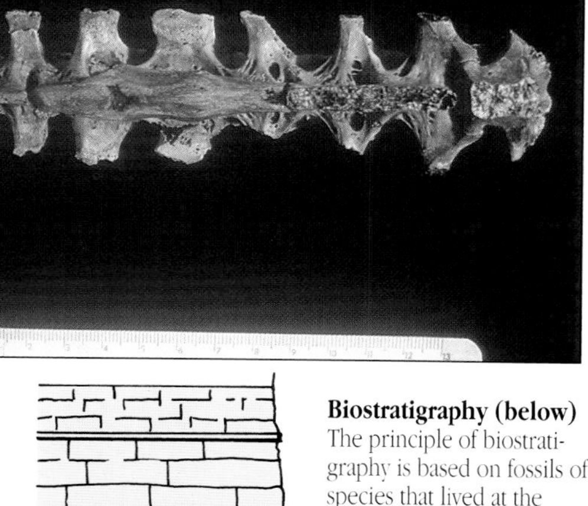

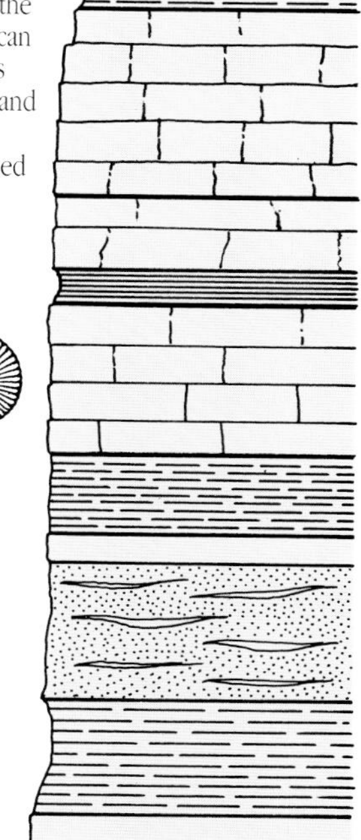

**Biostratigraphy (below)** The principle of biostratigraphy is based on fossils of species that lived at the same time. These are called index fossils if they had a limited life span (this span is called a biozone). Formations containing the same index fossils must have been deposited at the same time, and thus be the same age. Index fossils can be used as time markers with which to compare and correlate strata from different, widely separated parts of the globe.

How do geologists arrive at such high geological ages? In the last resort rocks and the fossils occurring in them just do not reveal their absolute age.

In 1650, Archbishop James Ussher of Armagh worked out from biblical evidence that the Creation took place on Sunday 23 October in the year 4004 BC, at nine o'clock in the morning. The calculation made in 1862 by William Thomson (the eminent British physicist who later became Lord Kelvin), working on the time it would take the Earth to cool from its red-hot molten condition, is founded on a physical basis. He arrived at an age for the Earth of between 20 and 400 million years.

But it was not until the early twentieth century that physicists Ernest Rutherford in England and Bertram B. Boltwood in America discovered that it was possible to use radioactive elements as a means of measuring time and determining the age of rocks. Many rocks contain small quantities of radioactive minerals. The principle is based on the fact that in the course of time radioactive elements decay to form stable end products and in a way that is completely constant and independent of any outside influence. The measurement of the rate of decay is the so-called half-life, which means the time it takes a radioactive isotope to go through half the decay and transformation process. From the measured relationship between original substance, the parent isotope, and end product, the daughter isotope, it is possible to calculate the time at which this atomic clock started to tick. This reveals the date of the rock's origin, and thus its age.

The isotopes uranium 238 and 235, thorium 232, rubidium 87 and potassium 40 are used as suitable radioactive elements today. Uranium 238 for example decays through various stages to form gaseous helium and the stable end product lead 206. So if rock containing uranium is examined, its age can be calculated from the ratio of remaining uranium to the newly formed lead. In this case the half-life is 4,510 million years. This means that after 4,510 million years half the uranium 238 has decayed to form lead 206.

For a dating up to a maximum of 50,000 years the radio-carbon method is used, working with carbon C14, with a half-life of only 5,570 years. The C14 method is based on the fact that in the structure of living organisms a type of carbon that has become radioactive in the upper layers of the atmosphere, the carbon isotope C14, occurs alongside normal carbon. On the death of the organism, i.e. the plant or animal, the radioactive carbon incorporated into bone or woody tissue begins to decay, as no new C14 is taken up from this point. The date at which decay began, and thus the age of the specimen, can be calculated if the very weak radio-active emission is measured. Because of its limited range the C14 method is of particular use for human prehistory.

Another method of numerical dating is dendrochronology, which has a span of a few thousand years, and works by counting annual rings of old trees and fossilized timber. Varve chronology uses the seasonal rhythm of meltwater deposits in areas in which glaciers and inland ice melt. The so-called varves, alternate light and dark layers of lake clay showing fine annual banding, were counted, and by combining and overlapping profiles from North Germany to North Sweden and America, a continuous sequence can be established for the past 10,000 years, thus dating the post ice age.

## Evolution of Life in Time

Absolute dating methods at our disposal today, which are continually being refined, have shown that rocks in which we find the first traces of the first, simple life are about 3,500 million years old, that the first multicellular organisms appeared about 2,000 million years ago, that genuine plants existed a thousand million years ago, and 590 million years ago, in other words at the beginning of the Palaeozoic Era, in the Cambrian, it is possible to observe a rapid spread of a great variety of organisms. These were exclusively marine life forms. Thus life came from the sea.

The first vertebrates were jawless, fish-like sea creatures which appear for the first time in 450 million year old strata of the Ordovician in the fossil record. Evidence of the first fish is not found until deposits which are 420 million years old. Other important evolutionary stages during the rise of the vertebrates were the first appearance of land-based tetrapods, of the first amphibians 370 million years ago, in the Devonian, and of the first reptiles over 300 million years ago, in the Carboniferous.

So reptiles (from the Latin *repere*, to crawl) flourished for the first time at the beginning of the Mesozoic, in the Triassic. Their success was

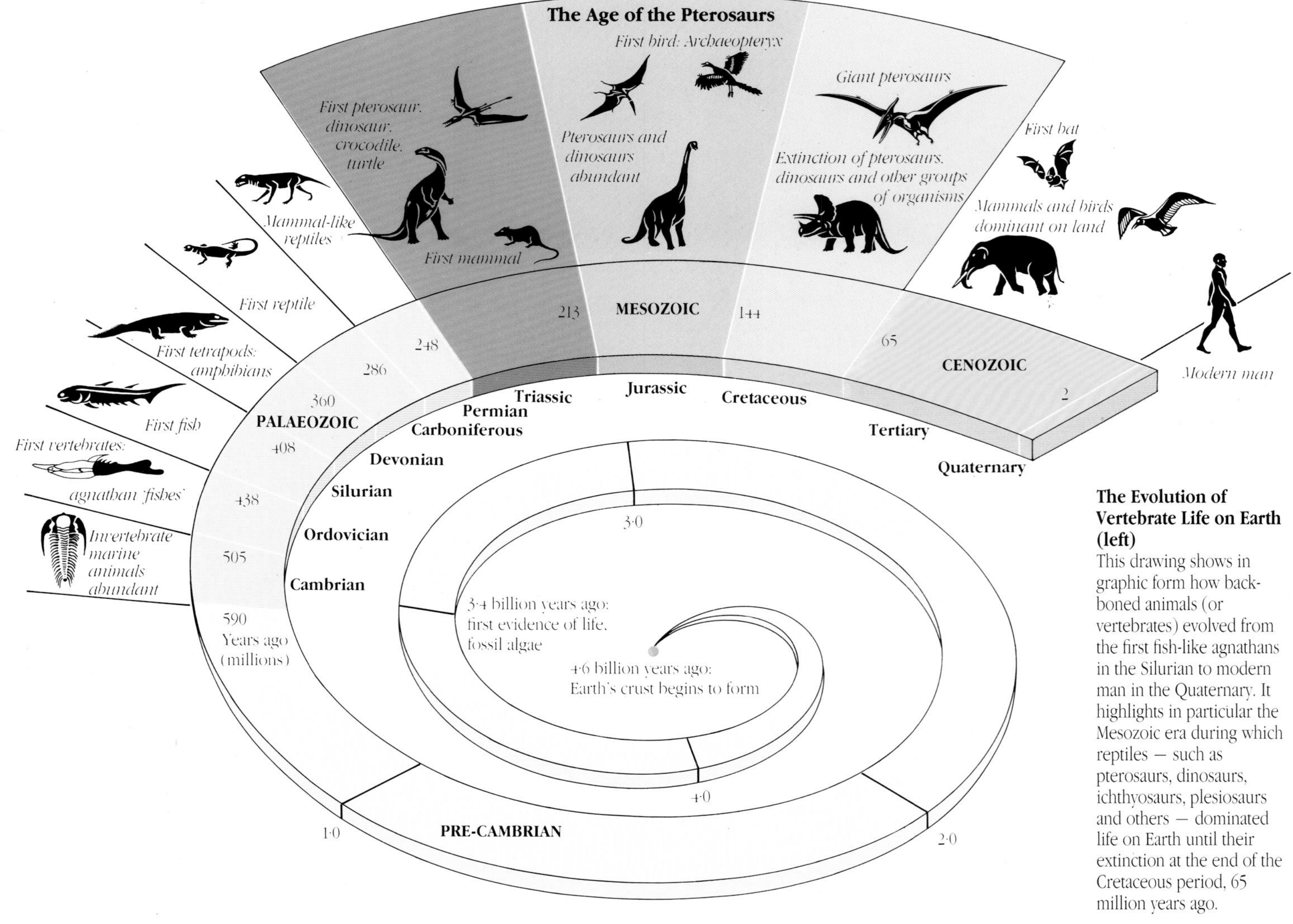


**The Evolution of Vertebrate Life on Earth (left)**
This drawing shows in graphic form how backboned animals (or vertebrates) evolved from the first fish-like agnathans in the Silurian to modern man in the Quaternary. It highlights in particular the Mesozoic era during which reptiles – such as pterosaurs, dinosaurs, ichthyosaurs, plesiosaurs and others – dominated life on Earth until their extinction at the end of the Cretaceous period, 65 million years ago.

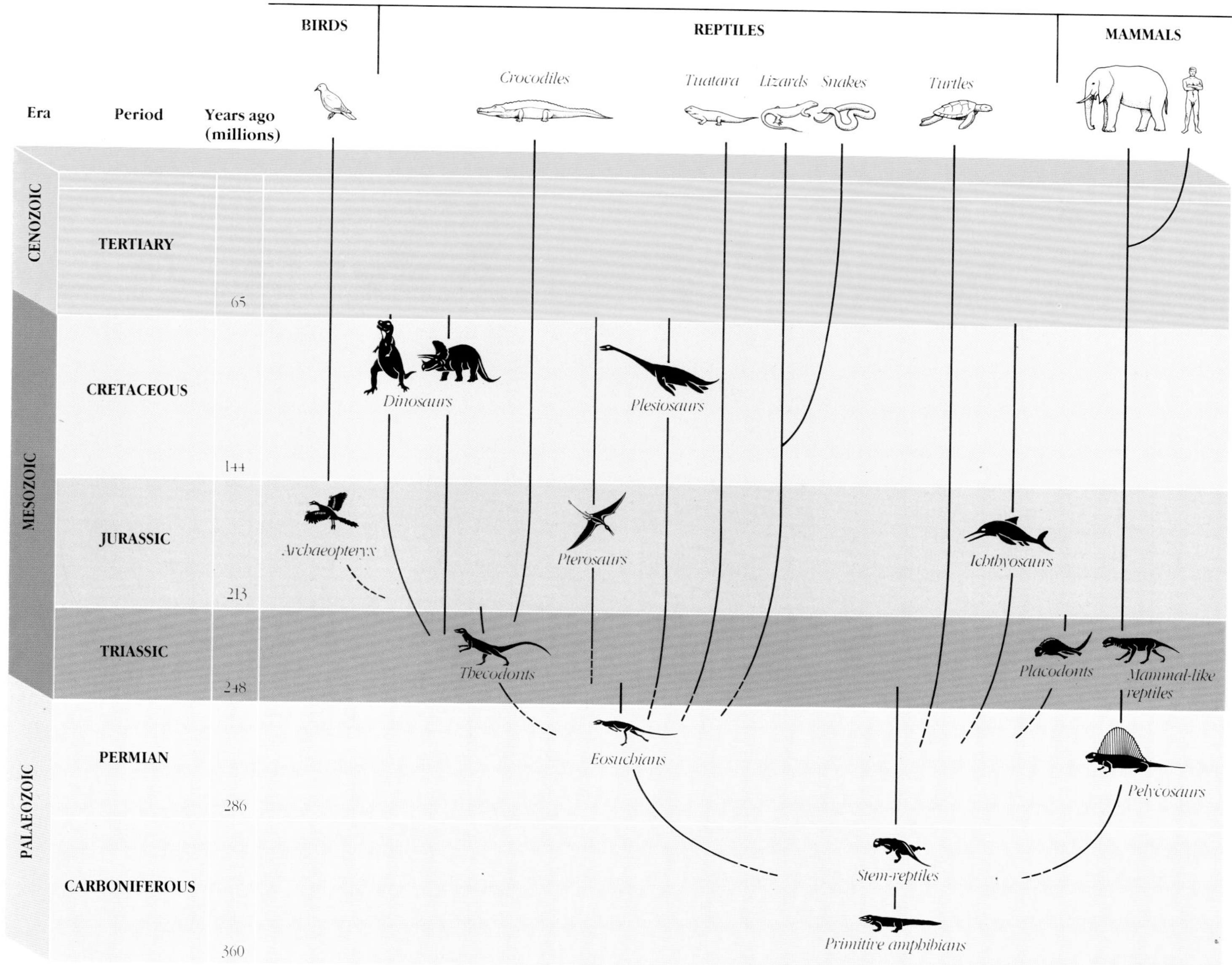


based on the fact that they were finally able to emancipate themselves from the water: reptiles lay their eggs on dry land. The eggs are large, with big yolks, and protected by a hard shell. Thus, unlike amphibians, they do not have to go through a larval stage in water. Their skin was protected against drying out. Thus they could make use of dry land as a new and extensive habitat.

Evolution grabbed this opportunity with great suddenness, as even as early as the Triassic all orders of reptiles, including pterosaurs, plesiosaurs, dinosaurs, placodonts and others were established. Some of these saurians returned to life in the water, with special adaptations, like for example the ichthyosaurs and plesiosaurs.

There is evidence of the earliest pterosaurs in the late Triassic. Their fossil remains were discovered in rocks in the Alpine foothills near Bergamo in northern Italy. At the same time it was proved that the pterosaurs were the *first* vertebrates to adapt to a life of active flight. They dominated the air without competition until the Late Jurassic, for almost 70 million years. Their first competitors were not to appear until 150 million years ago, with the first birds, represented by *Archaeopteryx* in the lithographic limestone of Solnhofen.

Throughout the Mesozoic, i.e. during the Triassic, Jurassic and Cretaceous, reptiles were absolute lords of the earth. For this reason the Mesozoic is also known as the Age of the Reptiles. In absolute figures their dominance lasted for over 180 million years. Certainly most of them became extinct either before or at the end of the Cretaceous, among them the pterosaurs. Latterly these reached enormous dimensions, with wing spans of 39ft (12m), making them the largest flying creatures of all times.

Pterosaurs first flourished in the Jurassic. The earliest pterosaur skeleton finds in Lower Jurassic strata on the Dorset coast of southern England are about 200 million years old. Finds at Holzmaden in Württemberg are somewhat younger, about 190 million years, but indicate a greater range. In the Upper Jurassic, about 150 million years ago, we see not only considerable evolution of a great variety of pterosaurs, but also world-wide distribution. The most important finds were made in the region of Solnhofen and Eichstätt in Bavaria. But pterosaur fossils have been found in Upper Jurassic strata in France, England, Portugal, Russia, East Africa, Cuba, the United States and China as well.

After long-tailed pterosaurs, the Rhamphorhynchoidea, became extinct in the late Jurassic, short-tailed pterosaurs, the Pterodactyloidea, developed considerably in the Cretaceous. The earliest Pterodactyloidea appeared in the Upper Jurassic, but they evolved to the largest extent in the early Cretaceous, about 135 million years ago. The strangest pterosaurs,

**The Age of Reptiles (above)**
The Mesozoic era was the age of the reptiles in general. Of many different groups only few escaped the great extinction at the end of the Cretaceous, 65 million years ago, which accounted for dinosaurs, pterosaurs, plesiosaurs and ichthyosaurs. Those that have survived until today are: crocodiles, the tuatara (*Sphenodon*), lizards, snakes, and turtles. Birds as well as mammals are considered to be descendants of different reptilian ancestors.

like *Pterodaustro* for example, a creature with filter dentition from the Cretaceous in Argentina, lived in this period.

Other pterosaurs, some of them enormous, lived later, in the Upper Cretaceous in China, Australia and Brazil. The pterosaur fossils described in the last century from the Greensand in Cambridge in England are somewhat more recent. Giant pterosaurs of the genus *Pteranodon*, found by O.C. Marsh's fossil hunters in the Kansas Chalk of the United States, can be dated to about 80 million years ago.

Geologically the most recent and also the largest known pterosaur, the famous *Quetzalcoatlus*, lived in the region which is now West Texas only towards the end of the Cretaceous, about 65 million years ago.

At the turn of the Cretaceous to the Tertiary, 65 million years ago, the reptiles' age of splendour was over. Of the 17 orders of reptiles only four survived, crocodiles, snakes and lizards, tortoises and the tuatara. Subsequently mammals and birds evolved in their place. During the Mesozoic they had eked out an undistinguished existence, and are scantily represented in the fossil record. At the beginning of the Cenozoic, in the Tertiary, mammals also produced an actively flying representative, the bat. Here the oldest fossil find is *Icaronycteris*, from 50 million year old lake deposits in Wyoming, USA. The last scion of this evolution of the vertebrates, only roughly sketched here, is man, the genus *Homo*. He appeared late, that means a mere two million years ago, and modern man only at the beginning of the last ice age, about 70,000 years ago.

We now want to present the enormous timespans of the geological past and the evolution of life on Earth in a form which it is easier for our minds to grasp. To do this we want to represent the total duration of the history of the Earth from the moment in which it came into being until the present day as a single 24 hour day. Thus the beginning of the day is the formation of the Earth 4,600 million years ago: 00.00 hours. The present moment is reached at the last stroke of midnight: 24.00 hours. Thus an hour represents 191·7 million years, a minute 3,194,000 years and a second still lasts for 53,240 years.

The most significant dates in the history of the Earth and the evolution of vertebrates can be read from this clock like a timetable of life:

00.00 h
Formation of the Earth
03.07 h
Formation of the Earth's crust
06.15 h
First signs of life
13.34 h
First multicellular organisms
20.55 h
Beginning of the Cambrian
21.39 h
First vertebrates
22.04 h
First land-based tetrapods (amphibians)
22.26 h
First saurians (reptiles)
22.51 h
First pterosaurs
23.13 h
First birds (*Archaeopteryx*), long-tailed pterosaurs become extinct
23.35 h
Short-tailed pterosaurs flourish
23.39 h
Pterosaurs, dinosaurs and others become extinct
37 seconds before 24.00 h
Appearance of early man (*Homo*)
2 seconds before 24.00 h
Appearance of modern man (*Homo sapiens*)

## Dragons of the Myths

If we pursue the history of the investigation of pterosaurs, the flying saurians of prehistoric times, there is a natural link in our minds with the myths and legends of dragons. These were usually also seen as winged lizards or snakes.

For 16th and 17th century scholars dragons were still a reality. For example, in the Schlangenbuch (Snake Book) by the famous Swiss naturalist and town doctor Conrad Gessner, dating from 1589, there is a chapter called 'Von den Tracken', in which he describes and illustrates various dragons. He also describes a battle between a Swiss called Winkelried and a dragon which took place near the Swiss village of Wyler.[19] The scholarly Jesuit father Athanasius Kircher provided a picture of this fight in his great work on natural history *Mundus Subterraneus* (The world below the Earth) in 1678. According to this the dragon had a long neck and tail, four legs, and wings. The Viennese palaeontologist Othenio Abel suggested in this context that the drawing could have been based on fossil reptile finds, possibly long-necked plesiosaurs from the Jurassic strata of Württemberg.

At a time when even naturalists believed in fabulous creatures and monsters, the discovery of fossil bones and remains of skeletons in caves must have reinforced ideas of dragons. Old names like dragon's cave, dragon's rock or dragon's stone still occur on modern maps.

Another picture of a dragon by Athanasius Kircher has come down to us. It was said to have been killed by a knight of St. John on the island of Rhodes. This picture is also said to have been the inspiration for Schiller's ballad 'The Fight with the Dragon'.

19 According to an ancient legend, in the early days of Swiss settlement a cruel dragon lived above the village of Wyler, and drove out men and cattle. A countryman called Winkelried, who had been banished for murder, offered to kill the dragon, in exchange for which he would be allowed to return. After he had defeated the dragon he held the bloody sword high in the air and the dragon's blood dripped on to his body, causing his death. Bölsche, W., 1929, *Drachen. Sage und Naturwissenschaft*, Stuttgart (Kosmos).

**Below:** The Swiss countryman Winkelried killing a dragon that had menaced the village of Wyler. This illustration appeared in *Mundus Subterraneus* by the Jesuit scholar Athanasius Kircher in 1678. It was conceivably based upon fossil finds.

**Left:** Every year in August a traditional festival called the *'Drachenstich'* (the slaying of the dragon) takes place in the small town of Furth im Wald in eastern Bavaria, Germany. A huge fire-breathing, winged dragon, which is actually mounted on wheels and powered by an engine, is ritually 'killed' by a prince on horseback during the performance. Such celebrations recall Christian allegories such as that of St George and the Dragon which express the triumph of good over evil. St Michael, St Margaret, St Sylvester and St Martha are all depicted as slaying dragons.

**Right:** This 18th century sculpture depicts a dragon as part of the fountain in front of the pilgrimage church of Loreto in Italy. Again it reminds us that in the Christian tradition the dragon has always figured as the symbol of the devil.

Even in the early seventeenth century such legends persisted, like that of the flying dragon on Mount Pilatus near Lucerne in Switzerland. It is reported that the creature flew out of a cave on Mount Pilatus in 1619, and flapped across the valley with slowly beating wings. Athanasius Kircher also created an imaginative picture of this, and it was still being printed on the map of Switzerland in Mattaeus Seutter's Atlas of the World in 1730.

There is still a ceremony of 'dragon-slaying' in a festival in the small town of Furth im Wald in eastern Bavaria. This involves a large, fire-spewing winged dragon being killed by a knight. When one remembers that even in our century the teeth of fossilized mammals were sold as 'dragons' teeth' by Chinese chemists, this gives a sense of how deeply notions of dragons were rooted in the peoples of Eastern Asia.

In China dragons were symbols of the might of the Emperor and of happiness for thousands of years, whilst in the culture of the West the dragon was usually a symbol of evil and the devil. Pictures in which the Archangel Michael, St. George or Christ himself are portrayed as dragon-killers are ancient in origin and very widespread. Fights with dragons are a recurrent myth in various forms amongst many peoples. They always deal with a god fighting with a dragon, for example Indra, Apollo, Hercules, Jason, Thor or Siegfried. The well-known Greek legend of Cadmus tells how he killed a dragon, from whose teeth the dragon's seed, armed men, sprang up.

Ancient notions of dragons suggest they had a snake-like body, two legs and bat's wings. A second pair of legs was not added until the 16th century.[20] These different types of dragons are impressively presented in Conrad Gessner's 1589 *Book of Snakes*. There are similar pictures in Sebastianus Munsterus' *Cosmographia Universa*, printed in Basel in 1544. They may have been the model for the creator of the Lindwurm Monument in Klagenfurt in Austria. In fact this sculpture was based on a fossil find from the region, the skull of an ice-age woolly rhinoceros. Clearly this was thought to be the skull of a prehistoric dragon.[21]

However, none of these concepts of dragons has anything to do with pterosaur fossil finds. Even when they really were based on fossilized remains, in many cases those of ice-age cave bears, the wings are always represented as bird- or bat-like. Actual pterosaur fossils could hardly have given rise to dragon legends, as the significance of such remains was disputed as late as the early nineteenth century, when scientific investigation had already begun.

**Below:** The Lindwurm Monument in Klagenfurt dates back to the late 16th century. The head is based on the skull of an ice-age woolly rhinoceros which had been found in 1335 near the town, and taken to be the skull of a dragon that had lived nearby.

20 Smith, G.E., 1919. *The Evolution of the Dragon*. London.

21 Abel, O., 1939. *Vorzeitliche Tierreste im Deutschen Mythus, Brauchtum und Volksglauben*. Jena.

Round about 1757 Karl Theodor, the Elector Palatine, discovered a number of assorted shells in a cupboard in his palace in Mannheim. He was so fascinated by their colours and shapes that he decided to start his own collection of natural objects. In the 18th century it was quite the fashion for princes and noblemen to collect minerals, zoological and botanical treasures, fossils, ethnological items and above all natural rarities and curiosities. So Karl Theodor established a *Naturalienkabinett* (cabinet of natural objects), an act which was in keeping with his desire to instruct; in other words it was a service to the public. Today we would call such a collection a natural history museum, although at first it occupied only two rooms in the east wing of the Mannheim palace, later extended to four galleries containing mineralogical and palaeontological collections, and also specimens of extant vertebrates, birds, insects and rare plants.

In 1764 the Elector handed over direction of the development of the *Naturalienkabinett* to historian and naturalist Cosimo Alessandro Collini (1727-1806).[1] He was to be the first man to examine a pterosaur fossil and write a scientific treatise on it; this appeared in 1784 in the Acta Academiae Theodoro-Palatinae in Mannheim.[2] The object of this description was an exceptionally attractive fossil found in the limestone quarries at Eichstätt in Bavaria. We know that Elector Karl Theodor received fossils for his natural history collection from Graf Friedrich Ferdinand of Pappenheim, a small town not far from the famous quarries of Solnhofen and Eichstätt. The fossil must have arrived in Mannheim between 1767 and 1784, as Collini did not list it in his 1767 catalogue of the collection.

Like many 18th century naturalists, Collini no longer thought that fossils were mineral formations, freaks of nature or even objects left behind after the Great Flood. He realized they were remains of living things from earlier epochs and compared them with modern plants and animals. However, faced with the fossilized vertebrate of Eichstätt he got into considerable difficulty: there was nothing in the animal kingdom comparable with the object in front of him, a remarkable skeleton with a long, toothed snout, claws on hands and feet and long, thin bones for the forelimbs.

**Left:** Karl Theodor (1733-1799), Elector of the Palatinate and Bavaria, who founded the Mannheim Natural History Collection in the middle of the 18th century. The first known pterosaur fossil specimen was housed in this *Naturalienkabinett*. This engraving was made in Paris in 1768.

Despite this Collini provided an astonishingly precise reproduction of the fossil, a copper engraving by Verhelst, which has proved an important basis for later research. Strangely enough he thought it possible that the right hand and right foot were not part of the creature, as they were not positioned at the point where they actually belonged. But he rightly recognized that the creature's arms could be folded, and expressed a supposition that a membrane could have been attached to them.

In an attempt to categorize this fossilized vertebrate, he established that it was impossible to place it in any known group of animals. He expressly excluded it from the class of birds, a view later put forward by Professor Friedrich Blumenbach[3] of Göttingen in particular. As far as the long folding arms, tail, hind legs and feet were concerned he recognized a similarity with bats, but rejected this interpretation because of the long, toothed beak. Finally he thought the most reasonable supposition was that the animal was a sea creature, but without being able to interpret the long legs with any clarity.

Collini concluded his treatise with a remarkable observation for its period, which modern palaeoecologists would fully endorse. He writes: 'In order to understand the function of all parts of its body, one must also know its habitat, its diet, its enemies, the other circumstances of its natural behaviour and the way in which the species survived and reproduced.'

### Georges Cuvier

Seventeen years passed before attention again turned to the still nameless Eichstätt fossil. The Parisian anatomist Georges Cuvier (1769-1832),[4] realized that this creature must have been a reptile.[5] He recognized the long bones on the forelimbs as highly elongated phalanges of one digit of the hand, on which a flight membrane must have been mounted. Naturally this membrane had not survived as a fossil. Thus the creature was capable of flight, a flying saurian comparable to *Draco* (dragon), the modern flying lizard. Cuvier based his classification of the creature within the zoological system solely on Collini's description and illustration of 1784, he had never seen the fossil itself. About 50 years later pterosaur fossils were found in the Jurassic Solnhofen limestone with imprints of the flight membrane surviving on the surface of the rock. This completely confirmed Cuvier's assumption. The creature itself remained nameless, until in a later, detailed treatise written in 1809 Cuvier placed it in a reptilian genus of its own and gave it the name *'Ptero-dactyle'*, meaning roughly 'flight finger'.[6]

---

1 Cosimo Alessandro Collini was born on 14 October 1727 in Florence, first studied law in Pisa, then went to Switzerland in 1749 and Prussia in 1750, to Frederick the Great's Berlin, intending to study Pure Science and undertake historical research. He met a number of scholars here, and in 1752 became secretary to the French writer, philosopher and historian Voltaire, who was living in Berlin at the time, and considered to be the embodiment of the Age of Enlightenment. In 1756 Collini left Voltaire and took a post as tutor in Strasbourg. During this period he became interested in natural science, especially zoology and anatomy, with which he concerned himself intensively. On Voltaire's recommendation he became an official at the Mannheim court of the Elector Palatine, Karl Theodor, in 1760, and was subsequently appointed supervisor of the natural history collection. At the same time he became a member of the Mannheim Academy of Science and later published several essays on animal fossils that had found their way into the Mannheim natural history collection.

2 Collini, C.A., 1784. *Sur quelques Zoolithes du Cabinet d'Histoire naturelle de S.A.S.E. Palatine et de Bavière, à Mannheim*. Acta Academiae Theodoro-Palatinae Mannhein, 5, pars physica: 58-103.

3 Johann Friedrich Blumenbach (1752-1840) was Professor of Medicine in Göttingen and in his time a prominent exponent of comparative anatomy and anthropology. Thus he was also very interested in fossil forms, and described and named the ice-age woolly rhinoceros and the mammoth. His principal work is the *Handbuch der Naturgeschichte*, which appeared in many editions.

**Above:** Cosimo Alessandro Collini (1727-1806), the first keeper of the Mannheim Natural History Collection established by Karl Theodor. In 1784 Collini published a description of the first known pterosaur, without, however, coming to a definite conclusion about its true identity as a flying reptile.

4 Georges Cuvier (1769-1832) was born on 23 August 1769 as Georg Küfer in Mömpelgard, then part of Württemberg, now Montbéliard in the Département of Doubs, France, in the same year as Napoleon, whom he later served, and Alexander von Humboldt, the eminent naturalist, whose close friend he was to become. He established himself as the foremost comparative anatomist of his day, and was honoured with many administrative and political appointments, notably: in 1796 member of the *Institut National*, 1808 University council member, 1811 Chevalier of the Légion d'Honneur, 1814 made a councillor of state by Napoleon and chancellor of the University, in 1818 he refused an offer of the interior ministry and became a member of the Académie Française. He was made a baron by the king in 1819 and finally a Peer of France in 1832. He died unexpectedly of cholera in May of the same year. Cuvier used his influence to promote science in schools. He also made the Musée d'Histoire Naturelle and Jardin des Plantes in Paris the leading scientific research institution of its day.

5 Cuvier, G., 1801. *Reptile volant. Extrait d'un ouvrage etc.*, an 9:6; Paris.

6 Cuvier, G., 1809. *Mémoire sur le squelette fossile d'un Reptil volant des environs d'Aichstedt, que quelques naturalistes ont pris pour un oiseau, et donc nous formons un genre de Sauriens, sous le nom de Ptero-Dactyle.* Annales du Musée d'Histoire Naturelle Paris, 13:424,

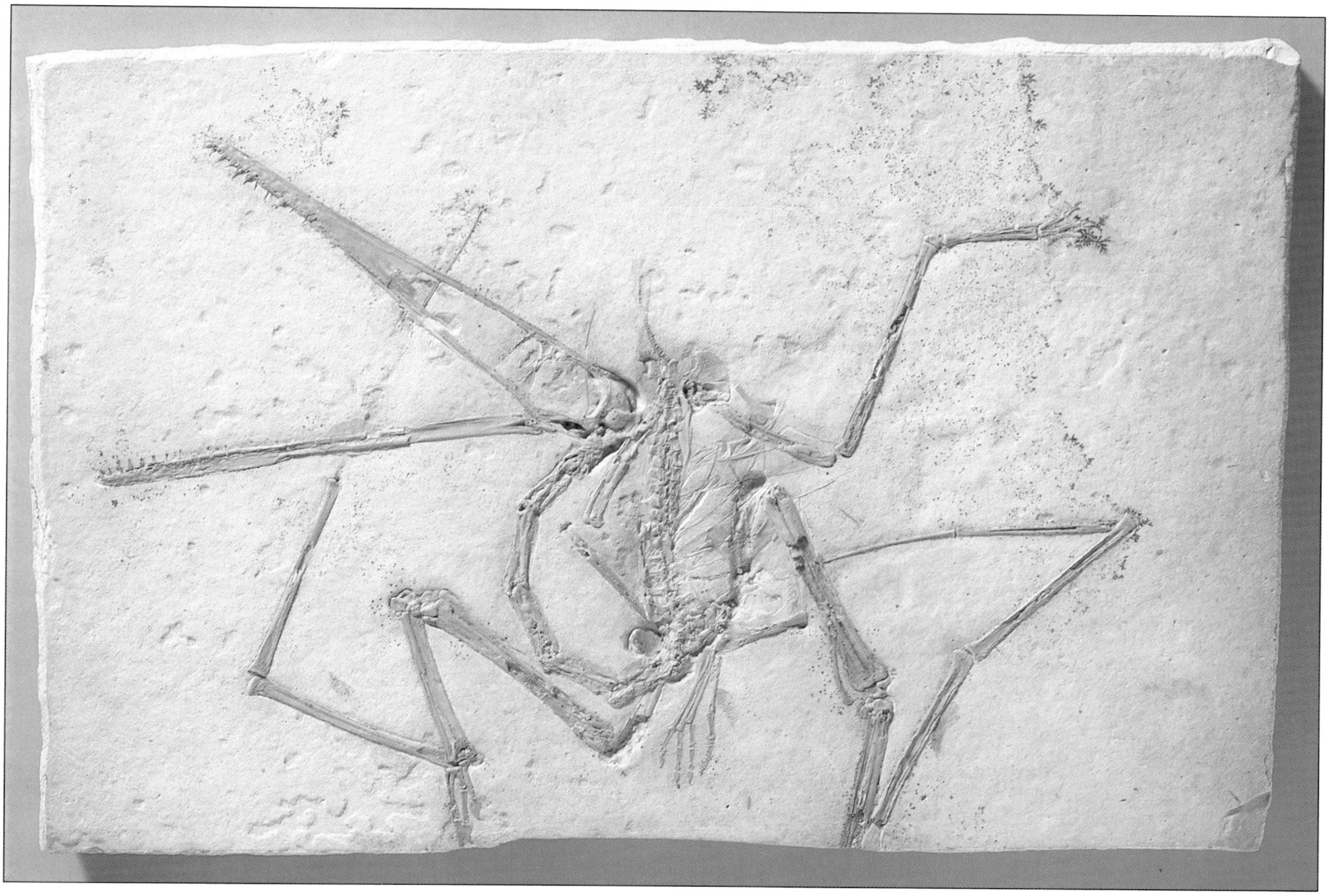

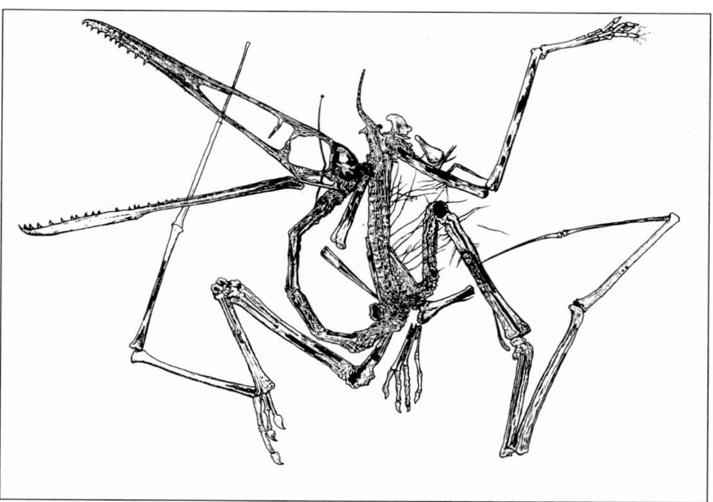

**Above and left:** The actual specimen of *Pterodactylus antiquus* from Eichstätt which Collini studied is seen above, while to the left is reproduced the original copper plate engraving by Verhelst which appeared in Collini's 1784 treatise entitled *Sur un animal fossile d'un genre particulier.*

**Right:** Georges Cuvier (1769-1832) is regarded as the father of vertebrate palaeontology. Cuvier recognised the reptilian nature of the Eichstätt fossil in his study of 1801.

Cuvier's particular academic strength lay in the field of comparative anatomy. He is considered the father of scientific vertebrate palaeontology. He came from modest circumstances. His father commanded the guard at the castle of Mömpelgard. Cuvier's interest in science was established at an early stage. In 1784, the same year that Collini described his mysterious Eichstätt fossil, the first pterosaur, Cuvier went as a fourteen-year-old student to the Hohe Karlsschule in Stuttgart to study economics. Even at this time he took every opportunity to collect plants and insects, and to immerse himself in the scientific works of the French zoologist, Leclerc de Buffon, and the Swedish botanist Carl Linnaeus.

After his period at the Karlsschule, Cuvier took a job as a residential tutor in Normandy. This enabled him to spend the dangerous years of the French Revolution by the sea, where he again took up the study of plants, insects and sea creatures and found fossils, which stimulated him to compare them with living specimens. He also maintained a lively correspondence with distinguished naturalists in Paris, who inevitably recognized the talents of the young scientist and offered him a professorship at the *École centrale* of the Panthéon. Thus in 1795 he went to Paris, where the political situation was slowly calming down, and embarked upon his remarkable career.

His first great publication on comparative anatomy appeared as early as 1800. His 'correlation principle' states that the shape of missing parts of a creature can be deduced from the shape of each isolated piece. As fossil skeletons are often fragmentary and incomplete, Cuvier's principle of correlation was of extraordinary significance for vertebrate palaeontology in general. Cuvier's precise knowledge of skeletal structure in living reptiles also meant that he was able to classify the Eichstätt vertebrate skeleton as a reptile.

He dealt with this interesting fossil in detail in his treatise of 1809, which appeared in the annals of the Natural History Museum in Paris. In the meantime other interpretations had appeared, such as that of Friedrich Blumenbach, who argued that it was a waterfowl. In this examination Cuvier again had to rely on Collini's first description of 1784, as it was thought that the original specimen was missing. Cuvier was in fact aware that Karl Theodor's natural history collection had been transferred to Munich, but it seemed that no-one could find it there. We now know that the specimen really was in Munich, but the Munich anatomist Samuel Thomas von Soemmerring (1755-1830) was working on the fossil at the time and preparing a scientific treatise of his own about it.

But how did the exhibit get to Munich? For political reasons, closely connected with the line of succession of the house of Wittelsbach. In 1777 the old Bavarian Wittelsbach line died out with the Bavarian Elector Max III Joseph. The succession passed to his cousins in the Palatinate, to Karl Theodor von Pfalz-Neuburg-Sulzbach, who moved his residence from Mannheim to Munich in the following year. It was not until 1802, after his death and under the regency of his successor, Elector Max IV Joseph, that the Mannheim natural history collection was brought to Munich and with it the rare fossil of the Eichstätt pterosaur, which was still unique. It was handed over to the natural history collection of the Bavarian Academy of Science, into the care of Samuel Thomas von Soemmerring.[7]

## Soemmerring

Soemmerring was one of the most versatile scholars of his time. He was an anatomist and surgeon, but also undertook palaeontological research, and concerned himself with astronomy and technical problems. Thus he was the inventor of an electro-chemical telegraph that is still kept and shown in the Deutsches Museum in Munich. In Munich Soemmerring became a member of the Bavarian Academy of Science, where he was made director of the natural history collection, which had considerably increased in size only a few years earlier through the acquisition of Karl Theodor's Mannheim collection. The collection included among its many zoological specimens, plants, minerals, rocks and fossils the fossil described by Collini and recognized by Cuvier as a flying reptile, the first *Pterodactylus*.

This fossil must have immediately roused Soemmerring's interest and stimulated him to examine this controversial vertebrate skeleton himself and produce an interpretation of his own. He presented the results of his studies on 27 December 1810 in the form of a lecture to the mathematics and physics class at the Academy of Science. At that time the Academy was housed in the former Jesuit monastery at St Michael's in Neuhauserstrasse in Munich, where the Bavarian state scientific collections, the successors of the Academy collection, were housed until 1944.

The lengthy title of Soemmerring's lecture was: 'About an *Ornithocephalus* or the unknown creature of the prehistoric world, whose fossil skeleton was described by C. Collini in the fifth volume of the Actorum Academiae Theodoro-Palatinae, along with a pictorial representation in actual size, and which skeleton is at present to be found in the Royal Academy of Science in Munich.' In his lecture, later printed in the Memoirs of the Academy in 1812,[8] Soemmerring addressed Collini's views critically. He did not see Cuvier's work of 1809 until 1811, and he considered his interpretation of the Eichstätt fossil in an appendix.

**Left:** Samuel Thomas von Soemmerring (1755-1830) restudied the Eichstätt pterodactyl, but concluded that it was a mammal which he named *Ornithocephalus*.

**Above:** The Academy of Sciences in Munich as it appeared in 1826, shortly after Soemmerring had become keeper of its Natural History Collections.

His analysis comes to the conclusion that the creature must be a mammal, a hitherto unknown kind of bat. This was a view similar to that held by Professor Johann Hermann of Strasbourg, who had pointed out the fossil in the Mannheim collection to Cuvier, and had also suggested that he thought it was a mammal, to be classified between bats and birds.

Soemmerring too was convinced that the creature was a transitional form between the mammal and the bird class. He even speaks of a 'graduated sequence' of animals between flying mammals and actual birds. It seems that Soemmerring was an early adherent of the ideas of Jean Baptiste de Lamarck, whose theory of evolution assumed a gradual sequence of living things, becoming increasingly complex. Thus Lamarck's view was in complete contrast with that of Cuvier, who worked on the basis that there were times when the entire living world was extinguished by catastrophe, and replaced with a completely new one.

Soemmerring called the Eichstätt fossil *Ornithocephalus antiquus*, which means 'old bird-head'. Although, unlike Cuvier, he had the advantage of being able to study the original fossil, he made serious mistakes, especially in his interpretation of the forelimbs. For example, he did not recognize the bones of the upper arm for what they were, but thought they were breast bones. This meant that he identified the actual lower arm bones as those of the upper arm, and the long bones of the middle hand as those of the lower arm. But he correctly established that the hand had four digits and that the highly elongated fourth digit with its four long phalanges must have been a 'mast' to stretch a flight membrane. He thought the creature was a bat-like mammal, closest to the modern Indian flying fox. Independently of Cuvier he also thought it probable that it fed on insects which it caught in flight. Soemmerring wrote of the habitat and environment of *Ornithocephalus* 'that at that time the present Danube region must have had a hot, southern Indian climate.'

In 1817 Soemmerring also described the second pterosaur fossil[9] from Jurassic limestone slabs, also from the Eichstätt region. He gave it the name *Ornithocephalus brevirostris* (=short-snouted bird-head), as it was a species with a short snout. He thought that it was even more bat-like than the first and compared it with the parti-coloured bat *Vespertilio murinus*. He felt his earlier view was reinforced by

7 Samuel Thomas von Soemmerring (1755-1830) was born on 28 January 1755 in Mainz. He lectured in anatomy and surgery at the Collegium Carolinum in Kassel, from 1784 he was Professor of Anatomy and Physiology at the university in his home town of Mainz. From 1795-1805 he worked as a doctor in Frankfurt and was a founder member of the Senckenbergische Naturforschende Gesellschaft. In 1805 he was appointed Professor of Anatomy and Surgery at the University of Munich and was personal physician to Maximilian Joseph, the first King of Bavaria. In 1819 he settled in Frankfurt again, and died there in 1830.

8 Soemmerring, S.T.v., 1812. *Über einen Ornithocephalus*. Denkschriften der Akademie der Wissenschaften München, math.-phys. Classe, 3: 89-158.

9 Soemmerring, S.T.v., 1817. *Über einer Ornithocephalus brevirostris der Vorwelt*. Denkschriften der Akademie der Wissenschaften München, math.-phys. Classe, 6: 89-104.

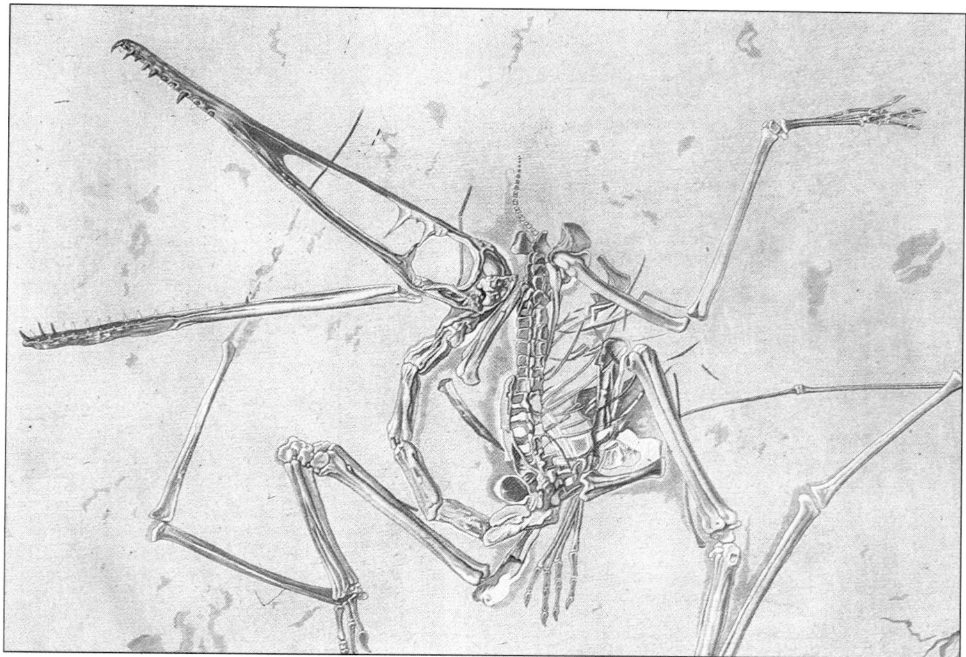

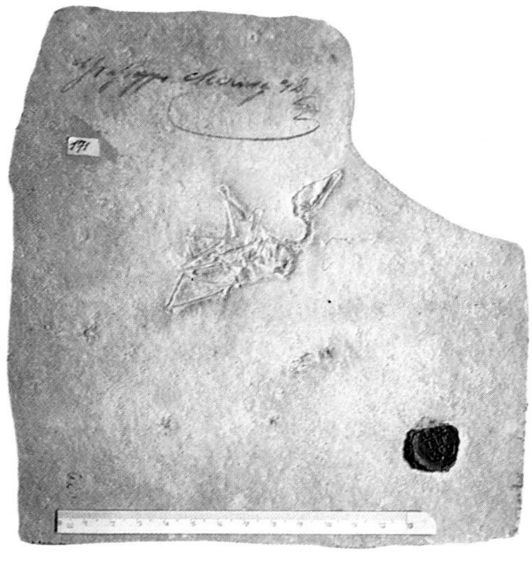

**Above:** In 1817 Soemmerring described a second pterodactyl from near Eichstätt. Because of the short beak he named it *Ornithocephalus brevirostris*. This specimen, long thought to be lost, was rediscovered in a school collection in 1969.

**Above:** The Eichstätt pterodactyl as illustrated in Soemmerring's treatise of 1812. He considered the skeleton to be that of a bat-like mammal.

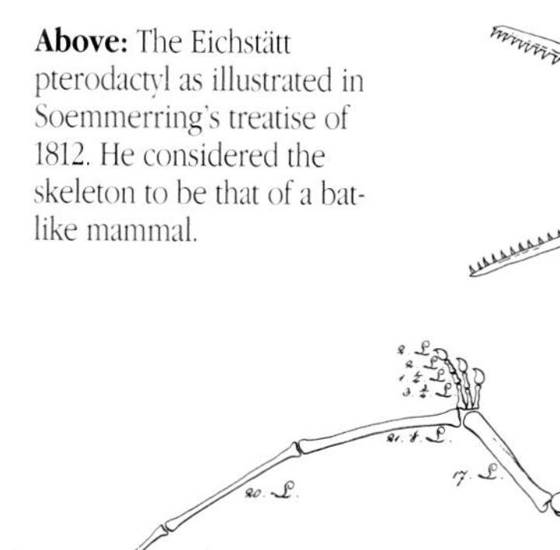

**Left:** The first skeletal restoration of a pterosaur as produced by Soemmerring in his 1812 treatise. His interpretation of the forelimb bones, however, was seriously in error.

**Above:** A skeletal restoration of *'Ornithocephalus' (=Pterodactylus) brevirostris* by Soemmerring, 1817, drawn on the basis of the second known pterodactyl from the Jurassic limestone of Bavaria. By marking the outlines of the wing membranes, Soemmerring gave it an even more bat-like appearance.

this and classified both forms as a new genus of bat, supposed to be similar to the flying fox.

Soemmerring's authority was apparently so great that of the German naturalists only Lorenz Oken (1779-1851) sided with Cuvier.[10] In 1819, in the magazine Isis, edited by Oken, Cuvier had called the Eichstätt pterosaur first known as *Ptero-dactyle* by its correct name *Pterodactylus* and given it the specific name *longirostris* (=long-snouted). According to international rules for the naming of zoological genera and species priority is given to Cuvier's *Pterodactylus*, but not to his specific name *longirostris*. Here the name *antiquus*, given by Soemmerring seven years earlier, is valid. Thus the first two pterosaur species should correctly be called in scientific terms *Pterodactylus antiquus* and *Pterodactylus brevirostris*. Later it turned out, however, that the species identified as *brevirostris* was simply a young animal of the species *antiquus*, and thus had to carry the same specific name as the adult individual, namely *antiquus*.

In the meantime, Cuvier had started to bring out his major work *Recherches sur les Ossemens fossiles* (Examinations of fossil bones) in 1812, which was to be a standard work on vertebrate palaeontology for a long time. He deals with *Pterodactylus* and its position in the zoological system in great detail in this work. With the aid of a cast and some detailed drawings that he had received from colleagues travelling through Munich, he once again took it upon himself to speak out against Soemmerring's bat

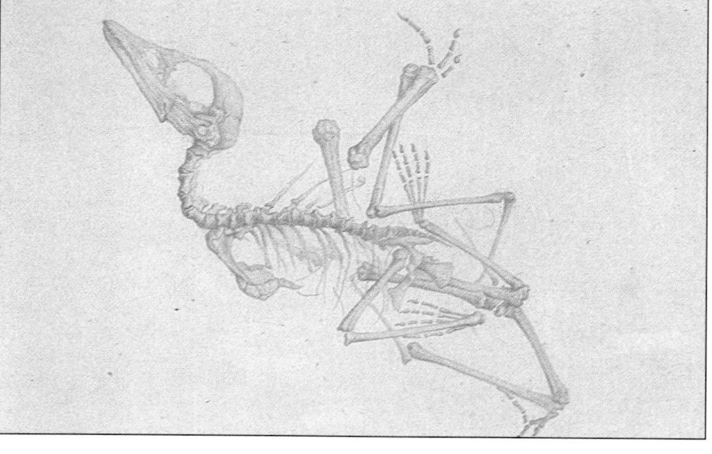

**Left:** Soemmerring's drawing of the *'Ornithocephalus' brevirostris* fossil pictured above. This appeared in his treatise of 1817. Today, this specimen is recognised as a juvenile individual of a larger species of the genus *Pterodactylus*. It is a baby pterosaur with a wing span of only 10in (25cm).

10 Lorenz Oken (1779-1851) was Professor at the University of Jena, but had seen the original *Pterodactylus* fossil in Munich himself. He wrote in 1819 in the magazine Isis, of which he was the editor: 'Consequently each individual piece of bone of this creature says loudly and clearly that it is an amphibian, and indeed of the order of lizards.' A year earlier he had taken Cuvier's side in the quarrel between Cuvier and Soemmerring, with the words: 'Truly, we never thought that we would find ourselves defending Cuvier! On other occasions we are always fleet to deny him something. But in this case! No! That is too bad!' The nature of these differences of opinion with Cuvier is clear if one compares Oken's nature philosophy with Cuvier's doctrine of catastrophe and his views on the constancy of species.

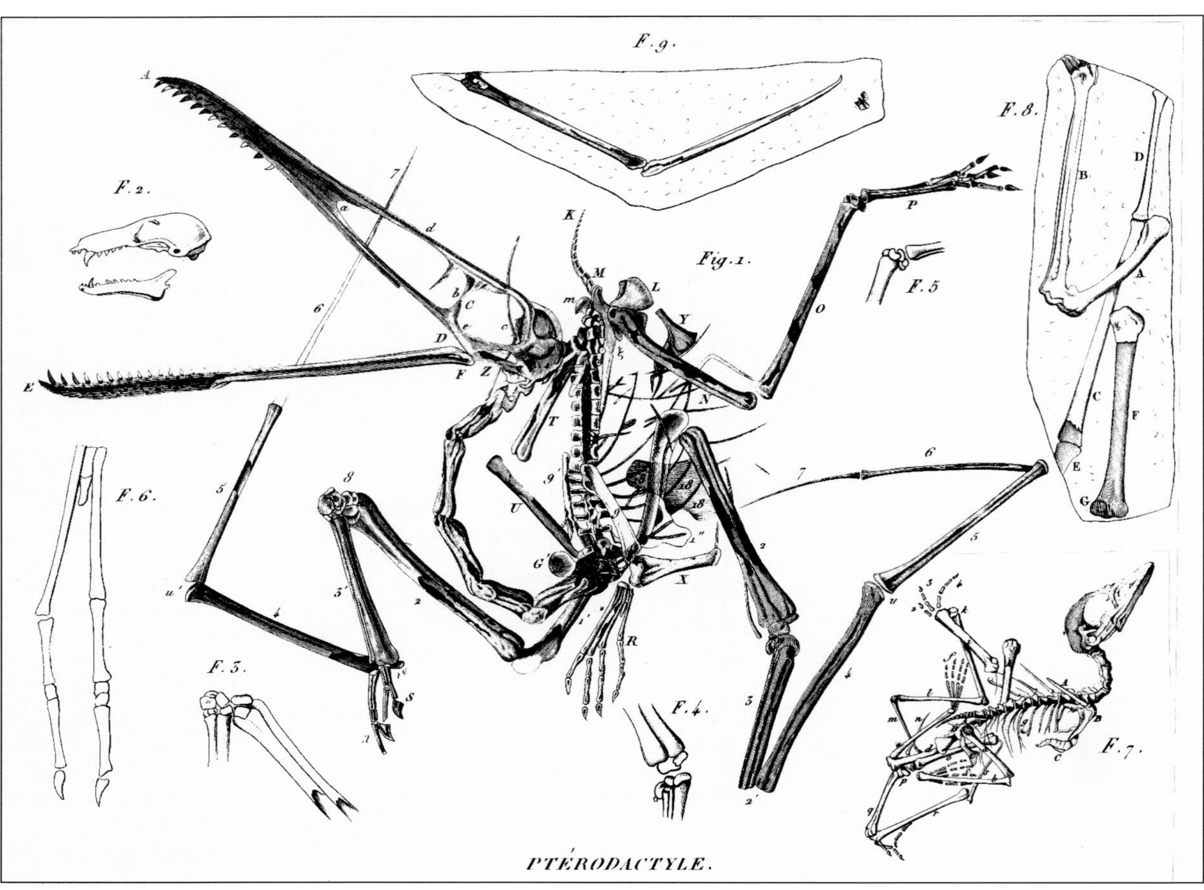


**Left:** A plate from Cuvier's fundamental work *Recherches sur les Ossemens fossiles* showing the Eichstätt pterodactyl, *Pterodactylus antiquus*, in the centre, with several drawings of osteological details (F.3-6), *Pterodactylus brevirostris* (F.7), and two more fragmentary pterosaur fossils (F.8 and 9). Cuvier also included a drawing of the skull of a bat, *Pteropus minimus* (F.2), taken by Soemmerring to be very similar to the skull of *Pterodactylus*. Cuvier, however, could demonstrate its great difference.

interpretation. In particular he pointed out the great differences between *Pterodactylus* and bats, in which it is possible to make a distinction in the dentition between incisors, molars and canines. But in *Pterodactylus*, as in reptiles, the teeth are simple, pointed and uniform. He also stressed other reptilian characteristics of the skeleton, especially in the vertebrae, ribs and pelvis. The skeleton of the foot in particular was completely different from that of birds and bats, and much more like that of a lizard. The short tail, which Soemmerring considered batlike, did not prove anything, as some reptiles, tortoises for example, also had short tails. Of course neither Cuvier nor Soemmerring could have known at the time that long-tailed pterosaurs would later be discovered; this would have emphasized lizard-like characteristics all the more.

Because of *Pterodactylus*' long hindlimbs, Cuvier assumed that the creature could only stand upright on its hind legs, and that the forelimbs could be folded back like birds' wings, and had not been an aid to standing. Finally Cuvier summed up his comparative anatomical investigation of *Pterodactylus* as follows: these creatures were reptiles that flew using a membrane supported by a single digit of the four-fingered hand and which could hang from tree branches with their three other, smaller digits. They could perhaps also crawl on the ground, but could only stand upright on their hindlimbs. They had large heads with jaws full of small, pointed teeth that were only suitable for catching insects and other small creatures. Cuvier thought these flying reptiles were the most extraordinary of living things, and that if one had met them alive they would seem the strangest creatures in nature. Scientific proof, using methods of comparative anatomy and Cuvier's authority, supported this assessment of *Pterodactylus* as a flying reptile, a pterosaur, and it is still recognized today.

## Other Finds – Other Ideas

Soemmerring clung to his bat hypothesis to the end. In 1820 he was still describing some hollow bones which without doubt came from a Solnhofen pterosaur as the fossil remains of a genus of large bat.[11] In the same year the Munich zoologist Johann Baptist von Spix (1781-1826) published a short treatise[12] on two phalanges from a pterosaur, also from Solnhofen, which he said were those of the southern Asian red-necked fruit bat. Incidentally in the same year, 1820, Spix had returned from a journey of exploration in Brazil. He had undertaken this with the botanist Carl Friedrich Philipp von Martius (1794-1868) and had returned with rich zoological and botanical collections. The two Munich naturalists had found large quantities of fish fossils in the north-eastern province of Ceará; in the 1970s pterosaur fossil remains were discovered here for the first time.

In 1825 the great Bayreuth fossil collector and palaeontologist Georg Graf zu Münster (1776-1844) asked Soemmerring's opinion about a presumed *Pterodactylus* head from Solnhofen that had come into his possession. In November of the same year Soemmerring replied: 'The Ornitholith, which is as rare as it is valuable, seems to belong to a particular genus of waterfowl which could have been similar to *Larus tridactylus* (a seagull) and *Colymbus* (a diver).' From that time this skull was counted as the first remains of a bird from the Jurassic, long before the discovery of *Archaeopteryx*, the so-called *Urvogel*, or primordial bird, in 1861. Later Graf Münster sent a cast of this fossil slab to Georg August Goldfuss (1782-1848), Professor of Natural History at the University of Bonn. In his *Beiträge zur Kenntnis verschiedener Reptilien der Vorwelt* (Contributions to the knowledge of various pre-

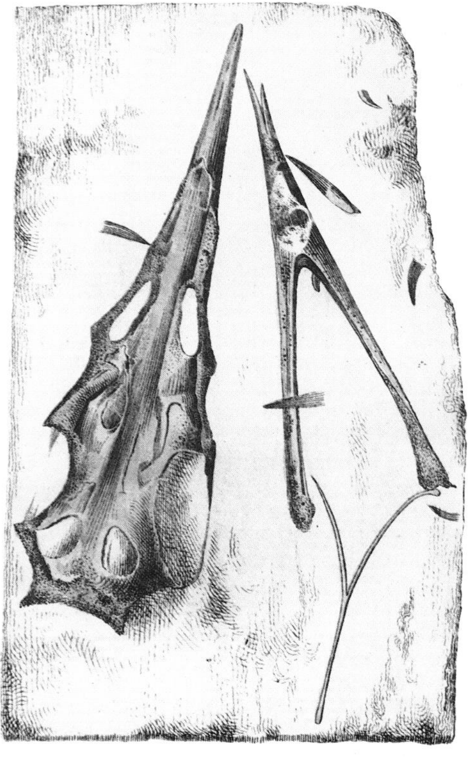

**Below:** Soemmerring thought that this fossil skull from the Solnhofen limestone belonged to a sea bird. In 1831 Professor August Goldfuss of Bonn University recognised it as belonging to a pterosaur. He named it *Pterodactylus muensteri*. Later it was realised that in fact it represented a completely new type of pterosaur, the rhamphorhynchids.

11 Soemmerring, S.T.v., 1829. *Über die fossilen Reste einer großen Fledermausgattung, welche sich zu Karlsruhe in der Großherzoglichen Sammlung befinden*. Denkschriften der Akademie der Wissenschaften München, math.-phys. Classe, 6: 105-112.

12 Spix, J.B.v., 1820. *Über ein neues, vermutlich dem Pteropus Vampirus Linn. zugehöriges Petrefikat aus dem Solenhofer Kalkbruch in Bayern*. Denkschriften der Akademie der Wissenschaften München, math.-phys. Classe, 6: 59-68.

**Left:** The first more complete skeleton of a long-tailed pterosaur was also described by Goldfuss in 1831. The specimen from the Solnhofen limestone was first named *'Pterodactylus' crassirostris,* because its long tail was not yet discovered. Today its correct scientific name is *Scaphognathus crassirostris.* To give an idea of scale, its skull is only 4·57in (11·6cm) long.

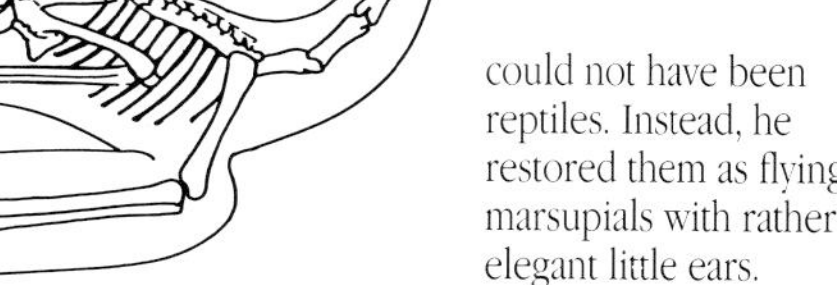

**Below:** The Munich zoologist Johann Georg Wagler restored *Pterodactylus* in 1830 in the guise shown below. Wagler supposed that it was an aquatic animal which may have used its wings like flippers for swimming, like penguins.

historic reptiles) of 1831 Goldfuss suggested that this could be a pterosaur skull.[13] In honour of Graf Münster he immediately named it *Ornithocephalus (Pterodactylus) muensteri.*

Certainly Soemmerring's mistake was understandable. In comparison with the *Pterodactylus* species *antiquus* and *brevirostris* the skull in the Münster collection was very different. Goldfuss on the other hand could compare it with the *Pterodactylus crassirostris* he had just acquired from Solnhofen, later given the generic name *Scaphognathus* (=tub jaw), whose skull was much more like Graf Münster's fossil. Münster wrote later, after further preparation and freeing of the skull bones from the rock: 'the toothless, spiniform point of the beak justifies the assumption of a subgenus of the genus *Pterodactylus* or perhaps, on closer acquaintance with the remaining bones, the formation of a new genus of these most wondrous creatures of the prehistoric world.' It was later established that this was the first long-tailed pterosaur find (=Rhamphorhynchoidea). All previous finds had been short-tailed pterosaurs (=Pterodactyloidea).

Goldfuss expressed views about the way of life of pterosaurs that seem very modern for 1831. He also thought they were flying reptiles which 'only used their claws to cling on to cliffs, crevices or trees, if they were available, and to climb up steep walls. Like bats they could fly and probably hovered above the surface of the water to catch insects and probably aquatic creatures as well.' And yet the Bonn professor could not escape the fascination exerted by these flying reptiles, and wrote at the end of his treatise: 'The image of this creature always seems more like a painting created by the unbridled imagination of a Chinese artist and less like a representation of a product of nature that really existed.' Goldfuss also believed that he had seen signs of hair on his specimen of *Pterodactylus crassirostris.* This was later seen to have been a mistake. Certain proof of a covering of hair for pterosaurs was successfully established, but not until 1927, by the Munich palaeontologist Ferdinand Broili.

The Munich zoologist Johann Georg Wagler had a completely different view of the position of *Pterodactylus* in the animal kingdom. In his *Natural System of Amphibians*[14] he combined it with other fossil groups like ichthyosaurs and plesiosaurs in a class of vertebrates of its own that he called Gryphi, placing them between birds and mammals. For this reason Wagler called *Pterodactylus* an arm griffin. He thought it had been hairless and that its feet were fin-shaped and covered with a kind of sheath of strong skin, but that some claws protruded beyond their outer edge 'to hold the female during the act of copulation'. Wagler had a strange idea of the way of life of these creatures. He thought they were aquatic, and used their wings as paddles in the water.

The English zoologist Edward Newman imagined pterodactyls quite differently in 1843.[15] He thought they were furry flying creatures with pouches, marsupials in other

13 Goldfuss, A., 1831. *Beiträge zur Kenntnis verschiedener Reptilien der Vorwelt.* Nova Acta Academiae Leopoldinae, 15: 61-128.

14 Wagler, J.G., 1830. *Natürliches System der Amphibien.* München, Stuttgart, Tübingen.

15 Newman, E., 1843. *Note on the Pterodactyle Tribe considered as Marsupial Bats.* Zoologist, 1: 129-131.

**Bottom of page:** A rather strange life restoration of pterodactyls was presented by Edward Newman in 1843 He thought that pterosaurs were warm-blooded and covered by a coat of fur, and so concluded that they could not have been reptiles. Instead, he restored them as flying marsupials with rather elegant little ears.

words. For this reason they have pretty little ears in his reconstruction drawing. The assumption that they must have been hairy also arose from the theory that these active flying animals were warm-blooded, and thus needed a covering of hair for reasons of heat conservation, like bats and other mammals.

Until 1827 all known pterosaur fossils came from the lithographic limestone in the quarries of Solnhofen and Eichstätt in Bavaria. Then finds were announced at other sites. The Proceedings of the Geological Society in London contained a description of a new species of *Pterodactylus* from early Jurassic strata from Lyme Regis, on the coast of Dorset.[16] These skeletal remains from the Blue Lias were dealt with by William Buckland (1784-1856), Reader in Geology at the University of Oxford. He was one of the 'fathers of British geology', and had described the first dinosaur, *Megalosaurus*, in England. Buckland's field was not just the geology of various parts of England and fossil reptiles in southern England, but also the structure of the Alps and fossil mammals of the Ice Age. He called the new species of pterosaur *Pterodactylus macronyx*, after the great claws on its digits. It later became clear that the genus was new as well. Richard Owen, later to be director of the Natural History Museum in London, gave it the name *Dimorphodon* (=two-form tooth) because of the double shape of its teeth. It was a flying creature with a wing span of 4·6ft (1·4m).

Buckland had acquired the fossil from Mary Anning (1799-1847), one of the first professional fossil collectors. She spent her whole life in the little town of Lyme Regis, on the Dorset coast of southern England. It is said that she was struck by lightning as a baby, and that her nurse was killed in the accident. She was a bright child, never married, and earned a living by collecting and selling fossils. The tongue-twister 'she sells sea shells sitting on the sea shore' is said to have been inspired by her. As an eleven-year-old girl she found the first articulated skeleton of a Jurassic ichthyosaur in the fossil-rich cliffs near her home town, and later the first complete plesiosaur skeleton. In December 1828 she discovered the first pterosaur in England, which she sent to Professor Buckland in Oxford. Mary Anning's customers included the King of Saxony, as well as many of the great palaeontologists and geologists of her time. The king bought fossils from her for his natural history collection in Dresden.

To be strictly accurate, the first English pterosaur remains had already been described by Gideon Mantell (1790-1852), but he thought they were the bones of a bird.[17] They were very fragmented, hollow bones originating from

**Above:** Dean William Buckland (1784-1856). Originally a scholar at Corpus Christi College, Oxford, he was appointed a Reader in Geology in 1818. In 1829 he described the first English pterosaur, *'Pterodactylus' (=Dimorphodon) macronyx.*

**Above:** Mary Anning (1799-1847) was one of the first professional fossil collectors. She made a living out of collecting and selling fossils from the Dorset coast near her home town of Lyme Regis. It was she who sold the specimen of *Dimorphodon* pictured left to William Buckland in 1828.

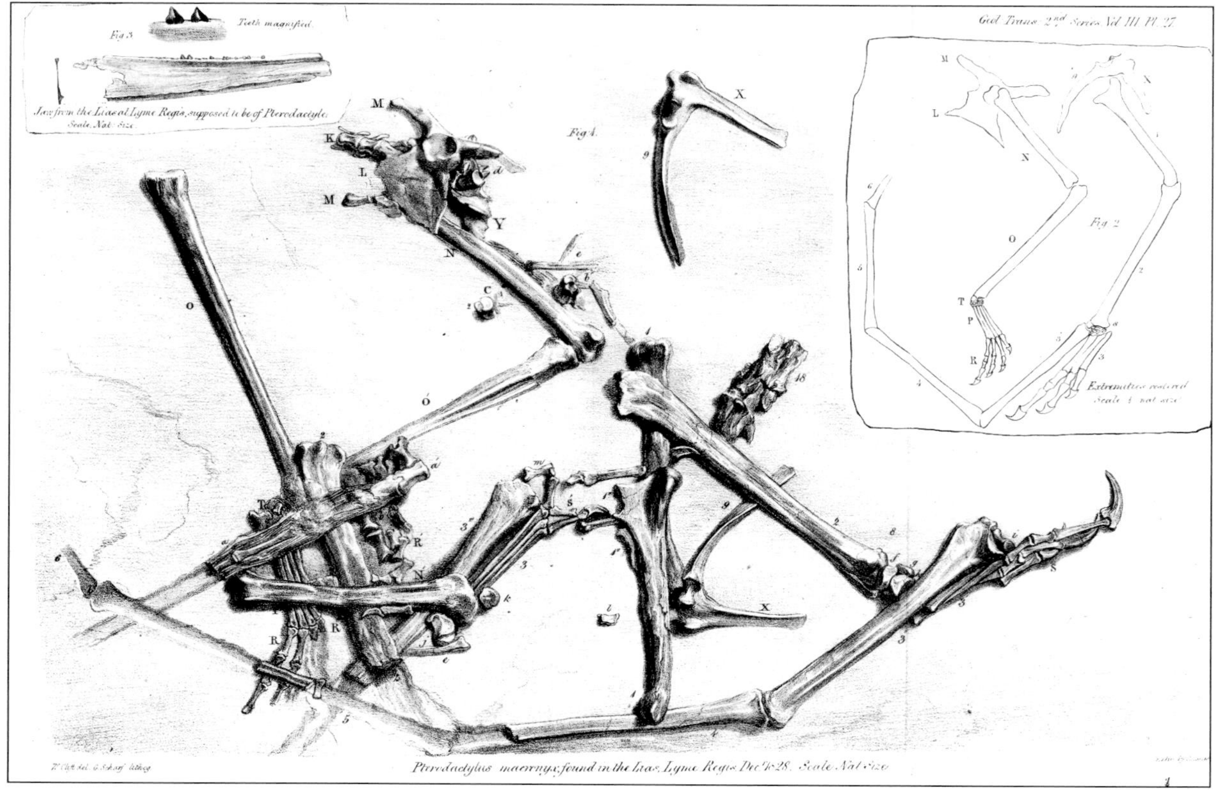

**Left:** The skeletal remains of the first Jurassic pterosaur in England were discovered by Mary Anning in the cliffs of the 'Blue Lias' near Lyme Regis. The skeleton was somewhat disarticulated and the skull was missing. The elements preserved were merely the incomplete wing bones and hind legs including the basin and shoulder girdle. This is the first illustration of *Dimorphodon macronyx* by Buckland in the 1835 Transactions of the Geological Society London.

16 Buckland, W., 1829. Proceedings of the Geological Society London, 1: 127.

17 Mantell, G.A., 1827. *Illustrations of the Geology of Sussex*. London.

**Above:** Gideon Mantell (1790-1852), a country doctor from Lewes in Sussex, actually described the first pterosaur remains found in England in 1827, but he mistakenly identified the hollow bones as those of a bird. He had collected them from the Wealden clay of Tilgate Forest in Sussex. Mantell is more famous for his discovery of the first remains of the dinosaur *Iguanodon* — some teeth which had originally been picked up by his wife, Mary Ann, near quarries in the Cuckfield area of Tilgate Forest.

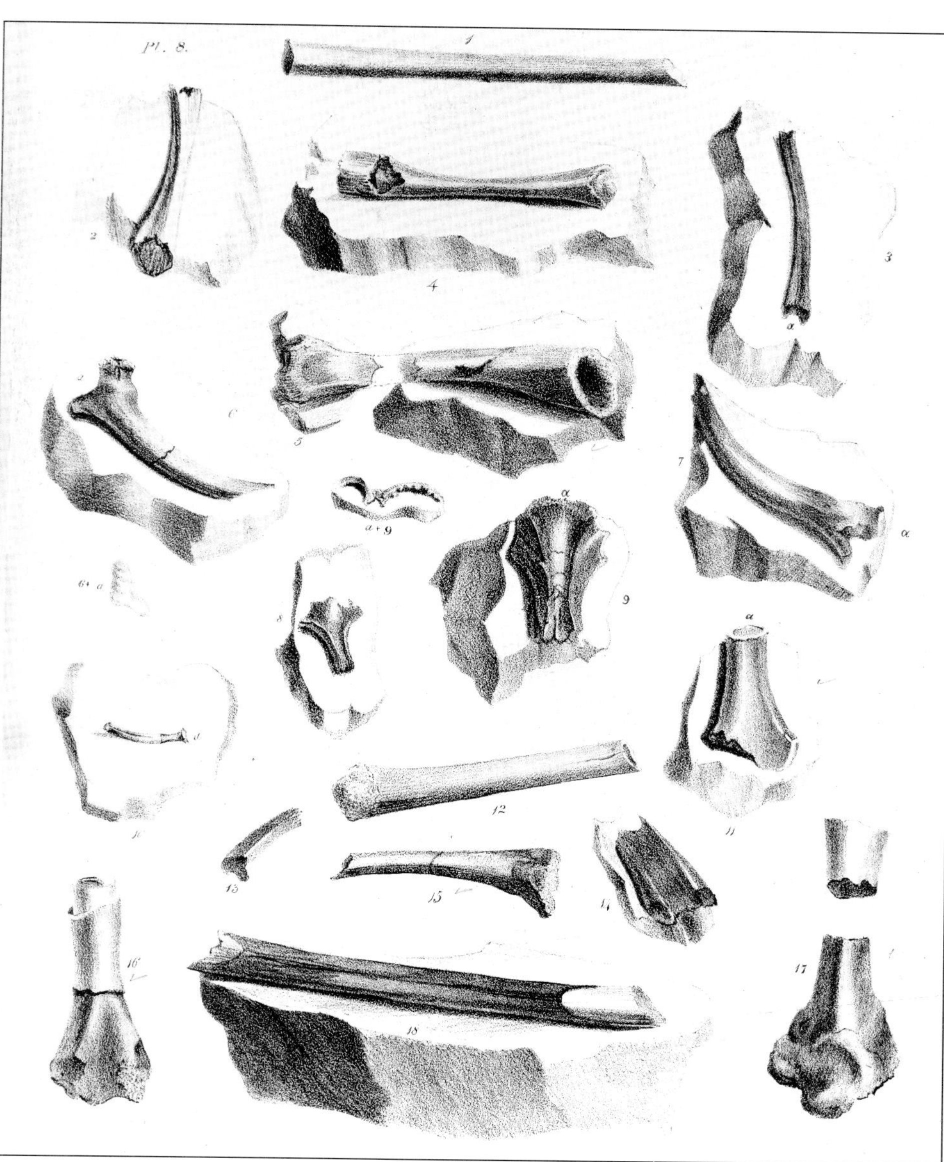

**Right:** A plate from Mantell's *Illustrations of the Geology of Sussex*, published in 1827. Mantell described these remains as 'bones of birds'; only later were they recognised as pterosaur bones.

**Below:** Carl Theodori (1788-1857), founder and keeper of the *Petrefaktensammlung* (fossil collection) in the castle of Banz on the river Main in Upper Franconia. In 1830 he announced the discovery of the first pterosaur bones from the Lias in Germany.

Lower Cretaceous strata in Tilgate Forest in Sussex. Mantell was a country doctor in Lewes, a small town in Sussex. He was a great lover and collector of fossils from the area around his home and wrote books and treatises on fossils and the geology of Sussex. In 1822 his wife Mary Ann had found the first remains of dinosaurs on English soil. They were only single teeth, which Mantell described as *Iguanodon* (=iguana tooth) because of their shape. Most of the more complete *Iguanodon* skeletons later discovered came from the same strata in Tilgate Forest as the pterosaur bones.

Pterosaur fossils from the Lias had also been found in Germany at the same time as the English finds. In 1830 Carl Theodori (1788-1857) reported the discovery of isolated bones from pterosaur skeletons around the monastery of Banz near Staffelstein on the upper Main in Franconia. Theodori, born in Landshut in Bavaria, was private secretary and chancellery councillor of Herzog Wilhelm in Bavaria, who in 1814 had acquired the former Benedictine monastery of Banz high above the Main, north of Bamberg, after it had been dissolved in the secularization of 1803. Herzog Wilhelm wanted to use the Brothers Dientzenhofer's magnificent monastery buildings with their splendid church, a superb example of Main-Franconian baroque, as a summer residence for himself and his family. For this reason Theodori spent the summer months here each year and began

**Left:** The baroque cloister of Banz in the Main valley, formerly a Benedictine monastery, became the castle of Wilhelm, Duke of Bavaria, in 1814. His secretary, Carl Theodori, collected fossils from the neighbourhood, and assembled a celebrated collection in the castle. This collection is still housed in Banz. It was refurbished in 1988 and exhibits many interesting specimens including a giant ichthyosaur skull, 6·6ft (2m) in length.

**Below:** A plate from Carl Theodori's memoir of 1852 illustrating the Liassic pterosaur bones from Banz, comprising jaw bones, vertebrae, ribs, upper arm, and shoulder girdle of a long-tailed pterosaur. Theodori named this as *'Pterodactylus' banthensis*. This species, the name is derived from Banz, was later assigned to a separate genus *Dorygnathus* (=spear jaw).

a systematic geological investigation of the environs of Banz, especially the Lias and the Dogger, the Lower Jurassic rocks that formed the basis of the Banz hills. With the former Benedictine father and priest Augustin Geyer he assembled a famous collection of fossils from the immediate neighbourhood, and this was displayed in the monastery, now palace, of Banz as the 'Petrefaktensammlung'.[18]

Theodori was in active contact with the leading naturalists of his time. The Banz collection was visited by Buckland, Owen, Goldfuss and Leopold von Buch, the preeminent German geologist at the time. The famous Frankfurt vertebrate palaeontologist Hermann von Meyer also visited the Banz collection in summer 1830 and later wrote: '. . . I really succeeded in finding remains of *Pterodactylus macronyx*, which had been discovered in England shortly before, for the Banz region.' Theodori himself had described the Banz pterosaurs as *Pterodactylus banthensis*,[19] thus distinguishing them from the English finds in Lyme Regis. Later they were even separated as a different genus called *Dorygnathus* (=spear jaw).

Fossil pterosaur remains were also found later in Liassic strata in Württemberg. The first find was reported by Albert Oppel (1831-1865), later to be Professor of Palaeontology in Munich. It was a lower jaw recovered from the

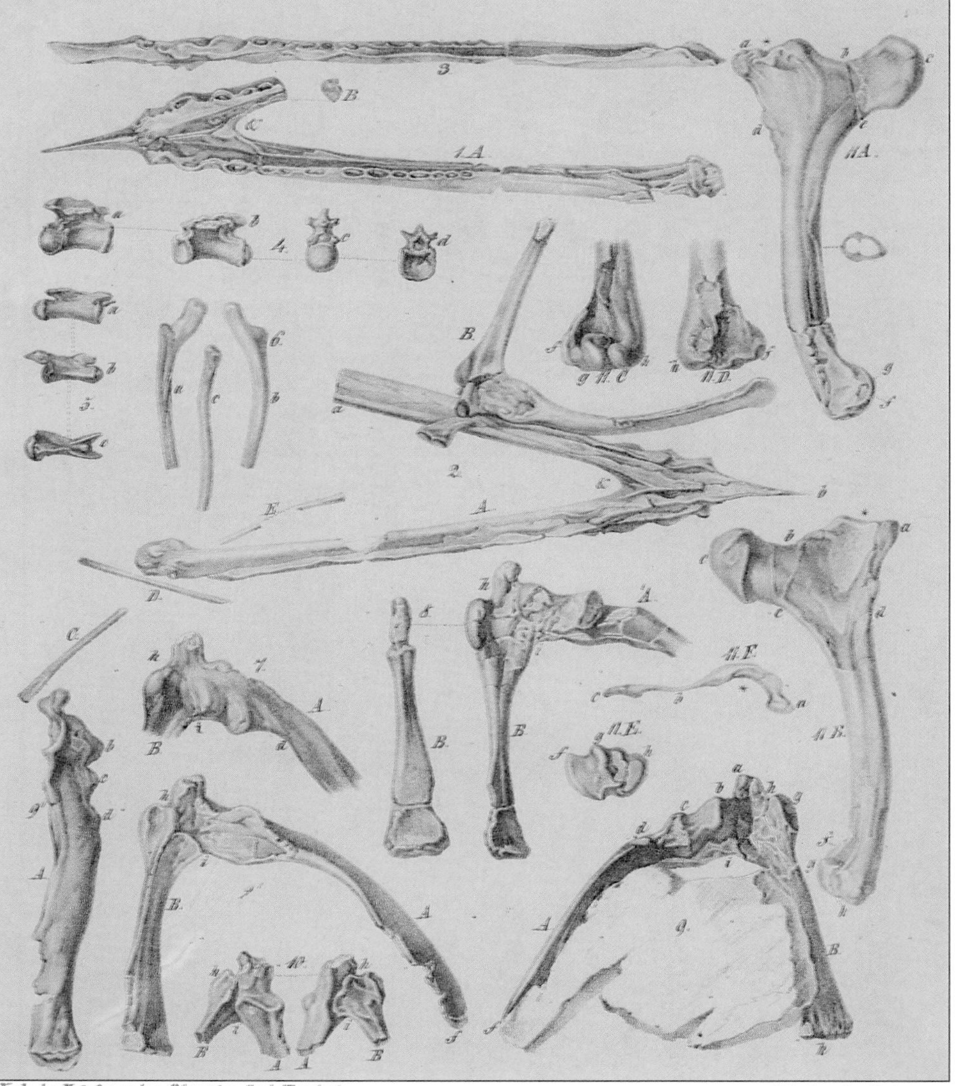


18 The collection is still there today. It was completely refurbished in 1988 and reopened in new rooms. The finest object in the little museum was and is a huge, 6·6ft (2m) long fossilized skull of an ichthyosaur, discovered in 1842 during building work in nearby Unnersdorf and then described by Theodori as *Ichthyosaurus trigonodon*. Of course Theodori suffered from the seclusion and isolation of Banz, especially from the lack of a library, essential for his scientific work.

19 Theodori, C., 1830. *Knochen von Pterodactylus aus der Liasformation von Banz*. Frorieps Notizen für Natur und Heilkunde, 632: 101.

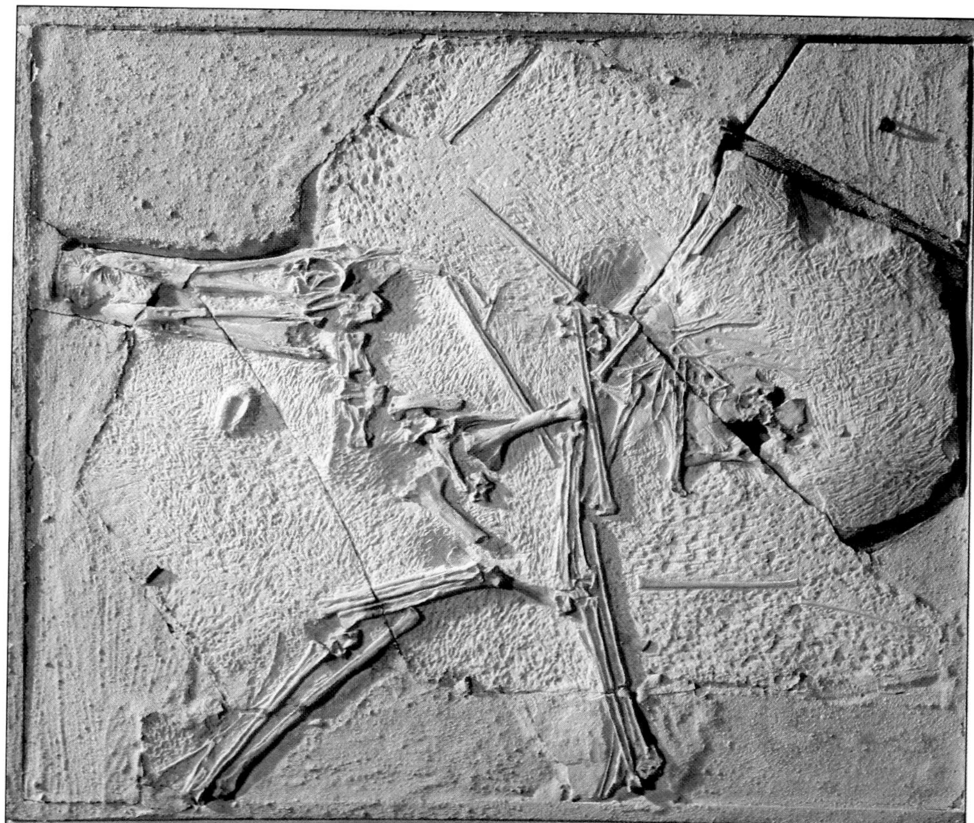

Lias at Wittberg near Metzingen in 1856, and he classified it as a *Pterodactylus* of the Banz species, *Pterodactylus banthenis*.[20] Two years later the Tübingen professor Friedrich August Quenstedt (1809-1889), a trail-blazing geological explorer, particularly of the Jurassic formation in Württemberg, reported on a *Pterodactylus liasicus* from the same site.[21] There were a few wing bones, scattered and embedded. Quenstedt thought the English, Franconian and Swabian pterosaur finds were of different ages, but saw them as examples of evolution of the species in geological time sequence. This shows that he too was a supporter of the ideas of the French zoologist Jean Baptist de Lamarck, as he writes: 'Then proof will also emerge that there were no crises in creation, but generally speaking only gradual development.' Here he was clearly taking up a position opposed to the catastrophe approach supported by Georges Cuvier. In fact it later emerged that the English Lyme Regis Lias pterosaurs are older than the Swabian and Franconian finds. But the latter two are the same age, dating from the late Liassic.

It was also Quenstedt who made known the first Swabian pterosaur find, in a letter to the Heidelberg professor Heinrich Georg Bronn, editor of the 'Neues Jahrbuch für Mineralogie' of 29 July 1854. 'At last I can tell you something about the first *Pterodactylus württembergicus* from the limestone slabs of our White Jurassic.' The fossil came from the limestone quarries of Nusplingen in the Schwäbische Alb, where the rocks are similar in age and origin to the Solnhofen limestone slabs. A year later Quenstedt described this pterosaur skeleton as *Pterodactylus suevicus*, from an animal with a wing span of about 4·3ft (1·3m).[22]

**Above:** The first pterosaur from Württemberg was announced by August Quenstedt as *Pterodactylus suevicus* in 1845. The skeleton was discovered in a limestone quarry near Nusplingen. Today this species is assigned to *Gallodactylus*, a genus first described from late Jurassic limestone from France.

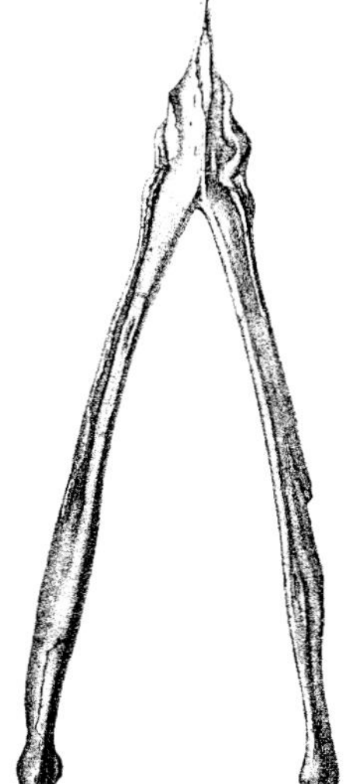

**Right:** This mandible was collected by Albert Oppel in 1856 near Bad Boll, not far from Holzmaden. The illustration is from von Meyer's monograph of 1859-60 in which this specimen is assigned to *Dorygnathus banthensis*.

Later more skeletal remains were discovered at Nusplingen quarry, but the principal area for finds in Württemberg was the region of Holzmaden, Ohmden, Bad Boll and Zell near Kirchheim/Teck on the northern edge of the Schwäbische Alb. Black bituminous shale from the Upper Liassic had been quarried there for years. It was also called *Posidonienschiefer* after the *Posidonia* shells that frequently occurred there.

Here again it was Albert Oppel who was the first to report a pterosaur find at Bad Boll, a lower jaw,[23] which he sent to the Frankfurt palaeontologist Hermann von Meyer for investigation. More complete pterosaur skeletons from Holzmaden were first described from 1895 by the Stuttgart professor Felix Plieninger. He was able to present evidence of two different genera, *Dorygnathus* and *Campylognathus* (=crooked jaw),[24] both long-tailed varieties. It was also Plieninger who introduced the division of the pterosaur order into two sub-orders, Rhamphorhynchoidea (for long-tailed forms) and Pterodactyloidea (for short-tailed forms).

Solnhofen and Eichstätt in Bavaria and Holzmaden in Württemberg have remained the most important sites for pterosaur finds until today. The Solnhofen limestone slabs continued to provide new species. Thus in 1839 Graf Münster reported a '*Pterodactylus* from the Solnhofen limestone quarries", which differed from other species in respect of its long, thin tail. For this reason he called it *Pterodactylus longicaudus*, long-tailed *Pterodactylus*. It was the first indication of a second type of pterosaur, which could be distinguished from short-tailed forms, with a few very short caudal vertebrae, by its long tail with a large number of vertebrae.[25]

## A New Genus

In 1846 Hermann von Meyer[26] had the opportunity of examining another long-tailed pterosaur from Solnhofen. Because of the 'beak-like projection on the snout' he gave this new genus the name *Rhamphorhynchus* (=beak-snout). Hermann von Meyer (1801-1869), the actual founder of vertebrate palaeontology in Germany, also gave the first summary of pterosaurs of the Upper Jurassic, in a magnificent folio volume which he published in 1859-60 under the title *Die Reptilien aus dem Lithographischen Schiefer des Jura in Deutschland und Frankreich*. At the time lithographic limestone meant limestone slabs of the Solnhofen limestone type, which were used in lithography, a stone-printing process invented by Alois Senefelder in 1796, because they were particularly fine-grained and dense.

There were also fossiliferous late Jurassic limestone slabs with fossil fish, small lizards, crocodiles and turtles in south-western France, near the little village of Cerin in the Département of Ain. However, only two bones suggested the existence of pterosaurs, an upper arm and a shin bone from a *Pterodactylus* with a wing span of about 6·5ft (2m), named *Pterodactylus cerinensis* by von Meyer.

20 Oppel, A., 1856. *Die Juraformation*. Jahreshefte des Vereins für Vaterländische Naturkunde in Württemberg, 12.

21 Quenstedt, F.A., 1858. *Über Pterodactylus liasicus*. Jahreshefte des Vereins für Vaterländische Naturkunde in Württemberg, 14: 299-336.

22 Quenstedt, F.A., 1855. *Über Pterodactylus suevicus im lithographischen Schiefer Württembergs*. Tübingen.

23 Oppel, A., 1858. *Die geognostische Verbreitung der Pterodactylen*. Jahreshefte des Vereins für Vaterländische Naturkunde in Württemberg, 14: 55.

24 Plieninger, F., 1895. *Campylognathus Zitteli. Ein neuer Flugsaurier aus dem oberen Lias Schwabens*. Palaeontographica, 41: 193-222.

25 Münster, G. zu, 1839. *Über einige neue Versteinerungen in den lithographischen Schiefern von Baiern*. Neues Jahrbuch für Mineralogie etc.: 676-682.

26 Hermann von Meyer (1801-1869) was born in Frankfurt on 3 September 1801. He was an extremely versatile researcher and the outstanding vertebrate palaeontologist of 19th century Germany. He was 'Bundescassier' to the Deutscher Bundestag in Frankfurt. From 1851-1852 he was director of the museum of the Senckenbergische Naturforschende Gesellschaft in Frankfurt. He described pterosaurs from the Upper Jurassic from Solnhofen in Bavaria, Nusplingen in Württemberg and Cerin in France in a magnificently presented monograph: *Die Reptilien aus dem Lithographischen Schiefer des Jura in Deutschland und Frankreich*, 1859-1860.

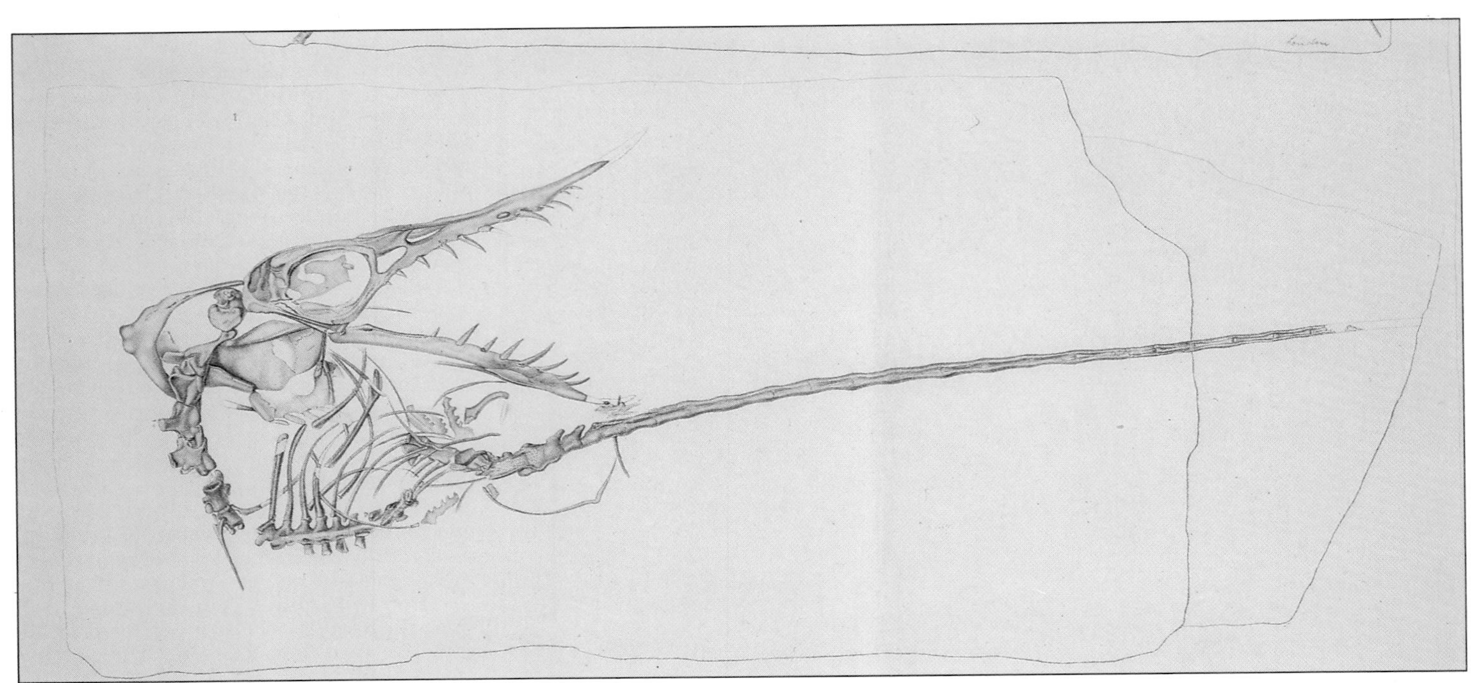

In Hermann von Meyer's great monograph there is also a description of skeletal remains found in Jurassic limestone slabs from Riedenburg in the Altmühl valley, about 25 miles (40km) east of Eichstätt. Because of its different, strong feet this species was given the name *Pterodactylus crassipes*, the thick footed. The fossil was later acquired by the Teyler Museum in Haarlem, Holland. In 1970 it was examined there by John H. Ostrom, Professor of Geology at Yale University, New Haven, USA. Professor Ostrom was more than a little surprised to discover that the sparse fragments of the hindlimbs and the hand did not come from a *Pterodactylus*, indeed they were not even part of a pterosaur, but came from a bird, the famous primordial bird *Archaeopteryx*. At that time there were only three specimens of this rare fossil, deposited in London, Berlin and Maxberg near Solnhofen.

John Ostrom discovered indistinct impressions on the rock surface of the limestone slab which had already confused Hermann von Meyer. Meyer wrote: 'I have never, on any other *Pterodactylus*, seen phenomena that one is inclined to ascribe to the folds of the flight membrane as clearly as on this specimen. But even here I cannot think them to be what I would dearly like to call them, because, apart from the fact that the flight digit is nowhere near them, they are not sharp and definite enough for folds of skin, particularly in a compressed condition. Therefore the reason for this phenomenon must be unevenness of the bed and movement of the water, which have caused this formation.'

Under oblique light these weak impressions on the surface of the stone showed up quite clearly for John Ostrom as imprints of feathers. Comparison of the skeletal remains with other specimens of prehistoric birds removed any remaining doubts. The *Pterodactylus crassipes* in the Teyler Museum in Haarlem was not a pterosaur, but an *Archaeopteryx*. Thus this primordial bird, the fourth specimen, had been woken like Sleeping Beauty after 110 years.[27]

For many years the curator of the Palaeontological Museum in Munich, Johann Andreas

27 Ostrom, J.H., 1970. *Archaeopteryx: Notice of a 'New' Specimen*. Science, 170: 537-538.

**Above:** This illustration of a *Rhamphorhynchus gemmingi* from Solnhofen appears in Hermann von Meyer's magnificent monograph *Die Reptilien aus dem Lithographischen Schiefer des Jura in Deutschland und Frankreich*. It shows the well preserved skull and typical long tail very nicely. The wings were obviously lost before the skeleton was embedded in the limy mud. Today this specimen is housed in the Teyler Museum, Haarlem.

**Below:** This is a plate from E.T. Newton's description of *'Scaphognathus' purdoni*, a fossil skull of a pterosaur discovered by the Rev D. W. Purdon near Whitby in Yorkshire. It shows the skull from both sides (Figs. 2 and 3) and from behind (Fig. 5). The preserved brain cast is seen from the left (Fig. 6) and from above and behind (Fig. 7). For comparison a skull of the Tuatara (*Sphenodon*) (Figs. 10 and 11) and a back view of the skull of a fowl (Fig. 12) are also included.

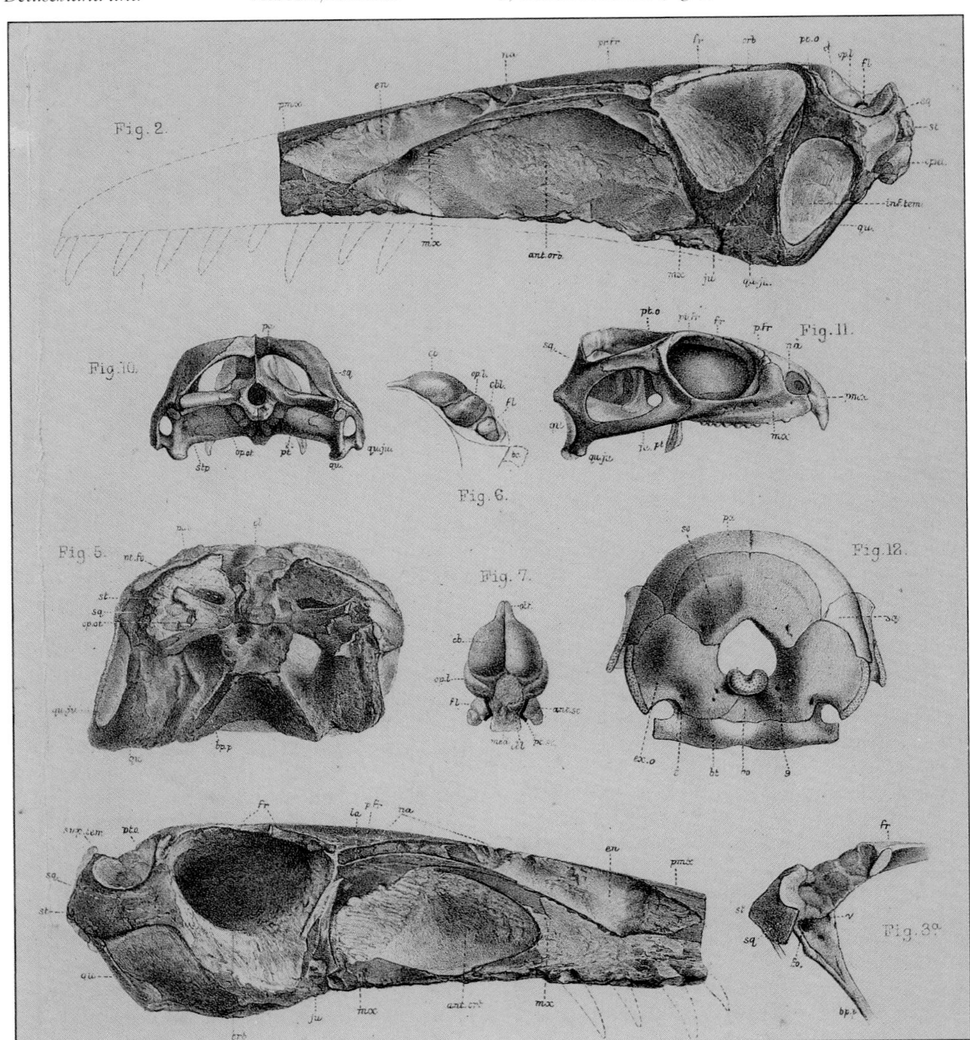

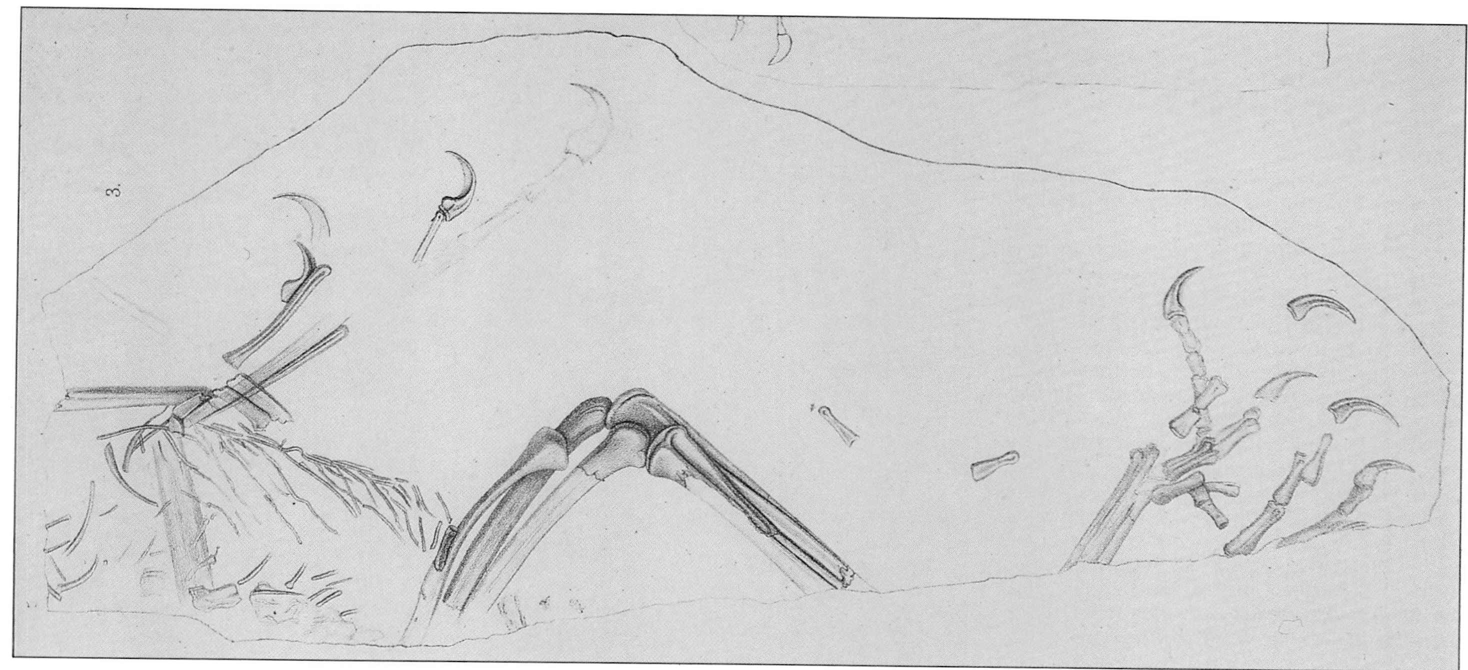

**Above:** Also figured in his great monograph of 1859-60, Hermann von Meyer assigned these remains from the Solnhofen limestone to a new species of pterodactyl, as *Pterodactylus crassipes*. It was not until 1970 that it was recognised as another specimen of the famous primordial bird *Archaeopteryx* by John H. Ostrom of Yale University. The fossil is also housed in the Teyler Museum, Haarlem, Netherlands.

**Right:** Sir Richard Owen (1804-1892) with a mounted skeleton of the fossil giant bird *Dinornis*. In his time Owen was a leading comparative anatomist, and eventually became the first superintendent of the British Museum (Natural History) in London. In several monographs Owen described the English pterosaurs, which he regarded as cold-blooded reptiles. His view conflicted with that of Harry Govier Seeley, who insisted that pterosaurs must have been warm-blooded, and a violent controversy between the two scientists ensued.

Wagner (1797-1861), devoted himself to investigating Solnhofen pterosaurs.[28] He described a number of new species. Many of these specimens came to light as a result of the purchase of Dr Carl Haeberlein's collection. He was a country doctor from Pappenheim, and the same Carl Haeberlein who in 1862 sold a large collection of Solnhofen fossils, including the first *Archaeopteryx* skeleton, to the British Museum (Natural History) in London. Interestingly Wagner saw pterosaurs as a transitional phase between reptiles and birds, although he was a convinced supporter of the Biblical creation story and violently rejected Darwin's ideas even in the last year of his life, 1861.

Remains of pterosaurs from strata of the Middle and Upper Jurassic had also come to light in England, for example from the so-called Stonesfield Slate in Oxfordshire, called *Pterodactylus bucklandi* by Hermann von Meyer in 1832, and in 1874 from the Kimmeridge Clay on the coast of Dorset in southern England. In the 1880s the Reverend D.W. Purdon found a fossil skull in the Liassic rocks of Whitby in Yorkshire, which he sent to the Geological Survey in London for investigation. There it was described by E.T. Newton in 1888, who named the species *Scaphognathus purdoni*, in honour of its finder. The genus *Scaphognathus* had been established by Andreas Wagner in 1861.

The fossil discovered by the Reverend Purdon was an unusually well-preserved pterosaur skull, in which the petrified contents of the brain capsule could be seen through an opening in the top of the skull. This kind of preservation is called an endocast, and it occurs when ooze is pressed into the hollow parts of the skull after the soft parts have decayed. This becomes firm, along with the surrounding sediment and also turns into stone. After removing the bones of the skull, Newton had a faithful cast of the brain that had controlled the pterosaur's life functions 180 million years ago. It showed remarkable similarity to the brain of a bird and was clearly different from the brain of a reptile.

In 1844, after Gideon Mantell himself recognized that the bones he had found in Tilgate Forest, thought to be bird bones, were in fact pterosaur bones, skeletal remains of pterosaurs were found at other Cretaceous sites in England, for example in 1851 in the Cambridge Greensand, which provided numerous specimens in subsequent years, although they were always isolated bones. Two researchers in particular devoted themselves to scientific investigation of these finds: Sir Richard Owen (1804-1892), director of the British Museum (Natural

28 Johann Andreas Wagner (1797-1861) was born in 1797 in Nuremberg. He was the first lecturer in zoology at the University of Erlangen, then went to Munich in 1836, became curator of the state palaeontological collection and was appointed to the first chair of palaeontology in Germany. He published numerous works, including material on fish and reptiles from Solnhofen, Tertiary primates from Greece and ice-age mammals from caves in Franconia. He was a profound believer in the Biblical creation story and was moved to oppose Charles Darwin's 'adventurous' ideas in the last years of his life. Thus for him the primeval bird *Archaeopteryx*, found in 1861, was not a bird, but a reptile, which he called *Griphosaurus* (=puzzle lizard), despite its feathers.

History) in London, and Harry Govier Seeley (1839-1909), Professor of Geology at King's College London. In 1901 Seeley published the first complete and popular book on pterosaurs, *Dragons of the Air*.

Seeley published a whole series of essays on pterosaurs (his Saurornia), which he later called Ornithosauria, following the Italian ornithologist Prince Charles Bonaparte. (But the name *Pterosauria* has priority, as it was suggested by the Darmstadt palaeontologist Johann Jakob Kaup as early as 1834). Seeley was concerned in particular with lavish finds of pterosaur bones in the Cretaceous Greensand of Cambridge. He gives an idea of the sites at which the bones were found in 1901 (p.34), when he writes: 'To give some idea of their abundance, it may be stated that they were mostly gathered during two or three years, as a matter of business, by an intelligent foreman of washers of the nodules of phosphate of lime, which, in commerce, are named coprolites. He soon learned to distinguish Pterodactyle bones from other fossils by their texture, and learned the anatomical names of bones from specimens in the University Museum. This workman, Mr Pond, brought together not only the best of the remains at Cambridge, but most of those at the museums at York and in London, and the thousands of less perfect specimens in public and private collections.'

In 1864, by analogy with birds, he insisted that pterosaurs, which he called Saurornia, must have been warm-blooded, which in his view justified separation from the reptile class.[29] Seeley felt that pterosaurs (he now used the name Ornithosauria) could not have been genuine reptiles. He wrote in *Dragons of the Air*. '. . . Ornithosaurs may now with more accuracy be described as dinosaurian. The dinosaurs, like the pterodactyles, must be re-

29 Seeley, H.G., 1864. *On the pterodactyle as evidence of a new subclass of Vertebrata (Saurornia)*. Reports of the British Association of Scientists, 34th meeting: p.69.
Seeley, H.G., 1870. *The Ornithosauria. An elementary study of the bones of Pterodactyles*. Cambridge University Press.
Seeley, H.G., 1901. *Dragons of the Air*. New York. Reprinted 1967 by Dover Paperback. This was the first popular book devoted exclusively to pterosaurs as a group. In it Seeley summarized knowledge about pterosaurs as it stood at the time.

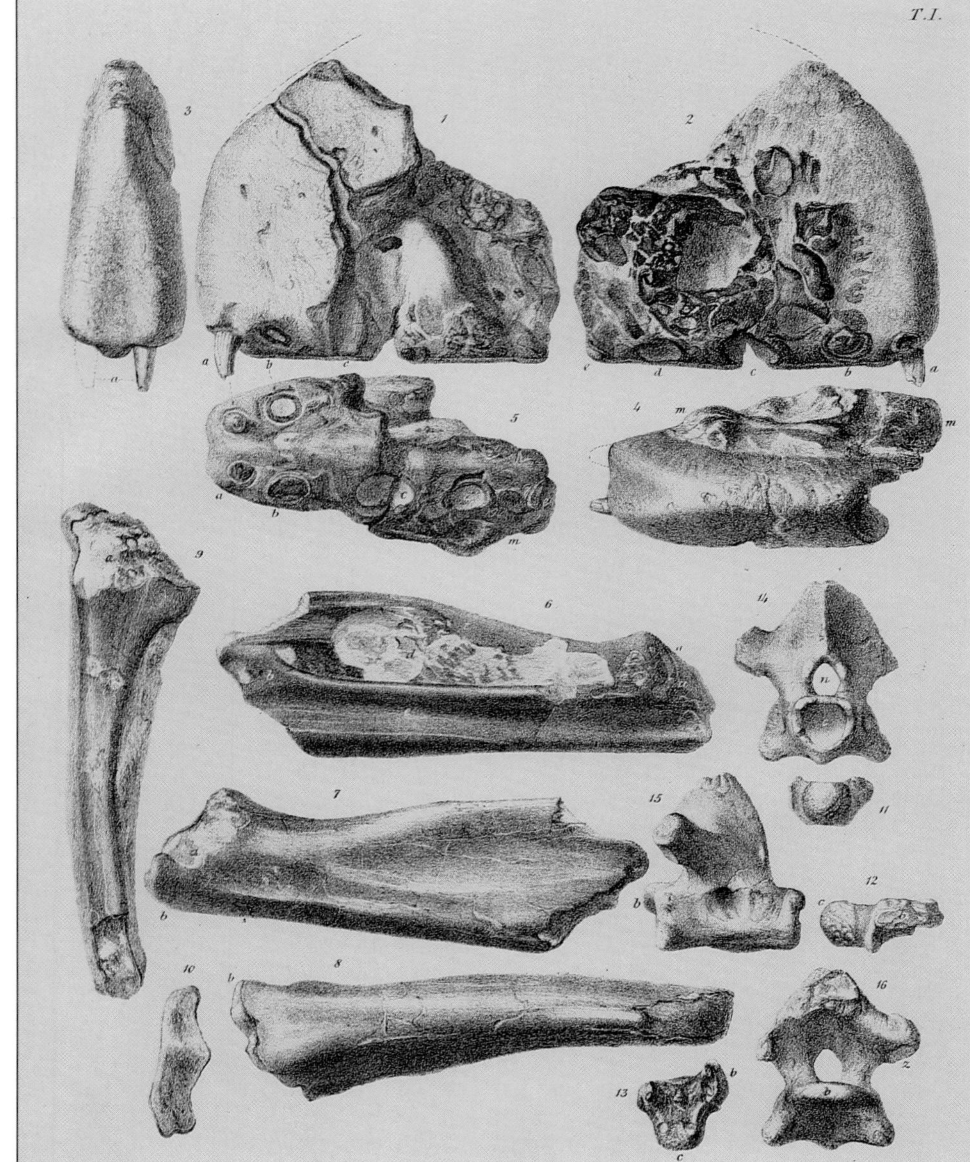

**Above:** A plate from one of Owen's monographs on the *Fossil Reptilia* depicting jaw fragments and vertebrae of *Criorhynchus* from the Cambridge Greensand.

**Below:** A life restoration of *Dimorphodon macronyx* from the Lias of Lyme Regis by H.G. Seeley, as seen in his popular book *Dragons of the Air* (1901).

**Right:** The Yale expedition of 1870 with O.C. Marsh standing in the centre. It was this party that discovered the first American pterosaur remains in Kansas. Because the West was still Indian territory, standard equipment included not only geological hammer, but also rifle and bowie-knife.

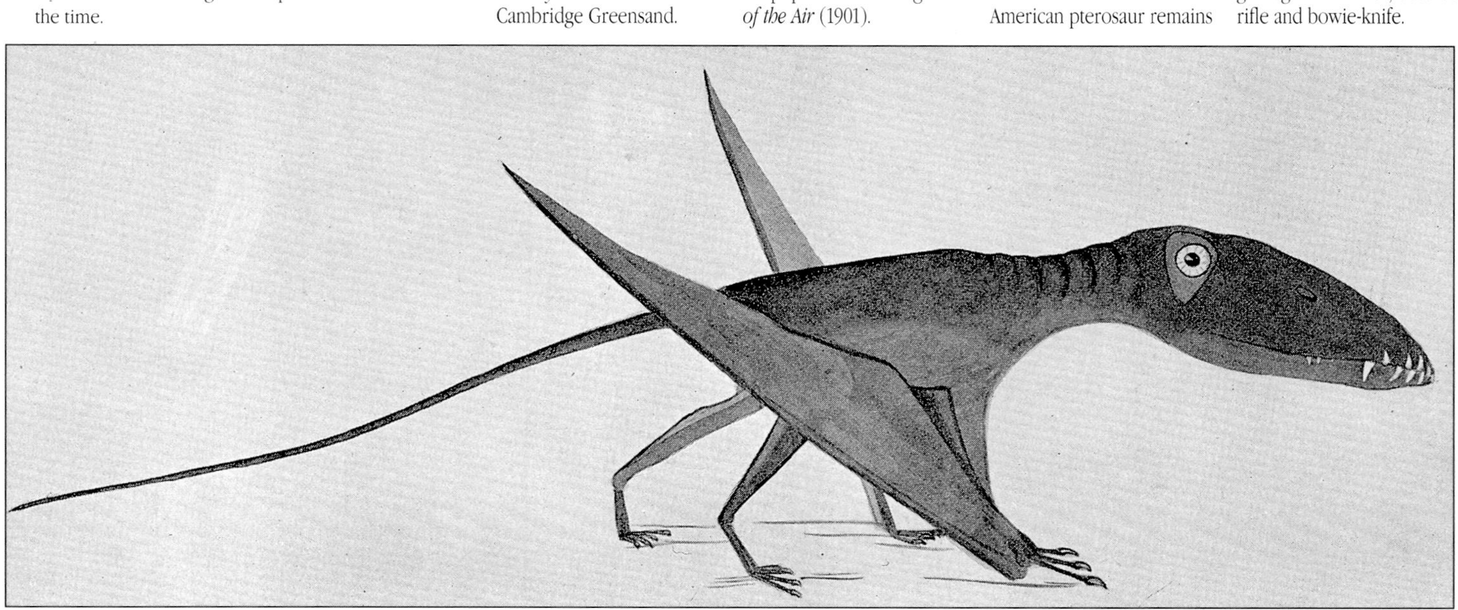

garded as intermediate in some respects between reptiles and birds.' Seeley then suggested a position of their own for pterosaurs, warm-blooded in his opinion, in the system of vertebrates. They were to be classified parallel with birds between reptiles and mammals.

Richard Owen's opinions were quite different from Seeley's.[30] He believed for example that the size of pterosaurs was limited from the outset. He thought they were cold-blooded and thus physiologically inferior to warm-blooded flying creatures like birds and bats. No larger pterosaurs were in fact known until about 1840. But in 1845 the secretary of the London Palaeontographical Society, John Scott Bowerbank, described a new species of pterosaur from chalk strata in Kent, whose wing span must have been at least eight to nine feet (2·5m). And somewhat later he discovered fossil bones of an even larger species, which must have had a span of almost 16·5ft (5m) with wings extended. For this reason Bowerbank called the species *Pterodactylus giganteus*.[31] This did not mean that Owen changed his views about the physiology of pterosaurs; no, he now declared, as a convinced supporter of Biblical teaching on creation, that God's power as a creator had been greater in the Earth's past, and thus went beyond calculations based upon contemporary nature.

**Above:** Edward Drinker Cope (1840-1897) was one of the pioneers of North American palaeontology, especially in exploring the Western territories for fossil vertebrates. His rivalry with Marsh is legendary.

A violent controversy developed between Owen and Seeley about the warm-bloodedness and physiology of pterosaurs. In 1870 Owen had received new skeletal remains of the Liassic pterosaur *Dimorphodon* from Lyme Regis in Dorset and compared its osteological characteristics with modern crocodiles and lizards in particular.[32] For Owen, as an anti-evolutionist, pterosaurs must have been reptilian and cold-blooded; they could not be warm-blooded and equally ranked with birds. The decisive fact was not that pterosaurs were actively flying animals, but that there was no evidence that they had an insulating skin covering to conserve warmth, in other words no feathers or hairs. In Seeley's eyes Owen was going against physiological principles by separating metabolic level and an ability to fly actively. Owen's reaction to much later evidence that pterosaurs had hair would have been interesting.

Immediately after the appearance of Owen's monograph Seeley published a critical statement.[33] For him pterosaurs were not reptiles, but closely related to birds. Like these they had a high metabolic level and similar physiology. This was also the case for lungs, heart and brain. He supported this on the basis of his excellent knowledge of the osteology of English Cretaceous pterosaurs. But essentially the quarrel between Seeley and Owen was not about the interpretation of skeletal structures, but a debate on the validity of species transformations and evolutionary progress.

## American Discoveries

In the 1870s much bigger pterosaurs were discovered, the largest of all flying creatures. These were found in America. Investigation of these giant pterosaurs is closely associated with Edward Drinker Cope (1840-1897) and Othniel Charles Marsh (1831-1899), both pioneers of geological and palaeontological exploration of the North American West, but also bitter rivals. Their principal service was the discovery and exploitation of famous dinosaur remains. Cope was a member of the Academy of Science in Philadelphia, Marsh was a professor at Yale College in New Haven.

In summer 1870 O.C. Marsh mounted an expedition to the Rocky Mountains to look for fossils. One of his companions was Colonel William F. Cody, better known as Buffalo Bill. In November, on the way back, Marsh's group began to explore the Cretaceous strata of this region, the Niobrara Chalk of western Kansas,

30 It was Richard Owen (1804-1892) who introduced the name *Dinosauria* in 1841, although only three specimens of these giant reptiles were known from English Jurassic and Cretaceous strata. After the appearance of Darwin's book *The Origin of Species* in 1859 he became a leading anti-Darwinist, opposing Darwin's theory, which stated that animal and plant species on Earth evolved one from another by a gradual process of transformation, and thus were the result of evolution controlled by natural selection. Only the best-adjusted organisms survive in the 'struggle for life'. Owen described the first skeleton find of the primeval bird *Archaeopteryx*, bought by the British Museum from the Pappenheim doctor Carl Haeberlein in 1862, as a primitive, but genuine bird. Unlike the Darwinists he did not see it as a 'missing link' in evolution from reptile to bird.

31 Bowerbank, J.S., 1846. *On a new species of Pterodactyle of the upper Chalk*. Quarterly Journal of the Geological Society London, 1(5):7.

32 Owen, R., 1870. *Monograph of the fossil Reptilia of the Liassic Formations. III*. Monographs of the Palaeontographical Society London, pp.41-81.

33 Seeley, H.G., 1870. *Remarks on Professor Owen's Monograph on Dimorphodon*. Annals and Magazine of Natural History, (4), 6: 129.

from their camp on the Smoky Hill River. Kansas was in fact E.D. Cope's territory, and he had recently received fossils of mosasaurs and plesiosaurs from the same strata. Cope, in fact, had never visited the area himself. He had collectors, his 'bone hunters', who sent material to Philadelphia for him. By contrast, Marsh went to explore the West himself. At that time this was quite a dangerous adventure, as the Indians could attack at any moment.

After reaching the Smoky Hill River, Marsh's group immediately found three new species of mosasaur, great marine lizards, including a skeleton almost 33ft (10m) long. Some problematical bones were also eventually excavated. They were long, hollow and thin-walled, reminscent of bird bones. But their joints were the same shape as those of the English pterodactyls, although these were much smaller. The fragment of a metacarpal bone was 6·7in (17cm) long, from which Marsh calculated a wing span for this truly gigantic flying creature of 20ft (6·1m).[34]

In the following summer (1871) Marsh's hopes of more complete pterosaur finds on the Smoky Hill River were fulfilled. He found the other half of the metacarpal bone he had come across the previous year, and this gave an overall length of 16in (40cm). The first phalanx of the flight digit was 16·5in (42cm) long. These new finds confirmed Marsh's first calculations of overall size. Somewhat higher in the Chalk profile he discovered the wing bones of an even bigger creature, whose wing span he estimated at about 21·6ft (6·6m). He named the two forms in 1872 as two new species of *Pterodactylus*, *Pterodactylus ingens* (the huge) and *Pterodactylus occidentalis* (the western).[35]

It was a triumph for Marsh to have discovered and named the first pterosaurs on American soil, also the largest so far known. His rival Cope had not been inactive in the meantime. Immediately after Marsh's departure at the end of the 1871 season, Cope travelled to Kansas and found the same sites on the Smoky Hill River. He started to dig feverishly to establish his own collection of Cretaceous reptiles, so that he could publish before Marsh if possible. On 1 March 1872 he presented a paper to the American Philosophical Society, describing his Kansas pterosaurs.[36] But Marsh's mouthpiece, the American Journal of Science, which he edited, had published the description of *Pterodactylus occidentalis* and *Pterodactylus ingens* five days earlier, and thus secured priority for Marsh.

The Kansas pterosaurs were not only gigantic, but surprisingly their jaws were toothless, in complete contrast with pterosaurs found in the slightly older English Cretaceous deposits. But above all they had a long, thin bone crest at the rear of the head, which must have made them look very peculiar. In 1876 Marsh called the American form *Pteranodon* (=toothless flyer), thus separating them from the European genera.[37] He also distinguished a second genus from the Kansas Chalk, the so-called Niobrara Formation, which was smaller and had no bone crest on the skull. He called it *Nyctosaurus* (=naked reptile). In subsequent years the Kansas sites were so productive that George F. Eaton, curator of Osteology and Vertebrate Palaeontology at the Peabody Museum at Yale College in New Haven, listed a collection of pterosaur bones from a total of 465 individual specimens.[38]

**Above:** Othniel Charles Marsh (1831-1899) discovered the first pterosaur bones in the New World in the autumn of 1870. These were fragments of a wing bone in the Niobrara Chalk of Kansas.

One of the most active researchers into North American Cretaceous pterosaurs was Samuel Wendell Williston (1852-1918). In his younger years he had been one of the most successful of O.C. Marsh's 'bone hunters' in the famous Western dinosaur sites. In 1882 he became geological assistant at Yale College, in 1887 Professor of Anatomy at Yale, in 1890 Professor of Geology at the University of Kansas and in 1902 Professor of Palaeontology at the University of Chicago. It was in his Kansas period that Williston was most concerned with pterosaur finds from the Niobrara Chalk. He wrote a total of nine essays on the 'Kansas Pterodactyls'[39], about the genera *Pteranodon* and *Nyctosaurus*, which had earlier been named by Marsh. Williston provided highly detailed observations about the skeleton of these pterosaurs, on the basis of considerably more complete skeletal material. He also believed that the genus *Ornithostoma*, described in England by Seeley, was identical with the American *Pteranodon*, a question that has still not been conclusively settled. In 1902 he reported on a remarkable specimen of *Nyctosaurus*, found shortly before in the Niobrara Chalk.[40] It was so complete that many new anatomical characteristics were observed, like for example the peculiar joints of the hind legs, from which he concluded that the creature must have walked most awkwardly on the ground. From this specimen, now in the Field Museum in Chicago, Williston provided an outstanding skeletal reconstruction of *Nyctosaurus* with a wing span of 7·9ft (2·4m); this is still reproduced in some modern textbooks.

34 Marsh, O.C., 1871. *Note on a new and gigantic species of Pterodactyle*. American Journal of Science, 1: 472.

35 Marsh, O.C., 1872. *Discovery of additional remains of Pterosauria etc*. American Journal of Science, 3: 241.

36 Cope, E.D., 1872. *Two new Ornithosaurians from Kansas*. Proceedings of the American Philosophical Society, 12: 420-422.

37 Marsh, O.C., 1876. *Principal characters of American Pterodactyles*. American Journal of Science, 12: 479.

38 Eaton, C.F., 1910. *Osteology of Pteranodon*. Memoires of the Connecticut Academy of Arts and Sciences, 2: 1-38.

39 Williston, S.W., 1892-1893. *Kansas Pterodactyls*. Kansas University Quart., I, II.

40 Williston, S.W., 1902. *On the skeleton of Nyctodactylus, with restoration*. American Journal of Anatomy, 1: 297-305.

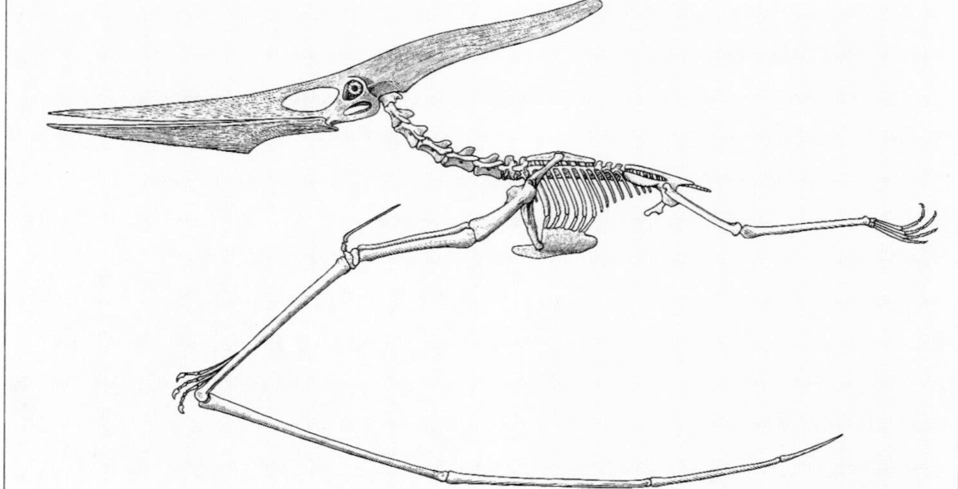

**Above:** George F. Eaton published a monograph on the *Osteology of Pteranodon* in 1910, on the basis of Marsh's finds. For the first time he reconstructed the skeleton of this giant pterosaur.

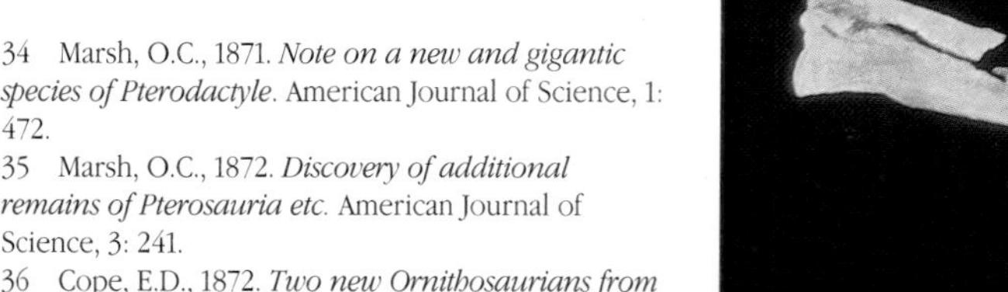

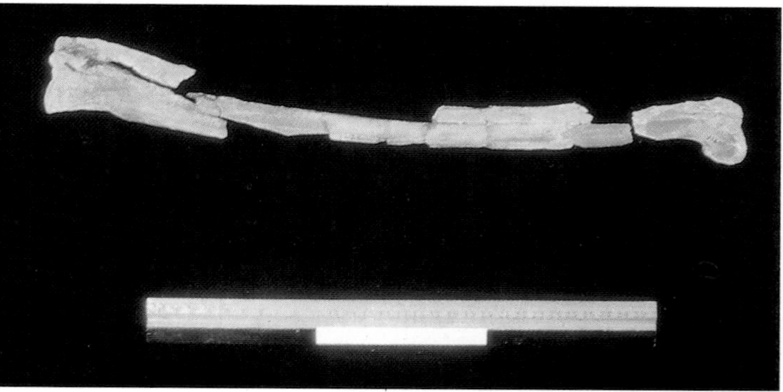

**Left:** The first evidence of pterosaurs in America was this metacarpal bone, the fragments of which were discovered by O.C. Marsh.

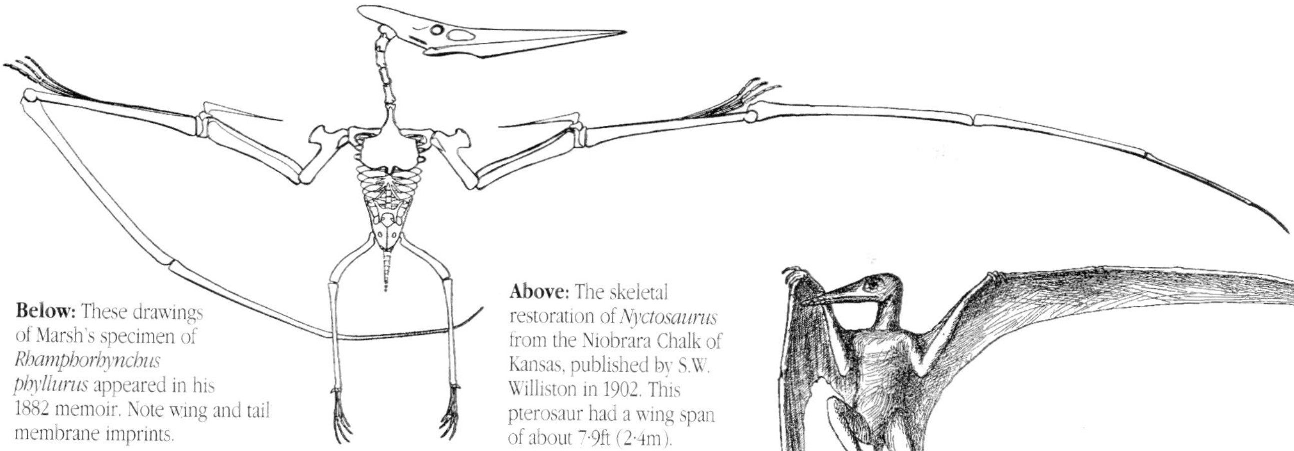

**Below:** These drawings of Marsh's specimen of *Rhamphorhynchus phyllurus* appeared in his 1882 memoir. Note wing and tail membrane imprints.

**Above:** The skeletal restoration of *Nyctosaurus* from the Niobrara Chalk of Kansas, published by S.W. Williston in 1902. This pterosaur had a wing span of about 7·9ft (2·4m).

**Left and below:** In 1882, the same year in which O.C. Marsh published his *Rhamphorhynchus phyllurus*, his friend Karl A. Zittel in Munich described an isolated wing of a *Rhamphorhynchus* from Solnhofen with amazingly sharp impressions of the wing membrane preserved. Even the internal strengthening system of fibres was clearly delineated. Based on this wing Zittel prepared the life restoration (left) which depicts the wings as being much narrower than those of Marsh's version.

**Above:** Karl Alfred von Zittel (1839-1904), Professor of Geology and Palaeontology in Munich, was a leading 19th century palaeontologist. Under his direction, the Bavarian State Collection became one of the most important collections in Europe.

In 1873 O.C. Marsh heard of the discovery of a Solnhofen pterosaur with wing membrane imprints. Through a friend he snapped up this sensational find from under the noses of German museum curators, for a thousand dollars. It was a magnificently preserved *Rhamphorhynchus*, to which Marsh gave the name *phyllurus* (=leaf-tail) in his description published in 1882.[41] *Rhamphorhynchus*' flight membrane was unknown until this time, but in this specimen it was imprinted on the surface of the rock with complete clarity. Surprisingly Marsh also found a skin imprint at the end of the long tail. This showed a rhomboid, terminal tail vane, which he oriented vertically, and interpreted as a steering rudder.

In his reconstruction drawing of the creature in life he also assumed the existence of another flight membrane between the tail and the hind legs, looking like the uropatagium of a bat. Apparently Marsh was influenced by Owen to make this restoration, who had shown a similar flight membrane for his *Dimorphodon*. However, there is no evidence in the fossil material itself for a bat-like 'uropatagium' of this kind in either *Rhamphorhynchus* or *Dimorphodon*.

By chance Karl Alfred Zittel[42] also described a *Rhamphorhynchus* wing membrane from the State Collection in Munich in the same year, 1882. Only an isolated wing had been preserved, but there was a very detailed imprint of the wing membrane, not only in outline, but with the internal strengthening system of stiff fibres, which were embedded very densely in the membrane. Zittel concluded from this find that *Rhamphorhynchus*' wings must have been very narrow, not broad and including the hind legs, as is the case with bats.

A particular controversy developed around the question of how the terminal tail vane was oriented in long-tailed pterosaurs, vertically or horizontally? Was it to be interpreted as intended to control height or sideways movement? Marsh oriented it, as we have seen, vertically, as he had noticed a slight asymmetry in the outline. Later for aerodynamic reasons it was seen as a height control and oriented horizontally. But several indications suggest that Marsh was right after all.

In Germany the so-called lithographic limestone from the many quarries in the area of Solnhofen, Eichstätt and even further east as far as Kelheim at the confluence of the Altmühl and Danube rivers continued to provide many discoveries which led to new perceptions about pterosaurs of the Jurassic. Because of the extremely fine grain of the sediment these strata preserve soft parts that are usually unable to survive very well. Thus in 1908 Karl Wanderer observed imprints above and below the skull of a *Rhamphorhynchus* from the Dresden Museum that suggested a soft crest on the head and a throat pouch.[43] Also he was the first to find numerous dots like needle pricks on the flight membrane prints, which were later (1927) established as being caused by hair folli-

41 Marsh, O.C., 1882. *The wings of Pterodactyles.* American Journal of Science, 3, no. 16: 223.

42 Zittel, K.A., 1882. *Über Flugsaurier aus dem lithographischen Schiefer Bayerns.* Palaeontographica, 29: 47-80.

43 Wanderer, K., *Rhamphorhynchus Gemmingi H.v. Mayer. Ein Exemplar mit teilweise erhaltener Flughaut aus dem Kgl. Mineralog.-Geol Museum zu Dresden.* Palaeontographica, 55: 195-216.

cles by the Munich palaeontologist Ferdinand Broili.[44] This meant that pterosaurs were probably warm-blooded, on the basis of direct evidence from the fossil, confirming the view of Seeley and others. In the same publication Broili also reported on the observation of webs between the toes of a Solnhofen *Rhamphorhynchus*. This confirmed another of Seeley's assumptions, that pterosaurs could swim.

It was also in 1927 that the important palaeoneurologist Tilly Edinger published her findings on the brain structure of pterosaurs.[45] Brain endocasts had been known since 1888, when Newton wrote about the skull of *Scaphognathus purdoni* from the Whitby Lias. But some Solnhofen pterodactyls and rhamphorhynchids showed evidence of brains in the form of endocasts. Tilly Edinger's research showed that, even in the Upper Jurassic, pterosaurs had developed brains that were more like those of birds than the brain of their contemporary, the 'primordial bird' *Archaeopteryx*. Thus the pterosaur brain was by no means reptile-like and small, as in modern crocodiles and lizards, but closer to that of a bird in shape and size. This was an important prerequisite for flight control and steering. As for Seeley and many palaeontologists after him, this was both a sign of a high metabolic rate and of warm-bloodedness, and thus a reason for not classifying pterosaurs as reptiles, but for placing them in a separate class of vertebrates.

If pterosaurs were still alive today and had not become extinct 65 million years ago, we would certainly never group these hairy, warm-blooded and possibly intelligent creatures with crocodiles, lizards or tortoises, but give them a place of their own in the zoological system of vertebrates. But this problem will be discussed in the following chapter.

**Above:** Tilly Edinger (1897-1967) was the founder of modern palaeoneurology, a science for the investigation of brain structures in fossil animals. She studied in detail the structure of pterosaur brains.

**Above:** D.M.S. Watson (1886-1973) was one of the first palaeontologists to regard pterosaurs as highly efficient mechanisms. He studied their flight behaviour from an aerodynamic point of view.

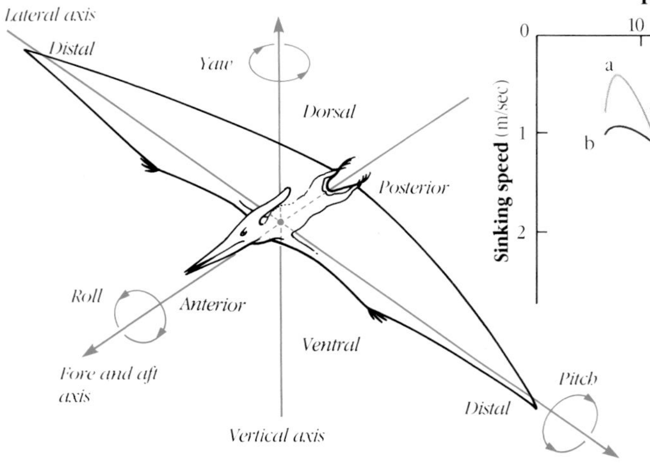


**Above:** This diagram (based on Bramwell and Whitfield's monograph on the *Biomechanics of* Pteranodon) shows the three axes of a flying object as applied to *Pteranodon*. The flying animal is regarded like an aircraft requiring the necessary control of motion about the roll, pitch and yaw axes.

**Flying speed** (m/sec)

0 10 20 30 40

**Sinking speed** (m/sec)

1 2

a b c d

**Above:** These polar curves plot flying speed against sinking speed for *Pteranodon* (a), a falcon (b), an albatross (c) and a glider (d). It can be seen that the best flying speed for *Pteranodon* was about 26ft/sec (8m/sec) when the sinking speed was at its minimum.

## Researching Pterosaur Flight

Stimulated by the beginnings of air travel with motor-driven aircraft in the early years of the century, interest was aroused in the flight characteristics of pterosaurs from the technical and aerodynamic point of view. Typically one of the first publications on this fascinating subject did not appear in a zoological or palaeontological magazine, but in the official organ of the Aeronautical Society of Great Britain, the Aeronautical Journal of October 1914. The essay by E.H. Hankin and D.M.S. Watson[46] was called 'On the Flight of *Pterodactyls*' and dealt with the flight of *Pteranodon*, the giant pterosaur from the Kansas Chalk. But they also used English skeletal material, with which they could test the movements of the individual wing joints. The pterosaur bones from the Cambridge Greensand were particularly suitable for this, as they were completely uncrushed. This was how they summed up their judgement of *Pteranodon*: 'Other flying animals can walk, run or swim, besides fly. But in the case of the higher pterodactyls their structure is such that it is difficult to understand how they can have had any other means of progression than flying. With a body little larger than that of a cat they had a span of wing asserted in some cases to have reached 21 feet or more.' And they added: 'The weakness of the flapping muscles makes it highly probable that their habitual mode of flight was by soaring, rather than by flapping.'

Subsequently *Pteranondon* in particular was the object of biomechanical and aerodynamic analyses, most recently by Cherrie D. Bramwell and George R. Whitfield[47] of the University of Reading in 1974. They calculated that Pteranodon, with a wing span of about 23ft (7m) and weighing 36lb (16·6kg) would have had a maximum flight speed of about 26ft/sec (8m/sec), and reached a lowest flight speed of 22ft/sec (6·7m/sec). This extremely slow flight also made it possible to land on the ground without danger. Bramwell and Whitfield were also of the opinion that an increase of average wind speed when the climate deteriorated at the end of the Cretaceous might have been one of the factors that brought about the extinction of the pterosaurs.

Finally scholars were not content with calculating the flight of pterosaurs theoretically, but even simulated it with flying models. The first attempt was by the German zoologist and behavioural researcher Erich von Holst.[48] In 1957 he built a flapping flight model of the Jurassic pterosaur *Rhamphorhynchus* with a wing span of 4ft (1·2m). He wanted to find out whether the terminal, rhomboid tail vane on the long tail of this pterosaur was originally oriented vertically or horizontally. The model, made of Japanese paper and balsa wood and driven by a rubber band motor, did in fact fly by flapping its own wings, but only with a horizontal tail vane functioning as a height control.

44 Broili, F., 1927. *Ein Rhamphorhynchus mit Spuren von Haarbedeckung*. Sitzungsberichte der Bayerischen Akademie der Wissenschaften München: pp.49-67.

45 Edinger, T., 1927. *Das Gehirn der Pterosaurier*. Zeitschrift für Anatomie und Entwicklungsgeschichte, 82 (1/3): 105-112.

46 Hankin, E.H. and Watson, D.M.S., 1914. *On the Flight of pterodactyls*. Aeronautical Journal, 18: 324-335.

47 Bramwell, C.D. and Whitfield, G.R., 1974. *Biomechanics of Pteranodon*. Philosophical Transactions of the Royal Society of London, B. Biol. Sci., 267: 503-592.

48 Holst, E.v., 1957. *Der Saurierflug*. Paläontologische Zeitschrift, 33: 15-22.

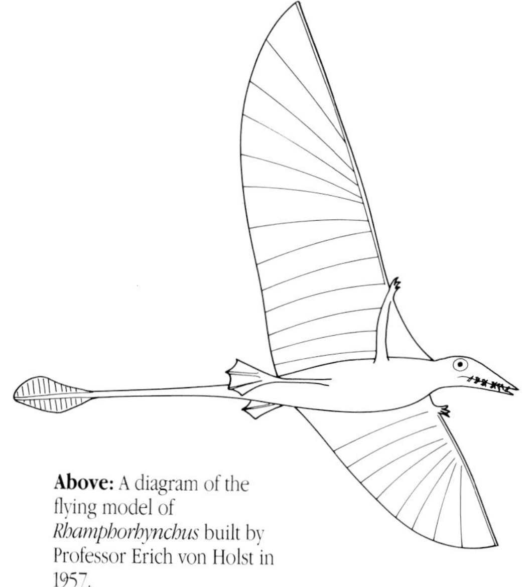

**Above:** A diagram of the flying model of *Rhamphorhynchus* built by Professor Erich von Holst in 1957.

**Above:** Stephen Winkworth launches his radio-controlled gliding model of *Pteranodon* into the air in 1985. The model flew successfully above the cliffs of the Dorset coast in southern England.

**Below:** The half-size model of *Quetzalcoatlus* built by Dr Paul MacCready and his team at AeroVironment Inc. in Monrovia, California. This model actually flapped its 18ft (5·5m) span wings during flight.

In 1985 an Englishman called Stephen Winkworth built a gliding model of a *Pteranodon* with built-in radio control.[49] And finally the American aeronautical engineer Paul MacCready[50] built a flapping flight model of the giant Texan pterosaur *Quetzalcoatlus*, half actual size, but still with a wing span of 18ft (5·5m). After successful test flights in Death Valley in California the model *Quetzalcoatlus* crashed in May 1986 in front of a large number of spectators in Washington.

In the last few decades it has become increasingly clear that the pterosaurs of the Mesozoic were an extraordinarily varied and successful group of animals. They have been found on all continents with the exception of the Antarctic. In the last few years further finds have been made in Europe and North America, and skeletal remains have also been found in South America, Asia, Australia and New Zealand. The first Chinese pterosaurs were particularly significant. They were found in the Lower Cretaceous of the province of Sinkiang, and described by C.C. Young in 1964.[51] There was also the strange pterosaur from the Lower Cretaceous in Argentina with filter dentition made up of hundreds of long, thin, bristle-shaped 'teeth',[52] and last but not least the excellently preserved pterosaur bones in the limestone concretions of the Santana Formation on the Araripe Plateau in Brazil, which has developed into one of the world's most important pterosaur localities.[53]

49 Winkworth, S., 1985. *Pteranodon flies again*. New Scientist: 32-33.
50 MacCready, P., 1985. *The Great Pterodactyl Project*. Engineering and Science, 49 (2): 18-24.
51 Young, C.C., 1964. *On a new pterosaurian from Sinkiang, China*. Vertebrata Palasiatica, 8: 221-256. Description of *Dsungaripterus* from the Lower Cretaceous in Sinkiang.
52 Bonaparte, J.F., 1970. *Pterodaustro guinazui gen. et sp. nov.. Pterosaurio de la formación Lagarcito, provincia de San Luis, Argentina*. Acta Geologica Lilloana, 10 (10): 207-226.
Sanchez, T.M., 1973, *Redescription del Craneo y Mandibulas de Pterodaustro guinazui Bonaparte (Pterodactyloidea, Pterodaustridae)*. Ameghiniana, 10 (4): 313-325.
53 Price, L.I., 1971. *Presenca de Pterosauria no Cretáceo Inferior da Chapada do Araripe, Brasil*. Annals of the Brazilian Academy of Sciences, 43 (suppl.): 451-461.

Among the most important discoveries of recent times are two superlatives, the largest pterosaur and the oldest pterosaur. In 1975 Douglas Lawson, then a student at the University of Texas in Austin, while doing field work for his master's thesis, found the skeletal remains of the largest pterosaur so far known, which he called *Quetzalcoatlus northropi*, (after the Mexican god Quetzalcoatl).[54] The fossils came from deposits from the Upper Cretaceous in the Big Bend National Park in West Texas. A reconstruction of the skeleton resulted in a wing span of 36 to 39·4ft (11 to 12m). What would Richard Owen have said about that?

*Quetzalcoatlus* is not just the largest pterosaur so far found, but also the geologically most recent pterosaur known to us. The oldest was discovered in 1973 in limestone of the Upper Triassic in the Bergamo Alpine foothills in Italy.[55] The Italian geologist Rocco Zambelli called it *Eudimorphodon* (=true two-form tooth), following the previous oldest, which Owen had christened *Dimorphodon* (=two-form tooth).

All these finds were documents of evolution and mosaic stones in the overall picture that we have gradually been able to form of this fascinating animal group called pterosaurs. The future will certainly bring further discoveries, and present us with a number of unexpected and surprising forms. Such is the nature of scientific inquiry, and we shall then, as always, have enthusiastic collectors and researching scientists to thank for this.

54 Lawson, D.A., 1975. *Pterosaur from the Latest Cretaceous of West Texas. Discovery of the Largest Flying Creature*. Science, 187: 947-948.

55 Zambelli, R., 1973. *Eudimorphodon ranzii gen. nov., sp. nov., uno pterosauro triassico*. Rendiconti Istituto Lombard. Scienze, B, 107: 27-32.
Wild, R., 1978. *Die Flugsaurier (Reptilia, Pterosauria) aus der Oberen Trias von Cene bei Bergamo, Italien*. Bolletino Società Paleontologica Italiana, 17 (2): 176-257.

# What are Pterosaurs?

Ever since 1801, when Georges Cuvier defined the Eichstätt *Pterodactylus* as a flying reptile, pterosaurs have been thought of as reptiles. The modern class Reptilia includes tortoises and turtles, the tuatara, which is now only found in New Zealand, lizards and snakes (Squamata) and crocodiles. These are the only surviving four of about 17 orders of reptiles that lived on earth in the Mesozoic Era, the age of the reptiles. They included creatures as diverse as dinosaurs, ichthyosaurs, placodonts, mammal-like reptiles, the pterosaurs themselves, and several others. For this reason it is difficult to give a definitive description of the class as a whole.

Reptiles form a common group with birds and mammals, the Amniota: in their embryonic stage they are protected by a fluid-filled sac, the amnion, not present in amphibians. Because they produce eggs with large yolks and hard shells, reptiles are able to live exclusively on dry land, and their young emerge fully developed from eggs laid there. Unlike amphibians such as frogs and newts, they do not need to spend the early stages of their life as larvae with gills. The hard shell prevents the amniotic egg from drying out. This 'invention' about 300 million years ago was the essential step needed to enable the reptiles successfully to conquer dry land, and to evolve in the astonishing way they did. Their descendants, birds and mammals, and by extension we human beings as well, owe their existence to this crucial step.

We could make it easy for ourselves and define reptiles as Amniota that are neither birds nor mammals. Modern reptiles are easily distinguishable from both amphibians and mammals. They are cold-blooded, so their body temperature rises or falls with the ambient air temperature. Their skin is horny, usually scaly. Their hearts are incompletely chambered, and so oxygen-rich and oxygen-poor blood is not as strictly separated in their circulatory system as it is in warm-blooded creatures such as birds and mammals. Like birds, reptiles lay eggs with hard shells and large yolks. Amphibians' eggs are soft, with small yolks, and have to be spawned in water, while embryonic development of mammals takes place in the mother's body. Young mammals are born alive and fed with milk from special glands in the mother.

We shall quickly run into difficulties if we try to apply the above list of modern reptile characteristics to pterosaurs. Even though the only evidence that is usually available to us is their fossilized skeletons, we can still draw indirect conclusions from these about pterosaur physiology, and thus establish the regular and recurring features of their lives. The fact that pterosaurs were flying creatures implies a high energy requirement, comparable to the needs of other flying vertebrates like birds and bats, with a significantly higher metabolic rate than reptiles. This can only be 'financed' by warm-bloodedness. In order to maintain a high and constant body temperature birds have a body covering of feathers, and mammals hair or fur. This is intended to prevent loss of body heat, so primarily has an insulating function. Protection is a secondary function, and in the case of birds feathers are also an aid to flight. Pterosaurs had a body covering of hair, as fossil finds have shown, and so they must have been warm-blooded.

This characteristic alone makes pterosaurs different from modern, cold-blooded reptiles like crocodiles or lizards. It is also possible that they had hearts with four chambers, which prevented a mixture of oxygen-rich and oxygen-poor blood circulating in the body. Their young may possibly also have been born alive, like the ichthyosaurs, and fed for as long as they remained in the nest. In this respect too pterosaurs would be different from typical modern reptiles.

We cannot really avoid the question: 'Are pterosaurs reptiles at all?' Formerly many scholars would have answered no. They wanted to establish a class of vertebrates especially for pterosaurs, placed between reptiles and birds, and between reptiles and mammals, or even



**The Relationships of Amniotes (left)**
Amniotes are vertebrates that develop within an amnion, a fluid-filled sac that protects the embryo before birth. The diagram takes the form of a family tree that shows in a simplified way the phylogenetic relationships of amniotes that evolved from a single stock of primitive tetrapods. About 300 million years ago, during the Upper Carboniferous, three major lineages can be distinguished: one that gave rise to mammals, a second to turtles, and a third to other reptilian groups and to birds. The class Reptilia includes all the lineages in solid colour. Reptiles can be defined as amniotes that lack the specialized characters of birds and mammals. Within modern fauna, crocodiles share a more recent common ancestry with birds than they do with lizards and snakes.

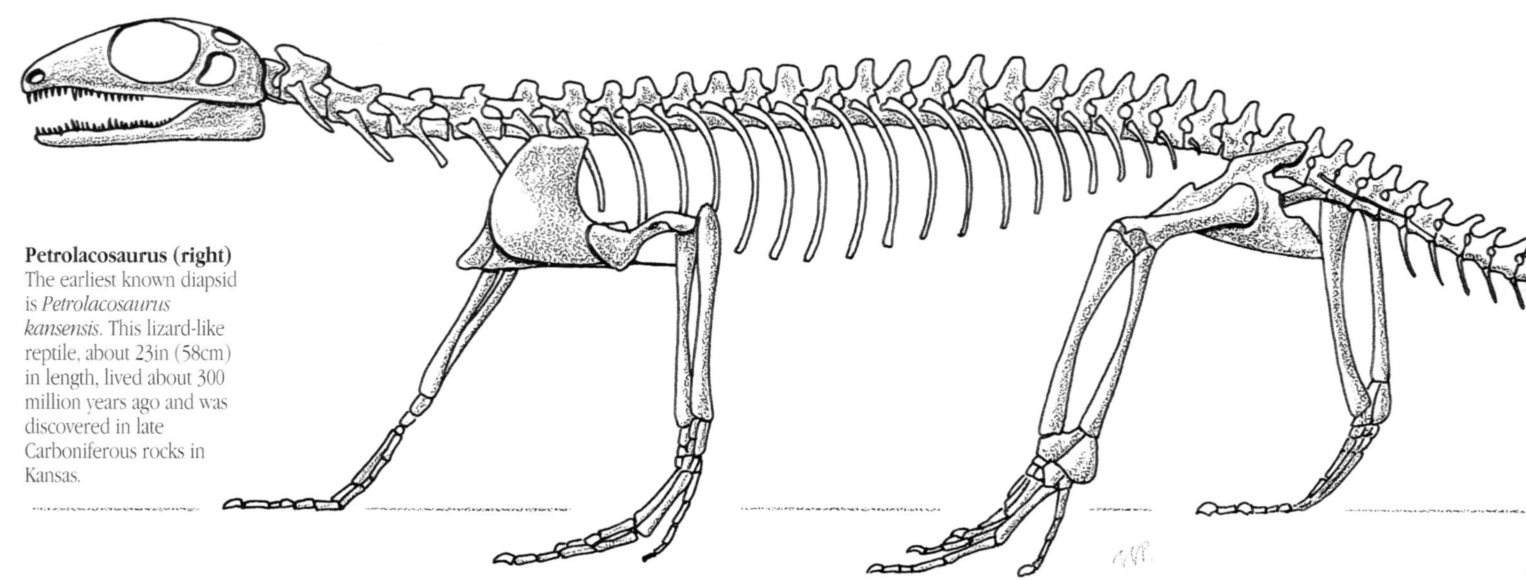

**Petrolacosaurus (right)**
The earliest known diapsid is *Petrolacosaurus kansensis*. This lizard-like reptile, about 23in (58cm) in length, lived about 300 million years ago and was discovered in late Carboniferous rocks in Kansas.

**Synapsid**

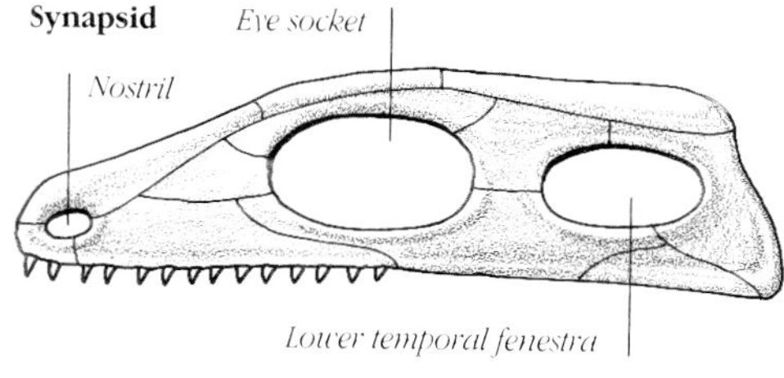


**Euryapsid**

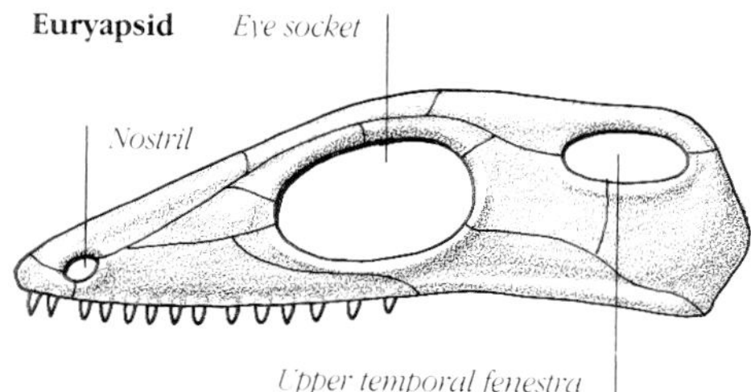


**Anapsid**

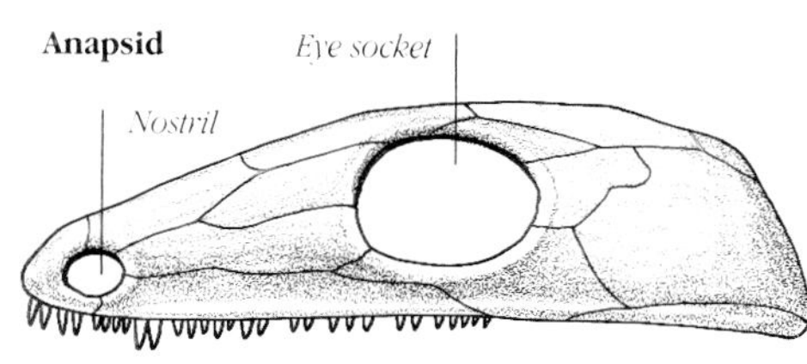


**Diapsid**

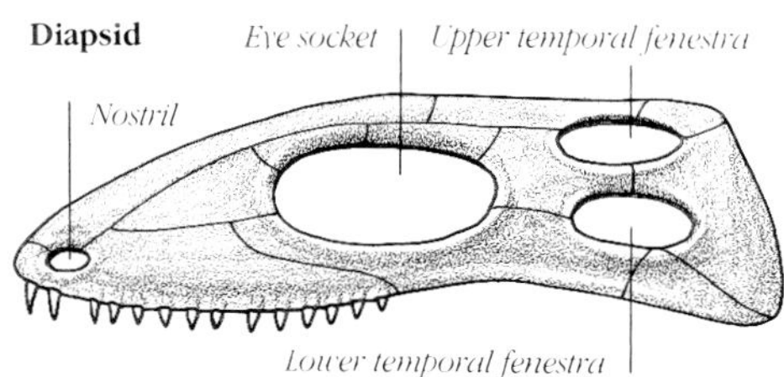


**Reptile Classification**
The subclasses of reptiles are recognized by the pattern of skull openings behind the eye socket, called temporal fenestrae. The synapsids have a single temporal fenestra low down on the side of the skull. The euryapsids also have one temporal fenestra but it is higher in position. Anapsids have no temporal opening at all, while diapsids have two, an upper and a lower one. During the Mesozoic diapsids were particularly abundant; they included the dinosaurs and pterosaurs in their number.

between birds and mammals. However, the problem can also be solved by defining reptiles in a different way, within a much broader framework. Such a definition could also accommodate warm-blooded creatures like pterosaurs, and certain dinosaurs like the coelurosaurs, also thought to have been warm-blooded. Despite this the Reptilia, if we include the fossil groups, are a motley crew, probably without a common, natural phylogeny, thus not monophyletic.

The absence or presence of certain openings in the skull, like the temporal openings behind the eye socket, is considered a significant pointer when reconstructing the phylogeny and classification of reptiles. A distinction is made here between **anapsids** without a temporal opening (tortoises for example), **synapsids** with only one, lower temporal opening (the mammal-like reptiles), **euryapsids** with only one, upper temporal opening (ichthyosaurs, for example) and finally **diapsids** with two temporal openings, an upper and a lower. According to this scheme pterosaurs are diapsids, as they have *two* temporal openings on each side of the skull behind the eye sockets.

The earliest diapsid reptile known is from the Upper Carboniferous, or Pennsylvanian system, about 260 million years ago. It was a lizard-sized creature called *Petrolacosaurus*.[1] There are two groups of diapsid reptiles, lepidosaurs and archosaurs. The lepidosaurs include lizards, snakes and tuataras, and the extinct rhynchosaurs and eosuchians. Crocodiles and alligators are the only remaining archosaurs. In the geological past they also included dinosaurs and a large and extremely diverse group of reptiles, the thecodonts.

Archosaurs and pterosaurs have *one* particular characteristic in common. They have another aperture in the skull wall between the eye and nose sockets, a so-called preorbital opening. Thus pterosaurs can be classified as archosaurs. Their closest living relatives are crocodiles and alligators. Their origin and family relationships will be discussed in more detail below.

## Origin and Relationships

We have already established that from an osteological point of view pterosaurs can be classified as diapsids, and then as archosaurs because of their characteristic skull openings. According to the classic system established by the American vertebrate palaeontologist Alfred Sherwood Romer,[2] archosaurs include dinosaurs, crocodiles, pterosaurs and thecodonts. As the oldest archosaurs are the Triassic thecodonts, the origin of pterosaurs has been thought to lie with these, usually terrestrial, reptiles.

The Tübingen reptile specialist Friedrich Freiherr von Huene investigated the skeletal remains of a small reptile from Lossiemouth in Scotland[3] in 1914. The fossils came from the Upper Triassic Elgin sandstone and had already been named *Scleromochlus taylori* by Arthur Smith Woodward of the British Museum in London in 1907.[4] Although the bones had survived only as prints in the coarse sandstone, by no means complete and very fragmented, Huene risked a reconstruction of the entire skeleton of this tiny reptile which was only about 9in (23cm) long. He classified it as a pseudosuchid, a sub-order of the thecodonts, and because of its long hind legs suggested that *Scleromochlus* was a creature that lived in trees and could jump from branch to branch or tree to tree. Huene even thought it possible that *Scleromochlus* was a gliding creature, with folds of skin on its forelimbs that could be used as wings. He therefore assumed that it represented a stage of development that must be postulated as a direct precursor of pterosaurs: a climbing, jumping creature living in trees, which gradually developed a flight membrane like that of the parachute animals.[5] Essentially Huene was suggesting an arboreal origin for pterosaurs, in other words they were descended from creatures that lived in trees, in which an active ability to fly had developed from a passive parachute and gliding phase.

The view that pterosaurs were descended from Triassic thecodonts survived for a long time, and has appeared in textbooks. In *Scleromochlus* there is a great disproportion between the fore- and hindlimbs: the hindlimbs being considerably longer than the forelimbs. In pterosaurs exactly the reverse is the case. Their forelimbs, the wings, are considerably longer and more powerful than the hindlimbs.

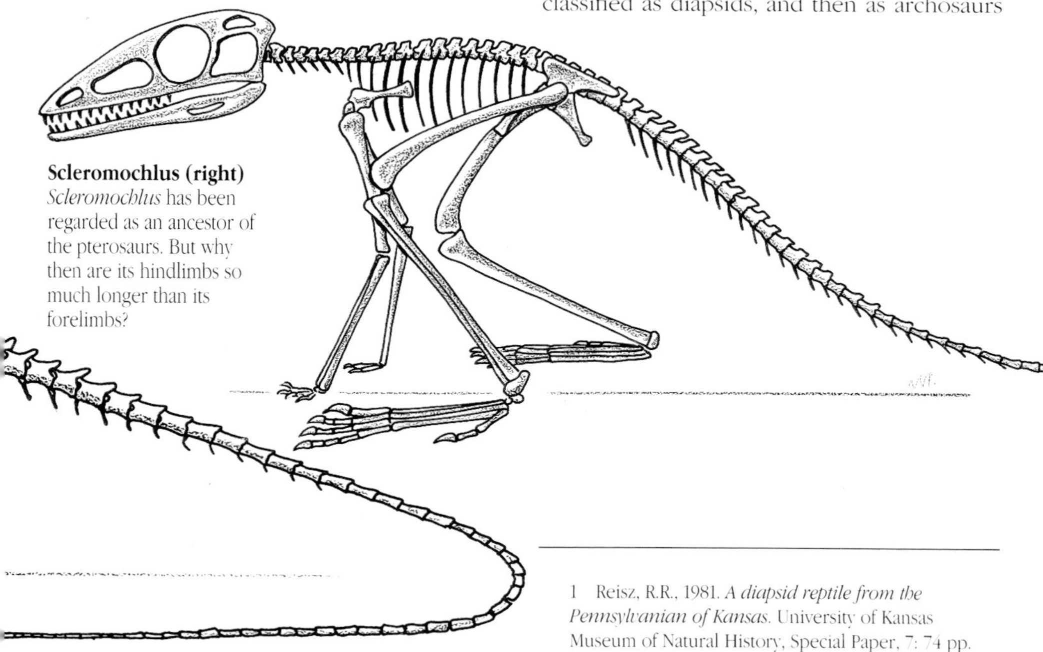

**Scleromochlus (right)**
*Scleromochlus* has been regarded as an ancestor of the pterosaurs. But why then are its hindlimbs so much longer than its forelimbs?

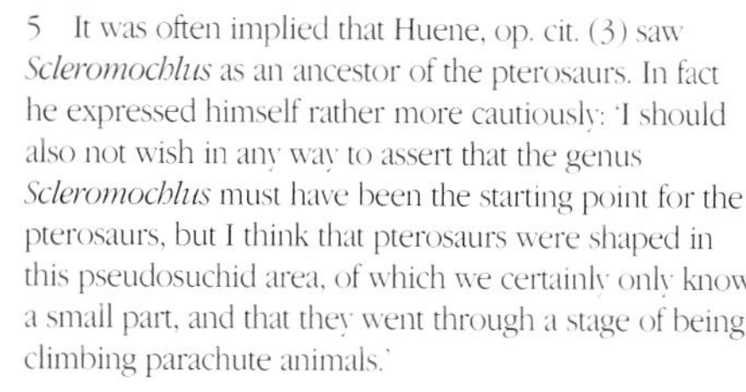

1 Reisz, R.R., 1981. *A diapsid reptile from the Pennsylvanian of Kansas*. University of Kansas Museum of Natural History, Special Paper, 7: 74 pp.

2 Romer, A.S., 1956. *Osteology of the Reptiles*. Chicago.

3 Friedrich Freiherr von Huene was born in Tübingen on 22 March 1875 and died there on 4 April 1969. He was Professor of Palaeontology at the University of Tübingen and taught there for over six decades. He produced over 300 scientific publications, mainly dealing with fossil reptiles, including pterosaurs, especially of the Mesozoic. He was one of the most important experts on fossil reptiles of his time. Huene, F.v., 1914. *Beiträge zur Geschichte der Archosaurier*. Geologische und Paläontologische Abhandlungen, N.F. 13: 1-53.

4 Woodward, A.S., 1907. *On a new dinosaurian reptile (Scleromochlus taylori, gen. et sp. nov.) from the Trias of Lossiemouth, Elgin*. Proceedings of the Geological Society London, 63: 140-144.

5 It was often implied that Huene, op. cit. (3) saw *Scleromochlus* as an ancestor of the pterosaurs. In fact he expressed himself rather more cautiously: 'I should also not wish in any way to assert that the genus *Scleromochlus* must have been the starting point for the pterosaurs, but I think that pterosaurs were shaped in this pseudosuchid area, of which we certainly only know a small part, and that they went through a stage of being climbing parachute animals.'

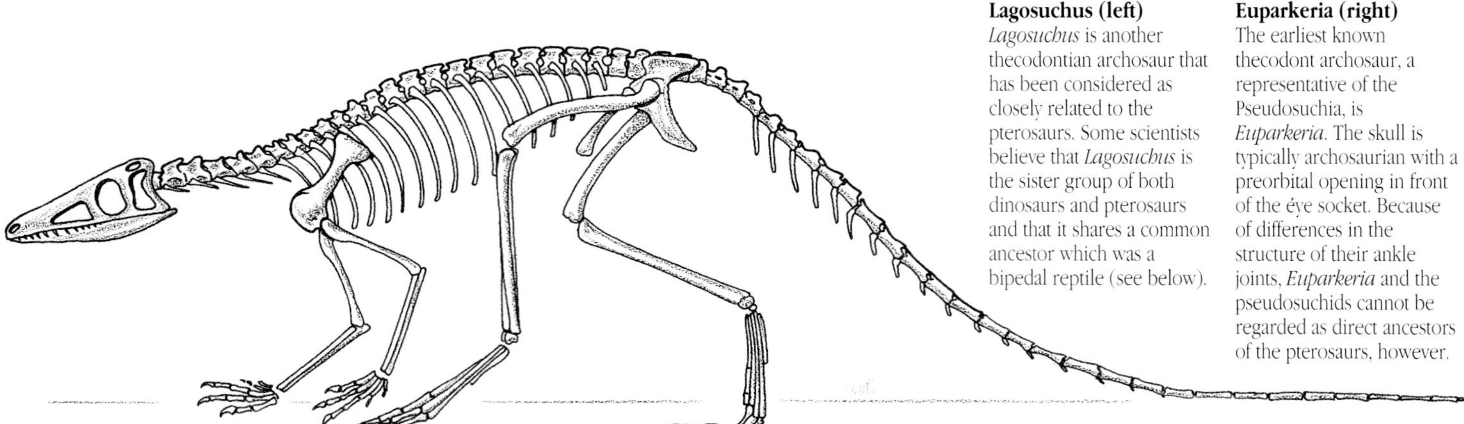

**Lagosuchus (left)**
*Lagosuchus* is another thecodontian archosaur that has been considered as closely related to the pterosaurs. Some scientists believe that *Lagosuchus* is the sister group of both dinosaurs and pterosaurs and that it shares a common ancestor which was a bipedal reptile (see below).

**Euparkeria (right)**
The earliest known thecodont archosaur, a representative of the Pseudosuchia, is *Euparkeria*. The skull is typically archosaurian with a preorbital opening in front of the éye socket. Because of differences in the structure of their ankle joints, *Euparkeria* and the pseudosuchids cannot be regarded as direct ancestors of the pterosaurs, however.

Direct predecessors of the pterosaur must therefore have shown a tendency in this direction. No thecodont fossil has limb proportions distorted in this way, and thecodonts also differ from pterosaurs in other skeletal characteristics. It is thus not possible to consider any particular thecodont as a pterosaur ancestor.

However, *one* fossil has been found that was considered to relate closely to the pterosaurs. It is a reptile about 12in (30·5cm) long with extremely long, slender limbs. It was found in the Chañares formation (Middle Triassic) in Argentina. This small thecodont, *Lagosuchus*, like *Scleromochlus* also has hindlimbs which are much longer than its forelimbs.[6] But it seems to have close affinities with dinosaurs, and to represent an intermediate stage between them and the original thecodonts. *Lagosuchus* has also been even more closely related to pterosaurs.[7] Kevin Padian of the University of Berkeley, California, assumes that *Lagosuchus* is related both to dinosaurs and pterosaurs. He believes that the common ancestor of

6 Bonaparte, J.F., 1975. *Nuevos materiales de Lagosuchus talampayensis Romer (Thecodontia-Pseudosuchia) y su significado en el origen de los Saurischia*. Acta Geologica Lilloana, 13, 1: 5-90; Tucuman.

7 Padian, K., 1984. *The Origin of Pterosaurs*. Third Symposium on Mesozoic Terrestrial Ecosystems (Reif, W.-E. and Westphal, F., eds.), pp.163-168; Tübingen, Attempto Verlag.

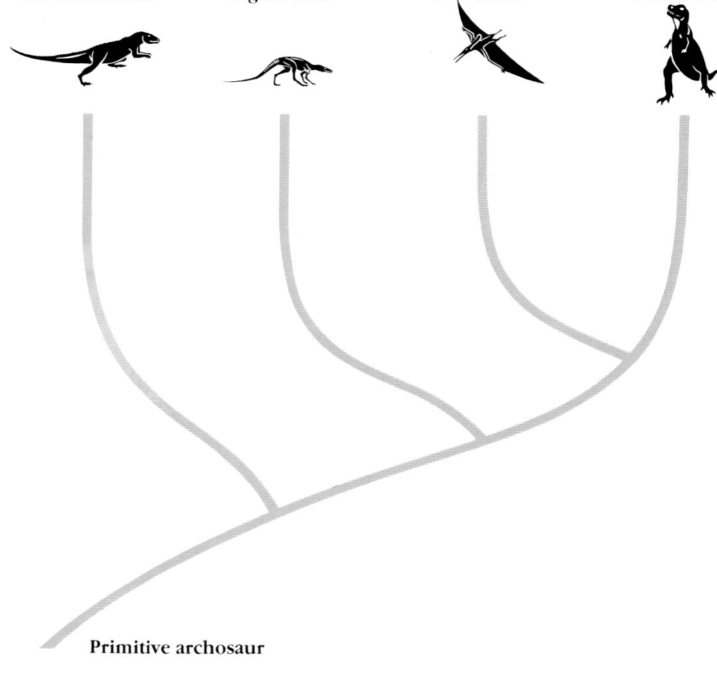


**Family Relationships**
This cladogram shows the hypothetical phylogenetic relationships between the pterosaurs, dinosaurs, *Lagosuchus*, and ornithosuchids as suggested by Kevin Padian of Berkeley University. In this concept dinosaurs and pterosaurs are regarded as sister-groups sharing a common ancestor with *Lagosuchus* and the ornithosuchids.

**Below:** This life restoration of *Lagosuchus talampayensis* suggests that this small archosaur might have been able to run bipedally. The extreme lengthening of the hind legs exhibits a tendency of limb proportion which is in marked contrast to the pterosaurs in which the forelimbs elongated and turned into wings.

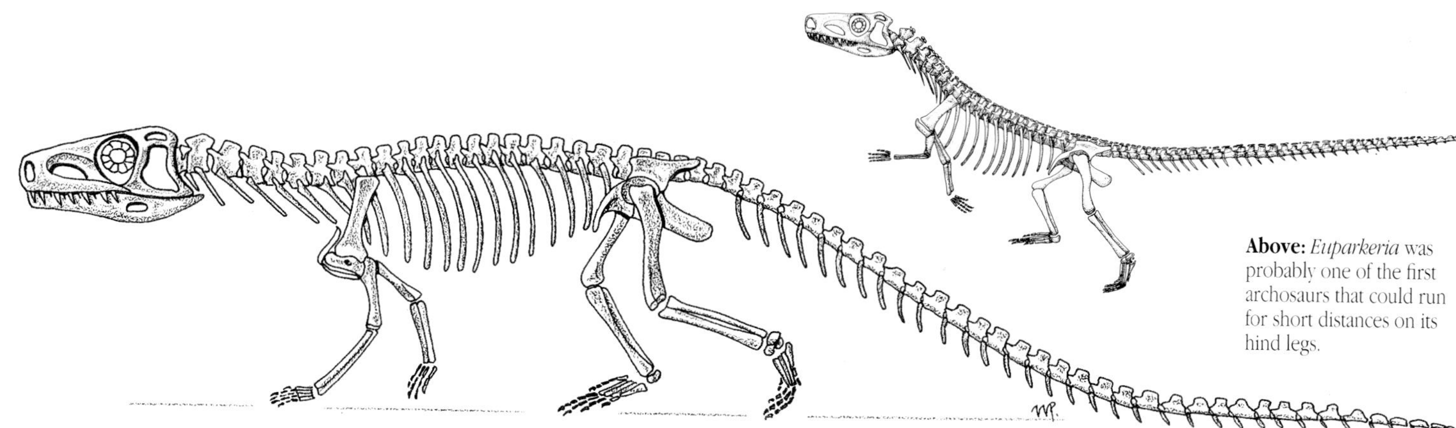

**Above:** *Euparkeria* was probably one of the first archosaurs that could run for short distances on its hind legs.

pterosaurs and dinosaurs was a biped with fully erect stance and gait. Expressed phylogenetically, *Lagosuchus* would be the sister group of both pterosaurs and dinosaurs, which would also themselves be sister groups. As an alternative to this scheme, pterosaurs could be seen as a sister-group of *Lagosuchus* and the dinosaurs, which would themselves be sister groups. In saying this, Padian presupposes that pterosaurs were bipeds and like birds could move along the ground on two legs. Consequently pterosaur flight would not have developed from the trees down, but from the ground up, a view which is disputed. According to this phylogenetic scheme *Lagosuchus*, dinosaurs, pterosaurs and the thecodont *Ornithosuchus* would have a common ancestor. The ornithosuchids were large, long reptiles (up to 13ft, 4m) of the Upper Triassic, partially capable of biped movement.[8]

It is interesting to note that as early as 1900 the German zoologist M. Fürbringer,[9] and H. G. Seeley in his *Dragons of the Air* of 1901, both put forward the view that pterosaurs could be traced back to dinosaur ancestors. But here too the fossil record presents no candidate as ancestor for the pterosaurs.

The earliest pterosaurs in the fossil record date from the Upper Triassic. In order to find out anything about their ancestors we have to look at appropriate fossil finds from the Middle and Lower Triassic, perhaps even the Permian. Of the thecodonts, only the second group, the pseudosuchians, are candidates here. Their earliest representative is the genus *Euparkeria*, a small reptile from the Uppermost Lower Triassic in South Africa, a creature afforded a central place in the evolution of archosaurs. *Euparkeria* is one of the first land animals which might have been able to walk on two legs, although it has a specialized ankle joint of crurotarsal or crocodiloid shape. In this type of joint the hinge articulation between leg and foot has a kink to allow a sideways twisting movement of the foot. Crocodiles also have an ankle of this kind, while dinosaurs, birds and pterosaurs have an ankle joint in which the joint articulation runs in a straight line, transversely between the tarsal bones. This is called a mesotarsal ankle joint. It therefore seems questionable that pterosaurs should originate from Triassic pseudosuchians. Certainly the pseudosuchid *Scleromochlus* seems to have a mesotarsal ankle joint[10] and in *Lagosuchus* the ankle has been interpreted as an intermediate form between pseudosuchid and dinosaur.[11]

Precise analysis of skeletal characteristics of the Triassic pterosaurs *Eudimorphodon* and *Peteinosaurus* from the Italian Alps led Rupert Wild of the Naturkundemuseum in Stuttgart to the conclusion that pterosaurs must be descended not from thecodonts, but, like the rest of the archosaurs, directly from eosuchians of the Permian or the Lowest Triassic.[12] The Triassic pterosaurs are already completely developed flying saurians with all the special adaptations to active flight and typical combinations of distinguishing features in their anatomy that

8 A similar view is put forward by Gauthier and Padian (1985). They relate *Euparkeria*, Ornithosuchidae, *Lagosuchus* and pterosaurs in this order more closely to dinosaurs (including birds) and use the taxon Ornithosuchia for this combination.

Gauthier (1986) argues similarly by including dinosaurs, pterosaurs, *Lagosuchus* and the Triassic Herrerasauridae in a new taxon Ornithodira, and also categorizes these, together with Ornithosuchidae, as Ornithosuchia ('birds and archosaurs closer to birds than to crocodiles'). Ornithosuchia and Pseudosuchia ('crocodiles and archosaurs closer to crocodiles than to birds') together make up the Archosauria, according to Gauthier (1986) 'all the descendants of the most recent common ancestor of crocodiles and birds.'

Gauthier, J. and Padian, K., 1985. *Phylogenetic, Functional and Aerodynamic Analyses of the Origin of Birds and their Flight*. The Beginnings of Birds, Proceedings of the International Archaeopteryx Conference Eichstätt 1984: 185-197.

Gauthier, J., 1986. *Saurischian Monophyly and the Origin of Birds*. The Origin of Birds and the Evolution of Flight (K. Padian, ed.). Memoires of the California Academy of Science, 8: 1-55.

9 Fürbringer, M., 1900. *Zur vergleichenden Anatomie des Brust-Schulterapparates und der Schultermuskeln. 5. Teil. Reptilien*. Jenaische Zeitschrift für Naturwissenschaften, 34, N.F. 27: 215-718; Jena.

10 Padian, K., op. cit. (7), p.165.

11 Bonaparte, J.F., op. cit. (6).

12 Wild, R., 1983. *Über den Ursprung der Flugsaurier*. Weltenburger Akademie, Erwin Rutte-Festschrift, pp. 231-238; Kelheim/Weltenburg.

Wild, R., 1984. *Flugsaurier aus der Obertrias von Italien*. Naturwissenschaften, 71: 1-11; Springer-Verlag.

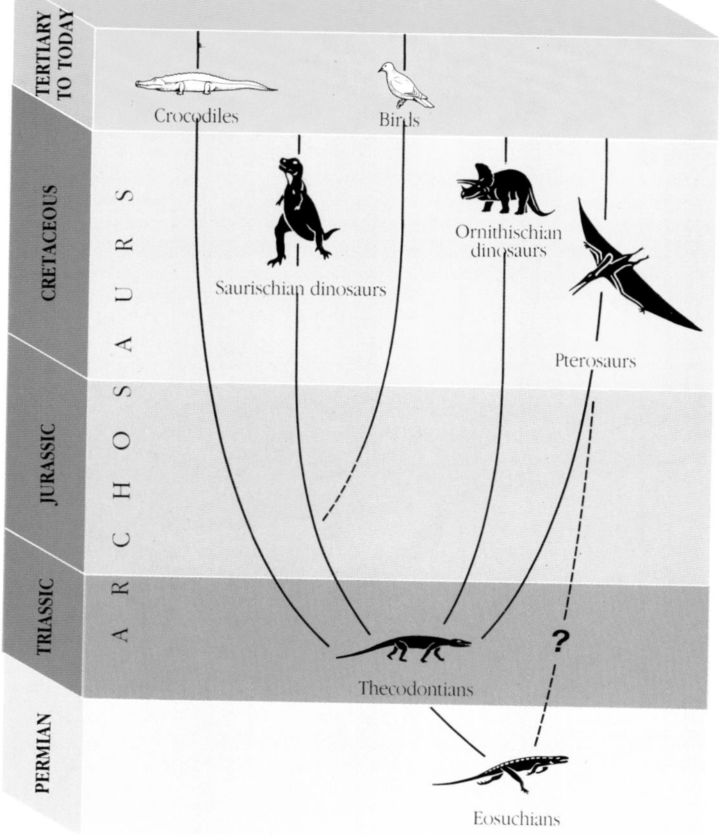


**Probable Lines of Descent (right)**
As a result of his studies on the oldest known pterosaurs – the Triassic forms *Eudimorphodon* and *Peteinosaurus* from the Italian Alps – Rupert Wild of the Stuttgart Natural History Museum concluded that the pterosaurs cannot be direct descendants of the Thecodontia, the ancestral stock of dinosaurs and crocodiles, but that more likely both have a common ancestor in the Eosuchia, a diapsid stem-group of small Permian reptiles which gave rise to the lepidosaurs as well as to the archosaurs as shown in this diagram. Although fossil evidence of intermediate forms is not known, we may suppose that the origin of the pterosaurs, and the beginnings of their evolution from land-bound reptiles to active fliers, lies in early Triassic or even late Permian times, perhaps as much as some 250 million years ago.

**Learning To Fly**

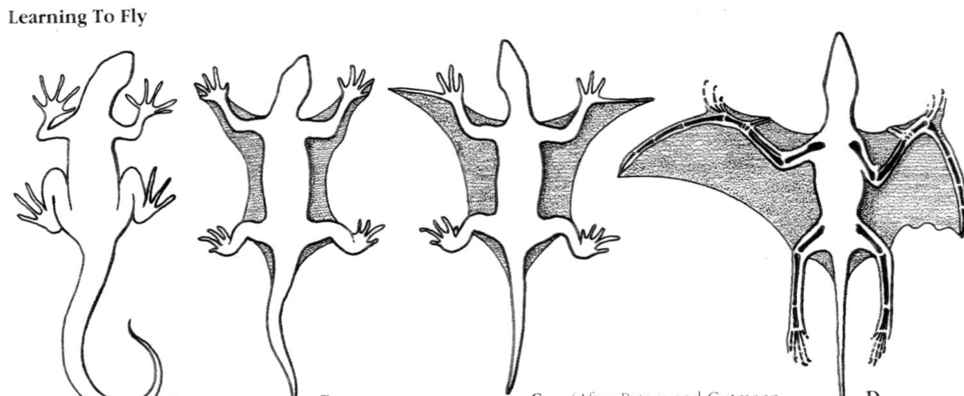


(After Peters and Gutmann, 1985)

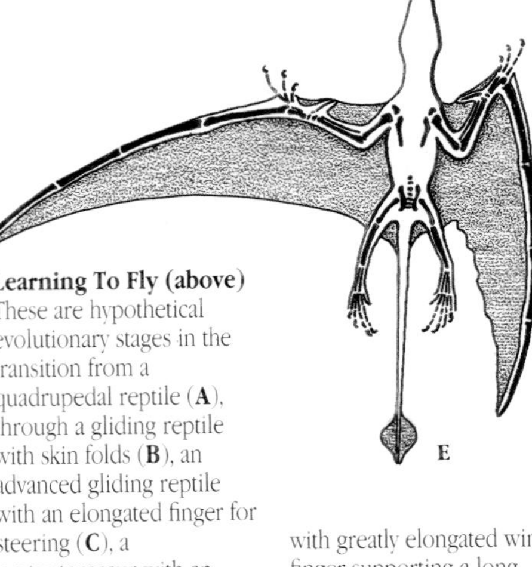


**Learning To Fly (above)** These are hypothetical evolutionary stages in the transition from a quadrupedal reptile (**A**), through a gliding reptile with skin folds (**B**), an advanced gliding reptile with an elongated finger for steering (**C**), a protopterosaur with an enlarged wing finger supporting a wing membrane for flapping (**D**), to a developed pterosaur with greatly elongated wing finger supporting a long wing membrane and a terminal tail membrane for steering and counterbalance (**E**).

we find in all pterosaurs. Thus the earliest forms in the fossil record are not transitional or intermediate links.

Additionally, these oldest known pterosaurs themselves represent various lines of development. They can be classified as three different families of Ramphorhynchoidea, the long-tailed pterosaurs, with at least one of them already seeming very specialized. But that means that their origin is to be found much further back in the geological past than had hitherto been assumed. The beginning of their development from small, land-bound reptiles via a presumed arboreal gliding stage to large-scale active flapping flight must have taken place in the Permian, about 250 million years ago, and so we should direct our attention there. The eosuchians present themselves as a potential ancestor group, small diapsid reptiles now generally held to come from the same ancestral stock as all later archosaurs and lepidosaurs.

The general structure of the eosuchians can be seen from *Heleosaurus*, a reptile about 20in (51cm) long from the Upper Permian in South Africa. It still had vestigial skin armour, but already showed a tendency to walk on two legs. Certain osteological features of the skull of *Eudimorphodon*, the best-known of the Triassic pterosaurs, were also found by Rupert Wild in eosuchians, but not in thecodonts. It is not known whether *Heleosaurus* had a preorbital opening in the skull, a feature that distinguishes archosaurs from other diapsids.

**Below:** *Heleosaurus scholtzi* reveals the general body form of an eosuchian reptile. It was a lizard-like animal about 20in (51cm) long. Here, too, a tendency to bipedal locomotion is discernible.

Other reptile groups are also descended from the eosuchians, the prolacertilians, for example. *Tanystropheus* is also one of these, the giraffe-necked saurian which in its juvenile stage had teeth with many cusps, very similar to the teeth of the Triassic pterosaur *Eudimorphodon*. Overall Triassic pterosaurs and eosuchians+prolacertilians have more features in common than pterosaurs and thecodonts. This means that the origin of pterosaurs probably lay with Permian eosuchians or certain transitional forms between eosuchians and prolacertilians, but not with thecodonts. Pterosaurs and thecodonts are branches of the diapsids which developed independently of one another from Upper Permian or Lower Triassic eosuchians.

For this reason Michael Benton of the University of Bristol has declared that pterosaurs were not archosaurs.[13] He classifies them with archosaurs and a few other groups of different early diapsids as archosauromorphs. But if pterosaurs are no longer to be considered archosaurs, then the question arises of the meaning and evaluation of the preorbital opening in the skull, because in Robert Carroll's view 'the (most primitive) archosaurs can be distinguished from other early diapsids only by a single character, the *antorbital fenestra*.'[14] Modern crocodiles, although they are archosaurs, in contrast to Jurassic and Cretaceous crocodiles have *no* preorbital fenestra, but it is assumed that some eosuchians still had an opening of this kind. This is obviously a matter of definition, and it can only be satisfactorily resolved as a result of more complete fossil finds in the future.

Pterosaurs can be regarded as an independent branch of the diapsids and assigned, following Kuhn-Schnyder and Rieber,[15] to a subclass of their own, Pterosauromorpha. In order to explain their phylogenetic relationship with the rest of the archosaurs we still need more thorough investigation and more detailed analysis of characteristics.

According to Rupert Wild a small, tree-climbing reptile can be reconstructed as a hypothetical pre-pterosaur or propterosaur, in which a tendency to enlargement of the body surface proceeded from a lateral band of skin. This skin extended from the rear of the forelimbs and a fourth digit of the hand that grew longer and longer with evolution, to the flanks of the body and to the upper legs. At the same time the fifth digit of the hand regressed, while the first three digits retained their normal length and had sharp, hook-shaped claws for climbing.

The formation of a flight membrane was of selective advantage for these climbing creatures, as it checked free fall and made a safe landing on the ground possible. At the same time airspace was increasingly used, both to escape from enemies and for locomotion and enlargement of the radius of action, with the associated exploitation of new sources of food over a large area. The flight membrane area gradually grew larger, while the fourth digit lengthened to twenty times the length of

13 Benton, M.J., 1985. *Classification and phylogeny of the diapsid reptiles*. Zoological Journal of the Linnean Society, 84: 97-194. Benton (Nature 296: 306-307, 1982) first reintroduced the sub-class Diapsida (Osborn 1903), but classified all diapsid reptiles with the exception of *Petrolacosaurus* as Neodiapsida. They were regarded as sister groups. According to this scheme the Neodiapsida include the Archosauromorpha (=Pterosauria, Rhynchosauria, Prolacertiformes and Archosauria) and the Lepidosauromorpha (=Younginiformes and Lepidosauria). In a note to his 1985 essay dated July 1985 Benton announced, however: 'I now accept that the pterosaurs are archosaurs, and a close sistergroup of the Dinosauria, as argued by Padian (1983, 1984) and Gauthier (thesis). M.J. Benton'.

14 Carroll, R., 1987. *Vertebrate Paleontology and Evolution*. pp.698. W.H. Freeman and Co., New York.

15 Kuhn-Schnyder, E. and Rieber, H., 1984. *Paläozoologie*. pp.390. Thieme Verlag, Stuttgart, New York.

**'Propterosaurus' (above)**
The hypothetical 'Propterosaurus' can be visualised as a small arboreal reptile which lived in late Permian or early Triassic times. It had already developed lateral skin folds, attached to the elongated fourth finger, which could be stretched between the fore- and hindlimbs. The fifth finger was reduced, whereas the first three fingers were freely movable and could be used to help climb trees. Further skin folds may have been developed in front of the forelimbs and between the tail and the hind legs, in order to increase surface area and so reduce sinking speed while gliding. This reconstruction is based on a similar life restoration published by Rupert Wild in 1984. It corresponds to stage **C** in the diagram above left.

the normal digit and of the metacarpal. Associated with this was a strengthening of the extremities of the forequarters and the pectoral and shoulder apparatus, with a bird-like shoulder girdle and an ossified sternum, in order to afford an appropriate area of attachment for a powerful system of flight muscles.

Such a hypothetical propterosaur has not actually been discovered in the fossil record. It developed relatively rapidly in the Upper Permian or Lower Triassic. The '*Propterosaurus*' was not itself a pterosaur, but no longer an eosuchian. Perhaps this 'missing link' will be found one day. The oldest known Triassic pterosaurs have evolved well beyond this stage: they are 'complete' pterosaurs.

## Osteology

Fossil finds so far have shown that pterosaurs occurred in a great diversity of shapes, but that nevertheless their skeleton has a uniform general structure which makes them an easily distinguishable animal group.

Generally speaking, pterosaurs have a relatively large skull and a powerfully developed cervical vertebral column. Pectoral girdle and wing skeleton are disproportionately enlarged, while the trunk, the actual body, remained small and the hind legs were more weakly developed.

The elongated skull had a large number of openings and in many pterosaurs is merely a set of bony bars. The eye sockets were usually very large, and had a bony ring round the eye, the so-called sclerotic ring, which protected the eye as in modern birds. The nasal openings were set well back. Pterosaurs must have had an underdeveloped sense of smell, but outstanding eyesight. This is confirmed by the structure of the brain.

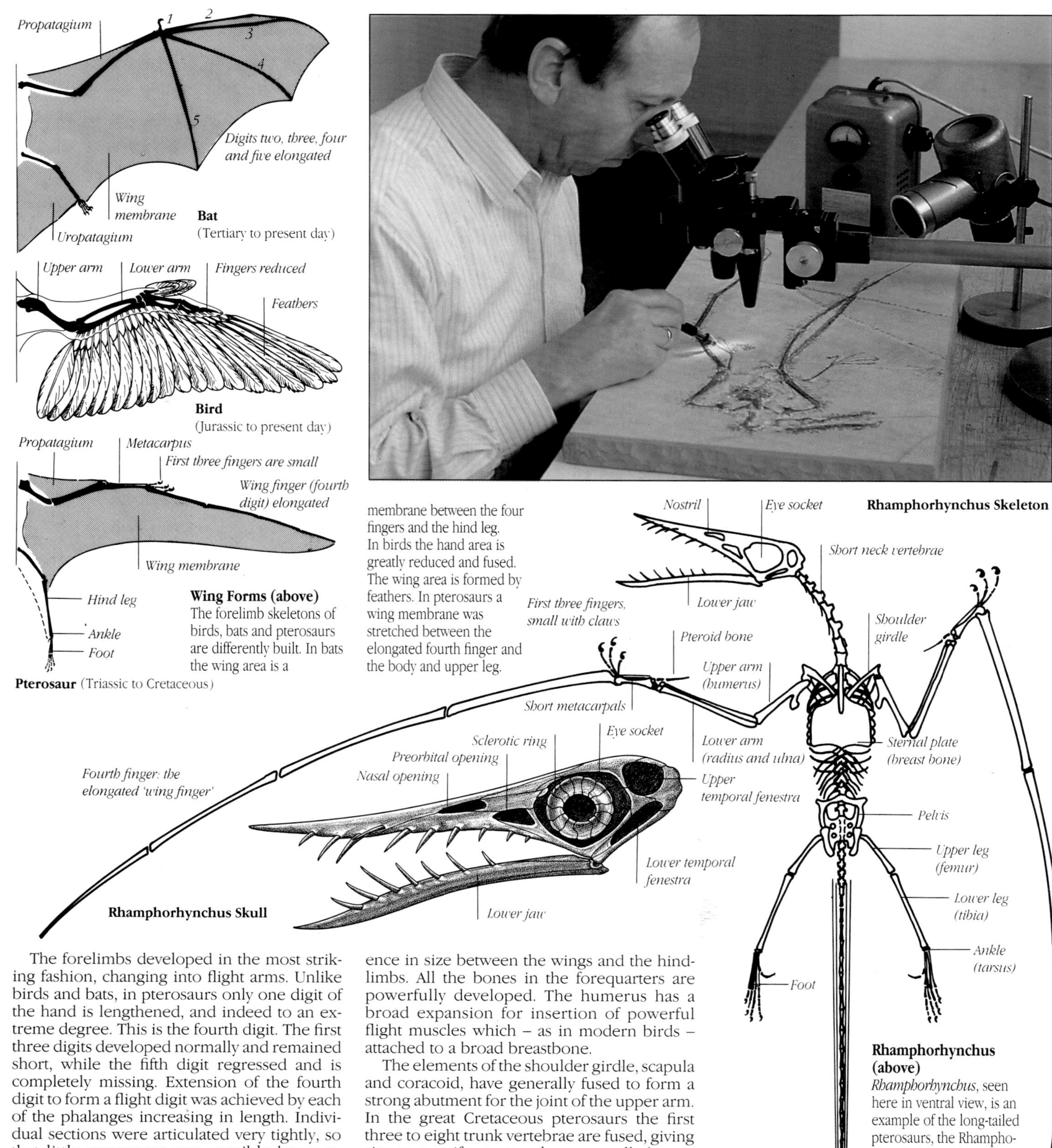


**Wing Forms (above)**
The forelimb skeletons of birds, bats and pterosaurs are differently built. In bats the wing area is a membrane between the four fingers and the hind leg. In birds the hand area is greatly reduced and fused. The wing area is formed by feathers. In pterosaurs a wing membrane was stretched between the elongated fourth finger and the body and upper leg.

The forelimbs developed in the most striking fashion, changing into flight arms. Unlike birds and bats, in pterosaurs only one digit of the hand is lengthened, and indeed to an extreme degree. This is the fourth digit. The first three digits developed normally and remained short, while the fifth digit regressed and is completely missing. Extension of the fourth digit to form a flight digit was achieved by each of the phalanges increasing in length. Individual sections were articulated very tightly, so that little movement was possible between them.

Bending was only possible between the first wing phalanx and the wing metacarpal. This joint consists of a bowl-shaped double articular facet on the wing phalanx and the end of the wing metacarpal, which is developed as a pulley. This roller joint is set somewhat at an angle, so that folding back the wing was associated with a twisting movement. In this way the wing was protected when at rest because only its bony leading edge pointed downwards, and not the vulnerable flight membrane.

The great extent to which the pterosaurs were adapted to flight is revealed by the difference in size between the wings and the hindlimbs. All the bones in the forequarters are powerfully developed. The humerus has a broad expansion for insertion of powerful flight muscles which – as in modern birds – attached to a broad breastbone.

The elements of the shoulder girdle, scapula and coracoid, have generally fused to form a strong abutment for the joint of the upper arm. In the great Cretaceous pterosaurs the first three to eight trunk vertebrae are fused, giving rise to a uniform complex, a so-called notarium, to stiffen and anchor the shoulder girdle. The hind legs are much less developed and seem, particularly in large pterosaurs of the Cretaceous period, hardly to have been able to support the weight of the body.

If all pterosaur fossil finds are considered together, one can identify two distinct groups. Firstly, the Rhamphorhynchoidea, which we know from strata of the Upper Triassic (about 220 million years ago). They flourished in the Jurassic and became extinct at the end of this period, about 150 million years ago. Their most striking characteristic is a long vertebral tail. All of them had teeth.

**Rhamphorhynchus (above)**
*Rhamphorhynchus*, seen here in ventral view, is an example of the long-tailed pterosaurs, the Rhamphorhynchoidea. A long vertebral tail, stiffened by rod-like ossified 'tendons' is the most distinctive character of this more primitive group of pterosaurs. The neck is quite short, and, compared to the wing span, the body is small. The skull reveals the diapsid pattern of temporal openings. The long teeth were ideally adapted for catching slippery fishes.

**Left:** For preparation and study of smaller pterosaur specimens a binocular microscope has to be used. Fine details, such as teeth, skull sutures, or small bones are sometimes smaller than one millimetre in length, as in this *Rhamphorhynchus* skeleton exposed on a slab of Solnhofen limestone.

**Pterodactylus (right)** *Pterodactylus*, seen in ventral view, is an example of the short-tailed pterosaurs, the Pterodactyloidea. Here the tail is reduced, neck and skull are elongated, and the elements of the wing skeleton have different proportions. In the Upper Cretaceous this advanced group of pterosaurs evolved into toothless and giant forms with wing spans of up to 39ft (12m).

**Pterodactylus Skeleton**

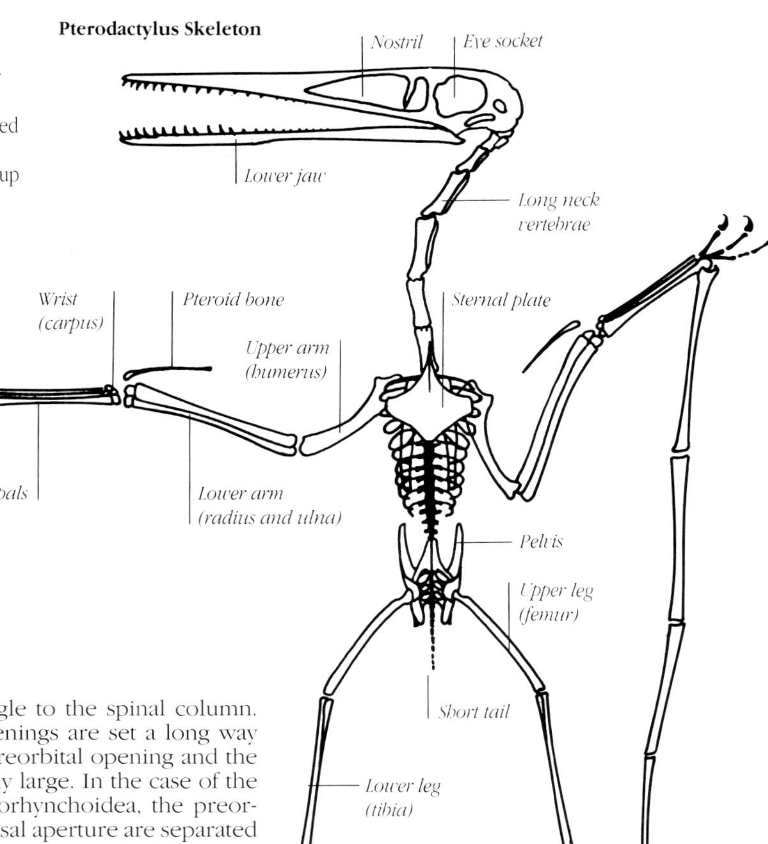


Secondly, the Pterodactyloidea, which first appeared in the Jurassic, in other words about 150 million years ago. They certainly split off from a branch of the Rhamphorhynchoidea, probably in the Lower Jurassic. But we do not know their direct precursors. Typical of Pterodactyloidea is their short tail. They also differ from the long-tailed pterosaurs in other aspects of their skeletal structure. These short-tailed pterosaurs did not reach the culmination of their development until the Cretaceous (144-65 million years ago). They include toothless forms and the largest flying animals of all times, with wing spans of about 40ft (12·2m). They became extinct at the end of the Cretaceous, and were the last of the pterosaurs.

In order to appreciate better the anatomy of the pterosaur, we shall now consider in turn the basic components of its skeleton, beginning with the head.

## The Skull

As a rule the pterosaur skull is relatively large, low and very elongated, and set at a reasonably wide angle to the spinal column. The outer nasal openings are set a long way back and, like the preorbital opening and the eye sockets, are fairly large. In the case of the long-tailed Rhamphorhynchoidea, the preorbital opening and nasal aperture are separated by a bone bridge, in the short-tailed Pterodactyloidea this bone bridge is not present and both skull openings form a large naso-preorbital fenestra. The articular head for the first vertebra is on the longitudinal axis of the skull at the rear in Rhamphorhynchoidea, but more on the lower side of the skull in Pterodactyloidea. This meant that Rhamphorhynchoidea carried their heads in a rather extended position whereas in the latter the head was carried at a distinct angle to the neck.[16]

The teeth are set in the jaw in the same manner as thecodonts, that is to say they have individual sockets. The teeth may extend around the full length of the jaw, or only occupy part of it. In Rhamphorhynchoidea the teeth are either inclined forwards, or upright. The front teeth are usually longer and more curved, compressed at the sides, smooth and pointed. They become smaller towards the back of the jaw. In *Rhamphorhynchus* the long front teeth, which point forward and outwards, fit alternately into one another. Together with the toothless ends of the jaw, which were equipped with pointed horn beaks, they made an outstanding

16 Wellnhofer, P., 1978. *Pterosauria* in *Encyclopedia of Paleoherpetology*, (ed. P. Wellnhofer), part 19: 82 pp. Gustav Fischer Verlag, Stuttgart, New York.

**The Skull of Rhamphorhynchus (left)** The drawings reveal the cranial osteology of *Rhamphorhynchus* as presented in a scientific monograph. The abbreviations refer to the scientific names of various elements of the skull. Reconstructions like this are the result of painstaking studies of many fossil specimens. The skull is shown in lateral, upper and palatal views, and from the back (near left), while the lower jaw is seen in lateral and upper view. The occipital condyle (co) forms the ball and socket articulation with the first neck vertebra. The opening above it (the foramen magnum) leads from the brain to the spinal cord.

prehensile organ for catching fish.[17] In some forms the toothless end of the lower jaw is laterally compressed and juts out beyond the upper jaw. Probably these pterosaurs used it to plough through the surface of the water when catching fish, like the black skimmer.[18]

*Eudimorphodon* is the only Triassic pterosaur with both robust front teeth and a large number of small, tightly-packed teeth with three and five cusps, in the upper and the lower jaw. In *Peteinosaurus* and *Dimorphodon* a large number of small teeth are set closely behind a few large front teeth.

Most Pterodactyloidea have complete sets of teeth, like *Pterodactylus* and *Ornithocheirus*. By contrast with Rhamphorhynchoidea they all have smaller, more even teeth. Reduction of dentition occurs in two ways: either only the front part of the jaw has teeth, as for example in *Gallodactylus*, or the points of the jaw become toothless, as in *Germanodactylus* and *Dsungaripterus*. Some Cretaceous pterosaurs are completely toothless. They probably had horn beaks with sharp edges, like birds.

Among Pterodactyloidea the genera *Ctenochasma*, *Gnathosaurus* and *Pterodaustro* had teeth which were very long and set close together, and used to filter planktonic food out of the water.

One often finds the small bone plates which formed the sclerotic ring preserved fossilized in the eye socket. This ring of bone supports the cornea from the inside in modern birds. It must have had the same function in pterosaurs, as they had large eyes. The pterosaurs' sclerotic ring consists of 12 to 20 thin, overlapping bone plates according to genus.

Variously shaped crests on the skull are particular features of many Jurassic and Cretaceous pterosaurs. Some pterosaurs have a long, low, median crest in the middle of the skull, like *Germanodactylus*, *Gnathosaurus*, *Ctenochasma* and *Dsungaripterus*, for example. Others have shorter or longer crests starting at the rear of the skull, the so-called supraoccipital crest, like *Pteranodon* and *Dsungaripterus*, and others again have high crests at the front end of the jaw, looking like a reversed ship's keel, like *Criorhynchus* from the Cambridge Greensand or *Tropeognathus* from the Santana Formation in Brazil.

**Above:** The picture of *Pterodactylus kochi* shows the position of the skull in relation to the neck that is typical of short-tailed pterodactyloids. The point of articulation (occipital condyle) is located underneath the braincase; in rhamphorhynchoids it is in a more posterior position.

The function of these crests can be explained in various ways. The evidence suggests that they were of different sizes in male and female animals. In this case they would be seen as a sexual characteristic, and were perhaps also used for display. But, as in the case of *Pteranodon*, they could have functioned as a stabilizer for the large, long head while flying. It is also possible that they served as a counterweight to the long beak, so the skull balanced more or less in equilibrium on the neck. Thus weight could be saved in the neck muscles.[19]

It has even been suggested that an elastic membrane was stretched between the long parietal crest of *Pteranodon* and its back, and that this functioned like the rudder of an aeroplane.[20] But this would have severely limited head movement, especially the extreme downward inclination needed for catching fish.

Crests at the front end of the skull and corresponding crests on the lower side of the lower jaw also played an important part when a pterosaur plunged its beak into the water in flight. In this event the head would swivel downwards and a long way backwards, so that its top side cleaved through the water. The high central crest over the front end of the upper jaw had exactly the same effect as the keel of a ship, automatically stabilizing the head and reducing its water resistance. Thus the crest fulfilled a hydrodynamic function.[21] This also

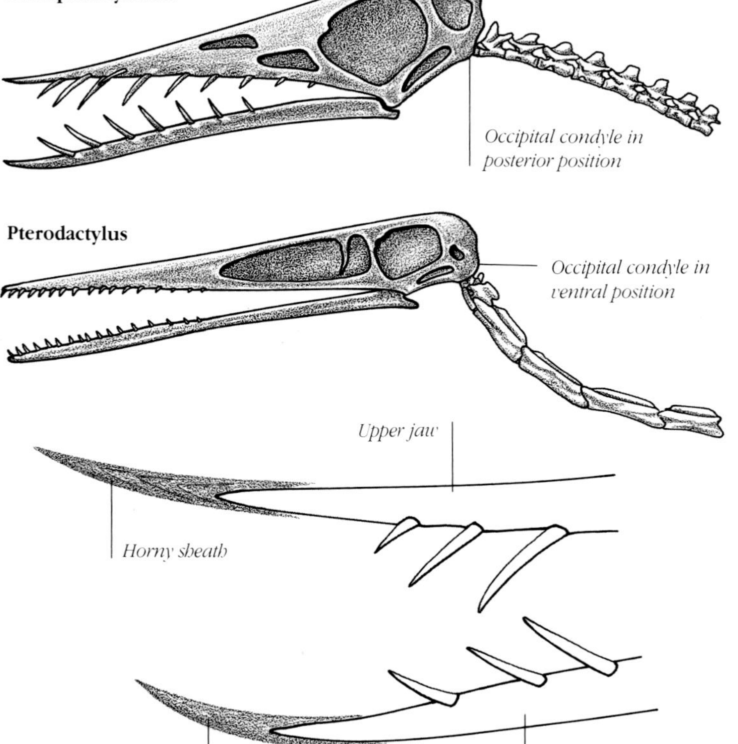


**Head Postures (left)**
Rhamphorhynchoid and pterodactyloid pterosaurs differed in the manner in which they carried their heads. Due to different positions of the occipital condyle, the head is in a straighter alignment with the neck in rhamphorhynchoids. In pterodactyloids a more angled arrangement is evident (see also photograph at top of page).

**Beaks (below left)**
Fossil preservation has indicated that in some cases the front ends of the jaws of *Rhamphorhynchus* were covered by long, pointed, horny beaks, attached like sheathes to the upper and lower jaws. They must have functioned like a pair of tweezers, enabling the pterosaur to winkle out and grasp its prey. They would certainly have been useful when fishing.

17 Wellnhofer, P., 1975. *Die Rhamphorhynchoidea (Pterosauria) der Oberjura-Plattenkalke Süddeutschlands.* Palaeontographica, 148: 1-33, 132-186; 149: 1-30, Stuttgart.

18 Zusi, R.L., 1962. *Structural adaptations of the head and neck in the Black Skimmer Rynchops nigra Linnaeus.* Publications of the Nuttal Ornithlogical Club, 3: 1-101, Cambridge, Mass.

19 Bramwell, C.D., and Whitfield, G.R., 1974. *Biomechanics of Pteranodon.* Philosophical Transactions of the Royal Society London, (B), 267: 503-581, London.

20 Stein, R.S., 1975. *Dynamic Analysis of Pteranodon ingens: a Reptilian Adaptation to Flight.* Journal of Paleontology, 49, 3: 534-548.

21 Wellnhofer, P., 1987. *New crested Pterosaurs from the Lower Cretaceous of Brazil.* Mitteilungen der Bayerischen Staatssammlung für Paläontologie und historische Geologie, 27: 175-186, Munich.

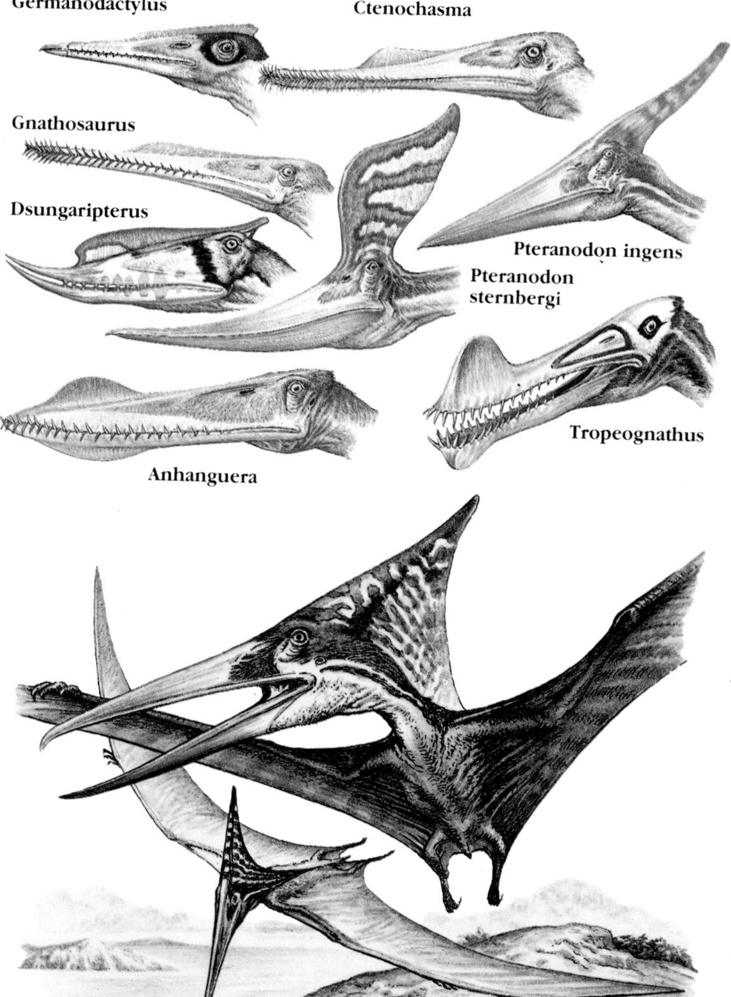


**Crested Forms (left)**
The drawing illustrates a variety of the forms of crest that we know pterosaurs exhibited. They vary from the low, median crests of *Germanodactylus*, to the large crests on the rear of the skull borne by *Pteranodon*, or the 'ship's keel'-like forms on the front of the jaws of *Tropeognathus*. Opinions differ as to their function. They may have served as an element in sexual display, or as counterbalances and stabilizers when flying, or even, in some cases, fishing on the wing.

**Jaw Articulation (right)**
The articulations of the lower jaw are functionally mirror-image screw joints as is seen in this specimen of *Pteranodon*. Obliquely arranged ridges and grooves forced the lower jaw to widen as the beak was opened, probably in order to expand a throat pouch to hold fish. The photographs below show the position of the jaws when closed (lower right) and open (lower left). The posterior process of the lower jaw can swing upward and slide over the quadrate bone of the skull above.

meant that less muscle power was needed to raise the head out of the water again and restore it to a flying position.

Normally, the lower pterosaur jaw is as long and slim as the upper jaw. The hinge of the jaw has a particular structure. It works like a screw joint: when the beak was opened wide it splayed out the branches of the lower jaw in a similar way to the method used by the pelican, so that it was easier to stow fish caught in the throat pouch.[22] Perhaps this is also an indication that pterosaurs had a throat pouch in which food was collected and predigested.

22 Wellnhofer, P., 1980. *Flugsaurierreste aus der Gosau-Kreide von Muthmannsdorf (Niederösterreich) – ein Beitrag zur Kiefermechanik der Pterosaurier*. Mitteilungen der Bayerischen Staatssammlung für Paläontologie und historische Geologie, 20: 95-112, Munich.

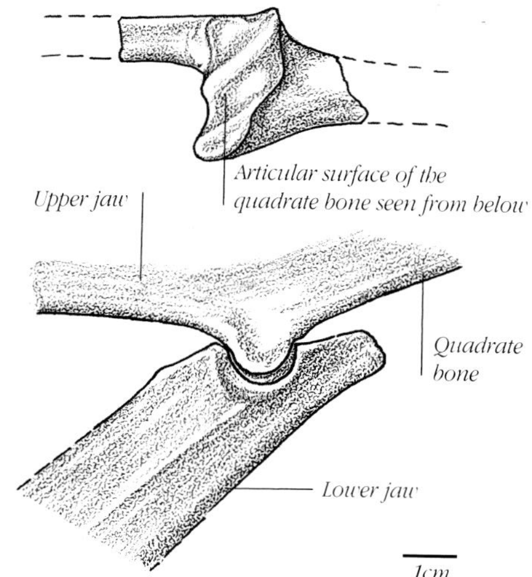

**Pteranodon's Crest (above)**
Did *Pteranodon ingens*' crest serve as a mast on which a membrane that stretched to its back was mounted? Such a 'sail' might have served as a flight rudder, but it would have severely limited the mobility of its head in the vertical plane.

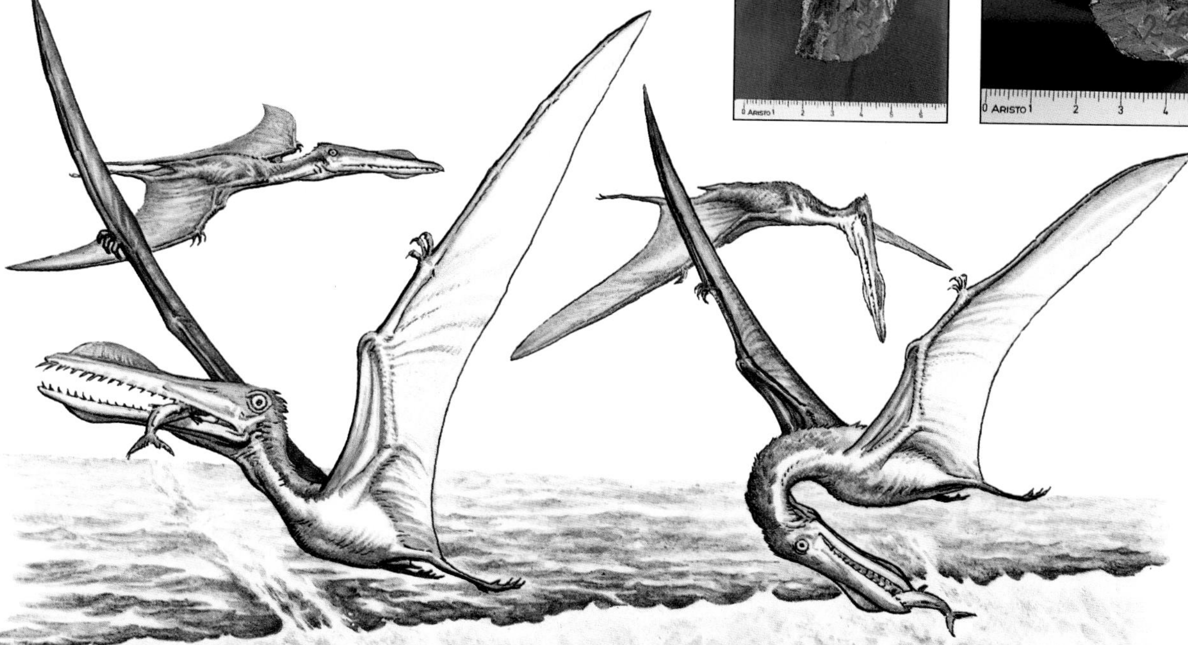

**Fishing Techniques (left)**
This sequence shows how the crest on the front of *Anhanguera*'s beak may have helped this pterosaur to fish when on the wing. As it dipped its jaws into the sea to snatch a fish, the crest would have ploughed through the water just below the surface, like the keel of a ship, reducing water resistance and stabilizing *Anhanguera*'s head at the critical moment of grasping its prey.

## The Spinal Column

The spinal column is usually divided into cervical, dorsal, sacral and caudal vertebrae. There is a considerable difference in the number and length of the caudal (tail) vertebrae between the long-tailed pterosaurs (Rhamphorhynchoidea) and the short-tailed pterosaurs (Pterodactyloidea). The number of cervical, dorsal and sacral vertebrae is not uniform in all pterosaurs either.

There can be seven, eight or nine cervical (neck) vertebrae. It is often not clear whether the last two cervical vertebrae can be counted as dorsal vertebrae. In terms of definition, however, the first dorsal vertebra is the one on which ribs are the first to be connected to the sternum.

The number of dorsal (back) vertebrae varies between 11 and 16, according to whether one counts the last cervical vertebrae as dorsal or not, and whether the last dorsal vertebrae are already part of the sacrum. In the sacrum there are between three and five vertebrae in Rhamphorhynchoidea and up to ten in Pterodactyloidea. Long-tailed pterosaurs have about 40 caudal vertebrae with the exception of *Anurognathus*, whose short stubby tail has only 11 vertebrae. *Anurognathus* is the only 'long-tailed' pterosaur with a short tail.

The joints of all pterosaur vertebrae are concave at the front and convex at the back; such vertebrae are termed procoeleous. Only the caudal vertebrae are concave at both ends, and they are termed amphicoeleous.

The cervical vertebrae of pterosaurs are large and robustly built, in contrast with the rest of the vertebrae, though like the dorsal vertebrae they have lateral openings, so-called pneumatic foramina, which helped to save weight. In Rhamphorhynchoidea the neck is always shorter than, or at most the same length as, the vertebral column between it and the tail. In Pterodactyloidea the neck is always longer. This is not achieved by an increased number of vertebrae, but rather by extension of the cervical vertebrae themselves. The shorter cervical vertebrae of Rhamphorhynchoidea have high upper neural spines. They have short, thin cervical ribs close to the vertebrae. Pterodactyloidea have ribs only on the last two cervical vertebrae, and in their case the neural spines are mostly low and crest-shaped. The cervical vertebrae of *Pteranodon* and other Cretaceous pterosaurs also have a high neural spine however. In the gigantic *Quetzalcoatlus* the cervical vertebrae are also extremely long with very low, crest-shaped neural spines. Furthermore, in this genus and in other large pterosaurs, additional processes, so-called exapophyses, have formed, jutting out ventrally at both ends of the vertebra. This five-point joint in the cervical vertebrae prevented vertebral torsion and major sideways movement. But the cervical vertebral column could be considerably bent upwards and downwards, which was particularly important for taking in food, i.e. for catching fish.

In most Cretaceous pterosaurs some of the dorsal vertebrae are fused together. This is called a notarium, in which the vertebrae and to an extent the neural spines as well have fused. In *Pteranodon* for example these form a supraneural plate with a shallow articular facet on each side to accommodate the shoulder blades (scapulae). Functionally this notarium is a uniform complex for support and anchorage of the pectoral girdle. The supraneural plate did not only serve to articulate the free end of the scapula but was also the attachment

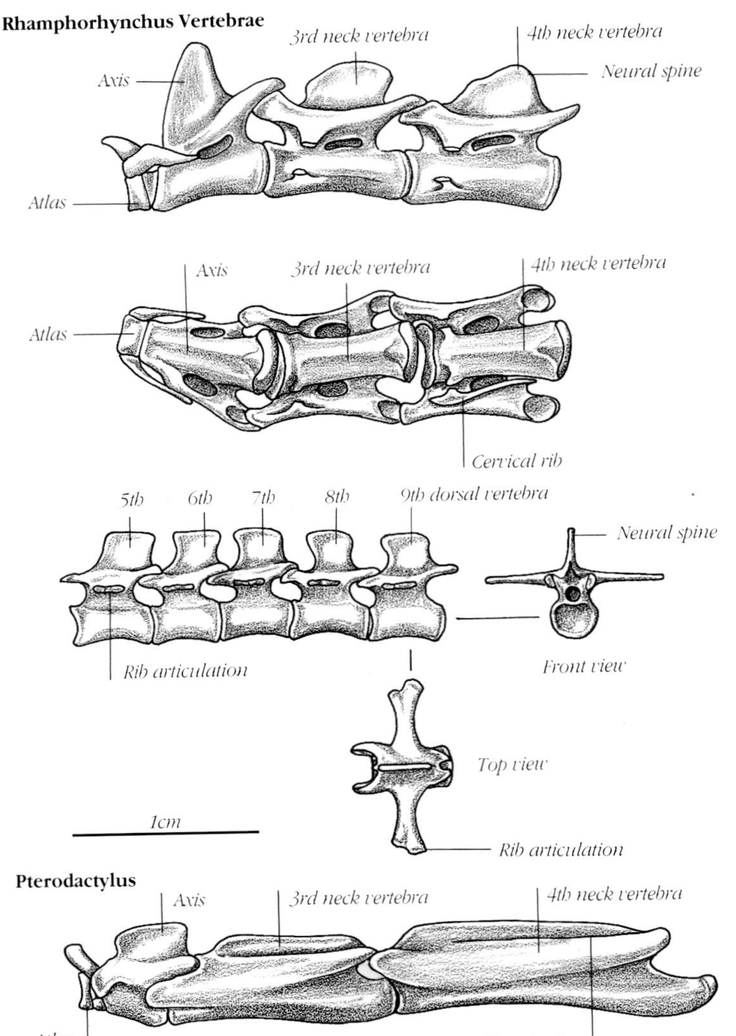


**Rhamphorhynchus Vertebrae (left)**
The general layout of the vertebrae of pterosaurs follows the archosaurian pattern. But compared to the trunk vertebrae (dorsals) the neck vertebrae (cervicals) are especially strong, providing large areas for the attachment of the neck musculature. Despite this, they are lightly built, partly hollow, and have holes in the bony walls, the pneumatic foramina, in order to save weight. The joints of all pterosaur vertebrae are generally concave at the front and convex at the back. Shown here are neck and trunk vertebrae in different aspects.

**Pterodactylus Neck Vertebrae (below left)**
The elongation of the neck in pterodactyloids is a consequence of the elongation of the individual neck vertebrae rather than of an increase in the number of neck vertebrae present. While the vertebrae grew longer, the neural spines on top of the vertebrae also became lower. As a result the head and neck could swing up and down quite freely, but sideways mobility was restricted.

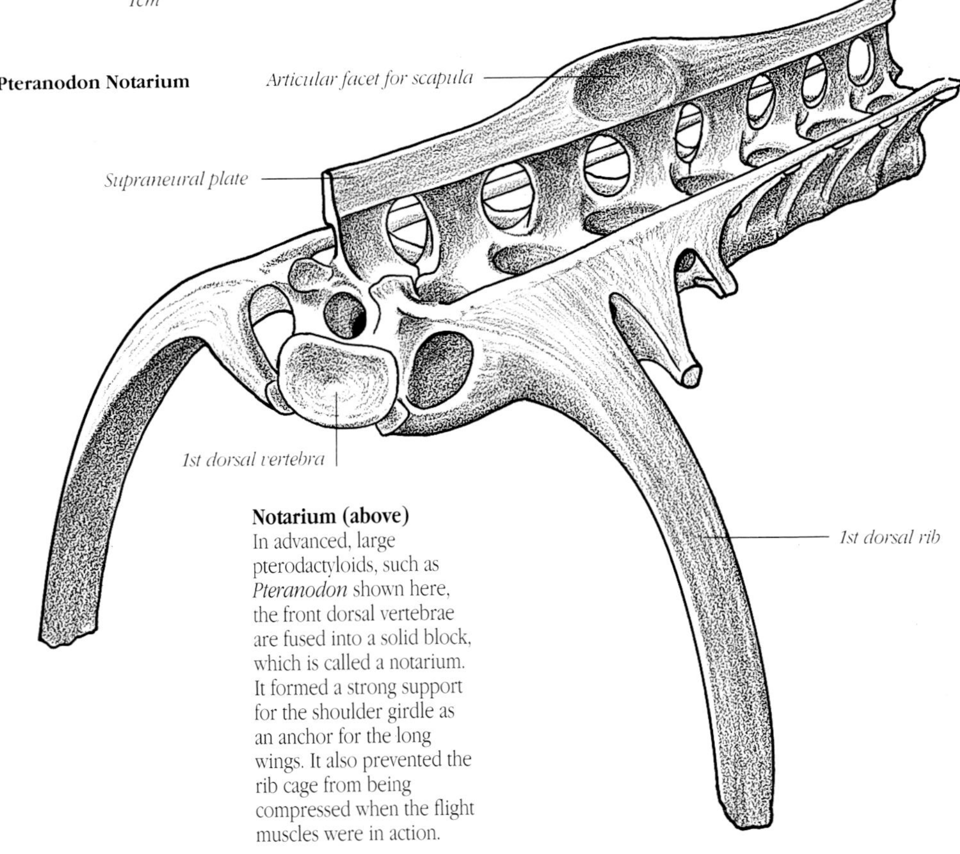


**Notarium (above)**
In advanced, large pterodactyloids, such as *Pteranodon* shown here, the front dorsal vertebrae are fused into a solid block, which is called a notarium. It formed a strong support for the shoulder girdle as an anchor for the long wings. It also prevented the rib cage from being compressed when the flight muscles were in action.

point for an important flight muscle, the latissimus dorsi, which made it possible to raise the upper forelimb backwards. The chest ribs decrease in length and strength towards the rear of the creature. They are connected to the breastbone (sternum) by short intermediate pieces, the so-called sternal ribs. This produced a rigidly fixed rib cage, which could not be compressed by flight muscle activity.

The sacral vertebrae fuse to form the sacrum and are connected to the ilia of the pelvis by broad spines or sacral ribs. Often the last dorsal vertebrae are still included in the sacrum and in the case of *Pteranodon* for example they fuse to form a synsacrum, as in birds.

Rhamphorhynchoidea have a long tail consisting of up to 40 vertebrae. The first five to six caudal vertebrae are still normally developed and can move interdependently. The subsequent caudal vertebrae are increasingly longer and thinner. Their mobility is severely restricted by a system of elongated bone spines which surround and stiffen the tail. These thin rod-like extensions originate in the extended front and rear vertebral processes, the zygapophyses, then fork and reach up to six times the length of the vertebrae. The ventral vertebral connections, the so-called chevrons, also have thin spines of bone stretching forwards and backwards.

**Right:** The tail of the long-tailed pterosaurs, the rhamphorhynchoids, is composed of about 40 vertebrae which are elongated and stiffened by long, rod-like, bony extensions of the zygapophyseal processes (sometimes incorrectly called ossified tendons). This *Rhamphorhynchus* specimen from the Solnhofen limestone shows the structure of the tail and these stiffening extensions of the vertebrae clearly.

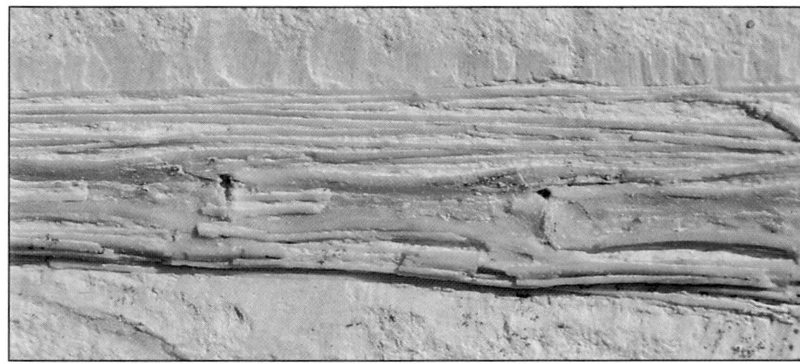

**Below:** This close-up of three *Rhamphorhynchus* tail vertebrae reveals that the bony rods originate as extensions from the vertebrae and from the ventral chevrons in between them (see also drawing below). The rods functioned as stiffening devices for the long, aerodynamic tail.

**Rhamphorhynchus Vertebra**

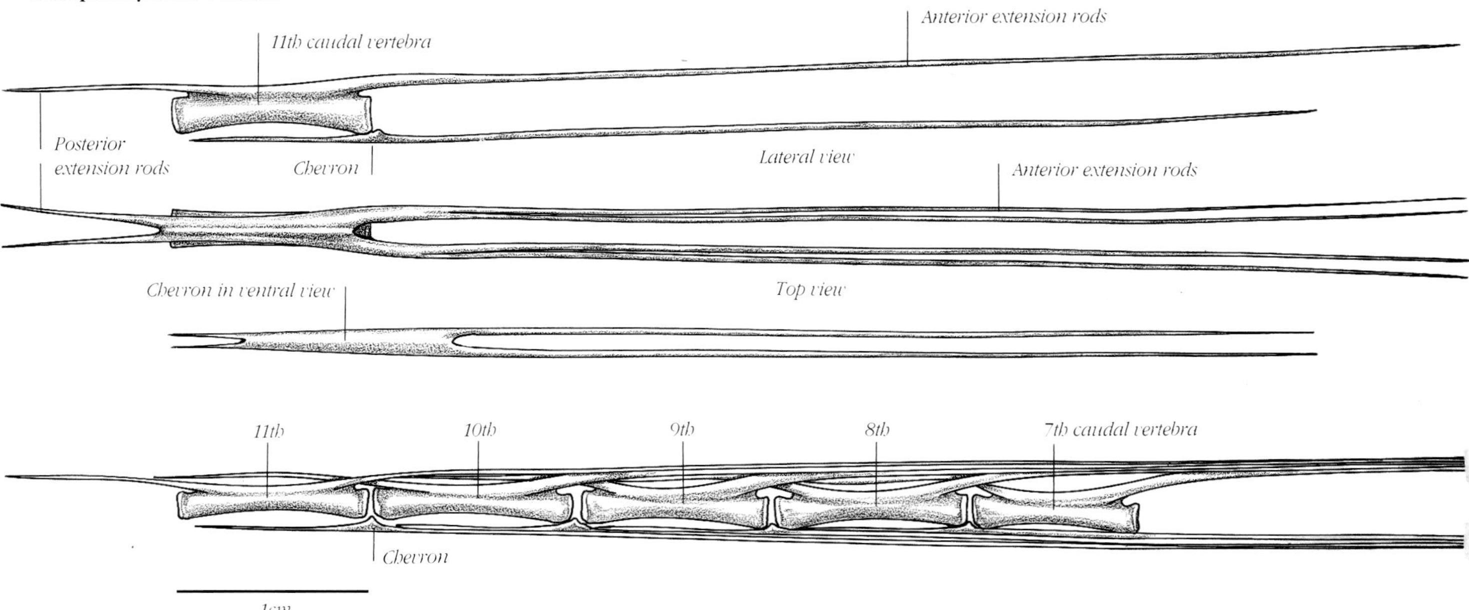


**Tail Stiffeners (above)**
This reconstruction shows the 11th tail vertebra of *Rhamphorhynchus* in isolation (in various views), and as part of a series of vertebrae. The intermediate vertebral elements, the chevrons, have also developed long, stiffening extensions. The tail was thus reinforced and stiffened both dorsally and ventrally.

**Pterodactylus Tail**



**Pterodactylus Tail (left)**
The tail of pterodactyloids is greatly reduced, and is composed of only a few small vertebrae which are not stiffened at all. This is *Pterodactylus*' tail.

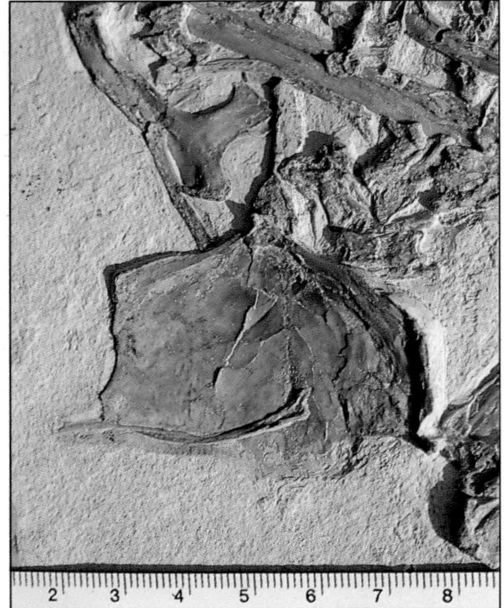

**Breastbones (right)** The pterosaur breastbone (seen here from below) is a wide plate with a crest (cristospina) protruding forward and ventrally. The large surface provided the area for the attachment of the large flight muscles.

**Left:** A *Rhamphorhynchus* breastbone (from below).

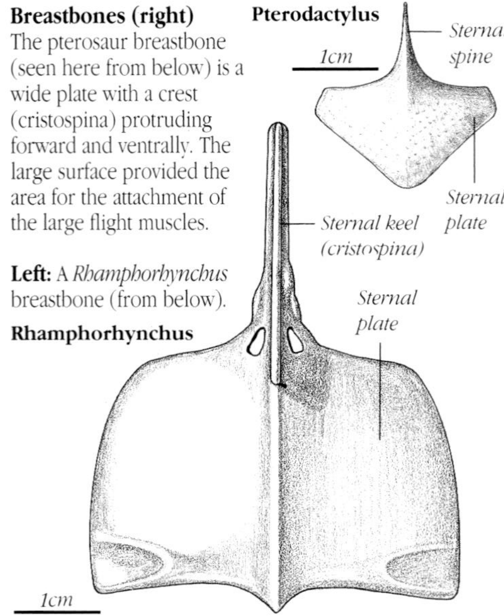


Thus long-tailed pterosaurs had a stiffened tail which moved principally upwards and downwards. A cross-section of the central tail area of *Rhamphorhynchus* reveals 26 dorsal and 12 ventral stiffening elements, which give the tail the stability of an elastic rod, similar to that of a carpet-beater. The function of a caudal vertebral column constructed in this way is clear: the tail was used for steering during sudden changes of direction in flight. This is also proved by the fact that at the end of this long tail there was a rhomboid tail membrane that must have had an aerodynamic function.[23]

While the posterior section of the tail of long-tailed pterosaurs was dominated by segmented axial musculature, the transverse processes of the front caudal vertebra still had epaxial muscles attached, which allowed the long tail to be moved sideways as well.

The tail of the short-tailed pterosaurs only contained a few short vertebrae, which rapidly taper, are not stiffened and apparently had no significance as far as flying was concerned. *Pterodactylus*' short tail had at most 16 vertebrae. The caudal vertebral column of *Pteranodon* was strange. It consisted of five very broad vertebrae with double joints. These were followed by six vertebrae which decreased in size, and at the end were long paired rods which were possibly integrated into the flight membrane. By means of an up-and-down movement, the tail of *Pteranodon* would have had a steering function in flight.[24]

## The Sternum

Like birds, pterosaurs possessed a large ossified breastbone or sternum. It consisted of a widened bone plate and a forward-pointing keel or crest (carina). According to genus it was triangular, heart-shaped or rectangular in shape. The slightly bulging bone plate of the breastbone and its keel functioned as the attachment surface for the massive system of pectoral muscles that moved the wings. On the side edges of the sternal plate short sternal ribs were attached, and they formed a connection with the thoracic ribs.

At the point of transition from the sternal plate to the sternal keel (cristospina sterni) two articular facets were located dorsally to take the coracoids of the pectoral girdle.[25] This support function of the coracoids at the same time prevented compression of the rib-cage of the pterosaur when the flight muscles were contracted to flap its wings.

## Gastralia

The gastralia or abdominal ribs are thin rods of bone set loosely in the skin of the abdomen. As a rule they are arranged in six rows one behind the other. Each row consists of a central piece angled in the middle with a slightly curved side-piece on either side. The gastralia are located immediately after the sternum, and bridge the space between sternum and pelvis. Together with this they served to protect the viscera. Gastralia are common in fossil and recent amphibians and reptiles, but are absent in modern birds.[26] It is assumed that they are skin ossifications of a former abdominal dermal armour that have been transferred inwards.

## The Pectoral Girdle

Shoulder elements found in other reptiles, like the clavicle and interclavicle, are absent in pterosaurs. The pectoral or shoulder girdle consists of scapula and coracoid. They are both long and powerfully developed, and meet at a more or less acute angle in a V or U shape. They are usually fused to form a single bone, the scapulocoracoid. In Cretaceous pterosaurs which have a notarium the pectoral girdle is anchored to the vertebral column. The free end of the scapula is articulated here to a facet of the ossified neural spines. The ventral end of the coracoid is levelled off and in the form of a saddle-shaped articular facet, which meshes with the sternum in an appropriate articular socket. Both scapula and coracoid are involved in the shoulder joint which faces to the side and slightly upward. As a result, the humerus was particularly well suited to execute dorsally directed movements. Seen from the front, the two coracoids form a V shape with one another and in articulation with the sternum. In the

23 Similarly stiffened caudal vertebrae are found in the theropod dinosaur *Deinonychus* from the Lower Cretaceous of Montana, in which the tail also had a steering function, when the creature was running quickly on the ground.
Ostrom, J.H., 1969. *Osteology of Deinonychus antirrhopus an Unusual Theropod from the Lower Cretaceous of Montana*. Bulletin of the Yale Peabody Museum of Natural History, 30, 165 pp.; New Haven.
24 Bennett, S.C., 1987. *New Evidence on the tail of Pterosaur Pteranodon (Archosauria: Pterosauria)*. Fourth Symposium on Mesozoic Terrestrial Ecosystems, Short Papers (ed. P.M. Currie and E.H. Koster), pp.18-23; Drumheller.

25 Rhamphorhynchoidea and Pterodactyloidea differ principally in the nature of coracoid articulation at the sternum. In Rhamphorhynchoidea the articular facet for the left coracoid is behind the facet for the right coracoid. In Pterodactyloidea the coracoid articular facets are arranged in symmetrical juxtaposition on the sternum.

26 It is remarkable that the oldest known bird, *Archaeopteryx* from the Jurassic did not have an ossified breastbone, but typically reptilian gastralia.

**Gastralia (right)**
Gastralia, sometimes called gastral ribs, are a typical structure in many amphibians and reptiles. They are dermal ossifications, and may have derived from the abdominal dermal armour protecting the underside of such creatures. In pterosaurs, such as in this *Rhamphorhynchus*, the gastralia are composed of three rod-like bones, an angled middle mediogastrale connected to two slightly curved lateral laterogastralia, arranged in six parallel rows one behind the other. They were originally embedded within the skin of the belly, between the sternal plate and the pelvis. Their function was probably to support and protect the intestines. Modern birds do not have gastralia.

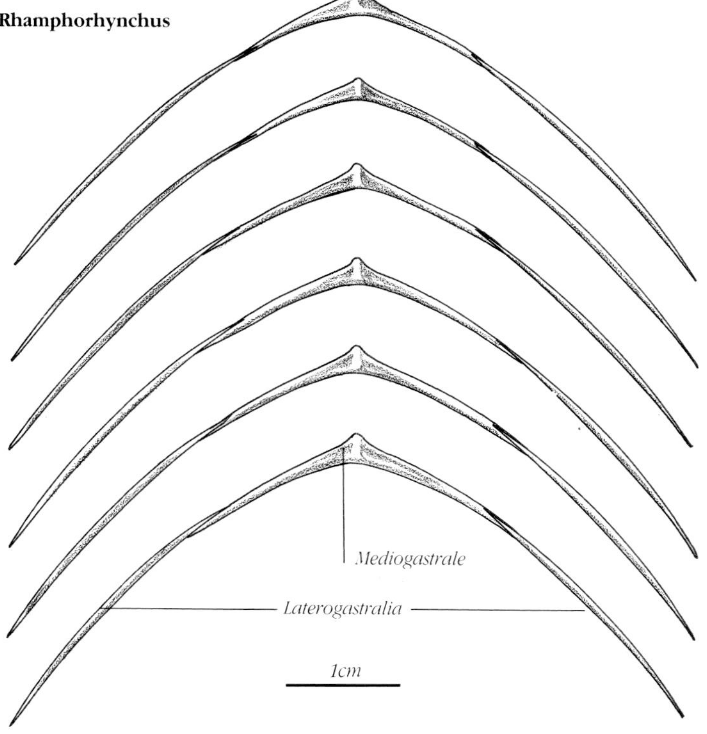

**Rhamphorhynchus Shoulder Girdle**

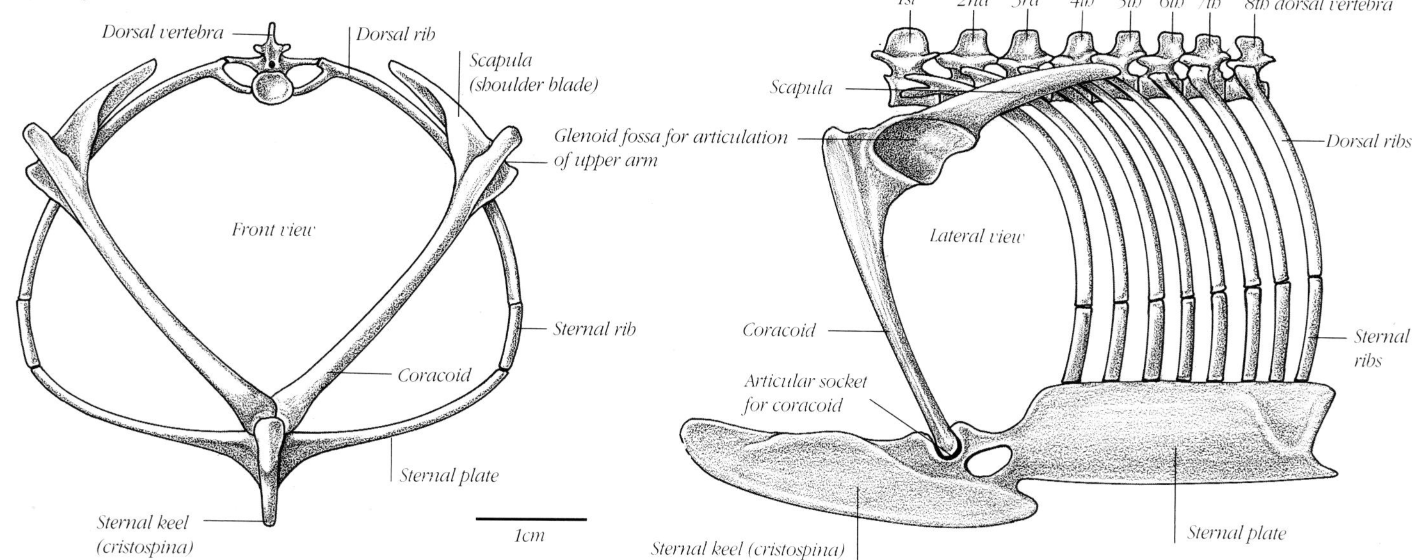


great Cretaceous pterosaurs both scapulacoracoids formed a closed ring with the notarium at the top and the sternum at the bottom, which created a stable part of the skeleton on which the long flight limbs could be mounted.

**The Shoulder Girdle (above)**
The shoulder girdle connected to the sternum, as shown here in *Rhamphorhynchus*. The glenoid fossa for the upper arm articulation faces slightly upward and backwards, indicating how the wing moved.

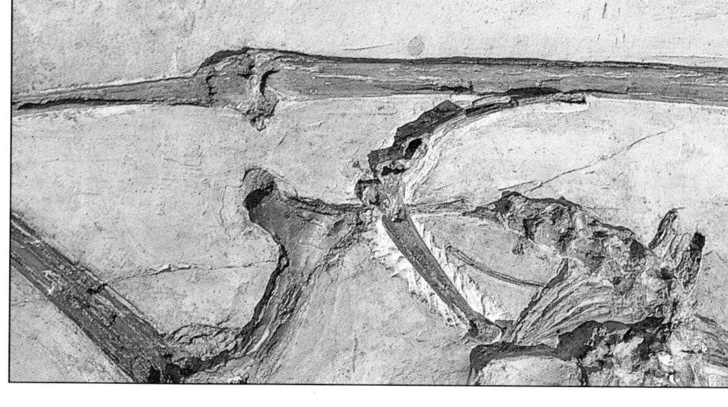

**Right:** The boomerang-shaped bone in the centre is the shoulder girdle of a *Rhamphorhynchus*.

## The Forelimbs

The forelimb of pterosaurs is developed into a wing. The fourth finger of the hand is greatly elongated and strengthened, while the first three fingers are normally developed and have claws. The fifth digit of the hand regressed in the course of evolution, and is absent.

In Pterodactyloidea a tendency to elongation of the wing is also reflected in the development of the metacarpals – the bones in the hand that form the palm. The bones of the flight limb are more powerfully developed in comparison with the bones of the hindlimbs. The long bones have very thin walls, and in some large Cretaceous pterosaurs, like *Pteranodon* for example, they are extremly thin, often only the thickness of a postcard.

A particular feature of pterosaur wings is the pteroid bone. It is connected by a joint to the distal, lateral carpal bone. Its function is disputed. Probably the pteroid reinforced the front edge of a small flight membrane between the upper and lower parts of the limb, the so-called propatagium.

## The Humerus

The pterosaur humerus (upper arm) is relatively short and solid. At the upper end (proximal) and usually near the axis of the shaft a saddle-shaped articular head is developed; this was in contact with the glenoid fossa of the pectoral girdle. Laterally at the upper end there is always a broad protruding crest, the delto-pectoral process. The pectoral flight muscles were attached to this.

The shaft of the humerus is usually bent somewhat forwards. The distal articular facets to radius and ulna (the bones of the forearm) permit quite major bending of the elbow. The humerus is a hollow bone. Air openings (foramina pneumatica) have been found in the bones of large pterosaurs. Spongy bone tissue is found in joints and processes. In large Cretaceous pterosaurs the cavity of the shaft is stiffened with thin bony struts. This gives maximum bone strength combined with the greatest possible lightness. The internal support structures are effectively lines of force made material. Maximum bracing of the humerus was possible when it was approximately at right angles to the longitudinal axis of the body. It could swing up to 65° backwards. In *Pteranodon* vertical movement of the humerus was possible in a sweep from 25° below the horizontal to 70° above it. In the course of this motion it was directed 17° backwards at its lowest point.[27]

27 Bramwell, C.D. and Whitfield, G.R., 1974, op. cit. (19).

## The Radius and Ulna

The lower part of the limb is always longer than the humerus. The radius and ulna (the two bones of the forearm) are next to, and touch one another. The ulna is always the stronger bone. Movement at the elbow was only possible in one plane. The maximum extension between humerus and lower arm was about 150°. When it was bent, in other words when the wing was folded, the radius was pushed distally along the ulna. When the radius was moved in this way it pressed on the proximal carpal, which was twisted and slid away

**The Upper Arm (right)**
The upper arm (humerus) is relatively short in pterosaurs, but it is quite robust with large processes for the attachment of the flight muscles (the delto-pectoral process). Despite its strength, this bone is hollow, and, except for the articular extremities, it has very thin walls which makes it light. In large pterosaurs the shaft is internally strengthened by bony struts which stiffened the outer walls transversely. These drawings show the left humerus of *Rhamphorhynchus* in lateral (left), anterior (middle), and medial (right) views.

**Rhamphorhynchus' Humerus**

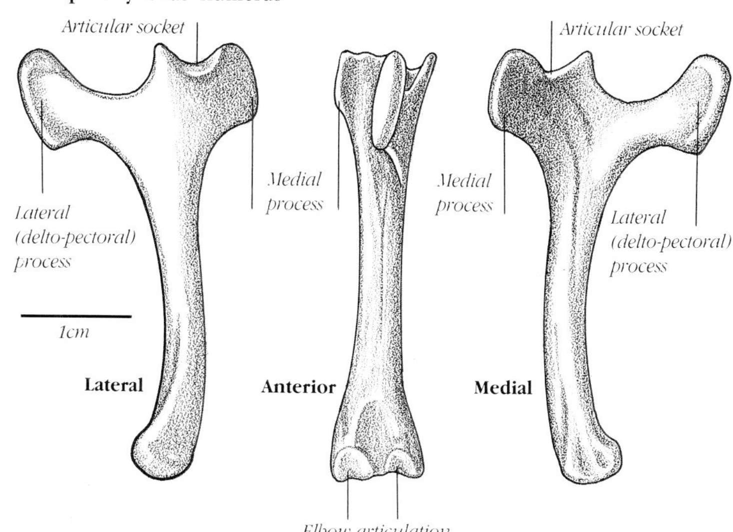

over a protrusion on the ulna. This caused the wing metacarpal to swing back, and with it the wing finger. Thus in pterosaurs there was automatic folding of the wing, a principle with which we are familiar in birds. It means that when the wing was folded the hand was automatically bent backwards in the wrist.

## The Carpus

Originally the carpus (or wrist) was made up of five bones: two proximal and three distal carpals. There is a tendency for proximal carpals to fuse into one bone. This is the case with Rhamphorhynchoidea and Cretaceous Pterodactyloidea. In advanced forms there is a further reduction to two distal bones. The larger of the two supports the solid wing metacarpal. The smaller, laterally placed distal carpal has a forward oriented glenoid fossa to take the pteroid. This is a specific pterosaur bone, which does not occur in other vertebrates. It was probably connected to a tendon running along the front edge of a small flight membrane between the upper and lower parts of the limb, the propatagium. Presumably the function of the pteroid bone was to alter the angle of attack and shape of the propatagium, and hence to alter flight performance. It has been observed that the pteroid is always directed towards the body in undisturbed fossil skeletons, which supports this interpretation of its position.

However, another school of thought suggests that the pteroid was directed forwards and downwards, and that for this reason pterosaurs had a movable forewing, flexed and controlled by the pteroid. If this were the case, the angle of incidence of this forewing would have been altered by upward and downward movement and would have caused variable camber of the wing.[28] Another interpretation of the function of the pteroid postulates that it could have been directed both forwards and downwards – during slow flight, for example, and also towards the body in rapid flight. In this case a tendon would have been stretched over the free end of the pteroid bone, which would have caused the pteroid to click into one or the other position according to the position of the flight digit.[29] However, the fact that in many pterosaurs the pteroid was very long and thin – often up to two thirds of the length of the lower arm – tends to argue against this view.

The wrist could be moved in three ways: motion could occur between proximal carpal and the lower arm, between proximal and distal carpal in the form of a limited sliding movement, and thirdly as a rotation between distal carpal and the wing metacarpal.

## The Metacarpus

The metacarpus (or palm of the hand) consists of four bones, of which the wing metacarpal is considerably stronger than the other three metacarpals. The wing metacarpal is jointed with the distal carpal in such a way as to allow it to twist via a tongue and socket joint. Distally it has a special joint formation to take the first joint of the flight digit. The three metacarpals of the three small digits are slender bone rods which lie one behind the other in close contact with the large metacarpal. The first two can also regress at their lower end, so that they no longer reach the carpus.

Long- and short-tailed pterosaurs also differ in the relative length of the metacarpal. In all Rhamphorhynchoidea it is shorter than half the length of the lower arm, in Pterodactyloidea it is longer than half the lower arm, and in Cretaceous pterosaurs it can often even be longer than the entire lower arm.

28 Frey, E. and Riess, J., 1981. *A new Reconstruction of the Pterosaur Wing*. Neues Jahrbuch für Geologie und Paläontologie, Abhandlungen, 161 (1): 1-27.
29 Pennycuick, C.J., 1988. *On the reconstruction of Pterosaurs and their manner of flight, with note on vortex wakes*. Biological Review, 63: 299-331.

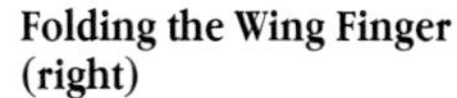

**Folding the Wing Finger (right)**
The principal folding joint in the pterosaurian wing was the articulation between the wing metacarpal and the first phalanx of the wing finger. The drawings show this section of the hand of *Rhamphorhynchus* with the wing finger in maximum flexion (near left) and maximum extension (far right).

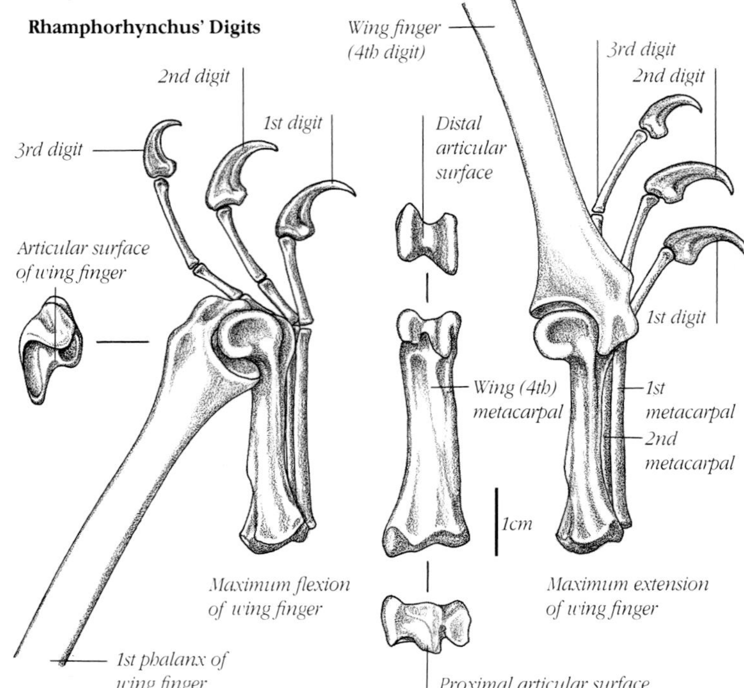

**Below:** A section of the wing skeleton of a *Pterodactylus* showing the principal folding joint of the pterosaurian wing. The first three fingers remained small, were equipped with sharp claws, and articulated with very slender metacarpals. The wing here appears folded to its maximum degree.

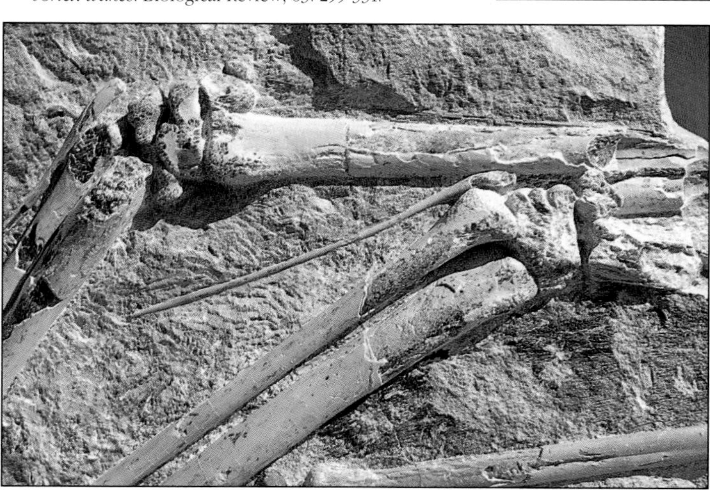

**Pterosaur Wrists (right)**
The wrist consists of two rows of small bones (carpals) which form the joint between the lower arm and metacarpus. They allowed twisting and sliding movements rather than much flexion in the wrist. A lateral carpal protruding to the front supported the slender pteroid bone, which is only known in pterosaurs.

**Left:** The wrists of a pterodactyloid from Brazil. The long, thin bone in the centre is the pteroid.

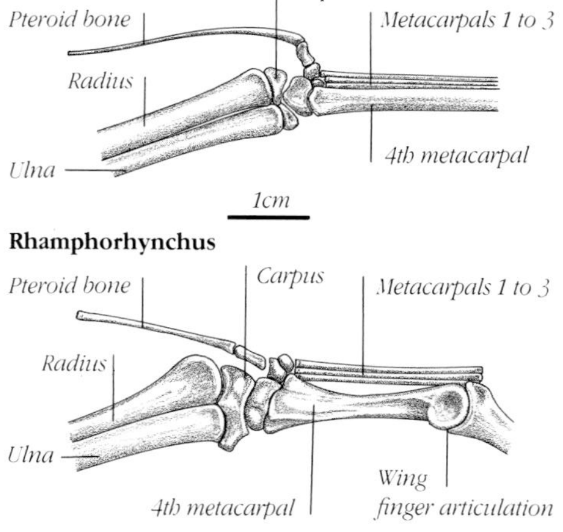

Appropriately to its function, the fourth metacarpal, the wing metacarpal, has a distinctive pulley on the distal end, into which the first flight digit joint was articulated. The axis of the joint is set somewhat at an angle, producing a twisting movement when the wing was folded, thus placing the flight digit against the body in such a way that its upper side pointed out sideways. To accommodate the double-bowled articular surface of the first flight digit phalanx there were corresponding depressions in the wing metacarpal, which indicate that the flight digit could be bent here to a very high degree, approximately to an angle of 25°-30°. At maximum extension the angle was 165°. Further extension was not possible, as a short process on the front side of the first flight phalanx, for the insertion of an extensor tendon, formed a stop and prevented forward hyperextension of the flight digit.

## The Digits

The pterosaur hand had only four digits. The first three were normally developed and had powerful, sharp, curved claws which projected in front of the wing and were oriented towards the body. These small digits could be moved freely and, including the claws, had two, three and four phalanges on the first, second and third digit. The claws had well-developed so-called flexor tubercles for the insertion of strong flexor tendons. This indicates that pterosaurs could grip rock ledges or trees with their digit claws and presumably could also climb.

The fourth digit was extremely elongated to fulfil its function as bearer of the flight membrane. It was almost twenty times longer than the small digits, and also much stronger. It consisted of four long phalanges. The proximal joint of the first and thickest phalanx consists of two bowled glenoid fossae to accommodate the joint pulley of the wing metacarpal. The articular capsules of the four wing phalanges produce joints which are appropriately tightly articulated. The flight digit phalanges are slightly bent, resulting in what must have been a leading edge to the wing that bent backwards and downwards.

In Rhamphorhynchoidea all the flight digit phalanges have a longitudinal furrow on the flight membrane side, which obviously permitted secure attachment of the flight membrane. The fairly sharp edges of these ridges are drawn further back at the top than at the bottom. The leading edge of the flight digit phalanges is rounded, like the leading edge of an aeroplane wing. The flight digit phalanges of Pterodactyloidea exhibit different characteristics: they have no longitudinal furrow, and are triangular in cross-section.

Maximum wingspan was achieved with regard to the maximum angle of extension between the individual joints of the flight arm. In *Santanadactylus* for example the humeri were set at a backward angle of 15°, the elbow had an angle open to the front of 150°, and between lower arm and metacarpus and between metacarpus and flight digit there was an angle of 165° in each case.[30] Folding the flight arm was essentially achieved by pulling the humerus backwards and bending the elbow joint and the joint between the wing metacarpal and the wing finger.

30 Wellnhofer, P., 1985. *Neue Pterosaurier aus der Santana-Formation (Apt) der Chapada do Araripe. Brasilien.* Palaeontographica, A, 187: 105-182; Stuttgart.

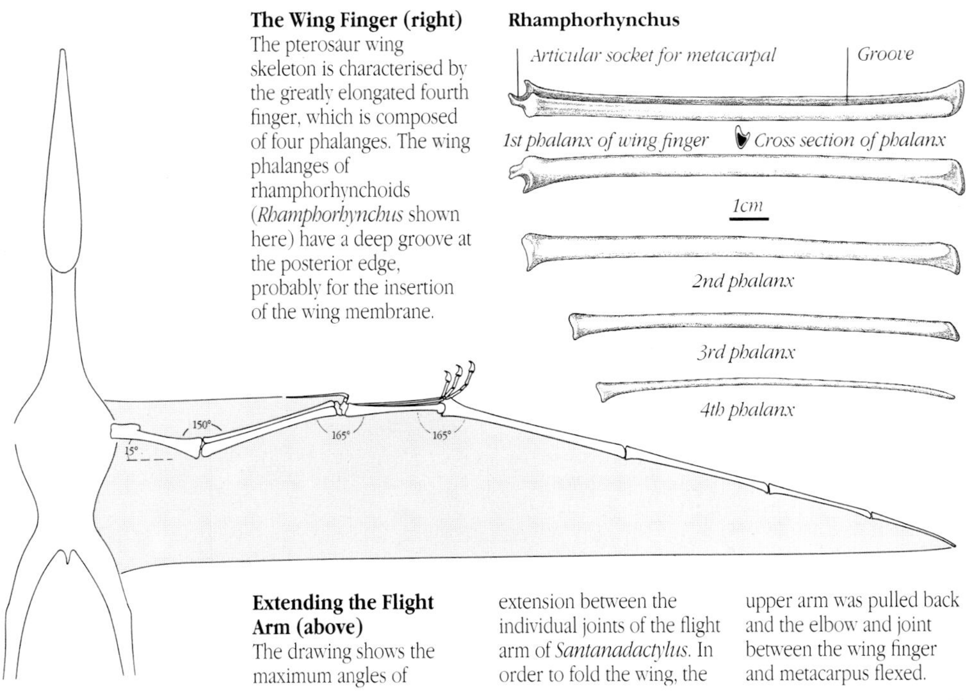


**The Wing Finger (right)** The pterosaur wing skeleton is characterised by the greatly elongated fourth finger, which is composed of four phalanges. The wing phalanges of rhamphorhynchoids (*Rhamphorhynchus* shown here) have a deep groove at the posterior edge, probably for the insertion of the wing membrane.

**Extending the Flight Arm (above)** The drawing shows the maximum angles of extension between the individual joints of the flight arm of *Santanadactylus*. In order to fold the wing, the upper arm was pulled back and the elbow and joint between the wing finger and metacarpus flexed.

## The Pelvis

In principle the pterosaur pelvis is an archosaur pelvis. It is composed of ilium, ischium and pubis on each side. Another pelvic bone typical of pterosaurs is the prepubis, which is situated in front of the pubis. The structure of the pterosaur pelvis is markedly different from that of birds.

As a rule ilium, ischium and pubis are more or less fused and form a unit with the sacrum of the spinal column. The degree of ossification in the pelvis is obviously also dependent on the age of the individual creature. The ilium is extended forward to form a narrow bone, bent slightly upwards. In contrast the section of the ilium behind the socket of the hip joint is shorter. The socket of the hip joint (acetabulum) is oriented laterally and obliquely upwards to accommodate the femur. It is not perforated, as is the case with birds. All three pelvic bones, ilium, ischium and pubis, are involved in the formation of the hip socket. This orientation of the hip sockets prevented the femur from being placed vertically and makes it improbable that pterosaurs could walk on the ground like birds.[31]

31 Molnar, R.E., 1987. *A pterosaur pelvis from western Queensland, Australia.* Alcheringa, 11: 87-94.
Unwin, D.M., 1987. *Pterosaur locomotion – joggers or waddlers?* Nature, 327: 13-14.
Wellnhofer, P., 1988. *Terrestrial locomotion in pterosaurs.* Historical Biology, 1: 3-16.

**Above:** An isolated pelvis of *Campylognathoides*. It is seen from above and shows the hip sockets clearly. Due to compression their orientation is unnatural.

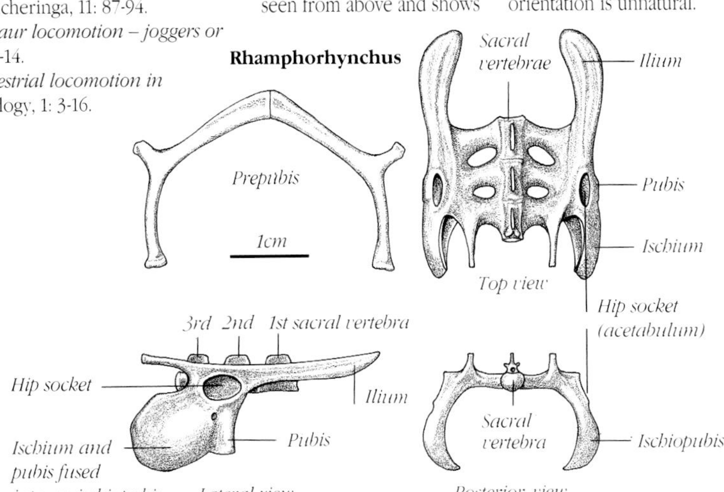


**Rhamphorhynchus Pelvis (right)** The pelvis is seen here from various angles. The arrangement of the ilium, ischium and pubis follows the general reptilian pattern, although the proportions are unique to pterosaurs. A paired prepubic bone, originally connected to the pubis by cartilage, is also typical of pterosaurs.

The short, ventrally directed pubis may be fused with the ischium, broadening towards the rear to form a uniform bone plate, the ischiopubis, as in *Rhamphorhynchus* for example. The pubes are never fused along the midline below, but the lower ischia can meet in the middle and close the pelvis ventrally, as in *Pteranodon*, *Nyctosaurus*, *Dimorphodon* and possibly in *Campylognathoides*.[32] In other pterosaurs the pelvis is open ventrally.

The prepubes are not firmly connected to the pelvis and are very variable in shape, so that they can serve as diagnostic features. They are articulated with the pubes and in Pterodactyloidea are broadened into a scoop shape at their free ends. In Rhamphorhynchoidea they partially form long, slender bars of bone which meet on the midline and are held together either by cartilage or by bony fusion. The function of the prepubes was to support the viscera, and perhaps also as a 'sitting bone' when the creature was at rest.

There is no doubt that Rhamphorhynchoidea had strong dorsal and ventral tail muscles to control the long tail. It is highly probable that these muscles were attached to the rear and inner sides of the ischium and on the dorsal side of ilium and sacrum.

## The Hindlimbs

By comparison with the forelimbs, the hindlimbs of pterosaurs are short, weak and slender, but relatively long when compared to the length of the trunk. In Triassic and Lower Jurassic pterosaurs they are relatively more strongly developed than in Upper Jurassic and Cretaceous genera. The femur is always shorter than the tibia.

32 Padian, K., 1983. *A functional analysis of flying and walking in pterosaurs*. Paleobiology, 9 (3): 218-239

**Above:** The pelvis of this *Pterodactylus*, seen here from the left, shows how it connected to the vertebral column and the tail. The prepubis is the spatulate bone below the pelvis. In life it was attached to the pubic bone by cartilage. This element is a typical pterosaurian bone, not found in other vertebrates. The prepubes probably supported the intestines.

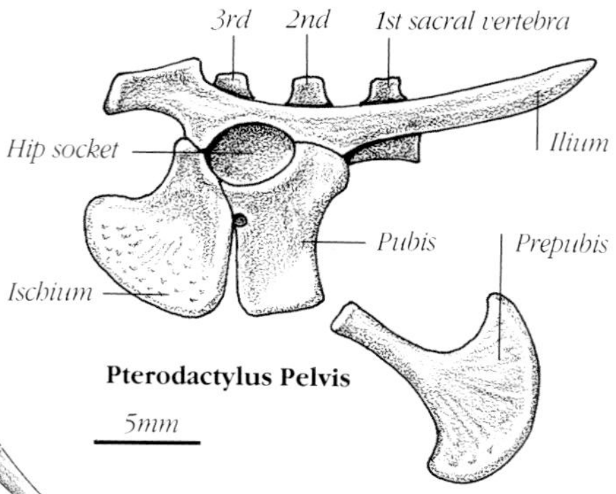

**Pterodactylus Pelvis (above)**
This pelvis is much like that of *Rhamphorhynchus*. Here, too, the hip socket is not perforated as in birds, and the ilium has a long extension to the front. However, the shape of the prepubis is different. It varies among all pterosaur genera, and can be interpreted as a diagnostic character.

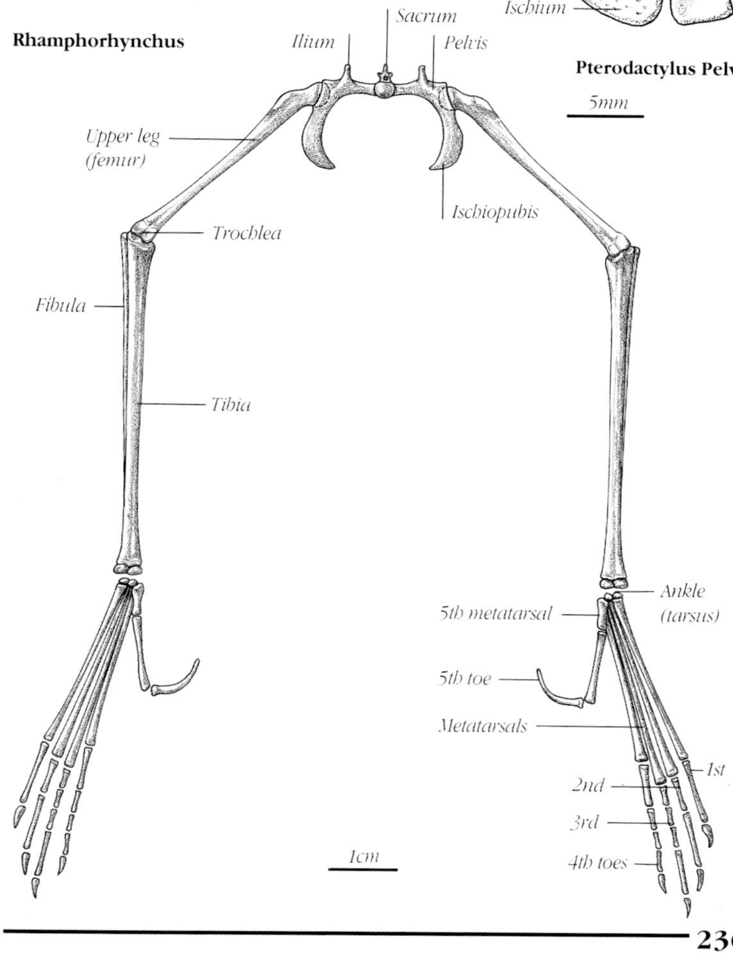

**The Hind Legs (left)**
This restoration shows how the hind legs of *Rhamphorhynchus* articulated in the pelvis. The hip socket pointed slightly upwards and backwards. The ball-like articular head of the femur (the caput) fitted into this socket in such a way that the femur pointed obliquely outwards rather than vertically downwards.

The femur (upper leg bone) has a straight or slightly curved shaft with a circular cross-section. The head of the femur is more or less distinctly separated from the shaft by a narrow neck (collum). The ball of the joint (caput femoris) is directed obliquely upwards. The collum bends at an angle to the shaft, in most pterosaurs this is between 130° and 160°. If one considers the lateral orientation of the hip sockets mentioned earlier, then the femur could only have been directed obliquely downwards and outwards. Thus biped locomotion, like that of a bird, was not a possibility. In the case of optimal articulation in the hip sockets, the femur would be in the horizontal plane, in other words in the flight position. The distal joint of the femur, the trochlea, was broadened and orientated obliquely to the longitudinal axis of the shaft.

The tibia (the main shin bone) is a completely straight, slender hollow bone, which is always longer than the femur. At its lower end the tibia broadens towards the tarsus. Flexion of the knee joint permitted the tibia to be in an upright position when moving on the ground, despite the oblique position of the femur.

In early pterosaurs like *Dorygnathus* and *Campylognathoides*, the fibula (the smaller shin bone) is developed to full length. In the more advanced Jurassic forms the fibula no longer reaches the tarsus at its lower end, but ends above it as a wedge-shaped bone pressed closely to the tibia. In Cretaceous pterosaurs the fibula is markedly reduced or completely absent.

## The Skeleton of the Foot

The foot of the pterosaur was generally narrow and long. Rhamphorhynchoidea differ from Pterodactyloidea in having a long fifth digit, which is flexed and has no claw. The phalangeal formula for the foot runs 2.3.4.5.2. in Rhamphorhynchoidea and 2.3.4.5.0. in Pterodactyloidea.

Pterosaurs have a typical mesotarsal ankle joint, i.e. the line of the joint runs between the proximal and distal bones of the tarsus. In early pterosaurs there were two proximal and three distal tarsals. In Cretaceous pterosaurs in particular the proximal tarsals fused with the tibia, while only two distal tarsals remain. The two proximal tarsals can also – particularly with age

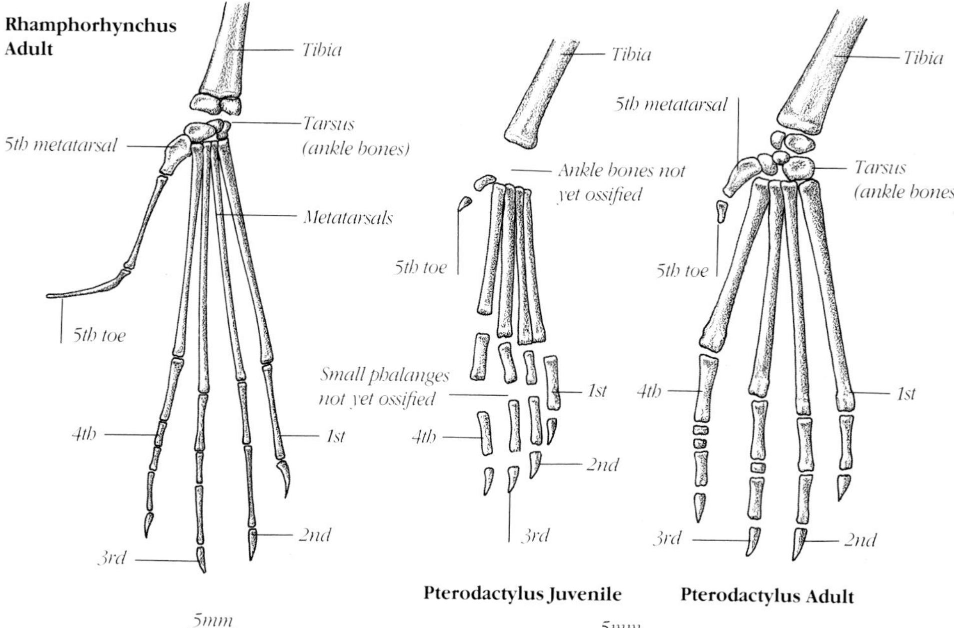

**Left:** The foot skeletons of *Rhamphorhynchus* (upper) and *Pterodactylus* (lower). In general the osteology of these feet suggests that pterosaurs were more likely to have walked on the soles of their feet, rather than on their toes like birds. Note that the fifth toe in pterodactyloids is reduced to a short stump.

**Pterosaur Feet (above)** The drawings compare the feet of an adult *Rhamphorhynchus* (left), and a juvenile and adult *Pterodactylus* (middle and right). The tarsal bones and small phalanges in the third and fourth toes of the juvenile are missing; they were not yet ossified when this individual died.

– fuse to form a single bone, as in some *Rhamphorhynchus* species for example.

Undisturbed skeletons show that the ankle could allow right-angled articulation of the foot with the tibia. This is an indication of a plantigrade position of the foot (i.e. with the sole on the ground) when walking. Thus pterosaurs were not digitigrade like birds – walking on the toes – but plantigrade – walking on the soles of the feet – like man. So far there have been no confirmed finds of pterosaur footprints, so no conclusive proof of this is available.[33]

The metatarsals (upper foot bones) of the first four digits of the foot are long, and slender; they are staggered, and have somewhat broader, flattened joint ends. The fourth metatarsal is usually somewhat shorter than the first three. The fifth is extremely short, and projects into the ankle. The four long metatarsals and thus the digits could be spread, perhaps to stretch a web between the digits. The short fifth metatarsal could apparently also be moved in another plane.

## The Foot Digits

All digits with the exception of the fifth had claws. But they were not as powerful as the claws on the digits of the hand, and also not as sharply curved. In Rhamphorhynchoidea the fifth digit has two phalanges, which are very long and meet at a marked angle. In Pterodactyloidea there is only a short phalanx on the fifth digit, and in *Pteranodon* and all other Cretaceous pterosaurs it has no phalanges.

In Pterodactyloidea the third and fourth toe has very short central phalanges, which only ossify in the adult growth phase. If these small intermediate phalanges are missing from a fossil specimen, then the creature is likely to be quite young. At that stage these small digital phalanges were still cartilaginous. As cartilage usually cannot be fossilized, there is a gap between the digital phalanges in such cases.

The long fifth digit on the foot of Rhamphorhynchoidea had more freedom of movement than the other digits and could apparently be moved in another plane as well. It is notable that in undisturbed skeletons the fifth digit is always flexed towards the tail. This position precludes stretching of the wing membrane by the fifth digit. There is also argument about whether this digit could have stretched a membrane on the inside of the hindlimbs, a so-called uropatagium. It must be assumed that the orientation of the other digits was vertical to this. Perhaps the feet of *Rhamphorhynchus* were held in flight in such a way that the soles pointed inwards, like those of modern flying foxes. The aerodynamic advantages of a uropatagium are not entirely clear. It was certainly a hindrance when swimming in water. But the long fifth digit could also have been used to stretch a web between the toes. However, the short-tailed pterosaurs no longer needed a long fifth toe of this kind.

**Principal Osteological Differences between Rhamphorhynchoidea and Pterodactyloidea**

| Rhamphorhynchoidea | Pterodactyloidea |
|---|---|
| Jaws always completely filled with teeth | Jaws completely, partially or not at all filled with teeth |
| Nasal and preorbital opening separate | Nasal and preorbital opening not separate or confluent |
| Occipital joint (condylus occipitalis) directed backwards | Occipital joint (condylus occipitalis) directed downwards and backwards |
| Cervical ribs present | Cervical ribs only present on the last two cervical vertebrae |
| No notarium | Notarium possible |
| Articular facets for the coracoids on the sternum one behind the other | Articular facets for the coracoids side by side |
| Long tail made up of extended vertebrae | Short tail |
| Short metacarpus | Long metacarpus |
| Flight digit phalanges with longitudinal furrow on the rear side | Flight digit phalanges without longitudinal furrow, triangular in cross-section |
| Long fifth digit on foot | Short fifth digit on foot |

33 The pterosaur tracks described by Stokes (1957) from the Jurassic Morrison Formation of Arizona clearly show the print of a plantigrade foot. However, in the meantime doubt has been expressed about whether these tracks were made by pterosaurs at all. Stokes, W.L., 1957. *Pterodactyl tracks from the Morrison formation*. Journal of Paleontology, 31, 5: 952-954.
Padian, K. and Olsen, P.E., 1984. *The fossil trackway Pteraichnus: Not pterosaurian, but crocodilian*. Journal of Paleontology, 58, 1: 178-184.
Unwin, D.M., 1989. *A Predictive Method for the Identification of Vertebrate Ichnites and its Application to Pterosaur Tracks*. Dinosaur Tracks and Traces, edited by D.D. Gilette and M.G. Lockley, pp.259-274; Cambridge University Press.

The Triassic period at the beginning of the Mesozoic era was highly significant for reptilian evolution. This was the time at which such diverse groups as tortoises, crocodiles and dinosaurs appeared. Fossil finds of the oldest pterosaurs so far known came from the Upper Triassic. Fossil remains from the so-called Rhaetic in Baden, Württemberg and England were identified as pterosaur bones by various researchers as early as the nineteenth century, but these remains were far too sparse for a precise impression of these Triassic pterosaurs to be formed.[1] Recently, the discovery of bone fragments of Triassic pterosaurs has been reported from Gloucestershire in England.[2] They were collected from Upper Triassic fissure deposits at Cromhall Quarry among a few thousand vertebrate elements of different reptile groups, such as sphenodontids, terrestrial crocodiles, flying lizards and others. Although incomplete, the bones represent the first definite record of pterosaurs from the British Upper Triassic. Two small bones could be identified as wing metacarpals. However, they lack diagnostic characters and cannot be assigned to any known pterosaur, except to the Rhamphorhynchoidea. They may even represent a new genus of pterosaur.

In 1899, E.D. Cope in America also believed that bone fragments and isolated vertebrae from Triassic strata in Pennsylvania could be those of a long-necked, long-tailed pterosaur. He called it *Rhabdopelix* (=rod-basin, after a rod-like pelvic bone).[3] The Tübingen expert on fossil reptiles Friedrich von Huene also reported later on similar pterosaur bones from the Pennsylvanian Triassic.[4]

However, identification of these very incomplete fossil remains as pterosaurs was frequently questioned. One of the assumptions was that *Rhabdopelix* may have been related to lizards, similar to the gliding reptile *Icarosaurus*, known from Triassic deposits in New Jersey.[5] But for a long time a fossil reptile skeleton from the Middle Triassic in the southern Alps in Italy called *Tribelesodon* was considered to be the oldest known pterosaur.

## Tribelesodon, a Triassic Pterosaur?

In 1886 Francesco Bassani (1853-1916), Professor of Geology in Milan, alluded to a pterosaur from Middle Triassic strata of Besano in Lombardy, northern Italy, in a monograph on fossils from the bituminous shales of Besano.[6] Milanese geologists had conducted systematic excavations there as early as 1863 and 1878, which had brought to light an interesting yield of hitherto largely unkown marine reptiles. Bassani identified a small fossil remnant of a skeleton as a pterosaur, which because of its tiny teeth with three cusps he called *Tribelesodon* (=three-cusped tooth).

**Above:** Franz Baron Nopcsa, Hungarian nobleman, geologist and acknowledged expert on fossil reptiles. He studied the specimen of *'Tribelesodon'* from Besano and interpreted it – in fact, erroneously – as the oldest known pterosaur.

Franz Baron Nopcsa (1877-1933), the Hungarian geologist and reptile expert, was the first to study these creatures from Besano in more depth. Baron Nopcsa was a many-sided, even enigmatic personality. He had extensive estates in Transylvania (modern Romania) and wrote numerous palaeontological treatises, even books. He was an internationally recognized specialist on fossil reptiles. In 1922 he produced a detailed description of the putative *Tribelesodon* pterosaur as well.[7] He even made a drawing of the reconstructed skeleton, showing it as a long-tailed pterosaur. The striking feature of this find, the only specimen of this creature, was a series of long bones, which both Bassani and Nopcsa took to be the elongated phalanges of a flight digit.

The Besano Triassic strata consists of black shale containing bitumen, a sort of mineral pitch, which was mined for commercial purposes. At the time it was distilled to produce raw materials for preparing 'Saurol', which like 'Ichthyol' (from the so-called fish-shale of Seefeld in the Tyrol) was used for pharmaceutical purposes, as an ointment. These were Middle Triassic marine deposits (Ladinian), about 235 million years old; they extend into the Swiss Canton Ticino and come to the surface at the southern end of Lake Lugano, on Monte San Giorgio. These strata, the 'Grenzbitumenzone', were also mined, and it was here that the Zürich palaeontologist Bernhard Peyer found reptile remains on a spoil heap in 1919. They sparked off very successful planned excavations, conducted by the University of Zürich on a regular basis in summer until the mid 1970s.

In September 1929 these produced an almost complete skeleton of a small reptile with extremely long cervical vertebrae. Vertebrae of this kind were already known from the Bayreuth Muschelkalk in northern Bavaria. In 1834 Georg Graf zu Münster had taken them to be limb bones, while in 1855 Hermann von Meyer in Frankfurt declared them to be the caudal vertebrae of a dinosaur, which he named *Tanystropheus* (=long vertebra).

1 Deffner, C. and Fraas, O., 1859. *Die Juraversenkung bei Langenbrücken*. Neues Jahrbuch für Mineralogie und Geologie: 1-38; Stuttgart. Flight digit phalanges from the Rhaet Bonebed are mentioned
Dawkins, W.B., 1864. *On the Rhaetic Beds and White Lias of Western and Central Somerset*. Quarterly Journal of the Geological Society, 20: 396-412; London. Dawkins discovered 'a crushed and hollow bone' in the Rhaetic (=Upper Triassic) of Somerset, England, and tentatively took it and two other bone fragments to be 'pterosaurian'.

2 Fraser, N.C. and Unwin, D.M., 1990. *Pterosaur remains from the Upper Triassic of Britain*. Neues Jahrbuch für Geologie und Paläontologie, Monatshefte, 1990 (5): 272-282; Stuttgart.

3 Cope, E.D., 1869. *Synopsis of the extinct Batrachia, Reptilia and Aves of North America*. Transactions of the American Philosophical Society Philadelphia, 14: 169-175; Philadelphia.

4 Huene, F.v., 1921. *Reptilian and Stegocephalian Remains from the Triassic of Pennsylvania in the Cope Collection*. Bulletin of the American Museum of Natural History, 44: 19, 561-574; New York.

5 Colbert, E.H., 1966. *A Gliding Reptile from the Triassic of New Jersey*. American Museum Novitates, 2246: 1-23; New York.

6 Bassani, F., 1886. *Sui fossili e sull'età degli schisti bituminosi triasici di Besano in Lombardia*. Atti Società Italiana Scienzi Naturali, 29: 15-72; Milan.

7 Nopcsa, F., 1922. *Neubeschreibung des Trias-Pterosauriers Tribelesodon*. Paläontologische Zeitschrift, 5: 161-181; Berlin.
Nopsca is a colourful figure with an interesting history. He worked as a spy for the Austro-Hungarian Empire in the First World War. After that he directed the Hungarian Geological Survey in Budapest for three years. In 1913, at the end of the Balkan War, he tried to become King of Albania. To this end he asked Vienna for 500 soldiers, artillery and two fast steamers, in order to invade Albania and have himself proclaimed king. At the end of the First World War, Baron Nopcsa lost the greater part of his estates, and sometimes it seemed likely that he would lose his reason as well. He used the last of his money for an extended motorcycle tour of Europe with his secretary, who was also said to have been his homosexual lover. He shot him, and then himself, in 1933.

Emil Kuhn-Schnyder, a successor of Bernhard Peyer in Zürich, was present as his assistant at the time, and described those dramatic September days like this: 'As a stratum of slate about a centimetre thick was being split the small skull of a reptile and the long topmost cervical vertebra attached to it appeared. After searching for hours we succeeded in finding two pieces of shale which were the precise continuation of the first. They contained the rest of the skeleton, right down to the end of the tail . . . Thus we had a successful find that increased our knowledge of *Tanystropheus* decisively . . . A few days later Peyer travelled to Milan to study the collection of Triassic fossils in the Museo Civico di Storia Naturale there. He came back from Italy beaming, and I suspected at once what he had discovered: he established that *Tribelesodon* was not a pterosaur, but a small *Tanystropheus*, in poor condition. He was later able to prove this beyond doubt by a thorough examination.[8]

The Monte San Giorgio find solved two riddles at a stroke. Firstly, that the long *Tanystropheus* vertebrae were cervical vertebrae of a reptile with an extremely long neck. For this reason it is also known as 'giraffe-necked saurian'. Secondly it was clear immediately that the series of long bones that Bassani and Nopcsa had interpreted as long flight digit phalanges in *Tribelesodon* were nothing more than cervical vertebrae of *Tanystropheus*, the giraffe-necked saurian, a partially aquatic creature of the eosuchian group. It is a sign of Baron Nopcsa's stature as a human being and a scientist that he later acknowledged his error. He wrote in a letter to Bernhard Peyer in 1931: 'It is crystal clear that I made a mistake.'

So, the Triassic 'pterosaur' *Tribelesodon* stood discredited. Were the finds made in England a hundred years earlier, in 1829, by Mary Anning in the Jurassic cliffs of the Dorset coast in southern England to remain the oldest pterosaurs known to man? *Dimorphodon* from the Early Lias in Lyme Regis, Dorset, was already a perfectly developed pterosaur, which suggested that it must have had more primitive ancestors, even in the Triassic Period. So there must have been Triassic pterosaurs. But there had been no unquestionable fossil finds. Palaeontologists had to wait until 1973.

**Nopcsa's Tribelesodon (right)**
This drawing shows how Franz Nopcsa reconstructed the skeleton of *'Tribelesodon'* as a long-tailed pterosaur on the basis of the fossil remains from Besano. Note the long bones which Nopcsa took to be elongated phalanges of the wing fingers.

## Eudimorphodon, the Oldest Pterosaur

In 1973 Mario Pandolfi of the Natural History Museum in Bergamo in northern Italy made a sensational find. He had unearthed an almost complete pterosaur skeleton in the course of palaeontological investigations on the western slopes of Monte Bò near the village of Cene in Val Seriana, in the Alpine foothills near Bergamo. He discovered it in a thin shale stratum from the rubble of a landslide in the former quarry of the village. The rock is one of the so-called Zorzino limestones, the geological age of which can be given as Upper Triassic (more precisely Middle to Upper Norian). These strata also correspond to the 'Hauptdolomit' of the southern Alps, with an absolute age of about 220 million years.

8 Kuhn-Schnyder, E., 1968. *Alles Lebendige meinet den Menschen*. Schweizer Spiegel, 12; Zürich
Kuhn-Schnyder, E., 1974. *Die Triasfauna der Tessiner Kalkalpen*. Neujahrsblatt der Naturforschenden Gesellschaft Zürich, 1974: 119 p., Zürich.

**The Giraffe-Necked Saurian (below)**
This skeletal restoration is of *Tanystropheus longobardicus*. Well preserved specimens of these long-necked eosuchian reptiles were discovered in Middle Triassic bituminous shale at Monte San Giorgio in Ticino, Switzerland. Its total length is about 10ft (3m). The supposed long bones of the wing finger of *'Tribelesodon'* turned out to be the elongated neck vertebrae of a small *Tanystropheus*.

**Above:** *Eudimorphodon ranzii* from the Upper Triassic limestone of Cene near Bergamo, northern Italy. It lived about 220 million years ago, and is thus one of the oldest known pterosaurs. The wing fingers and most of the hind legs are missing.

**Left:** *'Tribelesodon' longobardicus*, a small reptile from the Middle Triassic of Besano in northern Italy. Originally the long bones on the split slab were taken by Franz Baron Nopcsa as the phalanges of the wing finger of a pterosaur. Only later was the fossil recognized by Bernhard Peyer as the long-necked eosuchian reptile *Tanystropheus*, the long bones actually being extremely elongated neck vertebrae rather than pterosaurian wing bones.

This meant that the oldest pterosaur now really had been found, the first that could be conclusively proved to date from the Triassic. Rocco Zambelli, the curator responsible in the Bergamo museum, called it *Eudimorphodon* (=true two-form tooth), following the next oldest *Dimorphodon* from the English early Jurassic. It was a pterosaur with a wing span of about 3·3ft (1m).[9]

It was expected that the oldest pterosaurs would have particularly primitive characteristics. It now emerged that this was only partially true. Original characters were the long vertebral tail and a short metacarpal, as was also typical of long-tailed Jurassic pterosaurs. The general structure of *Eudimorphodon*'s skeleton is entirely characteristic of this group,

9 Zambelli, R., 1973. *Eudimorphodon ranzii gen.nov., sp.nov., uno pterosauro triassico*. Rendiconti Scienc. Istituto Lombardo, B, 107: 27-32; Milan.

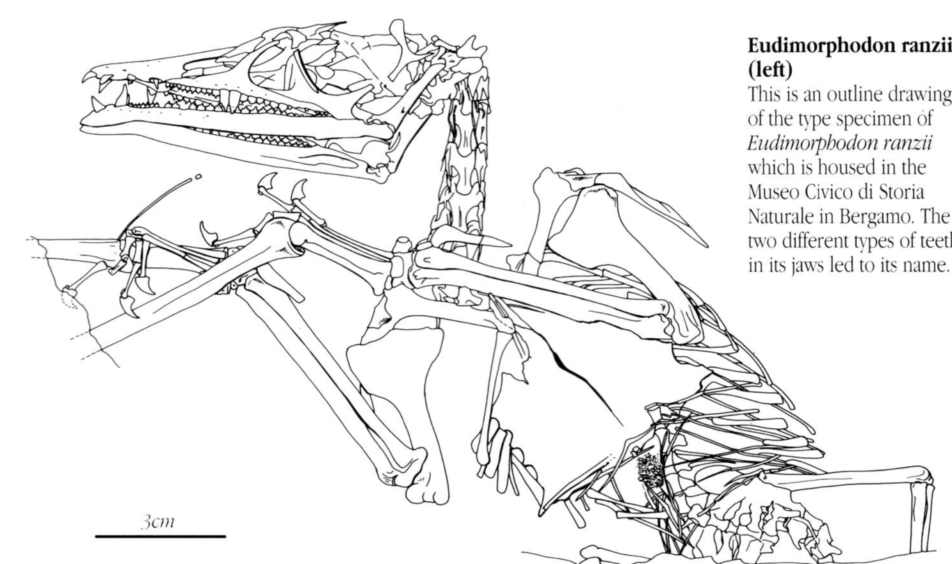


**Eudimorphodon ranzii (left)**
This is an outline drawing of the type specimen of *Eudimorphodon ranzii* which is housed in the Museo Civico di Storia Naturale in Bergamo. The two different types of teeth in its jaws led to its name.

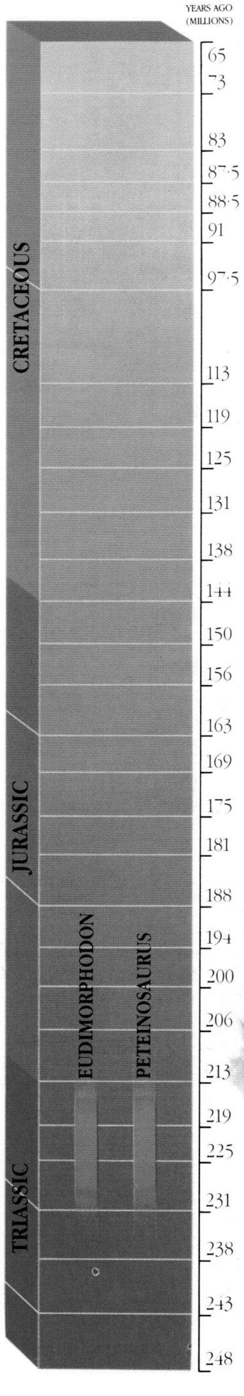

YEARS AGO (MILLIONS)

65, 73, 83, 87·5, 88·5, 91, 97·5, 113, 119, 125, 131, 138, 144, 150, 156, 163, 169, 175, 181, 188, 194, 200, 206, 213, 219, 225, 231, 238, 243, 248

CRETACEOUS

JURASSIC

TRIASSIC

EUDIMORPHODON

PETEINOSAURUS

**Time Chart (left)**
The first pterosaurs appear in the fossil record in the Upper Triassic in marine limestone of Norian age. *Eudimorphodon* and *Peteinosaurus* already represent two distinct evolutionary lines, indicating that pterosaurs originated much earlier, perhaps in early Triassic or even late Permian times.

1
2
1

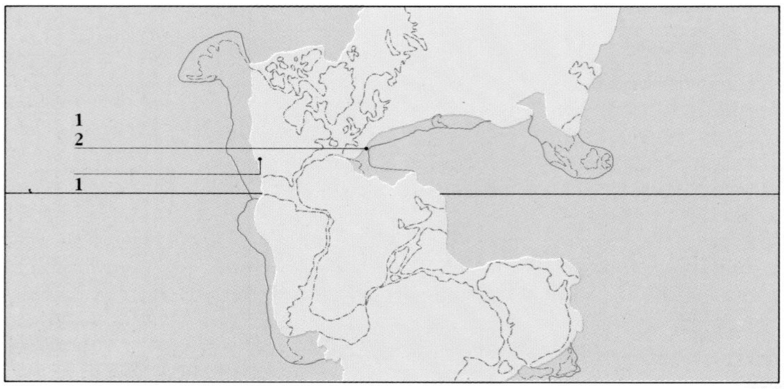

**Map (left)**
**1** *Eudimorphodon*
**2** *Peteinosaurus*

**Peteinosaurus (right)**
This long-tailed pterosaur, which lived on the shore of the late Triassic Tethys sea, was smaller than its contemporary *Eudimorphodon*. Its dentition consists of larger anterior fangs followed by a long series of small, pointed teeth which suggest that *Peteinosaurus* was insectivorous, perhaps catching insects on the wing. In the background we see the thecodont archosaur *Ticinosuchus*.

the Rhamphorhynchoidea, although the teeth are unique among pterosaurs.

The dentition does not consist, as is usual, of a row of teeth with a single cusp, but is divided into a few large front fangs and behind them a tight sequence of small teeth with three and five cusps. In the upper jaw there are two more large teeth with small additional cusps between the series with three and five cusps. In the upper jaw the dentition consists of 58 teeth, and in the lower jaw 56, thus a total of 114 teeth, and that in a jaw only 2·4in (6cm) long.

Dentition of this kind indicates a fish-catcher. Like other pterosaurs as well, *Eudimorphodon* must have lived by catching fish. And indeed hard scales of small ganoid fish, of the kind that frequently occur as fossils in Cene Triassic limestones were found in the region of this individual's stomach. On closer examination the Stuttgart museum curator Rupert Wild, an expert on Triassic reptiles, discovered wear facets in the teeth, which he attributed to

**Eudimorphodon (below)**
This Triassic pterosaur is one of the earliest known. Although it was a fully developed rhamphorhynchoid pterosaur with the characteristic long tail, it had unusual, unique dentition consisting of a series of teeth with single, three and five cusps. Such dentition would seem to belong to a fish eater, and indeed fossilized stomach contents have shown that *Eudimorphodon* preyed on small fishes such as *Parapholidophorus*, as shown here. Juvenile individuals had a different dentition and probably caught and ate insects such as the dragonfly seen at top right.

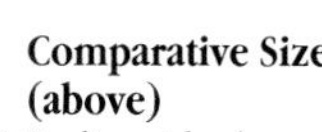


**Comparative Sizes (above)**
**1** *Eudimorphodon:* wing span 3·3ft (1m)
**2** *Peteinosaurus:* wing span 2ft (60cm)

**Left:** A close-up photograph of the skull of the type specimen of *Eudimorphodon ranzii*. The length of this skull is 3·4in (8·6cm). Rocco Zambelli, the curator of the Bergamo museum where the specimen is housed, named it *Eudimorphodon* which is Greek for 'true two-form tooth'.

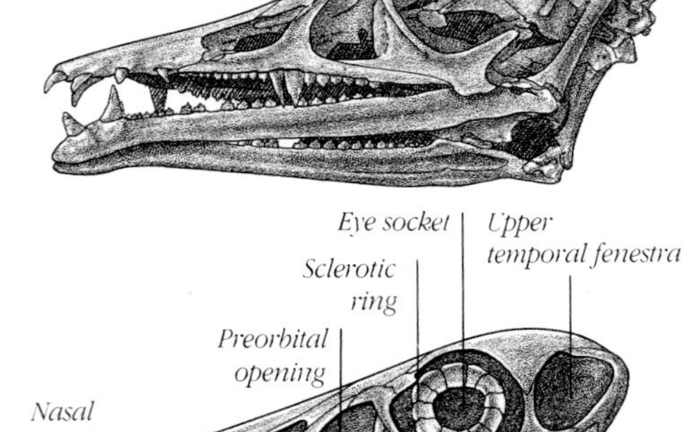


**Eudimorphodon Skulls (right)**
These drawings reveal the skull of *Eudimorphodon* as it was preserved (top), and as it was restored by Rupert Wild (below).

this pterosaur's fish diet. This is understandable, as the thick protective scales of these fish had to be crushed when the prey were caught.

The differentiated nature of the dentition and the fact that the teeth had more than one cusp are not primitive reptilian characters, but a specialization. The fact that no Jurassic pterosaur had multi-cusped teeth means that *Eudimorphodon* cannot be their direct ancestor, but represents a distinct line in the pterosaur family tree that became extinct in the Triassic.

## Peteinosaurus

In subsequent intensive investigations five more sets of pterosaur skeletal remains were found in the Triassic limestone of Cene, and they were thorougly examined by Rupert Wild in 1978.[10] As well as *Eudimorphodon* he identified another genus, a smaller one, which he called *Peteinosaurus* (=winged reptile), from the Greek words *peteinos* (=winged) and *sauros* (=reptile). This genus turned out to be more primitive than *Eudimorphodon* in many ways. In particular *Peteinosaurus* had only single-cusped teeth, which were flattened, with sharp cutting edges at the front and back. At the front of the lower jaw were two large teeth. The upper skull remains unknown. Rupert Wild believes that *Peteinosaurus* was insectivorous. In any case this is the most primitive of the known pterosaurs. Its wings were still relatively short, only twice as long as the hind legs. In all other pterosaurs the wings were at least three times as long, or longer.

Besides the type specimen of *Peteinosaurus* only one other specimen is known. Both are housed in the Bergamo Natural History Museum. This second skeleton is also lacking the skull and neck completely, but a section of the dorsal vertebral column, of the stiff tail typically reinforced by rod-like bony extensions, and the bones of the wings, the hind legs and the feet are preserved. The skeleton is still in articulation but was washed together by currents before it was embedded. Both individuals of *Peteinosaurus* originate from the Zorzino limestone (Norian) of Cene, and are about the same size

*Peteinosaurus* has a wing span of only 24in (60cm) and can best be considered as a direct ancestor of the oldest Jurassic pterosaur *Dimorphodon*. Both can be placed within the

10 Wild, R., 1978. *Die Flugsaurier (Reptilia, Pterosauria) aus der Oberen Trias von Cene bei Bergamo, Italien*. Bolletino Società Paleontologica Italiana, 17 (2): 176-256; Modena.

**Eudimorphodon Life Restoration (left)**
The drawing is a portrait illustrating how *Eudimorphodon* may have looked in real life. It is based on the type specimen which is pictured above left and on page 239.

**Eudimorphodon Jaw (left)**
The lower jaw of *Eudimorphodon ranzii* is seen from the outer side (above) and from the inner side (below). The peculiar dentition consists of large fangs at the front, and small three-cusped and five-cusped teeth along the posterior section of the mandible.

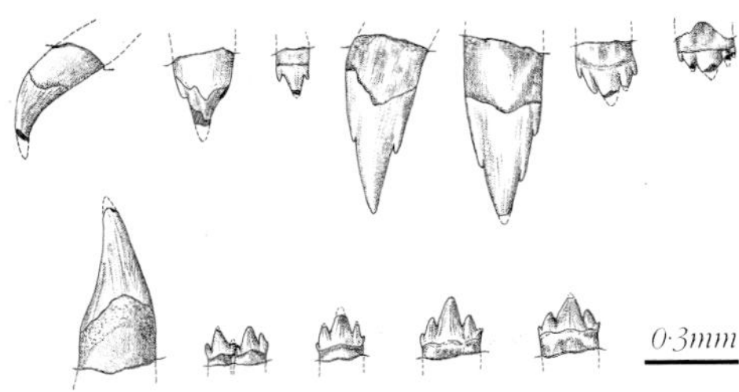


**Eudimorphodon's Teeth (right)**
In the upper drawing we see some typical teeth from the upper jaw (premaxilla and maxilla); in the drawing below are teeth of the lower jaw (mandible). The tips of the crowns are slightly worn from a diet of hard-scaled fish.

**Below:** The photograph shows in close-up detail the claws of the small fingers of *Eudimorphodon*. They are quite evidently robust and strong. They were probably used for climbing and for hanging on to tree trunks and steep cliff faces.

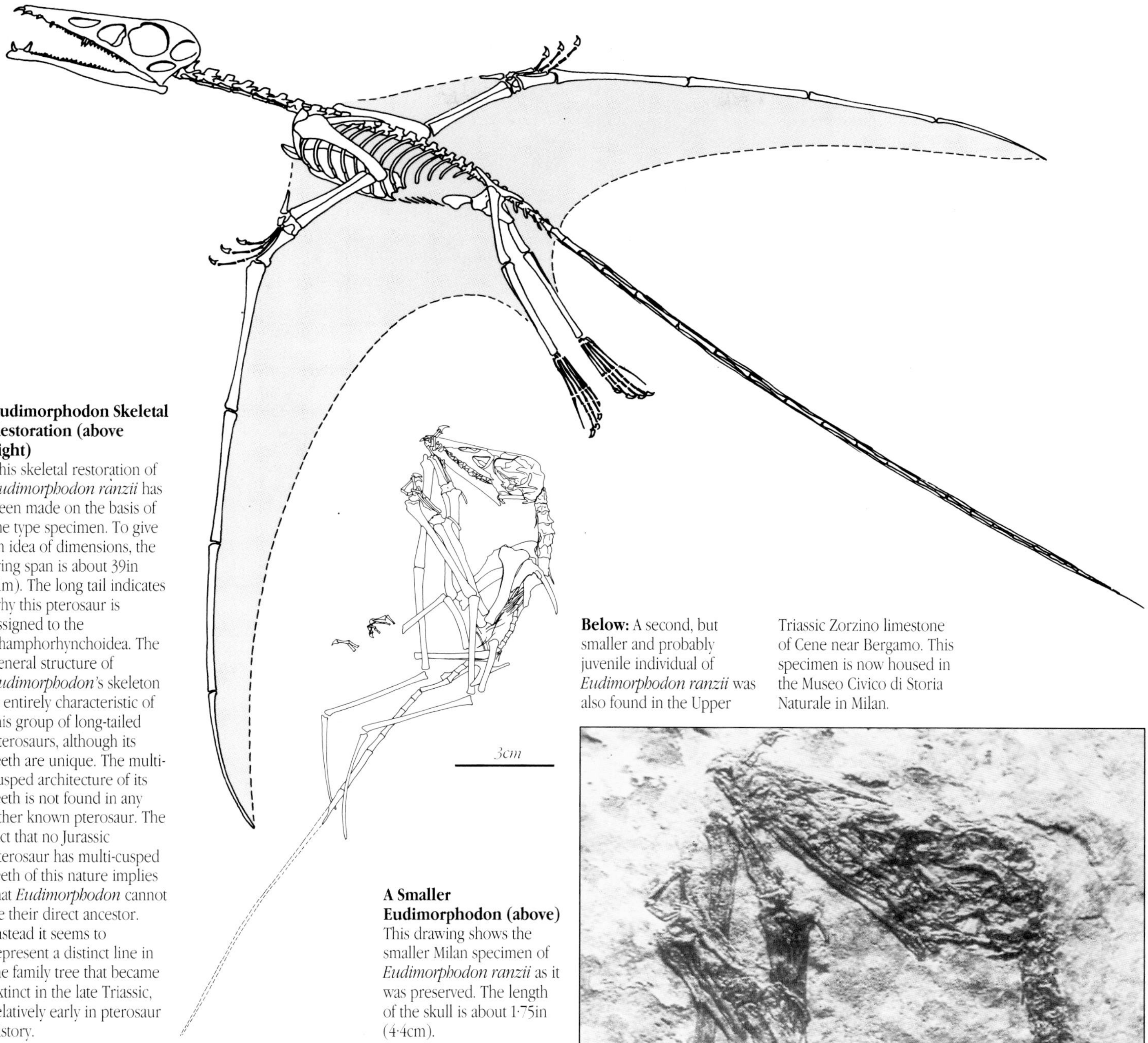

**Eudimorphodon Skeletal Restoration (above right)**
This skeletal restoration of *Eudimorphodon ranzii* has been made on the basis of the type specimen. To give an idea of dimensions, the wing span is about 39in (1m). The long tail indicates why this pterosaur is assigned to the Rhamphorhynchoidea. The general structure of *Eudimorphodon*'s skeleton is entirely characteristic of this group of long-tailed pterosaurs, although its teeth are unique. The multi-cusped architecture of its teeth is not found in any other known pterosaur. The fact that no Jurassic pterosaur has multi-cusped teeth of this nature implies that *Eudimorphodon* cannot be their direct ancestor. Instead it seems to represent a distinct line in the family tree that became extinct in the late Triassic, relatively early in pterosaur history.

**A Smaller Eudimorphodon (above)**
This drawing shows the smaller Milan specimen of *Eudimorphodon ranzii* as it was preserved. The length of the skull is about 1·75in (4·4cm).

**Below:** A second, but smaller and probably juvenile individual of *Eudimorphodon ranzii* was also found in the Upper Triassic Zorzino limestone of Cene near Bergamo. This specimen is now housed in the Museo Civico di Storia Naturale in Milan.

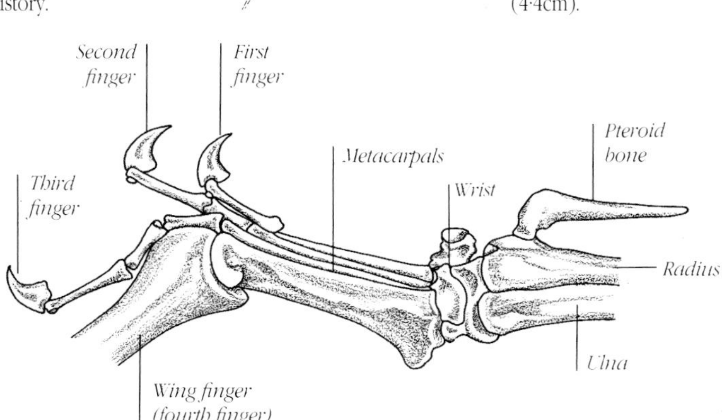


**Eudimorphodon's Wrist and Fingers (above)**
The wrist, the metacarpals, and the three small fingers (numbers one to three) of *Eudimorphodon* are seen here as preserved in the type specimen. The fourth finger, the wing finger, articulates with the wing metacarpal by means of a distinctive pulley-type joint on its distal end. It was this joint that enabled *Eudimorphodon* to fold its wing back. It is set at a slight angle which caused a twisting movement when the wing was folded, so positioning the flight digit against the body in such a way that the upper side of the wing faced outwards. Two of the claws are also to be seen in the photograph (bottom right of facing page).

family Dimorphodontidae, while *Eudimorphodon* is so far the only representative of an independent family, the Eudimorphodontidae.

### Preondactylus

Subsequently a third form of Triassic pterosaur came to light. In 1978 a fossil collector working in the Zorzino limestone of Endenna, only 6 miles (10km) from Cene, discovered three connected digital phalanges of a pterosaur wing, which Kevin Padian, a palaeontologist at the University of Berkeley, California traced back to a pterosaur with a wing span of about 4·9ft (1·5m).[11]

11 Padian, K., 1981. *Note of a new specimen of pterosaurs (Reptilia: Pterosauria) from the Norian (Upper Triassic) of Endenna, Italy*. Rivista Museo Civico Scienze Naturale 'E. Caffi', 2 (1980): 119-127; Bergamo.

**Time Chart (left)**
*Preondactylus* is the third genus of Triassic pterosaur known to date. It is of late Triassic (Norian) age and represents a family, the rhamphorhynchids, otherwise known only from Jurassic strata.

**Map (below)**
**1** *Preondactylus*

And in 1982 a collector in Udine in northern Italy found another pterosaur skeleton in bituminous, dolomitic limestone of the Upper Triassic (Early to Middle Norian) in the Preone valley in the Alps of the Veneto. Nando Buffarini, the finder, had a stroke of bad luck which is the nightmare of every fossil hunter. The slab of rock containing the valuable fossil shattered into several pieces as it was being extracted. The black bones were embedded in a marl stratum only fractions of an inch thick. When Signore Buffarini and his wife fitted the fragments of the slab of rock together again and washed them with water, the layer of marl was washed away with the bones, and lost. All that remained was the negative print of the skeleton on the surface of the rock. A cast of this negative relief was made with silicon rubber, and only then was the image of this pterosaur skeleton revealed in three dimensions, and in a form that allowed it to be studied.

Once more the investigation was conducted by Rupert Wild of the Museum für Naturkunde in Stuttgart.[12] His analysis enabled him to show that this was a specimen of an additional pterosaur family, hitherto known only in the Jurassic, the Rhamphorhynchidae. Rupert Wild gave the new genus from the Preone valley the name *Preondactylus* (=Preone finger) and established related characteristics with the Liassic pterosaur *Dorygnathus* (=spear-jaw). It is very probable that the three flight digit phalanges from Endenna described by Kevin Padian also belong to the genus *Preondactylus*. The dentition is differently developed from that of *Dorygnathus* from the Lias, consisting of single-cusped teeth. Skeletal proportions are also similar in the two genera. In 1984 one more pterosaur was discovered in the Preone valley of the Veneto Alps in northern Italy. This specimen too came from Upper Triassic dolomitic limestone like *Preondactylus*, but from a level that lay about 500-650ft (150-200m) deeper in the sequence of strata. Thus this fossil find can be dated as the oldest pterosaur yet known in geological history. The fossil consists of an accumulation of disarticulated skeletal bones, which are so tightly packed that they could be interpreted as the gastric pellet of a predatory fish.[13] This creature, probably

12 Wild, R., 1984. *A new pterosaur (Reptilia, Pterosauria) from the Upper Triassic (Norian) of Friuli, Italy*. Gortania, Atti Museo Friuliano di Storia Naturale, 5: 45-62; Udine.
Wild, R., 1984. *Flugsaurier aus der Obertrias von Italien*. Naturwissenschaften, 71: 1-11; Berlin, Heidelberg, New York (Springer).

13 Dalla Vecchia, F.M., Muscio, G. and Wild, R., 1989. *Pterosaur remains in a gastric pellet from the Upper Triassic (Norian) of Rio Seazza Valley (Udine, Italy)*. Gortania, Atti del Museo Friuliano di Storia Naturale, 10 (1988): 121-132; Udine.

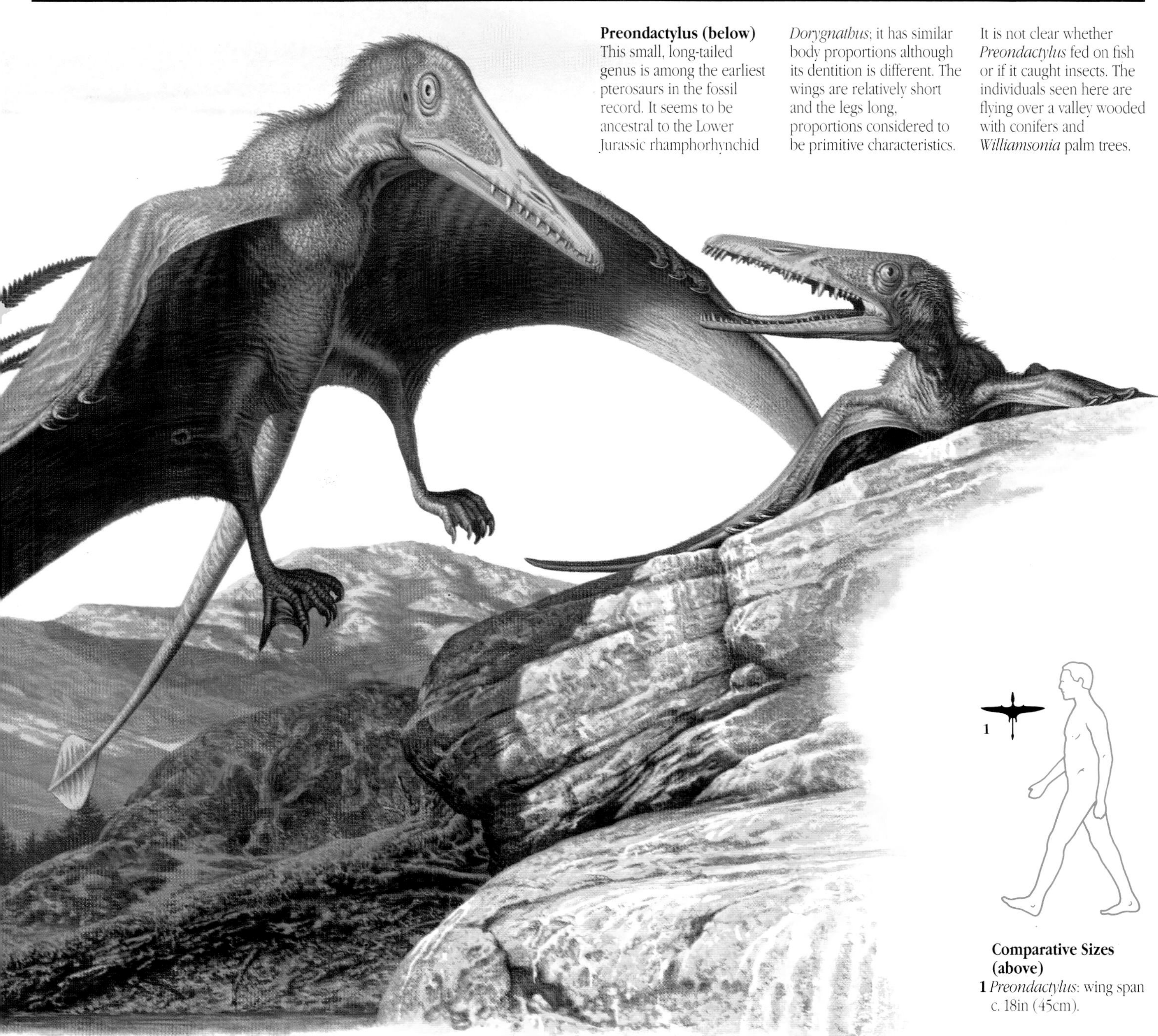


**Preondactylus (below)**
This small, long-tailed genus is among the earliest pterosaurs in the fossil record. It seems to be ancestral to the Lower Jurassic rhamphorhynchid *Dorygnathus*; it has similar body proportions although its dentition is different. The wings are relatively short and the legs long, proportions considered to be primitive characteristics. It is not clear whether *Preondactylus* fed on fish or if it caught insects. The individuals seen here are flying over a valley wooded with conifers and *Williamsonia* palm trees.

**Comparative Sizes (above)**
**1** *Preondactylus*: wing span c. 18in (45cm).

**Left:** The skeletal remains of a second specimen of *Peteinosaurus zambellii*. The skull was lost, perhaps when the carcass floated in the sea. The bones were washed together before fossilisation. The long tail, stiffened by rod-like bony fibres, shows up clearly.

3cm

**Peteinosaurus Skeleton (right)**
This drawing is of the second specimen which is also illustrated at left.

1cm

Tibia
Ankle
Metatarsal
Fifth metatarsal
1st
2nd
3rd
4th
5th toe

**Peteinosaurus' Feet (right)**
Seen here are the foot skeletons of *Peteinosaurus* as preserved in the second specimen (left) and as restored (right). The fifth toe is long, has no claw, and could be moved in a different plane from the other four toes. The function of this fifth toe is not clear. The specimens of *Peteinosaurus* are housed in the Museo Civico di Storia Naturale in Bergamo, northern Italy.

also a *Preondactylus*, fell prey to a predatory fish over 220 million years ago, and the fish then spewed up the indigestible remains of the skeleton. This gastric pellet sank to the bottom of the sea and was thus covered in ooze and fossilized.

Recently, reports of pterosaur remains from the late Triassic Dockum formation in West Texas suggest that the palaeogeographical distribution of Triassic pterosaurs was probably considerably more extended than hitherto assumed.[14] Although rather fragmentary, the teeth found in jaw fragments are multi-cusped and similar to *Eudimorphodon* from the Norian of Italy. If new finds confirm the pterosaurian nature of these remains, we may regard the pterosaurs as already well established and widespread in the Triassic.

Thus the oldest known pterosaurs occur in three distinct evolutionary lines: Eudimorphodontidae, Dimorphodontidae and Rhamphorhynchidae. Triassic pterosaurs are, as far as we know them, 'completely' developed and have all the typical skeletal characteristics of the order Pterosauria. They are not 'Propterosauria', or forerunners of the pterosaurs, and also not 'missing links' between pterosaurs and their ancestors. We must therefore accept that the evolutionary history of pterosaurs goes back much further into the past than was formerly believed. Perhaps they originated in the Lower Triassic, possibly even in the Permian, thus in the Palaeozoic Era. Certainly no fossils have so far been found that could be interpreted as ancestors of the pterosaurs or 'proto'-pterosaurs

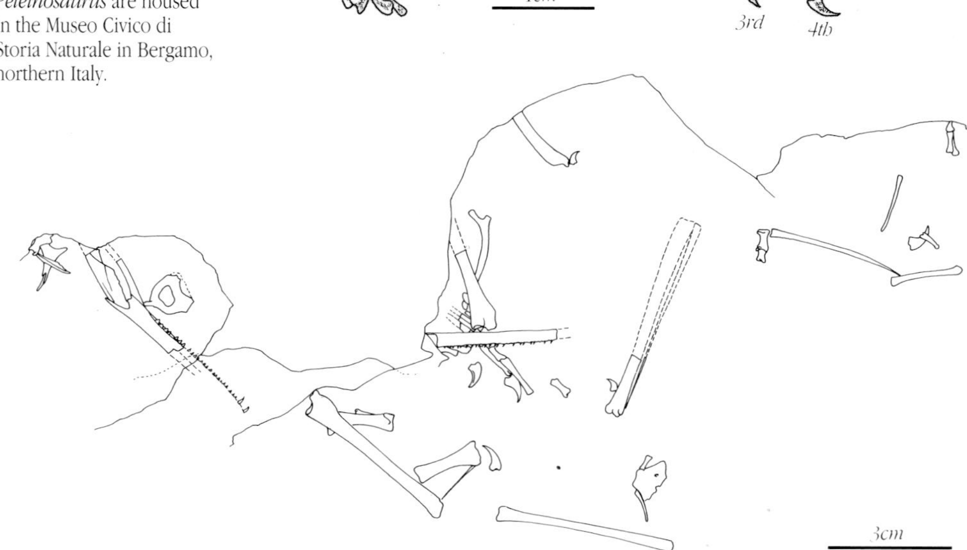


**Peteinosaurus zambellii (above)**
The drawing shows the type specimen of *Peteinosaurus zambellii* from the Upper Triassic Zorzino limestone of Cene near Bergamo. Only a few scattered bones are preserved including fragments of the lower jaw which can be seen in the upper left hand portion of the drawing. The two large teeth at the front of the lower jaw can be made out at centre left. The smaller teeth are single cusped, flattened, with sharp cutting edges at front and back. The upper skull is lost.

14 Murry, P.A., *Vertebrate paleontology of the Dockum Group, western Texas and eastern New Mexico.* The Beginning of the Age of Dinosaurs (K. Padian, ed.): 109-137; Cambridge University Press.

**Left:** The lower jaw of *Peteinosaurus* contains numerous small, single-cusped teeth. The jaw fragment is about 1·2in (3cm) long.

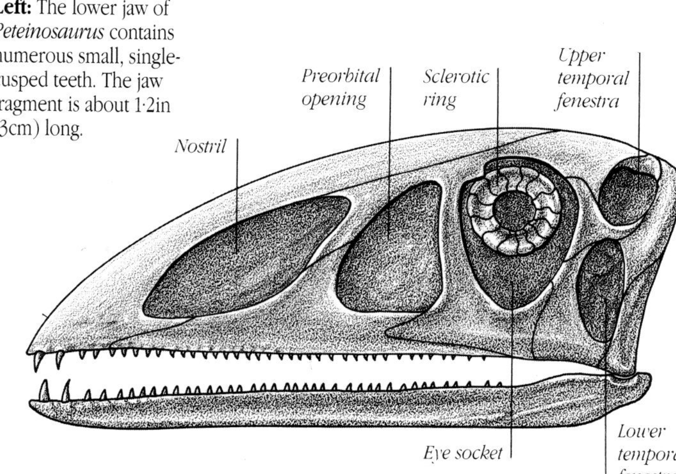


3cm

Sclerotic ring
Eye socket
Upper temporal fenestra
Preorbital opening
Nostril
Lower temporal fenestra

**Preondactylus (left)**
This is *Preondactylus buffarinii* from the Upper Triassic of the Preone valley near Udine. By misfortune only the impressions of the skeletal remains could be saved by the fossil collector, Nando Buffarini.

**Peteinosaurus Skull (above)**
This is a tentative restoration of the skull of *Peteinosaurus zambellii*. The shape of the skull is assumed to be similar to the Lower Jurassic genus *Dimorphodon*.

**Untimely End (below)**
This restoration shows a predatory fish, in this instance *Saurichthys*, about to consume an unwary *Preondactylus*. The indigestible bones of the pterosaur were vomited as a pellet by the predator.

**Preondactylus Skull (above)**
This is a tentative restoration of the skull of *Preondactylus buffarinii*. The posterior section of the skull was not preserved and is assumed here to have been similar to the Jurassic *Dorygnathus*.

**Gastric Pellet (below)**
This accumulation of bones has been interpreted as a gastric pellet spewed up by a predatory fish. The pigeon-sized pterosaur, *Preondactylus buffarinii*, may have been caught when it was itself fishing, or after it had drowned.

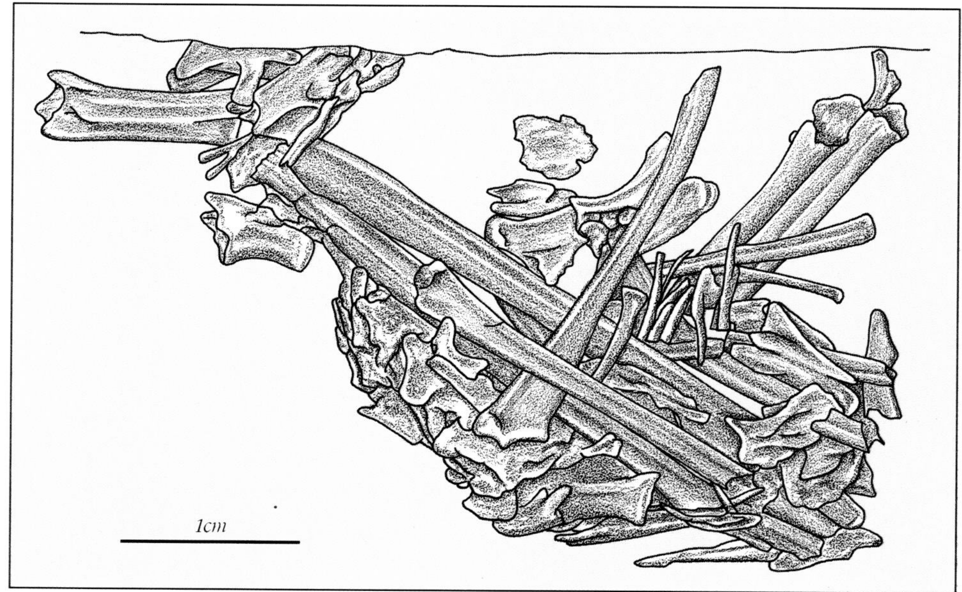


**SUMMARY OF TRIASSIC PTEROSAURS**

**Rhamphorhynchoidea**

Family Dimorphodontidae

*Peteinosaurus zambellii*

Upper Triassic, Middle to Upper Norian, Calcare di Zorzino, Cene near Bergamo, Italy.[10]

Family Eudimorphodontidae

*Eudimorphodon ranzii*

Upper Triassic, Middle to Upper Norian, Calcare di Zorzino, Cene near Bergamo, Italy.[10]

*Eudimorphodon*? sp.

Upper Triassic, Dockum Group, West Texas, USA.

In 1986, fragments of a lower jaw with two five-cusped teeth and of an upper jaw with multi-cusped teeth were reported from the Dockum Formation in West Texas.[14] The assignment of these jaw fragments must remain uncertain until more complete material is found

Family Rhamphorhynchidae

*Preondactylus buffarinii*

Upper Triassic, Early to Middle Norian, Dolomia di Forni, Madonna Peraries, Preone valley, province of Udine, Italy.[12]

?*Preondactylus* sp.

Upper Triassic, Middle to Upper Norian, Calcare di Zorzino, Endenna near Bergamo, Italy.[11,12]

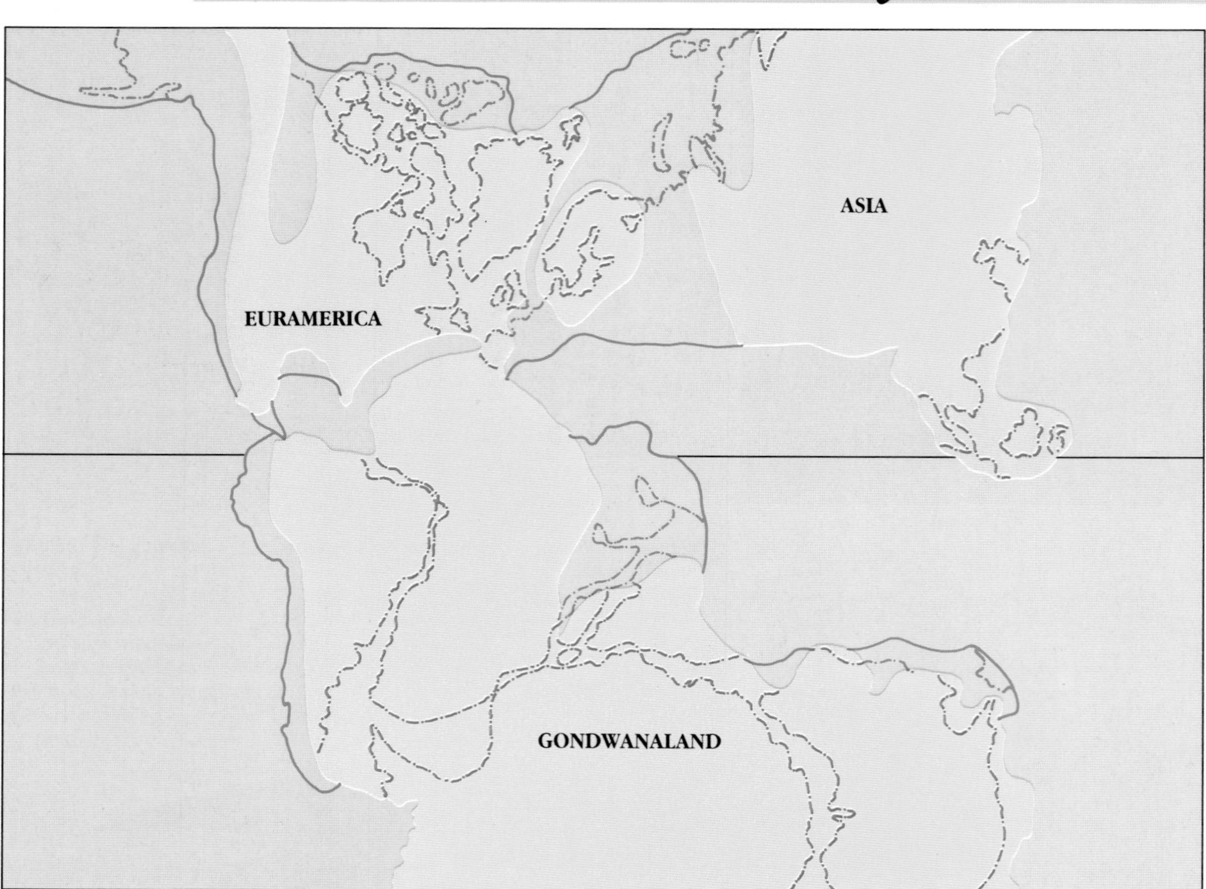


**Palaeogeographic Map of the Jurassic Period (left)** During the Triassic Period all the continents had been joined together to form the supercontinent of Pangaea. This began to split in the Jurassic Period as the sea flooded in and the Atlantic Ocean began to form. A sea also separated Europe from Asia. Despite this, as the map shows large land masses still existed in the form of Euramerica and Gondwanaland, which contained today's South America, Africa, India, Australia and the Antarctic. In the Jurassic Period fossil evidence shows that pterosaurs were distributed worldwide, and it is probable that they spread out from Europe where the oldest Triassic pterosaurs currently known have been found.

**Below:** A drawing (after Owen) of the skull of *Dimorphodon macronyx* as preserved from the Lower Lias of Lyme Regis, Dorset. The length of this skull is 8·5in (21·5cm).

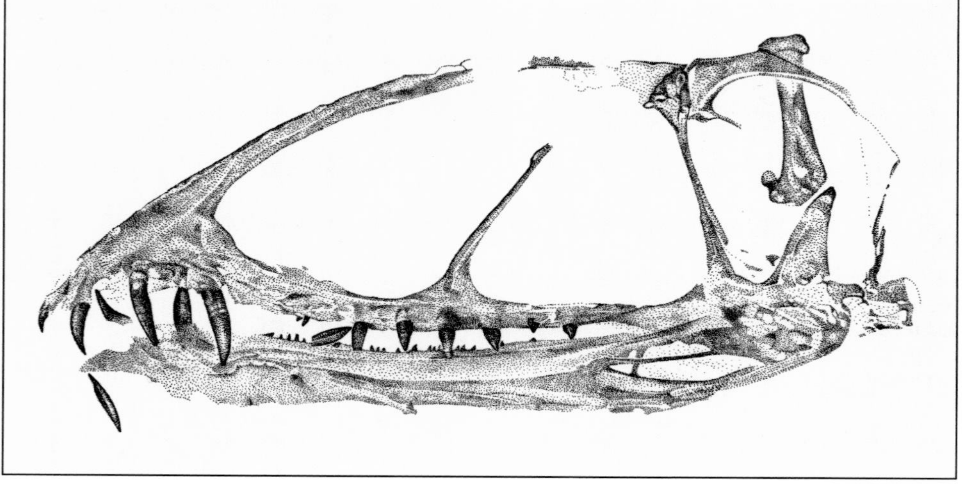

The middle division of the Mesozoic era is the Jurassic period, originally named after the Jura mountains in Switzerland. It followed the Triassic period and began about 213 million years ago. It ended 144 million years ago, and so lasted about 69 million years, or twice as long as the Triassic period.

The Jurassic is generally subdivided into Lias (Lower Jurassic), Dogger (Middle Jurassic) and Malm (Upper Jurassic). A major feature of the Jurassic period was extensive flooding of continents by the sea. For this reason finds of organisms that lived on land are particularly to be anticipated in near shore marine deposits. This is especially true of pterosaurs. The Atlantic Ocean began to open up in the Middle Jurassic. Despite this the map of the Earth still contained large, connected land masses, in the form of the supercontinents Euramerica and Gondwanaland, containing the modern continents of South America, Africa, India, Australia and the Antarctic. Asia was separated from Europe by a great seaway. The climate began to be differentiated in the course of the Jurassic. There was a wide tropical belt and only slightly cooler polar regions, but in comparison with today the Earth's climate was still warm and balanced. There were no polar ice caps as yet, and no distinct seasons.

So far Triassic pterosaurs have only been proved to exist in Europe, while it is probable that they already existed in North America. In the Jurassic, however, pterosaurs were distributed world-wide, and conditions were favourable for fossilization in numerous Jurassic 'fossil deposits' like Solnhofen in Bavaria, for example, or Holzmaden in Württemberg (southern Germany). We are familiar with pterosaur fossil finds from Jurassic deposits in Europe, Africa, Asia, North America, Central America and South America. The Lower Jurassic period saw pterosaurs spread all over the world, probably emanating from Europe, and also the development of various forms of pterosaur. Palaeontologists call this evolutionary process adaptive radiation: development in the course of the phylogeny showing adaptation to different life and environmental conditions.

In fact the first pterosaur finds came from Jurassic Solnhofen lithographic limestone: as we saw in Chapter 2, Cosimo Alessandro Collini described a fossil find from these strata as early as 1784.[1] However, the Solnhofen pterosaurs lived near the end of the Jurassic, about 150 million years ago. *Pterodactylus* appeared here as the first short-tailed pterosaur in the fossil record, while the last long-tailed pterosaurs on Earth existed at the same time in the same strata.

## Pterosaurs of the Lias

The oldest Jurassic pterosaurs were discovered in the Lower Lias, in England. To the east of the little town of Lyme Regis in Dorset on the south coast of England are the Church Cliffs, a massive series of blue-grey limestone alternating with shale. English geologists call these marine strata, which are about 85ft (26m) thick, 'Blue Lias Limestone'. They also extend west of the town beyond Pinhay Bay, forming enormous cliffs.[2] W.J. Arkell describes it like this, 'Almost the entire succession of the Lower Lias in its typical development across England from the Dorset coast consists of clays and shales, in the lower part of which numerous bands of calcareous mudstone or clay-limestone have been formed by secondary chemi-

1 Collini, C.A., 1784. *Sur quelques Zoolithes du Cabinet d'Histoire naturelle de S.A.S.E. Palatine et de Bavière à Mannheim.* Acta Academiae Theodoro-Palatinae Mannheim, 5, pars physica: 58-103.

2 Arkell, W.J., 1933. *The Jurassic System in Great Britain.* Clarendon Press, Oxford.

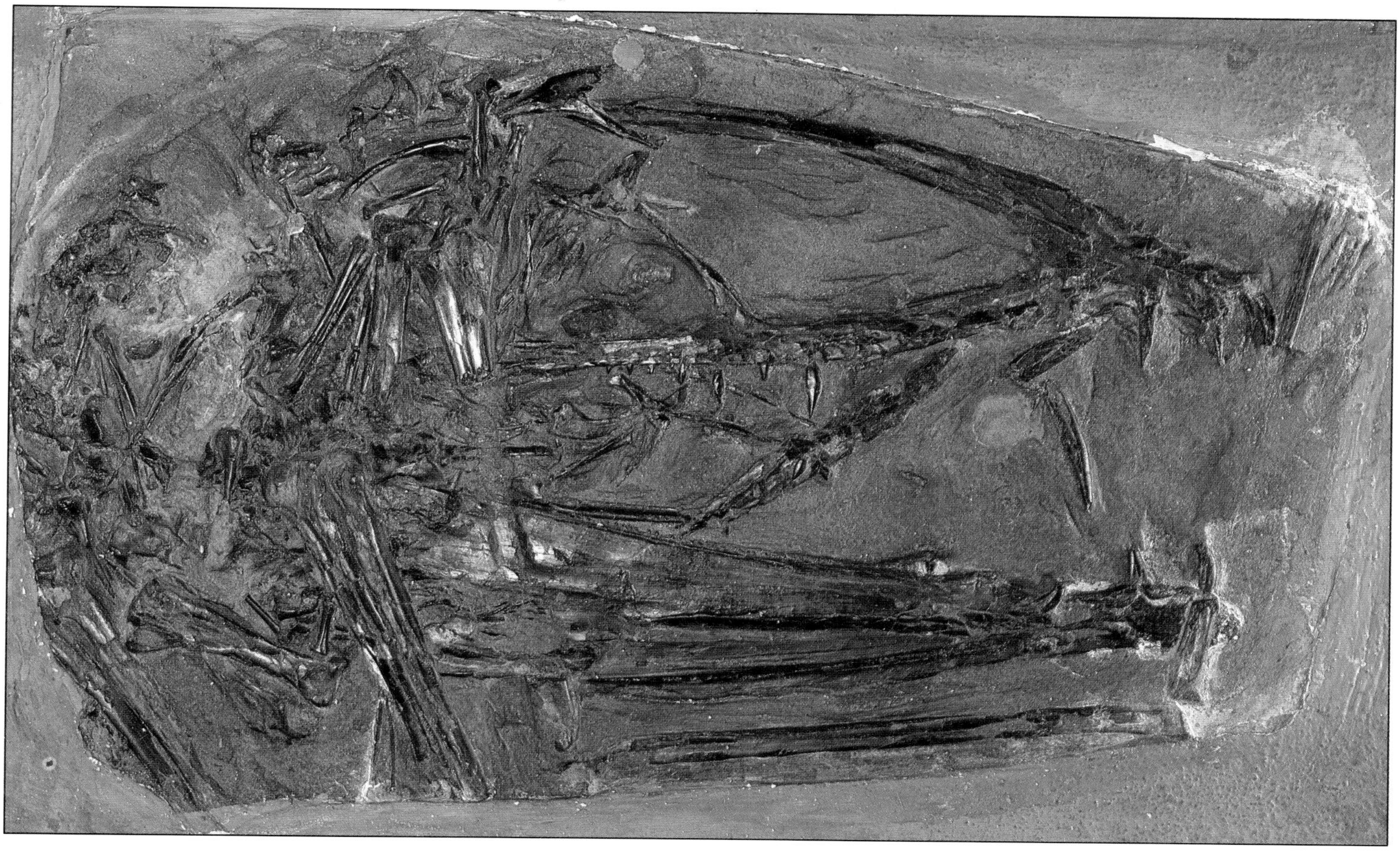

**Above:** *Dimorphodon macronyx*, a second specimen from Lyme Regis with the skull and lower jaw preserved. This specimen, which is now in the Natural History Museum in London, shows the large nasal and preorbital openings separated by thin bony struts which were a weight saving feature. The lower jaw is filled with a series of numerous tiny teeth, while the upper jaw contains larger teeth. The dual nature of the dentition in this genus gives rise to its name, *Dimorphodon* ('two form tooth').

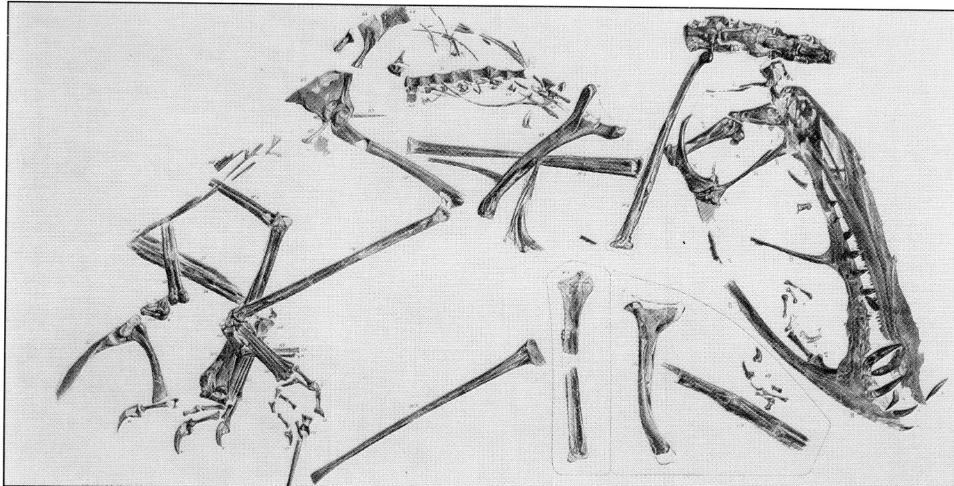

**Right:** These are the skeletal remains of *Dimorphodon macronyx* which Richard Owen received in 1858, as pictured in Owen's monograph of 1870. Again they are from the Lower Lias of Lyme Regis. Unlike previous finds, such as that acquired by William Buckland from Mary Anning, for the first time this skeleton had its skull preserved. It was so different from the late Jurassic *Pterodactylus* that Owen did not hesitate to establish a distinct genus for the Lyme Regis pterosaur.

cal processes ... The most conspicuous remains are the skeletons of great marine reptiles. The presence of these, and also of fossil insects, points to deposition, not in deep water as frequently deduced from the clayey sediment, but in a comparatively shallow continental sea. The rivers flowing into the Liassic sea had reached maturity, for instead of bringing down detrital material from the surrounding land, they carried only fine mud. Mixed with the sand in suspension came a high proportion of iron, which, in the form of minutely disseminated pyrites, gave the usual dark grey to black colour to the Lias shales.' (p.120).

The first professional fossil collector, Mary Anning, worked intensively and successfully as a collector here in the first half of the nineteenth century.[3] Her most famous finds were skeletons of great marine reptiles, ichthyosaurs and plesiosaurs, then in 1828 came the first pterosaur of the Lias, acquired by William Buckland, an Oxford professor, who described it in 1829 as *Pterodactylus macronyx*.[4] The name refers to the great claws on the small digits of the hand. At first, however, the skull of this pterosaur was not known. It was not until 1858 that Richard Owen of the British Museum in London received more pterosaur material from the Lias of Lyme Regis, including remains of skeletons with skulls, belonging to the same species. Owen immediately established that the skull of the genus *Pterodactylus*, formerly known only from the Upper Jurassic of Solnhofen, was very different. He therefore called the Lyme Regis pterosaur *Dimorphodon* (=two-form tooth), a reference to the two kinds of teeth in the dentition of this genus.[5] As well as the very rare pterosaurs – so far only the species *Dimorphodon macronyx* is known – there are numerous fish and many ammonites in the Lyme Regis Blue Lias, organisms that show these strata to be former marine deposits. Geologists place them in the Sinemurian age, on the basis of the internationally valid time scale (a diagram explaining this time scale can be found on page 96). They have an absolute age of about 205 to 200 million years.

---

3. Mary Anning (1799-1847) from Lyme Regis earned her living by selling fossils she collected from Blue Lias strata on the coast near her home town. She found the first skeletons of ichthyosaurs and plesiosaurs in England. In 1828 she found the remains of a pterosaur skeleton in the Blue Lias: this was the first pterosaur to be found in England.
4 Buckland, W., 1829. Proceedings of the Geological Society, 1: 127.
5 Owen, R., 1865 and 1870. *A monograph on the fossil reptilia of the Liassic formations.* Palaeontographical Society London.
Owen, R., 1874. *Monograph of the fossil reptilia of the Mesozoic Formations. I. Pterosauria.* Palaeontographical Scoiety London.

## Dimorphodon

*Dimorphodon* was a pterosaur about 3·3ft (1m) long overall with a maximum wing span of 4·6ft (1·4m). It had a relatively large, high skull with large side apertures. These 'windows', consisting of eye sockets, upper and lower temporal openings, preorbital openings and nostrils, were separated only by thin bars of bone. Thus despite its size the skull was very lightly built.

*Dimorphodon* had four large front teeth on each side of the upper jaw. Behind this was a row of smaller teeth. In the lower jaw as well four or five large front teeth were followed on each side by 30 to 40 tiny but pointed teeth. This specialization suggests that the creature was a fish eater. As a typical long-tailed pterosaur, *Dimorphodon* had a long vertebral tail made up of over 30 caudal vertebrae. The first five or six of these vertebrae were short, and could move against each other. Subsequent

Nasal opening
Preorbital opening
Eye socket with sclerotic ring
Upper temporal fenestra
Lower temporal fenestra


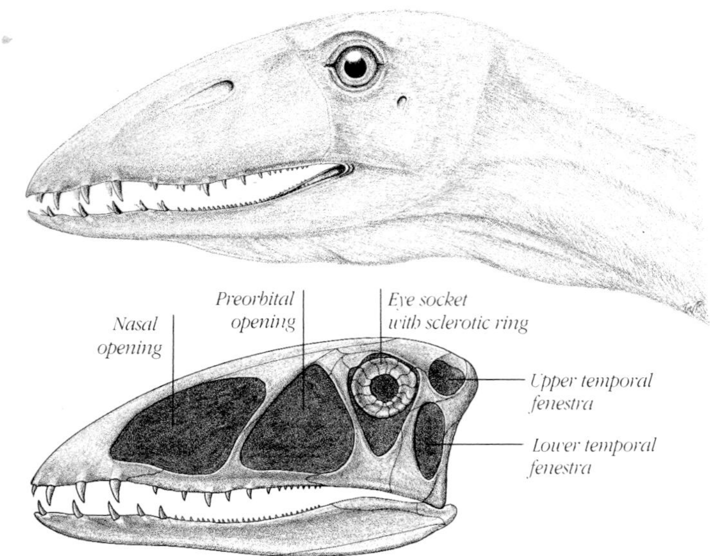

**Dimorphodon's Head and Skull (left)**
The life portrait of *Dimorphodon's* head seen at upper left is based on the fossil skulls from the Lower Lias of Lyme Regis. A restoration of one such skull is seen at lower left. The thin struts of bone separating the skull openings all helped to reduce the body weight that this creature needed to get airborne. The bony ring in the eye socket protected the eye against deformation. Note also the differently shaped teeth in the upper and lower jaws. These suggest that *Dimorphodon* was a fish eater.

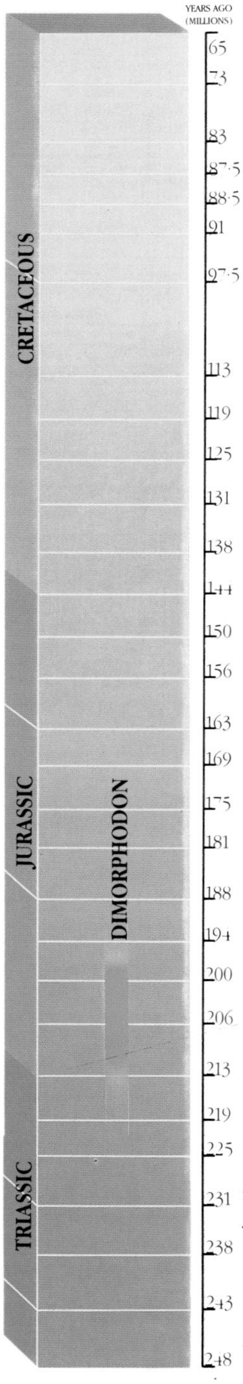

YEARS AGO (MILLIONS)
65
73
83
87·5
88·5
91
97·5
113
119
125
131
138
144
150
156
163
169
175
181
188
194
200
206
213
219
225
231
238
243
248
CRETACEOUS
JURASSIC
TRIASSIC
DIMORPHODON


**Time Chart (left)**
*Dimorphodon* is the earliest Jurassic pterosaur, discovered in early Liassic strata in Southern England. It is a long-tailed form, related to the Triassic *Peteinosaurus* which may have been its ancestor.

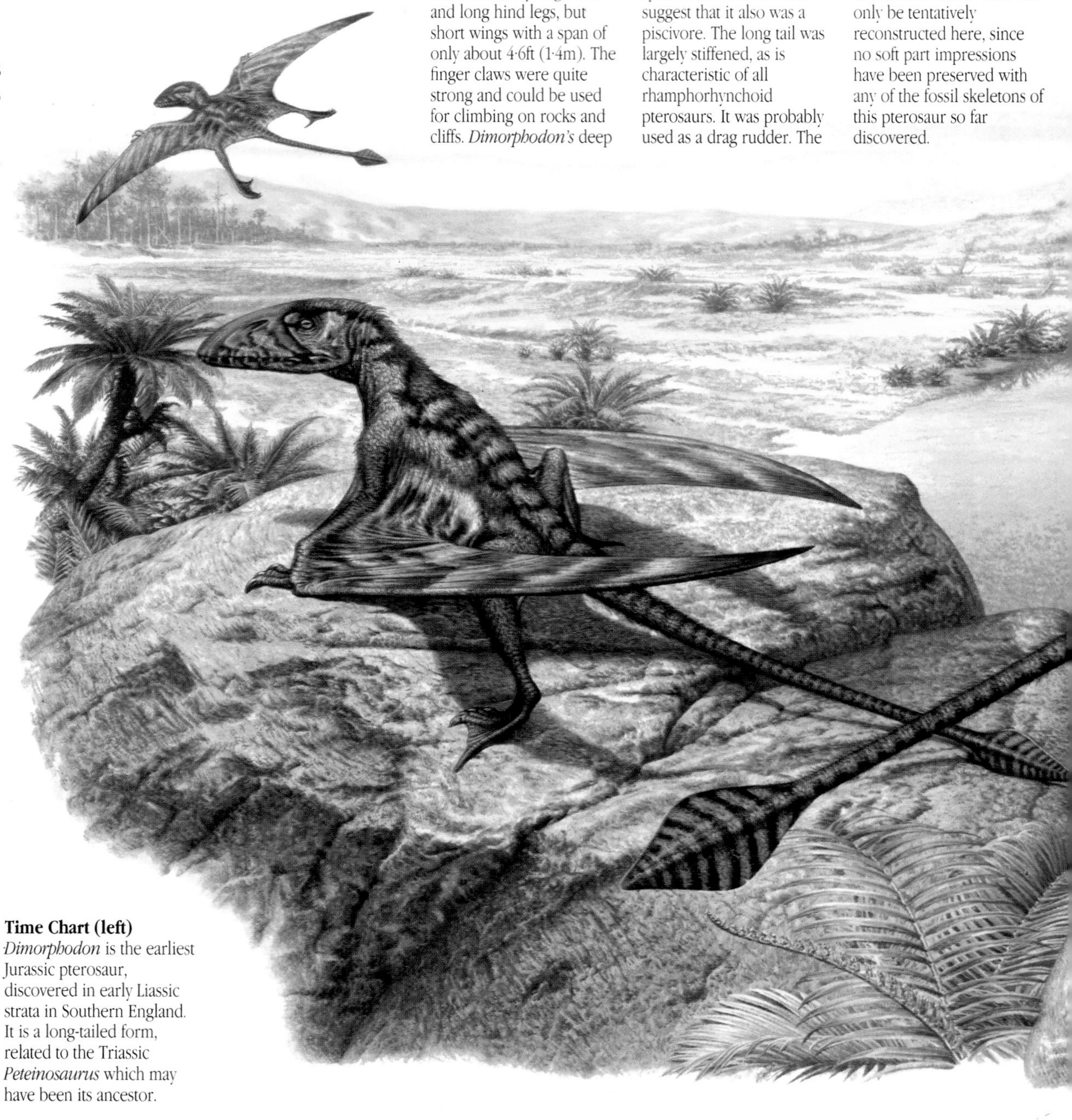

**Dimorphodon (below)**
This early Jurassic pterosaur had a relatively large head and long hind legs, but short wings with a span of only about 4·6ft (1·4m). The finger claws were quite strong and could be used for climbing on rocks and cliffs. *Dimorphodon's* deep snout is similar to the high beak of a puffin, and the specialization of its teeth suggest that it also was a piscivore. The long tail was largely stiffened, as is characteristic of all rhamphorhynchoid pterosaurs. It was probably used as a drag rudder. The extent of the wing membranes and the shape of the terminal tail vane can only be tentatively reconstructed here, since no soft part impressions have been preserved with any of the fossil skeletons of this pterosaur so far discovered.

caudal vertebrae were increasingly elongated, and were stiffened against one another by long, thin vertebral processes. This structure of a long, stiff tail, only articulated at the beginning, was linked with its function as a means of stabilizing the pterosaur in flight, which was further emphasized by the fact that there was a small vane at the end that was presumably used as a drag rudder. Further discussion of the function of this vane will be found in the 'Life Style' chapter.

*Dimorphodon*'s wings were still relatively short, a primitive characteristic. It is striking that the first of the four flight digit phalanges is only a little longer than the lower arm, and shorter than the second and third phalanges of the flight digit. The hind legs were extraordinarily powerfully developed and relatively long. The first four digits had claws; the fifth digit was fairly long and splayed sideways. A precise analysis of the structure of pelvis and hind leg led Kevin Padian to assume that *Dimorphodon* was well suited to biped, bird-like walking on the

**Comparative Sizes (above)**
**1** *Dimorphodon*: wing span 4·6ft (1·4m)

**Map (right)**
**1** *Dimorphodon*

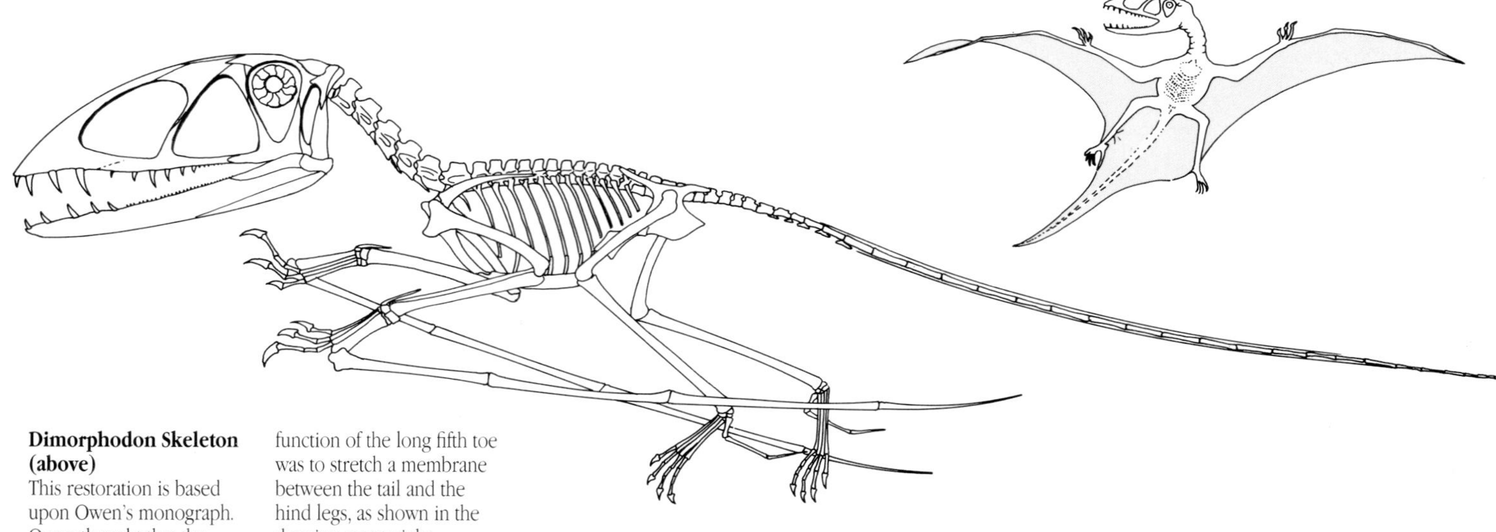

**Dimorphodon Skeleton (above)**
This restoration is based upon Owen's monograph. Owen thought that the function of the long fifth toe was to stretch a membrane between the tail and the hind legs, as shown in the drawing at top right.

ground, the long tail balancing the large head.[6] These problems of locomotion will be examined in greater detail in a later chapter.

Only a few specimens of *Dimorphodon* have been found, mainly incomplete skeletal remains. They all belong to the same species, *Dimorphodon macronyx*, and come from the Lower Lias of the Dorset coast in England. A single specimen, only a few bones of the flight arm and the hind legs, was found in the Lower Lias of Aust Cliff on the south bank of the Severn in Gloucestershire. With the exception of the Aust Cliff specimen, which was acquired for the Yale Peabody Museum, USA by O.C.Marsh from the London fossil dealer Bruce M. Wright in 1881, all the specimens are now in the Natural History Museum in London.

## German Finds

The first Liassic pterosaur finds on the European mainland were made only a year after William Buckland had introduced the Lyme Regis pterosaur. This time finds were made in Upper Lias strata near the former Benedictine monastery of Banz, high above the valley of the Main near Staffelstein in Upper Franconia in Bavaria. The Lias rocks around the monastery were known for their skeletal remains of ichthyosaurs and sea crocodiles. Isolated pterosaur bones and jaw fragments were found by ducal chancellery councillor Carl Theodori in 1830.[7] He saw the fossil remains as a new species, which he first called *'Ornithocephalus' banthensis*. Later Andreas Wagner, Professor of Palaeontology in Munich, established that it must also be a new genus, which he called *Dorygnathus*.[8] The name comes from the Greek *dorys* (=spear) and *gnáthos* (=jaw), from the toothless, lance-shaped point of the jaw.

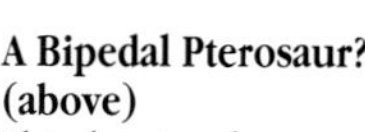

**A Bipedal Pterosaur? (above)**
This drawing shows *Dimorphodon* running along on its two hind legs, with its long tail counter-balancing its head. Dr Kevin Padian's work on the pelvis and hindlimbs of this pterosaur has led him to argue that *Dimorphodon* was well suited to this form of locomotion, although his hypothesis is disputed.

More complete *Dorygnathus* skeletons were later found, principally in Württemberg (southern Germany). As early as the late sixteenth century fossils had been found in the area around Bad Boll near Göppingen. In the mid eighteenth century, when the so-called Posidonian shale was mined, the first fossil vertebrates, ichthyosaurs and marine crocodiles, came to light. There were also quarries in the area near Holzmaden, Ohmden and Zell, small places in the northern foothills of the Schwäbische Alb, dominated by the towering Castle Teck.

Few of the quarries in this region are still worked today. Formerly roofing slate and flags for floors were mined here, but nowadays the decorative black slate slabs are only used for interior decoration. Here commercial mining is limited to a single stratum, the so-called Fleins, a layer 7in (18cm) thick, which gives three very firm slabs when split. This Fleins is up to 40ft (12m) below the surface of the site, so that some slate mines go down as deep as this. All the strata above this are technically unusable, although they still contain fossils, and find their way on to the spoil heaps.

Fossils are distributed throughout the profile of strata. Posidonian shale takes its name from a small frequently-occurring shell called *Posidonia bronni* (now called *Bositra parva*). Because of its bitumen content, many attempts have been made to extract oil from the rock, but the oil content is only 3-8 per cent, so the process is uneconomic.

Fossil content, especially ammonites as index fossils, mean that the Holzmaden Posidonian shale can be categorized as Lias epsilon, or the Lower Toarcian, according to the internationally accepted standard. The deposits came into being about 190 million years

6 Padian, K., 1983. *Osteology and Functional Morphology of Dimorphodon macronyx (Buckland) (Pterosauria: Rhamphorhynchoidea) Based on New Material in the Yale Peabody Museum.* Postilla, 189: 1-44; New Haven.
Padian, K., 1983. *A functional analysis of flying and walking in pterosaurs.* Palaeobiology, 9 (3): 218-239; Chicago.

7 Theodori, C., 1830. *Knochen vom Pterodactylus aus der Lias-Formation von Banz.* Froriep's Notizen für Natur und Heilkunde, 632: 101.
Theodori, C., 1831. *Über die Knochen vom Genus Pterodactylus aus der Lias-Formation von Banz.* Isis, p.277; Jena.
Theodori, C., 1852. *Über Pterodactylusknochen im Lias von Banz.* 1. Bericht des Naturforschenden Vereins Bamberg, 17-44; Bamberg.
On the subject of Carl Theodori and the Banz collection see also the chapter 'The History of Fossil Finds' and the accompanying footnote reference, no. 18.

8 Wagner, A., 1860. *Bemerkungen über die Arten von Fischen und Sauriern, welche im unteren wie im oberen Lias zugleich vorkommen sollen.* Sitzungsberichte der Bayerischen Akademie der Wissenschaften, math. – physikalische Classe, 36-52; Munich.

**Below:** This is another specimen of *Dorygnathus banthensis* from the Upper Lias of Holzmaden. The skull of this creature is particularly well preserved and shows clearly the formidable front teeth of this pterosaur which were used to grasp fish from the water. The skull length is 5in (12·8cm). This specimen is housed in the museum collection of Uppsala in Sweden.

**Above:** Dr Bernhard Hauff (1866-1950), the pioneer of fossil excavations in the Upper Liassic Posidonian shales around Holzmaden in Württemberg. His skilful preparations of ichthyosaurs, plesiosaurs, fishes, and pterosaurs from the quarries nearby became world famous, and his fossil specimens are housed in many collections, as well as in the fine Museum Hauff in Holzmaden itself.

**Above:** *Dorygnathus banthensis* from the Upper Lias of Holzmaden in Württemberg, Germany. This complete specimen of the Naturkundemuseum in Stuttgart comes from the Posidonian shale (*Posidonienschiefer*) and nicely shows the long, stiff tail, and the slender bones of the wing finger. The length of the skull is 3·8in (9·8cm).

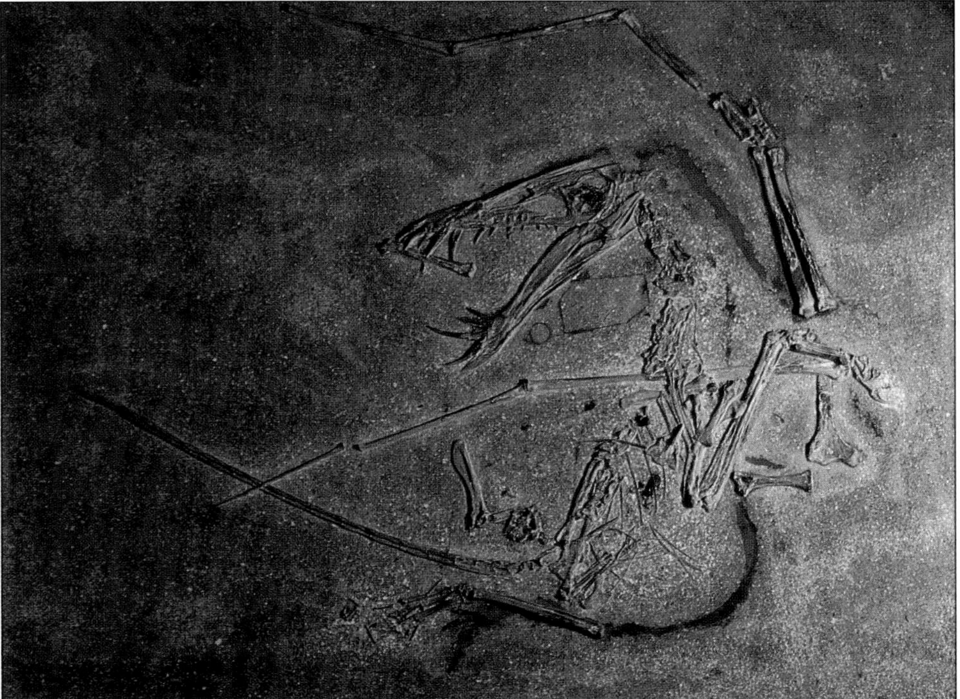

ago in an extended shallow sea that flooded broad areas of central Europe in the Lias. The area of modern Holzmaden must at the time have lain about 60 miles (100km) north-west of a large island, the Vindelician Land. The eastern limit of the Liassic sea was the coast of the Bohemian mainland, in the centre was the Ardennes-Rhenish island, the east coast of which was roughly on the line of modern Bielefeld-Marburg-Frankfurt.

Reptile finds from Holzmaden have become famous, and are to be found in many of the world's museums today. Ichthyosaurs are particularly abundant, but plesiosaurs, marine crocodiles, and even the remains of a dinosaur have also been found. There are also many fish, ammonites, squids, bivalves, sea lilies and crabs. Most of the fossils are in excellent condition. The great expert on Holzmaden fossils was Dr Bernhard Hauff. He began his careful preparations around 1890, and opened a small museum of his finds in Holzmaden in 1937. This has been considerably extended and modernized, and still attracts a large number of visitors.[9]

The first pterosaur fossil finds from the Posidonian shale of Württemberg were described by Albert Oppel in 1856,[10] but more complete skeletons were not found until the late nineteenth century. Numerous outstanding pterosaurs from the slate quarries around Holzmaden and Ohmden are known today, representing two genera, *Dorygnathus* and *Campylognathoides*.[11] The area was declared a protected area for excavation by the state in

9 Hauff, B. and Hauff, R.B., 1981. *Das Holzmadenbuch*. 136 p.; Holzmaden/ Teck.
Urlichs, M., Wild, R. and Ziegler, B., 1979. *Fossilien aus Holzmaden*. Stuttgarter Beiträge zur Naturkunde, C, 11: 34 p.; Stuttgart.

10 Oppel, A., 1856. *Die Juraformation*. Jahreshefte des Vereins für Vaterländische Naturkunde in Württemberg; 12.

11 Plieninger, F., *Die Pterosaurier der Juraformation Schwabens*. Palaeontographica, 53: 209-313; Stuttgart.
Arthaber, G. von, 1919. *Studien über Flugsaurier auf Grund der Bearbeitung des Wiener Exemplares von Dorygnathus banthensis Theod.sp.*. Denkschriften der Akademie der Wissenschaften Wien, math.-naturwiss. Klasse, 97: 391-464; Vienna.

1979, and can be considered the principal area for Liassic pterosaur finds. Other sites where only a few fragmentary pterosaur remains were found are the area around Bayreuth in Upper Franconia (Bavaria)[12] and Braunschweig in Lower Saxony.[13]

*Dorygnathus* (=spear-jaw) is a long-tailed pterosaur with a wing span of about 3·3ft (1m). Its skull is elongated. The eye sockets are the largest apertures in the skull. The front teeth in the upper and lower jaw are long, powerful and curved, and meshed alternately when the beak was closed. The rear parts of the jaw had only very small teeth. Dentition of this kind was a very effective organ for seizing and holding slippery prey, in other words fish. *Dorygnathus* had a relatively small, triangular sternum. This served as an area of attachment for flight muscles. The flight digits and thus the wings were relatively short. The fifth digit of the foot was very long, however, and set at a lateral angle. Its function is not clear. Possibly it was used to spread a small web which permitted the animal to take off more easily if it had had to land on the surface of the sea.

## Campylognathoides

The first pterosaur specimen from the Württemberg Lias was of the genus *Campylognathoides* (=curved jaw). However, the skeletal remains consisted only of a few bones of the flight arm, which had been described by Tübingen professor Friedrich August Quenstedt in 1858 under the name *Pterodactylus liasicus*.[14]

Upper temporal fenestra
Sclerotic ring
Nasal opening
Eye socket
Preorbital opening
Lower temporal fenestra

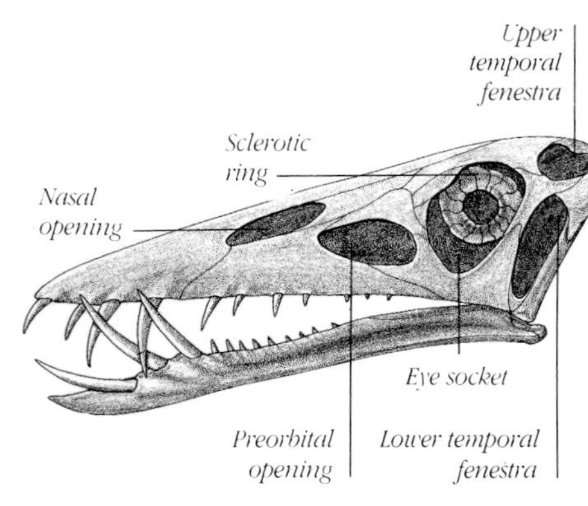

12 Wild, R., 1971. *Dorygnathus mistelgauensis n.sp., ein neuer Flugsaurier aus dem Lias Epsilon von Mistelgau (Fränkischer Jura).* Geologische Blätter von Nordost-Bayern, 21(4): 178-195; Erlangen.

13 Stieler, C., 1922. *Neuer Rekonstruktionsversuch eines liassischen Flugsauriers.* Naturwissenschaftliche Wochenschrift, N.F. 21(20): 273-280; Jena.

14 Quenstedt, F.A., 1858. *Über Pterodactylus liasicus.* Jahreshefte des Vereins für Vaterländische Naturkunde in Württemberg, 14: 299-336; Stuttgart.

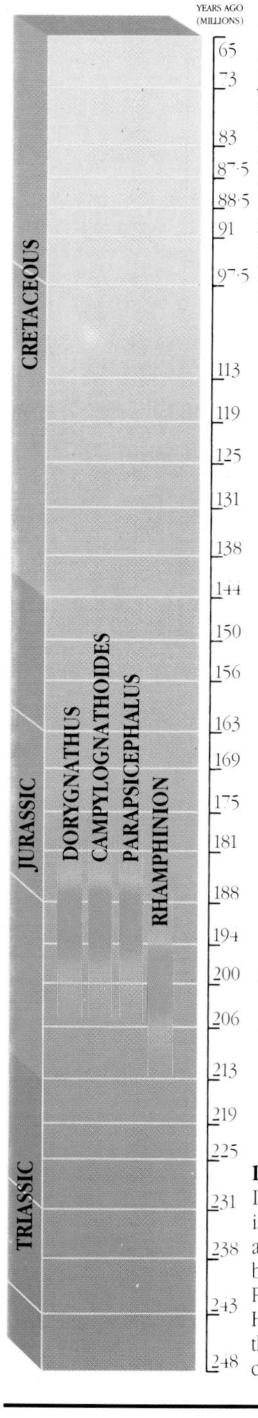

YEARS AGO (MILLIONS)
65
73
83
87·5
88·5
91
97·5
113
119
125
131
138
144
150
156
163
169
175
181
188
194
200
206
213
219
225
231
238
243
248
CRETACEOUS
JURASSIC
TRIASSIC
DORYGNATHUS
CAMPYLOGNATHOIDES
PARAPSICEPHALUS
RHAMPHINION

**Time Chart (left)**
*Rhamphinion* of the Lower Jurassic Kayenta formation of Arizona indicates a worldwide distribution of pterosaurs at that time. *Dorygnathus*, *Campylognathoides* and *Parapsicephalus* appear in the Upper Liassic (the Toarcian) of Germany and England.

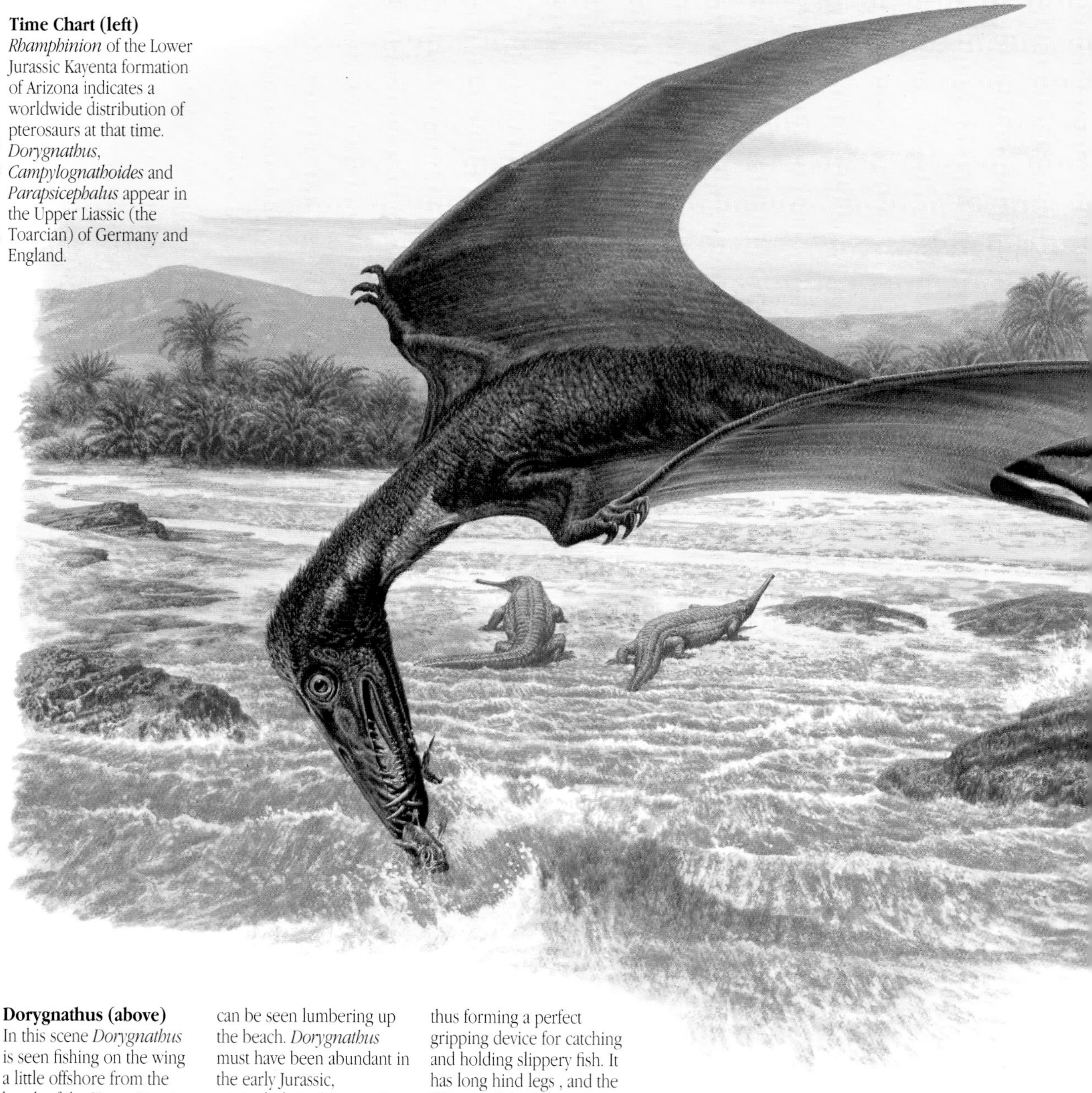

**Dorygnathus (above)**
In this scene *Dorygnathus* is seen fishing on the wing a little offshore from the beach of the Upper Liassic Posidonian shale sea of Holzmaden, Germany. In the background, marine crocodilians, *Steneosaurus*, can be seen lumbering up the beach. *Dorygnathus* must have been abundant in the early Jurassic, particularly in this area. It was a long-tailed pterosaur with a relatively small wingspan. Its front teeth are long and point forward, thus forming a perfect gripping device for catching and holding slippery fish. It has long hind legs , and the fifth toe of the foot is also long with a bent phalanx. It may have been used to spread a small web between the toes.

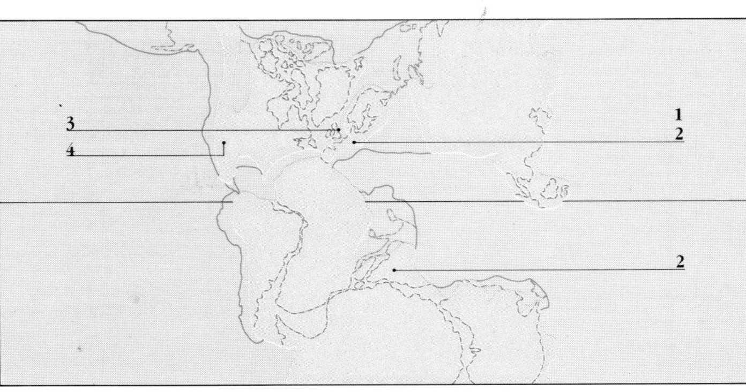


**Dorygnathus Heads (above)**
The drawings show restorations of the skull of *Dorygnathus* and a life portrait based on such fossil skulls. Note the curving front teeth.

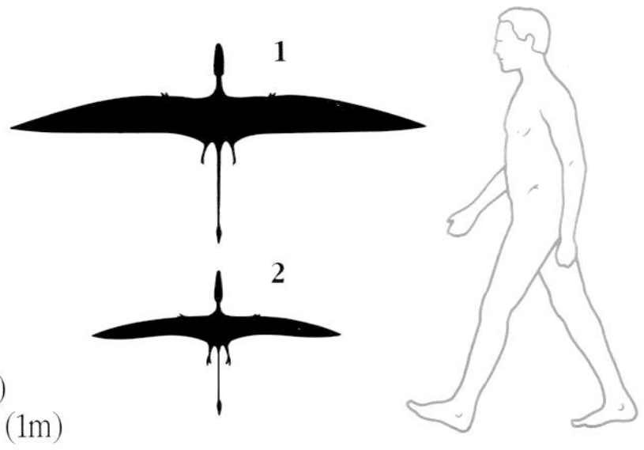

**Map (above)**
**1** *Dorygnathus*
**2** *Campylognathoides*
**3** *Parapsicephalus*
**4** *Rhamphinion*

**Comparative Sizes (right)**
**1** *Campylognathoides zitteli*: wing span 5·7ft (1·75m)
**2** *Dorygnathus*: wing span 3·3ft (1m)

**Campylognathoides (above)**
This pterosaur lived in the same environment as *Dorygnathus* in the Holzmaden area of the Upper Liassic Sea, but it is also known from northern Germany, and possibly even India. It is also a long-tailed, rhamphorhynchoid pterosaur, but it has a shorter head and smaller teeth than its contemporary *Dorygnathus*. The skull is dominated by the large eye sockets. So far, two species are known, *Campylognathoides liasicus*, with a wing span of about 3·3ft (1m), and the larger *Campylognathoides zitteli* with a span of around 5·7ft (1·75m). In the background is seen *Ohmdenosaurus*, a middle-sized sauropod discovered in this area.

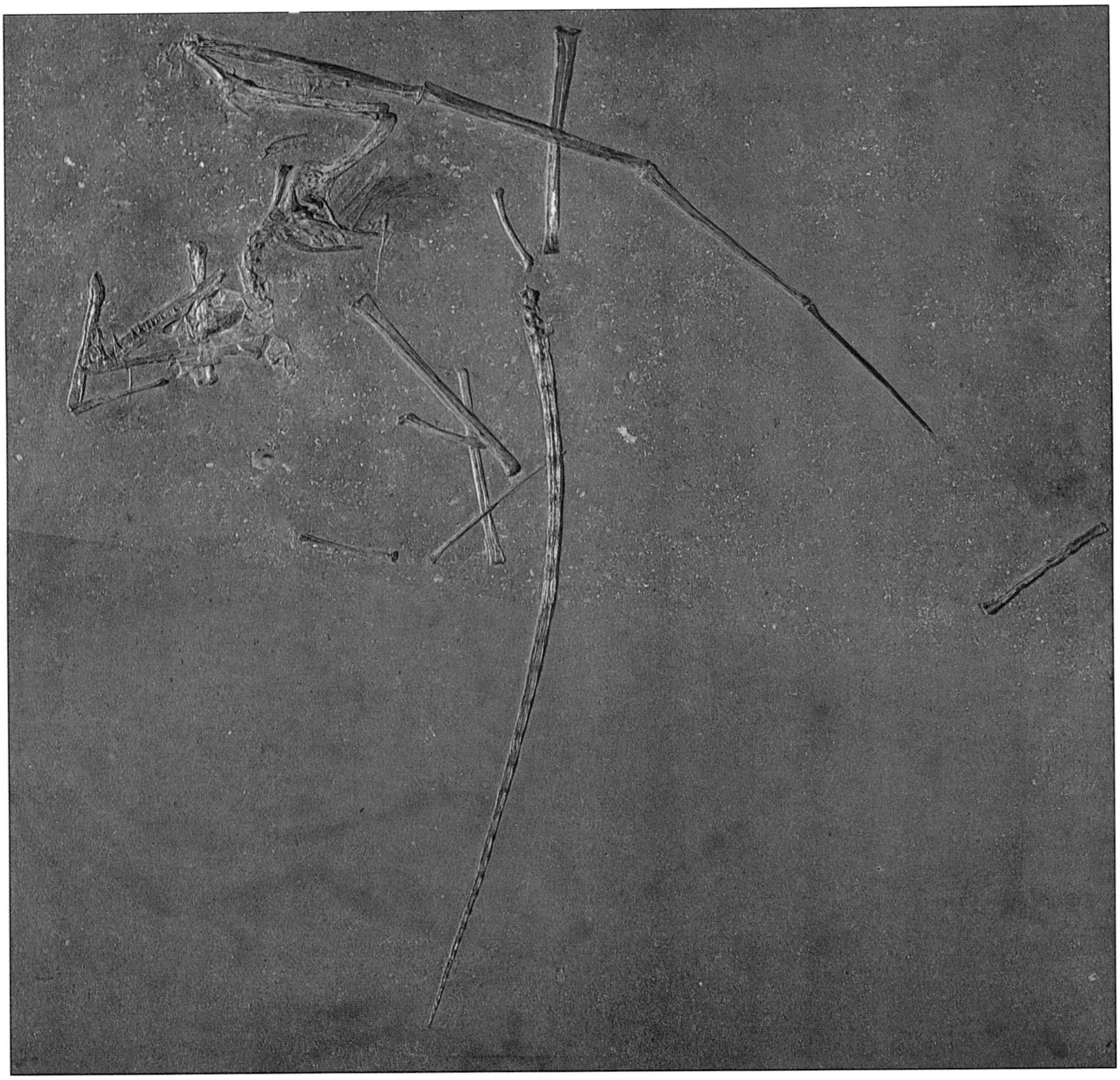

**Left:** These are the fossil remains of *Campylognathoides liasicus* which were excavated from the Upper Lias of Ohmden near Holzmaden in Württemberg, Germany. The skeleton is partly disarticulated, but it does show clearly the long tail characteristic of this genus and one wing. The tail is 10·2in (26cm) long, while the wing span is about 3·3ft (1m). This specimen is housed in the Staatliches Museum für Naturkunde, Stuttgart. It was as a result of the work of the Stuttgart palaeontologist Felix Plieninger that *Campylognathoides* was recognised as a genus in its own right, and not assigned to the genus *Pterodactylus* as Friedrich Quenstedt had originally suggested in 1858.

It was not until much more complete finds from the Holzmaden Posidionian shale had become known that the Stuttgart palaeontologist Felix Plieninger recognized that they were a genus in their own right.[15] The name *Campylognathoides* comes from the Greek *kampylós*, curved, and *gnáthos*, jaw, after the crooked ends to the jaw.

The genus has a characteristic relatively short skull, dominated by a large, circular eye socket. The end of the snout is pointed and toothed, with short, conical teeth set upright in the jaw. The sternum consists of a broad, rectangular plate of bone and has a short crest (cristopina) projecting forwards. In contrast with *Dorygnathus* the fifth toe is very short in this case. Two species of *Campylognathoides* are known from Holzmaden, *Campylognathoides liasicus* and *Campylognathoides zitteli*.[15,16] The former had a wing span of under 3·3ft (1m), and the latter had a span of about 5·7ft (1·75m).

In 1974 the Indian palaeontologist S.L. Jain described a fragment of a pterosaur skull with teeth as *Campylognathoides indicus*.[17] The fossil came from the Lower Jurassic of the Chanda district of India.

In 1986 a fossil collector found a small pterosaur pelvis that had survived in isolation in a Posidonian shale quarry in the area of Braunschweig in Lower Saxony, which could also be placed in the genus *Campylognathoides*.[18] In this case it was particularly significant that the hip sockets had survived in very good condition and their lateral and upward

15 Plieninger, F., 1895. *Campylognathus zitteli. Ein neuer Flugsaurier aus dem Oberen Lias Schwabens.* Palaeontographica, 41: 193-222; Stuttgart.
16 Wellnhofer, P., 1974. *Campylognathoides liasicus (Quenstedt), an Upper Liassic Pterosaur from Holzmaden. The Pittsburgh Specimen.* Annals of the Carnegie Museum, 45(2): 169-216; Pittsburgh.

17 Jain, S.L., 1974. *Jurassic Pterosaur from India.* Journal of the Geological Society of India, 15(3): 330-335.

18 Wellnhofer, P. and Vahldiek, B.W., 1986. *Ein Flugsaurier-Rest aus dem Posidonienschiefer (Unter-Toarcium) von Schandelah bei Braunschweig.* Paläontologische Zeitschrift, 60: 329-340; Stuttgart.

**Getting Airborne (bottom of page)**
While *Dorygnathus* had relatively short flight digits and wings, its feet had remarkably long fifth digits which were set at an angle which was laterally displaced from the remaining toes. The function of this fifth toe is not clear, but it may have served to spread a small web which could have helped the pterosaur to paddle to get airborne after it had alighted on water.

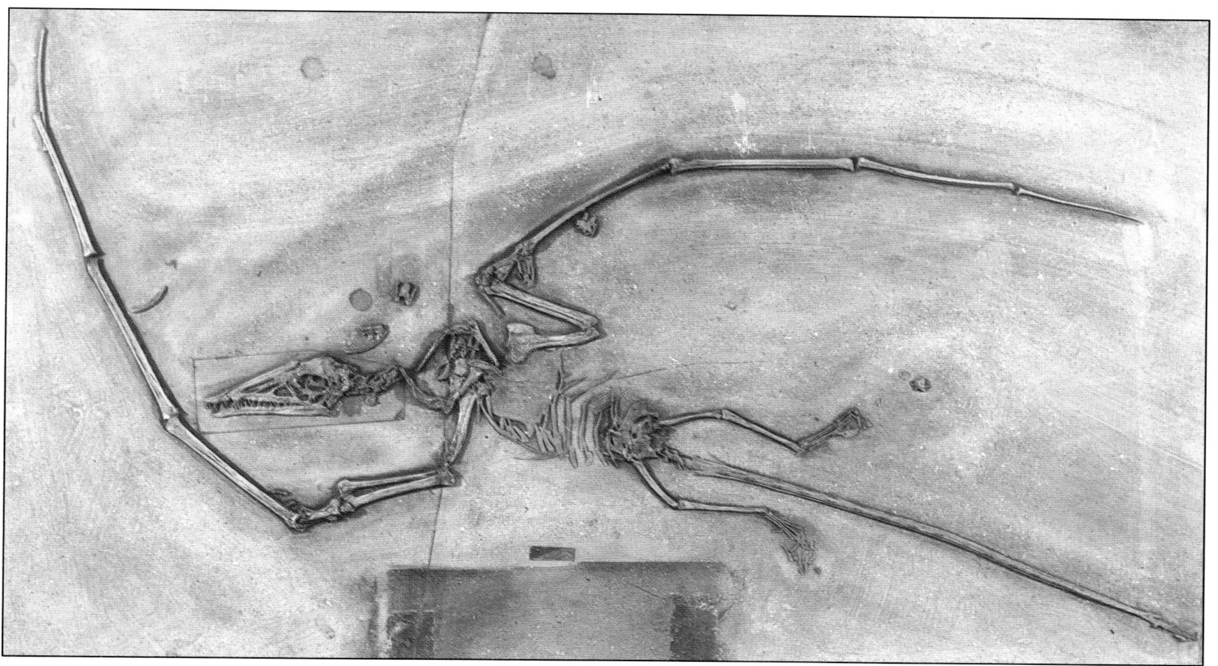

**Left:** This is one of the most complete specimens of *Campylognathoides liasicus* from the Upper Lias of Holzmaden. Called the Pittsburgh specimen, it is one of the prize fossils in the collection that the Carnegie Museum in Pittsburgh, Pennsylvania purchased from the Belgian Baron de Bayet in 1903. The Baron had bought this specimen from the noted Holzmaden palaeontologist Bernhard Hauff who had discovered it in 1897. Hauff had originally found the skeleton without the skull. It was not until a year later that he found the skull several yards away in the same part of the quarry, and was subsequently able to restore it to its rightful place. The length of the skull is 3·27in (8·3cm).

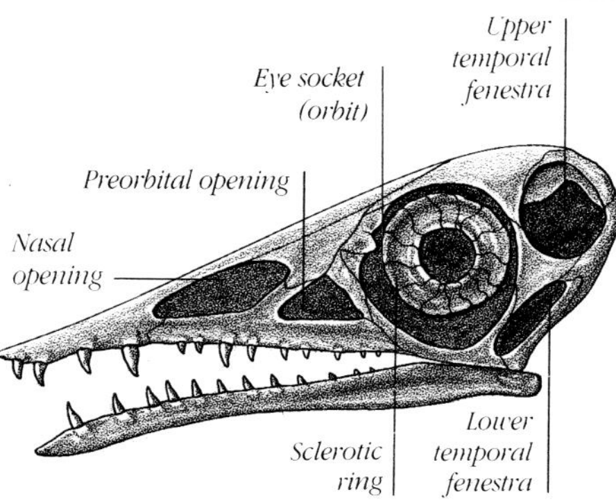


**Campylognathoides Skull and Head (left and right)**
*Campylognathoides liasicus'* eye sockets are very large, which suggests that it possessed acute eyesight. Some scientists argue that such large eyes indicate a nocturnal lifestyle. At right we see a life portrait based on the skull restoration shown left.

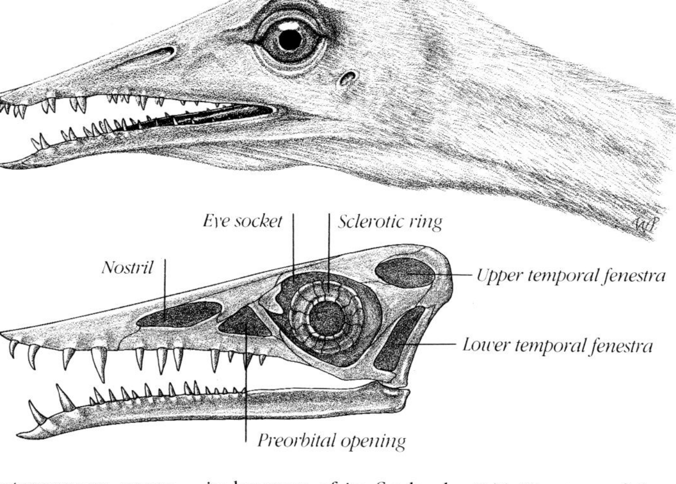


**Campylognathoides zitteli Skull (right)**
This second species of *Campylognathoides* was larger than *liasicus*. Its skull was 5in (13cm) in length.

**Campylognathoides Pelvis (below)**
The pelvis of a *Campylognathoides* specimen is seen here from the top (above) and the side. The hip sockets face laterally and slightly dorsally indicating that bipedal locomotion was unlikely.

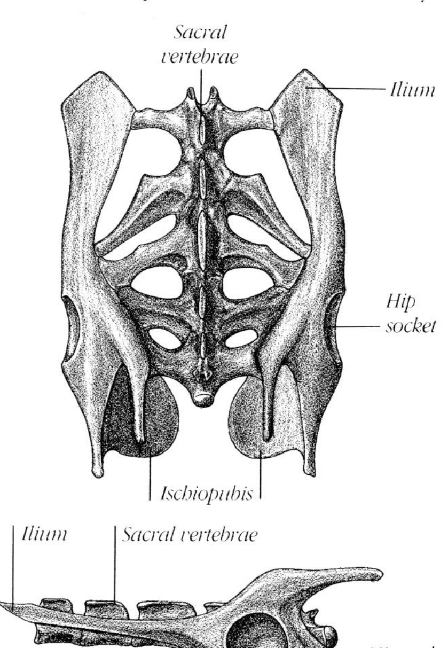


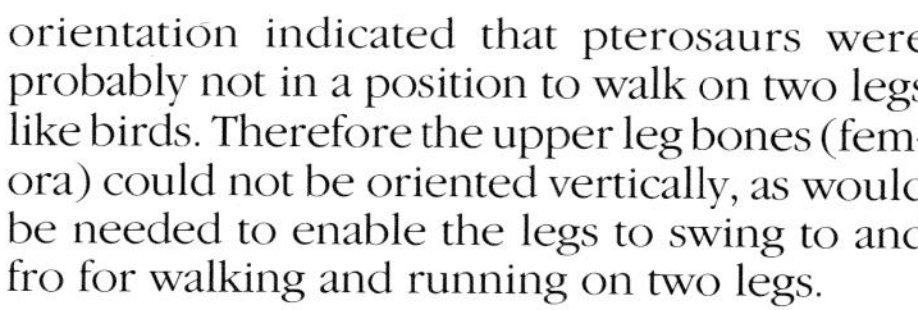

orientation indicated that pterosaurs were probably not in a position to walk on two legs like birds. Therefore the upper leg bones (femora) could not be oriented vertically, as would be needed to enable the legs to swing to and fro for walking and running on two legs.

## A Whitby Discovery

A very important Upper Liassic pterosaur find came from England. The 'alum shales' of Whitby on the Yorkshire coast in northern England are grey, crumbly shale with a high pyrites content, in the higher strata of which limestone geodes (or concretions) occur. These were formerly exploited to produce cement. The alum shales in the Whitby area were mined in the eighteenth and nineteenth century in particular, on numerous sites. Alum is a potassium aluminium sulphate, used among other things in paper factories and dyeing works. The alum industry flourished in the eighteenth century, but declined when a cheaper production method was found.

The first fossil reptile found in the alum shales of the Yorkshire coast was a marine crocodile described by William Chapman in 1758.[19] Then in the 1880s the Reverend D.W. Purdon found a well-preserved pterosaur skull 'from the Alum Shale at Lofthouse' (modern Loftus). It was named *Scaphognathus purdoni* in honour of its finder by E.T. Newton of the Geological Survey in London in 1888.[20] However it later became clear that this pterosaur was different from *Scaphognathus* (=tub-jaw), which was only known from the Solnhofen flaggy limestones of Bavaria. The Whitby genus was thus given the name *Parapsicephalus* (=double-vaulted skull). The bulk of the fossils from the Upper Lias of Whitby are ammonites, however. These also permit precise dating of the alum shales. Like the Posidonian shales they belong to the Lower Toarcian.

---

19 Chapman, W., 1758. *An account of the fossile bones of an allegator, found on the sea-shore near Whitby in Yorkshire.* Philosophical Transactions of the Royal Society London, 50: 688-691.
William Chapman: 'The bones were covered five or six feet with water every full sea, and were about nine or ten yards from the cliff, which is nearly perpendicular, and about sixty yards high.'
See also Benton, M.J., and Taylor, M.A., 1984. *Marine reptiles from the Upper Lias (Lower Toarcian, Lower Jurassic) of the Yorkshire Coast.* Proceedings of the Yorkshire Geological Society, 44(4), no. 29: 399-429.

20 Newton, E.T., 1888. *On the Skull, Brain and Auditory Organ of a new species of Pterosaurian (Scaphognathus Purdoni) from the Upper Lias near Whitby, Yorkshire.* Philosophical Transactions of the Royal Society, 179: 503; London.

The only specimen of this genus is a fragment of a skull 5·5in (14cm) long which has survived three-dimensionally. The front end of the jaw and the teeth are missing. It was a medium-sized, long-tailed pterosaur with a wing span of over 3·3ft (1m). This is one of the rare pterosaur skulls in which it is possible to examine the structure of the brain. Of course the brain itself cannot survive, it decays immediately after the death of the animal. But the skull filled with ooze on the sea bed, this ooze finally became petrified and formed an inner cast of stone, or endocast. This endocast is a faithful, three-dimensional copy of the pterosaur-brain, the various structures of which can be analysed precisely, almost as though it were real brain.

## Fragments from Arizona

In 1984 an interesting pterosaur fragment from the Kayenta formation in Arizona came to light. Some geologists date the Kayenta formation as Upper Triassic, others as Lower Jurassic. Kevin Padian of the University of California in Berkeley recognized that the fragmentary remains were a new species and genus, which he called *Rhamphinion jenkinsi*, named in honour of Dr Farish A. Jenkins Jr., who discovered the specimen.[21] Only four pieces were found. They come from the back of the head, the cheek-bone, the lower jaw and another indeterminate bone fragment. *Rhamphinion* (=beak and nape of the neck) is very probably a long-tailed pterosaur, a rhamphorhynchoid. Padian mentions another pterosaur bone from the Arizona Kayenta formation, a 1·65in (42mm) long flight digit metacarpal of a long-tailed pterosaur which must have had a wing span of about 4·9ft (1·5m).

21 Padian, K., 1984. *Pterosaur remains from the Kayenta Formation (?Early Jurassic) of Arizona.* Palaeontology, 27(2): 407-413.

**Above:** Cliffs of Lias rocks near Staithes north west of Whitby on the Yorkshire coast in England. Alum shales were mined in this area in the eighteenth and nineteenth centuries, and important fossil reptiles were discovered in the course of excavations.

**Right:** *Parapsicephalus purdoni*, a partial skull from the Upper Liassic alum shales of Whitby seen in top view. This important specimen is one of the few pterosaur skulls which have an endocast of the brain preserved within the brain cavity.

### The Skull of Parapsicephalus purdoni (right)

The drawings show the skull fragment of *Parapsicephalus purdoni* that was found near Whitby in Yorkshire. It is seen from the left side (upper drawing), and from below (middle drawing). The lower drawing shows a restoration with the supposed front end of the jaw outlined in dotted lines. When this specimen was examined, its brain cavity was discovered to be filled with petrified sediment, which thus revealed a three-dimensional image of the pterosaur's brain. Such endocasts are rare. They help scientists determine the possible mental abilities and consequent behaviour of pterosaurs.

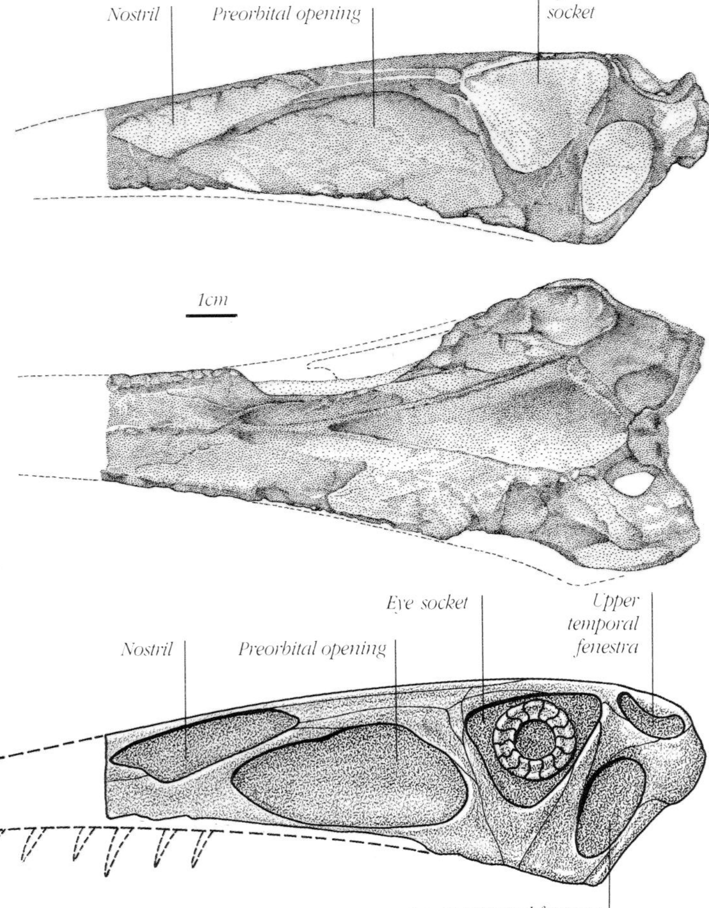

## Middle Jurassic Pterosaurs

The Stonesfield Beds in Oxfordshire consist of sandstone and sandy limestone. They are a striking set of geological strata, extending from the Cotswolds south of Bath into Oxfordshire. In the early nineteenth century these slab-like rocks were even mined in subterranean quarries, for use as roofing slates.[22] Large fossil bones were found in these Stonesfield strata as early as the eighteenth century, and at the beginning of the nineteenth century Stonesfield slate became famous because of the first dinosaur to be scientifically described, *Megalosaurus*, as well as finds of fish, crocodiles and the jawbones of early, primitive mammals.

As well as vertebrate fossils the Stonesfield slate also contains fossils of invertebrates, namely brachiopods, bivalves and ammonites. These index fossils also permitted stratigraphic dating of the Beds to the Bathonian age, a subdivision of the Middle Jurassic or Dogger, for which an absolute age of 175 to 169 million years is accepted today.

In 1832 the Frankfurt vertebrate palaeontologist Hermann von Meyer described the first pterosaur remains from Stonesfield, which he called *'Pterodactylus' bucklandi*, in honour of William Buckland.[23] Subsequently further remains of pterosaur skeletons were found in various places in the Oxfordshire Stonesfield Slate and ascribed by T.H. Huxley to various species of the genus *Rhamphorhynchus*.[24] This was the same Thomas Huxley who later became known as Darwin's 'bulldog', a passionate defender of his theory of evolution. Thomas Henry Huxley (1825-1895) was one of the most brilliant scientists of his time. He had studied medicine, but concerned himself particularly with physiology and natural history. He was Lecturer in Palaeontology and Natural History at the School of Mines in London, and studied fossils, including the pterosaurs from the Stonesfield Slate and later the primordial

**Right:** For hundreds of years Stonesfield slate has been widely used as roofing tiles, as is seen here in the main street of the Cotswold village of Chipping Camden in Gloucestershire. The slate, which is quarried near the village of Stonesfield, is a grey, fissile, calcareous sandstone. Its greatest recorded thickness is 6ft (1·83m). The fossils found in these slate beds are renowned worldwide. For example, *Megalosaurus*, the first dinosaur to be scientifically described, was found in them during the last century.

22 Arkell, W.J., 1933 (see reference 2), p. 277: 'The Stonesfield Slate Beds consist typically of thin sands and sandy limestones, often in the form of spheroidal doggers called 'pot-lids' or 'burs', some of which split under the weather into fissile roofing tiles.'
p. 278: 'A few miles farther north-east, in the North Cotswolds, the Stonesfield Slate Beds attain their maximum development and are still worked in several places under the name of Cotswold Slates. The activity of the industry in the past may be judged by the fact that at Kineton Thorns alone no less than 120,000 slates were made in one season.'

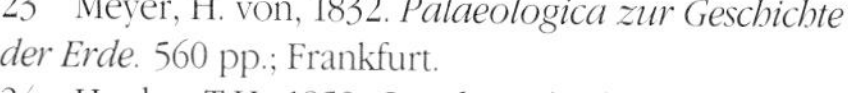

23 Meyer, H. von, 1832. *Palaeologica zur Geschichte der Erde*. 560 pp.; Frankfurt.
24 Huxley, T.H., 1859. *On Rhamphorhynchus bucklandi, a Pterosaurian from the Stonesfield Slate*. Quarterly Journal of the Geological Society, 15: 658; London.

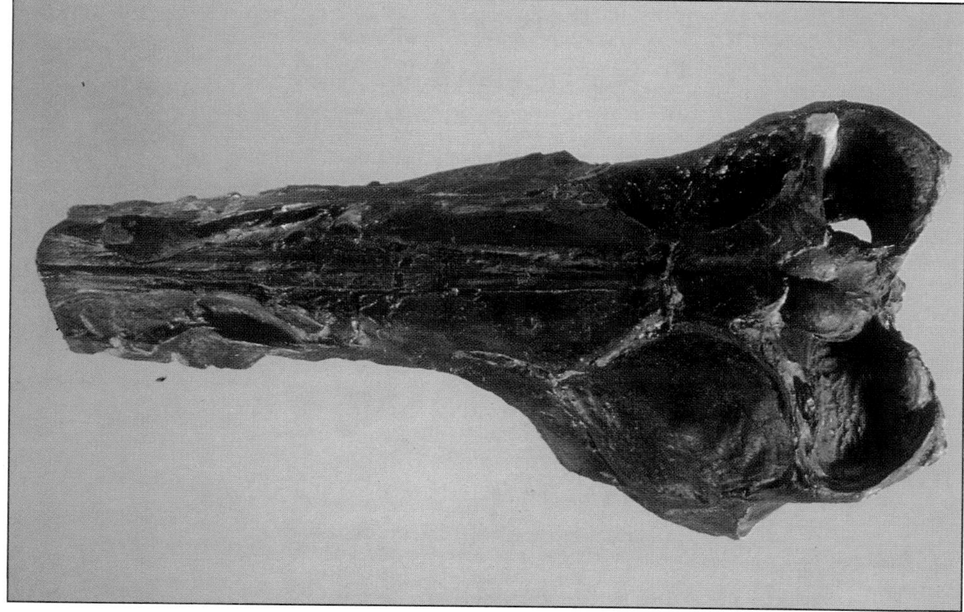

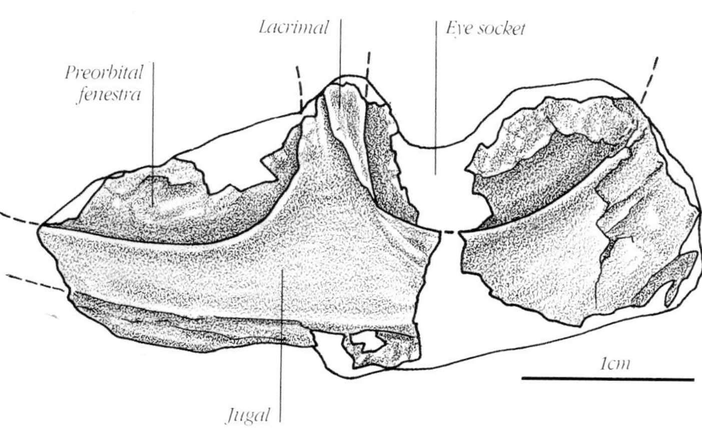


**Rhamphinion Skull Fragment (left)**
This is a fragment of the skull of *Rhamphinion jenkinsi* from the ?Lower Jurassic Kayenta formation of Arizona. We can see part of the jugal bone which forms the lower margin of the eye socket and the preorbital opening. This is one of a few, very scanty pterosaurian remains from these deposits which have also yielded dinosaurs. The drawing is based on an original by K. Padian who recognised *Rhamphinion* as a new genus.

**SUMMARY OF LOWER JURASSIC PTEROSAURS**

**Rhamphorhynchoidea**
Family Dimorphodontidae
*Dimorphodon macronyx*
Lower Lias, Blue Lias, Lyme Regis, Dorset; Aust Cliff, Gloucestershire, England.[5]

Family Rhamphorhynchidae
*Dorygnathus banthensis*
Upper Lias, Posidonian shale, Banz, Creez near Bayreuth, Bavaria; Holzmaden, Württemberg; Flechtorf, Lower Saxony, Germany.[11,13]
*Dorygnathus mistelgauensis*
Upper Lias, Mistelgau near Bayreuth, Bavaria, Germany.[12]
*Campylognathoides liasicus*
Upper Lias, Holzmaden, Württemberg, Germany.[15,16]
*Campylognathoides zitteli*
Upper Lias, Holzmaden, Württemberg, Germany.[15]
*Campylognathoides* sp.
Upper Lias, Schandelah near Braunschweig, Lower Saxony, Germany.[18]
*Campylognathoides indicus*
Upper Jurassic, Kota formation, Chanda District, Deccan, India.[17]
*Parapsicephalus purdoni*
Upper Lias, Alum shale, Whitby, Yorkshire, England.[20]

Undetermined family
*Rhamphinion jenkinsi*
Lower Jurassic, middle Kayenta Formation, Little Colorado River Valley, Arizona, USA.[21]

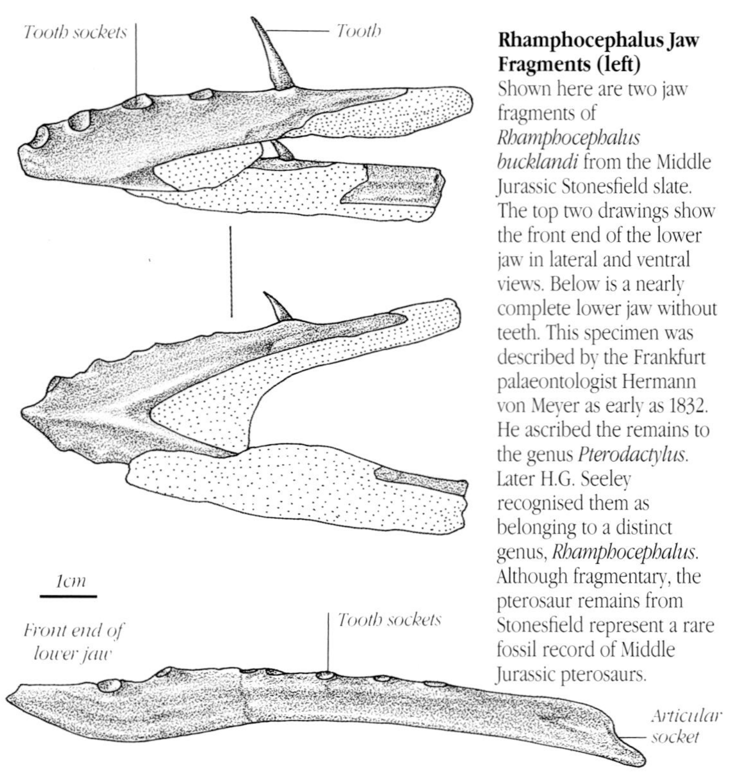


**Rhamphocephalus Jaw Fragments (left)**
Shown here are two jaw fragments of *Rhamphocephalus bucklandi* from the Middle Jurassic Stonesfield slate. The top two drawings show the front end of the lower jaw in lateral and ventral views. Below is a nearly complete lower jaw without teeth. This specimen was described by the Frankfurt palaeontologist Hermann von Meyer as early as 1832. He ascribed the remains to the genus *Pterodactylus*. Later H.G. Seeley recognised them as belonging to a distinct genus, *Rhamphocephalus*. Although fragmentary, the pterosaur remains from Stonesfield represent a rare fossil record of Middle Jurassic pterosaurs.

**Above:** This skull of the rhamphorhynchid pterosaur *Angustinaripterus* comes from the Middle Jurassic beds in Dashanpu Quarry, near Zigong in China. It is characterised by its large, interlocking teeth which are similar to those of *Dorygnathus*.

bird *Archaeopteryx*. This he interpreted by the application of Darwin's theory of evolution as a link between reptiles and birds, as the famous 'missing link'. As Darwin's 'bulldog' he came into conflict with Richard Owen of the British Museum (Natural History) in particular.

Later H.G. Seeley recognized a distinct genus in the Stonesfield slate pterosaurs, which he called *Rhamphocephalus* (=beak-head).[25] In no case were there complete skeletons, only fragments of lower jaw, skull and numerous individual bones like vertebrae, ribs, pectoral girdle and bones from the extremities. The dimensions of the fossil remains indicate that *Rhamphocephalus* must have reached a wing span of 3-4ft (0·9-1·2m).

The fragmentary state in which the remains of the skeletons have survived makes it difficult to ascribe Stonesfield slate pterosaurs to known species of the Jurassic. Skull and dentition of *Rhamphocephalus* indicate that they were long-tailed Rhamphorhynchoidea. On the other hand the wing phalanges have a triangular cross-section like the short-tailed pterodactylids, which do not occur until the Upper Jurassic. For this reason *Rhamphocephalus* is possibly a transitional form between the primitive Rhamphorhynchoidea and the more advanced Pterodactyloidea, as it seems to combine characteristics of both. Caudal vertebrae have not yet been discovered, however. More precise conclusions could only be drawn on the basis of more complete fossil finds, but such finds are hardly to be expected as the Stonesfield slate of Oxfordshire is now rarely quarried.

Pterosaurs from Middle Jurassic strata are found in very few places on Earth. Therefore *Rhamphocephalus* remains from the Stonesfield slate are of great significance despite their lack of completeness, as they form a link between the good fossil documentation in the Lower and Upper Jurassic.

## Discoveries at Dashanpu

An enormous dinosaur cemetery was discovered and excavated a few years ago near the city of Zigong in the province of Sichuan, and a large museum has now been built above it. The Sichuan basin in central China is a gigantic sedimentation basin containing continental deposits from the Upper Triassic to the Jurassic-Cretaceous boundary. The strata are over-

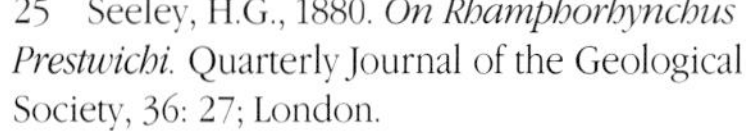

25 Seeley, H.G., 1880. *On Rhamphorhynchus Prestwichi.* Quarterly Journal of the Geological Society, 36: 27; London.

**Below:** Excavations underway at Dashanpu Quarry. A vast dinosaur 'cemetery' was discovered here in the red beds of Sichuan. Amongst the many Jurassic dinosaur remains uncovered was the skull of *Angustinaripterus longicephalus*.

**Angustinaripterus Skull (below)**
The well preserved skull of *Angustinaripterus longicephalus* reveals dentition similar to that of *Dorygnathus* from Holzmaden in Germany. These teeth must have been perfect for gripping fish.

*Eye socket*
*Preorbital opening*
*Upper temporal fenestra*
*Nostril*
*Lower temporal fenestra*

**Below:** The great limestone quarry of Solnhofen in Bavaria, Germany. This photograph was taken at the turn of the century when horses were still used to pull the carts laden with limestone slabs over the bridges to the workshops. The photograph shows nicely the typical layers of flaggy limestone which used to be used in this area for roofing. The series is composed of very fine grained, almost pure limestone slabs, deposited in the lagoons of the Jurassic Tethys Sea 150 million years ago.

10,000ft (3,000m) thick and consist mainly of reddish river and lake deposits, known overall as the 'Red Basin of Sichuan'.[26]

A number of different dinosaur faunas have been discovered throughout the strata of the Red Basin of Sichuan. They document the longest continuous sequence of Jurassic dinosaurs in the world. In one of these strata, the Lower Shaximiao formation of the Middle Jurassic, the skull of a pterosaur was found alongside the primitive sauropod dinosaur *Shunosaurus* and other vertebrate remains.[27] The rear end of the skull was missing, but nevertheless its shape and size can be reconstructed with some reliability. It is an elongated skull about 6·5in (16·5cm) long. The wing span must have been about 5ft (1·6m). The upper jaw had a total of 18 teeth and the lower jaw 18-20, which bit against each other alternately and must have been an excellent tool for catching fish. This dentition is similar to that of *Dorygnathus* from the Holzmaden Lias, but also shows similarities with *Rhamphocephalus* from the Stonesfield slate, to the extent that this can be judged.

The most striking characteristic of the Dashanpu pterosaur is the very narrow nostril. For this reason the genus was named *Angustinaripterus* (=wing with the narrow nostril), and because of its long head it was given the species name *longicephalus* (=long-skulled). Generally speaking the structure of the skull is the same as that of the long-tailed Rhamphorhynchoidea. This is recognizable not only from the dentition, but also from the fact that the pre-orbital opening and the nostril are divided by a bridge of bone. In short-tailed pterosaurs (Pterodactyloidea) these two skull openings are confluent and form a common nostril-preorbital opening in front of the eye socket.

Although *Angustinaripterus* from the Chinese Middle Jurassic shows similarities with pterosaurs from the European Lower and Middle Jurassic it can be considered as a representative of a distinct group of pterosaurs and thus is evidence of a wide distribution of flying reptiles to eastern Asia as early as the Middle Jurassic.

26 Dong Zhiming, 1988. *Dinosaurs of China*. English edition (text by A.C. Milner), 114 pp.; China Ocean Press, Beijing and British Museum (Natural History) London.
27 He Xinlu, Yan Daihan and Su Chunkang, 1983. *A new pterosaur from the Middle Jurassic of Dashanpu, Zigong, Sichuan*. Journal of the Chengdu College of Geology, supplement 1: 27-33; Chengdu, China.

## Evidence from Neuquén

In 1975 R.M. Casamiquela described fragmentary skeletal remains of a small reptile from the Callovian formation of Neuquén in northern Patagonia as a coelurid dinosaur with the name *Herbstosaurus pigmaeus*, named after R. Herbst, who collected the specimen, and because of its small size (pygmy).[28] Pelvis, femur and other remains were found, and first related to *Compsognathus*, a small dinosaur from the Upper Jurassic of Solnhofen. However, it later became clear that *Herbstosaurus* must be a pterosaur.[29] The pelvis and the shape of the femur are similar to those of the Rhamphorhynchoidea, the long-tailed pterosaurs. More precise assignment is not possible, however.

Very few pterosaurs are known from Middle Jurassic strata. The lack of significant fossil sites is explicable on geological grounds. Nevertheless finds of *Rhamphocephalus* in Europe, *Angustinaripterus* in China and *Herbstosaurus* in Argentina show that pterosaurs had managed to spread all over the world in the course of the Middle Jurassic.

## Upper Jurassic Pterosaurs

Solnhofen is a famous name for palaeontologists. It describes a classic fossil site, but is also used to identify an entire area in which fossils have been found in the Southern Franconian Alb in Bavaria. There the numerous quarries in which Solnhofen lithographic limestone is quarried extend over an area of about 50 miles (80km) in an east-westerly direction, essentially along the valley of the Altmühl, which flows into the Danube near Kelheim. For this reason one often finds the blanket term 'Solnhofen' in older museum collections, even when the fossil really comes from quarries in the region of Eichstätt, Pfalzpaint, Gungolding, Zandt, Painten or Kelheim.

28 Casamiquela, R.M., 1975. *Herbstosaurus pigmaeus (Coeluria, Compsognithidae) n.gen.n.sp. del Jurasico medio del Nequén (Patagonia septentrional). Uno de los más pequenos dinosaurios conocidos.* Acta primero Congreso Argentino Paleontologia et Bioestragrafia, 2: 87-102.
29 Ostrom, J.H., 1978. *The Osteology of Compsognathus longipes Wagner*. Zitteliana, 4: 73-118; Munich.

**SUMMARY OF MIDDLE JURASSIC PTEROSAURS**

**Rhamphorhynchoidea**
Family Rhamphorhynchidae
*Rhamphocephalus bucklandi*
Bathonian, Stonesfield Slate, Stonesfield, Oxfordshire, England.[23]
*Rhamphocephalus depressirostris*
Bathonian, Stonesfield Slate, Sarsden near Chipping Norton, Oxfordshire, England.[24]
*Rhamphocephalus prestwichi* Bathonian, Stonesfield Slate, Kineton near Stow-on-the-Wold, Gloucestershire, England.[25]
*Angustinaripterus longicephalus*
Middle Jurassic, Lower Shaximiao Formation, Dashanpu near Zigong, Sichuan, China.[27]

Undetermined family
*Herbstosaurus pigmaeus*
Callovian, Lotena Formation, Neuquén, northern Patagonia, Argentina.[28]

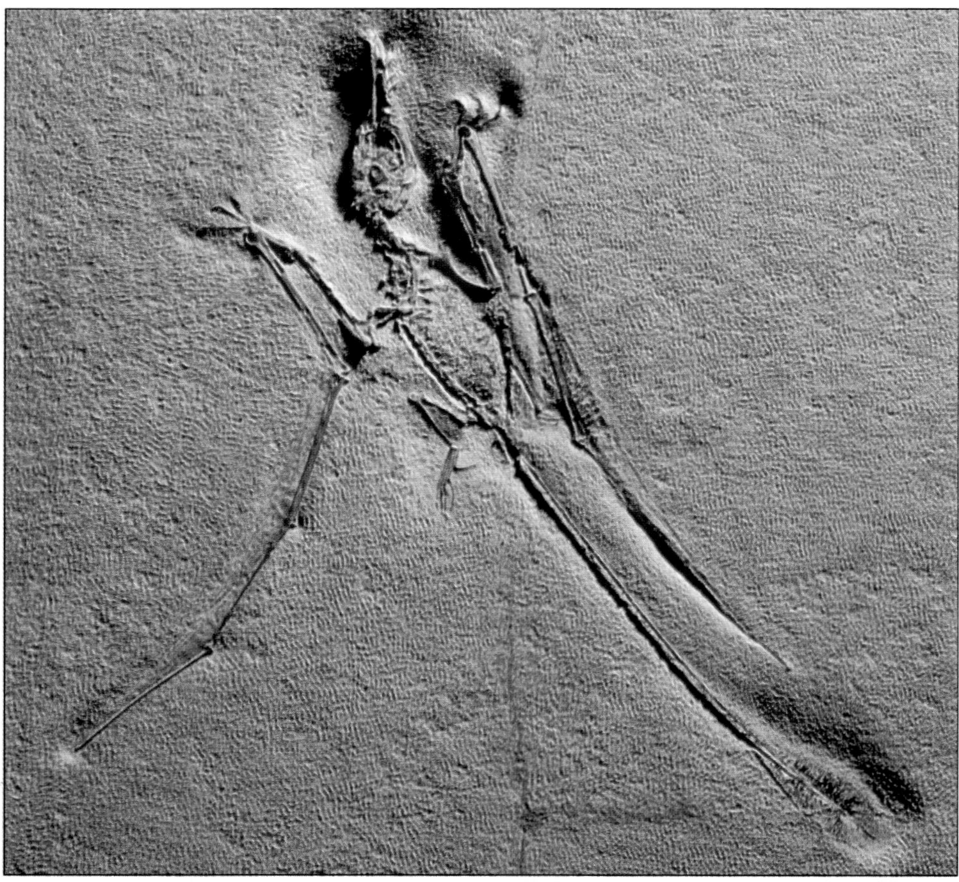

**Above:** *Rhamphorhynchus* is the most frequently occurring pterosaur to be found in the Solnhofen limestone of Bavaria. This individual is a *Rhamphorhynchus longicaudus* skeleton from Upper Jurassic Solnhofen deposits. The wing span of this long-tailed species was about 1·3ft (40cm).

We know from excavations that even ancient Roman builders used these flaggy limestones for building walls, as floor tiles and as slabs for inscriptions.[30] The Romans built a border wall, the so-called *limes*, a few miles north of the Solnhofen area. When the forts along the *limes* were being excavated, Solnhofen slabs were found that had been used by the Roman builders. The wide distribution and popularity of Solnhofen stone in the Middle Ages can be seen from the fact that even Hagia Sofia in Constantinople (now Istanbul, Turkey) was paved with it in the mid thirteenth century.

Alois Senefelder's invention of the lithographic printing process in 1796 gave a tremendous boost to the Solnhofen quarrying industry. It was not until lithographic printing was superseded by modern techniques that the light-coloured Solnhofen stone again became important as building material, especially for paving stones, wall tiles, steps and window sills, as well as stone for garden walls.

When Solnhofen stone is being quarried, which is still done by hand today, the quarry workers continually find fossils, but systematic collecting and research on the Solnhofen fossils did not begin until the late eighteenth century. It was at this time that the first pterosaur find, the Eichstätt *Pterodactylus*, arrived in Elector Karl Theodor's natural history collection in Mannheim (see page 22). Other fossil collections also played a significant role, like that of Duke Maximilian von Leuchtenberg, who became prince of Eichstätt in 1817, and that of the country doctor Carl Haeberlein in Pappenheim near Solnhofen. The most famous palaeontological finds passed through the hands of the elder and the younger Haeberlein, including the first two specimens of *Archaeopteryx lithographica*, the primeval bird. Carl F. Haeberlein (1787-1871) sold his collection of Solnhofen fossils with the first specimen of *Archaeopteryx* from Langenaltheim near Solnhofen for £700 to the British Museum (Natural History) in London in 1862. Ernst O. Haeberlein (1819-1896), his son, secured a price of 20,000 gold marks for the second *Archaeopteryx* specimen from Blumenberg near Eichstätt in 1881. Werner von Siemens, the industrialist, acquired the piece by means of interim financing for the Natural History Museum of the Humboldt-Universität in Berlin.[31]

As well as these famous and rare fossil specimens the Solnhofen strata have produced a mass of other fossil plants and animals for over 200 years. So far about 750 different species have been described. A striking feature of the fossil content is that it includes not only marine forms like ammonites, crabs, fish, and marine reptiles, but also terrestrial organisms like land plants, insects, tortoises and fresh-water crocodiles, sphenodontids, a small dinosaur, numerous pterosaurs and the six primeval birds so far known. This is a result of the way the Solnhofen flaggy limestones came into being: they were formed in a tropical lagoon about 150 million years ago (Lower Tithonian, early Upper Kimmeridgian).[32]

There are numerous theories about the origin of the Solnhofen limestone, and there is not space to discuss them all here. One theory proceeds on the assumption that in the warm climate of the Upper Jurassic the salt concentration of the sea water in the lagoon was raised by evaporation. This led to an oxygen deficit

**Below:** A disarticulated skeleton of *Rhamphorhynchus* from the Upper Jurassic Mörnsheim limestone. The skull, lower jaw, both wings, the long tail, and the large bony breastbone are preserved, as is the sclerotic ring of the eye (upper left corner).

30 In the first three centuries AD this area was part of the Roman province of Raetia, the capital of which was Augusta Vindelicorum, the modern Augsburg.

31 Viohl, G., 1985. *Carl F. and Ernst O. Häberlein, the Sellers of the London and Berlin Specimens of Archaeopteryx.* The Beginnings of Birds, Proceedings of the International Archaeopteryx Conference Eichstätt 1984: 349-352; Eichstätt.

32 In the later Jurassic the area of Solnhofen and the Southern Franconian Alb was a lagoon preceding a continent to the north and protected from the open sea, the Tethys, to the south by a belt of coral reef. However, a connection with deep areas of the Tethys existed via shallows with algal and sponge reefs in the south-west. The Central German continent and its islands were covered with palm and seed ferns, gingko plants and coniferous trees, and populated by insects, land reptiles, pterosaurs and primordial birds. Tributary rivers washed dead plants and animals into the Solnhofen lagoon, lying between the reefs and islands. The most common fossils in the Solnhofen strata are marine animals and plants, however, especially crustaceans, ammonites, squids and fish. Reptile finds suggest that this was a flourishing animal group. There are some well-preserved and complete skeletons of turtles, lizards, rhynchocephalia, tuatara, crocodiles, ichthyosaurs and pterosaurs.

and at times to the poisoning of the water near the bottom of the lagoon by decaying matter. There are hardly any signs of organisms living on the sea floor in the Solnhofen strata. On the other hand these conditions explain the excellent state of fossil preservation, as carrion-eaters could not exist there either.[33]

Although they occur only rarely, pterosaurs are so well documented in Solnhofen that it must be considered the most important site in which they have been found in the world: the unique quality of fossilization has led to the preservation of complete skeletons and the documentation of soft parts like flight membrane prints. Long-tailed pterosaurs were still extant in Solnhofen in the Upper Jurassic, like *Rhamphorhynchus*, together with the first short-tailed pterosaurs like *Pterodactylus*. Together with primeval birds they dominated the air, but certainly had different life styles, or ecological niches, as biologists put it. Solnhofen pterosaurs showed a variety of diverse forms. In size they ranged from small flying saurians with a wing span of only 14in (36cm) to 8·2ft (2·5m).[34]

At the time of writing 17 different species of pterosaur from the Solnhofen limestone have been identified. They can be placed in eight different genera. The many Solnhofen fossils in excellent condition have made a major contribution to better understanding of this extinct reptile group. We have the finds in Bavaria to thank for the fact that pterosaurs are among the best-researched fossil reptiles today. Since the first discovery of a pterosaur skeleton in Eichstätt, described by C. Collini in 1784 and named *Pterodactylus* by G. Cuvier, two to three hundred specimens of pterosaur fossil remains have been unearthed in the Solnhofen lithographic limestone down to the present day. Many of them have found their way into museums and public collections and been investigated scientifically.

**Above:** This small *Rhamphorhynchus* skeleton was a very young individual when it died. Its total length from the end of its snout to the tip of its tail is only 7in (17·5cm). The large eye socket is a typical feature of immature vertebrates. The wings and legs were probably lost when the body was floating in the sea.

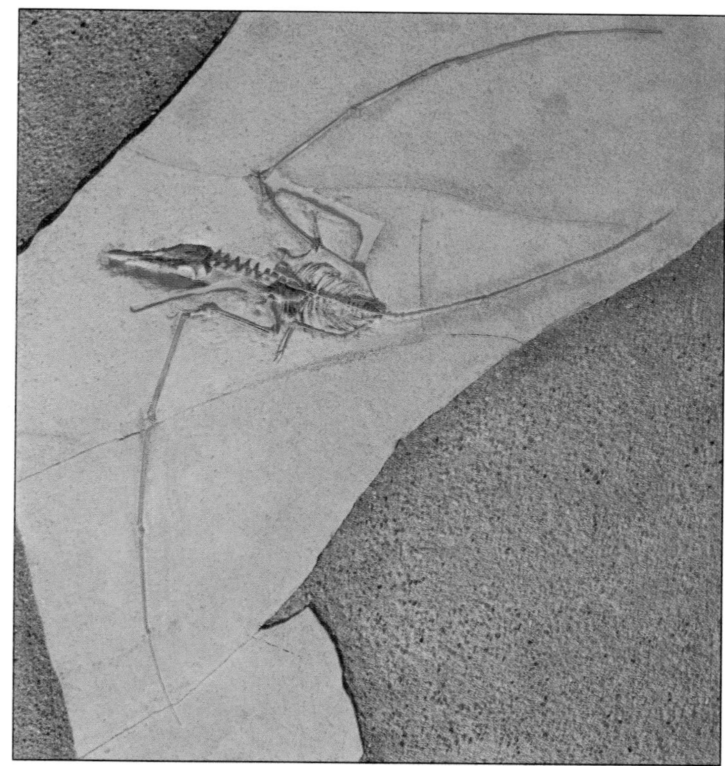

**Right:** A complete skeleton of *Rhamphorhynchus* from Solnhofen showing impressions of the wing membrane. Originally the right wing finger was folded beneath the body, but it has been removed and positioned symmetrically to the left wing. The traces where the bones were previously can still be made out. This masterpiece of the preparator of the Frankfurt Senckenberg-Museum is one of the most spectacular Solnhofen pterosaurs on display.

## Rhamphorhynchus

The most frequently occurring genus is *Rhamphorhynchus* (=beak-snout), a long-tailed pterosaur after whom the whole sub-order is named Rhamphorhynchoidea. In the Upper Jurassic, 150 million years ago, they already had a long period of evolution behind them then. The earliest known pterosaurs, those of the Upper Triassic, 220 million years ago, had been Rhamphorhynchoidea as well. They preserved the long vertebrate tail into the Jurassic, as a legacy of their reptilian ancestors. It is only on the basis of good fossil preservation in the rocks of Solnhofen that we know that there was a rhomboid membrane on the end of this long tail, which was certainly used as a rudder in flight.

Solnhofen long-tailed pterosaurs may have had a long past, but there was no future for them. They had reached the peak of their evolution, but it was also almost the end. Skeletons of *Rhamphorhynchus* have only been found subsequently in the strata above the Solnhofen limestone, the chronologically following geological unit, which is known as the Mörnsheim strata, or Malm Zeta 3. These strata were named

33 Barthel, K.W., 1978. *Solnhofen – Ein Blick in die Erdgeschichte.* 393 pp.; Ott-Verlag, Thun.
Malz, H., 1976. *Solnhofener Plattenkalk: Eine Welt in Stein.* (ed. Th. Kress). 109 pp.; Freunde des Museums beim Solenhofer Aktienverein, Maxberg.
Kuhn, O., 1977. *Die Tierwelt des Solnhofener Schiefers.* 5. Auflage, Neue Brehm-Bücherei, 318, 140 pp.; Ziemsen-Verlag, Wittenberg-Lutherstadt.
Viohl, G., 1985. *Geology of the Solnhofen Lithographic Limestone and the Habitat of Archaeopteryx.* The Beginnings of Birds, Proceedings of the International Archaeopteryx Conference Eichstätt 1984: 31-44; Eichstätt.

34 Wellnhofer, P., 1970. *Die Pterodactyloidea (Pterosauria) der Oberjura-Plattenkalke Süddeutschlands.* Abhandlung der Bayerischen Akademie der Wissenschaften, Neue Folge 141, 133 pp.; Munich.
Wellnhofer, P., 1975. *Die Rhamphorhynchoidea (Pterosauria) der Oberjura-Plattenkalke Süddeutschlands.* Palaeontographica (A), 148: 1-33; 132-186; 149: 1-30; Stuttgart.
Wellnhofer, P., 1983. *Solnhofener Plattenkalk: Urvögel und Flugsaurier.* (ed. Th. Kress). 64 pp.; Freunde des Museums beim Solenhofer Aktienverein, Maxberg.

**Rhamphorhynchus Skeletal Restoration (below)**
This restoration shows an individual that had a wing span of about 3ft (91·5cm). The general body shape is suggestive of a skilful and active flier, as one would expect of a creature that had to hunt from the air to catch its prey. The sharp, forward pointing teeth are particularly evident. Note how delicate the skeleton was when compared to the strongly developed shoulder girdle and wings.

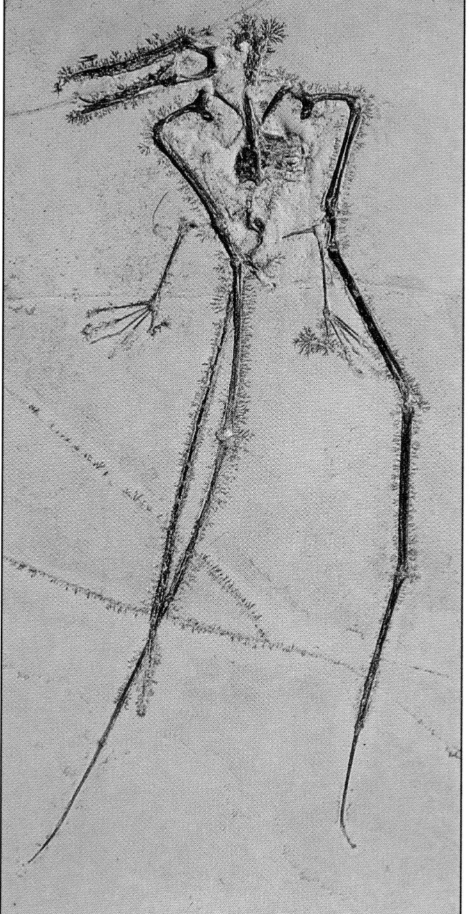

**Left:** This superbly preserved skeleton of *Rhamphorhynchus* is still fully articulated. It shows nicely both wings, the stiff tail, and the bony sternal plate on which the powerful flight muscles were attached. The wing span is c. 3·5ft (1·08m).

**Bottom of page:** This skull of *Rhamphorhynchus* from the Solnhofen limestone reveals the powerful teeth that this pterosaur possessed. In the eye socket the impression of the bony sclerotic ring which protected the eyeball is still visible.

**Below:** Another *Rhamphorhynchus* skull which shows how the long teeth which lined the jaws interlocked when the jaws were closed. This sort of dentition was a perfect adaptation for gripping slippery fish. This skull is 4·13in (10·5cm) long.

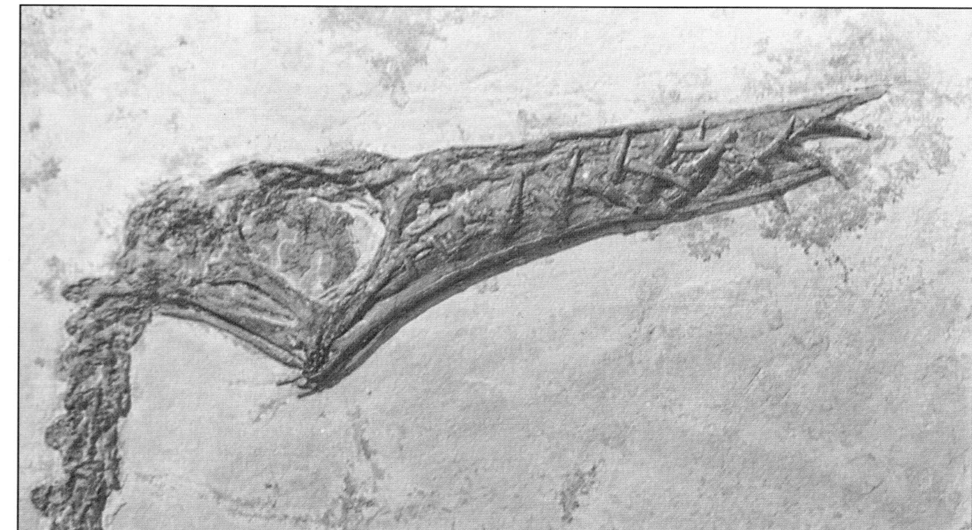

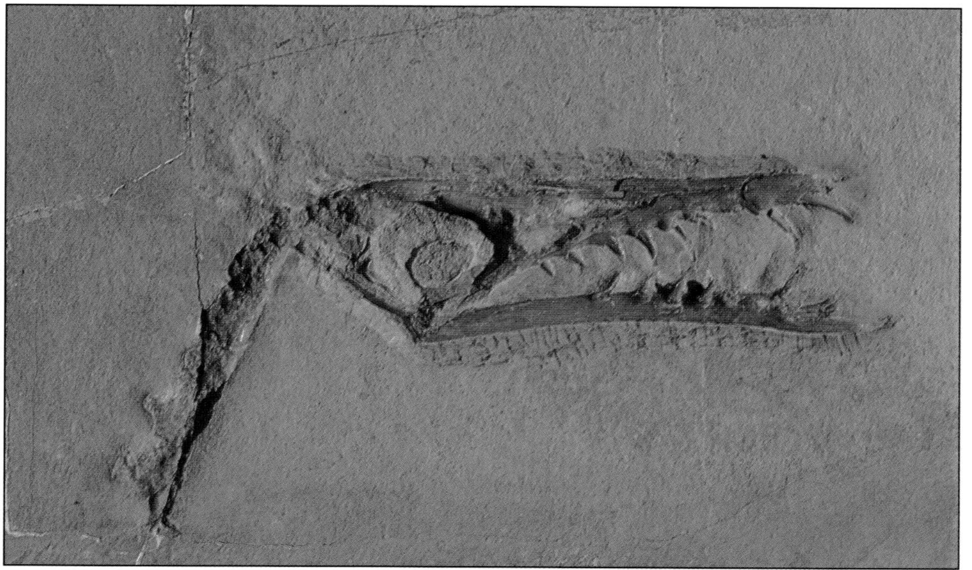

after the little village of Mörnsheim, which is near Solnhofen. They have also been quarried near Daiting, a few miles to the west.

Long-tailed pterosaurs do not occur in more recent Upper Jurassic strata or in the Lower Cretaceous. Thus they became extinct shortly after they had populated the coasts and islands of the Solnhofen lagoon.

*Rhamphorhynchus* was certainly a skilful flier. The sternum, where powerful muscles originated, was a broad plate of bone and had a forward-pointing crest, or cristopina. The neck is short, with compact, short vertebrae. The skull is always large, elongated and has a pointed front end. It has a large orbital opening and two smaller separate openings in the skull in front of the eyes, the nostril and the pre-orbital fenestra. The dentition is always powerfully adapted for catching prey, with long, pointed, slightly curved teeth directed forwards and outwards. When the jaw is closed they mesh alternately. There are 20 teeth in the upper jaw and 14 in the lower jaw. This denti-

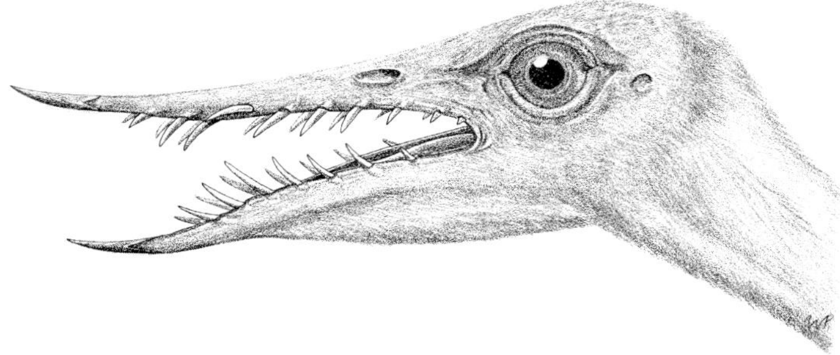

**Rhamphorhynchus Life Portrait (above)**
This restoration shows the head of *Rhamphorhynchus muensteri*, the most common pterosaur found at Solnhofen. The top jaws contains 20 teeth, the lower jaws 14.

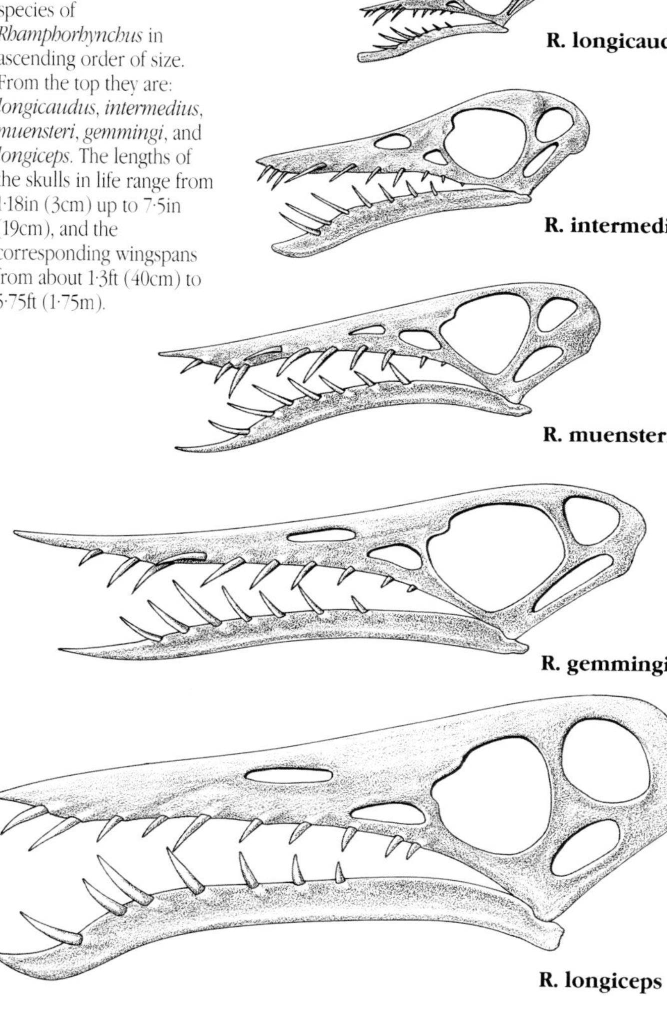


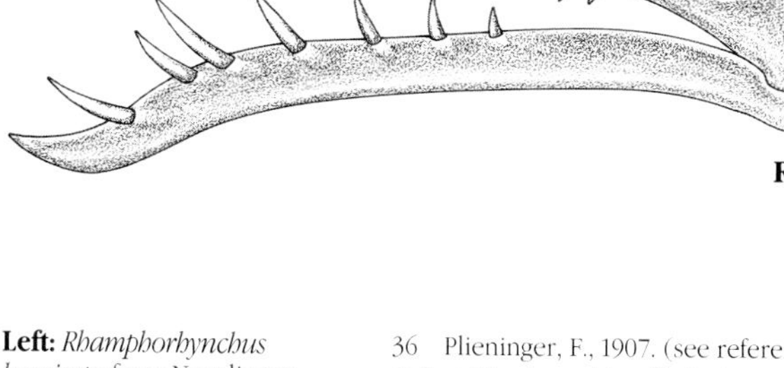


**Rhamphorhynchus Skulls (right)**
These drawings show the skulls of five different species of *Rhamphorhynchus* in ascending order of size. From the top they are: *longicaudus, intermedius, muensteri, gemmingi*, and *longiceps*. The lengths of the skulls in life range from 1·18in (3cm) up to 7·5in (19cm), and the corresponding wingspans from about 1·3ft (40cm) to 5·75ft (1·75m).

**Left:** *Rhamphorhynchus longiceps* from Nusplingen in Württemberg, Germany. This is the largest species of *Rhamphorhynchus* currently known. It has also been found in Solnhofen strata in Bavaria.

tion indicates that most species of *Rhamphorhynchus* were fish eaters. The remains of its last prey, a small fish, were in fact found in the stomach of a Solnhofen *Rhamphorhynchus*.

So far five different species of this genus have been found in Solnhofen. The smallest, *Rhamphorhynchus longicaudus* has a skull only 1·18in long (3cm) and a wing span of 15·75in (40cm). The largest species, *Rhamphorhynchus longiceps*, has a skull 7·5in (19cm) long and a wing span of 5·74ft (1·75m).

The most common species, *Rhamphorhynchus muensteri*, can be divided into two groups. One has a relatively long skull and a long flight digit, the other a relatively shorter skull and shorter flight digit. This suggests sexual dimorphism: the animals with larger skulls and longer wings could be assumed to be males, and the others females.[35] There are no distinctive characteristics on the skeleton to make it possible to distinguish male and female individuals in any other way.

*Rhamphorhynchus* also occurs in the Upper Jurassic flaggy limestone of Nusplingen in Württemberg (southern Germany).[36] This is the species *Rhamphorhynchus longiceps* (=long-skulled beak-snout), also known from Solnhofen in Bavaria. Remains of pterosaur skeletons from the somewhat older Oxford Clay (Upper Jurassic, Oxfordian) of Huntingdonshire in England were assigned to a new species, *Rhamphorhynchus jessoni*[37], and the same is true of individual bones from the Upper Jurassic Tendaguru strata of Tanzania, East Africa. These were discovered in the course of the famous German Tendaguru dinosaur expedition, 1909 to 1913.[38]

Finally individual teeth from the Middle Jurassic (Upper Callovian) and Upper Jurassic (Lower Kimmeridgian) of Portugal have also been assigned by R.A. Thulburn to the genus *Rhamphorhynchus*.[39]

35 Wellnhofer, P., 1975. Palaeontographica (A), 149, p. 3 (see reference 34).

36 Plieninger, F., 1907. (see reference 11).
At first Plieninger identified a large *Rhamphorhynchus* from the Upper Jurassic flaggy limestone of Nusplingen in Württemberg as a separate species, *Rhamphorhynchus kokeni*, but this species is identical with *Rhamphorhynchus longiceps* from the Solnhofen limestone of Eichstätt in Bavaria, described in 1902 by A. Smith-Woodward. With a skull 7·5in (19cm) long and a wing span of 5·74ft (1·75m) this is the largest known species of *Rhamphorhynchus*.
Smith-Woodward, A., 1902. *On two skulls of the Ornithosaurian Rhamphorhynchus*. Annals and Magazine of Natural History, (7), 9: 1-5; London.

37 Lydekker, R., 1890. *On Ornithosaurian Remains from the Oxford Clay of Huntingdonshire*. Quarterly Journal of the Geological Society, 46: 429; London. Description of pterosaur skeletal remains as *Rhamphorhynchus jessoni*.

38 Reck, H., 1931. *Die deutschostafrikanischen Flugsaurier*. Centralblatt für Mineralogie etc., B, 7: 321-336; Stuttgart.
Reck mentioned numerous individual bones and caudal vertebrae from the 'Obere Saurier-Mergel' of Tendaguru Hill in what was then German East Africa, modern Tanzania, and described them as a new species, *Rhamphorhynchus tendagurensis*. See also: Colbert, E.H., 1984. *The Great Dinosaur Hunters and Their Discoveries*. Dover Publications.

39 Thulburn, R.A., 1973. *Teeth of Ornithischian Dinosaurs from the Upper Jurassic of Portugal*. Servizio Geologico Portugal, Memoires, 22, N.S.: 89-134; Lisbon.

## Pterodactylus

The earliest evidence of short-tailed pterosaurs, called Pterodactyloidea after the indicative genus *Pterodactylus* (=flight finger) also comes from Solnhofen limestone. They are about as rare as the Rhamphorhynchoidea, and their principal distinctive characteristic is that they had only a short tail consisting of a few small caudal vertebrae, which was probably meaningless in terms of flight. This new, more 'modern' type of pterosaur appears in several different forms in the Upper Jurassic. This indicates that the Solnhofen Pterodactyloidea had already gone through a long phylogeny, a period in which very different genera came into being, able to conquer differing habitats.

A gap in the fossil record means that we know nothing about the direct ancestors of short-tailed pterosaurs. But as the general structure of their skeleton corresponds basically with that of the long-tailed Rhamphorhynchoidea, we must work on the basis that short-tailed pterosaurs were descendants of this older group of pterosaurs, from which they originated in the Lower or Middle Jurassic.

In order to preserve and possibly improve their ability to fly, proportions were generally altered in the Pterodactyloidea, along with the loss of the tail. The beak became more markedly elongated, and the neck is clearly longer too, as a result of elongation of the individual cervical vertebrae. The head was to a certain extent balanced on the neck and held like that of a pelican in flight, in complete contrast with the Rhamphorhynchoidea, who predominantly held the head extended. The two apertures in the skull before the orbital opening, nostril and preorbital opening, are no longer separated by a bridge of bone, but confluent. The metacarpal bones are relatively long, often even longer than the lower arm. In contrast the flight digit is shorter and the fifth foot digit is reduced and only rudimentarily developed.

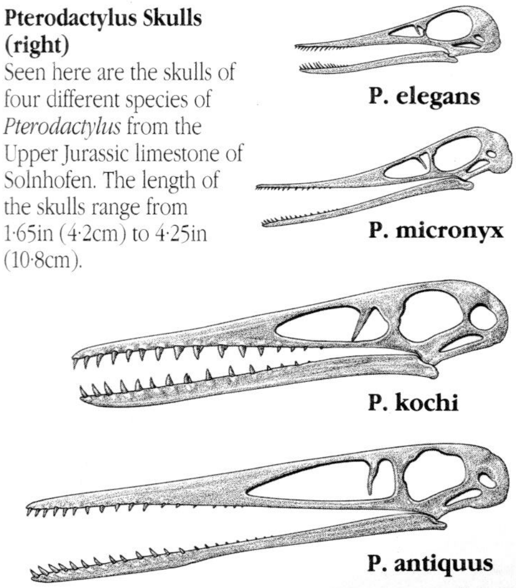

**Pterodactylus Skulls (right)**
Seen here are the skulls of four different species of *Pterodactylus* from the Upper Jurassic limestone of Solnhofen. The length of the skulls range from 1·65in (4·2cm) to 4·25in (10·8cm).

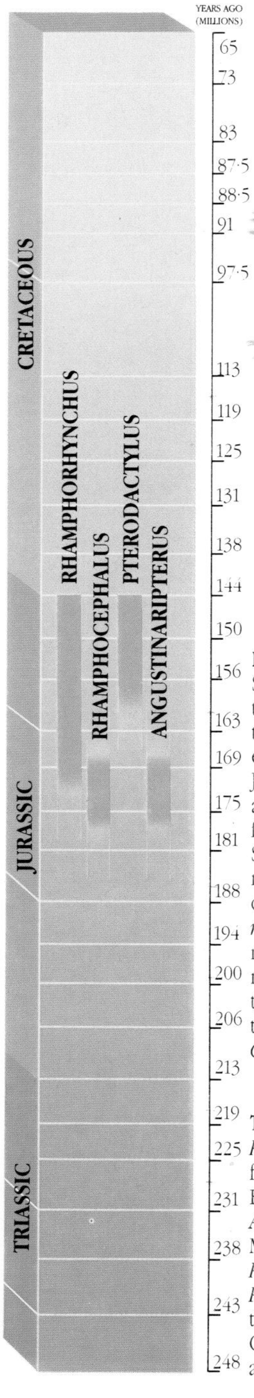

**P. elegans**

**P. micronyx**

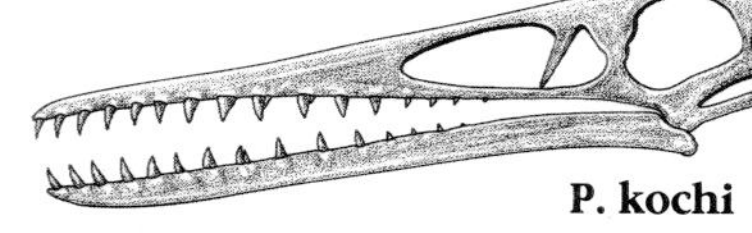

**P. kochi**

**P. antiquus**

**Pterodactylus (right)**
Seen here in a landscape that is probably typical of the Solnhofen near-shore environment in the late Jurassic, *Pterodactylus* was an agile flyer that may have fed on insects or small fish. Strikingly, its tail is very much shorter than that of its contemporary *Rhamphorhynchus*. It was obviously no longer required to maintain flight stability. In the background can be seen the small dinosaur *Compsognathus*.

**Time Chart (left)**
*Rhamphocephalus* is known from the Bathonian of England, and *Angustinaripterus* from the Middle Jurassic of China. *Rhamphorhynchus* and *Pterodactylus* both peak in the Upper Jurassic of Germany, England, France and East Africa.

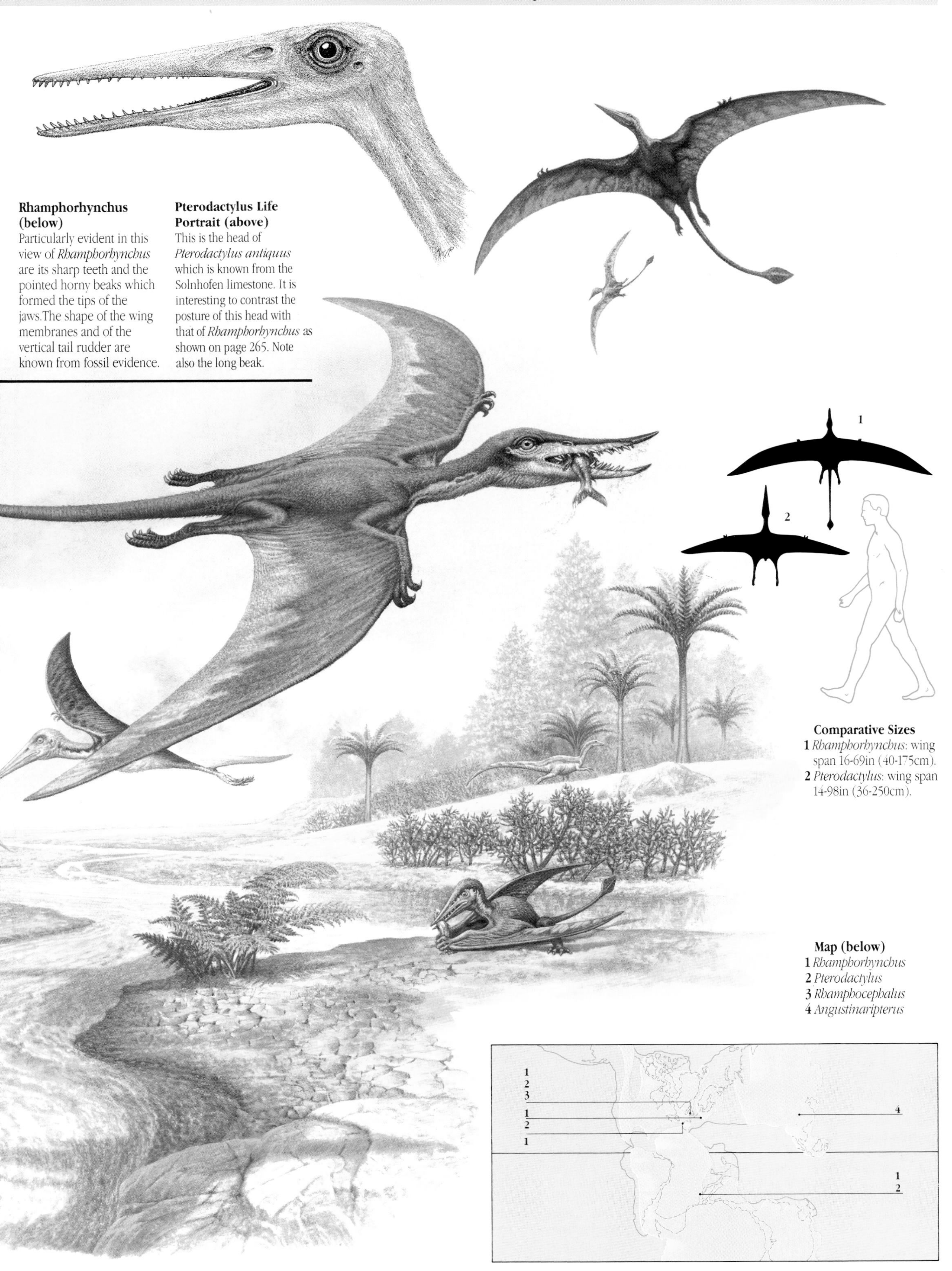


**Rhamphorhynchus (below)**
Particularly evident in this view of *Rhamphorhynchus* are its sharp teeth and the pointed horny beaks which formed the tips of the jaws.The shape of the wing membranes and of the vertical tail rudder are known from fossil evidence.

**Pterodactylus Life Portrait (above)**
This is the head of *Pterodactylus antiquus* which is known from the Solnhofen limestone. It is interesting to contrast the posture of this head with that of *Rhamphorhynchus* as shown on page 265. Note also the long beak.

**Comparative Sizes**
**1** *Rhamphorhynchus*: wing span 16-69in (40-175cm).
**2** *Pterodactylus*: wing span 14-98in (36-250cm).

**Map (below)**
**1** *Rhamphorhynchus*
**2** *Pterodactylus*
**3** *Rhamphocephalus*
**4** *Angustinaripterus*

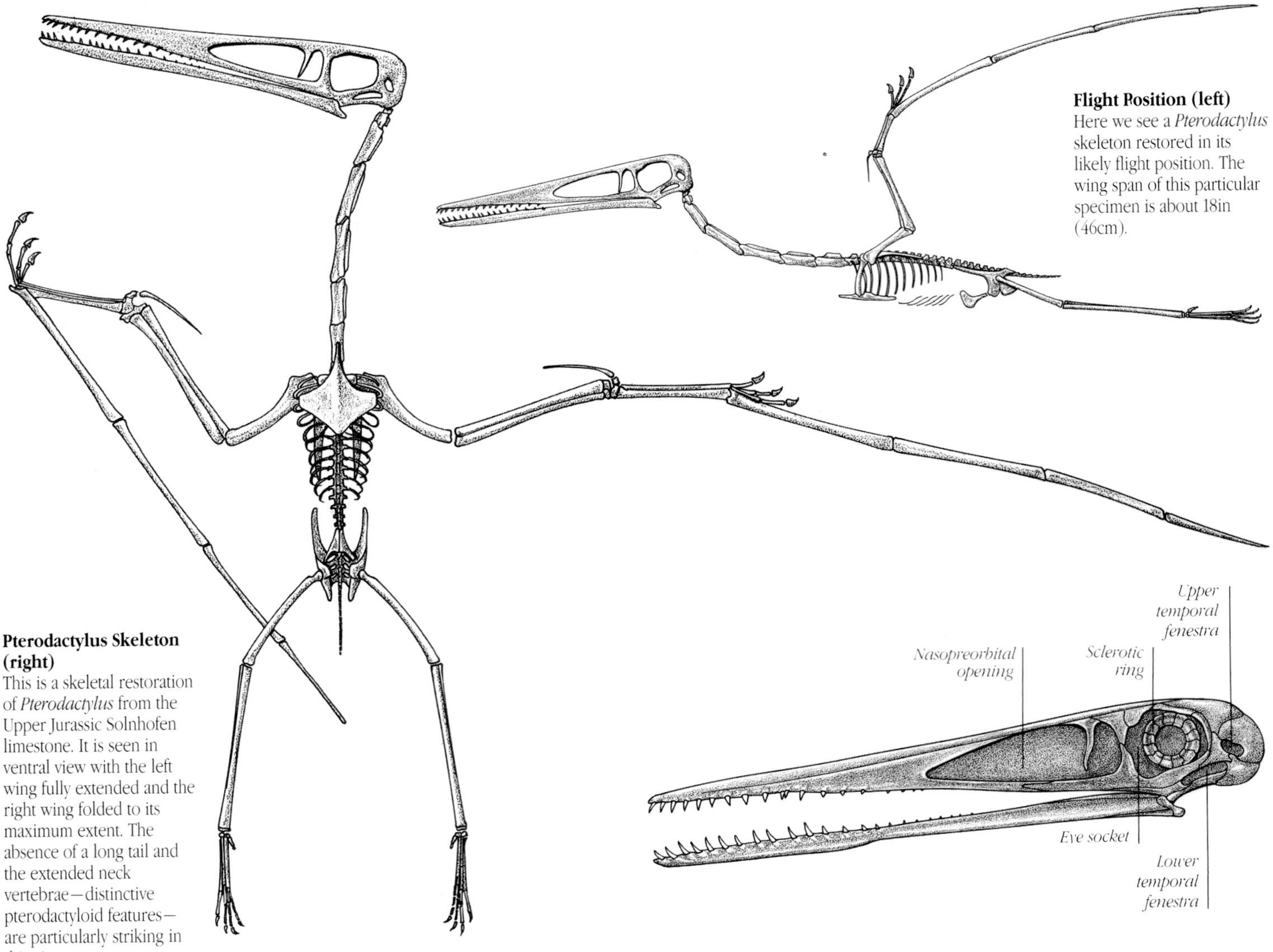

**Flight Position (left)**
Here we see a *Pterodactylus* skeleton restored in its likely flight position. The wing span of this particular specimen is about 18in (46cm).

**Pterodactylus Skeleton (right)**
This is a skeletal restoration of *Pterodactylus* from the Upper Jurassic Solnhofen limestone. It is seen in ventral view with the left wing fully extended and the right wing folded to its maximum extent. The absence of a long tail and the extended neck vertebrae—distinctive pterodactyloid features—are particularly striking in this view.

*Nasopreorbital opening*
*Sclerotic ring*
*Upper temporal fenestra*
*Eye socket*
*Lower temporal fenestra*

The short-tailed pterosaurs we encounter in the Solnhofen strata are still in the early stages of their evolution. They survived the change from the Jurassic to the Cretaceous, spread throughout the world even in the Lower Cretaceous and in their final form achieved bizarre shapes and gigantic dimensions. Five different genera of Pterodactyloidea have so far been found in the Solnhofen limestone, in which again a good ten species can be distinguished.[40] *Pterodactylus* specimens have also been found in the somewhat younger Mörnsheim strata as well (Malm Zeta 3).

Six species of this genus can be distinguished in the Solnhofen strata. The smallest is *Pterodactylus elegans*, diagnosed by its long, thin teeth, found only in the front part of the jaw. Its wing span is only 10in (25cm). The most common species is *Pterodactylus kochi*, of which there are fine, complete specimens in many museums and collections, some with surviving imprints of the flight membrane.[41] A series of smaller skeletons can be categorized as young animals of the species. When fewer finds were available, these small specimens were thought to be distinct species. However, it is possible to identify the younger animals quite definitively by the degree of ossification of the small toe phalanges. The smallest *Pterodactylus* and therefore probably the youngest ever found in the Solnhofen strata had a trunk length of only 0·75in (2cm) with a wing span of 7in (18cm). This baby pterosaur could only have been a few weeks old, but was certainly already able to fly properly.

Adult *Pterodactylus kochi* reach a wing span of about 20in (50cm). Thus they were about the size of a common moorhen. The larger Solnhofen *Pterodactylus* species like *Pterodactylus longicollum* (=long-necked flight finger), for example, reached wing spans of 4·75ft (1·45m), thus corresponding to the modern herring gull. We only know individual wing and leg bones of the largest species, *Pterodactylus grandis*. The bones suggest a wing span of about 8·2ft (2·5m), corresponding to the size of a bearded vulture. Thus this species was one of the largest of all the Jurassic pterosaurs.

Skeletal remains from Upper Jurassic strata in France, England and East Africa were also assigned to the genus *Pterodactylus*. Thus in 1859 H. von Meyer described a single bone from the upper arm (humerus) from the lithographic limestone of Cerin (Ain) in France as *Pterodactylus cerinensis*,[42] and a tibia was later assigned to the same genus.[43] In 1873 indivi-

dual skeletal remains of a large pterosaur from the Upper Jurassic of Boulogne-sur-Mer in northern France were described as *Pterodactylus suprajurensis*,[44] and again in 1874 R. Owen established two new species, *Pterodactylus manseli* and *Pterodactylus pleydelli* for indivi-

40 Wellnhofer, P., 1970. *Die Pterodactyloidea (Pterosauria) der Oberjura-Plattenkalke Süddeutschlands.* Abhandlungen der Bayerischen Akademie der Wissenschaften, N.F., 141 133 pp.; Munich.

41 Wellnhofer, P., 1987. *Die Flughaut von Pterodactylus (Reptilia, Pterosauria) am Beispiel des Wiener Exemplares von Pterodactylus kochi (Wagner).* Annalen des Naturhistorischen Museums Wien, 88 (A): 149-162; Vienna.

42 Meyer, H. von, 1859-1860. *Reptilien aus dem lithographischen Schiefer des Jura in Deutschland und Frankreich.* 144 pp.; Frankfurt.

43 Lortet, L., 1892. *Les Reptiles fossiles du Bassin du Rhône.* Archives du Musée d'Histoire Naturelle Lyon, 5: 1-139; Lyon.

44 Sauvage, H.E., 1873. *Note sur les reptiles fossiles.* Bulletin de la Société Géologique de France. ser. 3, 1: 365; Paris.

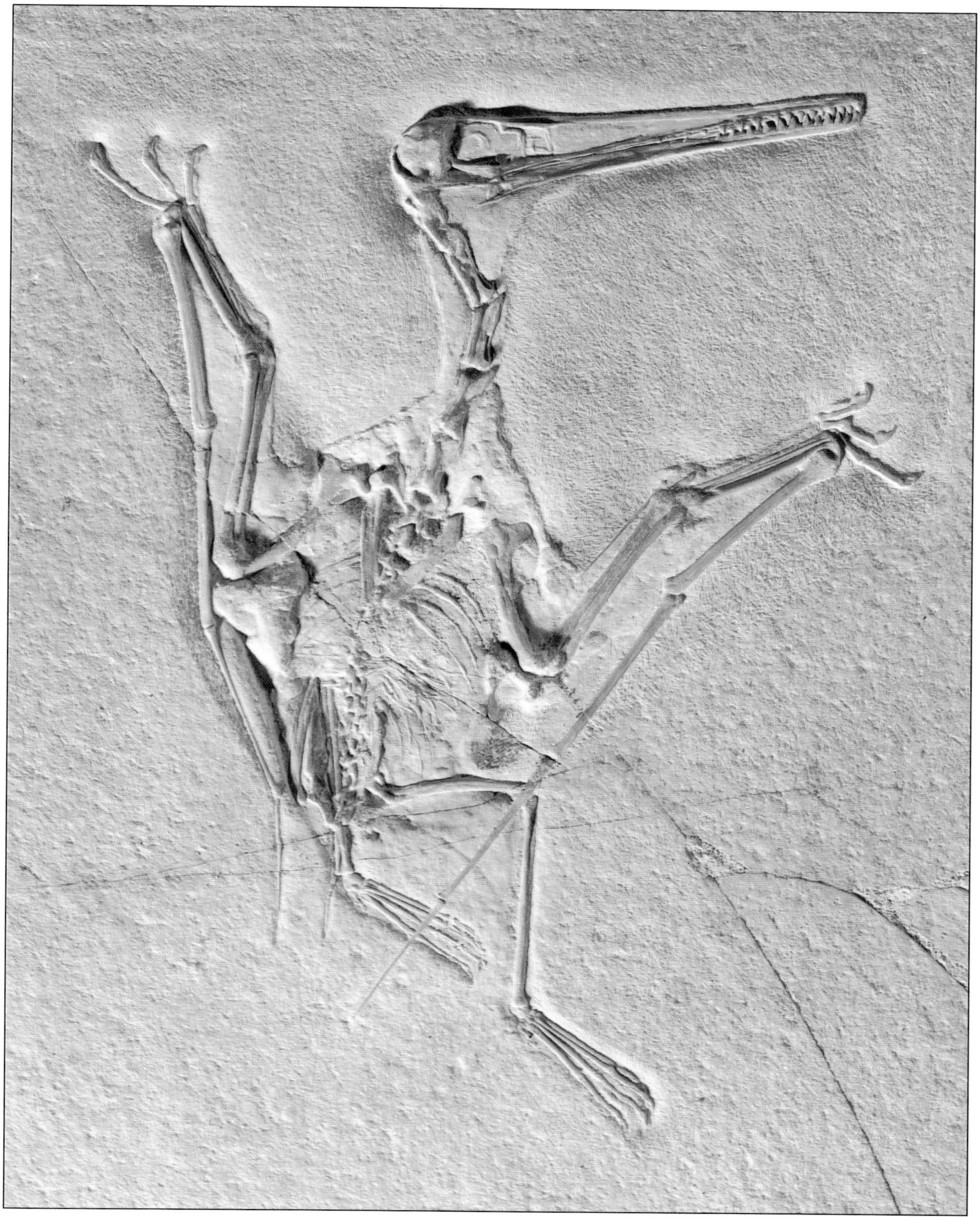

**Right:** *Pterodactylus kochi* from the Solnhofen limestone of Bavaria. *P. kochi* is the most common species of *Pterodactylus* to have been discovered. This Munich specimen is one of the most complete and best preserved pterodactyls in existence. Imprints of the wing membranes can be seen around the margin of the skeleton. The position of the head, rectangular on the neck, is typical of the short-tailed pterodactyloids. The wing span is 18in (46cm). Thus *Pterodactylus kochi* was about the size of a common moorhen. Larger species are known, the largest of all being *Pterodactylus grandis* which seems to have been about the size of a modern vulture.

**Pterodactylus antiquus Skull (left)**
This is a restoration of the skull of *Pterodactylus antiquus*, a species which is again known from the Solnhofen limestone of Bavaria. In contrast to *Rhamphorhynchus*, the nostril and the preorbital opening are not completely separated by a bridge of bone, but are confluent as shown here. The length of this particular skull is 4·25in (10·8cm). The drawing is based on the type specimen first described by Collini in 1784.

**Left:** The smallest pterodactyl ever discovered is a juvenile individual from the Solnhofen limestone. This baby pterosaur had a wing span of only 7in (18cm), and a body length of only 0·75in (2cm). It was probably just a few weeks old when it died. The indication that it is a juvenile, and not a distinct species in its own right, is the lack of complete ossification of the skeleton.

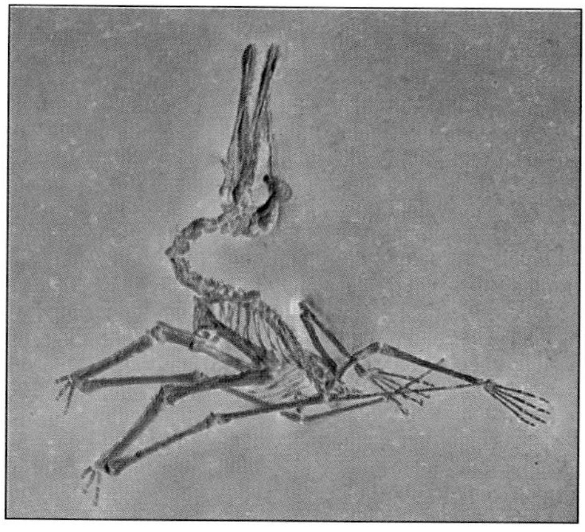

**Left:** *Pterodactylus elegans* from the Solnhofen limestone is one of the smallest pterosaur species. Its wing span was only about 10in (25cm). After death the head was pulled backwards by strong ligaments between the neck vertebrae, after the decay of the neck muscles. This bend of the neck may indicate that this animal died on dry land and was washed into the lagoon as a dried mummy.

dual pterosaur bones from the Kimmeridge Clay of Weymouth on the Dorset coast of south-east England.[5] Kimmeridge Clay, named after the small town of Kimmeridge east of Lyme Regis, corresponds in age in its higher layers to the Solnhofen Limestone of Bavaria. As well as large numbers of ammonite fauna it also contains fossil reptiles such as plesiosaurs, ichthyosaurs, crocodiles and, though very rarely, pterosaur bones as well. In the eighteenth century alum was mined from the clay and clay shales here. The famous, or rather infamous, 'Kimmeridge coal', a bituminous oil shale, had also been mined along the cliffs for centuries. The English geologist W.J.Arkell reported as late as 1933 that Kimmeridge oil shale was burned for heating purposes in the huts of the neighbourhood instead of coal, and that the inhabitants' noses had apparently become accustomed to the high sulphur content of the smoke produced.[2] In the second half of the nineteenth century oil was distilled from Kimmeridge Clay, but the high sulphur content and thinness of the strata that could be mined made the process uneconomic.

And finally, in the course of the dinosaur excavations on Tendaguru Hill in Tanzania, East Africa, *Pterodactylus* remains were found as well as *Rhamphorhynchus* fossils, and these were assigned to three different new species, *Pterodactylus arningi*, *Pterodactylus brancai* and *Pterodactylus maximus* by Reck in 1931,[38] though P.Galton of Bridgeport University believes that *Pterodactylus brancai* consisting of a bird-like tibiotarsus, corresponds better to the genus *Dsungaripterus* from the Lower Cretaceous of China than to the Solnhofen *Pterodactylus*.[45] There are also other species based on individual bones from France and England which cannot be assigned to the genus *Pterodactylus* with any certainty.

45 Galton, P., 1980. *Avian-like tibiotarsi of pterodactyloids (Reptilia: Pterosauria) from the Upper Jurassic of East Africa.* Paläontologische Zeitschrift, 54 (3/4): 331-342; Stuttgart.

**Time Chart (left)**
*Scaphognathus* and *Anurognathus* were contemporary rhamphorhynchoid pterosaurs known only from the Upper Jurassic (Tithonian) Solnhofen limestone. Along with all other long-tailed pterosaurs, they both died out before the end of the Jurassic.

**Anurognathus (right)**
This is one of the strangest pterosaurs which is known only by a single fossil specimen from the Solnhofen limestone. In its general body proportions it is a rhamphorhynchoid, but its tail is greatly reduced in length and forms a kind of bird-like pygostyl or 'Parson's nose'. *Anurognathus* was a slender pterosaur with extremely long wings. It had a short, deep head with a broad mouth and small, peg-like teeth. This suggests that *Anurognathus* was insectivorous, and was therefore an agile, highly manoeuvrable flyer. In this view it is snapping at a woodwasp (*Pseudosirex*) which is also documented in the fossil record of Solnhofen.

**Map (left)**
**1** *Scaphognathus*
**2** *Anurognathus*

## Scaphognathus and Anurognathus

The genus *Scaphognathus* (=tub-jaw) is hitherto known only from two specimens from the Solnhofen limestone. The first was one of the earliest pterosaur finds of all and was described as early as 1831 by Bonn professor August Goldfuss.[46] As the tail region had not survived, Goldfuss thought he was dealing with a *Pterodactylus*, which he called *Pterodactylus crassirostris* (=thick-beaked flight finger). The find was made in Eichstätt and is in the collection of the University of Bonn. The second specimen of *Scaphognathus* came from the Solnhofen limestone of Mühlheim near Solnhofen. Here the long tail was preserved, mean-

46 Goldfuss, A., 1831. *Beiträge zur Kenntnis verschiedener Reptilien der Vorwelt.* Nova Acta Academiae Leopoldinae Carolinae, 15: 61-128; Breslau and Bonn. Wellnhofer, P., 1983. (see reference 34), p. 42-43.

**Right:** A young, half-grown *Scaphognathus* from the Solnhofen limestone. It is the second known specimen of this rare pterosaur genus. The immature skeleton was not fully ossified: the tail was still flexible, and some small foot bones had not yet developed.

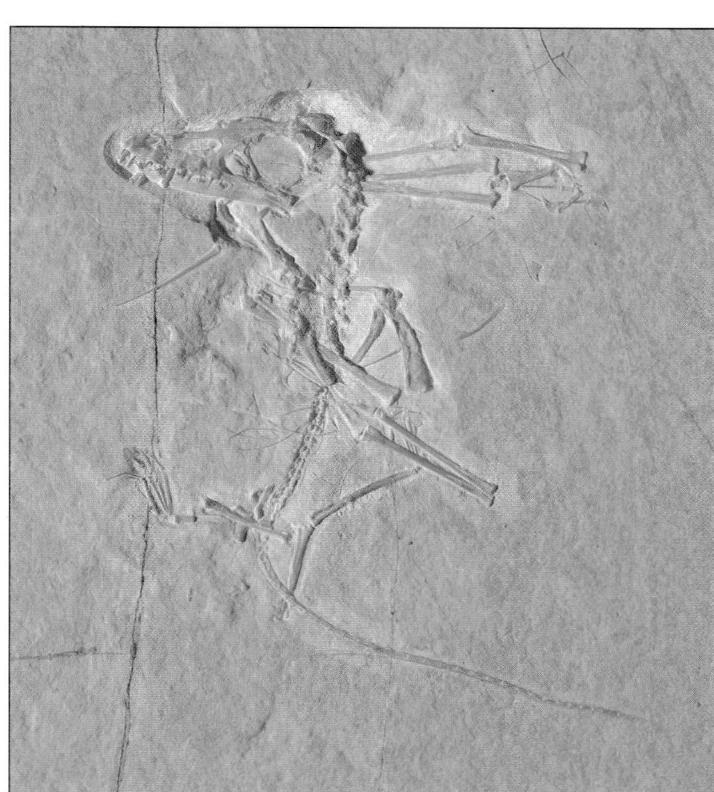

**Scaphognathus (below)**
In its general body proportions and with its long tail, *Scaphognathus* resembles *Rhamphorhynchus*, but it does have some peculiarities. *Scaphognathus* had a somewhat shorter head and long teeth which were set in an upright position. The tips of the jaws are not as pointed as in *Rhamphorhynchus*, but rather blunt. It is not clear, however, whether *Scaphognathus* was an insect feeder or a fish catcher.

**Comparative Sizes (above)**
1 *Anurognathus*: wing span 20in (50cm).
2 *Scaphognathus*: wing span 3ft (90cm).

**Right:** *Scaphognathus crassirostris* is a long-tailed rhamphorhynchoid pterosaur with long, upright teeth. The skull length of this specimen is 4·5in (11·5cm). Its wing span is relatively small: just 3ft (90cm). This specimen was described by August Goldfuss as early as 1831.

**An Immature Scaphognathus (below)**
This is a drawing of the juvenile, half-grown individual of *Scaphognathus* that is pictured on the previous page. This fossil comes from the Solnhofen limestone of Mühlheim. The preservation of the long tail meant that this genus could be confidently classified with the Rhamphorhynchoidea. We can deduce that this individual died before it was fully grown because its skeleton was not fully ossified; note that there are some small bones missing in the foot.

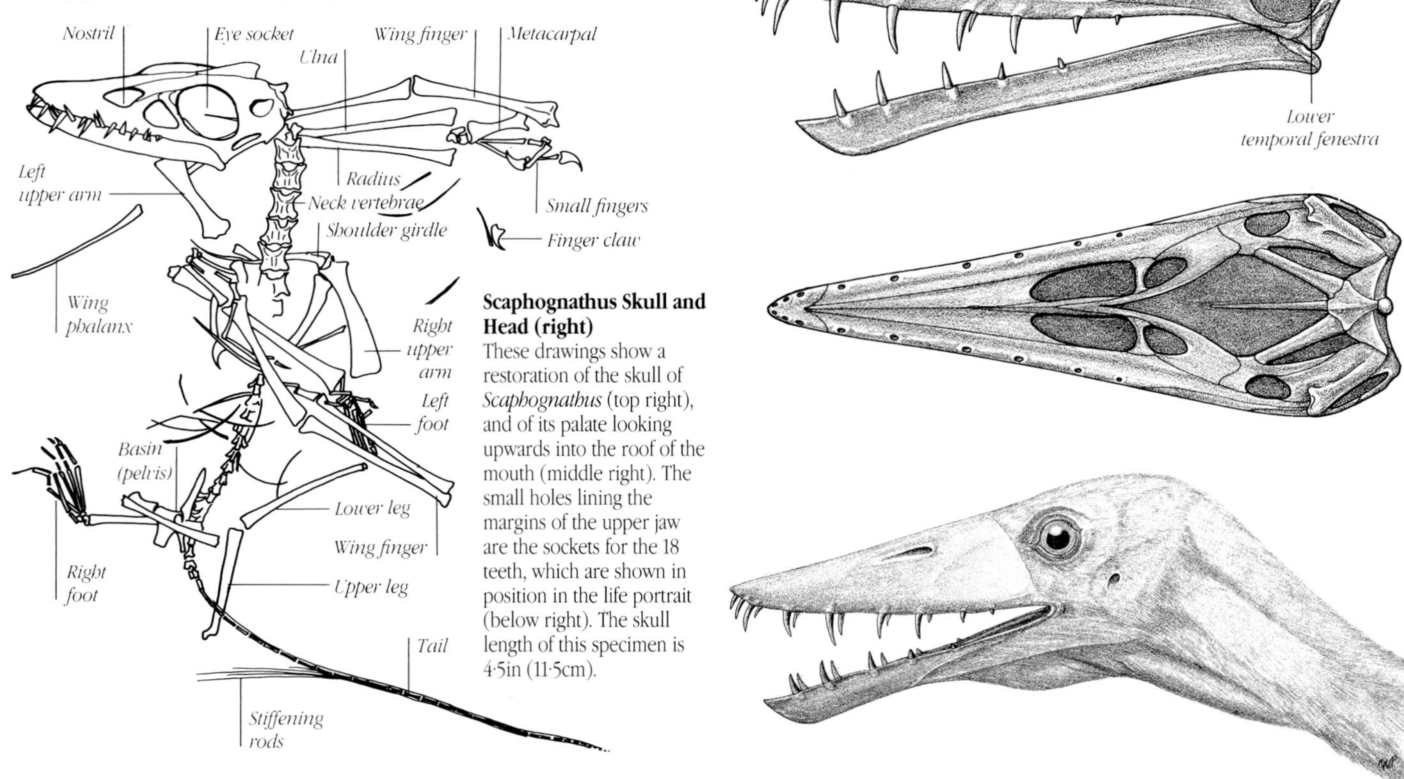

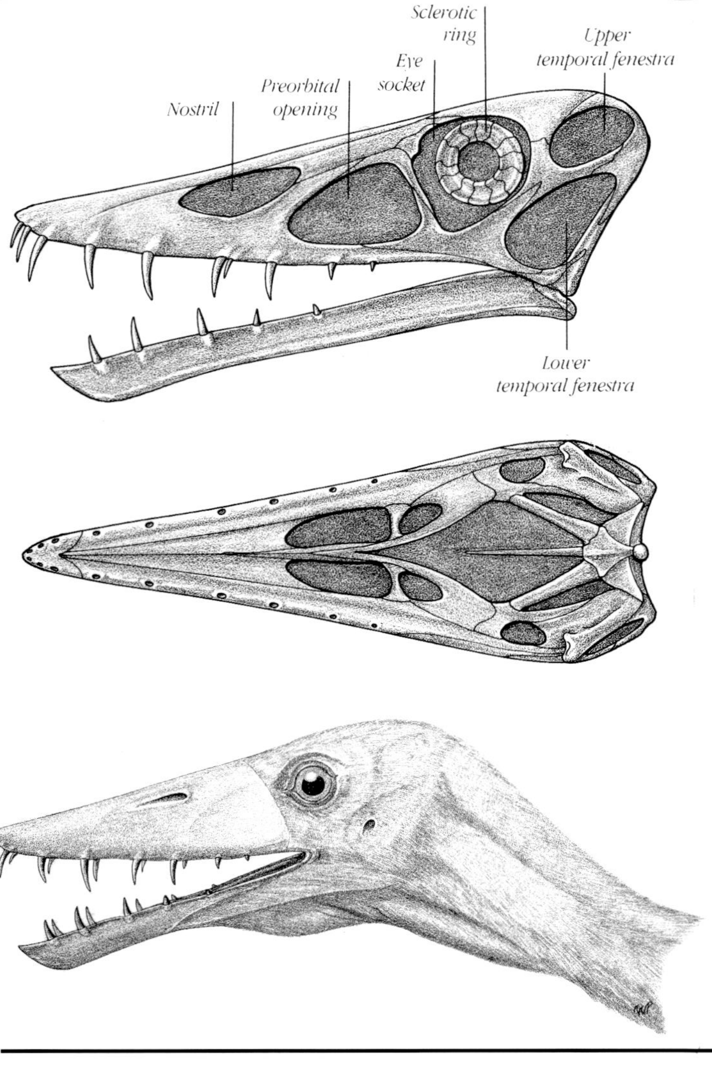

**Scaphognathus Skull and Head (right)**
These drawings show a restoration of the skull of *Scaphognathus* (top right), and of its palate looking upwards into the roof of the mouth (middle right). The small holes lining the margins of the upper jaw are the sockets for the 18 teeth, which are shown in position in the life portrait (below right). The skull length of this specimen is 4·5in (11·5cm).

ing that this genus could be classified with the long-tailed pterosaurs, the Rhamphorhynchoidea. The Mühlheim specimen is about half the size of the one from Eichstätt. From the small degree of ossification in the smaller specimen we must assume that this was a young animal that died before it was fully grown. But both specimens are of the same species. *Scaphognathus* had a shorter, more compact skull than *Rhamphorhynchus*. Its teeth, 18 in the upper jaw and 10 in the lower jaw, did not point forward, but were set upright in the jaw. The ends of the jaw do not meet at a point at the front, but are fairly blunt, like the bow of a boat, hence its name. Also the preorbital fenestrae are larger than in *Rhamphorhynchus*. The young *Scaphognathus* had a wing span of 20in (50cm), and the adult a span of 3ft (90cm).

So far only one specimen of *Anurognathus* (=tailless jaw) has been found, and this only as a negative imprint of skeletal remains on the surface of an Eichstätt limestone slab. It was described in 1923 as *Anurognathus ammoni*, after the Bavarian geologist Ludwig von Ammon, and is in the Paläontologische Staatssammlung in Munich.[47] This was a small and graceful pterosaur, one of the long-tailed group, the Rhamphorhynchoidea. It occupies a special place within this group, however. It has a short, reduced tail, a kind of 'Parson's nose' as in birds, but has to be classified as rhamphorhynchoid because of other skeletal characteristics. Thus it has a short metacarpus, a short neck and a long fifth digit on the foot. It also has a striking high, short skull, with small peg-like teeth. As *Anurognathus* apparently had a broad mouth it is to be assumed that it was insectivorous. Therefore it must have been an extraordinarily skilful flier if it caught its prey, dragonflies or wood-wasps, in flight. Its trunk was only 2in (5cm) long but it had extremely long wings with a span of 1·6ft (50cm).

**Above:** *Anurognathus ammoni* from the Solnhofen limestone of Bavaria. This is the only known specimen of this rhamphorhynchoid pterosaur which had a short tail.

**Anurognathus ammoni (below)**
This fragmentary skeleton is the unique specimen of *Anurognathus*. The actual fossil is shown in the photograph above. In fact, what we see are the impressions of bones rather than the bones themselves; it is like looking at a negative imprint of the skeleton. *Anurognathus* is an interesting genus because its tail is reduced to a short stump, similar to the Parson's nose or pygostyl of modern birds. Despite this feature, the general bauplan of the skeleton reveals that it must be grouped within the long-tailed pterosaurs; it is one of the rhamphorhynchoids.

**Anurognathus Skull and Head (below right)**
The skull of *Anurognathus* is short and broad, with large openings. Is is only 1·2in (3cm) in length. Its broad, rounded jaws which are studded with short, peg-like teeth suggest that this pterosaur may have been an insect eater. If that were the case, it must have been a very agile flier to hunt down its prey on the wing, just as insectivorous birds today are quick and nimble in the air. The poor fossil preservation resulted in a rather tentative restoration.

47 Döderlein, L., 1923. *Anurognathus Ammoni, ein neuer Flugsaurier.* Sitzungsberichte der Bayerischen Akademie der Wissenschaften, math.-naturwiss. Klasse, 117-164; Munich.
Döderlein, L., 1929. *Über Anurognathus Ammoni Döderlein.* Sitzungsberichte der Bayerischen Akademie der Wissenschaften, math.-naturwiss. Klasse, 47-63; Munich.

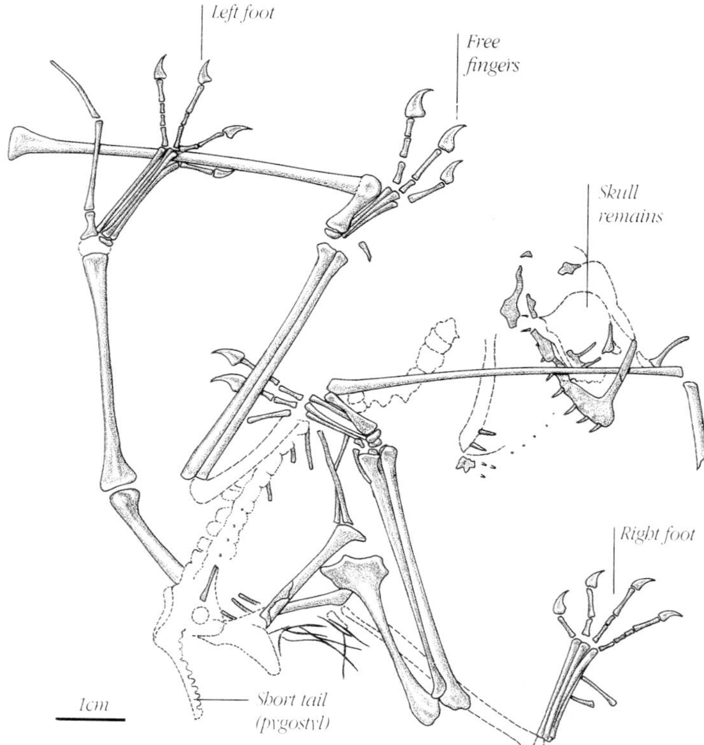


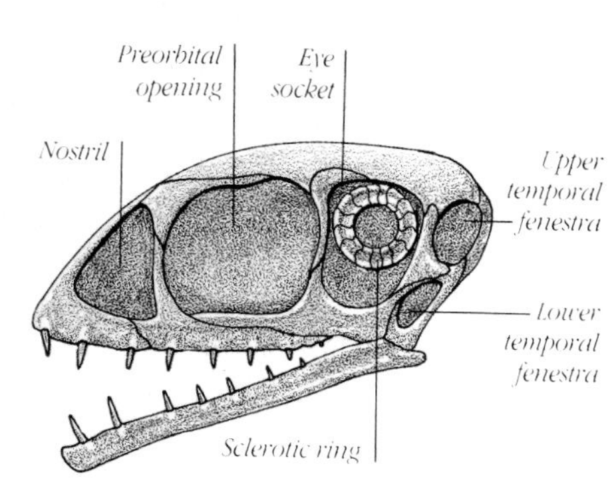


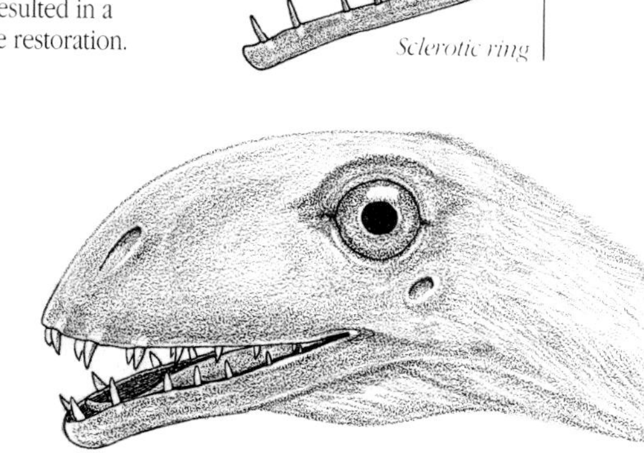

**Germanodactylus (left)**
Seen here in a late Jurassic landscape are two *Germanodactylus* short-tailed pterosaurs, one using its strong finger claws to climb up the trunk of a tree, and the other hanging head down from a branch by its feet in a bat-like fashion. Whether pterosaurs could actually rest in this position has been questioned by some scientists, however. The characteristic median crest on *Germanodactylus*' head is particularly evident in this view. It was probably covered with a horny carina. Two different species of this pterosaur have been discovered.

**Gallodactylus (right)**
In general appearance *Gallodactylus* resembled *Pterodactylus*. However, it had a number of distinct characteristics, such as the short medial crest at the rear of the head and teeth that were confined to the front ends of the long, slender jaws. The forwardly pointing teeth would have formed a very efficient gripping tool for grasping slippery fish from out of the water. *Gallodactylus* is known from late Jurassic strata in France and Germany.

**Above:** *Germanodactylus rhamphastinus*, the second species of *Germanodactylus* known from Bavaria. It is known only from the Mörnsheim limestone which is slightly younger than Solnhofen limestone.

## Germanodactylus

We now turn our attention back to a pterodactlyoid pterosaur. The genus *Germanodactylus* (=German finger) was introduced in 1964 by the Chinese palaeontologist C.C.Young for a Solnhofen pterosaur which C.Wiman had already described in 1925 as *Pterodactylus cristatus* (=*Pterodactylus* with crest).[48] So far there have been very few finds of this genus, representing two different species, *Germanodactylus cristatus* from the limestone of Solnhofen and *Germanodactylus rhamphastinus* from Daiting. The Daiting specimen comes from the strata above the Solnhofen limestone, and is thus somewhat younger. It is therefore possible that in terms of phylogeny it should be seen as a descendant of the older Solnhofen species.

*Germanodactylus*' typical characteristic is a low bone crest on the mid-line of the skull, starting above the nostril and extending above the openings for the eye sockets. The dentition consists of a long row of powerful and relatively short teeth. The smaller *Germanodactylus cristatus* had a skull length of 5·1in (13cm) with a wing span of 3·2ft (98cm), the larger *Germanodactylus rhamphastinus* a skull length of 8·3in (21cm) and wing span of 3·5ft (1·08m).

David Unwin of Reading University also assigns vertebrae, radius, ulna, a first flight digit phalanx, and tibia and fibula of a pterosaur from the Kimmeridge Clay of the Dorset Coast of south-east England to the genus *Germanodactylus*.[49] This is not only the first *Germano-*

48 Wiman, C., 1925. *Über Pterodactylus Westmani und andere Flugsaurier.* Bulletin of the Geological Institute of the University of Uppsala, 20: 1-38; Uppsala.
Young, C.C., 1964. *On a new pterosaurian from Sinkiang, China.* Vertebrata Palasiatica, 8: 221-256; Beijing.

**Comparative Sizes (above)**
1 *Gallodactylus*: wing span 4·4ft (1·35m).
2 *Germanodactylus*: wing span 3·5ft (1·08m).

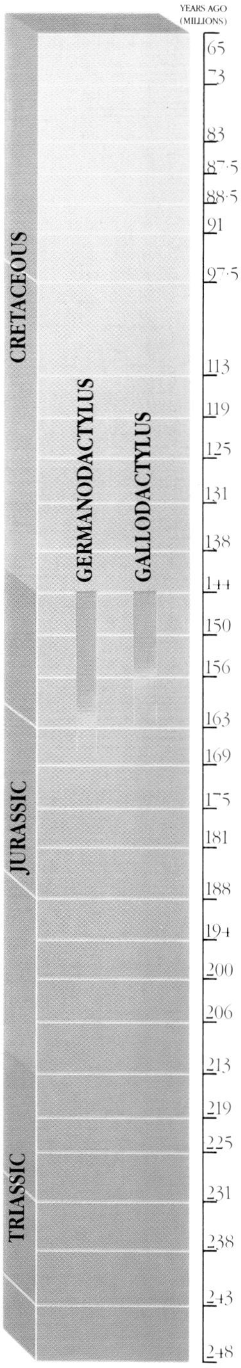

**Time Chart (right)**
*Germanodactylus* and *Gallodactylus* lived at the same time in the Upper Jurassic, and are known from the lithographic limestone of Germany and France. *Germanodactylus*, however, has been reported from slightly older strata of Kimmeridgian age in Dorset, southern England. Neither of these short-tailed pterosaurs survived into the Cretaceous.

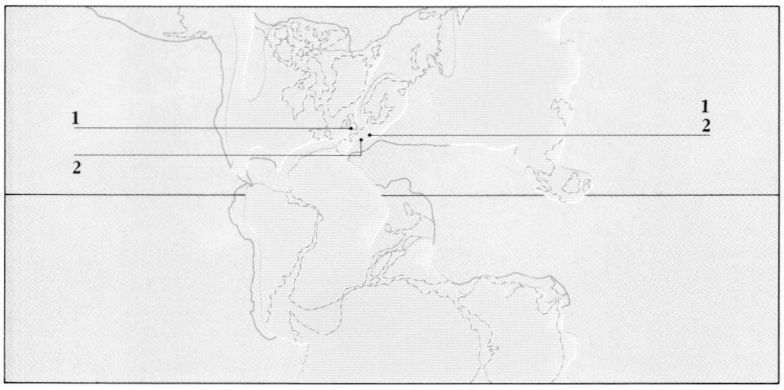

**Map (left)**
1 *Germanodactylus*
2 *Gallodactylus*

49 Unwin, D., 1988. *A new pterosaur from the Kimmeridge Clay of Kimmeridge, Dorset.* Proceedings of the Dorset Natural History and Archaeological Society, 109: 150-153.

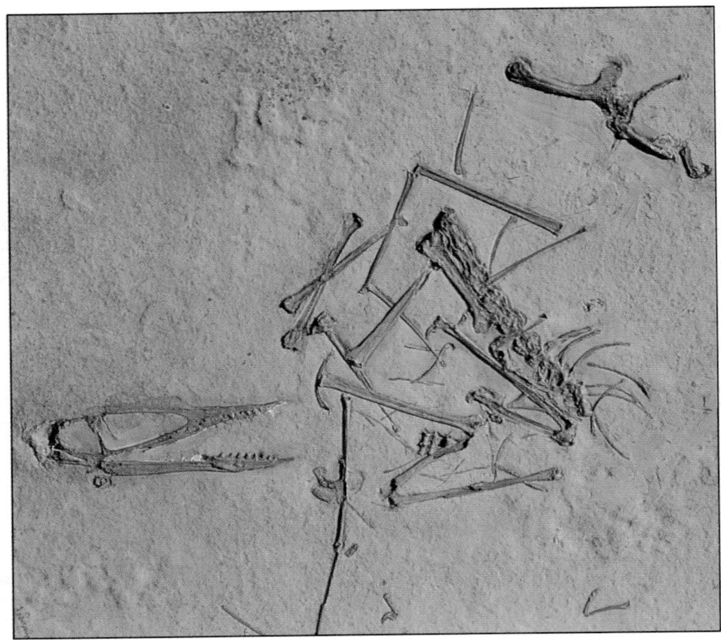

**Left and above:** Shown here are the skeletal remains and skull of *Germanodactylus cristatus* from the Solnhofen limestone of Bavaria. The skeleton is disarticulated, with the trunk, leg and wing bones, and skull having become separated. This smaller species of *Germanodactylus* had a wing span of about 3·2ft (98cm). The sagittal crest is clearly visible.

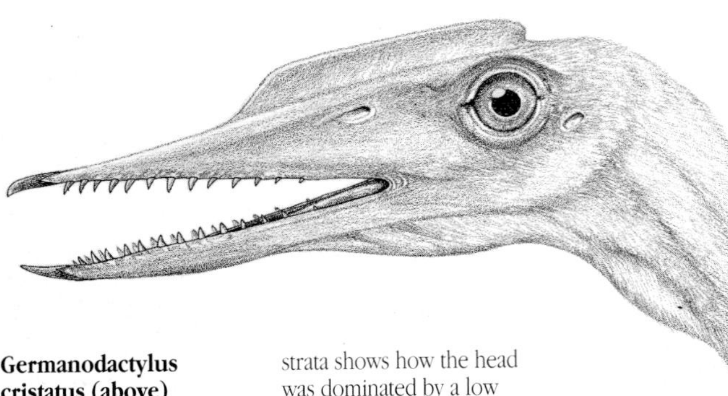

**Germanodactylus cristatus (above)**
This life portrait of the smaller of the species of *Germanodactylus* currently known from Upper Jurassic strata shows how the head was dominated by a low cranial crest. The tips of the jaws were toothless and were probably covered by pointed, horny beaks.

Nasopreorbital opening
Sagittal crest
Eye socket
Sagittal crest
Nasopreorbital opening

**Germanodactylus Skulls (right)**
These are skull restorations of *Germanodactylus cristatus* (upper) and *Germanodactylus rhamphastinus* (lower), the latter coming from the somewhat younger Mörnsheim limestone of Daiting in Bavaria. Both are characterized by having low, thin bony crests on top of their skulls.

dactylus to be found outside Bavaria, but also the oldest specimen of a pterodactyloid pterosaur, as the Lower Kimmeridge Clay is geologically somewhat older than the Solnhofen limestone.

## Gallodactylus

The name *Gallodactylus* (=Gallic finger) was introduced in 1974 by the French palaeontologist J.Fabre for a pterosaur from the Upper Jurassic of Canjuers (Var) in southern France.[50] There were many features in common with pterosaurs from the Upper Jurassic limestones of Bavaria and Württemberg. Thus the first pterosaur which had been described as *Pterodactylus suevicus* from Nusplingen in Württemberg by Tübingen professor August Quenstedt as early as 1855[51] could now be assigned to the genus *Gallodactylus*. This species is also known from Solnhofen. There *Gallodactylus* is among the larger short-tailed pterosaurs. Its particular characters are an elongated beak with a small number of slender teeth limited to

50 Fabre, J., 1974. *Un nouveau Pterodactylidae sur le gisement 'Portlandien' de Canjuers (Var): Gallodactylus canjuersensis nov.gen., nov.sp.* Annales de Paléontologie (Vertébrés), 62, fasc. 1: 35-70; Paris.
51 Quenstedt, F.A., 1855. *Über Pterodactylus suevicus im lithographischen Schiefer Württembergs.* 52 pp.; Tübingen.

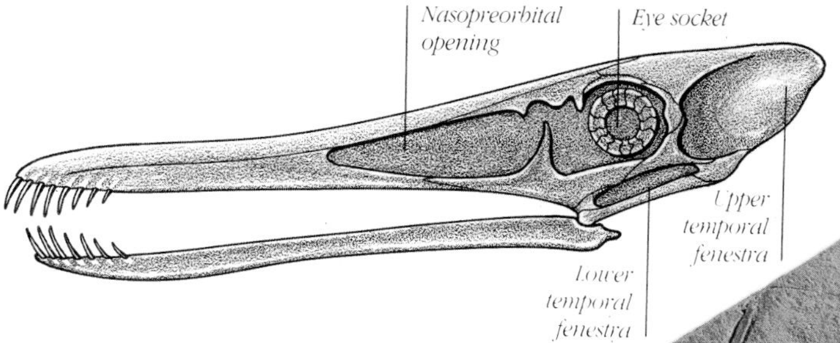

**Gallodactylus Skull (above)**
This is a restoration of the skull of *Gallodactylus suevicus*. The teeth are grouped together at the front of the jaws. The skull is 5·9in (15cm) long.

**Below left:** This is the only more or less complete skeleton of *Ctenochasma* of the six specimens known from the Solnhofen limestone. This filter-feeding pterosaur had a wing span of about 2·3ft (70cm). The specimen shows particularly well the very low skull with its long slender jaws which are slightly bent upwards and well adapted for filtering.

the front end of the jaw, and a short crest on the back of the head. *Gallodactylus* had a skull length of 5·9in (15cm) and a wing span of 4·4ft (1·35m).

## Ctenochasma

This striking short-tailed pterosaur is one of the rarities of the Solnhofen limestone. It is also known from Upper Jurassic strata in France and northern Germany, however. The first *Ctenochasma* (=comb-jaw) was described as early as 1851 by H. von Meyer[52] although the specimen consisted only of the front section of a lower jaw with numerous long, tightly-packed and strong teeth. It came from Upper Jurassic marine limestone in the Hannover area (Lower Saxony) and was given the name *Ctenochasma roemeri*, after the palaeontologist F.A. Roemer.

The first specimen from the Solnhofen limestone was described in 1862 by Munich Professor of Palaeontology Albert Oppel.[53] It was only the fragment of an upper jaw from the Solnhofen region that had been acquired by King Max II for the Munich state collection in a fossil collection of the Pappenheim country doctor Carl

**Right and below right:** *Ctenochasma*, the 'comb jaw', is one of the most intriguing pterosaurs to have been found in the Solnhofen limestone. Its long jaws were equipped with hundreds of long, curved, slender teeth which made it a perfect filter feeder. It presumably waded in the water and swept its jaws from side to side in order to strain small marine organisms from the water. The specimens illustrated here show *Ctenochasma's* upper and lower jaw (top right) and the upper jaw with bristle-like teeth seen from above (below right).

**Left:** *Gallodactylus suevicus* from the Upper Jurassic limestone of Nusplingen in Württemberg. The Nusplingen quarry has yielded only a few pterosaur fossils; this is one of the best preserved examples. It was described by A. Quenstedt in 1855.

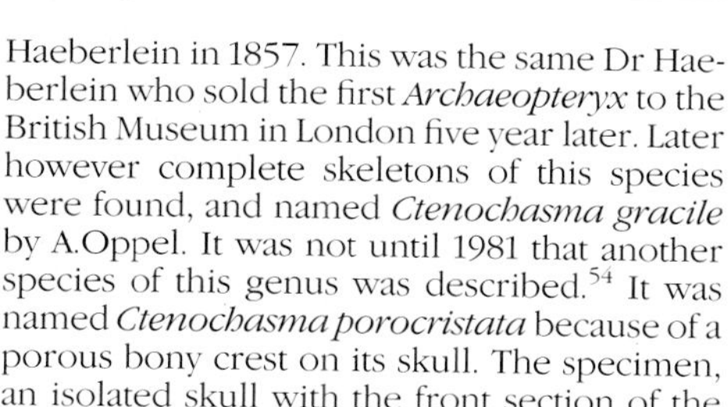

Haeberlein in 1857. This was the same Dr Haeberlein who sold the first *Archaeopteryx* to the British Museum in London five year later. Later however complete skeletons of this species were found, and named *Ctenochasma gracile* by A.Oppel. It was not until 1981 that another species of this genus was described.[54] It was named *Ctenochasma porocristata* because of a porous bony crest on its skull. The specimen, an isolated skull with the front section of the

52 Meyer, H. von, 1851. *Ctenochasma Roemeri*. Palaeontographica, 2: 82; Stuttgart.
53 Oppel, A., 1862. *Über Fährten im lithographischen Schiefer*. Palaeontologische Mitteilungen des Museums des kgl. bayrischen Staates, 1: 121-125; Stuttgart.
54 Buisonjé, P.H. de, 1981. *Ctenochasma porocristata nov. sp. from the Solnhofen Limestone, with some remarks on other Ctenochasmatidae*. Proceedings of the Koninklijke Nederlandse Akademie van Wetenchappen, B, 84(4): 411-436; Amsterdam.

dentition came from the Eichstätt quarry district.

The apt name *Ctenochasma* was chosen because of this pterosaur's strange dentition. This consisted of a large number of long, thin, inward-bending teeth, arranged in a dense row like the teeth of a comb in the upper and lower jaw. They formed a regular straining apparatus, with which these creatures could filter their food out of the water. For this reason the expression 'comb dentition' is also used to describe its arangement of teeth. *Ctenochasma* had a total of 260 individual teeth in its jaws. The largest of the six specimens so far known had a skull 7·9in (20cm) long and a wing span of at least 3·9ft (1·2m). As it can hardly be supposed that *Ctenochasma* fed in flight, we can only imagine that these pterosaurs swam in the water or waded in it near the beach, as do most modern sea birds.

The genus *Ctenochasma* has also been proved to exist in the Upper Jurassic (Lower

**Gnathosaurus (below)**
This view shows clearly the specialized dentition of *Gnathosaurus*. The long, slender jaws are lined with a series of teeth which get increasingly longer as they near the front of the snout. This suggests that *Gnathosaurus*, seen here in late Jurassic Solnhofen near-shore environment, must have been a filter feeder. When closed, the beak could be used for catching and filtering small creatures from the water. In the background we can see *Archaeopteryx*, the primordial bird, and a small theropod dinosaur, *Compsognathus*.

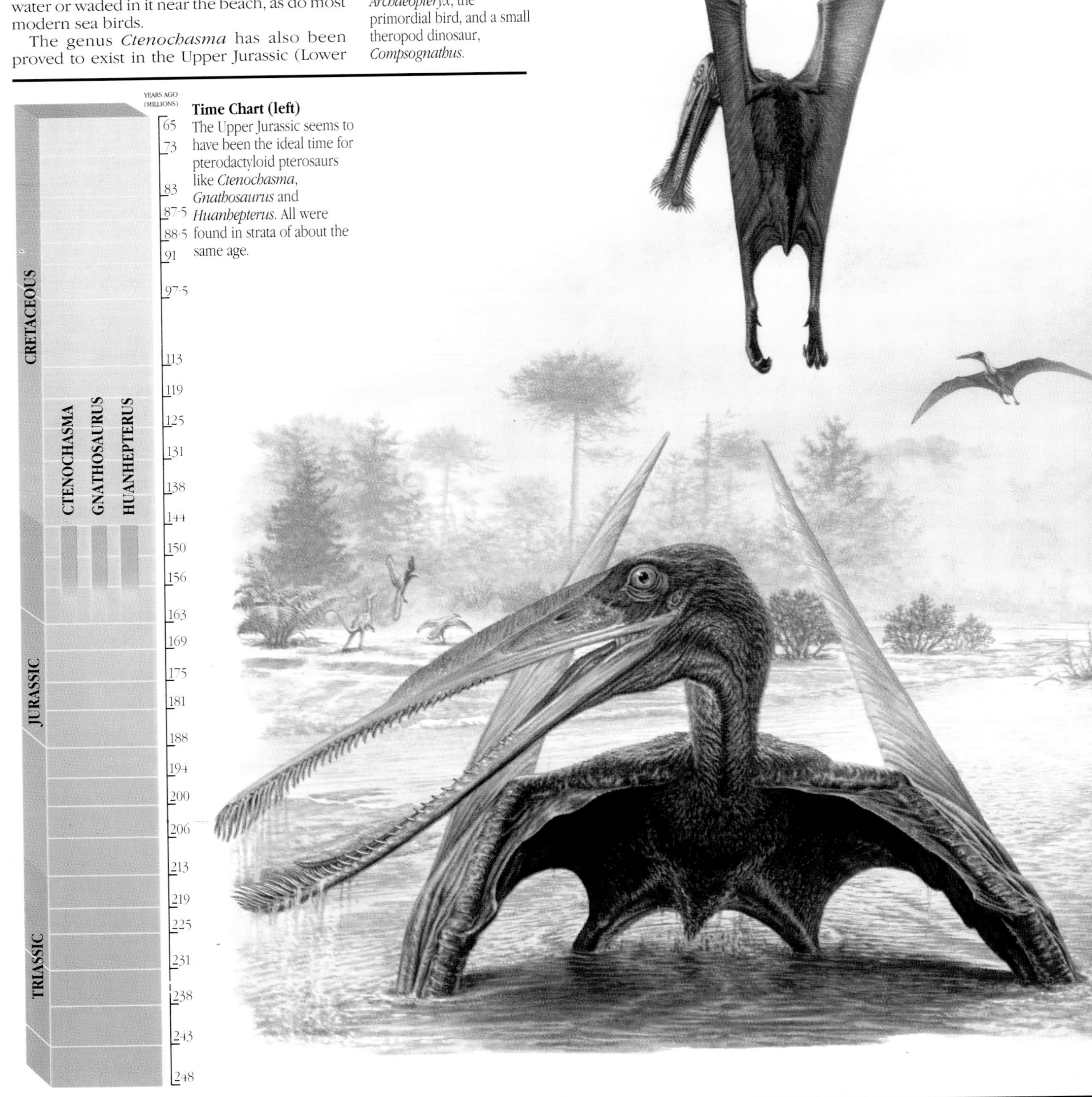


**Time Chart (left)**
The Upper Jurassic seems to have been the ideal time for pterodactyloid pterosaurs like *Ctenochasma*, *Gnathosaurus* and *Huanhepterus*. All were found in strata of about the same age.

Portlandian) of Haute Marne (France),[55] in the form of an isolated skull 9·5in (24cm) long, with dentition consisting of about 200 long, tightly-packed teeth, indicating a typical filter feeder.

## Gnathosaurus

The last Solnhofen pterosaur genus to be discussed here is *Gnathosaurus* (=jaw reptile). This is another extremely rare pterosaur. The two specimens so far discovered are the only remains of this form which is only known from the Solnhofen limestone. The first find, an isolated remnant of a lower jaw from Soln-

55 Taquet, P., 1972. *Un crâne de Ctenochasma (Pterodactyloidea) du Portlandien inférieur de la Haute Marne, dans les collections du Musée de Saint Dizier.* Comptes Rendus de l'Académie des Sciences, 274: 362-364; Paris.

**Ctenochasma Head and Skull (right)**
These drawings show a life portrait of *Ctenochasma gracile* (above), and a restoration of the skull and lower jaw which is also shown from below in the bottom drawing. As can be seen, the jaws contain an extraordinary number of teeth; there are over 250 in an adult pterosaur. The skull length is 4in (10·4cm). This species had no crest on its skull. *Ctenochasma porocristata* by contrast had a long para-sagittal crest running along the top of its skull which, in life, was probably covered by a thin horny crest.

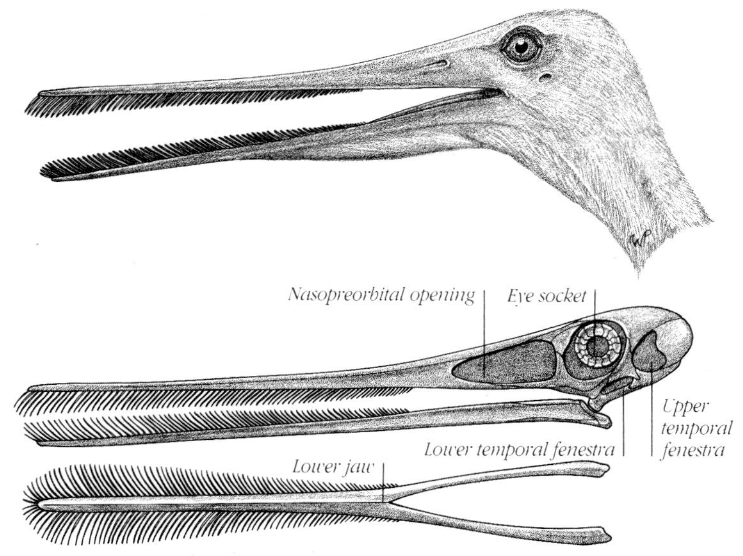


**Ctenochasma (below)**
*Ctenochasma* was even more extremely adapted as a filter feeder than *Gnathosaurus*. Its long jaws formed a filter basket for sifting out small aquatic planktonic organisms, such as crustaceans or the larvae of marine invertebrates, while standing in the shallows. Two distinct species are known, one (*porocristata*) with a bony crest along the midline of the skull.

**Map (right)**
**1** *Ctenochasma*
**2** *Gnathosaurus*
**3** *Huanhepterus*

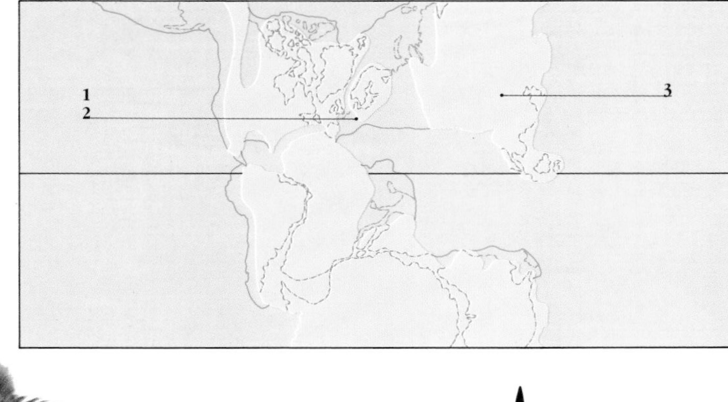

**Comparative Sizes (above)**
**1** *Ctenochasma*: wing span 3·9ft (1·2m)
**2** *Gnathosaurus*: wing span 5·6ft (1·7m)

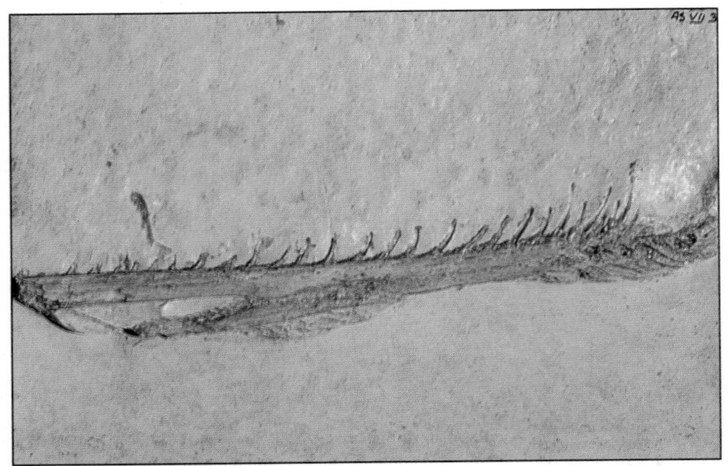

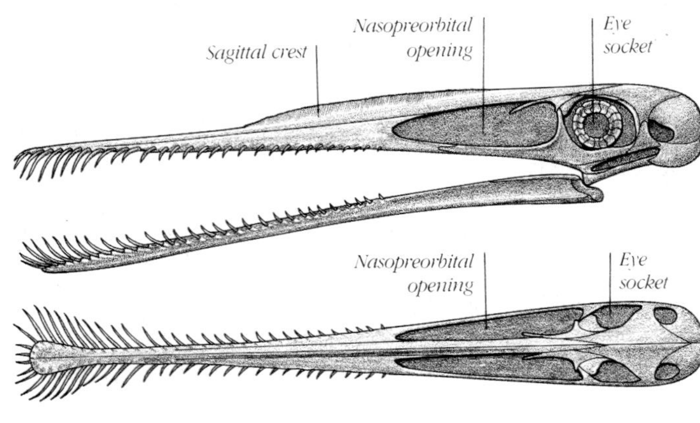


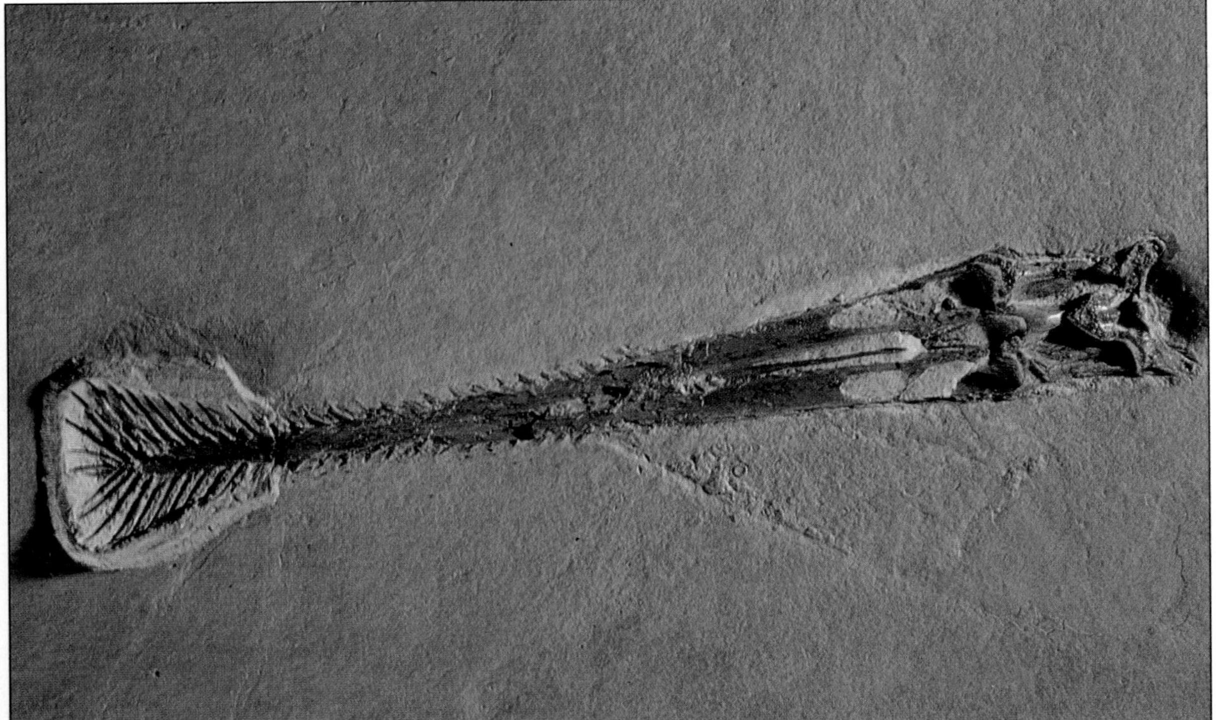

**Above left:** The first fossil of *Gnathosaurus* was recorded as early as 1832, but was mistaken for a crocodile. Only a partial lower jaw containing numerous teeth was known. It came from Solnhofen.

**Gnathosaurus Skull (above)**
This skull restoration of *Gnathosaurus* is seen in side and top view. A low, bony crest had developed along the midline of the skull roof. The dense arrangement of teeth points to a diet of small marine organisms. The skull length is 11in (28cm).

**Left:** A complete skull of *Gnathosaurus* discovered in 1951 in the Solnhofen limestone. The skull is exposed from the underside, and shows the complete dentition consisting of about 65 teeth.

hofen, was introduced as early as 1832 by the famous collector and palaeontologist Georg Graf zu Muenster in Bayreuth, and taken for a piece of crocodile jaw.[56] Later the Frankfurt palaeontologist Hermann von Meyer assigned the name *Gnathosaurus subulatus* (*subulatus* is the Latin for awl-like, after the shape of the teeth).[57]

It was not proved that the creature was a pterosaur until a second find was made in 1951, a skull 11in (28cm) long.[58] Nothing has so far been found of the rest of the skeleton, but it is not impossible that isolated bones from wings and hind legs of larger pterosaurs, as yet not classified with certainty, actually belong to the genus *Gnathosaurus*.

Even though this was a large pterosaur with a wing span of about 5·6ft (1·7m) we must assume that it was a filter feeder, though the teeth are more powerful than in the case of *Ctenochasma*, and less densely arranged, there being only 130. But here again the jaws have teeth extending well towards the back, with the longest at the front and set around the spoon-shaped jaw end. Like *Ctenochasma porocristata*, *Gnathosaurus* also has a low bone crest on its skull.

Because of their strange filter dentition *Ctenochasma* and *Gnathosaurus* are significantly different from other pterodactyloids. For this reason they are placed together in a family of their own, which is known as the Ctenochasmatidae.

## Russian Remains

Jurassic deposits in Kazakhstan in the southern Soviet Union have been noted for their rich fund of fossils for many years. Upper Jurassic limestone in the Karatau mountains, northwestern foothills of the Tien-shan, have provided fossil insects in excellent condition in particular, showing great similarity with insect fauna in the Solnhofen strata in Bavaria, which are approximately the same age.

A pterosaur from Karatau was first described in 1948.[59] These were the remains of a disarticulated and incomplete skeleton in which fragments of skull and jaw, vertebrae, ribs and bones from wings and hind legs can be recognized. In the jaws are peg-like teeth, with a total of 24 of them in the upper jaw. The shape of the jawbones suggests a high, short skull about 1·9in (48mm) long with a broad mouth, like a frog. For this reason the creature was given the name *Batrachognathus volans* (=flying frog-jaw). Very probably it was an insectivorous pterosaur that caught its prey in flight.

Thus this form is strikingly reminiscent of the somewhat smaller *Anurognathus* from the Solnhofen strata of Bavaria. It is not known whether *Batrachognathus* from Karatau had a reduced, partly fused tail, but the preserved characteristics and skeletal proportions in *Anurognathus* and *Batrachognathus* are very similar, and so they seem to be related, suggesting an assignment of both to the Anurognathidae family. It seems that only two speci-

56 Muenster, G. zu, 1832. *Bemerkungen über eine neue Art Pterodactylus aus Solenhofen.* Neues Jahrbuch für Mineralogie, etc., 412-416; Stuttgart.
57 Meyer, H. von, 1834. *Gnathosaurus subulatus, ein Saurus aus dem lithographischen Schiefer von Solenhofen.* Museum Senckenbergianum, I: 3; Frankfurt.
58 Mayr, F.X., 1964. *Die Naturwissenschaftlichen Sammlungen der Philosophisch-Theologischen Hochschule Eichstätt.* Festschrift 400 Jahre Collegium Willibaldinum Eichstätt: 302-334.

59 Rjabinin, A.N., 1948. *Remarks on a Flying Reptile from the Jurassic of the Kara-Tau.* Akademia Nauk, Paleontological Institute, Trudy, 15, (1): 86-93; Moscow and Leningrad (in Russian).

mens of *Batrachognathus* have been found. It was a small rhamphorhynchoid pterosaur with a wing span of about 20in (50cm).

### Sordes

In the sixties the Moscow zoologist A.G.Sharov discovered pterosaur remains while collecting fossil insects in the Upper Jurassic strata of the Karatau mountains, including an almost complete skeleton with imprints of soft parts of the body and flight membranes.[60] However, the sensational feature of this discovery was

60 Sharov, A.G., 1971. *New Flying Reptiles from the Mesozoic of Kazakhstan and Kirgizia.* Akademia Nauk, Paleontological Institute, Trudy, 130: 104-113; Moscow (in Russian).

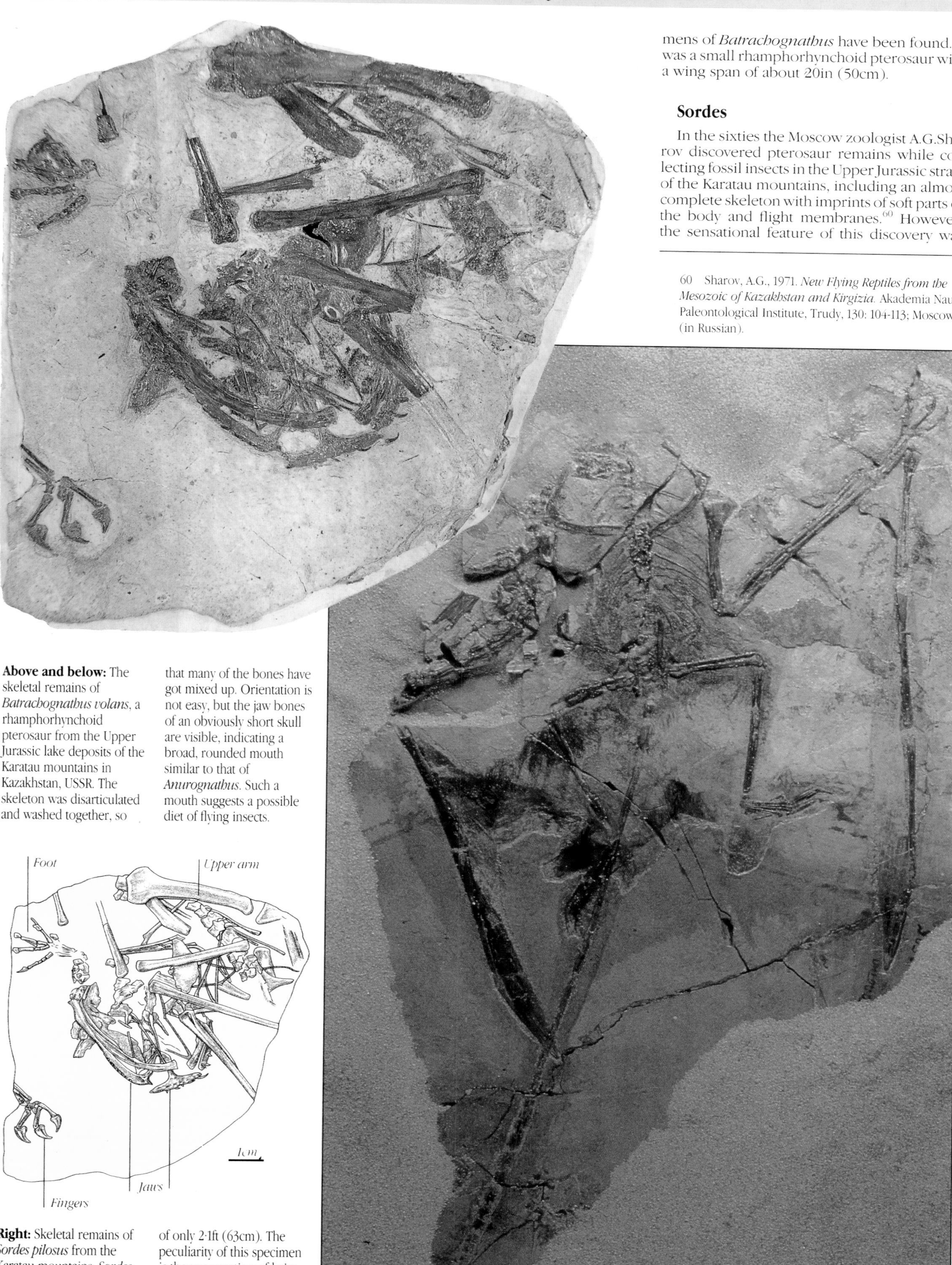


**Above and below:** The skeletal remains of *Batrachognathus volans*, a rhamphorhynchoid pterosaur from the Upper Jurassic lake deposits of the Karatau mountains in Kazakhstan, USSR. The skeleton was disarticulated and washed together, so that many of the bones have got mixed up. Orientation is not easy, but the jaw bones of an obviously short skull are visible, indicating a broad, rounded mouth similar to that of *Anurognathus*. Such a mouth suggests a possible diet of flying insects.

**Right:** Skeletal remains of *Sordes pilosus* from the Karatau mountains. *Sordes* was a rhamphorhynchid pterosaur with a wing span of only 2·1ft (63cm). The peculiarity of this specimen is the preservation of hairs covering the body, a sign of warm-bloodedness.

that because of the fineness of the sediment grain in which the Karatau fossils are contained, that even the hair that had covered the body of the creature in a thick fur was preserved. This was undeniable proof that pterosaurs were not naked or covered with reptilian scales, but that they were hairy, an indirect proof of their warmbloodedness. Traces of a hair covering had already been found in Holzmaden and Solnhofen pterosaurs,[61] but never the hairs themselves. Sharov called this new long-tailed pterosaur *Sordes pilosus* (=hairy evil spirit).

He writes in his examination, published in 1971, among other things: 'Long, dense and fairly thick hair covers the whole body, and the curvature of individual hairs suggests ample elasticity. There was also hair on the flight membrane, digits and the skin between the foot digits, although it was sparser here, and shorter. The root of the tail was also covered with hair, while the rest of the tail was apparently naked. The longest hairs on the body reached a length of 0·24in (6mm).'

The wing membrane outlines that have survived in *Sordes* show that the hind legs were integrated into the wing membrane. This left the long naked tail free to move, which was vital to its function as a rudder in flight. This all resulted in a fairly broad wing area.

*Sordes* was a rhamphorhynchoid pterosaur with the typical features of long-tailed pterosaurs, like a short metacarpal bone and long vertebrate tail. The end of the tail apparently flattened out slightly. There are no signs of the rhomboid terminal tail vane as in the Solnhofen *Rhamphorhynchus*. The fifth toe is very

61 Broili, F., 1927. *Ein Rhamphorhynchus mit Spuren von Haarbedeckung.* Sitzungsberichte der bayerischen Akademie der Wissenschaften, mathematisch-naturwissenschaftliche Abteilung: 49-67; Munich.

**Above:** A more complete specimen of *Sordes pilosus* from the Upper Jurassic of the Karatau mountains in Kazakhstan. The shape of the skull and the dentition resembles that of *Scaphognathus*.

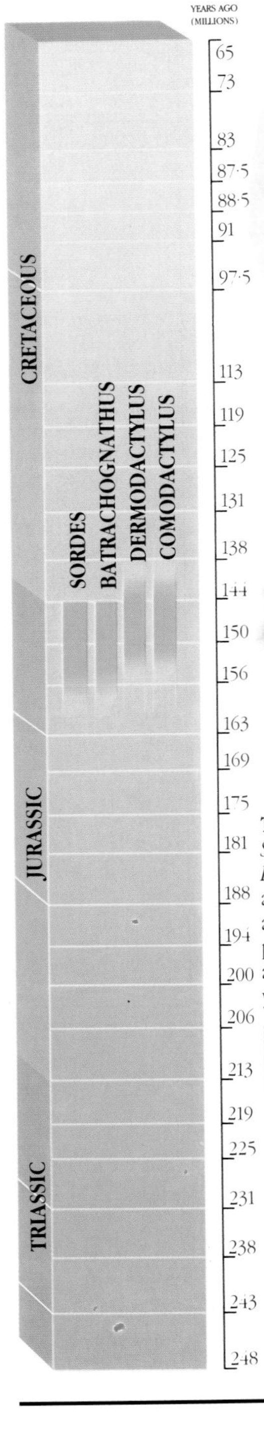

**Time Chart (left)**
*Sordes* and *Batrachognathus* are of about the same geological age as the Solnhofen pterosaurs. *Comodactylus* and *Dermodactylus* may be younger.

**Map (below)**
1 *Sordes*
2 *Batrachognathus*
3 *Dermodactylus*
4 *Comodactylus*
5 *Mesadactylus*

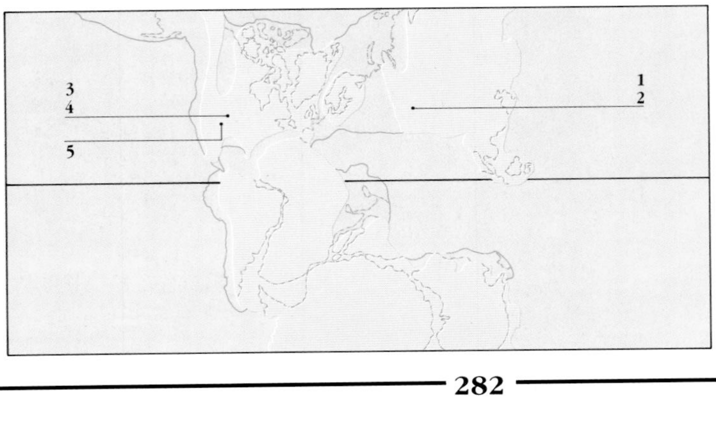

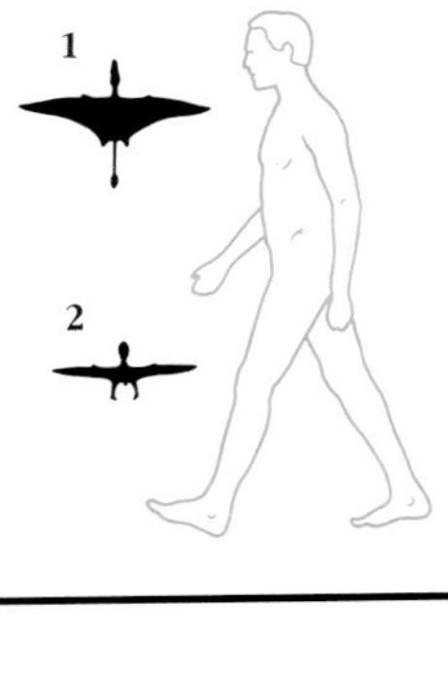

**Comparative Sizes (left)**
1 *Sordes*: wing span 24·8in (63cm).
2 *Batrachognathus*: wing span 20in (50cm).

**Sordes (right)**
*Sordes* is a small, long-tailed pterosaur that was probably a close relative of the Solnhofen *Scaphognathus*. The fossil preservation of its wing membranes shows that the wings were short and broad. A membrane also extended between the hind legs. *Sordes* is particularly fascinating because of the preservation of hairs which covered its body with a dense fur. This is evidence that *Sordes* and probably all pterosaurs were warm-blooded.

**Batrachognathus (right)**
Closely related to the Solnhofen *Anurognathus*, *Batrachognathus* was an insect eater as its name (='frog jaw') suggests. It had a short head and a wide mouth with small, peg-like teeth. It is known only by incomplete skeletal remains. Here it is shown with a short, reduced tail, by analogy to *Anurognathus* only.

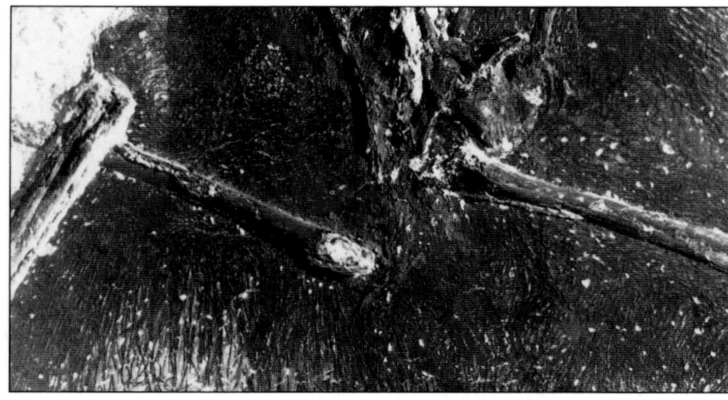

**Above:** A detailed photograph of the fur-like body covering of *Sordes pilosus*. Short hairs like these, up to 0·24in (6mm) long, covered the entire body except for the long tail which seems to have been naked.

long and hook-shaped. Sharov assumed that it was used to spread the trailing edge of the flight membrane in flight.

*Sordes*' skull and dentition are similar to that of the Solnhofen *Scaphognathus*, and a close relationship can thus be assumed. Both have few teeth, set upright and far apart in the jaw, and relatively short wing digits. *Sordes* can therefore also be classified as a member of the Rhamphorhynchidae family. A total of three specimens of skeletons have been found. Its skull was 3·15in (8cm) in length, and its wing span 24·8in (63cm). It was probably piscivorous, but could also have fed on insects.

Skull
Free fingers
Wing finger
Fur
Wing membrane
10cm
Long tail

**Sordes pilosus Skeletal Remains (above)**
These are the remains of *Sordes pilosus* from the Upper Jurassic of Kazakhstan as described and illustrated by the Moscow zoologist A.G Sharov in 1971. The impressions of the skin and membranes with the hairs still in place are very well preserved as this drawing reveals.

## Excavation in China

The Ordos basin is in the central section of the Yellow River in North Central China. This area is also known as the Shanxi-Gansu-Ningxia Loess Plateau, after the extensive loess deposits (rock dust and silt blown together by ice age winds), which extend over parts of all three provinces. Red Mesozoic strata containing fossils, so-called Redbeds, form the stratum below the loess and have provided skeletons of dinosaurs and also part of a pterosaur skeleton.

The Chinese palaeontologist Dong Zhiming described this pterosaur in 1982, using the name *Huanhepterus* (=wing from the River Huanhe).[62] The first bone was a vertebra found by a farmer in a quarry on the bank of the Huanhe River in Upper Jurassic sediments of the Zhiden Group near Senshilipou, Qinyan County in Gansu Province in 1978. Only an incomplete skeleton of *Huanhepterus* has been found, of which only the front 13in (33cm) of the end of the snout, some cervical, dorsal and sacral vertebrae, the sternum, the skeleton of the left wing and the left hind leg survived. It was a short-tailed pterosaur whose dentition showed similarity with the Solnhofen *Gnathosaurus*. The teeth are very long, slender and pointed, and tightly packed in the front section of the jaw. Thus *Huanhepterus* was grouped in the Ctenochasmatidae family. On the mid-line of the skull is a thin, low bone crest similar to that of *Gnathosaurus* or *Ctenochasma poro-*

62 Dong Zhiming, 1982. *On a new Pterosauria (Huanhepterus quingyangensis gen. et sp. nov.) from Ordos, China.* Vertebrata Palasiatica, 20, (2): 115-121; Beijing (Chinese with English abstract).

**Left:** The so-called Redbeds of North Central China have proved a fertile hunting ground for palaeontologists. Red Mesozoic strata lie below the extensive loess deposits that were blown together by ice age winds, and the skeletons of dinosaurs and a pterosaur have been found in this region. We see here late Jurassic sediments of the Zhiden group that have been exposed at Senshilipou, Qinyan County, Gansu Province. It was here that the specimen of *Huanhepterus* was found. This specimen was described by Dr Dong Zhiming in 1982. Its name signifies 'wing from the River Huanhe'. So far, this find is the only record of late Jurassic pterosaurs in China and fills the gap between the Middle Jurassic pterosaurs at Dashanpu, and the Lower Cretaceous pterosaurs from the Junggar Basin in Sinkiang.

**Above left:** The front end of the jaws of *Huanhepterus quingyangensis* as preserved. As well as the jaws, part of a long, slender hindlimb has also been discovered in the late Jurassic sediments of the Ordos basin in China.

**Huanhepterus quingyangensis (above)** The drawing shows *Huanhepterus quingyangensis* from the Upper Jurassic of Gansu, China. The jaws are fringed with long, slender teeth. The teeth are tightly packed towards the front of the jaw, a characteristic that recalls *Ctenochasma*. On top of the skull there extended a low sagittal crest.

*cristata* from Solnhofen. The lower jaw had a total of 50 and the upper jaw about 52 teeth. The largest, 1in (25mm) long, is the eleventh tooth in the upper jaw. The end of the snout is somewhat broader towards the front.

A striking feature is the very long neck with markedly elongated cervical vertebrae. In this case there is no notarium, i.e. a fusion of the anterior dorsal vertebrae to anchor the pectoral girdle. The sacrum consists of seven vertebrae. Measured by the size of the humerus (5·7in; 14·5cm) and the first phalanx of the flight digit (14·2in; 36cm), *Huanhepterus* was a relatively large pterosaur, whose wing span can be estimated at about 8·2ft (2·5m). Its comb-like dentition indicates that it filtered out small organisms under water.

## The Morrison Formation

The rarity of Jurassic pterosaur finds in North America is caused largely by the absence of fine-grained, Jurassic rocks like Solnhofen lithographic limestone or Holzmaden Posidonian shale, made up of fine, soft sediments in which the fragile and delicate pterosaur bones could survive as fossils. Skeletal remains of Jurassic pterosaurs have so far been found only in the Morrison formation of Wyoming and Colorado. It consists of a massive series of clay, silt and sandstones and also coarser conglomerates about 328ft (100m) thick. They originated from river and lake deposits about 135 million years ago, in the Jurassic, thus somewhat later than the Solnhofen strata in Bavaria.[63]

The Morrison Formation became famous because of the spectacular dinosaur finds made for the first time in Colorado in 1877, later continued very successfully in Utah and Wyoming. Here, near the place called Como Bluff, a station on the Union Pacific Railroad, already operating at the time, the principal explorers were the 'bone hunters' employed by O.C. Marsh, from Yale College, New Haven.[64] They excavated numerous skeletons of enormous dinosaurs, including *Apatosaurus* and *Diplodocus*, which can now be seen in the Yale Peabody Museum in New Haven.

## Dermodactylus

In the very early stages of the Como Bluff excavations, in Reed's Quarry 5, Samuel Wendell Williston, then still one of Marsh's collectors, found, along with other small bones, the fragment of a pterosaur bone which Marsh identified as the distal section of the right wing metacarpal of a pterodactyloid pterosaur. He described it in 1878, using the name *Pterodactylus montanus*,[65] but in 1881 changed the name of the genus to *Dermodactylus* (=skin-finger).[66] The bone is only 1·26in (32mm) long. When complete it must have been at least twice as long. In comparison with the thickness of its shaft it was thus a relatively long and slender metacarpal bone and is thus typical of the Pterodactyloidea. The double pulley at the end to take the flight digit has survived. In his description, Marsh mentions that the shaft of the bone is thin-walled and hollow, and oval in cross-section. It is only possible to speculate about the size of the whole animal. *Dermodactylus* could have had a wing span of about 3·28ft (1m).

Fragmentary as this fossil is, it was still the first proof of the fact that pterosaurs existed in the New World as early as the Upper Jurassic. Only a very few other fossil proofs have appeared since.

63 Jensen, J.A. and Padian, K., 1989. *Small Pterosaurs and Dinosaurs from the Uncompahgre Fauna (Brushy Basin Member, Morrison Formation: ?Tithonian), Late Jurassic, Western Colorado.* Journal of Paleontology, 63, (3): 364-373.

64 Ostrom, J.H. and McIntosh, J.S., 1966. *Marsh's dinosaurs. The collections from Como Bluff.* Yale University Press, 388 pp.; New Haven.

65 Marsh, O.C., 1878. *New pterodactyl from the Jurassic of the Rocky Mountains.* American Journal of Science, ser. 3, 16: 233-234.

66 Marsh, O.C.: 1878. *Notes on American Pterodactyls.* American Journal of Science, ser. 3, 21: 342-343.

10cm

**Huanhepterus Skeletal Restoration (above)** The drawing shows the skeleton of *Huanhepterus quingyangensis* as restored by Dong Zhiming in 1982. The bones drawn in dotted lines were not preserved with the fossil specimen. *Huanhepterus* was a large pterodactyloid pterosaur with a wing span of about 8·2ft (2·5m). One of the most striking features of the skeleton is the length of its neck vertebrae.

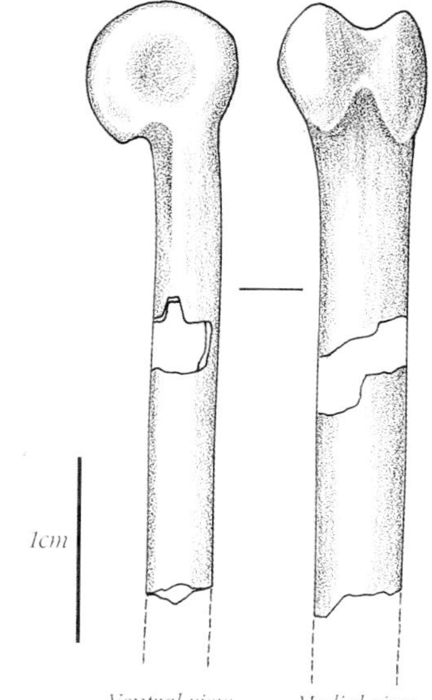


**Dermodactylus Wing Fragment (above)** *Dermodactylus montanus*, the fragment of a wing metacarpal bone of a pterodactyloid pterosaur from the late Jurassic Morrison Formation found by S.W. Williston at Como Bluff in Wyoming. Described by O.C. Marsh in 1878, this was the first record of a Jurassic pterosaur in the New World.

## Comodactylus and Mesadactylus

Another wing metacarpal, which was only discovered 100 years later in the Yale Peabody Museum collection, came from the famous Quarry 9 on the Como Bluff in Wyoming, the so-called Mammal Quarry. Peter Galton of Bridgeport University identified this bone, which came to O.C. Marsh in New Haven along with fossil material found by W. Reed in 1879 in strata from the Morrison Formation in Quarry 9.[67] This metacarpal survived complete. Its short, compact shape shows that it is rhamphorhynchoid, and it is reminiscent of the same part of the skeleton in the Solnhofen *Rhamphorhynchus*. Galton called this second Jurassic pterosaur from Como Bluff *Comodactylus* (=Como-finger). With a length of 2·26in (57·5mm) it is bigger than comparable bones from all other long-tailed pterosaurs so far known. Its wing span is estimated at 8·2ft (2.5m), and so it must have been one of the biggest Jurassic pterosaurs of all.

The second fossil site in the Morrison Formation in which remains of pterosaurs were found was the 'Dry Mesa' Quarry in Montrose County in western Colorado. Fossil skeletal remains were found in the 1970s in particular in the course of several palaeontological expeditions mounted by Brigham Young University, Provo, Utah under the direction of James A. Jensen.[68] The most spectacular fossils from Dry Mesa Quarry were new large sauropod dinosaurs, including parts of the skeleton of the gigantic '*Supersaurus*' with an estimated height of 54ft (16·5m) and a body length of 82-98ft (25-30m). But there were also several skeletal remains of small vertebrates, including some from pterosaurs.[63] One bone was at first described as the shin bone of a bird, *Palaeopteryx thomsoni*,[69] but it later turned out to be a bone from the lower arm of a small dinosaur.

Finally Jensen and Padian identified numerous small bones as remains of a pterodactyloid pterosaur, including a synsacrum (fused sacral vertebrae in the pelvic region), vertebrae, pectoral girdle, wing bones and femurs. The new generic name *Mesadactylus* (=Mesa-finger) was introduced for them.[63]

The most remarkable find is the synsacrum, which consists of seven fused vertebrae, the first five forming a neural blade through fusion of the upper neural spines. It is this formation that is different from that of other pterosaurs and also that of many birds. The preserved upper arm bones (humeri), however, are more similar to pterodactylids from Solnhofen. The thickness of the walls of these bones is between 0·01-0·02in (0·25-0·5mm).

Finally a flight digit phalanx from the Dry Mesa Quarry, described by Jensen and Ostrom as an indeterminate pterodactyloid pterosaur in 1977,[70] also belongs to *Mesadactylus*.

The bones from the Morrison Formation are evidence for a diverse pterosaur fauna in North America during the late Jurassic.

67 Galton, P.M., 1981. *A Rhamphorhynchoid Pterosaur from the Upper Jurassic of North America.* Journal of Paleontology, 55, (5): 1117-1122.

68 Jensen, J.A., 1975. *Continuing study of new Jurassic/Cretaceous vertebrate faunas from Colorado and Utah.* National Geographic Society Research Reports, 1975: 373-381.

69 Jensen, J.A., 1981. *Another look at Archaeopteryx as the world's oldest bird.* Encyclia, 58: 109-128.

70 Jensen, J.A. and Ostrom, J.H., 1977. *A Second Jurassic Pterosaur from North America.* Journal of Paleontology, 51, (4): 867-870.

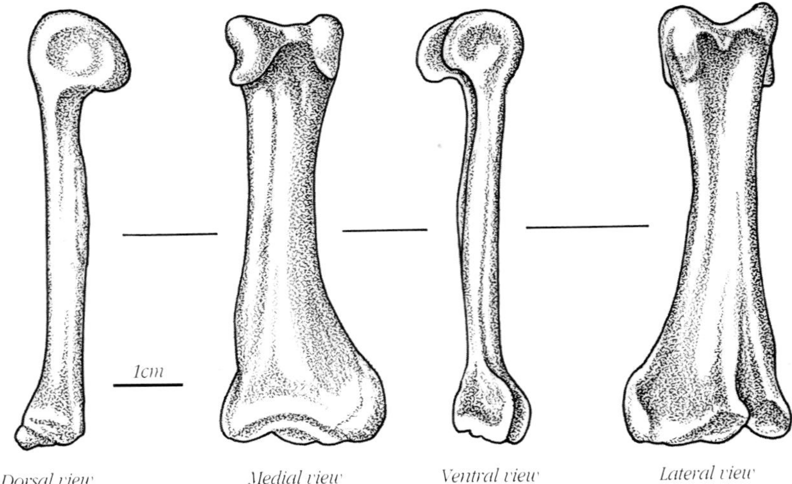


**Comodactylus ostromi (above)**
This is a metacarpal bone from the right wing of *Comodactylus ostromi* which was discovered at Como Bluff in Wyoming in 1879. However, it was not until 100 years later that Peter Galton identified it. For the first time it showed that rhamphorhynchoid pterosaurs lived in North America contemporary with the giant dinosaurs from the same area.

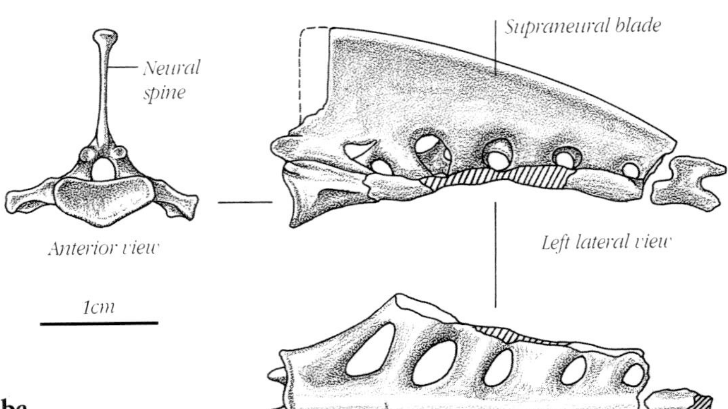


## A Pterosaur from Cuba

In the 1960s, when some pieces of Jurassic limestone were being prepared in acid in search of fossil fish some delicate reptilian bones were found which turned out to be those of a pterosaur. The fossil-bearing rock had been collected half a century earlier by Barnum Brown, for many years Curator of Fossil Reptiles at the New York American Museum of Natural History. It came from a site near Viñales in the province of Pinar del Rio in western Cuba, and was known for its marine fauna, ammonites, bivalves, fish and marine reptiles. The geological age of this black limestone is thus clear, and can be given as Upper Jurassic, Oxfordian to be more precise.

When Edwin H. Colbert, then Curator of Fossil Reptiles at the American Museum in New York examined this specimen scientifically in 1969[71] only one Jurassic pterosaur, indeed literally only a single bone, was known in the western hemisphere, and that was *Dermodactylus* from Como Bluff in Wyoming. This was a short-tailed pterosaur, but Colbert saw in this new and much more complete set of skeletal remains from Cuba the typical characteristics of a rhamphorhynchoid pterosaur, i.e. a long tail with long caudal vertebrae, surrounded by ossified 'tendons' (actually long processes of the vertebrae to stiffen the tail) and also the typical short metacarpal bone.

The specimen consists of skeletal remains of an individual preserved in seven small pieces of rock that had been treated with acid. What has survived are fragments of skull, isolated vertebrae, the two pectoral girdles, a sternum

71 Colbert, E.H., 1969. *A Jurassic Pterosaur from Cuba.* American Museum Novitates, 2370: 26 pp.; New York.

**Mesadactylus ornithosphyos (above)**
This specimen was discovered by Jim Jensen in the Dry Mesa quarry in Colorado. Of the several small bones, this synsacrum is the most diagnostic element. It was first taken to originate from a prehistoric bird, but was recently identified as pterosaurian.

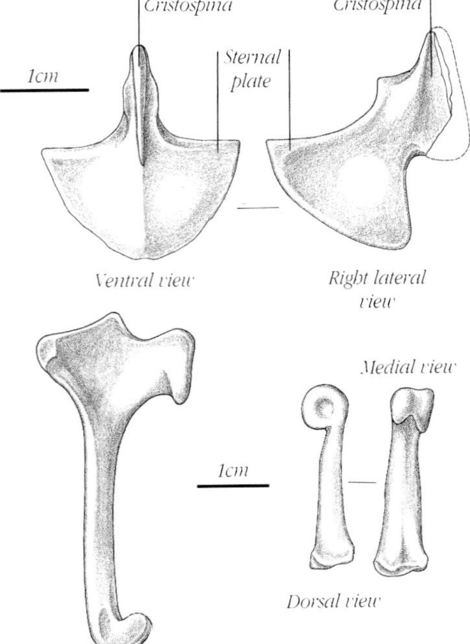

**SUMMARY OF PTEROSAURS OF THE UPPER JURASSIC**

**Rhamphorhynchoidea**

Family Rhamphorhynchidae

*Rhamphorhynchus longicaudus*
*Rhamphorhynchus intermedius*
*Rhamphorhynchus muensteri*
*Rhamphorhynchus gemmingi*
*Rhamphorhynchus longiceps*
Lower Tithonian, Solnhofen lithographic limestone, Bavaria; in part Nusplingen lithographic limestone, Württemberg; Germany.[34]
*Rhamphorhynchus jessoni*
Oxfordian, Oxford Clay, Huntingdonshire, England.[37]
*Rhamphorhynchus tendagurensis*
Upper Jurassic, Obere Saurier-Mergel, Tendaguru, Tanzania.[38]
*Rhamphorhynchus* sp.
Upper Callovian, Pedróga; Lower Kimmeridgian, Guimarota near Leiria, Portugal.[39]
*Odontorhynchus aculeatus*
Lower Tithonian, Solnhofen lithographic limestone, Bavaria, Germany.[34]
*Scaphognathus crassirostris*
Lower Tithonian, Solnhofen lithographic limestone, Bavaria, Germany.[34,40]
*Sordes pilosus*
Upper Jurassic, Karatau, Kazakhstan, USSR.[60]

Family Anurognathidae

*Anurognathus ammoni*
Lower Tithonian, Solnhofen lithographic limestone, Bavaria, Germany.[34,41]
*Batrachognathus volans*
Upper Jurassic, Karatau, Kazakhstan, USSR.[59]

Undetermined family

*Nesodactylus hesperius*
Oxfordian, Viñales, Pinar del Rio, Cuba.[71]
*Comodactylus ostromi*
Tithonian, Morrison Formation, Como Bluff, Wyoming, USA.[67]

**Pterodactyloidea**

Family Pterodactylidae

*Pterodactylus antiquus*
*Pterodactylus kochi*
*Pterodactylus micronyx*
*Pterodactylus elegans*
*Pterodactylus longicollum*
*Pterodactylus grandis*
*Pterodactylus grandipelvis*
Lower Tithonian, Solnhofen lithographic limestone; in part Mörnsheim strata; Bavaria, Germany.[34]
*Pterodactylus cerinensis*
Kimmeridgian, lithographic limestone, Cerin, Dept. Ain, France.[44]
*Pterodactylus suprajurensis*
Purbeckian, Boulogne-sur-Mer, France.[46]
*Pterodactylus manseli*
*Pterodactylus pleydelli*
Kimmeridgian, Kimmeridge Clay, Weymouth, Dorset, England.[5]
*Pterodactylus arningi*
*Pterodactylus maximus*
Upper Jurassic, Obere Saurier-Mergel, Tendaguru, Tanzania.[38]

Family Gallodactylidae

*Gallodactylus suevicus*
Lower Tithonian, Solnhofen lithographic limestone, Bavaria; Nusplingen lithographic limestone, Württemberg; Germany.[51]
*Gallodactylus canjuersensis*
Portlandian, Gisemens des Bessons, Canjuers, Dept. Var, France.[50]

Family Germanodactylidae

*Germanodactylus cristatus*
Lower Tithonian, Solnhofen lithographic limestone, Eichstätt, Bavaria, Germany.
*Germanodactylus rhamphastinus*
Lower Tithonian, Mörnsheim strata, Daiting, Bavaria, Germany.[34]
*Germanodactylus* sp.
Lower Kimmeridgian, Kimmeridge Clay, Kimmeridge Bay, Dorset, England.[49]

Family Ctenochasmatidae

*Ctenochasma roemeri*
Upper Jurassic, Deister near Hannover, Lower Saxony, Bavaria.[52]
*Ctenochasma gracile*
*Ctenochasma porocristata*
Lower Tithonian, Solnhofen lithographic limestone, Bavaria, Germany.[34,53,54]
*Ctenochasma* sp.
Lower Portlandian, Haute Marne, France.[55]
*Gnathosaurus subulatus*
Lower Tithonian, Solnhofen lithographic limestone, Bavaria, Germany.[34,57,58]
*Huanhepterus quingyangensis*
Upper Jurassic, Ordos, Gansu Prov., China.[62]

Family Dsungaripteridae

*Dsungaripterus brancai*
Upper Jurassic, Obere Saurier-Mergel, Tendaguru, Tanzania.[47]

Undetermined family

*Dermodactylus montanus*
Tithonian, Morrison Formation, Como Bluff, Wyoming, USA.[65,66]
*Mesadactylus ornithosphyos*
Tithonian, Morrison Formation, Dry Mesa Quarry, Colorado, USA.[63,68,69,70]
Pterodactyloidea indet.
Tithonian, Vacca Muerta Formation, Neuquén, Argentina.[72,73]

with an unusually large and deep keel, bones from the wing skeleton, pelvic bones, fragments of the femur, metatarsal bones and various ribs. The skeleton was no longer articulated naturally, but had fallen apart. Colbert called this Jurassic pterosaur from Cuba *Nesodactylus* (=island-finger) and placed it in the Rhamphorhynchidae family. *Nesodactylus* seems to have had somewhat longer and more heavily built wings and hindlimbs than the Solnhofen *Rhamphorhynchus*. Jaws and teeth are not preserved.

**Nesodactylus hesperius (left)**
Of the incomplete skeleton of this rhamphorhynchoid pterosaur from Cuba, we see here the breastbone (upper drawings), the upper arm bone (lower left) and the metacarpal bone of the left wing finger (lower right).

## Neuquén Fossils

Fossils that have survived in a very similar way to the Solnhofen fossils have been found in the Upper Jurassic flaggy limestones of the province of Neuquén in the eastern foothills of the Andes in central Argentina. These flaggy limestones can also be called lithographic limestone. They are part of the Vacca Muerta formation and because of the ammonite fauna they are placed in the Middle to Upper Tithonian age of the Upper Jurassic. Thus they are younger than the Solnhofen strata (which are Lower Tithonian) in Bavaria, and although they look very similar to them they were not formed in a lagoon protected by reefs but in an open shallow sea. It is estimated that the coast of the Jurassic sea at the time was about 62 miles (100km) away.[72]

The pterosaur specimens consist of one disarticulated and incomplete skeleton which palaeontologists are still studying and an isolated tibia 3·75in (95mm) long from an as yet undetermined pterodactyloid pterosaur, possibly a new species.[73]

But the find does show the important fact that short-tailed pterosaurs, the Pterodactyloidea, were distributed all over the world right at the beginning of their evolution in the Upper Jurassic. Fossil finds establish that at this time they lived in Europe, Africa, Asia, North and South America.

**Right:** The fossil remains of *Nesodactylus hesperius* from the late Jurassic of Pinar del Rio were preserved in several pieces of rock that were treated with acetic acid. In this way the bones could be exposed three-dimensionally.

72 Cione, A., Gasparini, Z., Leanza, H. and Zeiss, A., 1987. *Marine oberjurassische Plattenkalke in Argentinien.* Archaeopteryx, 5: 13-22; Eichstätt.
73 Gasparini, Z., Leanza, H. and Garata Zubilliga, J., 1987. *Un pterosauria de las Calizas Litograficas Tithonianas de Area de los Catutos, Neuquén, Argentina.* Ameghiniana, 24, (1-2): 141-143; Buenos Aires.
Leanza, H. and Zeiss, A., 1990. *Upper Jurassic Lithographic Limestones from Argentina (Neuquén Basin): Stratigraphy and Fossils.* Facies, 22: 169-186; Erlangen.

# PTEROSAURS OF THE CRETACEOUS

**Palaeogeographic Map of the Lower Cretaceous (left)**
At the beginning of the early Cretaceous, shallow seas had started to divide the southern continents although South America and Africa were still connected to one another. The Atlantic Ocean had started to develop, and the northern and southern continents were completely separated. The sea dividing Europe from Asia was growing.

**Palaeogeographic Map of the Upper Cretaceous (right)**
By late Cretaceous times the continents had moved to more familiar positions. Africa and South America were beginning to drift apart, and India was moving eastwards across the Indian Ocean. Australia and Antarctica had also detached themselves from what had been Gondwana. Extensive marine flooding in the north meant that seaways divided western from eastern North America.

The Jurassic was followed by the Cretaceous Period, which began about 144 million years ago and ended 65 million years ago. This final period of the Mesozoic Era was the longest, lasting for 79 million years. It is usually subdivided into Lower and Upper Cretaceous. Many of the geological and biological events of the time were highly significant for Earth as it is today.

In the Upper Cretaceous in particular there was extensive marine flooding all over the world, continents drifted apart and most of Earth's present high mountain ranges were formed. The two supercontinents, Laurasia in the north and Gondwana in the south, separated. At the beginning of the Cretaceous, South America and Africa were still connected, but towards the end of the period they had moved over 1,250 miles (2,000 km) apart: the South Atlantic had come into being. North America and Eurasia were still connected. In the south, Australia, Antarctica and India detached themselves from the Gondwana land mass and drifted apart.

These changes also affected the climate and further development of the plant and animal kingdoms. Thus this period also saw the first appearance of flowering plants and deciduous trees. Dinosaurs were still the dominant land animals in the Cretaceous as well, and some of their evolutionary lines reached their peak. Although birds were becoming more numerous and had conquered various habitats, pterosaurs continued to dominate the Earth's air space.

Cretaceous pterosaurs were found on all continents with the exception of the Antarctic, again overwhelmingly in marine deposits, although only short-tailed species, the Pterodactyloidea, lived in the Cretaceous. Long-tailed pterosaurs, the Rhamphorhynchoidea, did not survive the transition from the Jurassic to the Cretaceous. The major feature of the period was enormous increase in size. The largest Jurassic pterosaurs had a maximum wing span of 8·2ft (2·5m), but in the Lower Cretaceous pterosaurs with a 20ft (6m) wing span began to emerge, and in the Upper Cretaceous wing spans of nearly 40ft (12m) were found as well. These pterosaurs were the largest flying creatures that have ever lived on Earth.

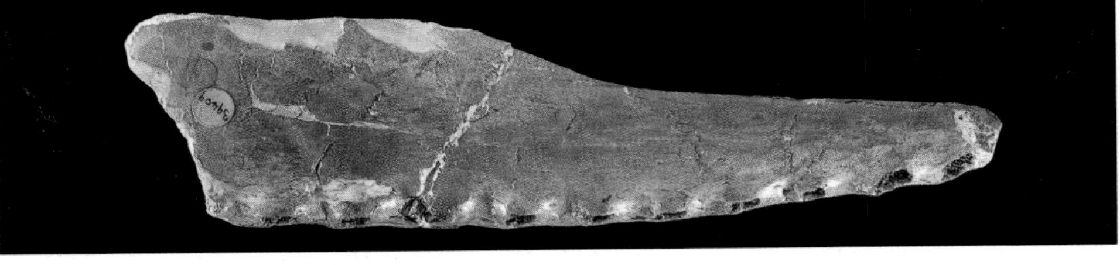

Towards the end of the Cretaceous the oceans withdrew from large continental areas. Subsequently global cooling occurred, and distinct climatic zones came into being on Earth. Then, 65 million years ago, at the end of the Cretaceous, it was all over. This amazing happening went into the annals of the history of the Earth as the 'mass extinction at the Cretaceous/Tertiary boundary'. Dinosaurs, ichthyosaurs, plesiosaurs, mosasaurs, and many fish and marine invertebrates disappeared from the Earth at that time, and the pterosaurs went as well. The reason for their extinction will be discussed in a separate chapter.

## English Finds

The first pterosaur bones in England were found by Gideon Mantell, a country doctor, in about 1827, in Tilgate Forest near Cuckfield in Sussex. A few years before he had discovered the first skeletal remains of the dinosaur *Iguanodon* there as well. The fossiliferous strata are sandy and clayey delta deposits from rivers and seas, and were formed in the south of England in early Cretaceous times. They are known as Wealden, a geological formation also found in Belgium, Northern France, and northwestern Germany. At first Mantell thought the delicate bones he had found in Tilgate Forest were those of birds. He described them as 'Bones of Birds' in his 'Illustrations of the Geology of Sussex' in 1827. He later gave them the new generic name *Palaeornis* (=old bird), but he finally diagnosed them as pterosaur bones and they were later placed in the genus *Ornithocheirus* (=bird-hand) by the English palaeontologist Harry Govier Seeley.

The first pterosaur remains from the Upper Cretaceous of England were described by James Scott Bowerbank in 1845. They were also the first pterosaurs so far known that were larger than the largest Jurassic pterosaurs. The material consisted of the front end of a snout with typical teeth, part of a pectoral girdle and a few other bones, and came from the Chalk (Turonian) of Burham in Kent.[1] Bowerbank estimated the wing span of this species at 8 or 9ft (2·75m). Richard Owen, who had hitherto thought it impossible that a cold-blooded reptile with a higher body weight than a warm-blooded mammal like the flying fox could lift itself into the air, had to revise his opinion. In an 1851 monograph (p.80),[2] he concedes: 'Of

1 Bowerbank, J.S., 1845. Proceedings of the Geological Society of London.

2 Owen, R., 1851. *Monograph of the fossil Reptilia of the Cretaceous Formations.* Palaeontographical Society London.

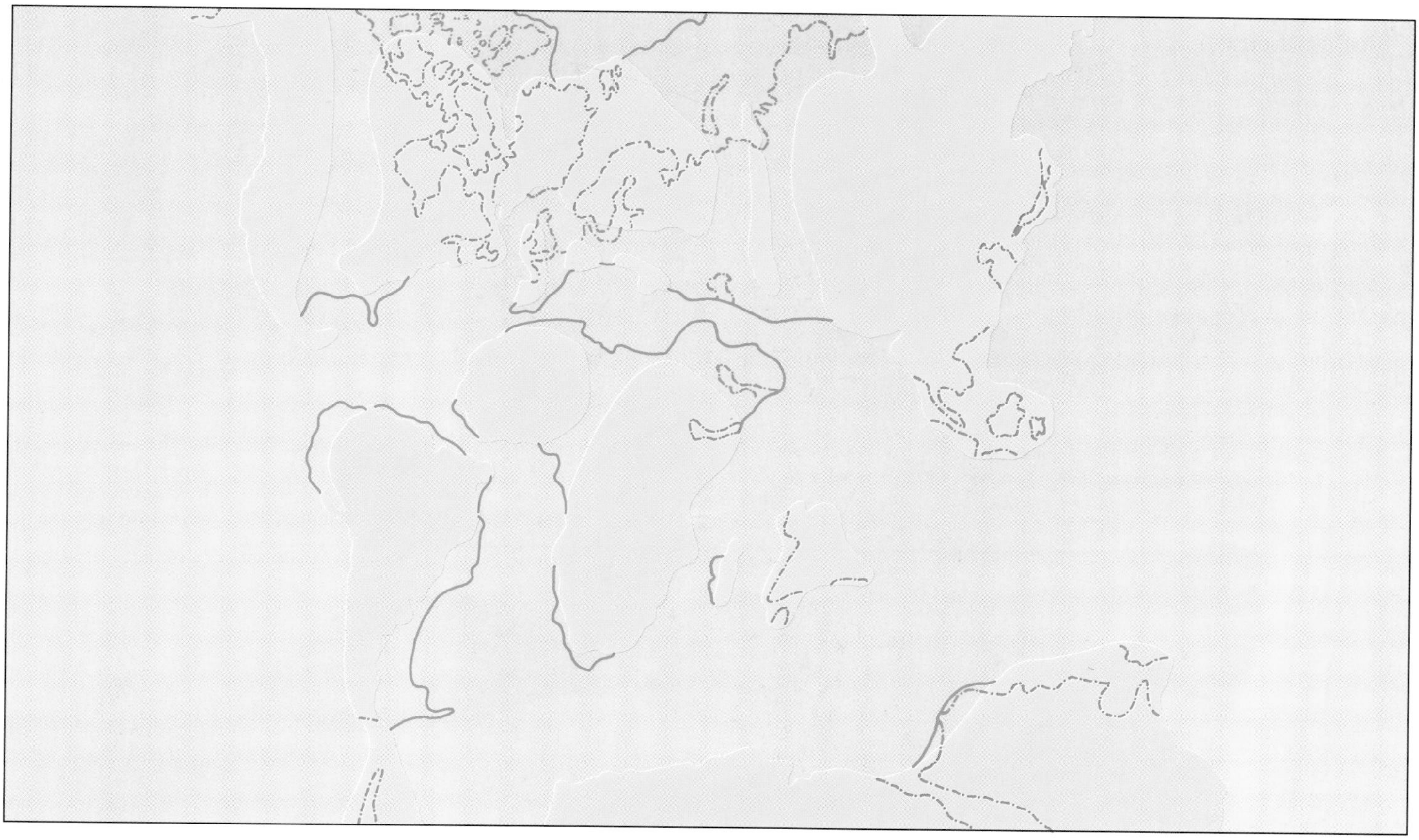

**Left:** The upper jaw of *Ornithocheirus cuvieri* from the Burham chalk pit in Kent. The fossil of this large Upper Cretaceous pterosaur was described by J.S. Bowerbank in 1845. This jaw measures 7in (18cm) in length.

**Below:** 'Mantell's Quarry' in Tilgate Forest near Cuckfield. It was in Wealden strata such as this that Gideon Mantell discovered the first pterosaur bones to be found in England. They were from the genus *Ornithocheirus.*

the remarkable Reptiles now extinct, which, like the Bats, had their anterior members modified for plying a broad membranous wing, no species had been discovered prior to 1840, which surpassed the largest of the *Pteropi*, or 'Flying-foxes', in the spread of those wings, and there was a *priori* a physiological improbability that the cold-blooded organization of a reptile should, by any secondary modification, be made to affect more in the way of flight, or be able to raise a larger mass into the air, than could be done by the warm-blooded mammal under an analogous special adaptation . . . The subsequent discovery of portions of the skull of the Pterodactyls shows that the manifestations of creative power in past time surpass the calculations that are founded upon actual nature.'

## Ornithocheirus

This genus was described by Harry Govier Seeley from fossil material found at English Cretaceous localities.[3] Despite the fact that no more complete skeletons were found, but essentially only fragments of jaws, individual bones or vertebrae, a total of 36 species were distinguished. Most of them are based on specimens from the Cambridge Greensand, a sandy marl full of phosphatic nodules. Numerous pits in the Cambridge area exploited the valuable phosphate of lime.

The Cambridge Greensand is a marine sediment deposited when the Cenomanian Sea expanded at the beginning of the Upper Cretaceous. As the fossils of pterosaur bones often seem to have been worn down, frequently as a result of rolling, it is suspected that they were washed out of older strata on the seashore and redeposited on a 'secondary deposit', this time in younger Cenomanian strata. Pterosaurs of the Cambridge Greensand could thus be considerably older, and possibly came from the late Lower Cretaceous, the Albian.[4]

3 Seeley, H.G., 1869. *Index to the fossil remains of Aves, Ornithosauria and Reptilia in the Woodwardian Museum Cambridge.* Proceedings of the Cambridge Philosophical Society, 3: 169.

4 Rawson, P.F. et al., 1978. *A correlation of Cretaceous rocks in the British Isles.* Geological Society London, Special Reports, 9: 70pp.
Seeley H.G., 1870. *The Ornithosauria. An elementary study of the bones of Pterodactyls.* 130 pp., Cambridge University Press. p.2: '. . . perfect bones are almost unknown. Even those bones like the carpals, which almost retain their entirety, invariably show indications of having been rolled on the sea-shore among the nodules of phosphate of lime with which they now occur, in their angular margins being rounded . . .'

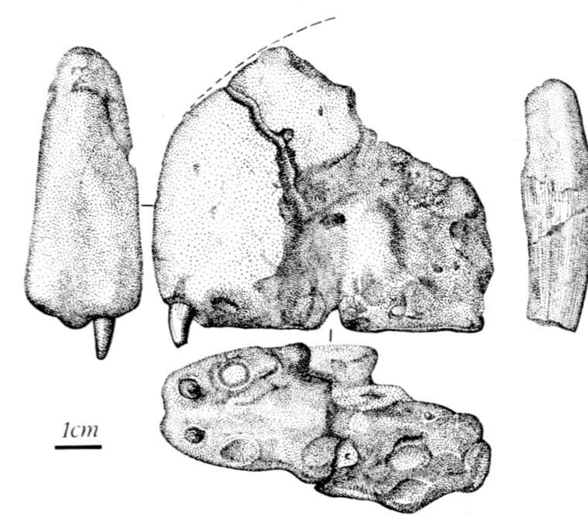


**Criorhynchus Jaw Fragments (above)**
This jaw fragment is seen from the front (top left), from the left side (middle top) and from below (lower middle). Enlarged is a single incomplete tooth.

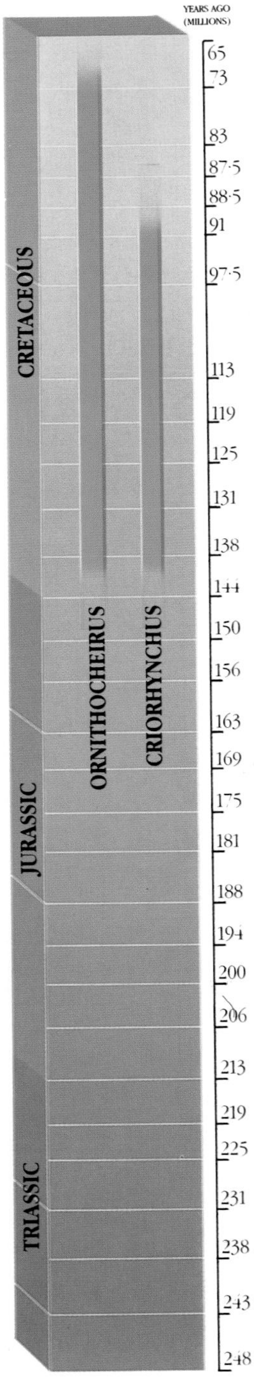

YEARS AGO (MILLIONS)
65 73 83 87·5 88·5 91 97·5 113 119 125 131 138 144 150 156 163 169 175 181 188 194 200 206 213 219 225 231 238 243 248

CRETACEOUS JURASSIC TRIASSIC
ORNITHOCHEIRUS CRIORHYNCHUS

**Time Chart (left)**
*Ornithocheirus* is something of a 'waste bin' generic name which may include several distinct genera. Most of the indisputable fossil material comes from the Upper Cretaceous (Cenomanian) of England. *Criorhynchus* is probably related. It is known from early Lower to early Upper Cretaceous.

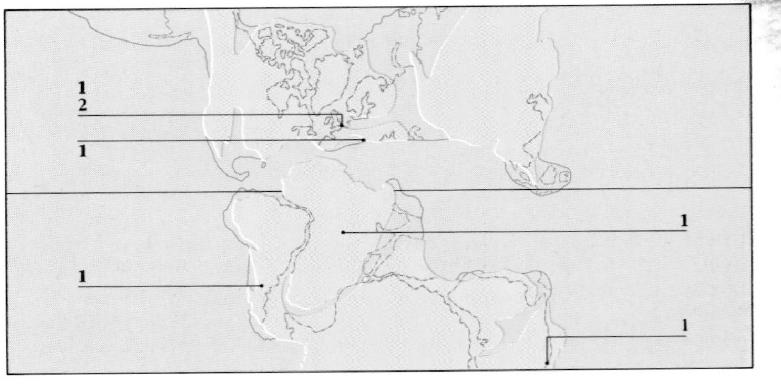

**Map (right)**
**1** *Ornithocheirus*
**2** *Criorhynchus*

**Criorhynchus (below)**
Formerly known only by fragments of the snout, *Criorhynchus* has turned out to be a close relative of *Tropeognathus* discovered more recently in early Cretaceous strata of Brazil. *Criorhynchus*, known only from England, must have looked similar, although the cranial crest at the front end of its snout was blunter and more robust. Its dentition of few, quite strong teeth suggests that this pterosaur was probably a fish eater.

In 1869 Seeley was commissioned to arrange and catalogue the pterosaur collection of the Woodwardian Museum (now Sedgwick Museum) of the University of Cambridge. Almost all the specimens came from the Cambridge Greensand, over 1,000 bones, all 'more or less broken and battered'. The name *Ornithocheirus* (=bird-hand) occurs for the first time in his 'Index to the fossil remains of Aves, *Ornithosauria* and Reptilia'. Because of the fragmentary and incomplete condition of the skeletal remains, controversy persists about what belongs to this genus and the family Ornithocheiridae named after it. In any case they were mainly large or very large pterosaurs with long, slender skulls, some probably with a bony crest on the snout, all armed with powerful teeth, coming right to the foremost point of the jaw. The fact that this genus was not too clearly defined meant that as time passed *Ornithocheirus* and the Ornithocheiridae became something of a 'waste bin' for many finds

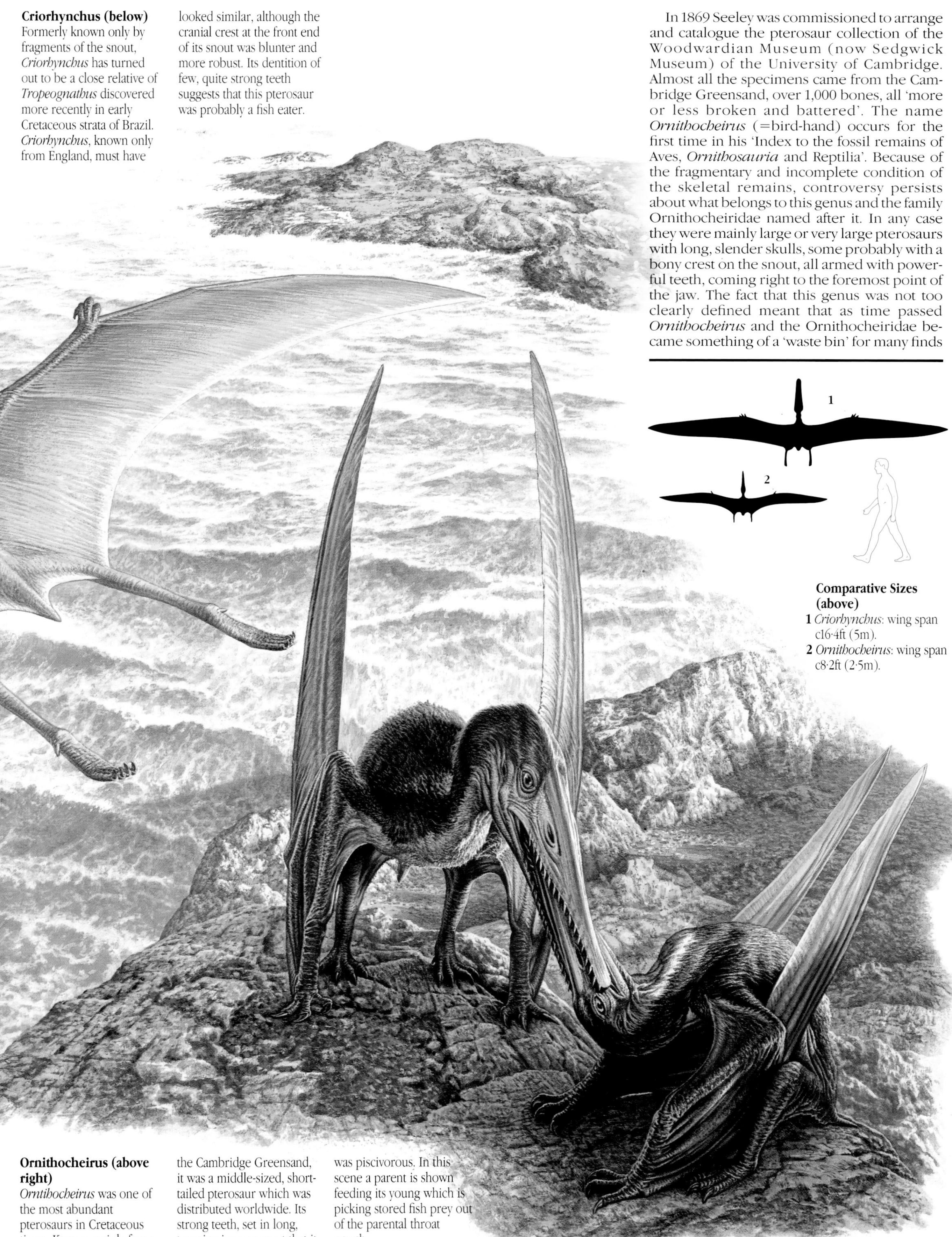


**Comparative Sizes (above)**
**1** *Criorhynchus*: wing span c16·4ft (5m).
**2** *Ornithocheirus*: wing span c8·2ft (2·5m).

**Ornithocheirus (above right)**
*Orntihocheirus* was one of the most abundant pterosaurs in Cretaceous times. Known mainly from the Cambridge Greensand, it was a middle-sized, short-tailed pterosaur which was distributed worldwide. Its strong teeth, set in long, tapering jaws, suggest that it was piscivorous. In this scene a parent is shown feeding its young which is picking stored fish prey out of the parental throat pouch.

in England, France, Germany, Bohemia, Austria, Africa, South America and Australia.

In 1914 R.W. Hooley tried to bring an element of order into the English *Ornithocheirus* material. He distinguished between five different groups, to which he gave names of their own, particularly on the basis of jaw fragments.[5]

As well as the pterosaur bones G. Mantell had found in the Sussex Wealden, Richard Owen also described part of a tibia from there as *Ornithocheirus curtus* (=short *Ornithocheirus*), and an incomplete lower jaw of a large species as *Ornithocheirus sagittirostris* (=arrow-beaked *Ornithocheirus*),[6] from the somewhat older 'Hastings Beds' of St. Leonards-on-Sea.

More remains of *Ornithocheirus* skeletons came from the late Lower Cretaceous, the so-called Albian of Folkestone in Kent. The latest English Cretaceous pterosaurs come from the Chalk (Turonian). They too are known only from fragments of bones, and were also assigned to *Ornithocheirus*.

**Ornithocheirus Skull (below right)**
This is a restoration of the skull of *Ornithocheirus* made on the basis of several fragmentary remains from the English Cretaceous. The skull is long and slender and the jaws are armed with numerous short, sharp teeth which extend to the very front of the upper and lower jaws. It was probably a fish eater.

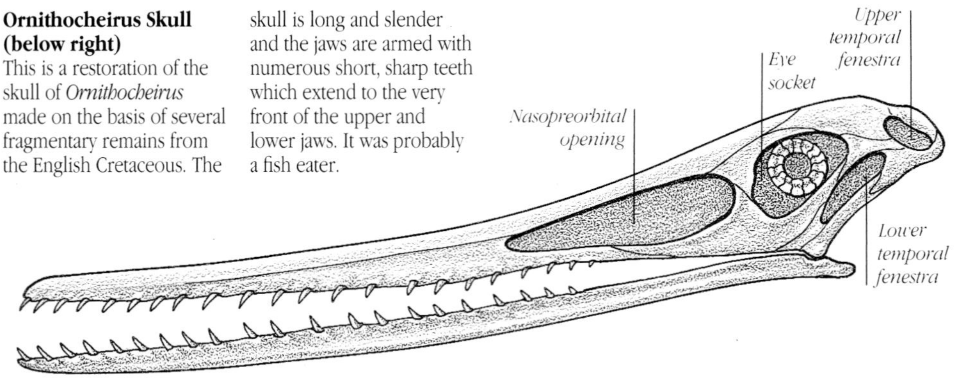

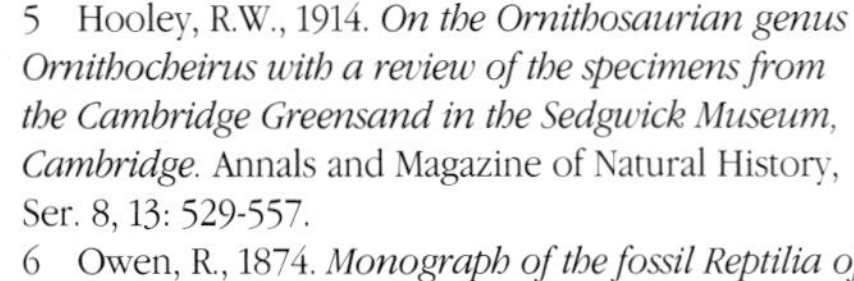

## Criorhynchus

Richard Owen identified a second type of large pterosaur in the copious pterosaur material from the Cambridge Greensand, and called it *Criorhynchus* (=ram-snout). Only fragments of bones have been found for this species as well. The most marked characteristic is the front end of the jaw. Unlike *Ornithocheirus* it is not slender and pointed, but blunt and solid, though compressed laterally. The front end of the upper jaw is slightly flattened and dented at the front. The jaws had powerful teeth, set upright, and curved slightly backwards. These typical features of the genus *Criorhynchus* were based only on a fragment of a front end of a snout. Owen did place other bones from the Cambridge Greensand in this genus, but definite classification was impossible.

Palaeontologists had always been puzzled about what *Criorhynchus*, a pterosaur with a wing span of about 16·4ft (5m), might have

5 Hooley, R.W., 1914. *On the Ornithosaurian genus Ornithocheirus with a review of the specimens from the Cambridge Greensand in the Sedgwick Museum, Cambridge.* Annals and Magazine of Natural History, Ser. 8, 13: 529-557.

6 Owen, R., 1874. *Monograph of the fossil Reptilia of the Mesozoic Formations. I. Pterosauria.* Palaeontographical Society, 27: 1-14; London.

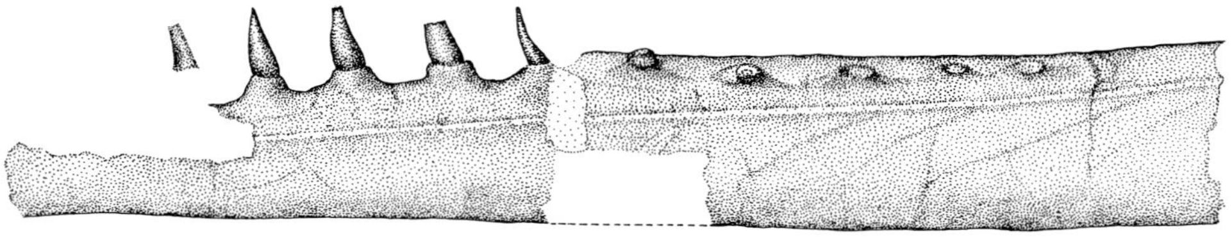

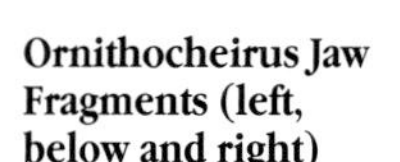

**Ornithocheirus sagittirostris**

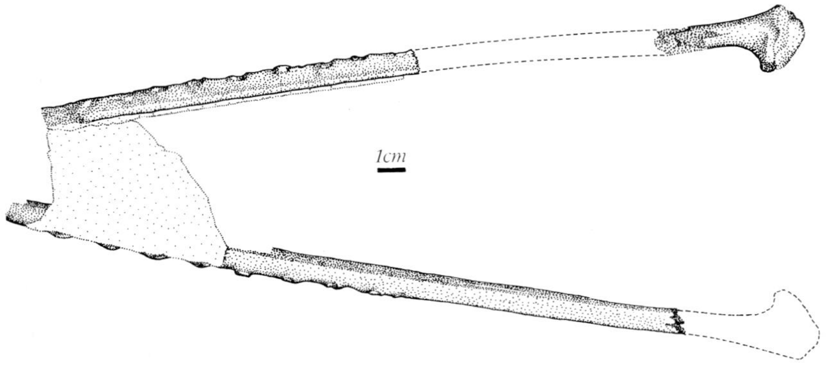

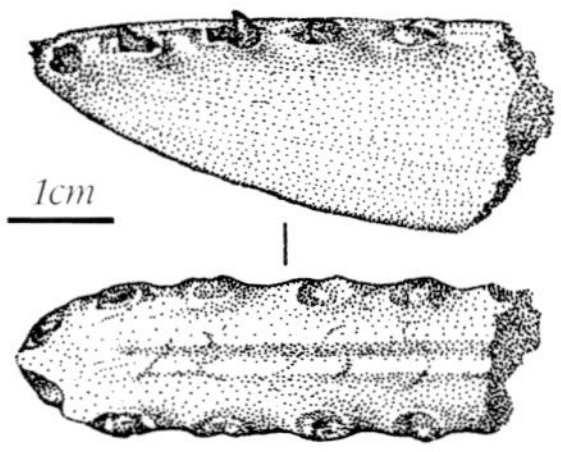

**Ornithocheirus daviesi**

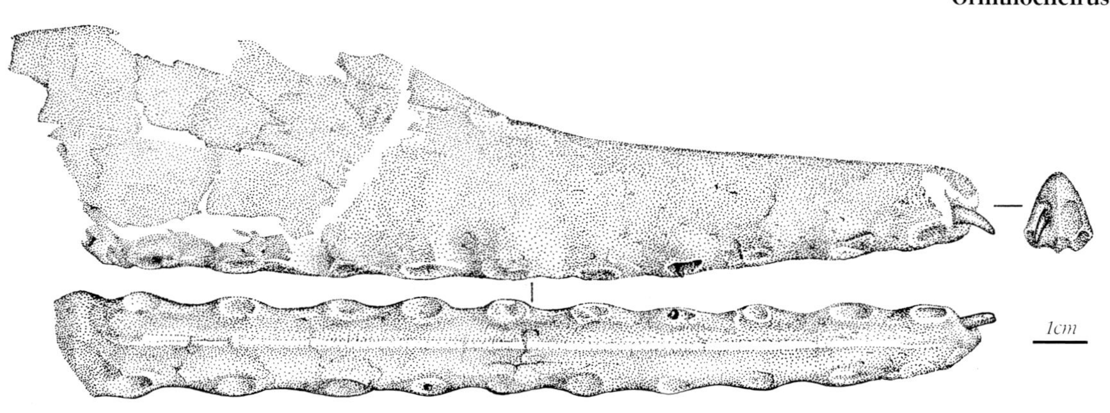

**Ornithocheirus cuvieri**

**Ornithocheirus Jaw Fragments (left, below and right)**
The drawings on this page and at near left on the opposite page show jaw fragments of different species of *Ornithocheirus* from various English Cretaceous localities. Immediately to the left is a lower jaw of *Ornithocheirus sagittirostris* seen in lateral view and, below that, from above. *O. sagittirostris* is from the Wealden of Sussex. At the foot of this page we see the upper jaw of *Ornithocheirus cuvieri* in lateral view and from below. *O. cuvieri* is from the Burham chalk pit in Kent, as is *O. giganteus* which is illustrated on the opposite page (middle left). The remaining specimen on this page is a jaw fragment of *O. daviesi* from the late Lower Cretaceous (Albian) of Folkestone in Kent. The final specimen illustrated at the foot of the opposite page is *O. sedgwicki* from the Cambridge Greensand. Here we see the tip of the upper jaw in lateral and dorsal views, and below that the tip of the lower jaw in lateral and dorsal views. No complete skeletons of *Ornithocheirus* are known; we only have jaw fragments such as this, individual bones or vertebrae. Despite this, 36 species have been distinguished, most of them based on specimens from the Cambridge Greensand. Many fragmentary remains from Europe, Africa, South America, Australia and New Zealand have also been assigned to *Ornithocheirus* on the basic of insufficient diagnostic characters. As a result, the generic name has become something of a 'waste bin' which needs clearer definition.

**Above:** Richard Owen, the British comparative anatomist who became the first superintendent of the British Museum (Natural History). It was Owen who first identified specimens from the Cambridge Greensand as belonging to a genus distinct from *Ornithocheirus*. He named it *Criorhynchus*. Owen conducted a fierce debate with Harry Govier Seeley on whether pterosaurs were warm-blooded or not.

looked like. The Viennese palaeontologist G. von Arthaber attempted a reconstruction of the skull in 1919. The result was a fairly short, tall head about 7in (18cm) long, which looked different from all the Cretaceous pterosaurs so far known.[7] The solution came from a South American find.

A few years ago a complete pterosaur skull in good condition from the Santana Formation (Aptian) in Brazil was discovered and described as *Tropeognathus* (=keel-jaw).[8] The front end of the jaw was startlingly similar to that of *Criorhynchus* from the Cambridge Greensand. It sloped sharply at the front and extended backwards in the form of a bony crest tapering towards the top. This crest is almost semicircular at the top and limited to the front end of the upper jaw. It was presumably drawn through the water like the keel of a ship while fish were being caught in flight, and helped to stabilize the head in this phase.

7 Arthaber, G. von, 1919. *Studien über Flugsaurier auf Grund der Bearbeitung des Wiener Exemplares von Dorygnathus banthensis Theod. sp.*. Denkschriften der Akademie der Wissenschaften, 97: 391-464; Vienna.
8 Wellnhofer, P., 1987. *New Crested Pterosaurs from the Lower Cretaceous of Brazil.* Mitteilungen der Bayerischen Staatssammlung für Paläontologie und historische Geologie, 27: 175-186; Munich.

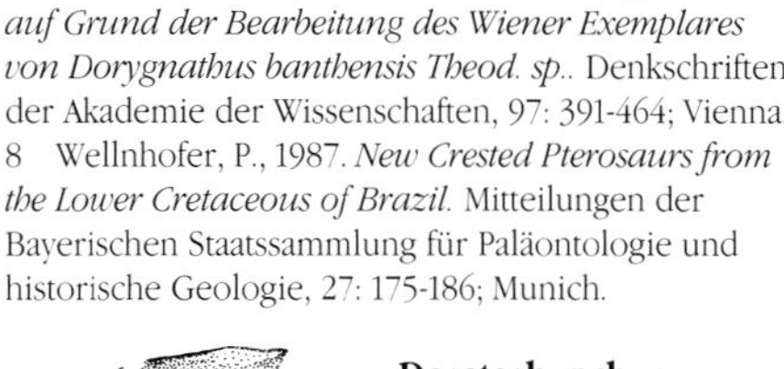

It now became clear that the high snout end in *Criorhynchus* was the front part of a bone crest that may have looked similar to that of *Tropeognathus*. *Criorhynchus* must thus have had a much longer skull than Arthaber thought. The common features of these two genera meant that they were closely related and placed together in the family Criorhynchidae.

## Doratorhynchus

In 1875 H.G.Seeley reported that at Christmas 1868, while staying in Swanage on the Dorset coast, he had been given a long vertebra and part of a large lower jaw found by a quarry worker in the Purbeck Limestone of Langton Matravers. The geological age of Purbeck Limestone is late Upper Jurassic to early Cretaceous (Tithonian-Berriasian). Seeley took the slender vertebra, about 5·2in (12 cm) long, to be the caudal (or tail) vertebra of a large long-tailed pterosaur to which he gave the name *Doratorhynchus* (=spear-snout).[9] He also included other bones in this, among them a wing phalanx 12in (30cm) long, described by Owen in 1870 as *Ornithocheirus validus*. Seeley had certainly allowed for the possibility that the vertebra could actually come from the neck, an assumption that later turned out to be correct. Further investigation of the cervical vertebrae of Cretaceous pterosaurs led to emphasis of the great similarity of this *Doratorhynchus* vertebra with the fifth cervical vertebra of the giant pterosaur *Quetzalcoatlus* from the Late Cretaceous of Texas.[10] This meant that many long vertebrae from the Cambridge Greensand that had formerly been taken for caudal vertebrae must be cervical vertebrae of pterosaurs. This shows that *Doratorhynchus* from the early Cretaceous in England was a large pterosaur with an extremely long neck, possibly an ancestor of the giant pterosaurs of Texas.

9 Seeley, H.G., 1875. *On an Ornithosaurian (Doratorhynchus validus) from the Purbeck Limestone of Langton near Swanage.* Quarterly Journal of the Geological Society London, 31: 465-468.
10 Howse, S.C.B., 1986. *On the cervical vertebrae of the Pterodactyloidea (Reptilia, Archosauria).* Zoological Journal of the Linnean Society, 88: 307-328; London.

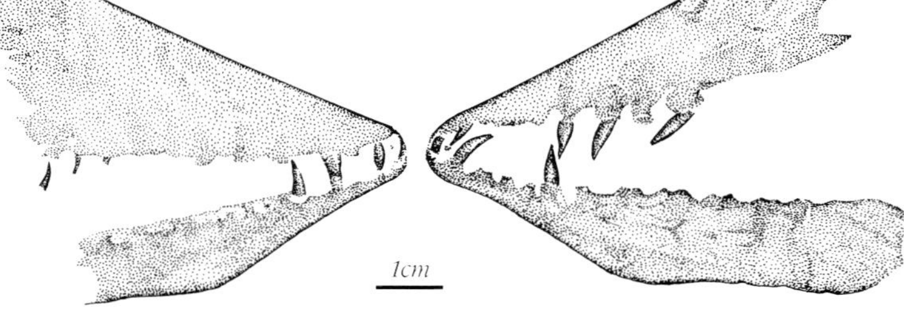


**Ornithocheirus giganteus**

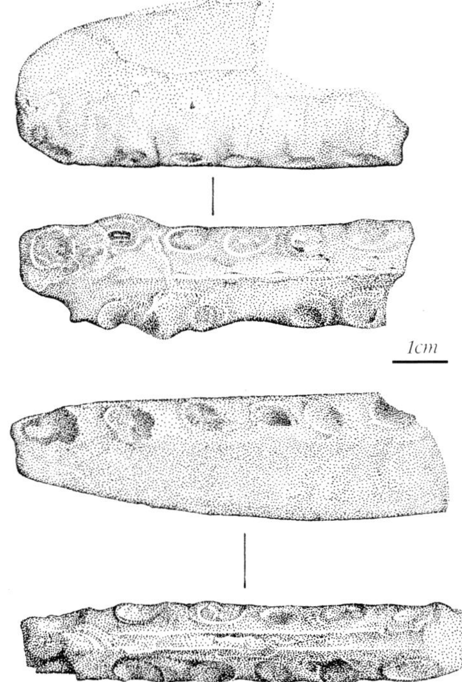


**Ornithocheirus sedgwicki**

**Doratorhynchus Vertebra (bottom of page)**
This long vertebra was discovered in the Purbeck limestone near Swanage on the Dorset coast in 1875. It was thought to have come from the tail of a long-tailed pterosaur, named as *Doratorhynchus* by H.G. Seeley. Later it was discovered that it is in fact the neck vertebra of a long-necked, short-tailed pterosaur similar to the giant Texan pterosaur *Quetzalcoatlus*, which is described at the end of this chapter. The vertebra is seen here in top view. It is about 5·2in (13cm) long.

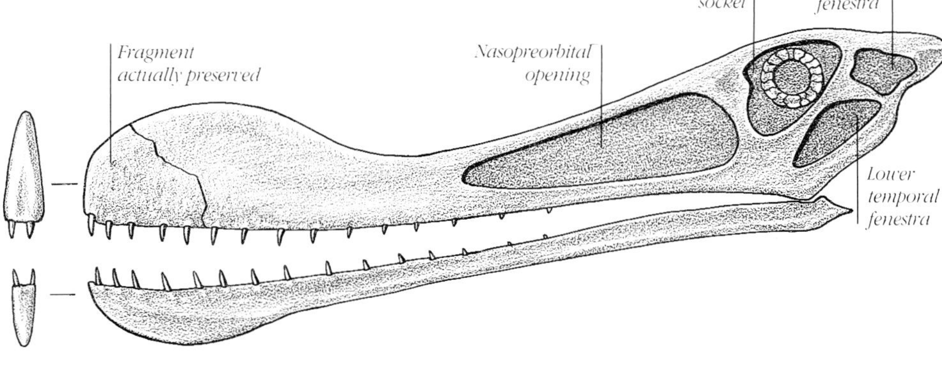


**Criorhynchus Skull (below right)**
This is a tentative restoration of the skull of *Criorhynchus* from the Cambridge Greensand. The most distinctive feature is the rounded crest at the front of the upper jaw. This is very similar to that of the Brazilian *Tropeognathus*, and as a result the two genera have been grouped in the family Criorhynchidae. We may deduce that this crest stabilized *Criorhynchus'* head while fishing. The skull length is about 20in (50cm).

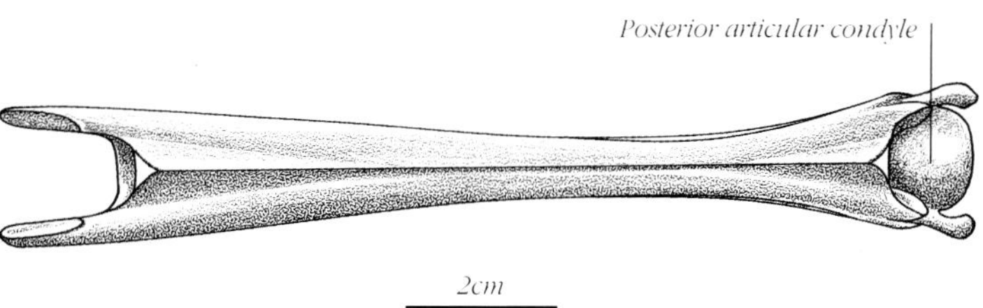

## Ornithodesmus

A fourth genus of Cretaceous pterosaur was discovered in England, from the Wealden of the Isle of Wight. It was again Seeley who in 1887 described a sacrum from the Lower Cretaceous of Atherfield (Aptian) which he thought came from a bird, and which he named *Ornithodesmus* (=bird-ribbon).[11] Later he diagnosed it as a pterosaur, and also placed in this genus parts of a skull, neck and dorsal vertebrae, the breastbone and parts of the wing skeleton of an individual which also came from Atherfield in the Isle of Wight. Because of the broad teeth of this individual he called the species *Ornithodesmus latidens*.[12]

11 Seeley, H.G., 1887. *On a sacrum apparently indicating a new type of Bird, Ornithodesmus cluniculus Seeley.* Quarterly Journal of the Geological Society London, 43: 206.

*Ornithodesmus* was a large pterosaur with a wing span of 16·4ft (5m). The front ends of the jaw were similarly formed to those of a duck. Despite this it was not a 'duck-billed pterosaur', as the jaws were equipped from back to front with a series of strong, lancet-shaped, laterally compressed teeth. The eye socket is small and placed fairly far back in the skull. The first six dorsal vertebrae are fused to form a notarium to which the pectoral girdle attached. The strong, alternately-meshing dentition and

12 It has recently become clear that the sacrum of *Ornithodesmus cluniculus* that Seeley at first thought came from a bird could not come from a pterosaur either, but belonged to a small theropod dinosaur. Thus the generic name *Ornithodesmus* designates neither a bird, nor a pterosaur, but a dinosaur. Therefore a new generic name will have to be given to the pterosaur species *'Ornithodesmus' latidens* (from a letter from Dr Andrew Milner, London).

**Ornithodesmus (below)**
*Ornithodesmus* was quite a large pterosaur; its wing span measured about 16·4ft (5m) while its skull length was about 22in (56cm). It is known from the Wealden (Lower Cretaceous) of England, and must have been a contemporary of the *Iguanodon* dinosaurs that can also be seen browsing on the vegetation in this Wealden landscape. To give an idea of comparative size, these *Iguanodon* were about 23ft (7m) long. *Ornithodesmus* is distinguished from all other Cretaceous pterosaurs by the peculiar broad and rounded front end of its beak This characteristic has given rise to its popular name of 'the duck-billed pterosaur'. However, unlike a duck, the front of its beak was lined with short, robust, alternately meshing teeth, a dentition that is suggestive of a diet of fish.

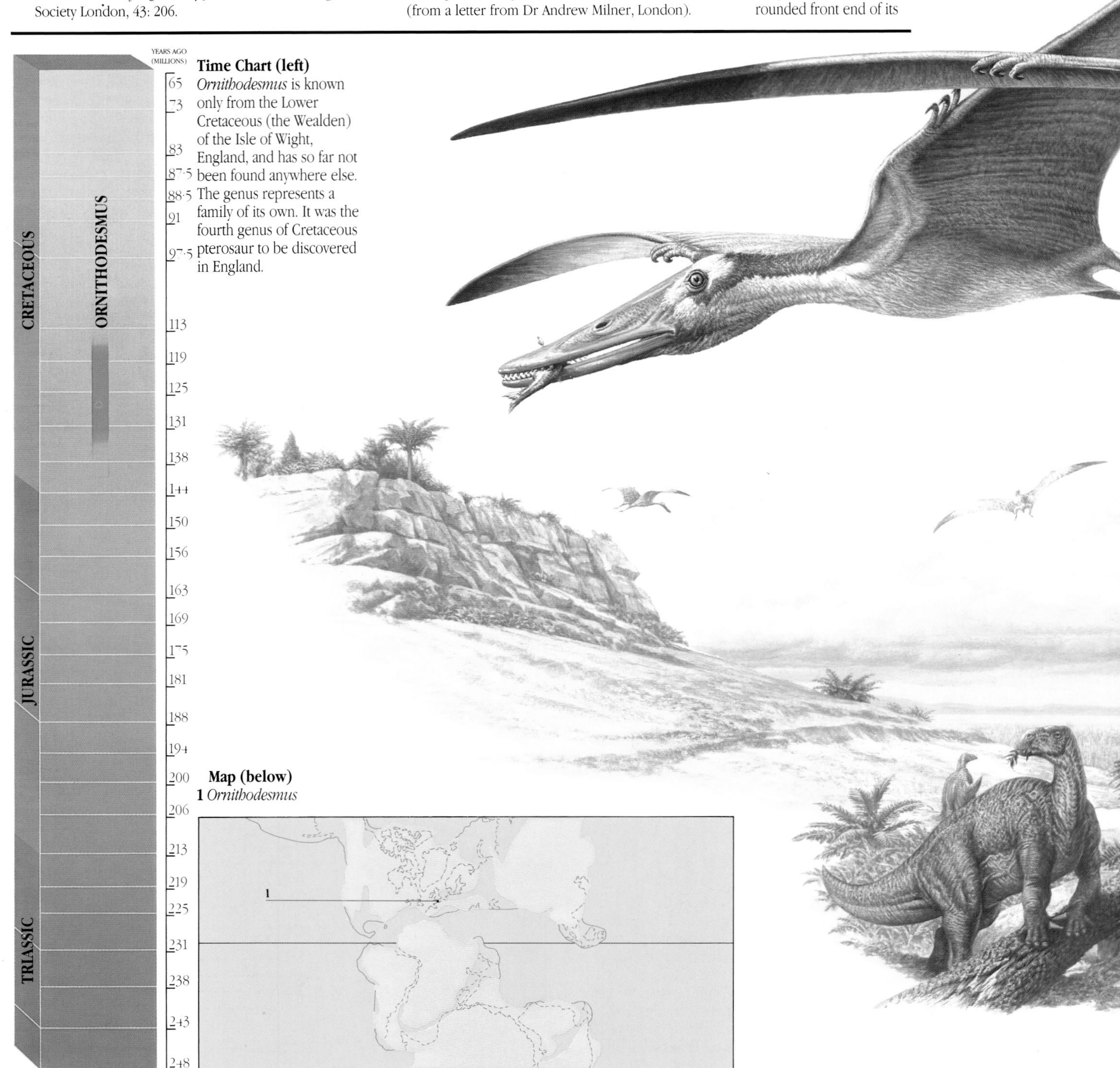


**Time Chart (left)**
*Ornithodesmus* is known only from the Lower Cretaceous (the Wealden) of the Isle of Wight, England, and has so far not been found anywhere else. The genus represents a family of its own. It was the fourth genus of Cretaceous pterosaur to be discovered in England.

**Map (below)**
**1** *Ornithodesmus*

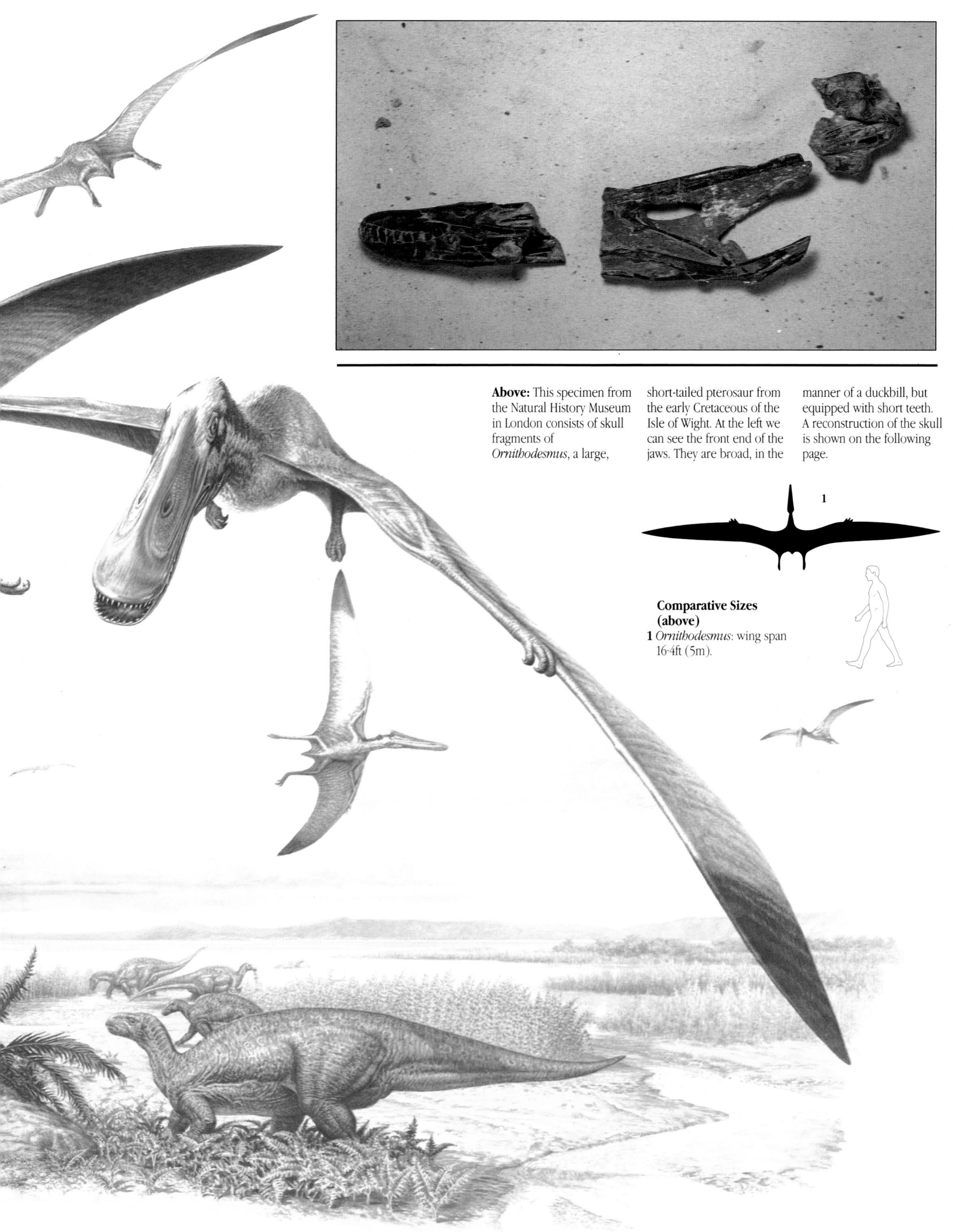

**Above:** This specimen from the Natural History Museum in London consists of skull fragments of *Ornithodesmus*, a large, short-tailed pterosaur from the early Cretaceous of the Isle of Wight. At the left we can see the front end of the jaws. They are broad, in the manner of a duckbill, but equipped with short teeth. A reconstruction of the skull is shown on the following page.

1

**Comparative Sizes (above)**
**1** *Ornithodesmus*: wing span 16·4ft (5m).

broad snout suggest that *Ornithodesmus* was a fish eater, and that it possibly used a different catching technique from its contemporaries, the Ornithocheirids, with their pointed snouts.

## European Finds

So far few Cretaceous pterosaurs have been found on the continent of Europe. Here too we are dealing with individual bones and fragments, fossils which were usually assigned to the English *Ornithocheirus*.

From the early nineteenth century onwards, hard Cretaceous coal has been mined in the so-called 'New World' near Grünbach in Lower Austria. It was formed in an estuary delta region about 70 to 80 million years ago. The deposits in which the coal seams are found are part of the Gosau Formation (Campanian) which occurs widely in the Northern Calcareous Alps. With the coal, which originated from ferns, conifers and palms, fossil remains of fauna have been found that suggest a tropical climate: dinosaurs, crocodiles, turtles and lizards. H.G. Seeley turned his attention to

**Ornithodesmus Skull (below)**
This drawing is a restoration of the skull of *Ornithodesmus latidens*, the species name *latidens* referring to the broad teeth which can be seen at the front of the upper and lower jaws. The drawing has been made on the basis of incomplete material from the early Cretaceous of the Isle of Wight. The eye socket is situated quite a long way back in the skull, and it extends downwards into a slot-like opening. The length of this skull is about 22in (56cm). When seen from above, the ends of the beak are rounded and broad, which gives the bill a characteristic rather duck-like appearance.

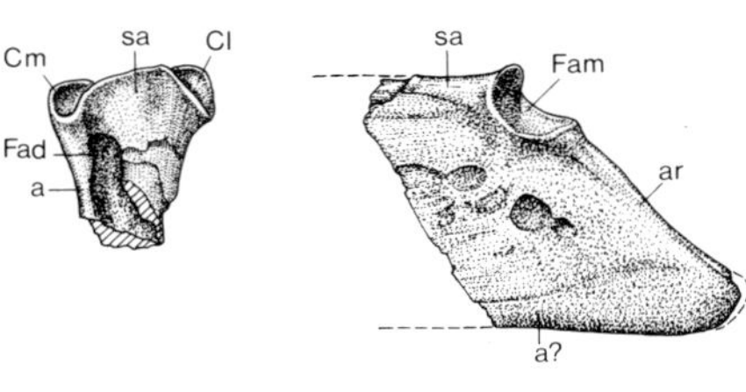


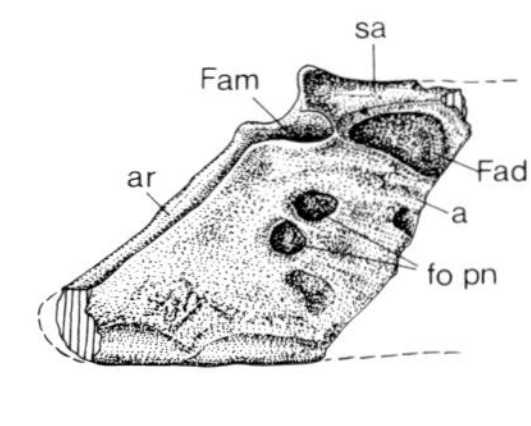


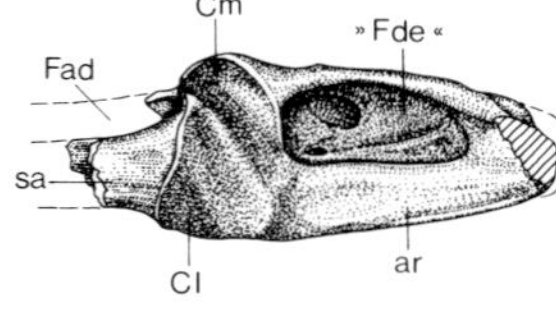


**Ornithocheirus bunzeli (above)**
Seen here are remains of the pterosaur *Ornithocheirus bunzeli* from late Cretaceous coal deposits that were mined near Grünbach in Lower Austria. The drawings show the articular end of the lower jaw in different aspects. These bones were described by H.G. Seeley in 1881. They showed that this pterosaur could open its jaws very wide indeed, presumably to grasp fish that it had caught.

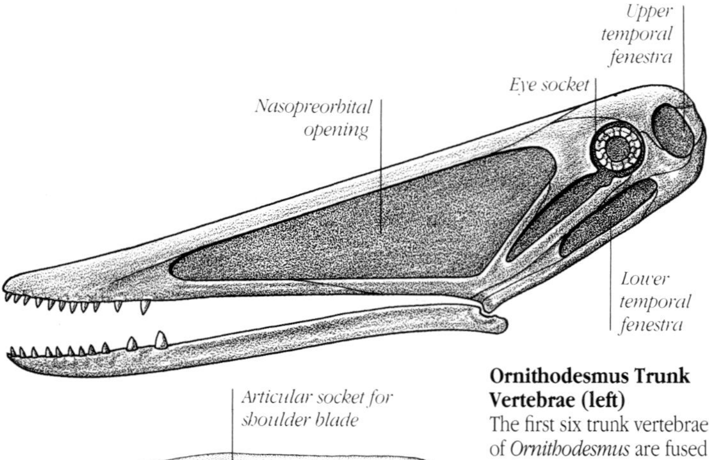


**Ornithodesmus Trunk Vertebrae (left)**
The first six trunk vertebrae of *Ornithodesmus* are fused to form a notarium. The shoulder blade was supported in a shallow depression in the fused neural spines. The length of this notarium is 6·8in (17·25cm).

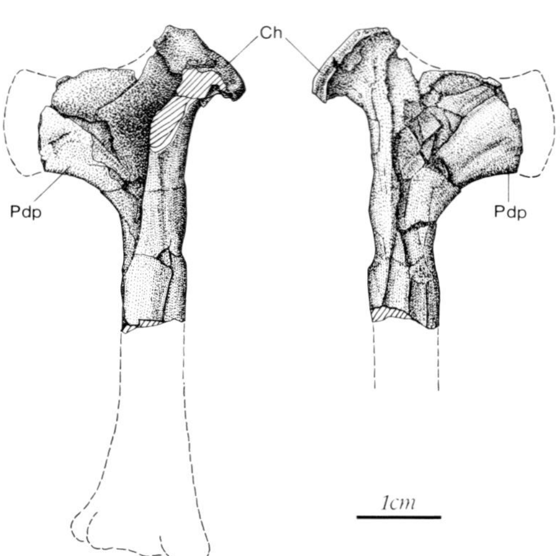


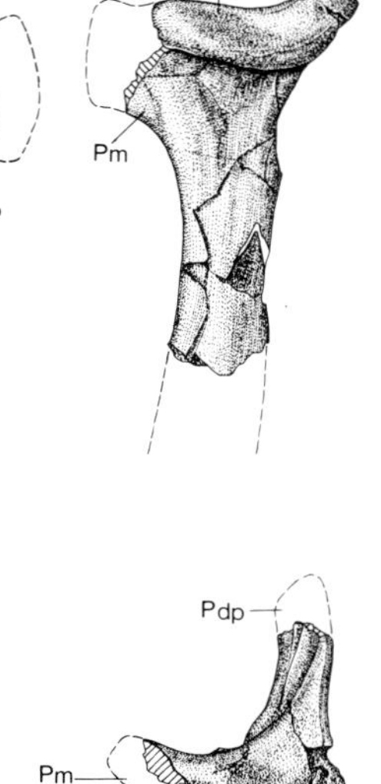


**Ornithocheirus Arm Fragments (above)**
These drawings show the upper arm of *Ornithocheirus* in various aspects. Although very incomplete, the bones of *Ornithocheirus* are the only fossil record of Cretaceous pterosaurs in the Alps.

**A Cretaceous Landscape (left)**
This drawing recreates the sort of landscape in which scientists believe *Ornithocheirus* flourished during the late Cretaceous, in the part of the world that is now Grünbach in Austria. It shows the mouth of a river with tropical vegetation: screw trees, reeds, willows and palms. A predatory *Ornithocheirus* is seen soaring above the water, while turtles and crocodiles bask on sand bars by the river. A lizard is perched on a creeper, while in the foreground and background hadrosaurs can be seen foraging for food. Such fauna have been preserved in the deposits of coal which originated from the lush plant material of this locality.

these reptiles in 1881, and described the articular bone of a lower jaw as *Ornithocheirus bunzeli*, because the bone had been described as a lizard by E. Bunzel in 1871.[13] Other pterosaur remains from this site were a humerus fragment and fragments of wing phalanges suggesting a wing span of 4·92-5·74ft (1·5-1·75m).

This lower jaw articular bone showed in particular that these pterosaurs could open their mouths very wide. At the same time the branches of the lower jaw widened, to create a larger opening for the throat pouch, in which fish that had been caught were stored.[14] As far as it is possible to determine, pterosaurs from the Gosau Cretaceous of Lower Austria were very similar to some *Ornithocheirus* species from the Cambridge Greensand.

In the Turonian strata of Bohemia (Czechoslovakia) A. Fritsch found fossil bones that he thought to be those of a bird, which he called *Cretornis* (=chalk-bird). Later the relatively small, well-preserved wing bones were recognized as those of a pterosaur, which was given the name *Ornithocheirus hlavatschi*, named after the collector of the fossils Hlaváč, a pharmacist in the town of Chotzen.[15]

In 1885 E. Koken described the metacarpal bone of a very large pterosaur with an estimated wing span of 28ft (8·5m) from the Lower Cretaceous of the Hannover region as *Ornithocheirus hilsenis* (from the Hils mountains).[16] However, other researchers doubted the pterosaurian nature of this bone, and thought it was the foot digit phalanx of a carnivorous dinosaur. Unfortunately this dispute cannot be cleared up, as the specimen has disappeared.

13 Seeley, H.G., 1881. *The Reptile Fauna of the Gosau Formation preserved in the Geological Museum of the University of Vienna.* Quarterly Journal of the Geological Society London, 37: 620-704.
14 Wellnhofer P., 1980. *Flugsaurierreste aus der Gosau-Kreide von Muthmannsdorf (Niederösterreich) – ein Beitrag zur Kiefermechanik der Pterosaurier.* Mitteilungen der Bayerischen Staatssammlung für Paläontologie und historische Geologie, 20: 95-112; Munich.
15 Fritsch, A., 1881. *Über die Entdeckung von Vogelresten in der böhmischen Kreideformation.* Sitzungsberichte der königlich-böhmischen Gesellschaft der Wissenschaften, 1880: 85; Prague.
16 Koken, E., 1885. *Über Ornithocheirus hilsensis Koken.* Zeitschrift der deutschen Geologischen Gesellschaft, 37: 214; Berlin.

**Above:** Exposures of the Tugulu Group, of early Cretaceous age, in the Wuerho region of the Junggar Basin in China. These deposits have yielded remains of *Dsungaripterus* and *Noripterus*.

Finally, fossil remains of Cretaceous pterosaurs were discovered also in France. As early as 1882 a dubious cervical vertebra and teeth were found in the Lower Cretaceous strata (Gault) of the Paris basin, and compared with *Ornithocheirus* species from the Cambridge Greensand by H.E. Sauvage. In 1983 the upper end of an ulna from the Lower Cretaceous (Hauterivian) of the Haute-Marne was discovered. This bone has also been placed in the genus *Ornithocheirus*. The size of the bone suggests a wing span of 12ft (about 3·7m).[17] And last of all a cervical vertebra that also came from the Lower Cretaceous (Aptian) of eastern France (Aube) has been described.[18]

However, it cannot be proved with certainty that all these finds belong to the genus *Ornithocheirus* or the family Ornithocheiridae.

17 Buffetaut, E. and Wellnhofer, P., 1983. *Un reste de Ptérosaurien dans l'Hauterivien (Crétacé Inférieur) de la Haute-Marne.* Bulletin de la Société Géologique de France, 1983 (7), 25(1): 111-115, Paris.

## Discoveries in Asia

The Junggar basin is in north-western China, between the Altai and Tianshan mountain ranges, in the province of Xinjiang. Its sequence of geological strata includes a long series of continental sediments, sandstones, slates and shales, deposited from the late Permian to the late Cretaceous. Some Upper Jurassic and Cretaceous horizons have produced dinosaurs. Pterosaurs have also been found in one of these formations, the Tugulu group. Their age can be given as late Lower Cretaceous.

## Dsungaripterus and Phobetor

It was Professor Young Chung-chien (C.C Young for western palaeontologists), the Grand Old Man of Chinese vertebrate palaeontology, who discovered the first Chinese pterosaur: *Dsungaripterus weii* (=Junggar-wing).[19] The fossil material consisted of the front sections of skull and lower jaw, and a large part of the rest of the skeleton, preserved in excellent three-dimensional condition. In 1973 a palaeontological expedition excavated more *Dsungaripterus* skeletal material on the same site near Wuerho, in the north west of the Junggar basin, including complete skulls, a sternum, a sacrum and pelvic bones.[20]

18 Buffetaut, E., Dubus, B. and Mazin, J.-M., 1989. *Une vertèbre de ptérosaure (Reptilia: Archosauria) dans l'Aptien de l'Aube.* Bulletin annual de l'Association Géologique Auboise, 11: 3-8.
19 Young, C.C., 1964. *On a new pterosaurian from Sinkiang, China.* Vertebrata Palasiatica, 8: 221-256; Beijing.
20 Young C.C., 1973. *Reports of Paleontological Expedition to Sinkiang (II). Pterosaurian Fauna from Wuerho, Sinkiang.* Memoirs of the Institute of Vertebrate Palaeontology and Palaeoanthropology, Academia Sinica, 11: 18-35; Beijing (in Chinese).

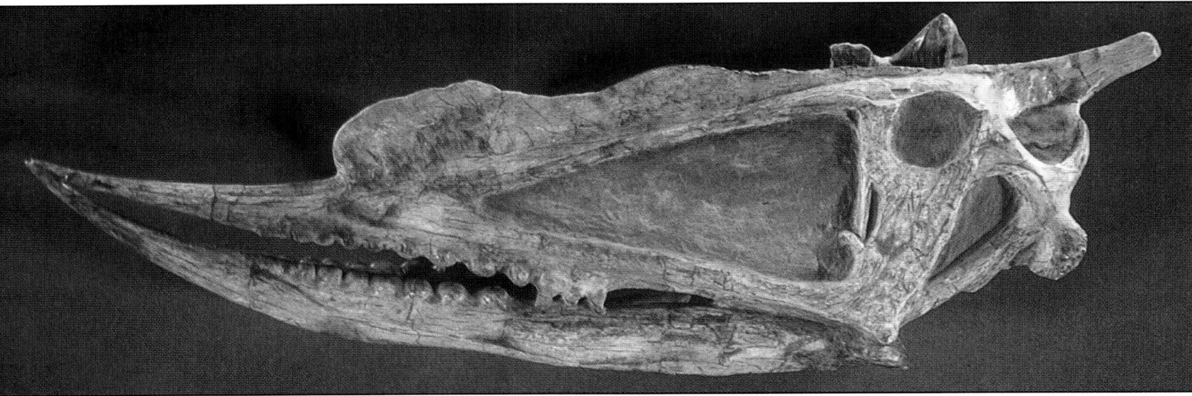

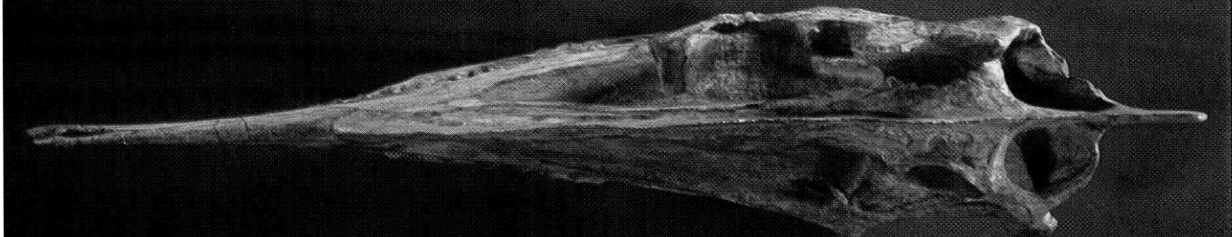

**Right:** The skull of *Dsungaripterus weii* from the Lower Cretaceous of Xinjiang Province, China, seen from the side (upper photograph) and from the top (lower). These views show particularly clearly the extremely pointed, toothless tips of the jaws which are bent upwards at the front. It seems possible that *Dsungaripterus* used these like a pair of forceps to winkle out small crabs and shellfish on the shore. Once caught, such creatures could have been broken open by means of the flattened bony knobs that are situated further back in the jaws. The crests running along the midline of the skull are also readily apparent in this view. The length of this skull is 16in (41cm).

*Dsungaripterus weii* was a fairly large pterosaur with a wing span of 9·8-11·5ft (3-3·5m), with a skull up to 1·6ft (50cm) long. The toothless tips of its jaws, slightly bent upwards, are a striking feature. They seem to have worked like a pair of tweezers. Further back, both upper and lower jaw have blunt knobs on their margins, which look like breaking tools. Perhaps *Dsungaripterus* used its jaw like the beak of a shore bird, in order to find and crack open bivalves, snails and crabs.

Other particular features of *Dsungaripterus* are cranial crests on the skull: an elongated crest on the snout along the mid-line extending over the eyes, and a short crest rising above the back of the head. The eye socket is quite high in the skull, and relatively small. The largest aperture in the skull is the nasopreorbital opening. *Dsungaripterus* had a series of fused front dorsal vertebrae, a so-called notarium, and fused sacral vertebrae, a synsacrum, similarly to birds.

**Phobetor (right)**
*Phobetor* was a close relative of *Dsungaripterus*, although only about half its size. It had similar bony crests adorning its head. Its pointed jaws are straighter than those of *Dsungaripterus* and they contain real, conical teeth rather than tooth-like bony knobs. *Phobetor* is seen here skimming over the water and feeding in the fast-moving river shallows.

YEARS AGO (MILLIONS)

CRETACEOUS
JURASSIC
TRIASSIC
DSUNGARIPTERUS
PHOBETOR
NORIPTERUS

65
73
83
87·5
88·5
91
97·5
113
119
125
131
138
144
150
156
163
169
175
181
188
194
200
206
213
219
225
231
238
243
248

**Time Chart (left)**
There is evidence that *Dsungaripterus* existed in the late Jurassic of Africa, and survived into the early Cretaceous where it was found in China along with the related genus *Noripterus*. Another dsungaripterid pterosaur, *Phobetor*, is recorded from the early Lower Cretaceous of West Mongolia.

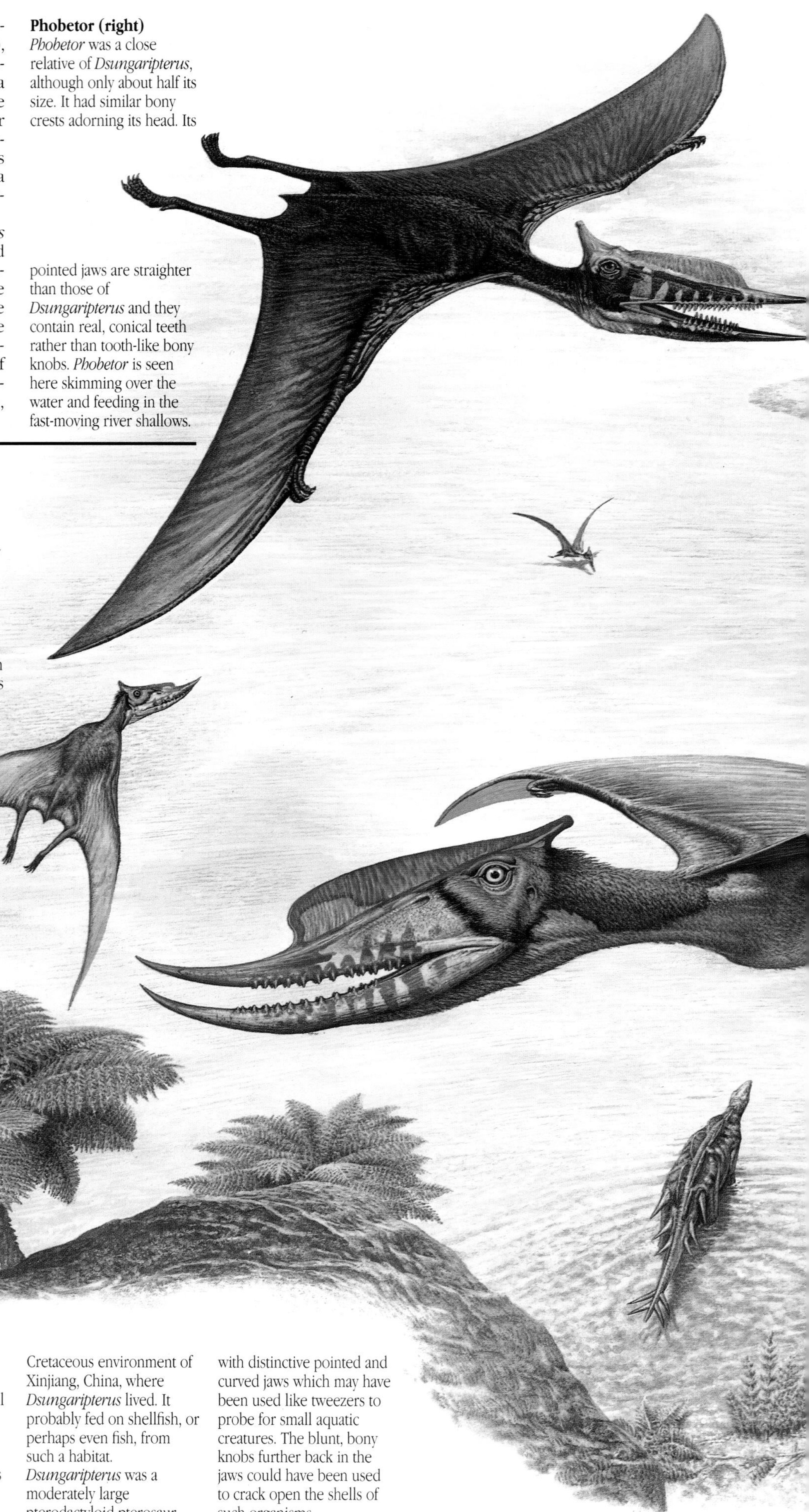

**Dsungaripterus (above right)**
In this scene we see a small river flowing into a lake. The stegosaur *Wuerhosaurus* is entering the shallows with one of its young. It is a landscape typical of the early Cretaceous environment of Xinjiang, China, where *Dsungaripterus* lived. It probably fed on shellfish, or perhaps even fish, from such a habitat. *Dsungaripterus* was a moderately large pterodactyloid pterosaur with distinctive pointed and curved jaws which may have been used like tweezers to probe for small aquatic creatures. The blunt, bony knobs further back in the jaws could have been used to crack open the shells of such organisms.

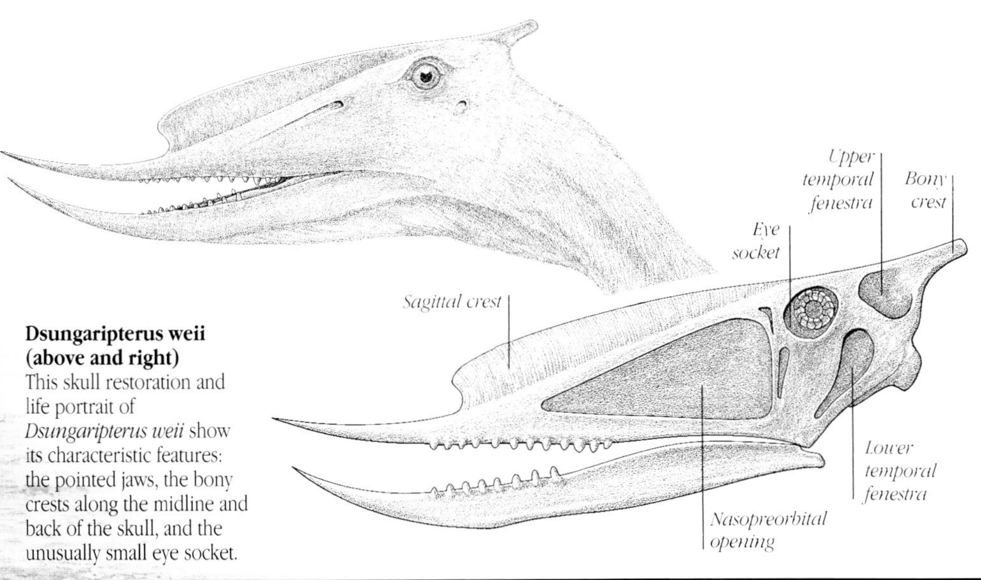


**Dsungaripterus weii (above and right)**
This skull restoration and life portrait of *Dsungaripterus weii* show its characteristic features: the pointed jaws, the bony crests along the midline and back of the skull, and the unusually small eye socket.

In 1982 N. Bakhurina of the Moscow Palaeontological Institute described skeletal remains of a small *Dsungaripterus (D. parvus)* from the early Lower Cretaceous, Zagan Zabsk Formation, of western Mongolia. At first there were only bones from the wing skeleton and the hind legs. Later skulls were also discovered, and there were such clear distinctions between these bones and the Chinese *Dsungaripterus* specimens that a new genus, *Phobetor* (=the frightening one) was suggested for the Mongolian form. *Phobetor* did have *Dsungaripterus*' toothless jaw points and a cranial crest, but also had genuine pointed teeth. Its wing span was about 4·9ft (1·5m).[21]

21 Bakhurina, N.N., 1982. *Pterodactyl from the Lower Cretaceous of Mongolia.* Palaeontological Journal, 4: 104-108; Moscow (in Russian).
Bakhurina, N.N., 1986. Priroda, Akademia Nauk SSR; Moscow (in Russian).

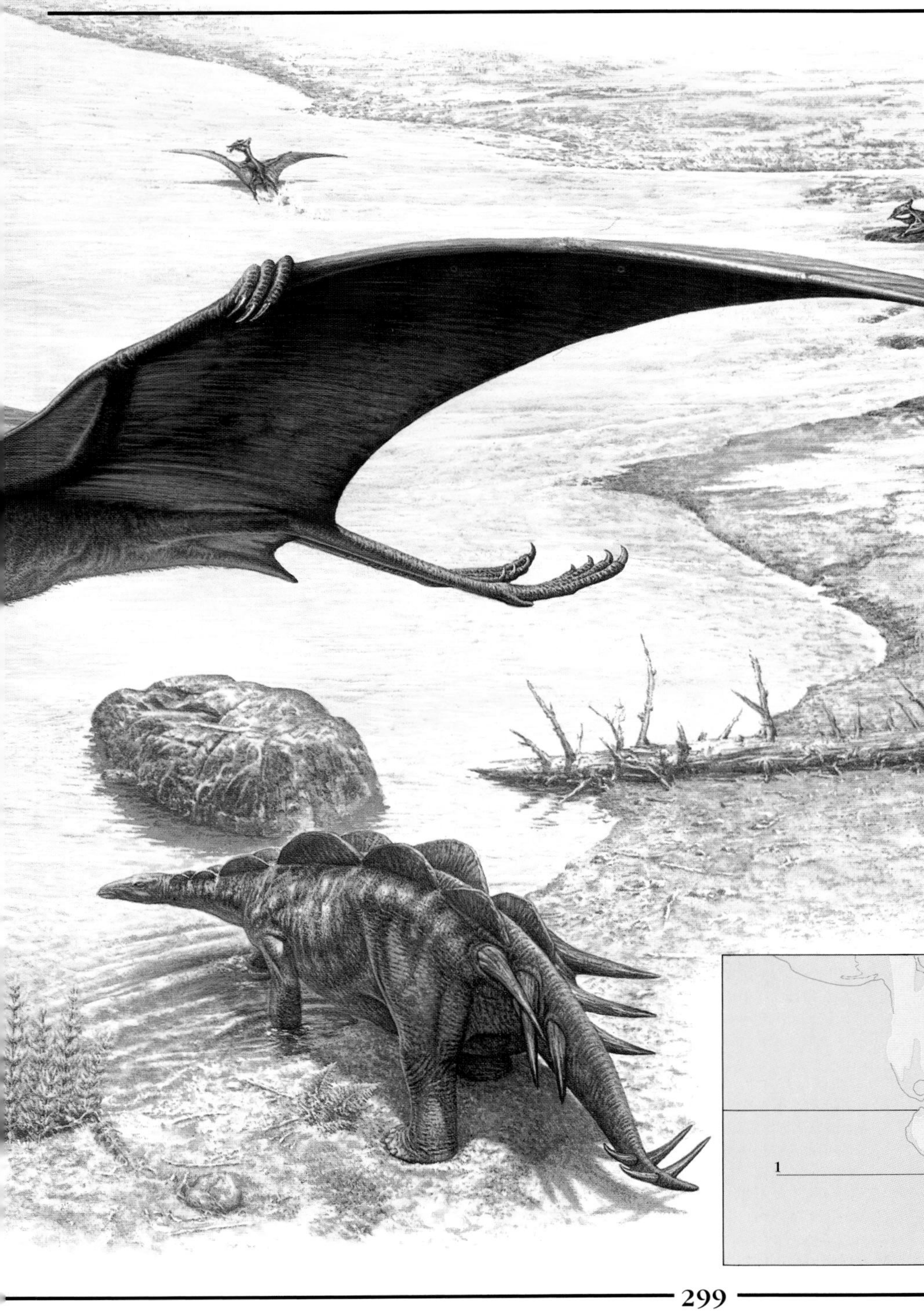

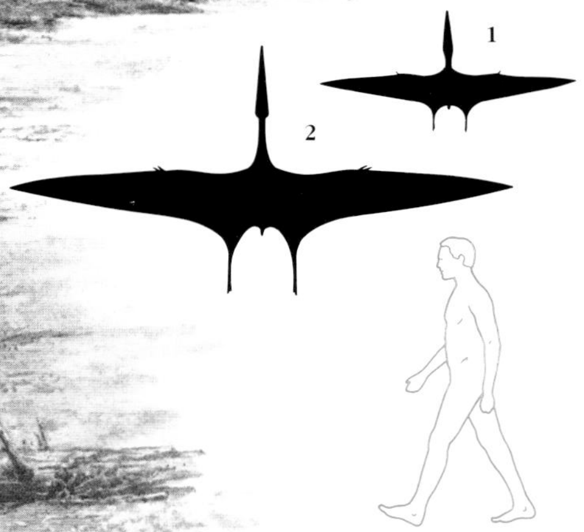

**Comparative Sizes (above)**
**1** *Phobetor*: wing span 4·9ft (1·5m).
**2** *Dsungaripterus*: wing span 9·8ft (3m).

**Map (below)**
**1** *Dsungaripterus*
**2** *Phobetor*
**3** *Noripterus*

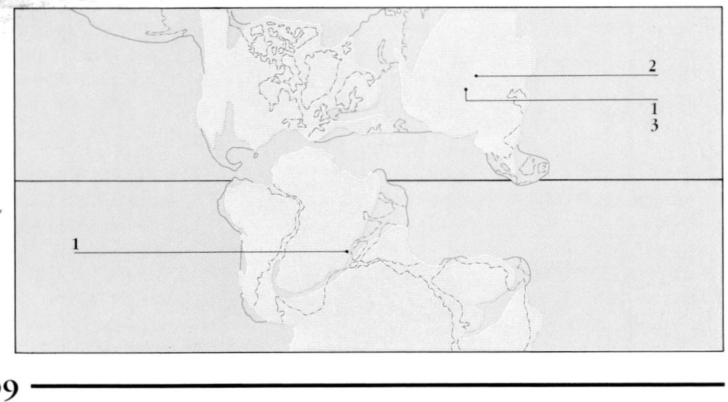

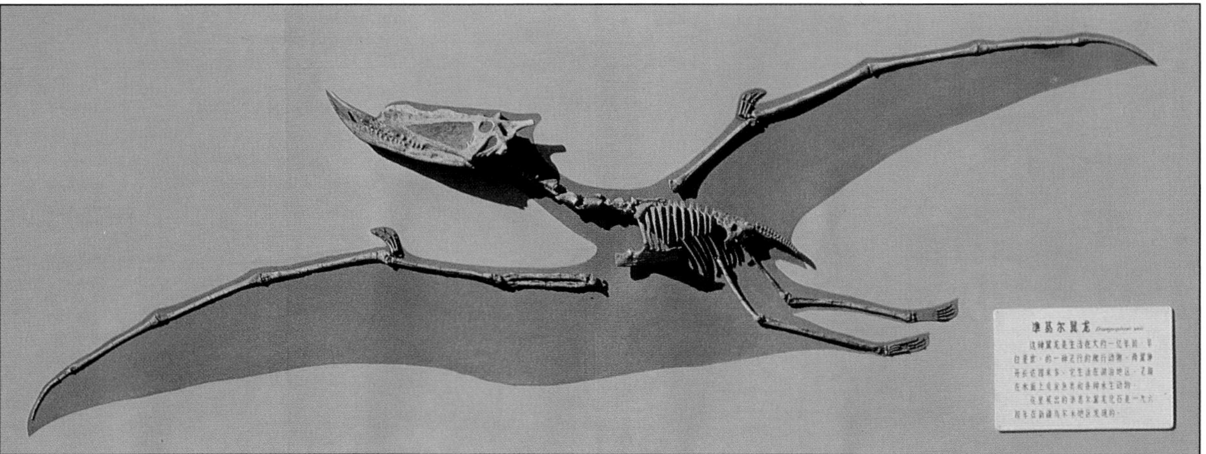

**Left:** A wall mount of the skeleton of *Dsungaripterus weii* from early Cretaceous sediments in Xinjiang, China which is on display in the Natural History Museum, part of the Institute of Vertebrate Palaeontology and Palaeoanthropology in Beijing. Missing bones have been restored and put in their correct places. The outlines of the body and the wing membranes are indicated against the blue background. The wing span of this mounted skeleton is nearly 10ft (3m).

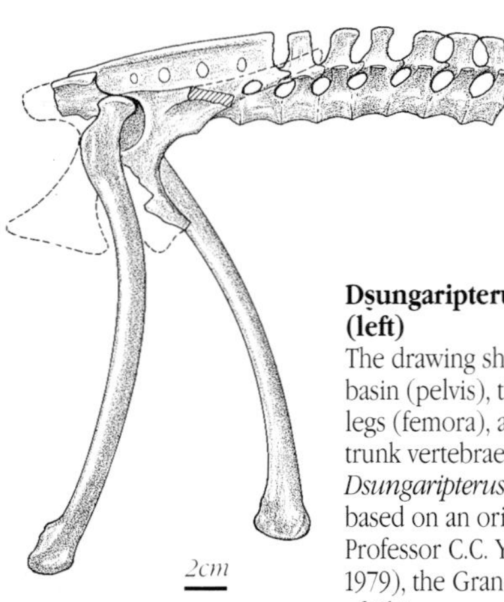


**Dsungaripterus Pelvis (left)**
The drawing shows the basin (pelvis), the upper legs (femora), and the last trunk vertebrae of *Dsungaripterus weii.* It is based on an original by Professor C.C. Young (1896-1979), the Grand Old Man of Chinese vertebrate palaeontology who discovered and described this, the first Chinese pterosaur, in 1964.

**Above and below:**
This is the skull of *Phobetor parvus* from early Lower Cretaceous rocks of Western Mongolia. This dsungaripterid pterosaur had toothless pointed tips to its jaws, and crests along the top and at the rear of its skull.

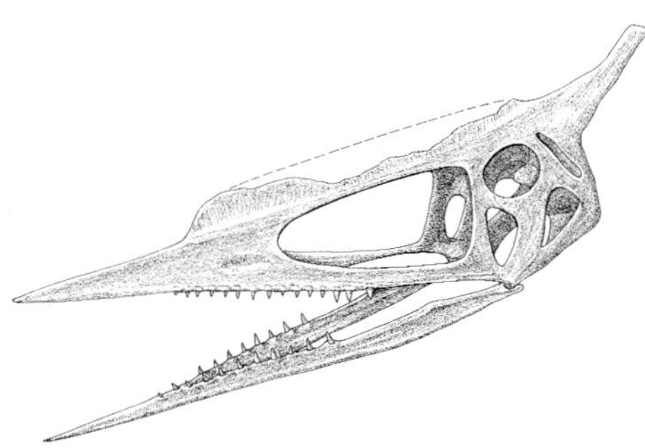

## Noripterus

During the second palaeontological expedition to the Junggar basin of Xinjiang another pterosaur was discovered, which was a third smaller than *Dsungaripterus.* Professor Young gave it the name *Noripterus* (=lake-wing).[20] The skeletal remains were of various individuals, including the front end of an upper jaw and bones from the wing skeleton and hind legs. Like that of *Dsungaripterus*, the lower jaw was toothless at the front. The rest of the teeth were strong, and set fairly far apart. *Noripterus*' neck vertebrae were long and narrow. Both Lower Cretaceous pterosaurs from Xinjiang are closely related and have therefore been placed in the family Dsungaripteridae.

Professor Young tentatively placed pterosaur skeletal remains from the Lower Cretaceous of Shantung and Inner Mongolia in this category.[19] Dsungaripterid pterosaurs apparently occurred all over the world. They lived in East Africa in the Upper Jurassic,[22] and in South America in the Lower Jurassic,[23] as well as in China and Mongolia.

The first mention of a Cretaceous pterosaur in Russia was by N.N.A. Bogolubov, who described a fragment of a neck vertebra of considerable size in 1914.[24] It was found in Upper Cretaceous deposits in Saratov in the Petrovsk district and given the name *Ornithostoma* (=bird-mouth) *orientalis*. The genus *Ornithostoma* had already been suggested by H.G. Seeley in 1871 for the jaws of toothless pterosaurs from the Cambridge Greensand, but later synonymized with the North American *Pteranodon* by S.W. Williston. The incompleteness of the English finds has not so far made it possible to confirm this.

## Long-necked Giants

No more Cretaceous pterosaurs were found in the Soviet Union until 1984. L.A. Nessov of the University of Leningrad found skeletal remains of a large pterosaur in Upper Cretaceous strata of Uzbekistan in that year, and gave them the name *Azhdarcho lancicollis*, from the Uzbek name for a mythical dragon.[25] The species name *lancicollis* refers to the species' long neck. The neck vertebrae are very long and slender, and also very similar to the long cervical vertebrae of the giant pterosaur *Quetzalcoatlus* from Texas. For this reason they were classified in a common family which was named Azhdarchidae.[26]

A very long neck vertebra described by the French palaeontologist C. Arambourg in 1959 is also assigned to the Azhdarchidae family.[27] The fossil came from Cretaceous strata in the Amman region of Jordan, and was allotted the

22 Galton, P., 1980. *Avian-like tibiotarsi of the pterodactyloids (Reptilia: Pterosauria) from the Upper Jurassic of East Africa.* Paläontologische Zeitschift, 54: 331-342; Stuttgart.
23 Bennet, S.C., 1989. *A Pteranodontid Pterosaur from the early Cretaceous of Peru, with comments on the Relationships of Cretaceous Pterosaurs.* Journal of Paleontology, 63(5): 669-677.
24 Bogolubov, N.N.A., 1914. *A propos d'une vertèbre de Ptérodactyle des dépots crétacés supérieurs du gouvernement de Saratoff.* Annales de géologie et minéralogie de la Russie, 16 (1): 1-7.
25 Nessov, L.A., 1984. *Pterosaurs and Birds from the Upper Cretaceous of Middle Asia.* Paleontological Journal, Academy of Sciences SSSR, 1984 (1): 47-57; Moscow (in Russian).
26 Padian, K., 1986. *A taxonomic note on two pterodactyloid families.* Journal of Vertebrate Palaeontology, 6 (3): 289.
27 Arambourg, C., 1959. *Titanopteryx philadelphiae nov. gen., nov. sp., ptérosaurien géant.* Notes et Mémoires du Moyen Orient, 7: 229-234.

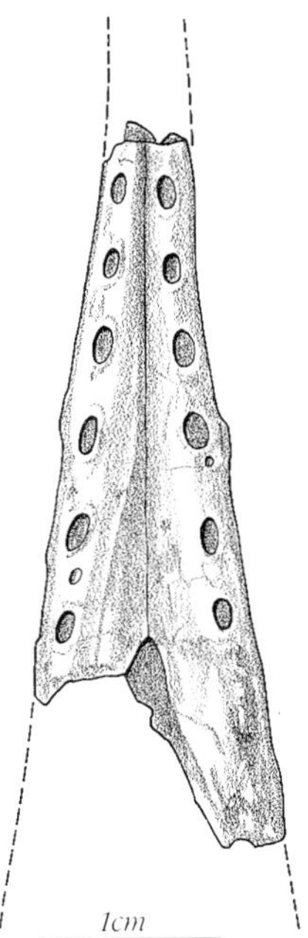


**Noripterus Jaw (above)**
We see here, from below, a fragment of the upper jaw of *Noripterus*. The holes are empty tooth sockets.

**Right:** These are remains of *Noripterus*. On the left is a nearly complete folded wing, in the centre the main folding joint of the wing which connected the wing finger to the metacarpal bone, and on the right a complete hind leg.

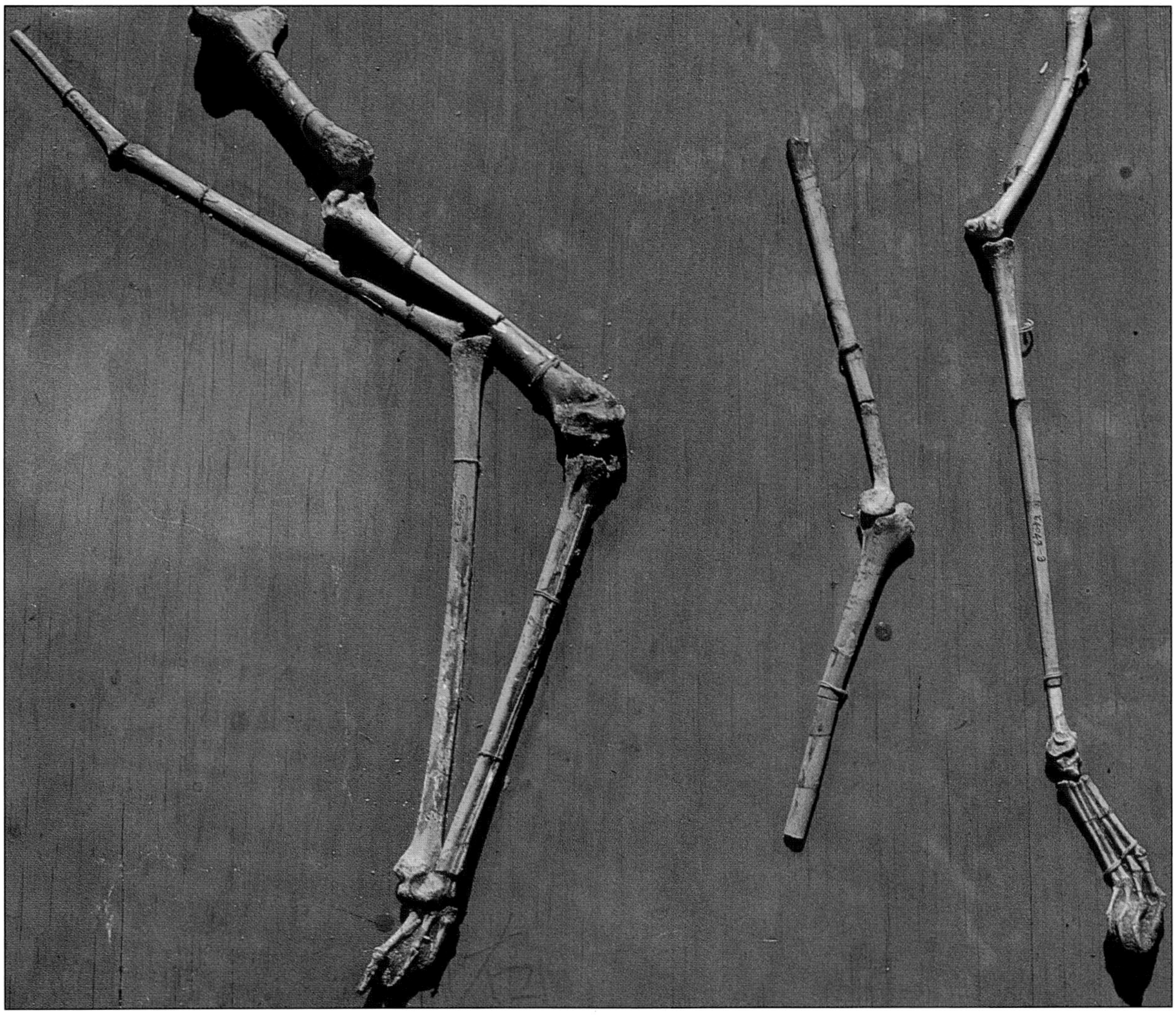

name *Titanopteryx* (=titan-wing) as a new genus. In fact Arambourg believed that the 2ft (60cm) long bone was the wing metacarpal of a giant pterosaur. It was not until the extremely long neck vertebrae of *Quetzalcoatlus* were found in Texas that it became clear that the *Titanopteryx* bone was also a neck vertebra. It thus achieved comparable size with the giant pterosaurs of Texas.

Long-necked giant pterosaurs occurred all over the world in the Cretaceous, as is shown by the discovery of fossil remains of *Quetzalcoatlus* in Texas and possibly also in Alberta, *Azhdarcho* in Uzbekistan, *Titanopteryx* in Jordan, a long vertebra in Senegal and perhaps *Doratorhynchus* in England. They must have been soaring fliers of great stamina, able to cover great distances.

The find of a 'limb bone' in the Upper Cretaceous of Hokkaido in Japan, classified in the genus *Pteranodon*[28] and a fragment of a pterosaur jaw with three teeth from Rajasthan in India[29] should also be mentioned. Both finds are too incomplete to be determined more accurately. They are simply proof of the palaeogeographic distribution of pterosaurs in the Cretaceous.

28 Ikuwo, O., Hasegawa, Y, and Otsuka, H., 1972. *Preliminary Report on the Cretaceous Reptile Fossils from Hokkaido.* Memoirs of the National Science Museum, 5: 213-222; Tokyo.

29 Dubey, V.S. and Narain, K., 1946. *A Note on the occurrence of Pterosauria in India.* Current Science, 15 (10): 287-288; Bangalore.

## Out of Africa

Proof that pterosaurs also lived on the African continent in the Cretaceous rests upon two examples only. The first is an incomplete wing metacarpal of a large pterosaur from Cretaceous (Cenomanian-Turonian) deposits in the former Belgian Congo, modern Zaïre. W.E. Swinton described it in 1948 and established similarities with *Ornithocheirus* species from the English Cambridge Greensand.[30] The total length of this metacarpal was about 14in (36cm), and thus the wing span of this creature can be estimated at 13-16ft (4-5m) at least.

30 Swinton, W.E., 1948. *A Cretaceous Pterosaur from the Belgian Congo.* Bulletin de la Société Belge de Géologie, Paléontologie et Hydrologie, 47: 234-238; Brussels.

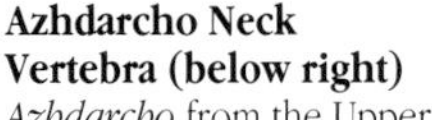

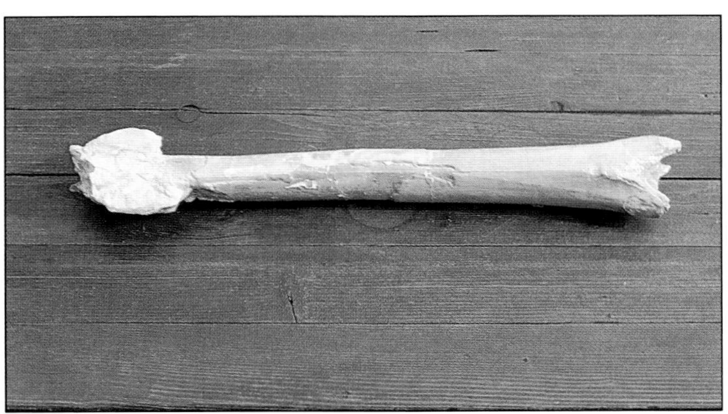

**Azhdarcho Neck Vertebra (below right)**
*Azhdarcho* from the Upper Cretaceous of Uzbekistan, was a large pterosaur with an extremely long neck. The long neck vertebrae, one of which is seen here in different aspects, are of the same type as those of the giant Texas pterosaur, *Quetzalcoatlus*. They have been assigned to the same family, Azhdarchidae.

**Below:** This 2ft (60cm) long neck vertebra (first taken to be a wing bone) is the only record of the giant pterosaur *Titanopteryx* which was discovered in Cretaceous rocks in Jordan. With its extremely long neck, *Titanopteryx* can also be assigned to the Azhdarchidae.

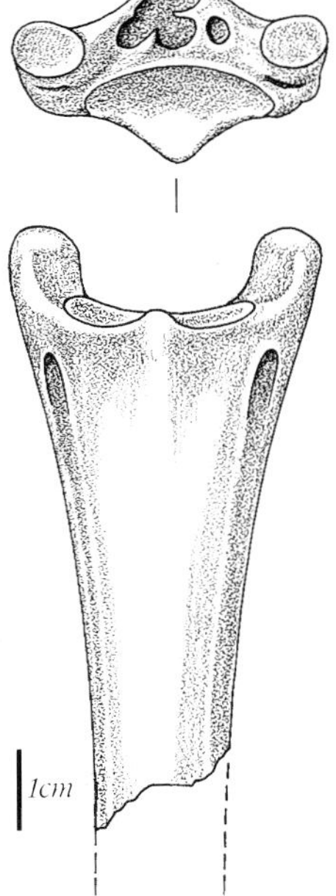

The other specimen of an African Cretaceous pterosaur is an elongated neck vertebra 9·6in (24·5cm) long, from the Upper Cretaceous (Campanian-Maastrichtian) of Paki in Senegal.[31] The vertebra is similar in form to those of the giant pterosaurs *Quetzalcoatlus* of Texas and *Titanopteryx* of Jordan, and shows that Azhdarchidae occurred in Africa as well.

This sparse fossil record of Cretaceous pterosaurs in Africa is surprising as pterosaurs were amply documented in South America in this period, particularly in the Lower Cretaceous, thus at a time when the two continents were not yet separated by the South Atlantic, so that unrestricted interchange of fauna must have been possible. Other reptiles, like crocodiles and turtles, occur correspondingly in Lower Cretaceous strata of equal age, in both Brazil and Niger. Brazilian Cretaceous pterosaurs must have extended their habitat to the African section of the Gondwana continent 110 million years ago. Clearly there were less favourable conditions for fossil preservation in suitable sediments on the African side. Perhaps in future more intensive searches for fossils, and geological exploration, will also lead to the discovery of more, and more complete, Cretaceous pterosaurs in Africa.

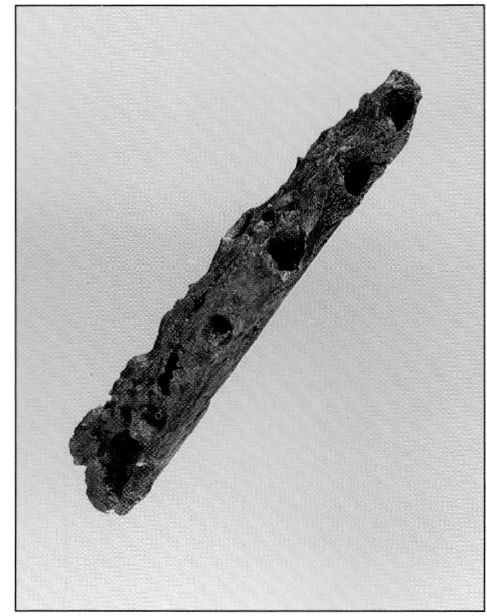

**Above:** The front end of a lower jaw from the Lower Cretaceous Toolebuc Formation of Western Queensland collected by Ralph Molnar in 1979. The fossil is similar to some species of *Ornithocheirus*.

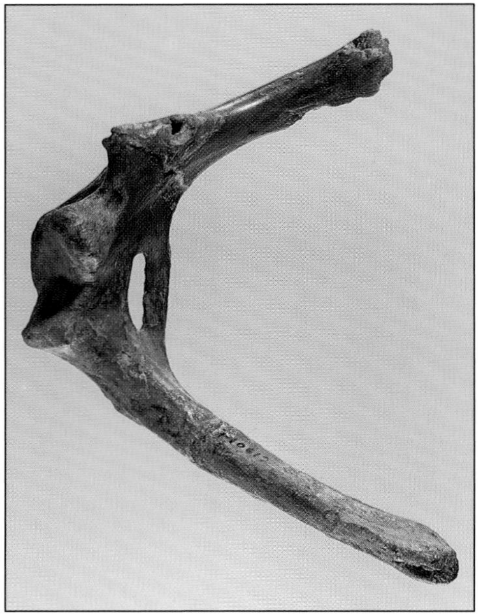

**Above:** A shoulder girdle of the 'Toolebuc pterosaur' also discovered by Ralph Molnar. This boomerang-shaped bone shows close similarities to the Upper Cretaceous *Pteranodon* from North America.

### Australian Excavations

It was a long time before pterosaur fossils were discovered in Australia as well: the first confirmed find was reported by R.E. Molnar and R.A. Thulborn in 1980.[32] The fossil material consisted merely of the front end of a lower jaw with empty tooth sockets, a single vertebra and an isolated scapulocoracoid. All these skeletal remains were found in marine Lower Cretaceous sediments in the Eromanga Basin in western Queensland. The fossil strata are part of the Toolebuc Formation and dated to the late Lower Cretaceous (Albian). Thus they are about 100 million years old and were deposited alongside plentiful marine fauna, especially bivalves, snails, belemnites, ammonites, fish and marine reptiles.

The characteristics of the lower jaw of this Toolebuc pterosaur are reminiscent of parts of the jaw of *Ornithocheirus* in England. The vertebra, also incomplete, is similar to those of English and Chinese pterosaurs of the Lower Cretaceous, and the pectoral girdle like that of *Pteranodon* and *Nyctosaurus* from the Upper Cretaceous of North America.

It seems that in any case the early Cretaceous Australian pterosaurs belonged to various genera, but that there were clearly close links with English, American and Chinese forms.

In 1987 R.A. Molnar identified another pterosaur fragment from the Toolebuc Formation in Queensland.[33] It was part of a pelvis, successfully freed from the rock, complete and in three dimensions, with acid. It corresponded in many ways with *Pteranodon*. The hip socket still showed its natural orientation, in other words sideways, upwards and backwards. This leads one to assume that the hind legs could not have functioned like those of birds, an argument against bipedal locomotion.

31 Monteillet, J., Lappartient, J.R. and Taquet, P., 1982. *Un Ptérosaurien géant dans le Crétacé supérieur de Paki (Sénégal).* Comptes rendus Académie des Sciences Paris, 295, série II: 409-414; Paris.

32 Molnar, R.E. and Thulborn, R.A., 1980. *First pterosaur from Australia.* Nature, 288 (5789): 361-363.

33 Molnar, R.E., 1987. *A pterosaur pelvis from Western Queensland, Australia.* Alcheringa, 11: 87-94.

However sparse and fragmentary the Australian pterosaur material may be, so far only four fragments of bones, it still shows that pterosaurs had penetrated a considerable distance into southern latitudes in the Lower Cretaceous, that they probably belonged to various groups of Pterodactyloidea, and that there were close correspondences with pterosaur fauna in America, Europe and possibly China as well.

The most southerly occurrence of pterosaurs is documented by a single fragment of bone from Upper Cretaceous strata in New Zealand. It is the distal section of an ulna from a middle-sized pterodactyloid coming from marine sandstone in the Mangahouanga Stream on the North Island of New Zealand, described by J. Wiffen and R.E. Molnar in 1988.[34] A single pterosaur tooth was found with the ulna, proving that toothed pterosaurs still lived at this late stage of the Cretaceous (Campanian-Maastrichtian).

The bone shows certain similarities with English and Brazilian genera, but cannot be classified with certainty. The special feature of this find, however, is its palaeogeographic situation. It is not only the first New Zealand pterosaur, but also the most southerly. In the Upper Cretaceous this area of New Zealand was at a latitude of 60°S. That proves that even shortly before they became extinct pterosaurs were in a position to live in extremely high latitudes and in a cool to cold-temperate climate with clear seasonal variations. This was only possible if these large, actively flying reptiles were warm-blooded.

### South America's Nyctosaurus

It was Arthur Conan Doyle who told of the exciting discovery of pterosaurs that were still alive in South America, in his Professor Challenger story *The Lost World*. Of course this notion sprang from the imagination of a brilliant writer. In 1912, when the book appeared, the inventor of the legendary Sherlock Holmes could certainly not have suspected that some of the most significant fossil pterosaur finds were to be made in South America. It was not until 1953 that the Brazilian L.I. Price described the first South American pterosaur find.[35]

34 Wiffen, J. and Molnar, R.E., 1988. *First pterosaur from New Zealand.* Alcheringa, 12: 53-59.

The fossil was the upper part of a humerus from the Upper Cretaceous (Gramame Formation) of Paraiba in Brazil. The complete bone would have been about 6·5in (16·5cm) long. This suggests a larger pterosaur with a wing span of about 11·5ft (3·5m).

The form of this humerus corresponds very well with specimens from the Chalk of the Niobrara Formation in Kansas, already named as *Nyctosaurus* (=naked reptile) by O.C. Marsh as early as 1876. For this reason Price called this first South American pterosaur *Nyctosaurus*

35 Price, L.I., 1953. *A presenca de Pterosauria no Cretáceo superior do Estado da Paraiba.* Divisão Geologia Mineralogia, Notas preliminares, Estud., 71: 1-10; Rio de Janeiro.

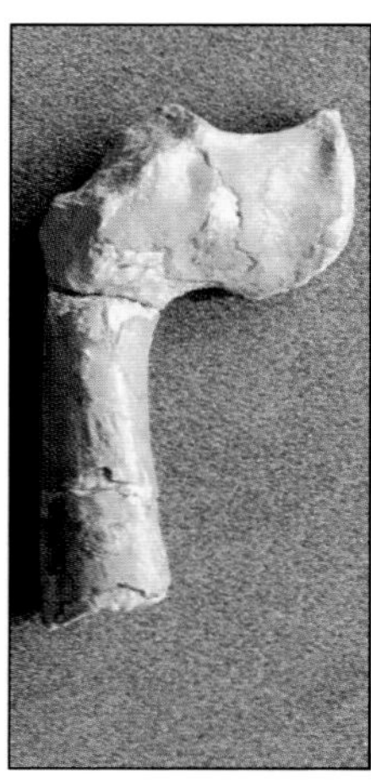

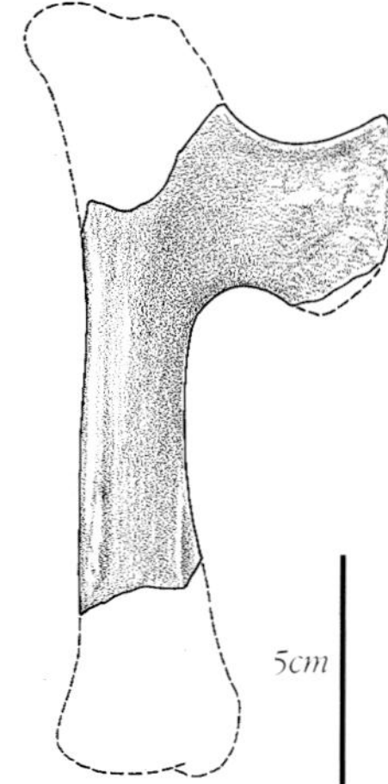


**Above:** This upper arm from late Cretaceous rocks in Paraiba, Brazil was the first discovery of pterosaur remains in South America. It was described as *Nyctosaurus lamegoi* in 1953. The wing span of this animal may have reached 11·5ft (3·5m).

**Above:** The city of Juazeiro do Norte in Ceará in north-eastern Brazil with the Araripe Plateau in the distance. The area has become famous for the fossils occurring in the early Cretaceous Santana Formation exposed along the edge of the vast plateau.

*lamegoi* (named after A.R. Lamego, then director of the geology and mineralogy division of the Department of Mineral Production in Rio de Janeiro), a species which was clearly larger than *Nyctosaurus gracilis* from Kansas. *Nyctosaurus* was a toothless pterodactyloid, which differed from its giant contemporary *Pteranodon* not only by being smaller, but also by having no crest at the back of its head. Of course a single arm bone cannot tell us anything about such particular features of the skull; we can only make these deductions by assuming that it belongs to the genus *Nyctosaurus*. If more complete skeletal material of *Nyctosaurus lamegoi* should ever be found, it could very well turn out that it is different from the Kansas forms and perhaps represents a new genus.

It was again L.I. Price who announced the first pterosaur skeletal remains from the Santana Formation in north-eastern Brazil, from a stratum that has produced finds among the most significant and productive in the world. Probably the best known fossils of the Santana Formation are the fish, which are preserved typically in limestone concretions. Local fossil collectors split these nodules, also known as geodes, and thus reveal the fossil. This kind of fossil preservation is particularly favourable for the delicate, thin-walled pterosaur bones, as the calcareous concretions form a protective case for the bones and skeletal elements, in which they are mostly preserved in three-dimensional form, and have thus survived the passage of millions of years as if they had been kept in a safe.

Preparation of the fossils is a lengthy process, using hammer and chisel or a chemical method with acid, but it produced individual bones with which it is often possible to test the possibilities of articular movement, just as though these were the bones of living creatures. These unique fossil preservations and the range of new pterosaurs, some of them looking very strange indeed, all contributed to the fame of the Santana Formation in Brazil.

The site is on the slopes of the Araripe Plateau (Chapada do Araripe), at the border of the states of Piauí, Ceará and Pernambuco in north-eastern Brazil. The Santana Formation reaches a thickness of about 656ft (200m). But it is only in the uppermost stratum, the Romualdo Member, that the fossil concretions that were formed about 115 million years ago, in the late Lower Cretaceous (Aptian), in a marine environment near the coast, are to be found. Even though it is only in recent decades that increasing attention has been paid to pterosaur remains, the fossil manifestations of the Araripe Plateau have been known for a long time. In fact it was two Bavarian naturalists, zoologist J.B. Spix and botanist C.F.P. Martius, who undertook an expedition to Brazil from 1817 to 1820, into country that at the time was completely unexplored. In 1819 they reached the province of Pernambuco and discovered the fossil sites of what is called the Santana Formation today, with their fish fossils.[36] Zoologist Dr Johann Babtist Spix and botanist Dr Carl Friedrich Philipp Martius undertook an extended scientific and anthropological expedition to north-eastern Brazil from 1817 to 1820 on behalf of the Bayerische Akademie der Wissenschaften in Munich. At the time an ocean voyage was accompanied by privations, hardship and danger. The Munich scientists found this out all too quickly. On the very second night, after they had sailed from Trieste, the Bora, the cold north wind of the Adriatic, struck their frigate *Austria* with full force, so that they were nearly shipwrecked.

Three months later, on 15 July 1817, they reached Rio de Janeiro at last and began their journey of exploration, which was to last over three years, into the north-east of the country and the Amazon region. They covered about 6,200 miles (10,000km), mostly on foot or by boat. At that time the Brazilian interior was still wild, completely unexplored territory. Their journey was undertaken under the most primitive conditions, and they suffered unbelievable hardship, hunger, thirst and severe illness.

In the three-volume description of their journey, published after their return to Munich, they also report on the discovery of sites in the Araripe region where fossils were found: 'Almost on the south-eastern border of the province, near the little Villa do Bom Jardim, in the Cayriris Novos district, there is a fairly extensive marly lime formation, in which there are numerous fossils of fish. The same appear both in the bedded strata of rock and in the segregated and rolled pieces.' They also provide an illustration of a fossil fish in their work, the front part of a *Rhacolepis*, a marine fish similar to the tarpon.

## Santana Specimens

Price called the first pterosaur from the Araripe Plateau *Araripesaurus*, (=Araripe reptile) and classified it as an ornithocheirid.[37] The specimen consisted of skeletal remains of an individual preserved in a calcareous concretion typical of the Santana Formation. They in-

36 Spix, J.B. and Martius, C.F.P., 1828. *Reise in Brasilien*. 3 volumes; Munich.

37 Price, L.I., 1971. *A Presença de Pterosauria no Cretáceo Inferior da Chapada do Araripe, Brasil.* Anais Academia Brasileira Ciencias, 43 (suppl.): 451-461.

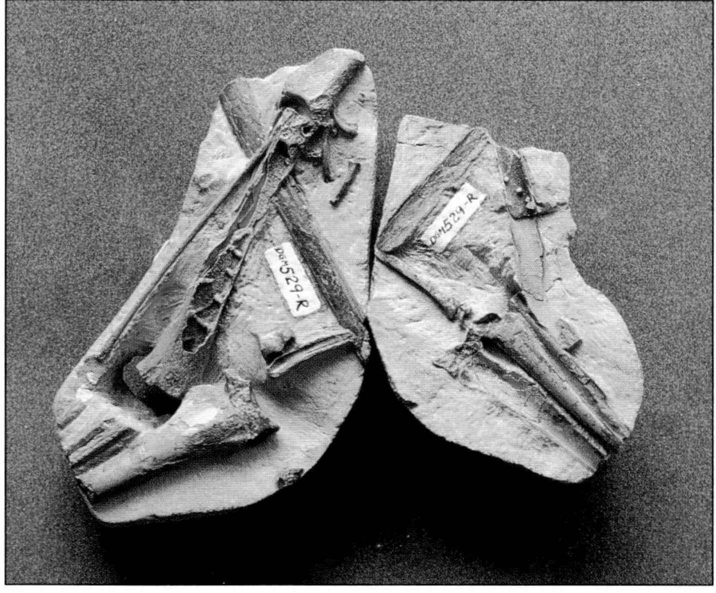


**Right:** These wing bones encased in a limestone nodule were the first pterosaurian fossils discovered in the Lower Cretaceous Santana Formation of the Araripe Plateau. They were recorded in 1971, and described as *Araripesaurus castilhoi* by the Brazilian palaeontologist Llewellyn Price. Not only was the concretion split in half, the individual bones were split and present mirror images. The specimen consists of a section of the lower arm, wrist and metacarpals, and the upper end of the wing finger. The wing span of this particular individual can be estimated at 7·2ft (2·2m).

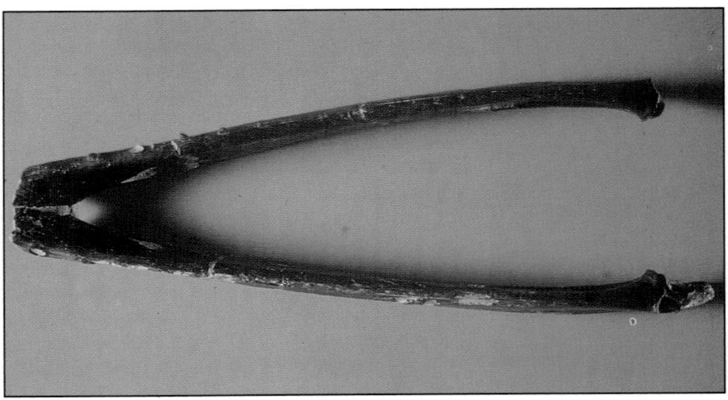

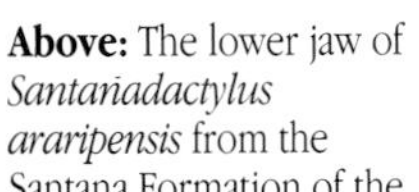

**Above:** The lower jaw of *Santanadactylus araripensis* from the Santana Formation of the Araripe Plateau in northeastern Brazil. We are here looking down on the lower jaw from above.

**Above right:** The incomplete skull of *Santanadactylus araripensis* shown after preparation. It was found in a limestone nodule.

cluded parts of the right-hand wing skeleton of a short-tailed pterosaur. The only full-length bone to have survived is the fourth metacarpal, which supported the flight digit. On the basis of its size (4·6in; 11·8cm) the wing span of this individual can be estimated at 7·2ft (2·2m). It is true that the skull is missing, and this is the most important part of the skeleton for diagnostic purposes. For this reason the classification of *Araripesaurus* as an ornithocheirid must remain dubious.

The second pterosaur find from the Araripe Formation also belongs to an undetermined family. It is a single flight digit phalanx, discovered in 1977 and named *Araripedactylus* (=Araripe finger).[38] This long, robust bone 1·8ft (55cm) long was the first proof that large pterosaurs also occur in the Santana Formation; their wing span was at least 16ft (4·8m). Here too more complete skeletal material is needed before the relationships of *Araripedactylus* to other genera can be cleared up.

In 1980 another pterosaur genus from the Santana strata was described, and named *Santanadactylus* (=Santana-finger).[39] But again there were only isolated bones, fragments of a humerus and shoulder articulation, and of two neck vertebrae; they came from different individuals, however. The neck vertebrae are elongated, and suggest a long-necked form. The characteristics of the humerus make it possible to classify *Santanadactylus* as an ornithocheirid. However, these have short neck vertebrae, which means it is doubtful whether the long neck vertebrae belong to *Santanadactylus* at all, or to a hitherto unknown genus.

Later further and more complete examples of *Santanadactylus* skeletal remains were discovered.[40] They included a spinal column that was still connected, with dorsal vertebrae fused to form a notarium, skull, bones of the wing skeleton and even the two almost complete wings of an individual.[41] So far four distinct species of *Santanadactylus* have been identified. Most of them were relatively large ornithocheirid pterosaurs with teeth, with a wing span of 9·5-18·7ft (2·9-5·7m). One species, *'Santanadactylus' spixi*, was probably a dsungaripterid, and represents a new genus.

The genus *Brasileodactylus* (=Brazil-finger) was based on the front end of a lower jaw from the Santana Formation in Brazil.[42] The surviving section is 4·4in (11·2cm) long, slightly bent upwards and triangular in cross-section. The jaw was toothed, but the teeth had fallen out, so that only the empty alveoli could be seen. These are rounded-elliptical, and more widely spaced towards the back. Characteristics suggest that it belongs to the Ornithocheiridae. Only more complete finds would help to determine whether *Brasileodactylus* is identical to *Santanadactylus*.

**Santanadactylus araripensis Skull Restoration (right)**
This restoration shows the skull and lower jaw of *Santanadactylus araripensis* as far as it is preserved. *Santanadactylus* is classified as an ornithocheirid pterosaur with teeth. Its wing span was over 10ft (3m).

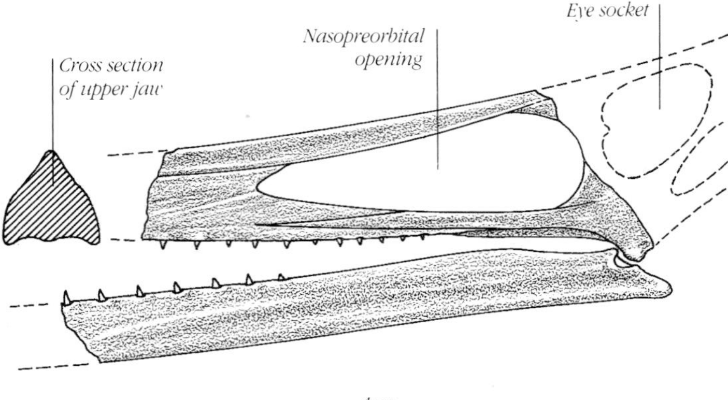


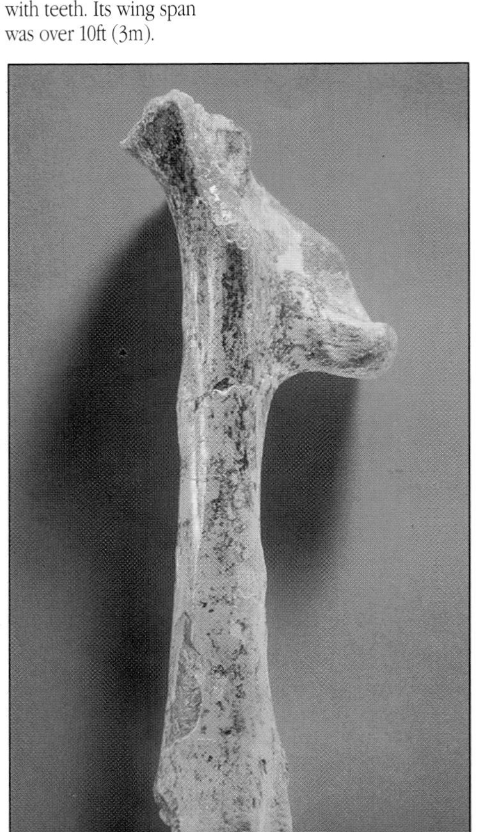

**Above:** An upper arm of *Santanadactylus* from the Santana Formation of the Araripe Plateau in northeastern Brazil. The length of this humerus is 6·7in (17cm). It was the characteristics of this bone that enabled scientists eventually to classify *Santanadactylus* as an ornithocheirid.

## The 'Old Devil'

D.A. Campos and A.W.A. Kellner described a new pterosaur genus from the Santana Forma-

38 Wellnhofer, P., 1977. *Araripedactylus dehmi nov. gen., nov. sp., ein neuer Flugsaurier aus der Unterkreide von Brasilien.* Mitteilungen der Bayerischen Staatssammlung für Paläontologie und historische Geologie, 17: 157-167; Munich.

39 Buisonjé, P.H. de, 1980. *Santanadactylus brasilensis nov. gen., nov. sp., a longnecked, large pterosaur from the Aptian of Brazil.* Proceedings of the Koninklijke Nederlandse Akademie van Wetenschappen, B, 83 (2): 145-172; Amsterdam.

40 Wellnhofer, P., Buffetaut, E. and Gigase, P., 1983. *A pterosaurian notarium from the Lower Cretaceous of Brazil.* Paläontologische Zeitschrift, 57: 147-157; Stuttgart.
Wellnhofer. P., 1985. *Neue Pterosaurier aus der Santana-Formation (Apt) der Chapada do Araripe, Brasilien.* Palaeontographica, A, 187: 105-182; Stuttgart.

41 Leonardi, G. and Borgomanero, G., 1987. *The skeleton of a pair of wings of a pterosaur (Pterodactyloidea, ?Ornithocheiridae, cfr. Santanadactylus) from the Santana Formation of the Araripe Plateau, Ceará, Brazil.* Anais do X Congresso Brasileiro de Paleontologia, 1987: 123-129; Rio de Janeiro.

42 Kellner, A.W.A., 1984. *Ocorrencia de uma mandíbula de pterosauria (Brasileodactylus araripensis, nov. gen., nov. sp.) na Formaçao Santana, Cretáceo da Chapada do Araripe, Ceará, Brasil.* Anais XXXIII Congresso Brasileiro de Geologia, 1984: 578-590; Rio de Janeiro.

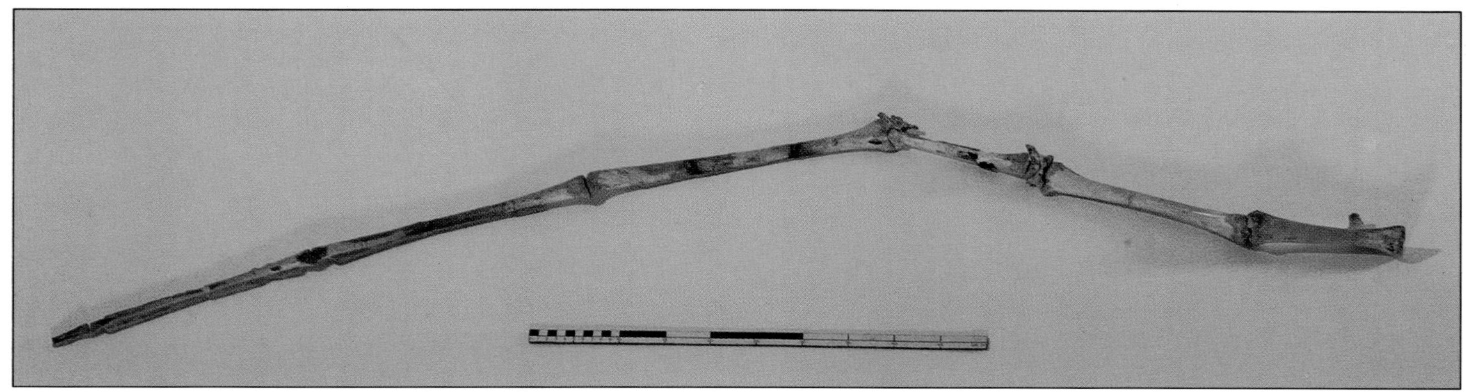

**Above:** A complete wing of *Santanadactylus* after the wing bones had been isolated from the large limestone nodule in which they were preserved. The length of the wing is 5ft (1·52m).

**Above:** The wrist of *Santanadactylus* with the pteroid bone pointing towards the body. The bones were isolated from the limestone with acid.

**Below:** This front end of the lower jaw is the only known skeletal fragment of the genus *Brasileodactylus*. It measures 4·4in (11·2cm) in length.

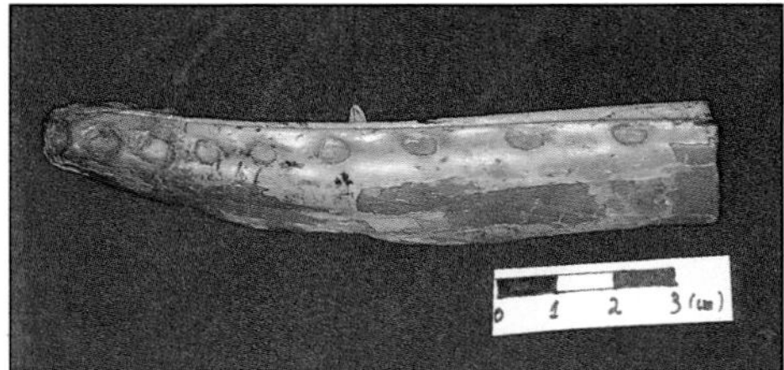

tion, which they called *Anhanguera* (=old devil) after a name from the Indian Tupi culture.[43] The type specimen is a slender skull 1·6ft (50cm) long with a medial crest on the snout. This crest is an outgrowth of the upper jaw bone. A similar crest may also have developed on the lower side of the lower jaw. *Anhanguera* had teeth, and was probably a fish eater. The crest on the snout stabilized the head when the tip of the snout was drawn through the water while fishing in full flight.

*Anhanguera* is now one of the best-known pterosaurs from the Santana Formation. Two more skeletal remains of this genus were found, including a fairly complete specimen, in which the skull and a large proportion of the post-cranial elements had survived, like spinal column, ribs, pectoral girdle, pelvis and parts of the wings and hind legs. Some of the bones were found still articulated naturally in a large

43 Campos, D.A. and Kellner, A.W.A., 1985. *Panorama of the Flying Reptiles Study in Brazil and South America.* Anais da Academia Brasileira Ciencias, 1985, 57 (4): 453-466; Rio de Janeiro.

**Right:** This is the skull of *Anhanguera blittersdorffi* from the Lower Cretaceous Santana Formation. It was a large pterodactyloid pterosaur with a considerable wing span. The bony crest on top of the snout is characteristic.

**Anhanguera Skull Restoration (right)**
The drawing shows a restoration of the skull of *Anhanguera blittersdorffi* which is pictured above. The lower jaw is not preserved. Skull length is 1·6ft (50cm).

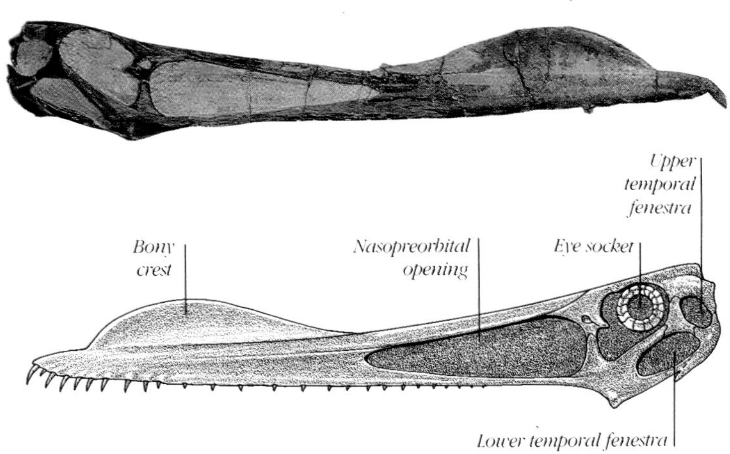


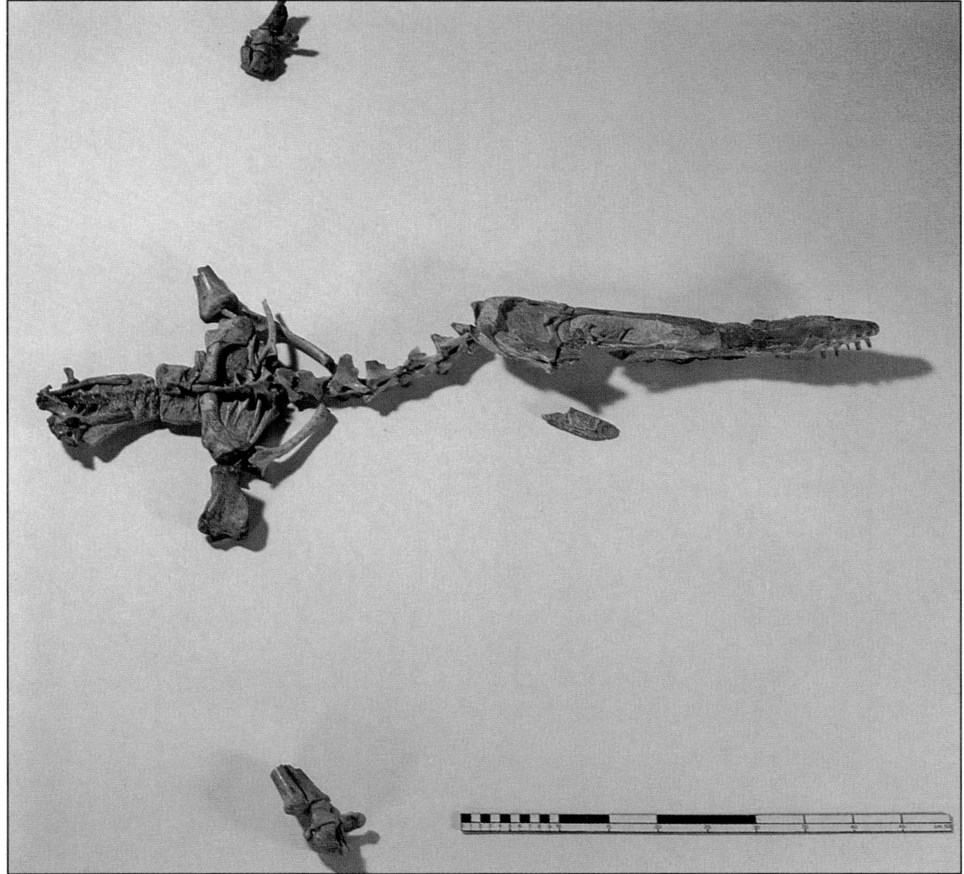

**Above:** This is *Anhanguera santanae*, a specimen in the collection of the American Museum of Natural History in New York. It was preserved in a large calcareous nodule from the Lower Cretaceous Santana Formation. The photograph shows the New York specimen after preparation, revealing skull, vertebral column, shoulder girdle, pelvis, and parts of the wings. When found, some of the bones were still in their natural articulation. This is the most complete skeleton of a pterosaur of this size range known. This individual had a wing span of 13·6ft (4·15m). Note how long the skull is in comparison to the body.

calcareous concretion and it was to a large extent possible to free them completely from the rocks. The proportions of this large pterosaur with a wing span of more than 13ft (4m) are unusual: in comparison with the actual body the skull is twice as long.[44] The great disproportion between wings and hind legs is expressed by the fact that the pectoral girdle is large and robust, but in comparison the pelvis is quite small.

Three-dimensional reconstruction of the pelvis of *Anhanguera* revealed that the hind legs could not be brought into a vertical position under the body, but were splayed slightly to the side. Thus bird-like, bipedal locomotion on the ground was scarcely possible. Orientation of the hip sockets obliquely upwards and the slight bend of the articular head of the thigh bone make quadrupedal locomotion on the ground more probable.[45]

So far only two species of *Anhanguera* are known. A separate family, the Anhangueridae, was suggested for them. They have a characteristic crest on the snout, and complete ossification of some elements of the skeleton (skull, pectoral girdle, notarium, carpus and pelvis) did not take place until very late in the growth of the individual, perhaps not until shortly before the adult stage. The different formation of the crest in the two species could also be interpreted as a sexual characteristic of male and female individuals.

### Cearadactylus and Tropeognathus

A long pterosaur skull with lower jaw from the Santana Formation was also established as a new genus *Cearadactylus* (=Ceará-finger) in 1985.[46] The skull is not preserved intact on the

44 Wellnhofer, P., 1991. *Weitere Pterosaurierfunde aus der Santana-Formation (Apt) der Chapada do Araripe, Brasilien.* Palaeontographica, A, 215; Stuttgart.
45 Wellnhofer, P., 1988. *Terrestrial locomotion in pterosaurs.* Historical Biology, 1: 3-16.
46 Leonardi, G. and Borgomanero, G., 1985. *Cearadactylus atrox nov. gen., nov. sp.: Novo Pterosauria (Pterodactyloidea) da Chapada do Araripe, Ceará, Brasil.* D.N.P.M., Coletana de trabalhos Paleontologicos, Séria Geológica, 27: 75-80; Brasilia.

**Above:** The skull of the New York specimen of *Anhanguera santanae*. Unfortunately the bony cranial crest has broken off this particular specimen.

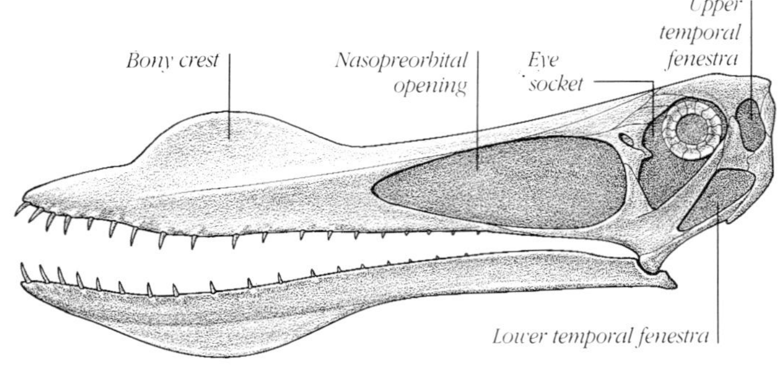


**Anhanguera Skull (left)**
This restoration of the skull of *Anhanguera santanae* is based on the New York specimen pictured above. Here the bony cranial crest has been restored in position.

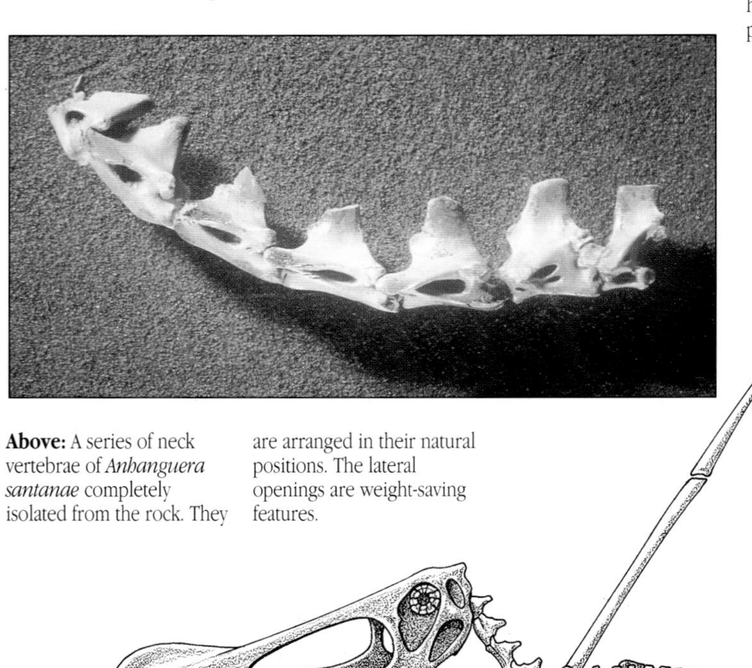

**Above:** A series of neck vertebrae of *Anhanguera santanae* completely isolated from the rock. They are arranged in their natural positions. The lateral openings are weight-saving features.

**Anhanguera Skeleton (right)**
This skeletal restoration shows *Anhanguera santanae* in a four-legged pose. The relative orientation of the hip sockets and the articular head of the thigh bones makes this more plausible than a bipedal posture.

**Above:** The shoulder girdle of *Anhanguera santanae* consisting of the shoulder blade and the coracoid bone which are not yet fused into a single element, but forming the articular socket for the upper arm.

**Above:** Left and right wrists of *Anhanguera santanae* with the bones arranged in their natural articulation. These bones can be seen with their associated pteroid bones in the skeletal restoration on the opposite page.

**Right:** The skull of the Munich specimen of *Anhanguera santanae* lacks the front end of the snout and the bony crest. This specimen was also collected from the Lower Cretaceous Sanatana Formation in north-eastern Brazil.

rear side. Its overall length must have been 1·9ft (57cm). The wing span can be estimated at 18ft (5·5m). A particular feature of *Cearadactylus* is its powerful dentition. The front teeth are much longer and much stronger than the back ones. When the snout is closed there was a gap in the front area. The long front teeth, set in jaws which broaden to a spoon shape at the front, suggest an excellent grip when catching slippery fish. Nothing is known of this genus except the skull. It is therefore perfectly possible that *Cearadactylus* is identical with other genera based only on post-cranial bones, perhaps with *Araripedactylus*, for example.

A complete skull with lower jaw and an isolated lower jaw documented another new pterosaur genus from the Santana Formation.[47] Its special characteristic is a tall, rounded medial crest at the front end of the snout and a similar crest on the lower side of the lower jaw, at the point where the two branches of the mandible have fused in the mid-line to form a symphysis. These crests are in the form of the keel of a ship, for which reason these ptero-

47 Wellnhofer, P., 1987. *New Crested Pterosaurs from the Lower Cretaceous of Brazil.* Mitteilungen der Bayerischen Staatssammlung für Paläontologie und historische Geologie, 27: 175-186; Munich.

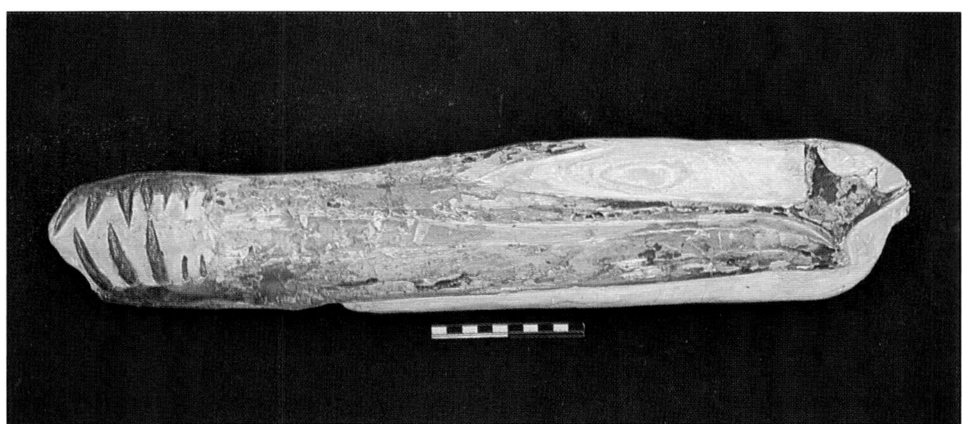

**Above:** This incomplete skull from the Santana Formation is the only evidence for the genus *Cearadactylus*.

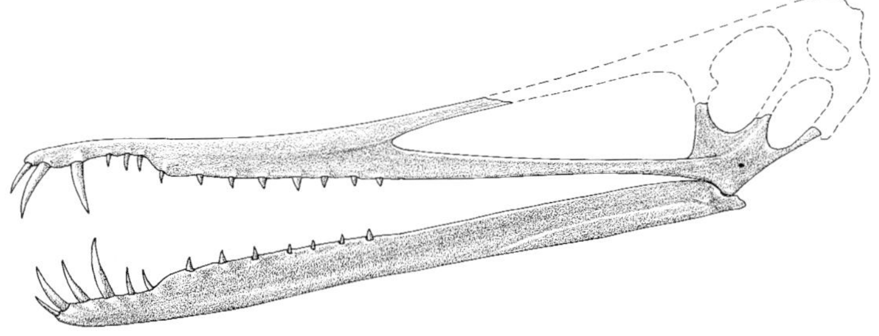

**Cearadactylus Skull (left)**
This is a tentative restoration of the skull of *Cearadactylus atrox*. Its length is about 1·9ft (57cm).

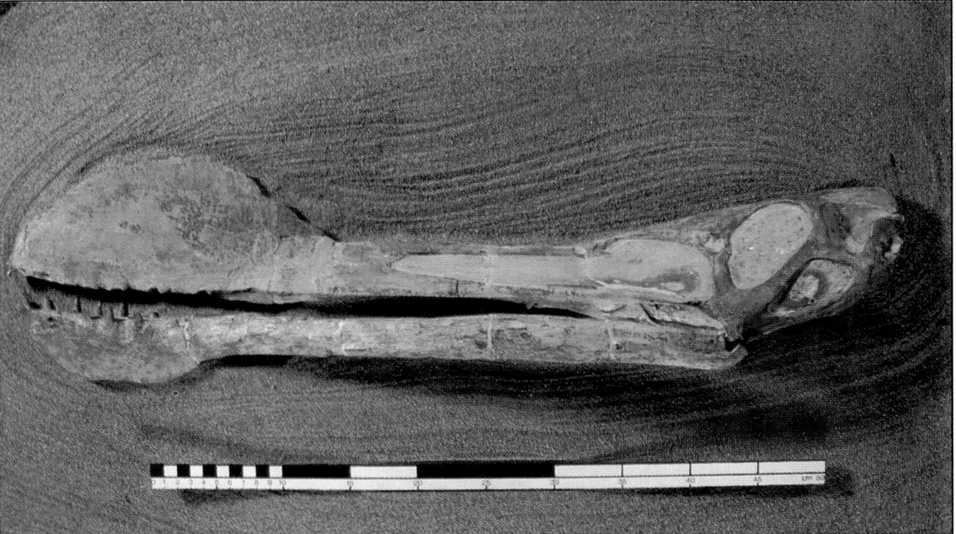

**Left and below:** These photographs show the skull and lower jaw of *Tropeognathus mesembrinus*, a large pterosaur from the Lower Cretaceous Santana Formation of Brazil. At the front end of the long jaws deep bony crests are developed. The photograph (left) shows these crests from the front. Their shape resembles the keel of a ship; perhaps they also served as stabilizing devices in the water when the pterosaur was skimming for fishes. The skull length is slightly over 2ft (63cm).

saurs were given the name *Tropeognathus* (=keel-jaw). Another shorter and blunter crest developed on the back of the skull. The dentition consists of a total of 26 teeth in the upper jaw and 22 in the lower.

The function of the crests on the tip of the snout was probably hydrodynamic. *Tropeognathus* also fed on fish. In flight the tip of the snout had to dip into the water and plough through the surface of the sea. The skull was so long that it had to be stabilized by the crest in this phase. This saved muscle mass on the neck, and thus weight.

*Tropeognathus* is so far known through only two species, represented by two specimens. The skull lengths are 2·0 and 2·2ft (63 and 67cm). *Tropeognathus robustus* had a wing span of 20ft (6·2m) and is thus the largest Santana pterosaur so far found.

The crest at the front end of *Tropeognathus*' snout is highly reminiscent of the high front end of the snout of *Criorhynchus* from the

**Tropeognathus mesembrinus Life Portrait and Skull (right)**
Shown here is a life portrait of *Tropeognathus mesembrinus*, a large toothed and crested pterosaur from Brazil, and below that is a restoration of the skull based upon the specimen illustrated on the previous page. It was almost certainly a fish eater, and its dentition consists of 26 teeth in the upper jaw and 22 in the lower jaw. The bony crests at the front end of the upper and lower jaws would most likely have been covered with a horny sheath. Two species of *Tropeognathus* are known.

Bony crest
Nasopreorbital opening
Eye socket
Upper temporal fenestra
Lower temporal fenestra

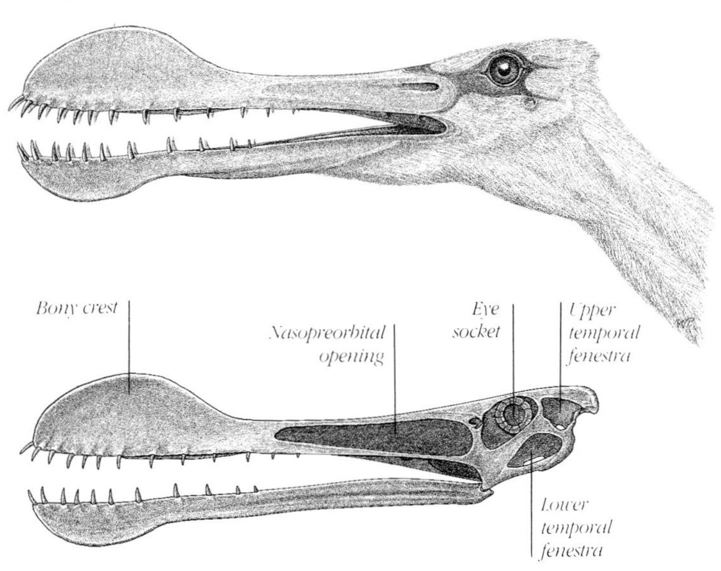

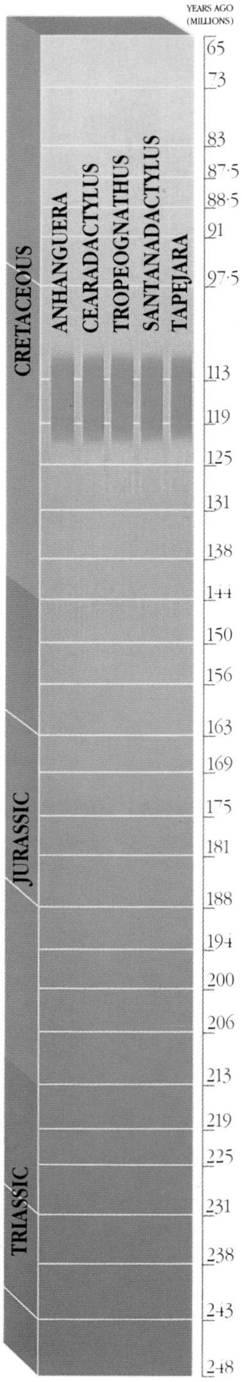

YEARS AGO (MILLIONS)
CRETACEOUS
JURASSIC
TRIASSIC
ANHANGUERA
CEARADACTYLUS
TROPEOGNATHUS
SANTANADACTYLUS
TAPEJARA
65
73
83
87·5
88·5
91
97·5
113
119
125
131
138
144
150
156
163
169
175
181
188
194
200
206
213
219
225
231
238
243
248

**Time Chart (left)**
During the early Cretaceous, in the Aptian age, a great variety of pterodactyloid pterosaurs lived in the region of modern north-eastern Brazil. Some of them may be related to English forms.

**Cearadactylus (right)**
Among the largest pterosaurs from the Santana Formation, *Cearadactylus* is viewed here sitting on a rock and holding its prey fish in a firm grip in its claws. Its long front teeth would have proved very effective tools for fishing in the shallows of near-shore lakes.

1
2
3
4
5
6
7
8
9

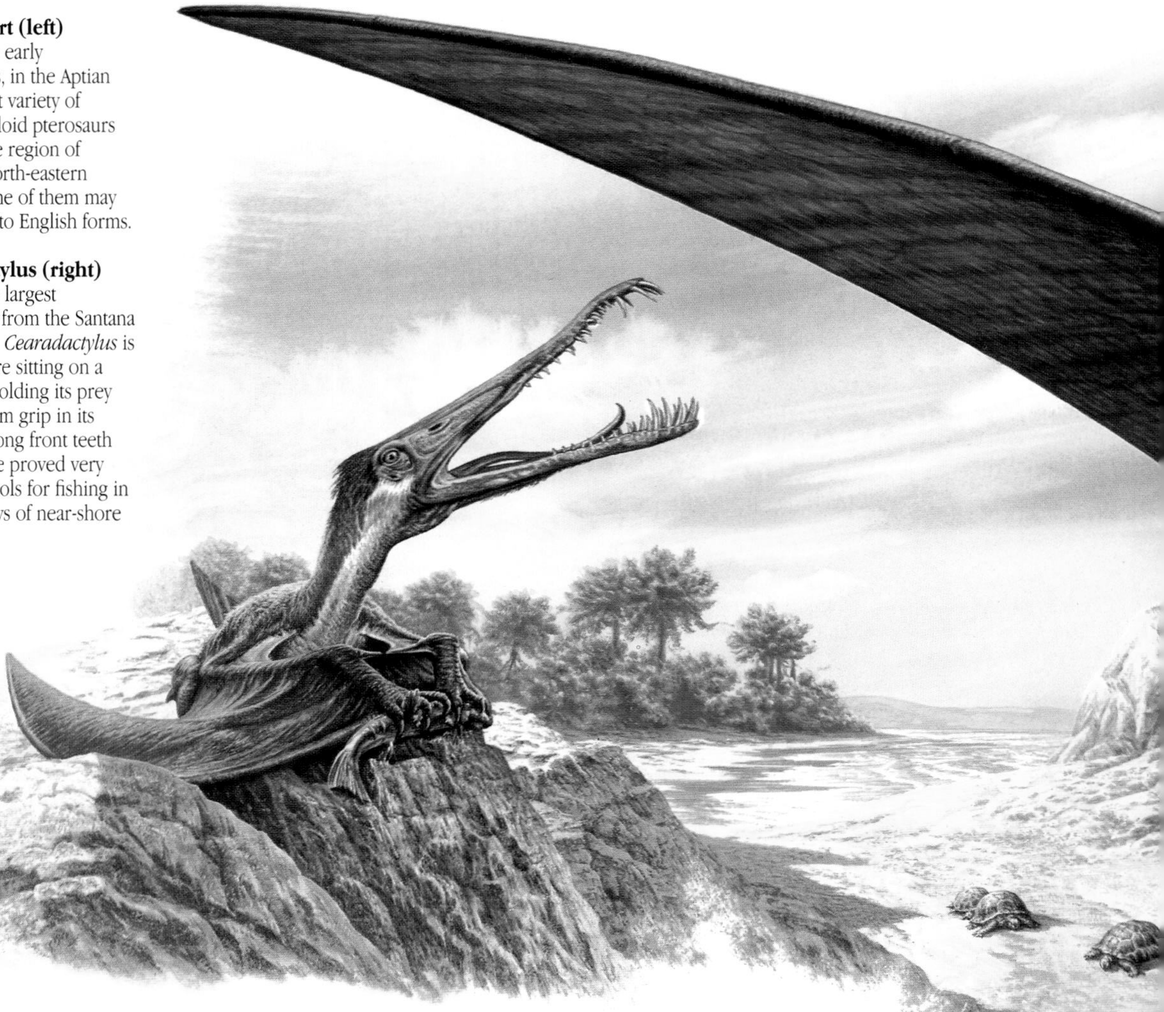

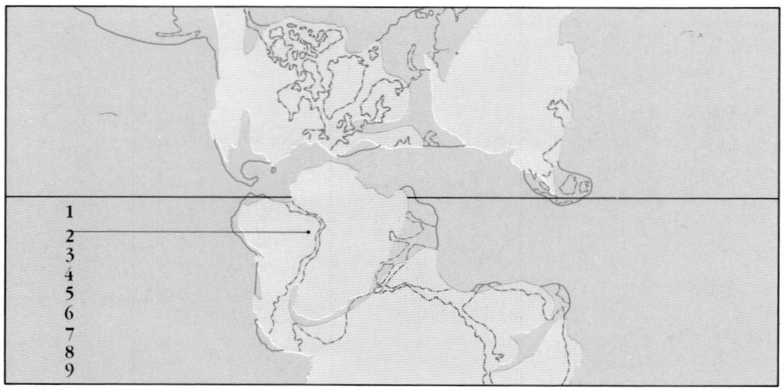

**Map (left)**
1 *Anhanguera*
2 *Cearadactylus*
3 *Tropeognathus*
4 *Santanadactylus*
5 *Araripedactylus*
6 *Araripesaurus*
7 *Brasileodactylus*
8 *Tupuxuara*
9 *Tapejara*

**Tropeognathus robustus Lower Jaw (above)**
Only the lower jaw of this second species of *Tropeognathus* is preserved. It is shown here from the front, from the side and from above.

**Tropeognathus (left)**
This is one of the most unusual pterosaurs known. It was named because of the resemblance of the crests on its jaws to a ship's keel (from the Greek word *tropis* meaning keel). These crests must have served to stabilize the head when the tips of the jaws were ploughing through the water. Two species are known, *Tr. mesembrinus* and *Tr. robustus*, which can be distinguished by their different crests and teeth.

**Comparative Sizes (above)**
**1** *Anhanguera*: wing span 13ft (4m).
**2** *Cearadactylus*: wing span 18ft (5·5m).
**3** *Tropeognathus*: wing span 20ft (6.2m).

**Anhanguera (left)**
*Anhanguera* is one of the best known early Cretaceous pterosaurs. It was quite large with very long wings and peculiar low medial crests on top of the skull and below the lower jaw. Like *Tropeognathus*, these served to stabilize the head when fishing. In this scene *Anhanguera* has just caught a fish and the front of its head on its extremely flexible neck is still ploughing through the water. In the background can be seen turtles on the beach leading to the sea.

Cambridge Greensand in England. It was therefore suggested that *Tropeognathus* should be included in the family Criorhynchidae as well.

## Toothless Forms

All species of pterosaur from the Santana Formation of Brazil so far mentioned were toothed forms, but in 1989 a toothless species was discovered for the first time. This was the front part of the skull with a medial crest and a few bones from the wing skeleton. The edges of the jaw are clearly toothless, thus indicating a different family from the ornithocheirids or the anhanguerids. A.W.A. Kellner and D.A. Campos named this pterosaur *Tupuxuara*, after a 'familiar spirit' from the culture of the Tupi, a tribe of Brazilian Indians.[48] The fossil remains are still too sparse to give more precise detail about this toothless pterosaur. They are however clearly different from other toothless genera of the Upper Cretaceous like *Pteranodon*, *Nyctosaurus* or *Quetzalcoatlus*.

A second toothless pterosaur from the Santana Formation in Brazil was not described until 1990, and was named *Tapejara* by A.W.A. Kellner.[48] The name means 'the old being' and comes from the mythology of the original inhabitants of Brazil, the Tupi Indians. So far only the skull is known, which like that of *Tupuxuara* has a tall crest in the mid-line. The eye sockets are relatively small, while the nasopreorbital opening on the other hand is very large. The ends of the jaws are directed downwards at the front, like a bird's beak. It was certainly one of the strangest Cretaceous pterosaurs that ever lived. Unfortunately little is known of the rest of the skeleton. Because of certain similarities *Tapejara* and *Tupuxuara* have been placed in a common family, the Tapejaridae. Their relationships to other toothless pterosaurs, like for example *Pteranodon* from the Upper Cretaceous, cannot be established, as yet.

The fossil sites of the Santana Formation of the Araripe Plateau in north-eastern Brazil seem to be inexhaustible. More completely new pterosaurs are being analysed by scholars at the time of writing, so that there will be additions to the nine genera and fourteen species so far known. Thus the Santana strata have similar significance for research into Cretaceous pterosaurs as the Solnhofen strata have hitherto had for pterosaurs of the Jurassic. From Solnhofen we so far know nine genera, with

48 Kellner, A.W.A. and Campos, D.A., 1989. *Sobre um Novo Pterossauro com Crista Sagittal da Bacia do Araripe, Cretáceo Inferior do Nordeste do Brasil.* Anais Academia Brasileira Ciencias (1988), 60 (4): 459-469; Rio de Janeiro.
Kellner, A.W.A., 1990. *A New Edentate Pterosaur of the Lower Cretaceous from the Araripe Basin, Northeast Brazil.* Anais Academia Brasileira Ciencias (1989), 61 (4): 1-7; Rio de Janeiro.

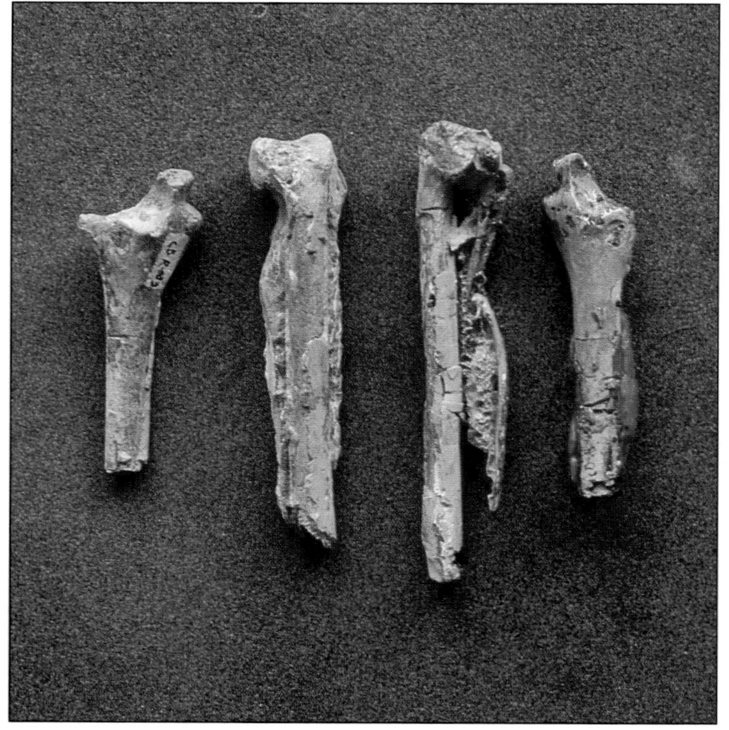

**Left:** The first toothless pterosaur discovered in the Santana Formation was called *Tupuxuara* after a mythical ghost in the culture of the Brazilian Tupi tribe. However, only a fragment of the upper jaw and a few fragments of the wing skeleton, metacarpals and wing phalanges (shown here) were preserved. The skull had a long bony crest above the nasal opening. The remaining parts of the skull are unknown so far.

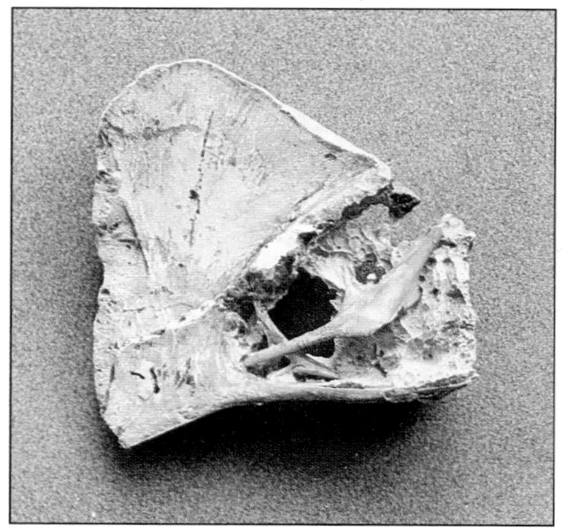

**Below:** A second toothless pterosaur from the Sanatana Formation was described and named as *Tapejara* after another figure in Tupi mythology. Originally, only this fragment of a skull was discovered. It is characterized by a high bony crest on top of its front end. A second, more complete skull was subsequently discovered.

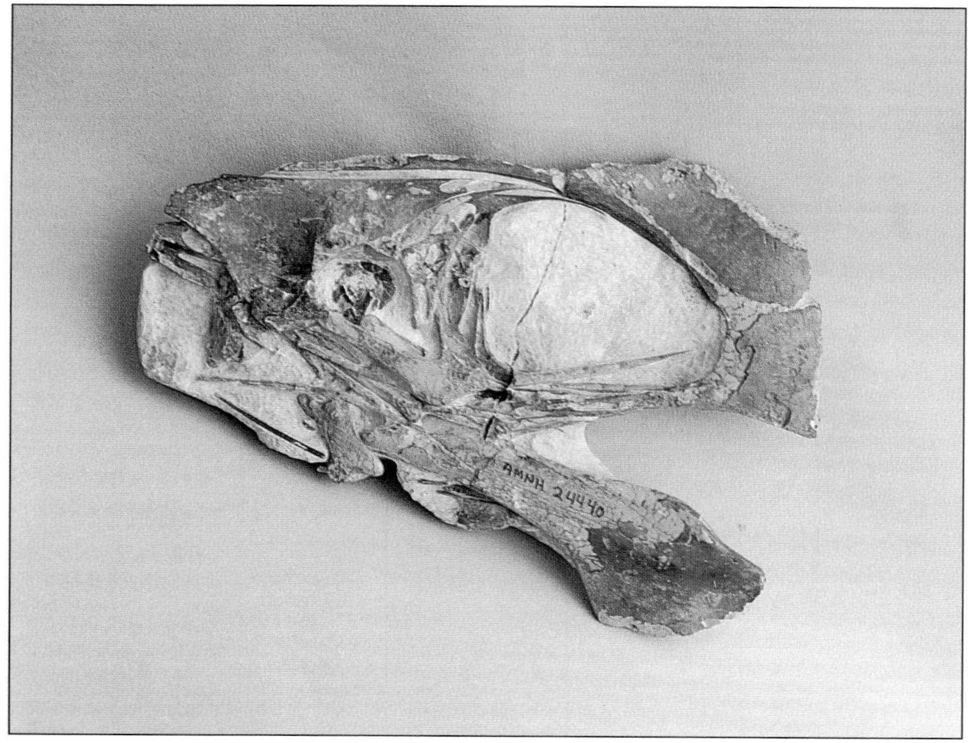


**Left:** This almost complete skull of *Tapejara* is the second specimen of this toothless pterosaur to be discovered in the Santana Formation of Brazil. It includes the lower jaw, and reveals the very unusual shape of the bony crest on top of the skull.

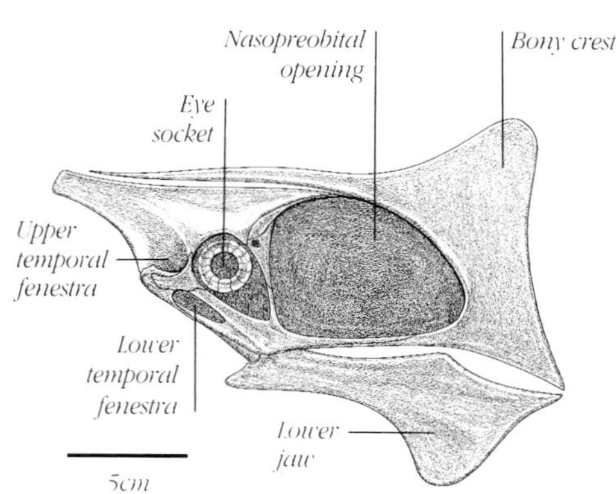


**Tapejara Skull Restoration (above)**
This is a restoration of the skull of *Tapejara*. The jaws are rather short and the eye socket is only small. The thin bony crest is separated from the back of the skull roof, rather like a cock's crest.

**Above:** *Pterodaustro* from early Cretaceous sediments of Argentina is the most extreme example of a filter feeder among pterosaurs discovered to date. This specimen is a disarticulated skeleton. The skull with its upwardly bent jaws can be seen at the bottom of the slab. The jaws are long and the lower jaw bears hundreds of long, seemingly flexible 'teeth' along its length.

eighteen different species. Many unusual and exciting new discoveries can be expected from the calcareous concretions of the Santana Formation in the future.

## Argentina's 'South Wing'

In 1970 Dr José Bonaparte discovered one of the most unusual pterosaurs to have been found to date. At first only a skull fragment, vertebrae and some elements of the appendicular skeleton were found, then later a complete skull and a complete skeleton including the skull came to light. They came from Lower Cretaceous (Lagarcito Formation) strata in the province of San Luis in Argentina.[49]

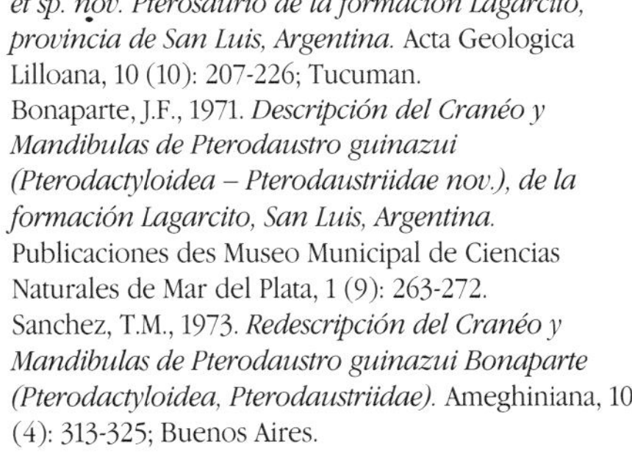

49 Bonaparte, J.F., 1970. *Pterodaustro guinazui gen. et sp. nov. Pterosaurio de la formación Lagarcito, provincia de San Luis, Argentina.* Acta Geologica Lilloana, 10 (10): 207-226; Tucuman.
Bonaparte, J.F., 1971. *Descripción del Cranéo y Mandibulas de Pterodaustro guinazui (Pterodactyloidea – Pterodaustriidae nov.), de la formación Lagarcito, San Luis, Argentina.* Publicaciones des Museo Municipal de Ciencias Naturales de Mar del Plata, 1 (9): 263-272.
Sanchez, T.M., 1973. *Redescripción del Cranéo y Mandibulas de Pterodaustro guinazui Bonaparte (Pterodactyloidea, Pterodaustriidae).* Ameghiniana, 10 (4): 313-325; Buenos Aires.

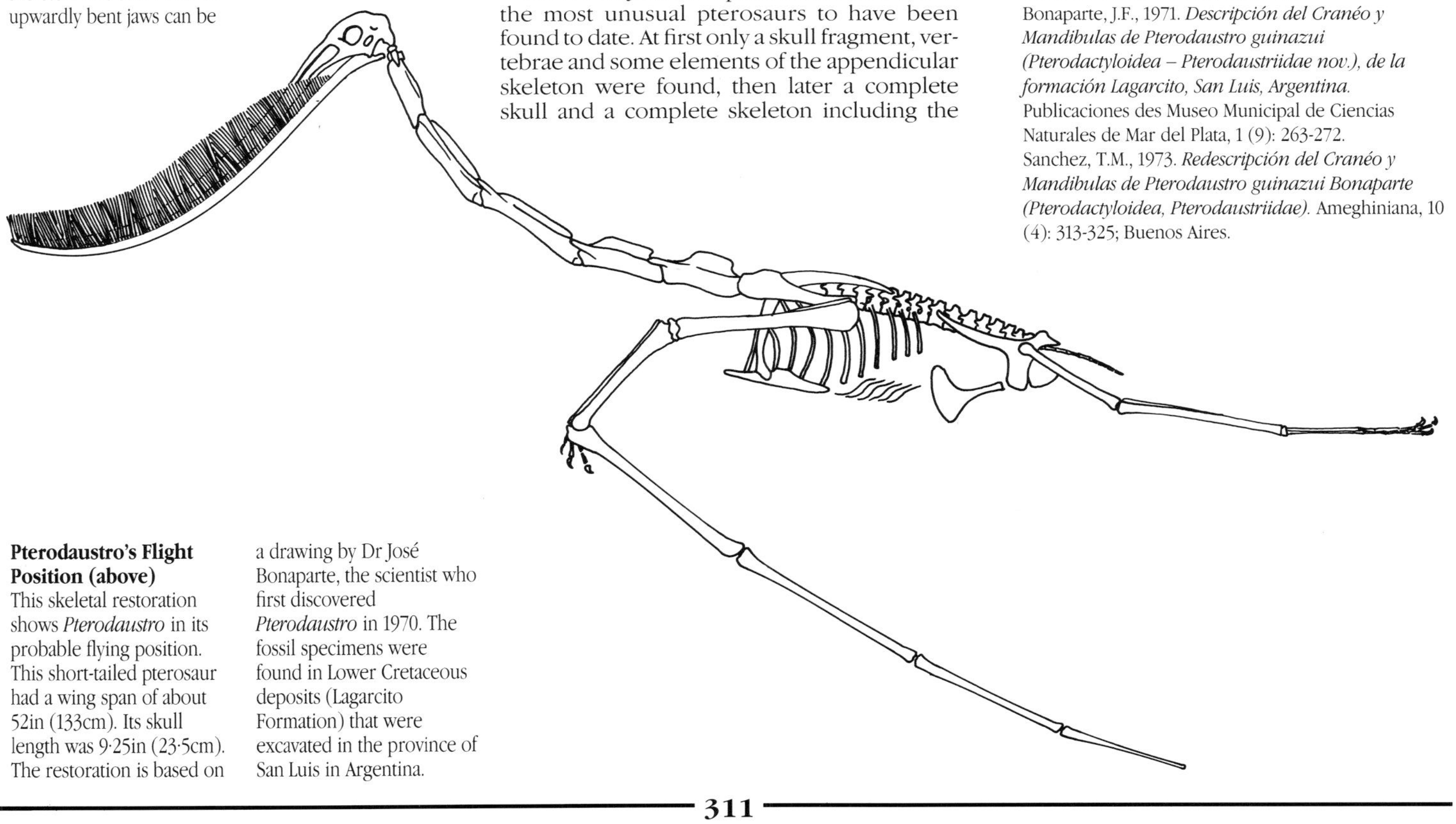

**Pterodaustro's Flight Position (above)**
This skeletal restoration shows *Pterodaustro* in its probable flying position. This short-tailed pterosaur had a wing span of about 52in (133cm). Its skull length was 9·25in (23·5cm). The restoration is based on a drawing by Dr José Bonaparte, the scientist who first discovered *Pterodaustro* in 1970. The fossil specimens were found in Lower Cretaceous deposits (Lagarcito Formation) that were excavated in the province of San Luis in Argentina.

Dr Bonaparte called this genus *Pterodaustro* (=south-wing); it is a short-tailed pterosaur with unique dentition. The skull is very markedly elongated and the front parts of the jaw are bent upwards. The lower jaw has a side groove in which are set a large number of long, tightly packed, apparently elastic 'teeth', which could more properly be called bristles. About 24 such lower jaw teeth occupy a centimetre of jaw length, which means that in a jaw 7·9in (20cm) long there are almost 500 teeth in each half of the jaw. *Pterodaustro*'s lower jaw was thus a highly effective sieving apparatus for filtering small organisms out of the water. The food content of this filter basket was chopped up into smaller bits by blunt, short teeth in the upper jaw.

*Pterodaustro*'s skull was 9·25in (23·5cm) long, but its wing span only 4·36ft (1·33m). Its filter dentition made it far more specialized than *Ctenochasma* from Solnhofen, which had filter dentition in the upper and lower jaw, but

**Left:** Dr José Bonaparte of the Museo Argentino de Ciencias Naturales in Buenos Aires, the discoverer of *Pterodaustro*, one of the most unusual pterosaurs to have been found to date. Dr Bonaparte is here pictured in the main hall of the museum.

**Pterodaustro (below)**
Dubbed the 'flamingo pterosaur', *Pterodaustro* was a remarkable filter feeder. It could not trap its food on the wing, but had to stand in the shallows and sieve small organisms out of the water with its filter basket.

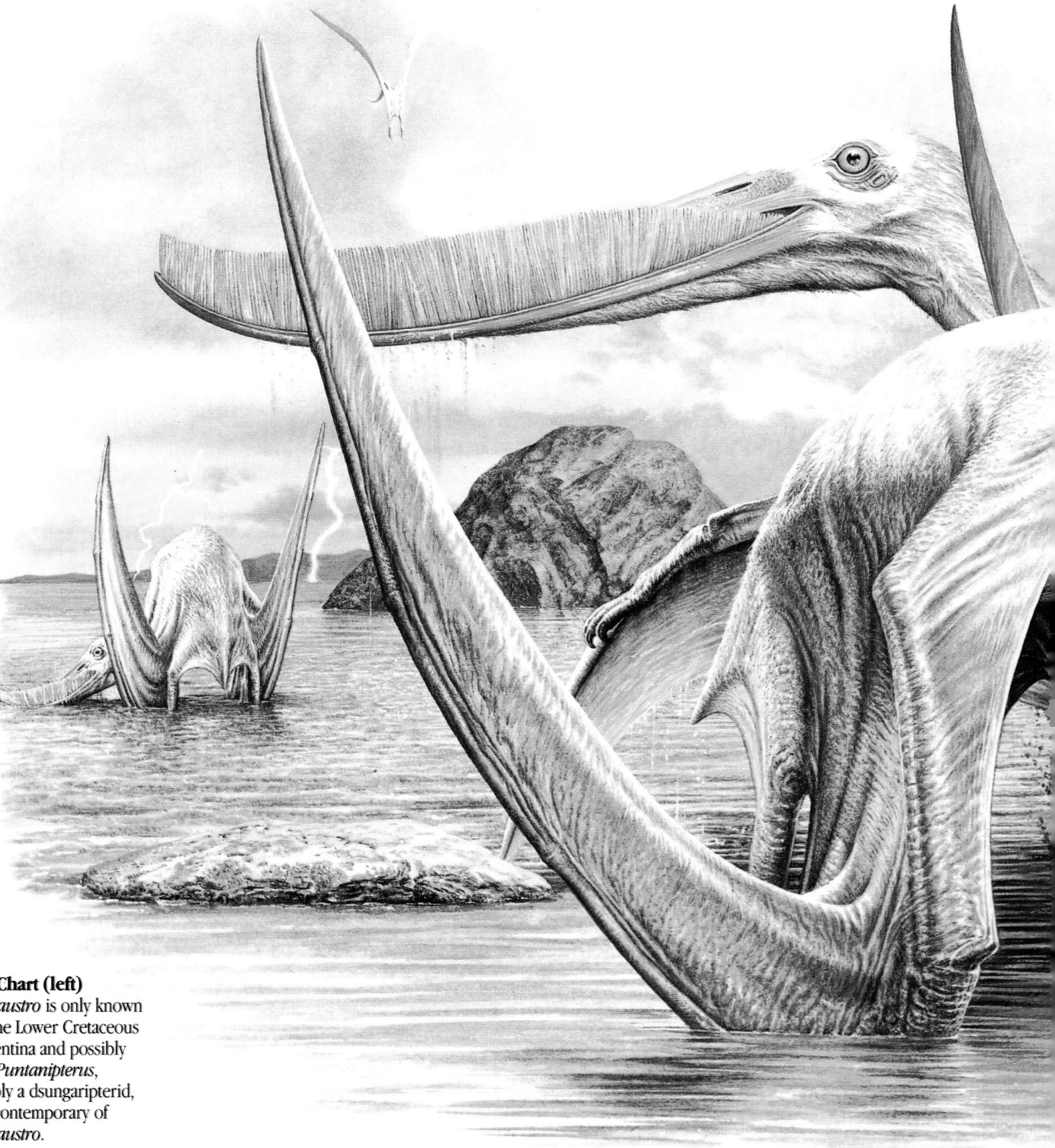

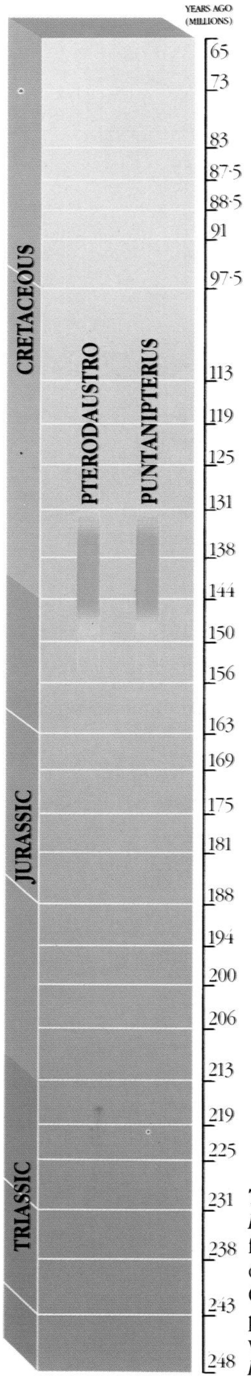

**Time Chart (left)**
*Pterodaustro* is only known from the Lower Cretaceous of Argentina and possibly Chile. *Puntanipterus*, probably a dsungaripterid, was a contemporary of *Pterodaustro*.

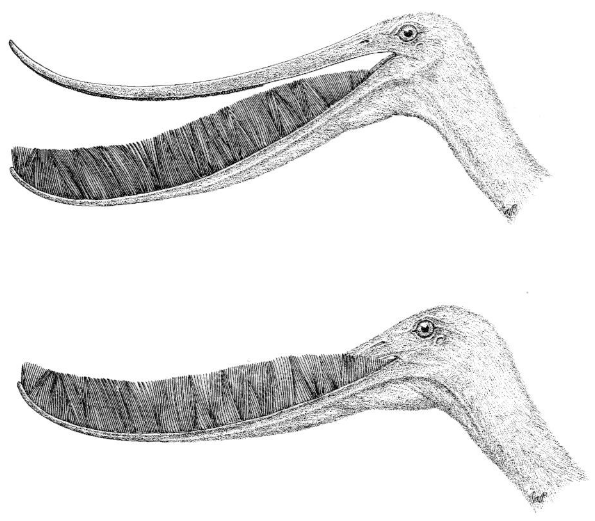

**Pterodaustro Life Portraits (left and above)** The head of *Pterodaustro* is here restored as in life with its beak open and closed. Its dentition consisted of a comb-like array of long, elastic bristles (not actually teeth) in the lower jaw for sieving creatures from the water. In its upper jaw was a series of short, blunt teeth for chopping up the food into smaller pieces to be swallowed.

**Map (right)**
**1** *Pterodaustro*
**2** *Puntanipterus*

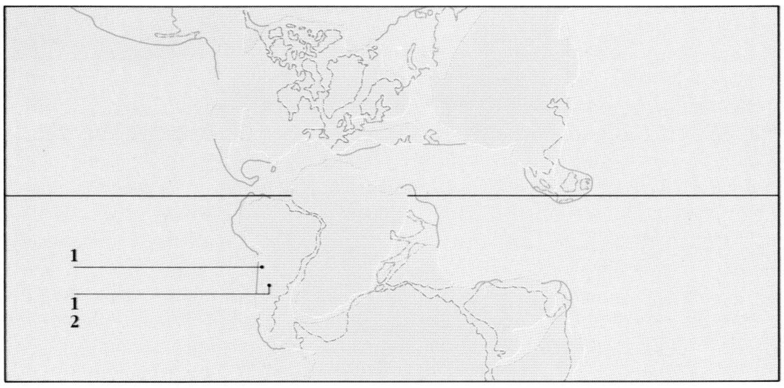

**Comparative Sizes (above)**
**1** *Pterodaustro*: wing span 4·36ft (1·33m).

consisting of considerably fewer teeth. For this reason *Pterodaustro* was placed in a family of its own, the Pterodaustridae.

Skull fragments and a humerus of *Pterodaustro* have also been discovered in the Lower Cretaceous of Chile, in the province of Antofagasta.[50]

J.F. Bonaparte and T.M. Sanchez reported on a second pterosaur genus from the Lower Cretaceous (La Cruz Formation) of the province of San Luis in Argentina in 1975.[51] What was found was a 3·5in (9cm) long tibia, which broadened at the end to form a bird-like roller-joint. With this were only a dorsal vertebra, a wing phalanx and a foot digit phalanx. The particular features of the tibia, which is fused with the fibula, are different from those of *Pterodaustro*, and were seen as diagnostic of a new genus, *Puntanipterus* (named after natives of the province of San Luis, called *puntanos* in Spanish). In the opinion of Peter Galton of Bridgeport University, *Puntanipterus* belongs to the family Dsungaripteridae, which was distributed from China via East Africa to South America.

One of the most southerly occurrences of pterosaurs was found in Lower Cretaceous strata of the province of Santa Cruz in Patagonia. They are bone fragments of a small ulna, which were questionably classified as ornithocheirid.[52] These Patagonian pterosaurs must have lived in a paleolatitude of 51°S, though not as far south as the New Zealand Cretaceous pterosaurs mentioned earlier.

**Above:** This photograph shows in detail the bristle-like dentition in the lower jaw of *Pterodaustro*. A mere centimetre of jaw might hold 24 such 'teeth', which meant that *Pterodaustro*'s entire lower jaw could accommodate nearly 1,000 of these bristles. They acted like a fine sieve which trapped aquatic organisms.

Part of a femur of a pterodactyloid pterosaur that cannot be any more precisely classified also came from Argentina. It was found in Lower Cretaceous deposits in Neuquén in northern Patagonia.[53]

In 1989 Christopher Bennett described a pterosaur humerus from the Chulec Formation (Lower Cretaceous, Albian) of Huanuco in Peru.[54] This well-preserved, fairly complete bone is 7·7in (19·6cm) long and suggests a wing span of about 13ft (4m). It is very similar to humeri from the Santana Formation of Brazil, like *Santanadactylus* for example, and thus proves that Brazilian Santana pterosaurs were distributed over large areas of South America in the Lower Cretaceous.

## North American Finds

The first fossil remains of North American pterosaurs were described as *'Pterodactylus' oweni* by O.C. Marsh in 1871.[55] A year later Marsh changed the name to *'Pterodactylus' occidentalis*, as the specific name *oweni* had already been allotted to an *Ornithocheirus* from the Cambridge Greensand in England by Seeley in 1870.[56] During the 1870 expedition mounted by Yale College, New Haven, to the American West, a stop was also made on the way back in West Kansas, and a very successful search for fossils carried out in the Kansas Chalk of the Niobrara Formation (Santonian) on the Smoky Hill River. One of the participants in the 1870 Yale College Expedition reported on the events in this vein: '. . . and finally reached Fort Wallace in Kansas. The last geological expedition was to be made from this post, along the Smoky River, and, with a small escort of cavalry, we started on the 20th of November. The nights had now become bitterly cold, and to avoid the piercing wind our

50 Chong, D.G., 1976. *Los relaciones de los Sistemas Jurásico y Cretácico en la zona preandina del Norte de Chile.* Actas I Congresso Geologico Chileno, 1976, 1: A21-A42; Santiago.

51 Bonaparte, J.F. and Sanchez, T.M., 1975. *Restos de un pterosaurio Puntanipterus globosus de la formación La Cruz, provincia San Luis, Argentina.* Actas Primo Congresso Argentino de Paleontologia e Bioestratigraphia, 2: 105-113; Tucuman.

52 Urreta, M.B.A. and Ramos, V.A., 1981. *Estratigraphia y Paleontologia de la Alta Cuenca des Rio Roble Cordillera Patagonia – provincia de Santa Cruz.* VIII Congresso Geologico Argentino, San Luis, Actas III: 101-138.

53 Montanelli, S.B., 1986. *Sobre e primer resto des Pterosauria (Reptilia) de la Formación La Amarga (Cretácico inferior), Neuquén, Argentina.* Boletin informativo Associación Paleontologie Argentina, 15: 13.

54 Bennett, S.C., 1989. *A pteranodontid Pterosaur from the early Cretaceous of Peru, with comments on the Relationships of Cretaceous Pterosaurs.* Journal of Paleontology, 63 (5): 669-677.

55 Marsh, O.C., 1871. *Note on a new and gigantic species of Pterodactyle.* American Journal of Science, 1: 472.

56 Marsh, O.C., 1872. *Discovery of additional remains of Pterosauria etc.* American Journal of Science, 3: 241.

**Right:** The lower jaw of *Pteranodon*, incompletely preserved, from the Upper Cretaceous Niobrara Formation of Kansas, from above. Instead of teeth, the outer margins of the jaws are developed as sharp ridges. These were covered by horny beaks.

**Left:** Exposures of the Niobrara chalk along the Smoky Hill River in West Kansas. These marine strata are deposits of a 'midcontinental seaway' that ran through the North American continent in late Cretaceous times. Here O.C. Marsh and his field party from Yale College in Connecticut found the first fossil remains of the giant pterosaur *Pteranodon* in 1870. The Niobrara chalk has produced hundreds of pterosaur bones, fish and marine reptiles in the course of excavations since that time.

**Right:** The field party led by Othniel Charles Marsh (standing in the centre) to the Western Territories in 1872. This expedition was very successful in collecting additional and more complete fossil bones of the large pterosaur *Pteranodon* from the late Cretaceous Niobrara chalk of Western Kansas. In those days, this was still Indian territory, and rifle, revolver and bowie knife took their places alongside the geological hammer as part of the standard equipment for palaeontological field work. On the evidence of this picture, hats were also *de rigueur* in Marsh's company.

**Below:** The skull of *Pteranodon* collected from the Niobrara chalk by S.W. Williston, and described by O.C. Marsh as *Pteranodon longiceps* in 1876. This skull shows nicely the long toothless jaws. However, the cranial crest at the rear is missing.

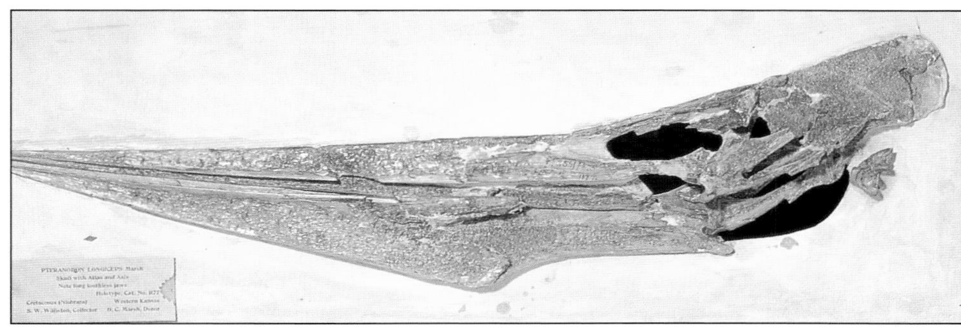

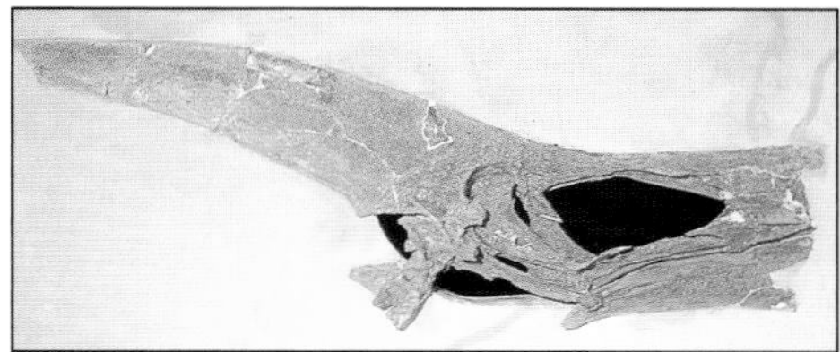

**Above:** A partial skull of *Pteranodon*, again from the West Kansas Niobrara Formation, showing the posterior half with the long bony crest extending from the back of the skull (on the left).

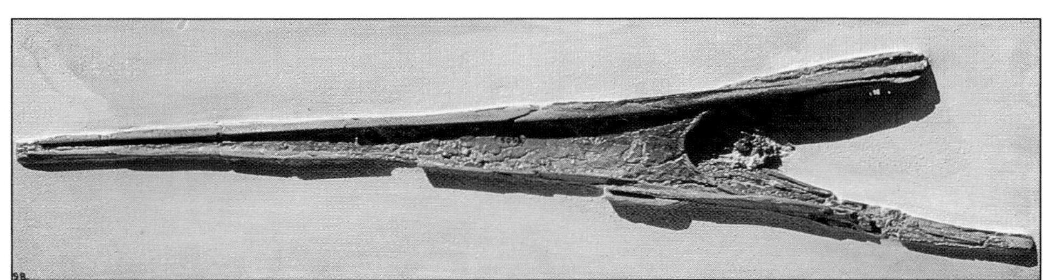

camp was pitched under a high bank. About midnight a wolf, attracted by the scent of meat, jumped off this bank, into the midst of our mules, and frightened them to such a degree that about a dozen broke loose and stampeded. The night was dark and the greatest confusion followed; for until the sentinels told us the true cause of disturbance we instinctively thought of Indians. The mules, with broken halters and lariats flying, reached the fort early in the morning, and caused great consternation among the officers, who naturally concluded that the Cheyennes had attacked us, and sent a company of soldiers to our rescue. The troops appeared more disappointed at losing the expected fight than gratified at our safety.

'The search for fossils met with great success, and remains of Cretaceous reptiles and fishes were collected in great quantities. One trophy was the skeleton of a sea serpent, nearly complete, and so large that we spent four days in digging out and carrying it to camp . . .

'The Smoky River runs through the great Kansas hunting grounds. Every day herds of the buffalo were around us, and we enjoyed many an exciting 'run' across the prairie.

'The weather day by day grew colder, and at length we saw indications of an approaching storm. Knowing the danger of exposure to snow on these open plains, we reluctantly bade farewell to our geological diggings, and satiated even with buffalo hunting, turned back to Fort Wallace . . .

'On commencing the journey homeward, and entering the palace cars, our ruffianly appearance created consternation among sober railroad tourists. Months of hardship, labor and adventure had made many a rent in our well-worn clothes; and the buckskin breeches and army blouses of several members gave to the party a wild and warlike character, in keeping with the open display of revolver and bowie knife, and bronzed faces covered with the untrimmed stubble of a season. We reached New Haven on the 18th of December, after six eventful months, during which no serious illness or accident had happened to any of our party.'[57] Among the fossil remains of fish and marine reptiles that they had collected was a single bone fragment from a large pterosaur. It was half a metacarpal bone, from which Marsh deduced this must have come from a giant pterosaur with a wing span of 20ft (6m).

In the following summer, 1871, at the same site he found the missing second half of this bone, which was 15·7in (40cm) long, confirming Marsh's estimate of the size of this individual. Further fossil discoveries on the Smoky Hill River in Kansas produced a large quantity of pterosaur material, including skulls. It now turned out, however, that in contrast with the English ornithocheirids these giant pterosaurs were toothless, and that they had a long crest at the rear end of the skull, which must have made this flying reptile look very bizarre indeed.

57 'Harper's New Monthly Magazine', volume 43, pp.663-671.

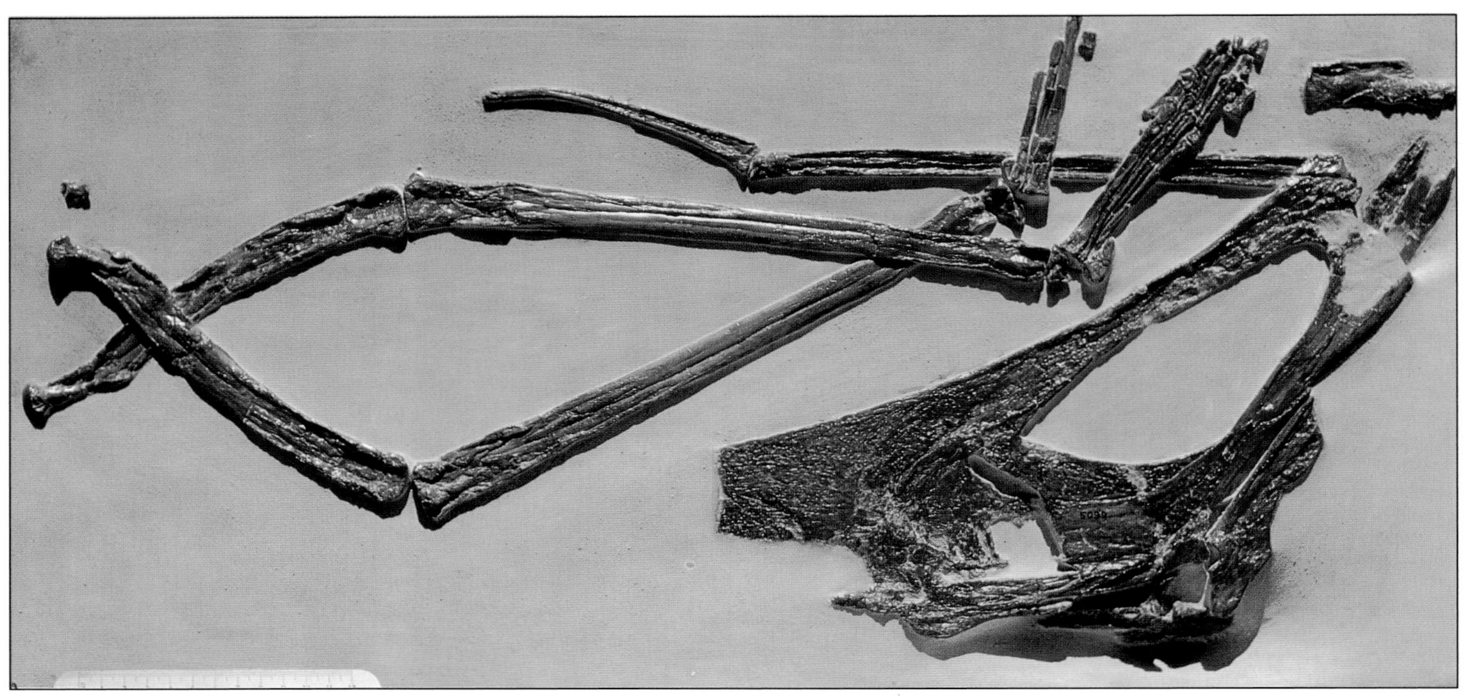

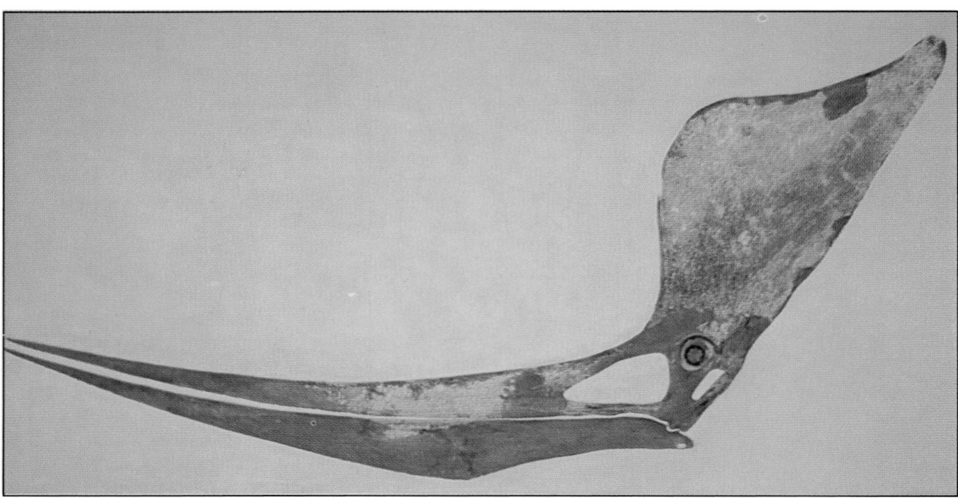

**Above:** These are incomplete skeletal remains of *Pteranodon* from the Upper Cretaceous of Kansas. This specimen comprises a fragment of the skull, the bones of the wing finger, which extend across the top of the picture from right to left, and both fairly complete hind legs. The skeleton of this large pterosaur is optimised for lightness. The bones are thin walled and hollow, and have openings which allow the penetration of air sacks which were connected to the lungs. Modern birds have a similar system.

**Above:** *Pteranodon sternbergi* is characterized by its high cranial crest. The length of the lower jaw is 3·9ft (1·2m). This is the largest species of *Pteranodon* known to date.

**Pteranodon sternbergi Skull (right)**
This is a skull restoration of *Pteranodon sternbergi*, the largest of the *Pteranodon* species recovered from Kansas.

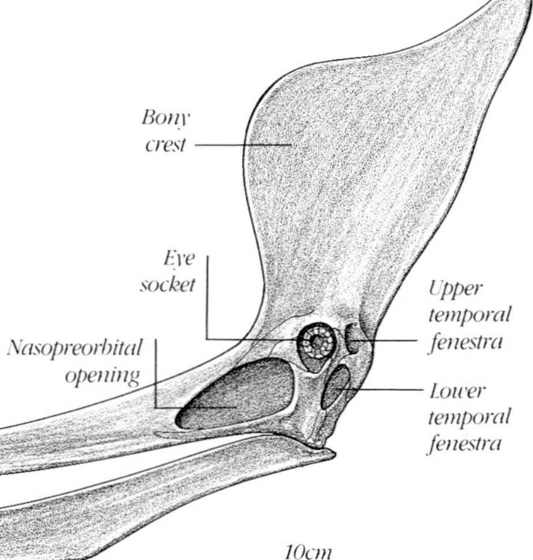


For this reason Marsh thought it necesssary in 1876 to distinguish the American Cretaceous pterosaurs from the English forms. He introduced the name *Pteranodon* (=toothless flier) for them,[58] and placed them in a family of their own, the Pteranodontidae, and even a sub-order of their own, the Pteranodontia. He also included another genus here, *Nyctosaurus* (=naked reptile), which had been found with *Pteranodon* skeletal remains in the Kansas Chalk.

None of the skulls collected or described by Marsh was originally attached to the bones of the rest of the skeleton, with the exception of neck vertebrae. It is therefore difficult to assign skeletal bones to particular skulls. Despite this, Marsh distinguished various different species of *Pteranodon*, which differed from each other particularly in the morphology of their skulls, especially in the shape of the crest. For example, *Pteranodon ingens* had a skull 5·9ft (1·79m) long, of which almost half consisted of the crest, rising well back over the rump. *Pteranodon sternbergi* had a crest which rose steeply and was broader at the top. The lower jaw alone of this species is 3·9ft (1·2m) long, thus longer by a third than *Pteranodon ingens*, which had an estimated wing span of about 23ft (7m). *Pteranodon sternbergi* was thus one of the largest known pterosaurs, and must have had a wing span of over 30ft (9m). This was only exceeded by the azhdarchids, like *Quetzalcoatlus* or *Titanopteryx*.

In contrast with these pterosaurs with extremely long necks, *Pteranodon* had a relatively short neck with powerful but short cervical vertebrae. Its long, pointed jaws are toothless, the eye socket is relatively small and placed fairly high in the skull. There is always a crest on the back of the head, but not on the snout or lower jaw. All the bones are extremely thin walled and pneumatic, meaning that they are hollow and had small air vents, possibly to allow the penetration of air sacks, which were connected with the lung, as in modern birds. The vertebrae also have large lateral openings, and are very lightly constructed.

After O.C. Marsh, S.W. Williston in particular devoted himself to research into 'Kansas Pterodactyls',[59] and in 1910 G.F. Eaton, Curator of

58 Marsh, O.C., 1876. *Principal characters of American Pterodactyls.* American Journal of Science, 12: 479.

59 Williston, S.W., 1892-1893. *Kansas Pterodactyls. Part I and II.* Kansas University Quarterly, I: 1-13; II: 79-81.

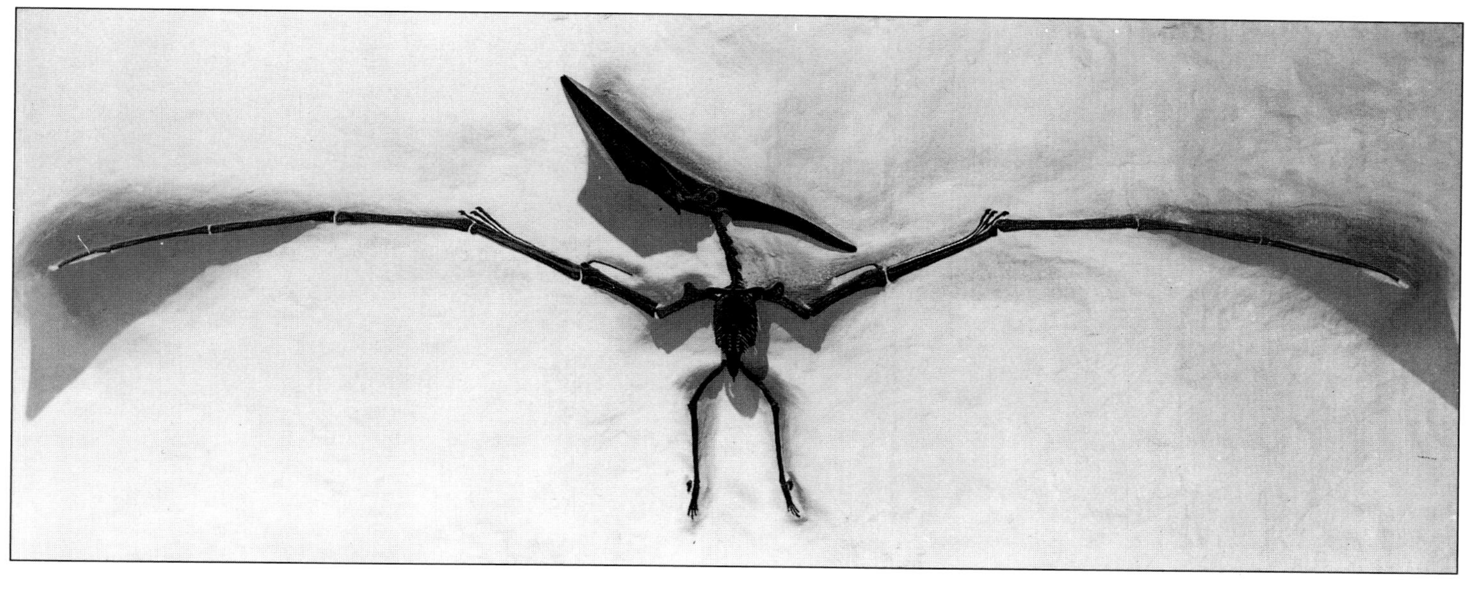

**Above:** A skeletal restoration of *Pteranodon* from the Upper Cretaceous of Kansas, mounted and on display in the Peabody Museum of Yale University in New Haven, Connecticut. The wing span of this particular specimen is 23ft (7m). The compactness of the body and hind legs when compared with the wings is remarkable in this view. The relative size of the skull with its long cranial crest is impressive.

Osteology and Vertebrate Palaeontology at the Peabody Museum of Yale College in New Haven could boast an inventory of *Pteranodon* skeletal remains featuring no fewer than 465 individuals.[60]

*Pteranodon* must have been able to sustain flying and soaring, ranging far out over the open sea to catch fish. The West Kansas strata in which finds were made are deposits of an extended sea that ran through the North

60 Eaton, G.F., 1910. *Osteology of Pteranodon*. Memoirs of the Connecticut Academy of Arts and Science, 2: 38 pp.; New Haven.

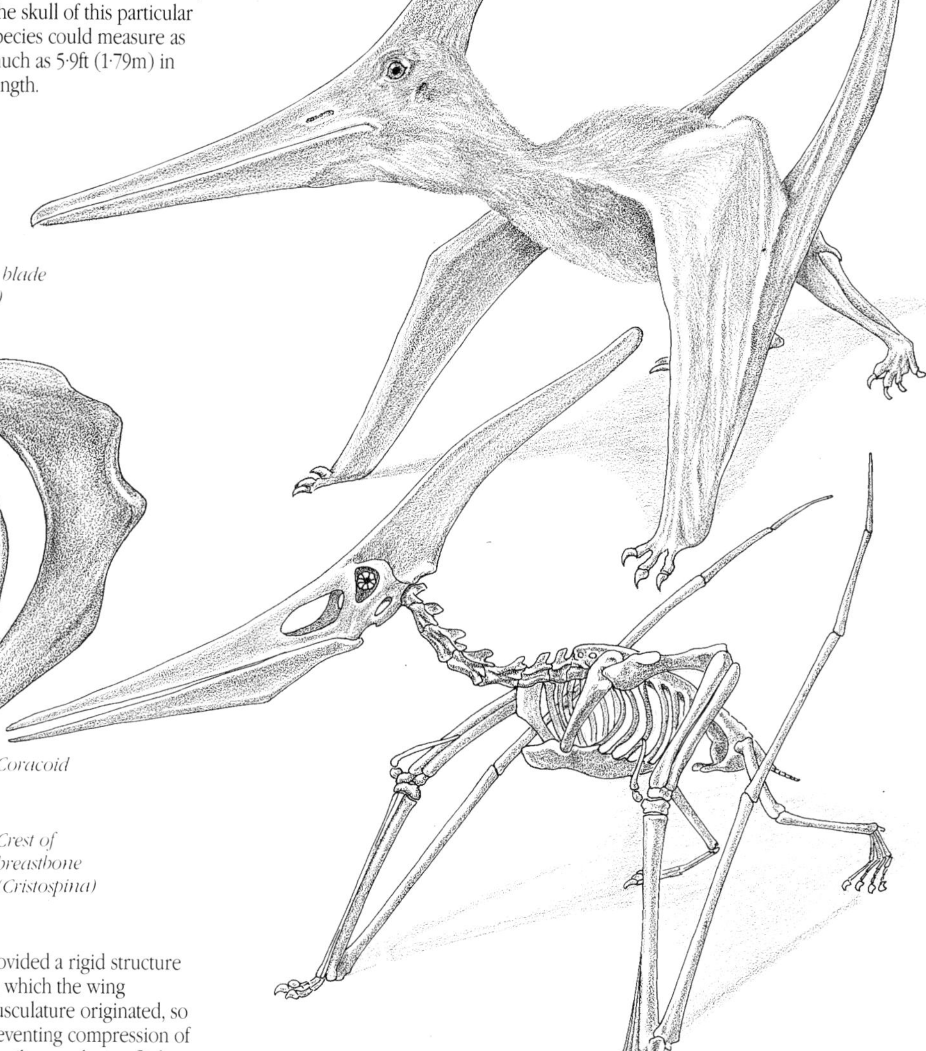

**Pteranodon ingens (below right)**
Shown here is a life portrait of *Pteranodon ingens* (above), and a comparable skeletal restoration (below). The skull of this particular species could measure as much as 5·9ft (1·79m) in length.



**Pteranodon's Shoulder Girdle (above)**
This drawing shows the shoulder girdle and the front section of the trunk of *Pteranodon*. The first eight dorsal vertebrae are fused and form a notarium providing strong support for the shoulder blades. In conjunction with the ribs and breastbone, this provided a rigid structure on which the wing musculature originated, so preventing compression of the rib cage during flight action.

American continent in the Cretaceous as a 'midcontinental seaway'. As the sites where *Pteranodon* remains were found are at least 100 miles (160km) from what was then the coast, it can be presumed that these pterosaurs perished in or over the water, far away from their nesting or resting places on the coast. Despite their large wings their actual bodies were rather small. Cherrie Bramwell and George Whitfield of Reading University calculated the body weight of *Pteranodon ingens* with a wing span of 22·8ft (6·95m) as a mere 36·6lb (16·6kg). With this the animal was able to achieve a maximum speed of 31mph (50km/h).

## Nyctosaurus

When more pterosaur material from the Smoky Hill River in West Kansas was found, O.C. March recognized that it also included skeletal remains of a second, smaller form, which he called *Nyctosaurus* (=naked rep-

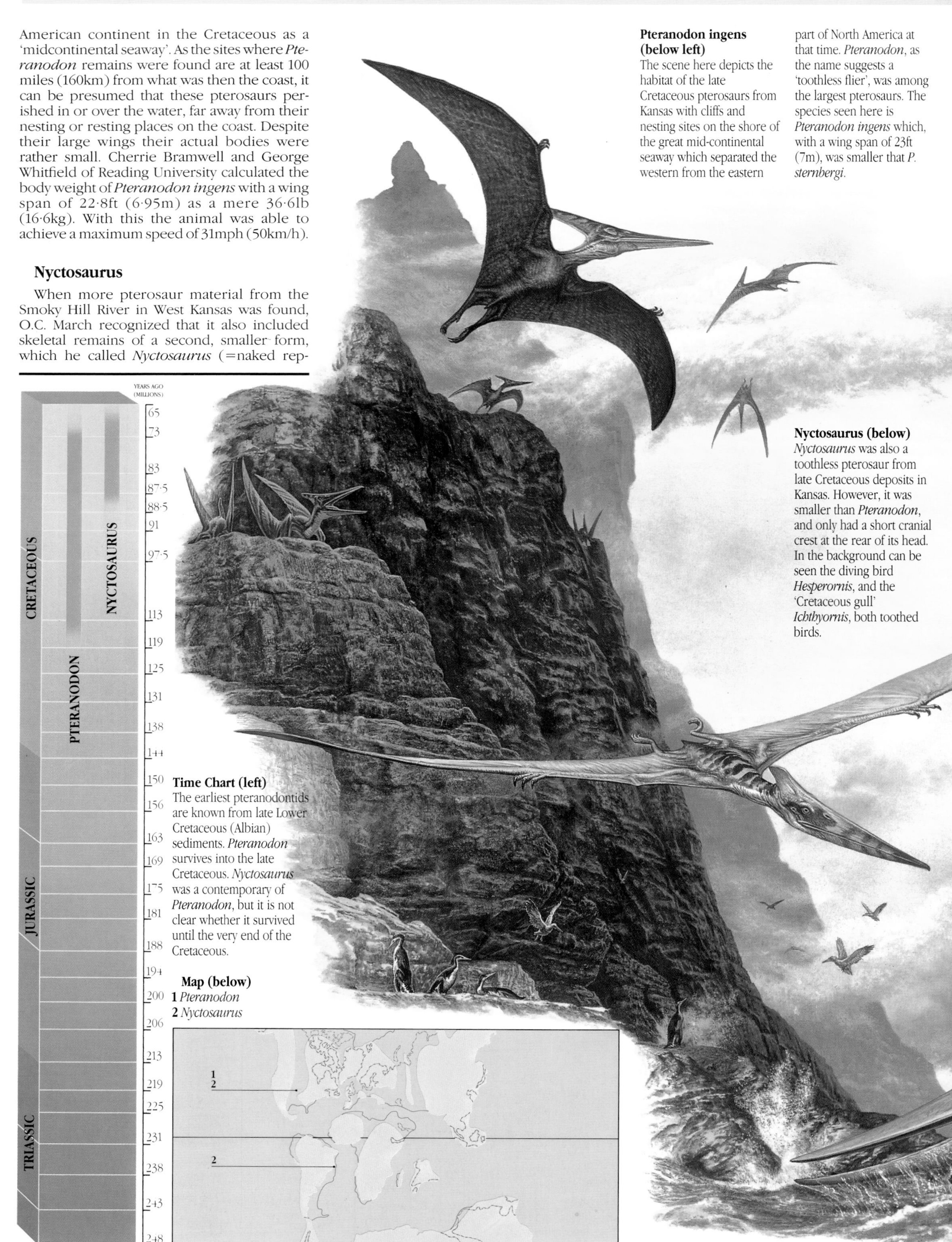


**Pteranodon ingens (below left)**
The scene here depicts the habitat of the late Cretaceous pterosaurs from Kansas with cliffs and nesting sites on the shore of the great mid-continental seaway which separated the western from the eastern part of North America at that time. *Pteranodon*, as the name suggests a 'toothless flier', was among the largest pterosaurs. The species seen here is *Pteranodon ingens* which, with a wing span of 23ft (7m), was smaller that *P. sternbergi*.

**Nyctosaurus (below)**
*Nyctosaurus* was also a toothless pterosaur from late Cretaceous deposits in Kansas. However, it was smaller than *Pteranodon*, and only had a short cranial crest at the rear of its head. In the background can be seen the diving bird *Hesperornis*, and the 'Cretaceous gull' *Ichthyornis*, both toothed birds.

**Time Chart (left)**
The earliest pteranodontids are known from late Lower Cretaceous (Albian) sediments. *Pteranodon* survives into the late Cretaceous. *Nyctosaurus* was a contemporary of *Pteranodon*, but it is not clear whether it survived until the very end of the Cretaceous.

**Map (below)**
**1** *Pteranodon*
**2** *Nyctosaurus*

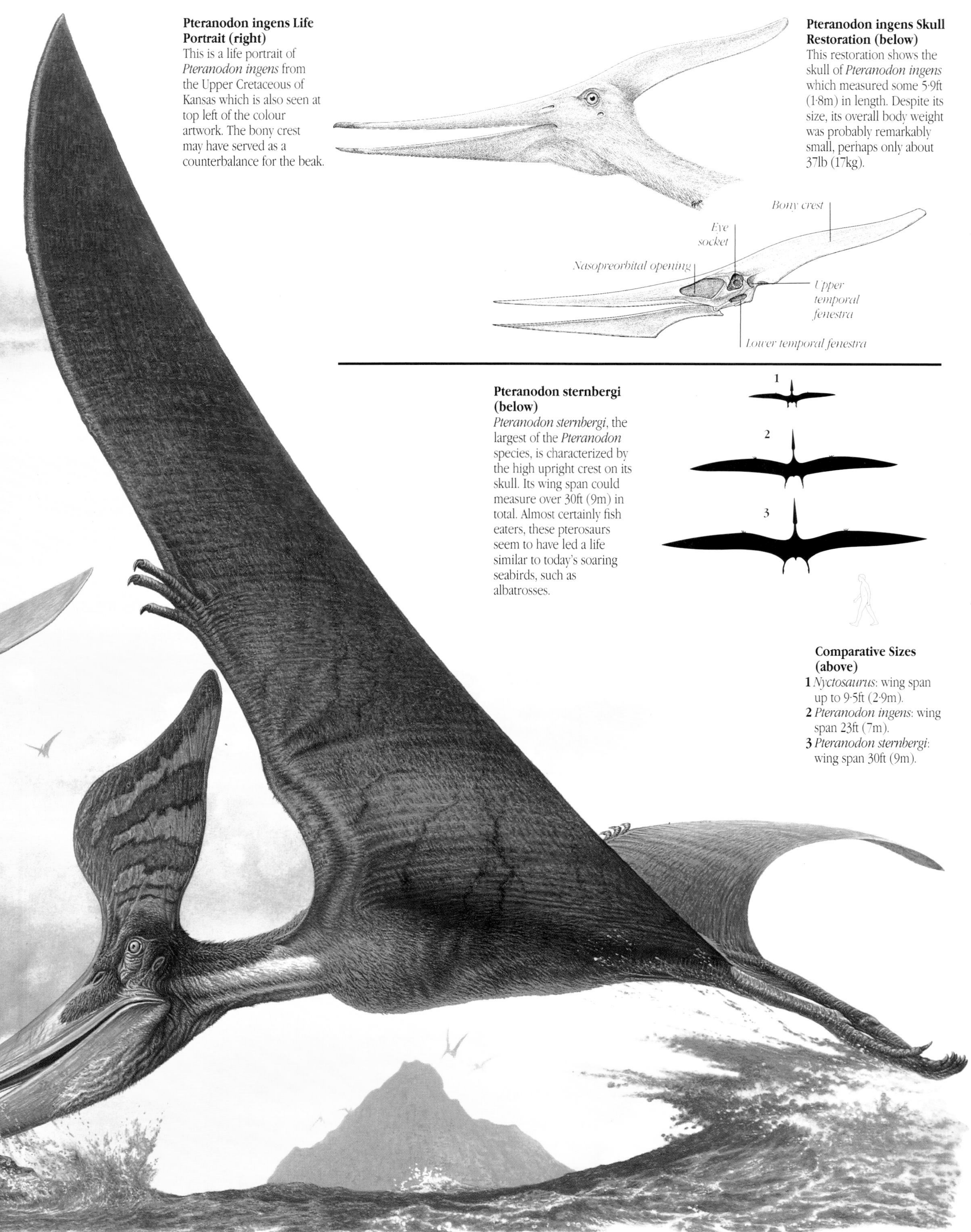


**Pteranodon ingens Life Portrait (right)**
This is a life portrait of *Pteranodon ingens* from the Upper Cretaceous of Kansas which is also seen at top left of the colour artwork. The bony crest may have served as a counterbalance for the beak.

**Pteranodon ingens Skull Restoration (below)**
This restoration shows the skull of *Pteranodon ingens* which measured some 5·9ft (1·8m) in length. Despite its size, its overall body weight was probably remarkably small, perhaps only about 37lb (17kg).

**Pteranodon sternbergi (below)**
*Pteranodon sternbergi*, the largest of the *Pteranodon* species, is characterized by the high upright crest on its skull. Its wing span could measure over 30ft (9m) in total. Almost certainly fish eaters, these pterosaurs seem to have led a life similar to today's soaring seabirds, such as albatrosses.

**Comparative Sizes (above)**
**1** *Nyctosaurus*: wing span up to 9·5ft (2·9m).
**2** *Pteranodon ingens*: wing span 23ft (7m).
**3** *Pteranodon sternbergi*: wing span 30ft (9m).

tile).[58] Relatively complete skeletons were later described by S.W. Williston, who also provided a first reconstruction of the skeleton.[61] *Nyctosaurus* was considerably smaller than *Pteranodon*. It has a wing span of 7·9-9·5ft (2·4-2·9m). Its skull is low and elongated. It is also toothless, and has no crest. As it is also different with regard to other skeletal features, it has been grouped in a family of its own, the Nyctosauridae.[54] Another characteristic is that the flight digit consisted of only three, rather than the usual four, phalanges.[62]

A humerus and fused dorsal vertebra from the marine Lower Cretaceous (Albian) of Oregon is similar to *Nyctosaurus*, but clearly a larger species, described in 1928 by C.W. Gilmore as *'Pteranodon' oregonensis*.[63]

Pterosaur remains from Upper Cretaceous strata have also been found in other sites in North America, and it may be that they are pteranodontids: in Delaware (early Campanian),[64] Georgia (Santonian),[65] Montana (early Campanian),[66] and Alberta (early Campanian).[67]

## Quetzalcoatlus

On the 'big bend' on the Rio Grande in western Texas on the border with Mexico is one of the lesser known but scenically most magnificent National Parks in the United States, the Big Bend National Park. Its landscape is made up to an equal extent of mountains of volcanic origin and also of terrestrial sediments from the late Cretaceous and early Tertiary, of which the soft, weathering forms are the typical 'badlands' of a dry, warm climate. There is little vegetation to prevent the erosion of these clayey sediments. For this reason fossil remains, dinosaurs, crocodiles and mammals are continually washed free by occasional violent rain storms, but they are also destroyed if they are not collected and saved.

The Cretaceous and Tertiary strata of the Big Bend National Park have long been known to contain fossils. They are particularly interesting because the transitional strata between the youngest Cretaceous and the oldest Tertiary, the Cretaceous/Tertiary boundary (K/T boundary for short), are revealed. This is one of the few places on Earth where the factors that led to the extinction of dinosaurs and other land vertebrates at the end of the Cretaceous, 65 million years ago, can be studied.

In 1975 *Science* published a short report entitled 'Pterosaur from the Latest Cretaceous of West Texas. Discovery of the Largest Flying Creature'.[68] Even palaeontologists, otherwise used to large prehistoric animals, could hardly

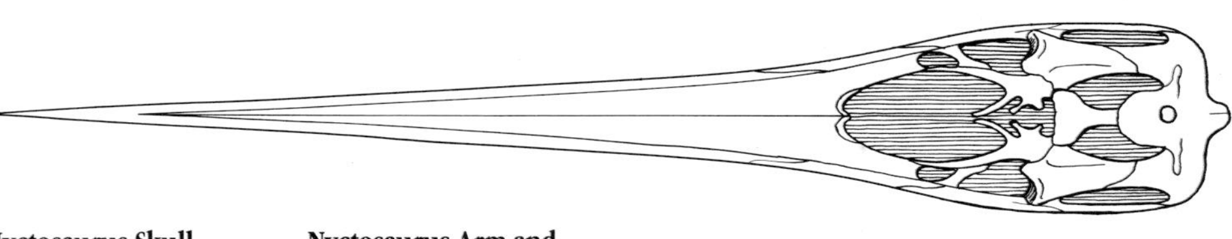

**Nyctosaurus Skull (above)**
We see here the skull of *Nyctosaurus gracilis* from below looking up into the palate. The length of this particular skull with its long, slender beak is about 1ft (30cm).

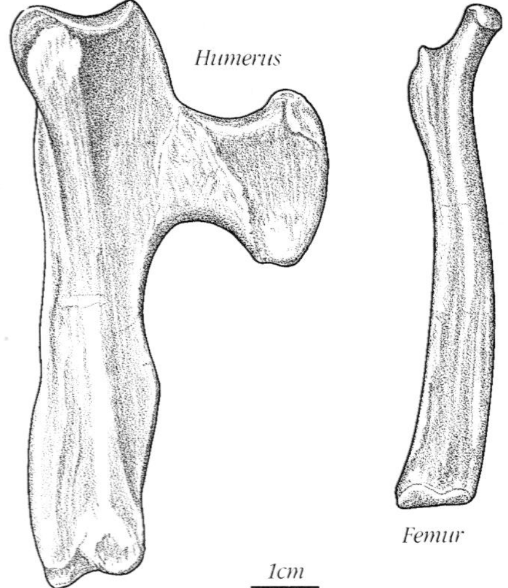


**Nyctosaurus Arm and Leg Bones (right)**
These drawings depict the upper arm (left) and upper leg of *Nyctosaurus gracilis* from behind. The humerus is characterized by its distinctive hatchet-like shape.

61 Williston, S.W., 1902. *On the skeleton of Nyctodactylus, with restoration.* American Journal of Anatomy, 1 (3): 297.
Williston, S.W., 1902. *On the skull of Nyctodactylus, an Upper Cretaceous Pterodactyl.* Journal of Geology, 10 (5): 520-531; Chicago.
Williston, S.W., 1903. *On the osteology of Nyctosaurus (Nyctodactylus), with notes on American pterosaurs.* Field Columbian Museum Publications, Geological Series, 2: 125-163.
62 Brown, G.W., 1986. *Reassessment of Nyctosaurus: new wings for an old pterosaur.* Proceedings, Nebraska Academy of Science, 1986: 47.
63 Gilmore, C.W., 1928. *A new pterosaurian reptile from the marine Cretaceous of Oregon.* Proceedings of the U.S. National Museum, 73 (24): 1-5.
64 Baird, D. and Galton, P.M., 1981. *Pterosaur Bones from the Upper Cretaceous of Delaware.* Journal of Vertebrate Palaeontology, 1 (1): 67-71.
65 Schwimmer, D.R., Padian, K. and Woodhead, A.B., 1985. *First Pterosaur Records from Georgia.* Journal of Palaeontology, 59, (3): 674-676.
66 Padian, K., 1984. *A large Pterodactyloid Pterosaur from the Two Medicine Formation (Campanian) of Montana.* Journal of Vertebrate Paleontology, 4 (4): 516-524.
67 Currie, P.J. and Padian, K., 1983. *A New Pterosaur Record from the Judith River (Oldman) Formation of Alberta.* Journal of Paleontology, 57 (3): 599-600.

68 Lawson, D.A., 1975. *Pterosaur from the Latest Cretaceous of West Texas. Discovery of the Largest Flying Creature.* Science, 187; 947-948.
Langston, W., Jr., 1978. *The Great Pterosaur.* Discovery 2 (3): 20-23; Austin.

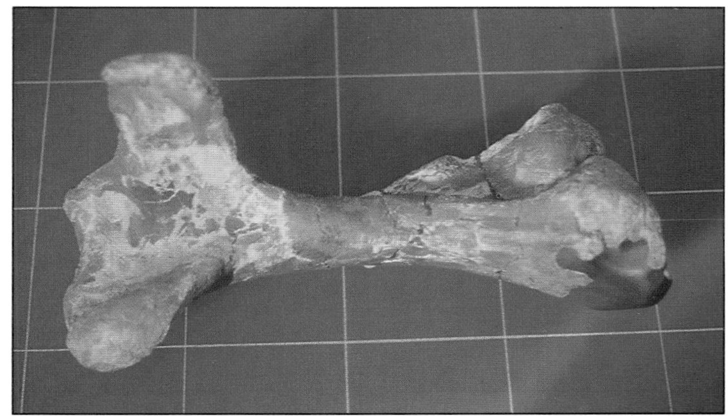

**Left:** The upper arm of *Quetzalcoatlus northropi* from the latest Cretaceous of West Texas. The bone is 1·7ft (52cm) long and very massively built. The wing span of this giant pterosaur has been calculated as up to 39ft (12m) in total.

**Right:** Dr Wann Langston Jr leading a field excursion in Big Bend National Park in 1989. Dr Langston has excavated many pterosaur bones from this important locality.

believe that this 'Texas pterosaur', as it came to be known, must have had a wing span of 51ft (15·5m), as the first calculation suggested. This was twice as big as the largest pterosaurs hitherto known, pteranodontids from the Kansas Chalk.

The history of its discovery began in 1971, when Douglas A. Lawson, a student at the University of Texas in Austin, was carrying out geological investigations for his master's thesis. He was especially interested in the sediments of the Javelina Formation, which were deposited at the end of the Cretaceous, about 65 million years ago: his aim was to find out about the environment and life conditions of the last dinosaurs, like the titanosaurids, for example. One afternoon, in a dry valley, Lawson found some bone fragments that must have been washed down from higher up. He followed the trail to a steep wall of rock, where he discovered the source of all these pieces of bone. He saw part of a bone 3ft (1m) long, still sticking in the rock. He brought part of this back to Austin with him and showed it to his professor, Dr Wann Langston Jr, as he had no idea what he had discovered. After thorough examination of the fragment and comparison with fossil remains in other museums, it rapidly became clear that this long, hollow, very thin-walled bone could only be a bone from a pterosaur wing.

There was no time to lose. Every day that passed would bring more weathering and destruction of the bones that had been revealed. Professor Langston and his student took the long road back from Austin to Big Bend, over 500 miles (800km), and investigated the site thoroughly. They dug out all the bones that were still to be found in the sediment. They even hoped they might rescue the entire skeleton of this giant of the air. But unfortunately it seemed that only a wing had survived. It must have been detached from the body after the creature died, and embedded further away.

But they still had the humerus and hundreds of small fragments of bones, which it was possible to assemble as lower arm and carpus in the laboratories of the Texas Memorial Museum. Other parts of the wing phalanges were added, one of which alone was 4ft (1·22m) long, but broken off at both ends. Lawson named this pterosaur *Quetzalcoatlus* after the Mexican deity Quetzalcoatl, who was worshipped by the Aztecs in the form of a feathered snake.

In subsequent years Dr Langston carried out regular investigations in the Javelina Formation of the Big Bend National Park, in the course of which he was able to collect numerous fossil bones and parts of the skeleton of smaller individuals in another part of the

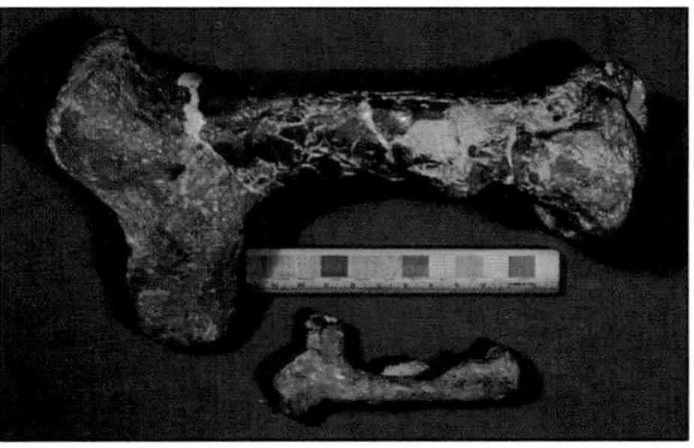

**Above:** A comparison of the upper arms of the giant *Quetzalcoatlus northropi* and of the smaller, almost half-sized species *Quetzalcoatlus* sp. (not yet named) which were both found in Big Bend NP.

**Left:** The fossil site where the giant Texas pterosaur *Quetzalcoatlus* was discovered in latest Cretaceous sediments of the Javelina Formation in Big Bend National Park, West Texas. This first discovery of a *Quetzalcoatlus* humerus was made in 1971 by Douglas Lawson, who was then a student working under the supervision of Dr Wann Langston of the University of Texas in Austin.

**Right:** Dr Wann Langston with a complete wing of the 'smaller' *Quetzalcoatlus* sp.. The bones are arranged in their natural articulation and suspended individually in order to allow them to be manipulated to aid study of their possible movements. These studies were undertaken to assist in the construction of a flying model of *Quetzalcoatlus* by Dr Paul MacCready.

park. Even so this 'little' *Quetzalcoatlus* had a wing span of at least 18ft (5·5m). These remains made it possible to establish a fairly good idea of the full skeleton of *Quetzalcoatlus*, and to calculate the probable wing span of the large individual at 36-39ft (11-12m).[69]

It is not yet clear whether these individuals, all found in a closely restricted area about 30 miles (50km) from the site at which the larger creature was found, were young individuals of the large species, or whether they represent a distinct, smaller species of *Quetzalcoatlus*. But because they are so complete they show us how these pterosaurs were constructed, and what they looked like. They were toothless, had sharp edges to their jaws, probably covered with horn, and long, narrow pointed beaks with a low, slender crest. The neck vertebrae were extremely long and show typical characteristics of the kind noted in *Titanopteryx* and *Azhdarcho*. The articulations of the cervical vertebrae allowed practically no lateral movement for the long neck. The long wing phalanges are constructed in a way that differs from other Pterodactyloidea. While the first of the four wing phalanges is hollow and oval in cross-section, the other three phalanges are made of solid bone tissue, with a T-shaped cross-section. Thus nature found a perfect solution for the technical problem of the accumulation of forces during the downstroke of the wing, and combined the highest possible strength with the lowest possible weight.

Aeronautical engineers quickly calculated that a pterosaur the size of the large *Quetzalcoatlus* must probably have weighed well over 220lb (100kg), and simply did not have enough muscular mass to raise this weight into the air and achieve continuous flapping flight. A glance at the massive bone crests on the humerus of *Quetzalcoatlus* is enough to show what powerful flight muscles must have been attached here.

The humerus is 1·7ft (52cm) long, and very robust in structure. One of the largest living birds, the wandering albatross, has a humerus 1·3ft (40cm) long and a wing span of 11ft (3·4m). On this basis *Quetzalcoatlus* would have had a wing span of only 14·4ft (4·4m). The fact that in reality its wings stretched almost three times as far is due to the completely different structure of the pterosaur skeleton. In *Quetzalcoatlus* the humerus is the shortest bone in the wing, whereas in the albatross it is the longest. Wing length in pterosaurs is determined above all by the metacarpus and the flight digit, whereas in birds the feathers protrude far beyond the skeleton of the wing. According to an estimate by Dr Langston, *Quetzalcoatlus* could have weighed 190lb (86kg). Bramwell and Whitfield's calculations gave a weight for *Pteranodon* of between 28·2 and 52·5lb (12·8 and

69 Langston, W., Jr., 1981. *Pterosaurs*. Scientific American, 244 (2): 122-136.

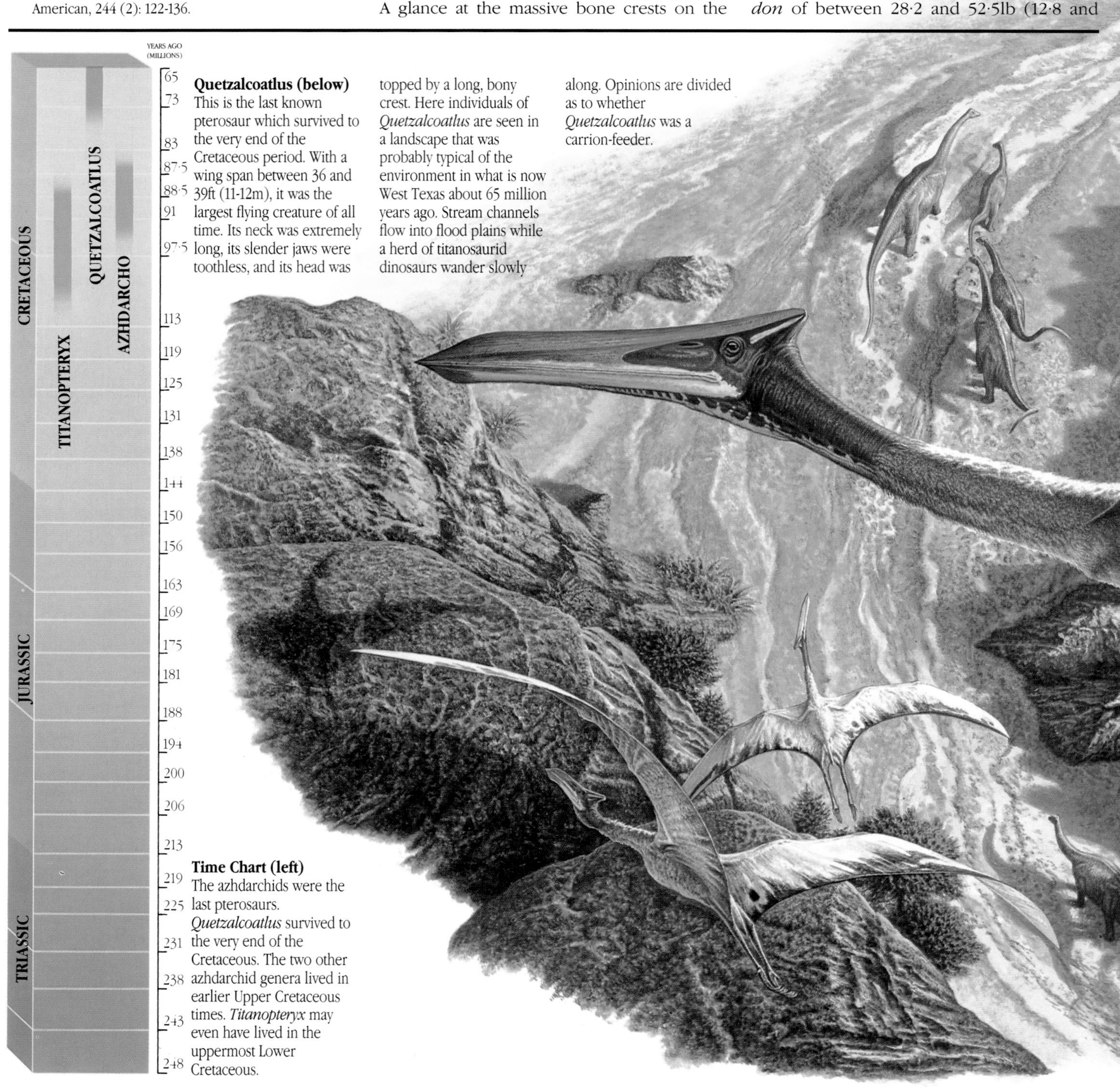


**Quetzalcoatlus (below)** This is the last known pterosaur which survived to the very end of the Cretaceous period. With a wing span between 36 and 39ft (11-12m), it was the largest flying creature of all time. Its neck was extremely long, its slender jaws were toothless, and its head was topped by a long, bony crest. Here individuals of *Quetzalcoatlus* are seen in a landscape that was probably typical of the environment in what is now West Texas about 65 million years ago. Stream channels flow into flood plains while a herd of titanosaurid dinosaurs wander slowly along. Opinions are divided as to whether *Quetzalcoatlus* was a carrion-feeder.

**Time Chart (left)** The azhdarchids were the last pterosaurs. *Quetzalcoatlus* survived to the very end of the Cretaceous. The two other azhdarchid genera lived in earlier Upper Cretaceous times. *Titanopteryx* may even have lived in the uppermost Lower Cretaceous.

**Right:** Technician Earl Yarmer of Texas Memorial Museum, Austin, is carefully chipping pterosaur wing bones out of the rock at Big Bend National Park. This is a partly articulated wing of a *Pteranodon*-sized *Quetzalcoatlus* in Upper Cretaceous floodplain sediments.

**Comparative Sizes (above)**
**1** *Quetzalcoatlus northropi*: wing span 36-39ft (11-12m).

**Map (below)**
**1** *Quetzalcoatlus*
**2** *Titanopteryx*
**3** *Azhdarcho*

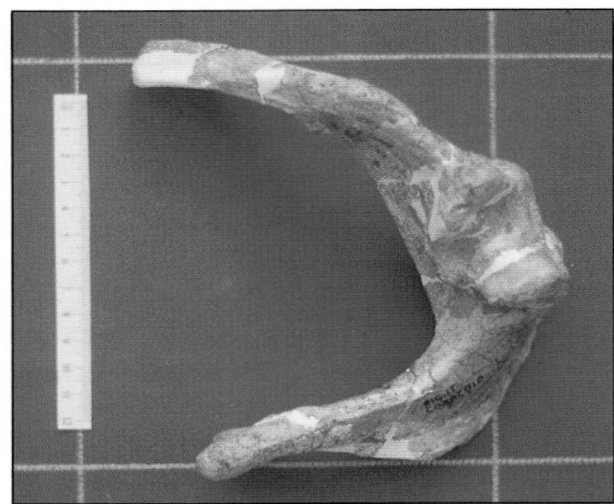

**Above:** This is the shoulder girdle of *Quetzalcoatlus* sp., a smaller species about half the size of the giant *Quetzalcoatlus northropi*. This specimen shows the glenoid fossa which was for articulation of the upper arm.

**Feeding Habits (right)**
*Quetzalcoatlus* lived inland from the sea. Perhaps, therefore, it was a carrion feeder, although its lack of teeth makes this seem improbable. Alternatively it may have probed for shellfish in small pools.

23·8kg), with a wing span of 23ft (7m).[70] Therefore *Quetzalcoatlus*, with a wing span of 36-39ft (11-12m), was possibly even lighter than the 190lb (86kg) that have been assumed, absolutely comparable in size and weight with a modern ultra-light aircraft.

Problems also arise when we try to imagine the habitat and way of life of these giant Texan pterosaurs. Unlike most other pterosaur fossils they were not found in marine strata, but in the sand and silt of the extensive flood plain of a former meandering river system which at that time, during the latest Cretaceous, was well inland, about 250 miles (400km) from the nearest sea coast. There is no geological evidence for large fresh-water lakes in the area. Lawson therefore took the view that *Quetzalcoatlus* might have lived rather like the modern vulture, that it was an eater of carrion who fed on the corpses of dinosaurs. Its long neck would have been well adapted for this. As a good soarer with considerable stamina it was certainly able to cover large distances in search of dead dinosaurs. Nevertheless many contradictions remain. Was the long, almost inflexible neck possibly not more of a hindrance for an eater of carrion? And could the pterosaur tear pieces of flesh from the corpse of an animal at all with its pointed, toothless jaws? On the

70 Bramwell, C.D. and Whitfield, G.R., 1974. *Biomechanics of Pteranodon*. Philosophical Transactions of the Royal Society London, (B), 267: 503-581.

**Above:** The front end of the jaws of the 'small' *Quetzalcoatlus* sp. from the latest Cretaceous of West Texas. The jaws are toothless. The length preserved is 31·5in (80cm).

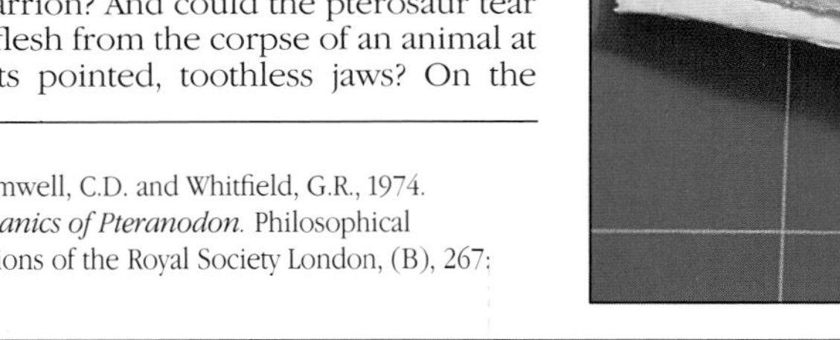

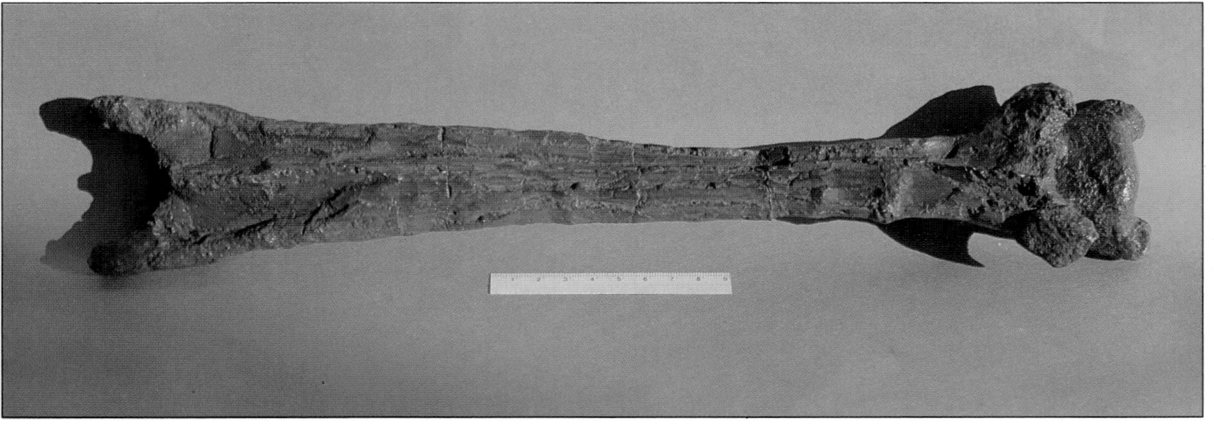

**Left:** This long neck vertebra also belonged to *Quetzalcoatlus* sp. These long and slender vertebrae are diagnostic for inclusion in the family Azhdarchidae which has a worldwide distribution during the Cretaceous.

**SUMMARY OF CRETACEOUS PTEROSAURS**

**Pterodactyloidea**
Family Ornithocheiridae
*Ornithocheirus compressirostris*
Upper Cretaceous, Turonian, Chalk, Kent, England.[1,2]
*Ornithocheirus cuvieri*
*Ornithocheirus fittoni*
*Ornithocheirus giganteus*
*Ornithocheirus microdon*
*Ornithocheirus sedgwicki* and other species
Upper Cretaceous, Cenomanian, Cambridge Greensand, England.[3]
*Ornithocheirus clifti*
*Ornithocheirus curtus*
Lower Cretaceous, Wealden, Sussex, England.[6]
*Ornithocheirus sagittirostris*
Lower Cretaceous, Hastings Beds, Sussex, England.[6]
*Ornithocheirus daviesi*
Lower Cretaceous, Gault, Albian, Kent, England.[6]
*Ornithocheirus diomedius*
Upper Cretaceous, Turonian, Kent, England.[6]
*Ornithocheirus bunzeli*
Upper Cretaceous, Gosau Formation, Campanian, Austria.[13,14]
*Ornithocheirus hlavatschi*
Upper Cretaceous, Turonian, Bohemia, Czechoslovakia.[15]
*Ornithocheirus hilsensis*
Lower Cretaceous, Neocomian, Hannover, Germany.[16]
*Ornithocheirus* sp.
Lower Cretaceous, Gault, Albian, La Meuse, France.
Lower Cretaceous, Hauterivian, Haute-Marne, France.[17]
Lower Cretaceous, Albian, Aube, France.[18]
?*Ornithocheirus*
Lower Cretaceous, Toolebuc Formation, Albian, Queensland, Australia.[32]
Lower Cretaceous, Rio Belgrano Formation, Barremian, Santa Cruz, Argentina.[52]
Upper Cretaceous, Campanian-Maastrichtian, New Zealand.[34]
Upper Cretaceous, Cenomanian-Turonian, Zaïre, Africa.[30]
*Santanadactylus brasilensis*[39]
*Santanadactylus araripensis*[40]
*Santanadactylus pricei*[40]
*Brasileodactylus araripensis*[42]
Lower Cretaceous, Santana Formation, Aptian, Araripe Plateau, Brazil.
Family Anhangueridae
*Anhanguera blittersdorffi*[43]
*Anhanguera santanae*[40,44]
Lower Cretaceous, Santana Formation, Aptian, Araripe Plateau, Brazil.
Family Tapejaridae
*Tupuxuara longicristatus*
*Tapejara wellnhoferi*
Lower Cretaceous, Santana Formation, Aptian, Araripe Plateau, Brazil.[48]
Family Cearadactylidae
*Cearadactylus atrox*[46]
Lower Cretaceous, Santana Formation, Aptian, Araripe Plateau, Brazil.
Family Criorhynchidae
*Criorhynchus simus* and other species
Lower Cretaceous, Wealden, Sussex;
Upper Cretaceous, Cenomanian, Cambridge Greensand, England.[5]
*Tropeognathus mesembrinus*
*Tropeognathus robustus*
Lower Cretaceous, Santana Formation, Aptian, Araripe Plateau, Brazil.[8]
Family Ornithodesmidae
*Ornithodesmus latidens*
Lower Cretaceous, Wealden, Isle of Wight, England.[12]
Family Dsungaripteridae
*Dsungaripterus weii*
Lower Cretaceous, Tugulu Group, Xinjiang, China.[19,20]
?*Dsungaripterus brancai*
Upper Jurassic, Tendaguru, Tanzania, Africa.[22]
*Noripterus complicidens*
Lower Cretaceous, Tugulu Group, Xinjiang, China.[20]
*Phobetor parvus*
Lower Cretaceous, Zagan Zabsk Formation, West Mongolia.[21]
*'Santanadactylus' spixi*
Lower Cretaceous, Santana Formation, Aptian, Araripe Plateau, Brazil.[23]
*Puntanipterus globosus*
Lower Cretaceous, La Cruz Formation, San Luis, Argentina.[51]
Family Pterodaustridae
*Pterodaustro guinazui*
Lower Cretaceous, Lagarcito Formation, San Luis, Argentina.[49]
*Pterodaustro* sp.
Lower Cretaceous, Neocomian, Antofagasta, Chile.[50]
Family Pteranodontidae
*Pteranodon longiceps*[58]
*Pteranodon ingens*[56]
*Pteranodon marshi*[72]
*Pteranodon occidentalis*[56]
*Pteranodon eatoni*[72]
*Pteranodon sternbergi*[72]
*Pteranodon walkeri*[72]
Upper Cretaceous, Niobrara Formation, Santonian, West Kansas, USA.
*Pteranodon* sp.
Upper Cretaceous, Santonian-Campanian, Hokkaido, Japan.[28]
*'Pteranodon' oregonensis*
Lower Cretaceous, Hudspeth Formation, Albian, Oregon, USA.[63]
*Ornithostoma seeleyi*
Upper Cretaceous, Cenomanian, Cambridge Greensand, England.[73]
*Ornithostoma orientalis*
Upper Cretaceous, Senonian, Saratov, Petrovsk, USSR.[24]
Indeterminated Pteranodontidae
Lower Cretaceous, Toolebuc Formation, Albian, Queensland, Australia.[33]
Lower Cretaceous, Chulec Formation, Albian, Huanuco, Peru.[23]
Upper Cretaceous, Merchantville Formation, Campanian, Delaware, USA.[64]
Upper Cretaceous, Two Medicine Formation, Campanian, Montana, USA.[66]
Upper Cretaceous, Eutaw Formation, Santonian, Georgia, USA.[65]
Upper Cretaceous, Judith River Formation, Campanian, Alberta, Canada.[67]
Family Nyctosauridae
*Nyctosaurus lamegoi*
Upper Cretaceous, Gramame Formation, ?Maastrichtian or Campanian, Paraiba, Brazil.[35]
*Nyctosaurus gracilis*
Upper Cretaceous, Niobrara Formation, Santonian, West Kansas, USA.[58]
Family Azhdarchidae
*Doratorhynchus validus*
Lower Cretaceous, Purbeck Limestone, Berriasian, Dorset, England.[9,10]
*Titanopteryx philadelphiae*
Upper Cretaceous, Maastrichtian, Rosaifa, Jordan.[27]
*Azhdarcho lancicollis*
Upper Cretaceous, Turonian-Coniacian, Uzbekistan, USSR.[25]
*Quetzalcoatlus northropi*
*Quetzalcoatlus* sp.
Upper Cretaceous, Javelina Formation, Maastrichtian, Big Bend National Park, West Texas, USA.[68]
?*Quetzalcoatlus* sp.
Upper Cretaceous, Judith River Formation, Campanian, Alberta, Canada.[71]
Indeterminated Azhdarchidae
Upper Cretaceous, Campanian-Maastrichtian, Paki, Senegal.[31]
Indeterminated Pterodactyloidea
*Araripesaurus castilhoi*[37]
*Araripedactylus dehmi*[38]
Lower Cretaceous, Santana Formation, Aptian, Araripe Plateau, Brazil.

other hand, there is much evidence of burrowing animals in the rock in which the fossil remains were found. The occurrence of large quantities of fossil tree trunks in the area suggests periodic flooding at the time. All this allows the possibility that *Quetzalcoatlus* used its slender, pointed beak to search in the ground for the molluscs and crabs that lived in the shallow pools of water.

These and many other questions will perhaps be answered when scientific investigation of the rich skeletal material of *Quetzalcoatlus*, still under study at the time of writing, is finally concluded.

Finds in the Judith River Formation (Campanian) in the Dinosaur Provincial Park in Alberta, Canada, make it probable that *Quetzalcoatlus* did not just live in Texas.[71] However, fragments of a femur and a neck vertebra do not permit definite classification in the same genus as the Texas finds.

The Texan pterosaurs from Big Bend National Park are especially significant for another reason. They were not only the largest, but also the last of these fascinating flying reptiles to live on Earth. The strata in which the finds were made have been dated as latest Upper Cretaceous (Maastrichtian). They are only a few metres below the boundary layer with the Tertiary, the time marker between the Mesozoic and the Cenozoic Eras. Above this boundary neither dinosaurs nor pterosaurs are found. Thus both groups of reptiles became extinct at the same time. The causes that led to this 65 million years ago were probably the same for both of them.

71 Currie, P.J. and Russell, D.A., 1982. *A giant pterosaur (Reptilia: Archosauria) from the Judith River (Oldman) Formation of Alberta.* Canadian Journal of Earth Sciences, 19 (4): 894-897.

72 Miller, H.W., 1972. *The Taxonomy of the Pteranodon Species from Kansas.* Transactions of the Kansas Academy of Science, 74, 1: 1-19.

73 Lydekker, R., 1904. *Vertebrate Palaeontology of Cambridgeshire.* in: J.E. Marr and A.E. Shipley, *Handbook to the Natural History of Cambridgeshire,* pp.51-79; Cambridge.

In The Lost World, Arthur Conan Doyle tells how Professor Challenger and his companions met living pterosaurs, survivors from the Jurassic, on a remote highland plateau in South America: '. . . and (it) flapped its twenty-foot span of leathery wings as it soared up into the air . . . It was a wonderful sight to see at least a hundred creatures of such enormous size and hideous appearance all swooping like swallows with swift, shearing wing-strokes above us.'

Pterosaurs have always stimulated the imagination of naturalists working on their fossil remains. For example, the Rev. William Buckland, Professor of Geology at the University of Oxford, saw the creature as 'a monster resembling nothing that has ever been seen or heard-of upon earth, excepting the dragons of romance or heraldry.'[1] And in a contribution to the 'Bridgewater Treatises on the Power Wisdom and Goodness of God as manifested in the Creation' he wrote in 1836: 'In external form, these animals somewhat resemble our modern Bats and Vampires . . . Their eyes were of enormous size, apparently enabling them to fly by night . . . It is also possible that the Pterodactyles had the power of swimming.'[2]

Buckland was not the first person to see pterosaurs as bat-like. Thomas von Soemmerring advanced this view in 1812 and defended it against Cuvier, and it seems that pterosaurs have retained this bat-like image right down to the present day.

The last living pterosaurs disappeared from the Earth 65 million years ago, long before man existed. All that is left are fossilized remains of their bones, although in a few cases we also have impressions of their skin and body-covering in the rock, casts of cavities in the skull like the brain case and finally – extremely rarely – fossilized remains of food in the stomach. How then can palaeontologists reconstruct the life style of pterosaurs, particularly as there are no directly comparable creatures in the modern animal kingdom? Bats and birds are very different from pterosaurs in the way their skeletons are constructed, especially in the structure of their flight equipment. Furthermore, the surface of the wing is made up of feathers in birds, and in bats of thin membranes which were probably very different from those of pterosaurs.

The fossilization process causes considerable loss of information. Fossil remains of an individual are inevitably fragmentary. An additional factor is that the pterosaur skeleton was lightly built, and as a rule the bones were thin-walled and fragile. This means that fossil survival was only possible under favourable conditions in soft sediments. Up to the time of writing more than 50 genera of pterosaur comprising almost 100 different species are known. They lived from the late Triassic to the end of the Cretaceous, that is to say for a period of about 155 million years. There have been birds on Earth for about as long. We may assume that pterosaurs achieved as great a variety of forms in the most varied environments as birds. However, this also means that our knowledge of pterosaurs may be limited to a mere one per cent of the pterosaur fauna that in fact once existed.

Almost all pterosaur fossil finds come from marine deposits near the coast. The potential for fossilization in terrestrial upland areas was much too slight for delicate, fragile pterosaur skeletons to survive. They were crushed and destroyed by weathering, erosion and the action of flowing river water. Thus we are faced with a situation comparable with knowing only the shore birds of the 9,000 species of bird alive today.

We must take this limitation into consideration when attempting to reconstruct the life style of the pterosaurs so far known to us. In detail this means answering the following questions on the basis of the fossil material:

1) Locomotion: how did pterosaurs fly and how did they move on the ground?
2) Nutrition: how did they feed and what did they eat?
3) Reproduction: how did they reproduce themselves? Did they lay eggs or produce living young?
4) Physiology: were they warm-blooded or cold-blooded? Was their physiology bird-like or reptilian?

The fossils themselves provide no direct answers to many of these questions. They can often only be answered by indirect, analogous inferences. Naturally there are also alternative interpretations, which have led to different, even contrary views of the life style of pterosaurs. But often a single fossil find in good condition is enough to knock a conventional theory on the head, or to defend a traditional view against a new hypothesis. Thus our present ideas on the life style of pterosaurs will also be called into question or refined by future fossil finds.

**Above:** Georges Cuvier, the great Parisian comparative anatomist, who, in the early years of the nineteenth century, engaged in a lively debate with Thomas von Soemmerring about the nature of pterosaurs and their likely behaviour. Like William Buckland, Soemmerring thought that pterosaurs were bat-like, to be classified as mammals somewhere between bats and birds. For his part, Cuvier stressed the reptilian nature of these remarkable flying creatures.

**Right:** William Buckland reconstructed the habits and behaviour of pterosaurs for the 'Bridgewater Treatises on the Power Wisdom and Goodness of God' of 1836, from which this illustration is reproduced. He regarded them as animals of bat-like appearance living on cliffs by the Jurassic Sea. Shown here is the genus *Dimorphodon* which Buckland first described in 1829. It was not known at that time that *Dimorphodon* actually had a long tail.

## Pterosaur Flight

Since the time of Georges Cuvier (1801) it has been known that pterosaurs were flying reptiles. Flying creatures need a propulsion system powerful enough for them to overcome Earth's gravity and at the same time drive themselves forwards. In tetrapod vertebrates evolution solved this problem by modifying the forelimbs to form wings. These wings are aerofoils that have to be moved by muscles to achieve active powered flight. In order to understand pterosaur flight we have to analyse first of all the structure of their wings, both the skeleton of the wing and its muscles, and also the aerofoil, the flight membrane.

The elements of the skeleton that are important for flight are powerfully developed in all pterosaurs. The shoulder girdle is fused into a hook-shaped bone made up of the scapula and the coracoid, the so-called scapulocoracoid. This, with its glenoid fossa, offers a strong abutment for the short, compact upper arm

1 Buckland, W., 1835. *On the discovery of a new species of pterodactyl in the Lias of Lyme Regis.* Geological Transactions, London, ser. 2, vol. 3: 217-222.

2 Buckland, W., 1836. *Geology and Mineralogy, Considered with reference to Natural Theology.* I, pp. 224-245, in volume 5 of the Bridgewater Treatises on the Power Wisdom and Goodness of God as manifested in the Creation, London.

bones of the wings. In the large Cretaceous pterosaurs this bone is still anchored over the scapula to the notarium, the fused dorsal vertebrae. Below, the shoulder girdle is articulated to the sternum via the coracoid, in a way similar to modern birds.

The sternum itself is a broad plate of bone which towards the front becomes a keel-shaped cristospine. As the most important flight muscles originated at the sternum, this braced structure of the shoulder girdle prevented compression of the rib cage during contraction of the flight muscles.

The shoulder joint is oriented laterally and in its normal position points slightly backwards. If the articular head of the upper arm bone is placed in the shoulder socket, it shows that in its optimum position and with maximum wing extension the humerus was directed 20° degrees above the horizontal. On the downstroke of the wing the humerus could be moved a maximum of 20° downwards from the horizontal plane, but at least 60° above it on the upstroke.

During the up- and downstroke of the wing the humerus could rotate around its longitudinal axis, thus altering the position of the wing. This is an essential prerequisite of powered flight, as it is the only way in which the flying body can move forward. Rotation of the wing in the nose-down sense was produced automatically by the muscles responsible for the downstroke of the wing, above all the pectoral muscles originating on the sternum and its protruding cristospine. They were inserted on the inside of the lateral delto-pectoral crest, thus causing a twisting movement forwards.

There are other muscle scars on the pterosaur humerus, marking the points at which the muscles for bending and stretching the lower arm and raising the upper arm on the upstroke were inserted. Thus the upstroke of the wing functioned on the same principle as that of a bird. In the latter it is brought about by two groups of muscles, one with its origin in the shoulder girdle that raises the humerus directly upwards (M. deltoidus), and a second, originating in the sternum, the coracoid and the wishbone (M. supracoracoideus). This supracoracoideus muscle is the second largest muscle in the front extremity of birds, after the great pectoral muscle (M. pectoralis).

Although this muscle lies below the humerus, it is responsible for raising it. This is done by means of a tendon that passes through a channel in the upper end of the coracoid and is anchored on the upper side of the humerus. Therefore a contraction of the supracoracoid muscles pulls the humerus upwards by means of this tendon, causing the wing upstroke.

In pterosaurs we find a similar channel on the coracoid as in birds, so that we can assume that in pterosaurs too the upstroke was brought about by the supracoracoid muscle and a tendon running over the coracoid as if over a pulley. Certainly pterosaurs did not have a wishbone like birds, which is created by the fusion of the clavicles. The pterosaurs' supracoracoid muscle thus originated principally at the sternum and probably partially at the coracoid as well, and was covered by the stronger pectoral muscle, which also originated at the sternum.[3] Deltoid muscles were certainly also responsible for the upstroke as well as the supracoracoid muscle; they originated at the shoulder blade and possibly at the notarium.

In comparison with the relatively short and compact humerus, the radius and ulna are longer and thinner. The ulna is always the thicker of the two bones, which are set close together and form a functional unit. No rotation was possible in the elbow joint, a hinge joint which could be opened up to 150° maximum extension. Flexion was only possible to an angle of 110°, to the front. These mechanical constraints are another reason for excluding the possibility that pterosaur wings could be as tightly folded and held close to the body, as is the case in birds.

3 Padian, K., 1983. *A functional analysis of flying and walking in pterosaurs.* Paleobiology, 9(3): 218-239.



**Flight Muscles (left)**
The main flight muscles of a Cretaceous pterosaur are seen here from the front. Two muscle groups operate the wing, the depressor (left) and the elevator (right) muscles. The principal depressor muscle (M. pectoralis) originated from the sternum and was attached to the humerus. The main elevator muscles (deltoideus and supracoracoideus) originated from the shoulder blade, and the sternum and coracoid.

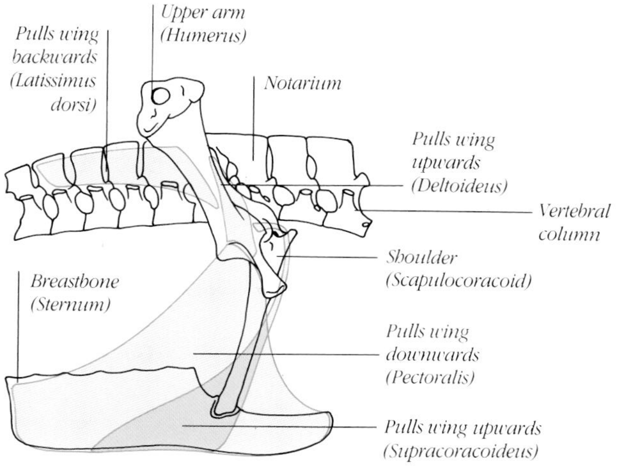

**Flight Muscles (left)**
The flight muscles are seen here from the side. The pectoralis muscle, the principal depressor, is the largest muscle of the flight apparatus. Underneath this the supracoracoideus pulled the humerus upwards by means of a tendon which ran around a pulley near the shoulder socket. The deltoideus muscle helped this movement. The latissimus dorsi muscle pulled the humerus, and so the wing, backwards.

## The Pterosaur Hand

The range of movement in the wrist encompassed sliding forwards and backwards, and rotation around the longitudinal axis. Thus the flight hand could be angled both backwards and downwards, although not very much, by about 30° in both directions. In advanced forms the wrist is composed of three carpal bones, a proximal carpal, articulated with the lower arm, a distal carpal, set between the proximal carpal and the metacarpus, and a lateral (actually medial) carpal articulated with the distal carpal at the front. All these carpal bones have very complex articular surfaces, to allow fine adjustment of the wing.

## The Pteroid Bone

A peculiarity of the wing skeleton of the pterosaur is a small bone articulated with the lateral carpal. This long, thin bone is always directed towards the body in undisturbed skeleton finds. This suggests that the pteroid was connected by a tendon to a muscle in the area of the shoulder, probably at the coracoid. Its function was apparently firstly to strengthen and tighten the leading edge of a small, triangular flight membrane between the base of the neck and the upper and lower arm, the so-called propatagium, and secondly to alter the position of the propatagium and achieve an aerodynamic effect in certain flight manoeuvres by means of various angles of attack.

The pteroid originates from the wrist but is regarded as an accessory bone, found only in pterosaurs. There are various hypotheses about its function, like that of E. Frey and J. Riess, who work on the assumption that in the flight position the pteroid was originally directed forwards and downwards. This leads them to a new reconstruction of the pterosaur wing.[4] According to this hypothesis the pteroid would have spread a large pre-wing membrane, extending between shoulder, upper and lower arm down to the small fingers and along the front side of the flight digit. The pteroid would have made this pre-wing adjustable, and assisted the camber. The leading edge may have been reinforced with a tendon, which could have extended along the whole of the leading edge of this pre-wing.

Another view of the function of the pteroid was put forward by C. Pennycuick.[5] According to him the pteroid could have been directed in turn both towards the body and also forwards and downwards. It would have been in the first, more streamlined position in the leading edge of the propatagium during rapid flight, and the second position, extended forwards and

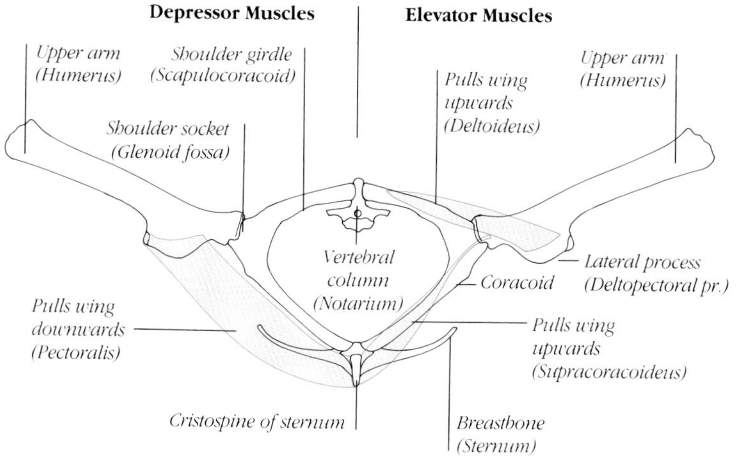

4 Frey, E. and Riess, J., 1981. *A new Reconstruction of the Pterosaur Wing.* Neues Jahrbuch für Geologie und Paläontologie, Abhandlungen, 161(1): 1-27; Stuttgart.

5 Pennycuick, C.J., 1988. *On the reconstruction of pterosaurs and their manner of flight, with notes on vortex wakes.* Biological Review, 63: 299-331.

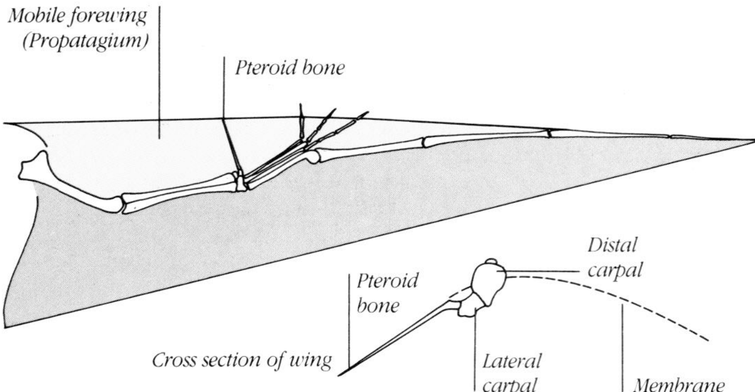

Wing reconstruction after Frey and Riess (1981)

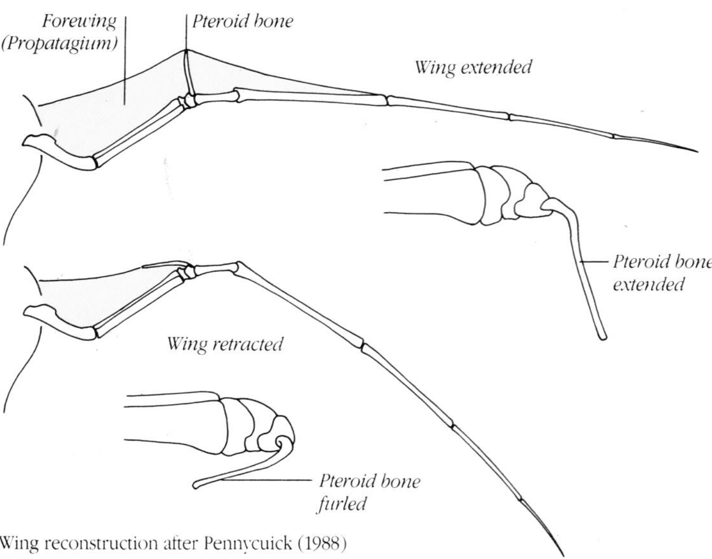

Wing reconstruction after Pennycuick (1988)

**Wing Reconstructions (left)**
Shown here are alternative wing reconstructions as proposed by E. Frey and J. Riess in 1981 (above) and C.J. Pennycuick in 1988 (below). Frey and Riess suppose that an enlarged forewing could be stretched by the pteroid bone which would have pointed forwards and downwards. The small digits of the hand would have been included in this forewing. Pennycuick's reconstruction assumes an automatic snap action of the pteroid bone whereby protraction of the wing finger deployed a drooped leading edge (upper drawing), while retraction would have furled the forewing. In this way, pterosaurs might have had the equivalent of variable geometry aircraft wings which could be modified in shape according to flight speed requirements.

**Below:** The first phalanx of the fourth finger, the wing finger, articulates in a pulley-like joint with the metacarpal bone (here partly covered). This was the main wing folding joint in pterosaurs.

ment of the flight digit, but not flexion. The distal joint of the flight digit metacarpal, however, is in the form of a pulley and made it possible for the flight digit to be folded a long way backwards. This is the principal folding joint in the pterosaur wing. To make this possible the proximal joint of the first wing phalanx is built asymmetrically. The slightly oblique arrangement of this joint made it possible for the first phalanx to slide in part laterally above the metacarpal when the flight digit was folded back to its maximum extent.

## The Digits

A strong process on the front side of the first wing phalanx joint served for attachment of a strong extensor tendon, running along the front side of the metacarpal via a bone channel to an extensor muscle on the lower arm (M. extensoris digiti). At the same time this extensor process on the digit joint prevented forward hyperextension of the flight digit. If the flight digit was at its maximum extension it was oriented at an angle of 165° to the metacarpus.

Between the four enormously elongated and reinforced phalanges of the flight digit are relatively shallow, oval, concave-convex articular facets at which little flexion was possible. The joint connections were relatively tight, and probably appropriate ligaments ensured a large degree of rigidity in the four-phalanged flight digit.

The first three small fingers could be moved freely and rose forwards out of the wing. They had scarcely any role to play in flight. Their sharp, bent claws had well-developed flexor processes to which strong flexor tendons were attached. Thus the digital claws were ideally suited for gripping and climbing steep surfaces like rocks, cliffs and tree trunks.

downwards, during slow flight, that is to say when landing and taking off. Pennycuick assumes that in this case a tendon was stretched from the shoulder area over the tip of the pteroid to the joint between the first and second wing phalanges. If the flight digit was swept back in rapid flight, then under this hypothesis the pteroid would have snapped automatically from a position in which it was directed forwards, to a furled position.

However, in pterosaur finds, particularly from the Solnhofen limestones, in which the imprints of the wing membranes are well preserved, there are never signs of a front wing extending over the propatagium and outwards as well over the pteroid down to the fingers. Besides, the pteriod is usually such a delicate, long and slender bone (up to 80 per cent of the length of the lower arm) that it could not have withstood the stress of a leading edge tendon of this kind.

The pterosaur metacarpus is an extended element of the wing skeleton, still relatively short in the long-tailed Rhamphorhynchoidea, but relatively long in the short-tailed Pterodactyloidea; in the extreme forms of the Upper Cretaceous it was even longer than the lower arm. The dominant bone is the fourth metacarpal, the flight digit metacarpal. The other three metacarpals supported the three small claw-bearing digits and are thinner, sometimes even reduced to splint-shaped rods of bone.

The powerful flight digit metacarpal had a shallow, convex articular facet with a pivot-shaped process that fitted into a corresponding socket in the distal carpal. This connection allowed limited rotation of the metacarpal around its longitudinal axis and thus adjust-

**Wing Extension (below)**
The extensor digiti was a special muscle for the extension of the wing finger. The pteroid bone was operated by the pteroid muscle at the coracoid. Its tendon formed the leading edge of the forewing. Over the pteroid muscle the angle of attack of the wing, and thus its camber, could be altered. The wing profiles show the camber at different cross sections.

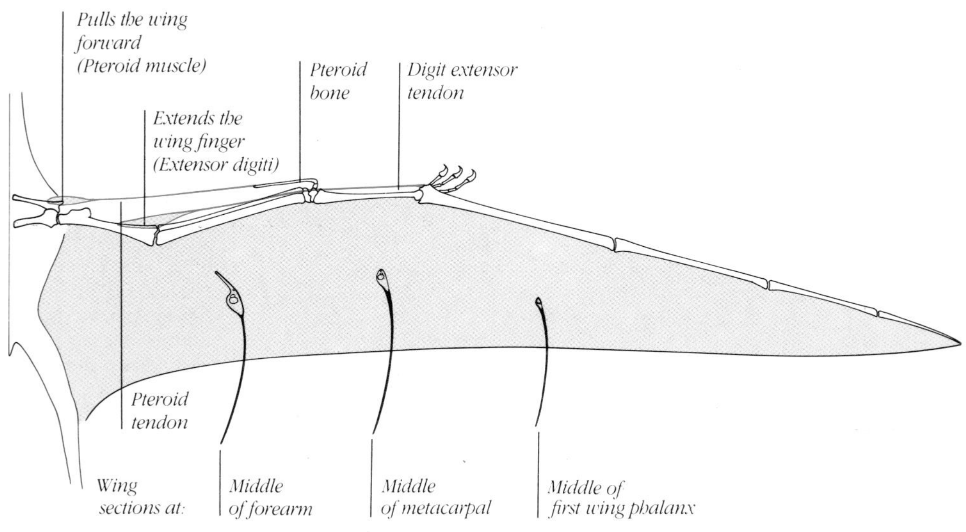

## Bone Structure

The bones of the pterosaur wing skeleton are hollow. Only in the area of the joints, at the ends of the long bones, is there an internal zone of spongy bone tissue, appropriate to the increased load on the articular facets. The wall thickness of the tubular bones of the wing is very slight, often only that of a postcard. In the wing phalanges the bone wall on the longitudinal edges is somewhat thicker, especially at the front, on the leading edge of the wing. This structure afforded optimal bending strength to these bones, which were under particular stress in flight. In the case of *Quetzalcoatlus*, the giant Texan pterosaur, the three outer wing phalanges were no longer hollow and thin-walled, but T-shaped in cross-section. They were constructed like T-bars and thus resisted the ever-increasing bending momentum on the outer sections of the wing.

Other bones in the pterosaur wing were not completely hollow either. In the large Cretaceous species in particular the bones of the upper and lower arm were reinforced internally by a system of thin bony struts. This can be seen particularly clearly in a specimen of *Santanadactylus* from a calcareous nodule in the Brazilian Santana Formation.[6] The humerus is 6·7in (17cm) long and has an average wall thickness of only 0·55mm. Numerous bony support struts run transversely through the shaft cavity, in part interconnected with each other. They run in the direction of the major mechanical forces that were exerted on the bones during the strokes of the wing.

This wing bone structure, similar to that of modern birds, resulted in maximum weight reduction combined with optimum rigidity and strength. This was the only way in which the long bones, particularly of large pterosaurs, could be so thin-walled. They were protected against breaks by internal supports. These were only as thick as was absolutely necessary, and were actually no more than materialized lines of force. An extremely lightly built skeleton was the secret of the great evolutionary success of the pterosaurs of the Mesozoic Era.

## Flight Membranes

In 1817, S.T. von Soemmerring published a reconstruction of a small *Pterodactylus* from the Solnhofen limestones, in which he drew the outline of the flight membranes. As he thought the pterodactyles were bats, it was only logical that he should give the Solnhofen *Pterodactylus* bat's wings. Flight membranes extended back to the feet, between the hind legs and the short tail, and in front of the arms to the neck. This was long before pterosaur flight membranes were discovered as detailed imprints on the surface of Solnhofen limestones.

The so-called 'Zittel-wing', a *Rhamphorhynchus* wing with an extremely well-preserved flight membrane, described by Munich professor Karl A. Zittel in 1882, was a famous specimen.[7] In the same year O.C. Marsh, who was friendly with Zittel, brought out a publication on a *Rhamphorhynchus* specimen that had survived complete, in which not only the flight membranes of the wings but also a membrane on the end of the long tail, the so-called tail vane, had been preserved.[8]

Pterosaur finds with wing membrane imprints are not as rare as is often thought. They are known from specimens from the Lower Jurassic of Holzmaden, the Upper Jurassic of Solnhofen in southern Germany, from the Upper Jurassic of Kazakhstan in the USSR, and from the Lower Cretaceous of Brazil, in the genera *Dorygnathus, Rhamphorhynchus* and *Sordes*, and in *Pterodactylus* and a genus from the Santana Formation in Brazil, as yet undetermined. The Solnhofen specimens in particular have made a great contribution to our knowledge of the extent and constitution of pterosaur flight membranes.[9]

Fossil finds show that pterosaur flight membranes were not bat-like in appearance. This is a consequence of the different construction of the hand. In bats the flight membrane is spread between the elongated second, third, fourth and fifth digits and the feet, but in the case of pterosaurs the flight membrane is spread by a single digit, the fourth, or flight digit. This flight digit is much thicker and longer than the wing digits of the bat. The extreme length of the flight digit alone means that the flight membrane must have been fairly narrow. Whether this was only attached to the sides of the body, so that the hind legs remained completely free,[10] or whether the flight membrane was also attached to the upper leg, or even to part of the lower leg,[9] or reached to the ankle and was spread by the fifth foot digit,[5] is a subject of scientific controversy.

The best-preserved flight membrane so far, in a Solnhofen *Pterodactlylus* in the Naturhistorisches Museum in Vienna, the 'Vienna specimen', suggests the following conclusions: the flight membrane of the wing, the brachiopatagium, was attached to the upper leg and ex-

6 Wellnhofer, P., 1985. *Neue Pterosaurier aus der Santana-Formation (Apt) der Chapada do Araripe, Brasilien*. Palaeontographica (A), 187, p.178; Stuttgart.

7 Zittel, K.A. von, 1882. *Über Flugsaurier aus dem lithographischen Schiefer Bayerns*. Palaeontographica, 29: 47-80; Stuttgart.

8 Marsh, O.C., 1882. *The wings of Pterodactyls*. American Journal of Science, 23: 251-256.

9 Wellnhofer, P., 1987. *Die Flughaut von Pterodactylus (Reptilia, Pterosauria) am Beispiel des Wiener Exemplares von Pterodactylus kochi (Wagner)*. Annalen des Naturhistorischen Museums Wien, 88, A: 149-162; Vienna.

10 Wellnhofer, P., 1975. *Die Rhamphorhynchoidea (Pterosauria) der Oberjura-Plattenkalke Süddeutschlands. III. Palökologie und Stammesgeschichte*. Palaeontographica (A), 149: 1-30; Stuttgart.

Padian, K., 1979. *The Wings of Pterosaurs: A New Look*. Discovery, 14(1): 20-29; New Haven.

**Right:** This humerus of *Santanadactylus* from Brazil has been split open to reveal the system of bony struts that strengthened the hollow, very thin-walled shaft of the bone. The outer wall of this bone is only 0·02in (0·5mm) thick. The internal struts can be regarded as materialized lines of force, and provided maximum lightness combined with optimum strength.

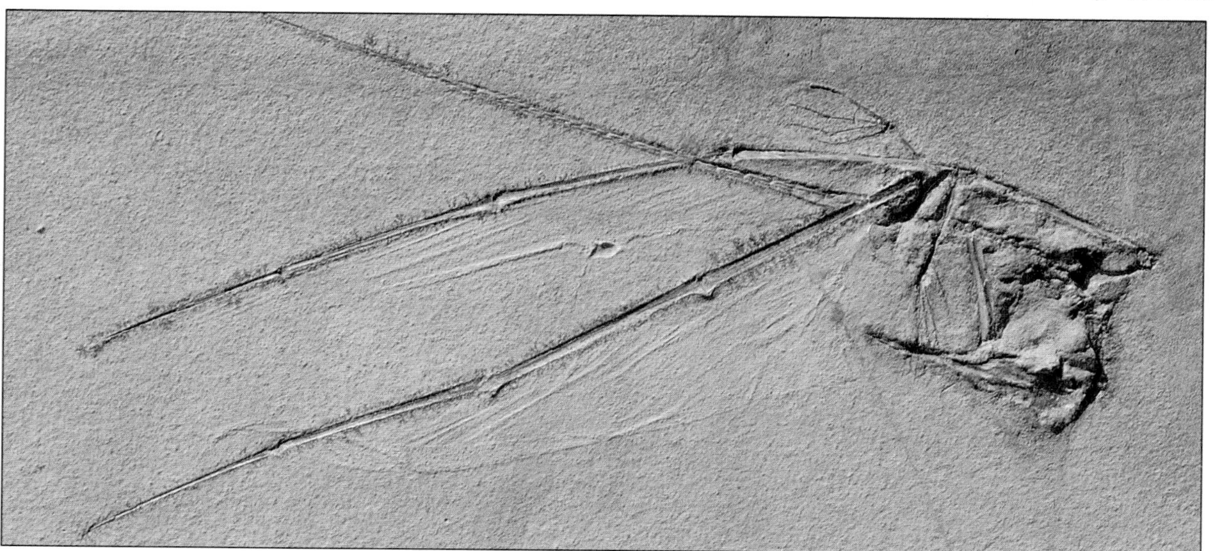

**Left:** This is a *Rhamphorhynchus* specimen from Solnhofen with the impressions of the wing membranes still attached to the wing fingers clearly visible. When this pterosaur died, its membrane must have been embedded in the Solnhofen sediment in a relaxed state. It is still possible to see folds parallel to the wing fingers. Finds such as this which preserve the imprints of the wing membrane are rather more common than might first be imagined. Several are known from Germany, while others come from the Soviet Union and Brazil.

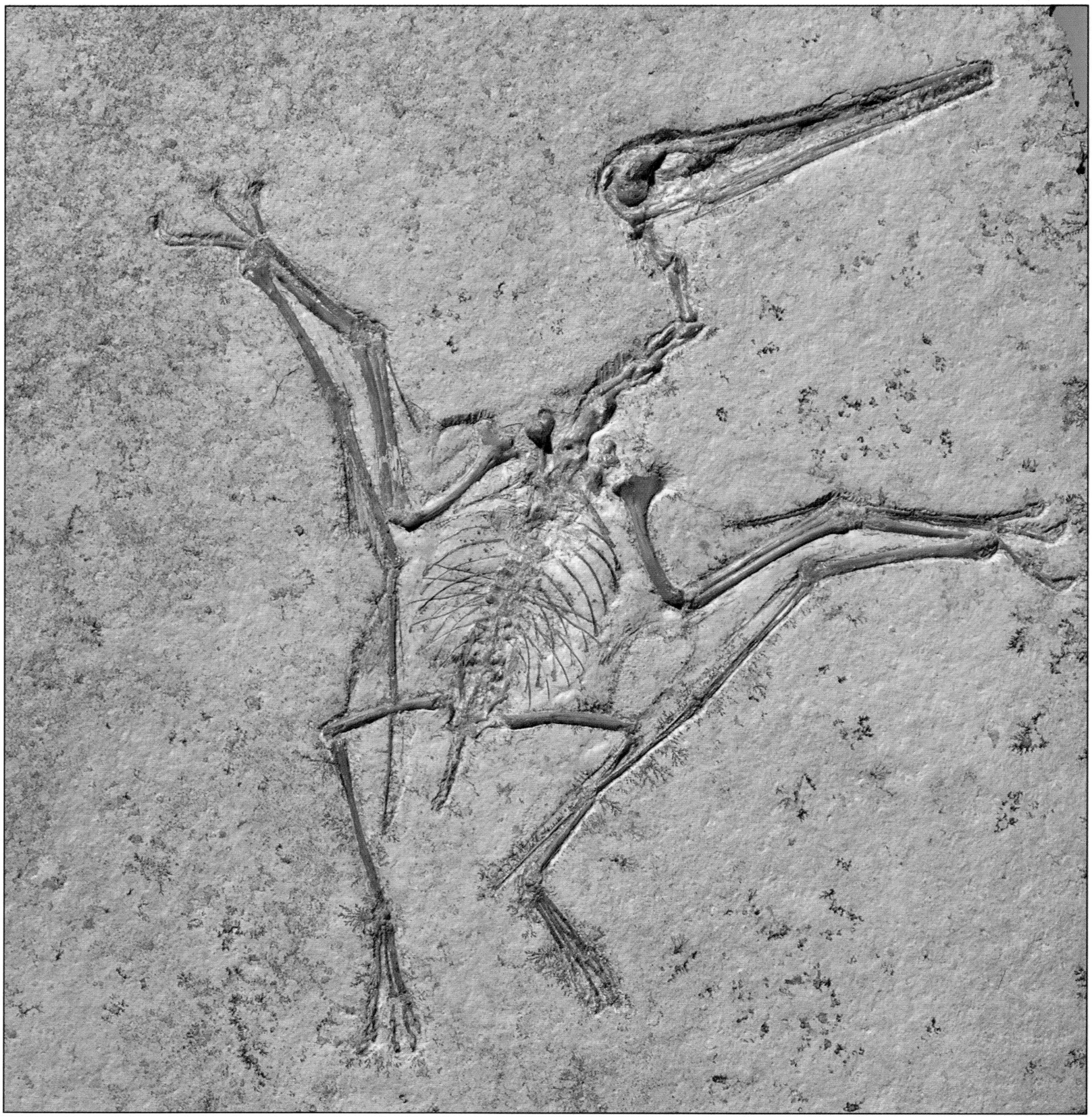

tended to the side of the upper part of the lower leg. Despite this the wing was very narrow and pointed. There is no indication of a broader membrane between the hind legs or between legs and tail, of a uropatagium in other words. A small front wing membrane, a propatagium, was spread on the inside of the arm between wrist and shoulder. This reconstruction corresponds fairly precisely with the version developed by the Viennese palaeobiologist Othenio Abel as early as 1919.[11]

The wing geometry of *Pterodactylus* was not necessarily valid for all Pterodactyloidea. Thus, as a result of new observations on *Pteranodon*, Chris Bennett came to the conclusion that the flight membrane of this large Cretaceous pterosaur was attached at the tail.[12] The last section

11 Abel, O., 1919. *Neue Rekonstruktion der Flugsauriergattungen Pterodactylus und Rhamphorhynchus.* Die Naturwissenschaften, 7, Heft 37: 661-665; Berlin.

12 Bennett, C., 1987. *New Evidence on the tail of Pterosaur Pteranodon (Archosauria: Pterosauria).* Short Papers of the Fourth Symposium on Mesozoic Terrestrial Ecosystems (ed. P.M. Currie and E.H. Koster): 18-23; Drumheller.

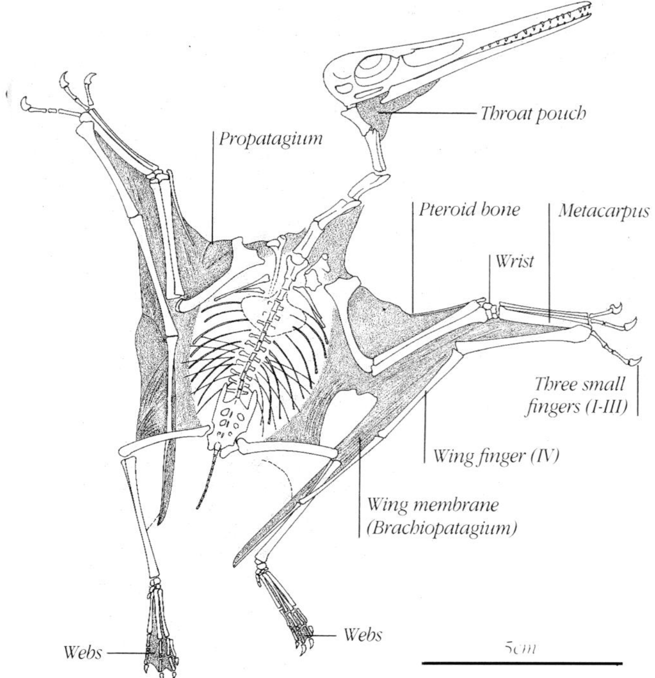


**Left:** The Vienna specimen of *Pterodactylus kochi* from the Solnhofen limestone of Bavaria has the impressions of the wing membranes superbly preserved. The animal, which has a wing span of 15in (38cm), was embedded lying on its stomach. The specimen is now housed in the Naturhistorisches Museum in Vienna.

**Pterodactylus Flight Membranes (right)**
This restoration of the flight membranes of *Pterodactylus*, based on the Vienna specimen illustrated at left, shows the extent of the main wing membrane, the brachiopatagium, and of the forewing, the propatagium, with the arrangement of the internal strengthening fibres, the aktinofibrils. There is no evidence of a uropatagium, a membrane between the hind legs and tail. The wing membrane did not reach the ankle, and generally was quite narrow in shape.

**Pteranodon's Tail (right)**
The tail of *Pteranodon* consisted of a series of short vertebrae with a double condyle articulation terminating in a pair of greatly elongated rod-like bones. Chris Bennett of the University of Kansas at Lawrence has suggested that these served for the attachment of the wing membrane, thus leaving the hind legs completely free of the wing.

**The Vienna Pterodactylus (left)**
This specimen of *Pterodactylus kochi* indicates that the wing membrane of this pterosaur genus extended to the upper leg rather than down to the ankle. The wings are preserved in a folded and relaxed position.

**Right:** A rhomboid vane was developed at the distal end of the long vertebral tail of rhamphorhynchoid pterosaurs. In life it was oriented vertically, and stretched by internal, transverse stiffening zones, the function of which was presumably to keep the tail membrane permanently spread. It probably served as a drag-rudder in flight in order to stabilize the position of the animal in the air.

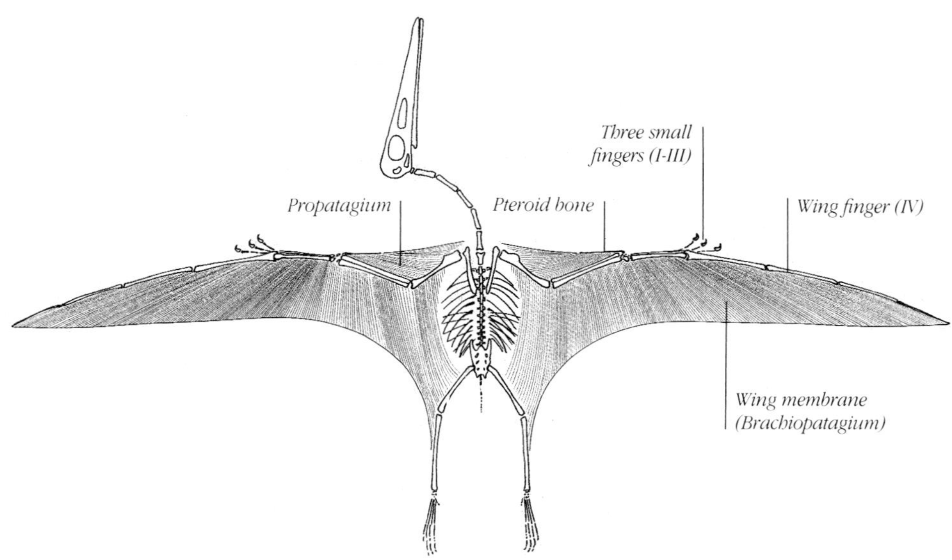


**Tail of Pteranodon from above and from the side**

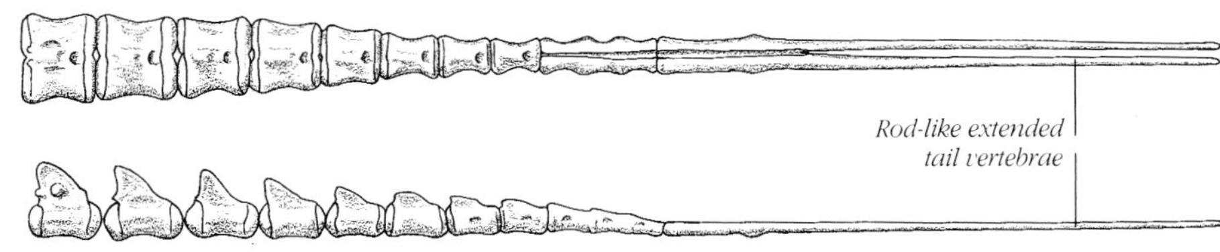


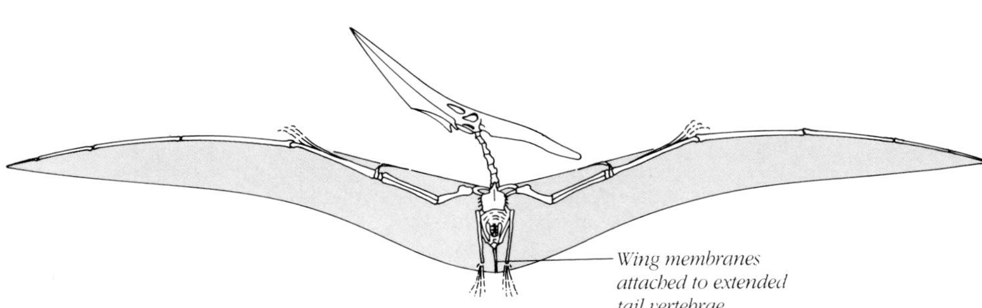


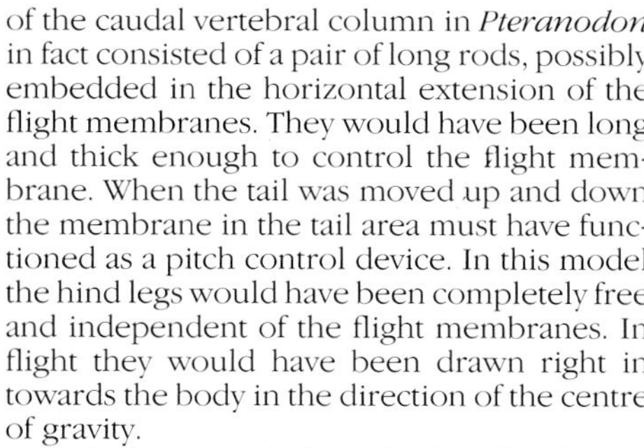

of the caudal vertebral column in *Pteranodon* in fact consisted of a pair of long rods, possibly embedded in the horizontal extension of the flight membranes. They would have been long and thick enough to control the flight membrane. When the tail was moved up and down the membrane in the tail area must have functioned as a pitch control device. In this model the hind legs would have been completely free and independent of the flight membranes. In flight they would have been drawn right in towards the body in the direction of the centre of gravity.

In the long-tailed Rhamphorhynchoidea the long vertebral tail had a small additional membrane at the end, the terminal tail membrane. In the case of *Rhamphorhynchus* it was rhomboid or triangular and somewhat asymmetrical. It was apparently a different shape in different species. A typical feature are bands running transversely, suggesting a system of reinforcement by means of which the tail membrane was kept permanently spread. In life and in flight the tail membrane must have been oriented vertically. It was very firmly anchored on the last 15 to 17 caudal vertebrae.

The tail of the Rhamphorhynchoidea was stiffened and not very elastic. The caudal vertebrae could only move in relation to each other in the front section. Vertebral processes on the sides indicate particularly great lateral mobility. The vertical terminal tail membrane could thus function like a rudder in flight, and possibly when swimming in the water as well.

## Internal Wing Structure

As early as 1882 Zittel observed fine parallel striations in the flight membrane of *Rhamphorhynchus*, which he took to be the result of a particular internal structure. What can be seen are the sharp imprints of very fine 'fibres', running through the flight membrane in tight sequence, in a longitudinal direction near the flight digit and increasingly obliquely towards the trailing edge of the flight membrane. The 'fibres' are 0·002in (0·05mm) thick, and a uniform 0·008in (0·2mm) apart. Thus within a millimetre width of skin there are four to five of these fibres, called 'aktinofibrils'. It is not known of what material they consist, but it may have been keratine, the horny material hairs, scales and claws are made of. Towards the edge of the flight membrane there are frequently additional aktinofibrils intercalated, so that when the wing was unfolded and the flight membrane spread these fibres were spread out like a fan, but an even arrangement was guaranteed overall.

Aktinofibrils have been observed in the

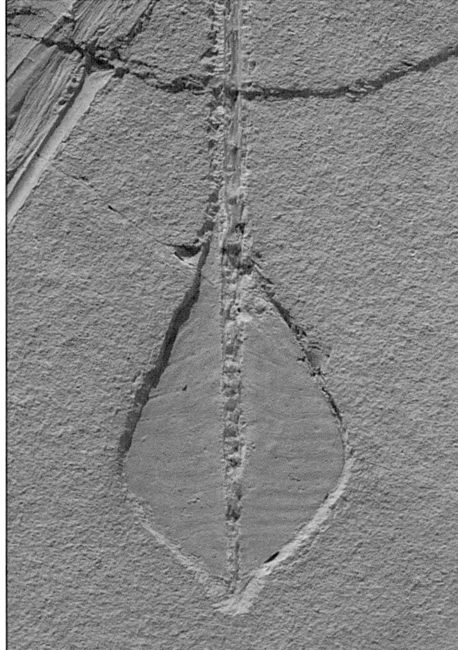

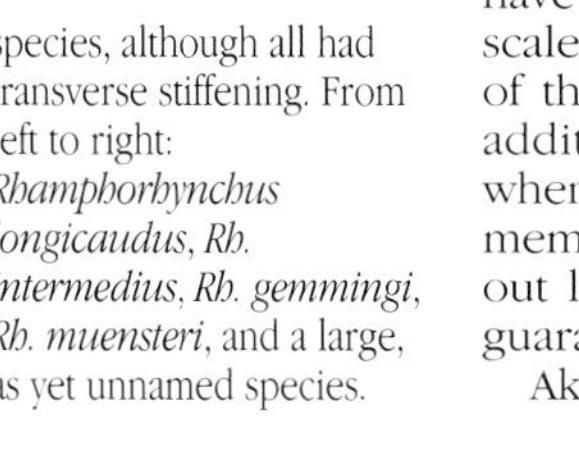

**Tail Membranes (below)** The tail membrane is preserved in several specimens of *Rhamphorhynchus* from the Solnhofen limestone. They show that its size and shape varied between different species, although all had transverse stiffening. From left to right: *Rhamphorhynchus longicaudus*, *Rh. intermedius*, *Rh. gemmingi*, *Rh. muensteri*, and a large, as yet unnamed species.

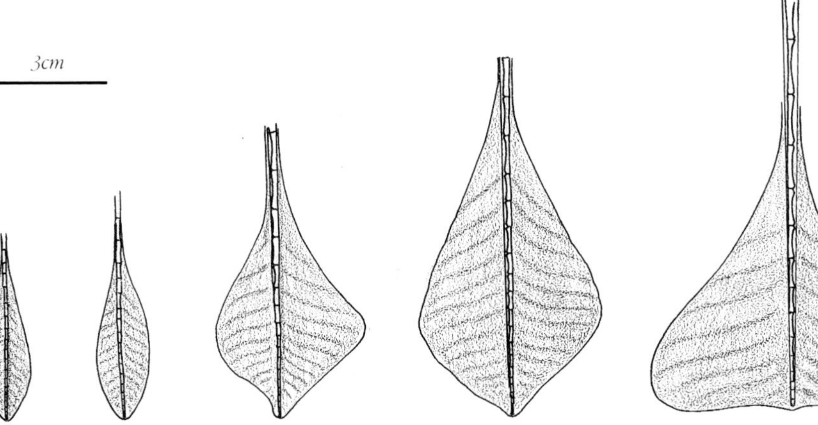

flight membrane of *Rhamphorhynchus* and *Pterodactylus*,[9] but also in Pterodactyloidea from the Santana Formation of Brazil.[13] In no case did folding take place at right angles to these supporting fibres. The flight membrane could only be folded parallel to the course of the aktinofibrils. This suggests an aerodynamic function for these structures. They were not just a system for reinforcing the flight membrane, but also prevented wobbling in flight, especially on the trailing edge of the wing, which the fibres met at right angles.

For this reason the pterosaur flight membrane was also called an 'aktinopatagium'. The internal fibres were covered with an upper and a lower layer of skin. It was a sandwich structure. The covering skin layers may have had fine muscles running through them to exert active tractive power to bend the aktinofibrils. This gave the cambering necessary to provide lift in flight.[14]

The stripes visible on the fossil flight membrane imprints have also been interpreted differently, as wrinkles in the relaxed flight membrane. According to this interpretation these wrinkles were formed by inner elastic fibres running diagonally.[5] But these fine structures are so sharply imprinted on the fossil itself that they could hardly have been produced by soft parts like skin. Surviving flight membrane in a Santana pterosaur does not show this ray system in relief, but in the form of dark coloured stripes. This would hardly be possible if we were dealing merely with wrinkles in the skin.

Finally a third model has been developed for the internal structure of the pterosaur wing membrane.[15] It is based on a small section of wing membrane near the lower arm of a pterodactyloid from the Lower Cretaceous of Brazil. Here the flight membrane in soft part preservation shows various layers of skin under the electron microscope: on the outside is a thin horny epidermis, below this a layer obviously with numerous capillary blood vessels, under this a layer with a network of organic

13 Campos, D.A., Ligabue, G. and Taquet, P., 1984. *Wing membrane and wing supporting fibres of a flying reptile from the Lower Cretaceous of the Chapada do Araripe (Aptian, Ceará State, Brazil).* Short Papers of the Third Symposium on Mesozoic Terrestrial Ecosystems: 37-39; Tübingen.

14 Schaller, D., 1985. *Wing Evolution.* The Beginnings of Birds. Proceedings of the International *Archaeopteryx* Conference Eichstätt 1984: 333-348; Eichstätt.

15 Martill, D.M. and Unwin, D.M. *Exceptionally well preserved pterosaur wing membrane from the Cretaceous of Brazil.* Nature, 340, No.6229: 138-140.

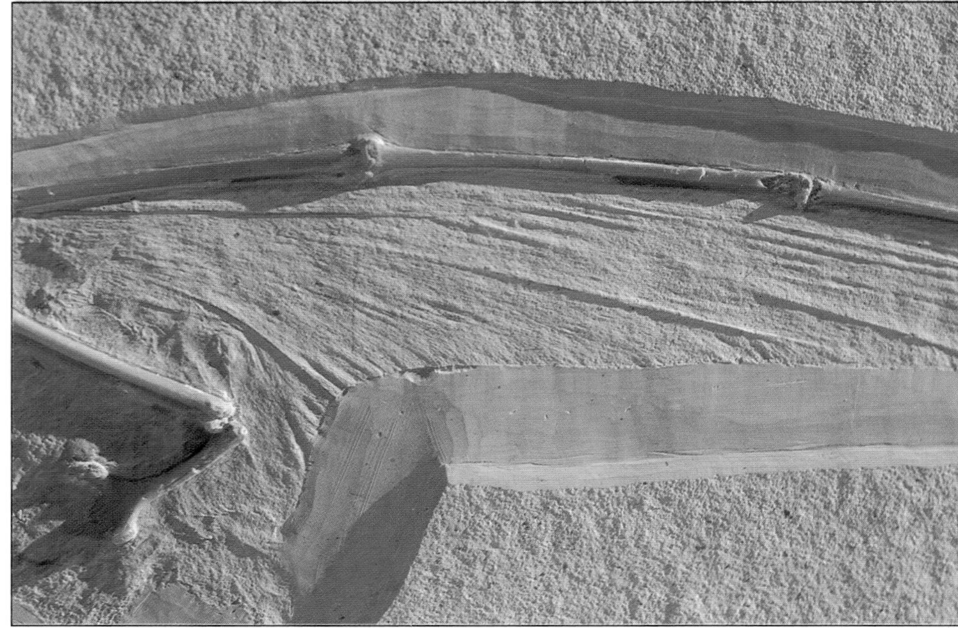

**Above:** The best preserved pterosaur wing membrane is still the *Rhamphorhynchus* wing described by K.A. Zittel in 1882, here seen in a section detail. It reveals particularly clearly the internal structure of the wing which shows up as sharp impressions on the surface of the limestone slab.

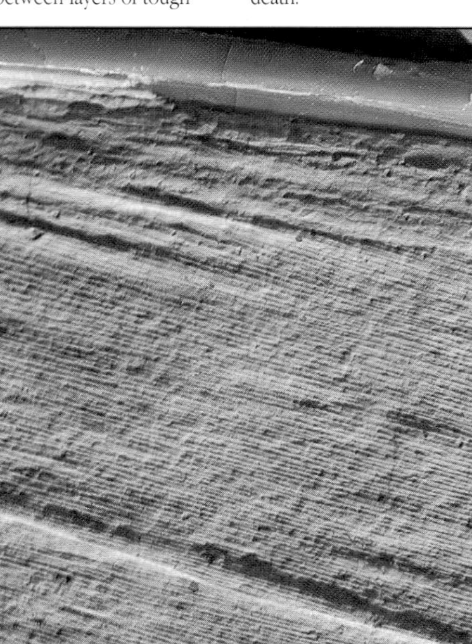

**Below:** A close-up view of the 'Zittel' wing reveals a system of fine, parallel fibres, called aktinofibrils, which were sandwiched between layers of tough skin. The fibres or rays can be clearly distinguished from the larger wrinkles which were caused by relaxation of the wing after death.

**Internal Strengthening (below)**
This is a model of the internal structure of the wing membrane in pterosaurs. The strengthening fibres, the aktinofibrils, were only 0·002in (0·05mm) thick. Folding of the wing membrane could only occur parallel to the course in which the aktinofibrils lay.

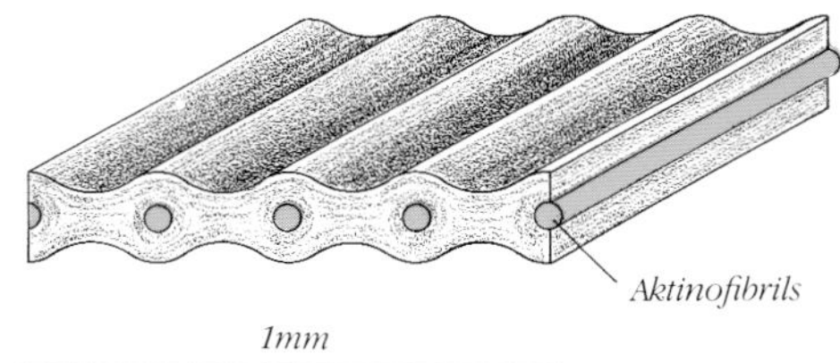

**Left:** A section of the wing membrane of a large pterodactyloid pterosaur from the early Cretaceous of Brazil shows the mannner in which the aktinofibrils were embedded in the membrane.

**Right:** A section of the trailing edge of the wing membrane of a Solnhofen *Rhamphorhynchus*. This shows that the aktinofibrils met the hind margin of the wing membrane at right angles to prevent it from flapping due to turbulence.

elastic fibres and finally the bottom layer with striated muscle fibres. The whole layer of skin must have been approximately 1mm thick.

Of course these observations only permit statements about a very small section of wing membrane, not from the actual aktinopatagium. Beyond this the flight membrane of pterosaurs seems to have been particularly well supplied with blood near the body, and it was assumed that here dilatation of the blood vessels developed a physiological mechanism to disperse excess metabolic heat.

Problems of the fine structure and histology of the pterosaur wing membrane have not been finally cleared up, but it is possible to establish that the skin structure of the membrane was stout, tough, relatively thick but elastic and fairly complex, of a kind that is not found in bats or other known modern animals.

## Pterosaurs' Ability to Fly

In the animal kingdom there are three different principles of aerial locomotion: gliding, soaring and powered flight. Gliding is a means of passive locomotion with the aid of enlarged body surfaces which transform vertical falling into a tranverse mode of transport, but always accompanied by loss of height. Examples are the flying lizard *Draco* or the flying squirrel *Petaurista*. But many birds glide between the active flapping phases.

Soaring is achieved by means of air currents, wind or rising columns of air in which height can be gained. Many modern birds use this flying technique.

Powered flight is always flapping flight, in which the energy comes from muscles that move the wings up and down, as in birds and bats. The wing surfaces have to fulfil the aerodynamic principles of an aerofoil, i.e. they have an upper side with convex camber and a flat or concave lower side. If an aerofoil with a wing profile of this kind is moved through the air, the airstream produces reduced pressure on the upper side and increased pressure on the lower side. According to this principle, discovered by physicist Daniel Bernoulli as many as 200 years ago, the aerofoil is subject to lift. The greater the camber on the aerofoil, the greater the lift.

It is assumed that pterosaurs were capable of powered flight because of the large areas for the origin and attachment of muscles on the breast bone and upper arm. Some, particularly the large Cretaceous pterosaurs, certainly also used soaring, although the areas for the origin of muscles on the breastbone are not as large as in modern flying birds.

To have functioned in accordance with the Bernoulli effect, pterosaurs' wings must have had cambered surfaces. Indeed they must have been in a position actively to control and alter this camber. Bats manipulate the camber of the flight membrane with the long digits of their hands. Pterosaurs, with only a single flight digit, had a system of aktinofibrils, fibre structures embedded in the flight membrane, that could be cambered by muscle power.

However, the greatest lift came from the section of the wing membrane nearest the body, in other words at places at which the front membrane, the propatagium, could alter its angle by means of the pteroid muscle at the front, and where the wing grew into the upper part of the hind leg, at the back. The outer section of the wing had, as in birds, a high speed profile with a more shallow camber,[16] at least in the more advanced pterosaurs with long wings. Thus the digital wing had a more shallow profile than the arm wing, and was the more important for active flight.

It is worth noting that aerononautical engineers were involved in early investigations of pterosaur flight mechanics. First E.H. Hankin and palaeontologist D.M.S. Watson published a paper entitled 'On the flight of pterodactyls' in the Aeronautical Journal in 1914,[17] and G.H. Short wrote in the same magazine on 'Wing adjustments of pterodactyls'.[18]

Hankin and Watson investigated in particular the mechanical structure of *Pteranodon*'s skeleton, especially possibilities of mobility in the individual joints of the wing skeleton. They believed that this large Cretaceous pterosaur was primarily a soarer, as they thought its flight muscles too weak to have been adequate for persistent flapping flight. This first biomechan-

16 Herzog, K., 1968. *Anatomie und Flugbiologie der Vögel.* 180 pp.; G. Fischer Verlag, Stuttgart.

17 Hankin, E.H. and Watson, D.M.S., 1914. *On the flight of Pterodactyls.* The Aeronautical Journal, 72: 1-12.
p.11: 'The weakness of the flapping muscles makes it highly probable that their habitual mode of flight was by soaring rather than by flapping . . . The implied suggestion that their flight was like that of an albatross agrees well with the little we are able to infer about their habits.'

18 Short, G.H., *Wing adjustments of pterodactyls.* The Aeronautical Journal, 72: 13-20.

**Below:** The flight of a soaring albatross with a wing span of about 10ft (3m) can best be compared to the flight of a large pterosaur like *Pteranodon*. Albatrosses are able to stay in the air for a long time, soaring very long distances over the sea without needing to land. *Pteranodon*'s wings would also have given it excellent soaring ability.

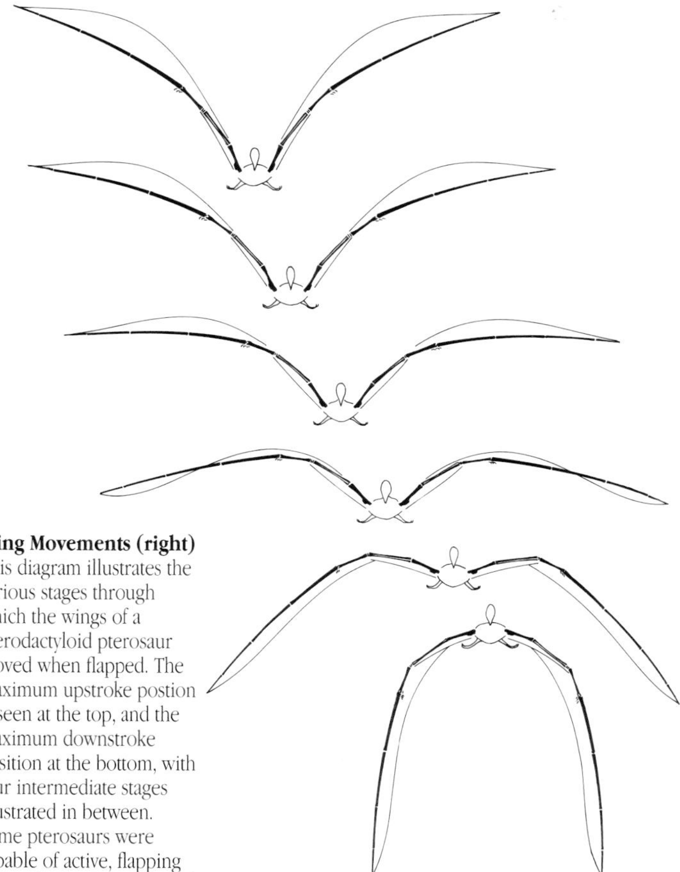

**Wing Movements (right)** This diagram illustrates the various stages through which the wings of a pterodactyloid pterosaur moved when flapped. The maximum upstroke postion is seen at the top, and the maximum downstroke position at the bottom, with four intermediate stages illustrated in between. Some pterosaurs were capable of active, flapping flight which was powered by their large flight muscles.

**Right:** *Pterodactylus* catching a fish in the Solnhofen lagoon as reconstructed by Othenio Abel in 1925. The wing membrane, the brachiopatagium, is drawn to the upper leg but not reaching as far down as the ankle, as is the case with bats. The accuracy of this restoration was confirmed a few years ago on the basis of the Vienna specimen of *Pterodactylus*.

ical study of pterosaur flight is considered a classic, and was for a long time the only one on the subject.

Othenio Abel, the Viennese palaeobiologist, thought *Pterodactylus* was a flapping flyer which flew in a similar way to bats. He saw *Rhamphorhynchus*' long tail with its terminal vane as a pitch control.[19] However, anatomical findings show that it cannot have been oriented horizontally, but vertically.[20] Thus it was a rudder, probably a drag rudder, used to stabilize the flight position. The short-tailed pterosaurs, the Pterodactyloidea, show that pterosaurs could fly without a tail vane.

Abel also assumed that *Rhamphorhynchus*' normal resting position was on the ground. Taking off would have been assisted by striking the tail against the ground. However, it is now thought that the tail muscles would not have been strong enough for this.

The first mathematical calculations of flight technique data were made by ornithologist D. von Kripp in 1943.[21] He designed a restoration of *Pteranodon* and compared it with the aerodynamics of tailless aircraft. With a wing span of 23ft (7m) its wing area was 37·7 sq ft (3·5m²). Its body weight was 66lb (30kg). This gives a wing loading of 1·75lb/sq ft (8·5kg/m²). The high aspect ratio, i.e. long, narrow wings, endowed *Pteranodon* with outstanding soaring qualities: it could soar skilfully, quickly and over long distances, indeed even better than the albatross. An updraft of only 2 to 3ft/sec (0·6 to 1m/sec) would have been enough for it to maintain level flight. Over the open sea updrafts of this strength could easily occur above the crests of the waves.

The sites where fossils were found in the Niobrara Chalk of Kansas were at least 100 miles (160 km) from the coast at the time *Pteranodon* lived, so it must have flown long distances. The animals discovered presumably flew out over the open sea and died there. Incidentally, Kripp thought it impossible that *Pteranodon* could land on the water, swim and take off again. He therefore believed that it must have caught mainly flying fish above the surface of the sea.

It was not until the seventies that *Pteranodon*'s flying abilities were investigated again. First, in 1971, W.B. Heptonstall produced computer calculations giving a weight of 50lb (22·7kg) for a wing span of 22·3ft (6·8m).[22] According to this estimate the pectoral muscles would not have been strong enough for the creature to take off from the ground. The muscles alone would have had to weigh 220lb (100kg). The weight of a bird increases with the square of the wing area, for which reason large birds like the albatross with a weight of 19lb (8·5kg) and a wing span of 11ft (3·4m) cannot sustain flapping flight but can only soar.

*Pteranodon*, or *Quetzalcoatlus*, which was almost twice as big, and other large pterosaurs could probably only take off with the assistance of a headwind or from an elevated site.

At about the same time Cherrie Bramwell and George Whitfield of the University of Reading turned their attention to *Pteranodon*'s flight mechanics.[23] They arrived at a body weight of only 36·6lb (16·6kg) with a wing span of 22·8ft (6·95m). They calculated a sinking speed of only 1·4ft/sec (0·42m/sec) with an optimum soaring flight speed of 26·25ft/sec (8m/sec) (18mph; 29km/h). According to this *Pteranodon* could fly extremely slowly and soar in thermals and rising air currents by cliffs. Its top speed was 46ft/sec (14m/sec) (31mph; 50km/h), its stalling speed was calculated at 22ft/sec (6·7m/sec) (15mph; 24km/h). This made a safe and gentle landing possible. A headwind of somewhat more than 22ft/sec (6·7m/sec) was sufficient for take-off: *Pteranodon* only needed to spread its wings to raise itself into the air.

Probably the wing area that forms the basis of these calculations, 46·07 sq ft (4·28m²) is somewhat too high. It assumes that the flight membrane extended to the feet, but more recent research suggests that this was not the case. It is possible that the wing membrane was only attached to the upper part of the hind legs, to just below the knee at most, or, as Chris Bennett suggested for *Pteranodon*, to the tail.[12]

Finally R.S. Stein even carried out wind tunnel tests for a biomechanical analysis of *Pteranodon*'s flight dynamics.[24] He concluded from this that *Pteranodon* was suitable for soaring and gliding flight, but primarily adapted to slow flapping flight. Stein calculated its weight at only 33lb (15kg), its stalling speed at 15ft/sec (4·5m/sec) (10mph; 16·2km/h) and its top speed at 49·2ft/sec (15m/sec) (33·55mph; 54km/h). Its muscular performance was 0·1hp. One stroke of the wings per second was enough to take off from the ground.

Stein also worked on the basis that the camber of the wings, and thus lift, could be controlled by flexion or extension of the flight digit. Stein also assumed that the wings extended as far as the feet, and relied on the reconstruction given by Eaton in 1910.

J.C. Brower, Professor of Geology at Syracuse University, New York, based his aerodynamic computer-supported calculations on a very narrow flight membrane, which left the legs completely free; this goes back to Kevin Padian's idea.[25] Despite the smaller wing area assumed by this hypothesis, Brower also came up with very low stalling speeds for *Pteranodon*. It was only capable of short periods of flapping flight, but was primarily a soarer. The smaller *Nyctosaurus* did have enough muscle power for continuous level flapping. However, its flight was probably alternating flapping and gliding flight, as in modern seagulls.

How can the giant Texas pterosaur *Quetzalcoatlus* with its wing span of 36 to 39ft (11 to 12m) and a weight of 165 to 190lb (75 to 86kg) have flown? Its muscle power can scarcely have been sufficient for continuous powered flight. It too was a highly specialized soarer.[26]

**Soaring Mastery (left)** *Pteranodon* had a wing span of about 23ft (7m). The long, narrow shape of these wings enabled *Pteranodon* to soar effortlessly in light winds. It may have used rising air in thermals on the upwind side of cliffs for lift, as we see in this restoration. Cherrie Bramwell and George Whitfield of the University of Reading made a study of the likely flight mechanics of *Pteranodon* and they concluded that it also could have soared over the sea in search of food. Because of its low sinking speed and its ability to stay airborne at low speeds, a temperature difference of just 1°C between the air and the water would have been sufficient for the formation of thermals in which *Pteranodon* could have soared. It may even have been able to alter the wing camber and so affect lift.

19 Abel, O., 1927. *Lebensbilder aus der Tierwelt der Vorzeit.* 2. Auflage, 714 pp.; G. Fischer Verlag, Jena.
20 Holst, E. von, 1957. *Der Saurierflug.* Paläontologische Zeitschrift, 31: 15-22; Stuttgart.
21 Kripp, D. von, 1943. *Ein Lebensbild von Pteranodon ingens auf flugtechnischer Grundlage.* Nova Acta Leopoldina, N.F. 12, Nr. 82: 217-246; Halle.
22 Heptonstall, W.B., 1971. *An analysis of the flight of the Cretaceous pterodactyl Pteranodon ingens (Marsh).* Scottish Journal of Geology, 7(1): 61-78.
23 Bramwell, C.D., 1970. *The first hot-blooded flappers.* Spektrum, 69: 12-14; Oxford.
Bramwell, C.D., 1970. *Those flappers again!* Spektrum, 72: 7; Oxford.
Bramwell, C.D. and Whitfield, G.R., 1970. *Flying Speed of the Largest Aerial Vertebrate.* Nature, 225, No. 5233: 660-661.
Bramwell, C.D. and Whitfield, G.R., 1974. *Biomechanics of Pteranodon.* Philosophical Transactions of the Royal Society of London, B, 267: 503-592.
24 Stein, R.S., 1975. *Dynamic analysis of Pteranodon ingens: a reptilian adaptation to flight.* Journal of Paleontology, 49(3): 534-548.
25 Brower, J.C., 1980. *Pterosaurs: How they flew.* Episodes, 1980 (4): 21-24.
Brower, J.C., 1982. *The Aerodynamics of an Ancient Flying Reptile.* Syracuse Scholar, 45-57; Syracuse, N.Y.
Brower, J.C., 1983. *The Aerodynamics of Pteranodon and Nyctosaurus, two Large Pterosaurs from the Upper Cretaceous of Kansas.* Journal of Vertebrate Palaeontology, 3(2): 84-124.
Brower, J.C. and Veinus, J., 1981. *Allometry in Pterosaurs.* University of Kansas Palaeontological Contributions, 105: 1-32; Lawrence.
See also:
Cox, B.C., 1980. *Trimming the pterosaur's wings.* Nature, 284: 400-402.
26 Langston, Jr., W., 1981. *Pterosaurs.* Scientific American, 244 (2): 122-136.

Overall pterosaur flying ability must have been very varied. The early Rhamphorhynchoidea still had relatively short, broad wings, the later ones already had narrow, long wings. Their long tail with a vertical terminal vane served as a rudder, probably as a drag rudder, to stabilize the animal in flight. They always had a relatively broad sternum with cristospina for the origin of powerful flight muscles. They were capable of continuous flapping flight. Later, advanced long-tailed pterosaurs, like *Rhamphorhynchus* of the Jurassic, had long, narrow wings, and thus good soaring ability, combined with low weight, calculated at 1·07lb (484g) for a *Rhamphorhynchus* with a wing span of 2·9ft (89cm).[27] A herring gull of similar span weighs more than double.

Pterosaurs' very low weight is due mainly to the fact that their bodies were relatively small in comparision with their wing span. Thus the trunk length of *Rhamphorhynchus* mentioned above is only about 4in (10cm) with a wing span of 2·9ft (89cm). Proportional differences are even more extreme in the large pterosaurs of the Cretaceous. An *Anhanguera* from the Lower Cretaceous had a trunk only 9·5in (24cm) long, but a wing span of 13·6ft (4·15m), a difference of more than seventeen times.

The small Pterodactyloidea of the Jurassic were short-tailed, powered flapping fliers. They were less stable in flight, but more able to manoeuvre, and more agile.

The large Cretaceous pterosaurs were all short-tailed. They were perfectly adapted to continuous gliding and soaring flight; they weighed very little, flew very slowly and thus used little energy. They were ideally built for gliding and soaring under mild and calm climatic conditions.

## Locomotion on the Ground

The problem of how pterosaurs were able to move on the ground is almost as old as the discovery of the first fossil remains of these flying reptiles.[28] Connected with this of course is also the question of how they took off from the ground, and how they could land on the ground.

Often the problem of pterosaur locomotion was polarized into two contrary views: bat-like versus bird-like, in other words quadruped versus biped. Hankin and Watson saw pterosaurs as completely helpless once they were on the ground: 'Perhaps the most feasible method of progression for them on land is that, having alighted on their feet, they fell over on their stomachs and pushed themselves along, after the manner of penguins, by means of the hind legs, perhaps with the occasional slight lift from the wings for surmounting an obstacle.'[17]

Othenio Abel, at the time the leading authority in the field of palaeobiology and the reconstruction of fossil vertebrates, explained: 'When a *Pterodactylus* moved on the ground, which can in any case only have happened very rarely, we will have to assume exactly the same position of the body for this means of locomotion as in a crawling bat, with the belly resting on the floor and only raised when the hind legs are pushed under the body and the rear part of the body thus lifted a little.'[29]

The opposing view was put by Carl Stieler, who thought the long-tailed Liassic pterosaur *Dorygnathus* capable of reaching the necessary speed for take-off by running with short steps (but with its legs wide apart) on its toes.[30] And Kevin Padian discussed the function of the pelvis and the hind legs of the Liassic pterosaurs *Dimorphodon* and *Campylognathoides*, and came to the conclusion that all pterosaurs were bipedal and did not crawl on all fours like bats, but could walk on two legs like birds.[3]

What characteristics of fossil pterosaur skeletons are significant for the one or the other hypothesis? To answer this we must first examine the structure of the pelvis and the hind legs.

Pterosaurs all have a very reptilian pelvis with an elongated ilium, and beneath this a broad plate of bone made up of the ischium and pubis fused, the so-called ischio-pubic plate. This is more like the construction of an archosaur pelvis as in *Euparkeria* than the pelvis of a bird. The primitive *Euparkeria* from the Triassic as a rule had sprawling or semi-erect stance and gait. The pelvic muscles were used both to draw the hind legs up to the body and to swing the lower leg backwards or forwards.

In birds the pelvis is markedly elongated, and ischia and pubes are not fused at the bottom, but wide open. The pelvic muscles work in such a way that the bird is suspended over its hind legs as in a seesaw, and the legs swing forwards and backwards. Thus the femur has to be articulated in the hip socket in such a way that it can be moved in this vertical plane parallel with the longitudinal axis of the body. In birds this is possible because the articular head of the femur is set almost at a right angle inwards from the bone shaft, and the sideways oriented hip socket is covered by a bony protuberance. Thus the weight taken by the hind legs is absorbed at the top.

27 Wellnhofer, P., 1982. *Zur Biologie der Flugsaurier.* Natur und Museum, 112 (9): 278-291; Frankfurt.

28 Seeley, H.G., 1870. *The Ornithosauria: An Elementary Study of the Bones of Pterodactyles.* 130 pp.; Deighton, Bell and Co., Cambridge. In this study Seeley gave a short review of the various points of view in the controversy. He noted that Soemmerring (1812) regarded *Pterodactlyus* from the Solnhofen limestone as an unknown kind of bat with comparable locomotion on the ground, and also quoted Goldfuss (1831) who argued for quadrupedal, bat-like locomotion, as follows: 'This animal was enabled by means of the pelvic bones and the long hind-legs to sit like the squirrels. We should regard this position as natural but for the long wing-finger hanging far down the sides. If it were to creep along it would have the same difficulties as a bat, and the length and weight of the head, as well as the proportional weakness of the hind limb, make it improbable that they progressed by leaping. These animals made use of their claws only to hang on to rocks and trees and to climb up steep cliffs . . .'
An early exponent of the opposing theory of bipedal, bird-like walking, a view strongly supported by Seeley himself, was Quenstedt (1855), who thought 'that the animal was able to walk upright, being probably still more upright than birds, since the great disproportion between the neck on the one hand, and the thigh on the other, could not have allowed a more appropriate position.'

29 Abel, O., 1925. *Geschichte und Methode der Rekonstruktion vorzeitlicher Wirbeltiere.* 327 pp.; G. Fischer, Jena.

30 Stieler, C., 1922. *Neuer Rekonstruktionsversuch eines liassischen Flugsauriers.* Naturwissenschaftliche Wochenschrift, N.F. 21, Nr. 20: 273-280; Jena.

**Rhamphorhynchus the Quadruped (left)**
Here we see *Rhamphorhynchus* as reconstructed in a quadrupedal stance and gait, after the idea of Manfred Reichel. The ungainly pose suggests somewhat clumsy terrestrial movements.

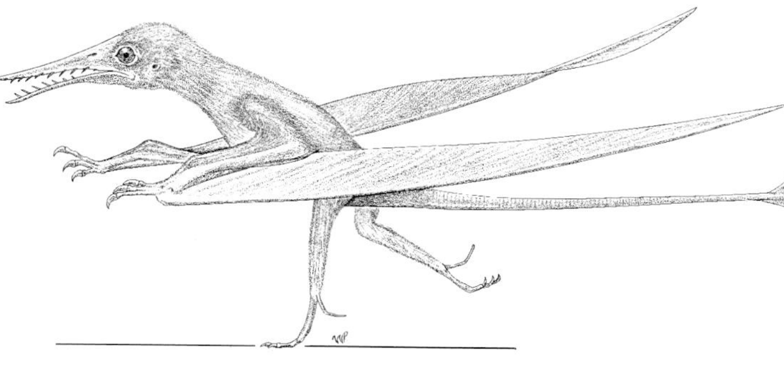

**Rhamphorhynchus the Biped (left)**
Here, by contrast, is *Rhamphorhynchus* reconstructed as a biped. The hind legs are positioned under the body in bird-like manner enabling the pterosaur to run on two legs. The wings, however, could not have been folded as closely to the body as in birds.

**Right:** As this picture of a roadrunner (*Geococcyx californianus*) clearly shows, birds are digitigrade; that is, they walk on their middle toes rather than on the soles of their feet. This makes them capable of quite rapid motion on two legs. The situation with pterosaurs is different. The structure of their hip joints and feet is not well adapted to motion on two legs. It is more likely that they moved on four legs on the ground.

Furthermore birds walk on their three middle toes, thus they are digitigrade, rather then plantigrade, which means walking on the soles of the feet. Thus many birds are capable of running rapidly and effectively, for example when escaping from danger or to achieve the speed necessary for take-off.

If we consider the construction of pelvis and hind legs in pterosaurs, we find that things are quite different. The hip sockets in the pelvis are not only oriented sideways, but also somewhat upward and backwards. There is no rim above the hip socket to support the femur. The articular head of the femur is never at right angles, as in birds, but in the best case bent at 120° to the bone shaft, usually at 130° to 160°. If the femur of a pterosaur is placed in the hip socket of the pelvis, the bone is splayed out and cannot be moved into a vertical position.[31]

However, the pterosaur femur was relatively mobile, and could rotate backwards into the horizontal plane, i.e. into the plane of the wings. This is the position that was adopted in flight, in order to spread the flight membrane, to give it camber and by alternate raising and lowering to steer the animal around its roll axis. The front edge of the hip socket is thickened to support the articular head. But the femur could also rotate to the side and the front for quadrupedal locomotion on the ground or for landing and climbing on trees and cliffs.

The knee joint also seems to have been relatively flexible and allowed the lower leg to turn inwards and the foot to move forwards and backwards parallel to the middle vertical plane when striding. The whole foot met the ground, thus the gait was plantigrade. The digits were of unequal length, the last penultimate phalanx being long, and they had sharp, pointed claws; they are very different from the three-toed foot of bipedal dinosaurs and birds.[32] These creatures also walk only on their toes, and are thus digitigrade. The middle digit is always the longest in such cases, and the first digit is reversed, i.e. directed backwards. The structure of the skeleton of the foot is thus fundamentally different in birds and pterosaurs.

Pterosaurs' long foot digits always have sharp claws with needle-fine points. They seem to have been better suited to gripping and climbing than walking on the ground.

A more recent reconstruction of the pelvis and hind legs of a pterodactyloid from the Brazilian Santana Formation suggests that the animal was biped, with an upright body, standing almost like a penguin.[33] This assumption refers only to short-tailed pterosaurs, but does run into great difficulties as far as the position of the wings is concerned.

Pterosaurs could not draw their wings close to the body and fold them, as birds can. The

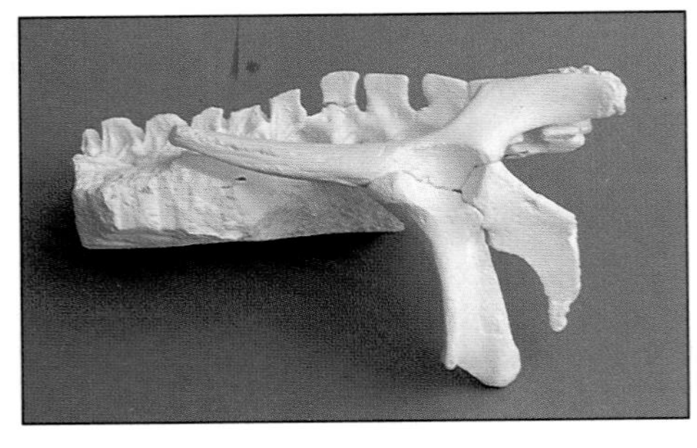

**Above:** The pelvis of *Anhanguera* was able to be reconstructed three-dimensionally in plaster. The hip socket points sideways and upwards, a position that would have made vertical orientation of the upper leg impossible.

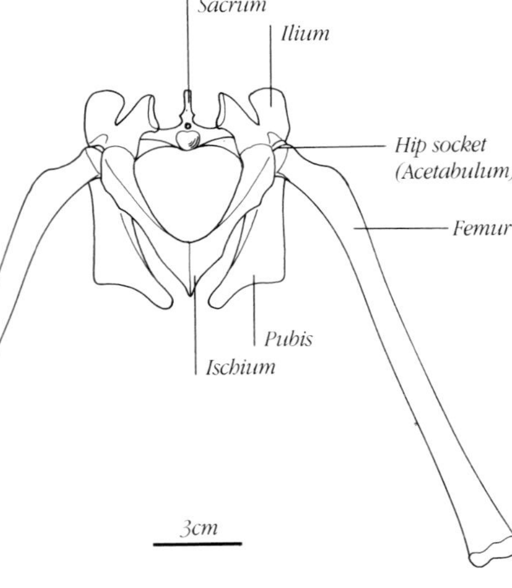


**The Pelvis of Anhanguera (above)**
The reconstructed pelvis of *Anhanguera* is seen here from behind with the upper leg bones articulating in the hip sockets. This is the maximum extent to which the upper legs can be moved into the vertical plane. Evidently *Anhanguera*'s legs would have been splayed out sideways if it had tried to stand bipedally.

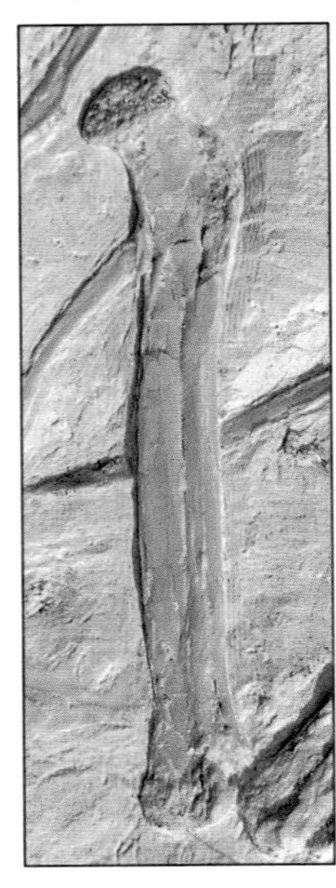

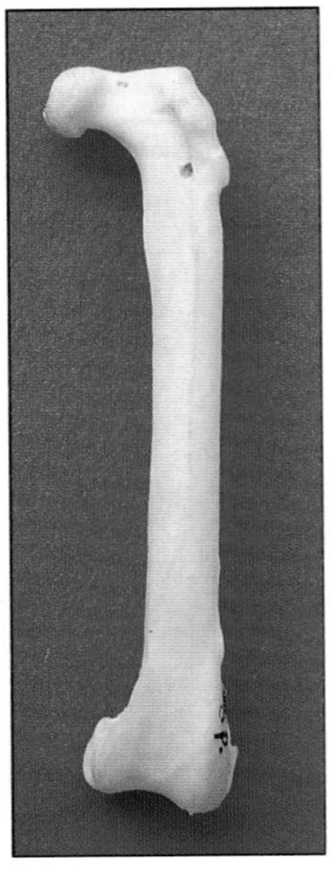

**Above and above right:** These photographs allow us to compare the femur of a pterosaur (*Rhamphorhynchus*, above) with that of a contemporary bird, a toucan (above right). Careful comparison reveals the different orientation of the femur head which articulates in the hip socket. In the case of the pterosaur the head is set at only a slight angle to the shaft, whereas in the bird it is set at a right angle. This makes it possible for the bird's legs to be swung vertically beneath its body, enabling it to walk and run bipedally.

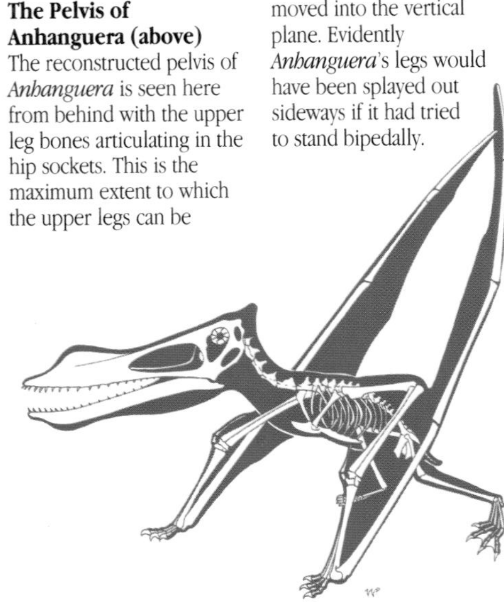

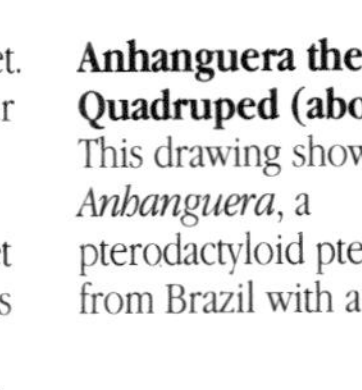

**Anhanguera the Quadruped (above)**
This drawing shows *Anhanguera*, a pterodactyloid pterosaur from Brazil with a wing span of about 13ft (4m), restored in a quadrupedal stance. The belly is lifted off the ground and the hind legs are splayed out to the sides.

**Anhanguera the Biped (right)**
This is *Anhanguera* from the early Cretaceous of Brazil restored according to the ideas of Chris Bennett. By adopting a rather steep position of the body, the pterosaur might have been able to walk bipedally in an upright posture. However, the fact that its wings could not have been folded as closely to its body as those of birds today, and the difficulty of balancing its large head in this position casts doubt on the likelihood of this kind of two-legged locomotion on the ground.

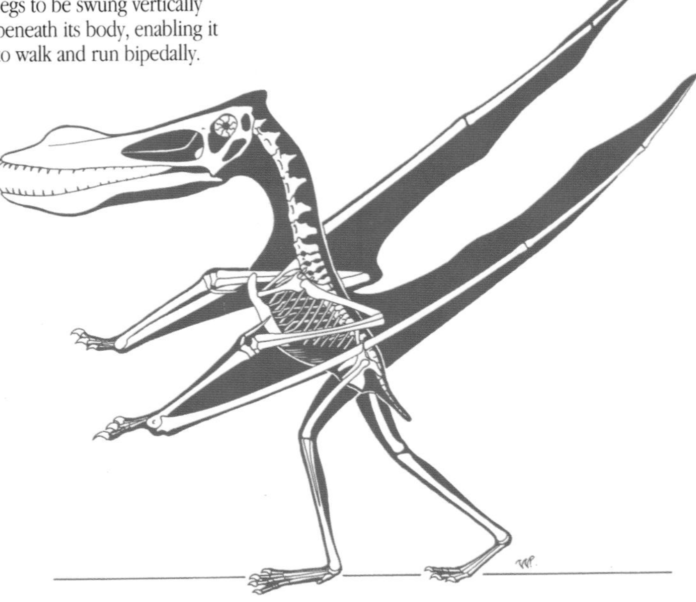

31 Wellnhofer, P. and Vahldiek, B.-W., 1986. *Ein Flugsaurier-Rest aus dem Posidonienschiefer (Unter-Toarcian) von Schandelah bei Braunschweig.* Paläontologische Zeitschrift, 60: 329-340; Stuttgart.
Wellnhofer, P., 1988. *Terrestrial Locomotion in Pterosaurs.* Historical Biology, 1: 3-16.

32 Unwin, D.M., 1987. *Pterosaur Locomotion. Joggers or Waddlers.* Nature, 327: 13-14.
Unwin, D.M., 1988. *New remains of the pterosaur Dimorphodon (Pterosauria: Rhamphorhynchoidea) and the terrestrial ability of early pterosaurs.* Modern Geology, 13: 57-68.

33 Bennett, S.C., 1990. *A Pterodactyloid Pterosaur from the Santana Formation of Brazil: Implications for Terrestrial Locomotion.* Journal of Vertebrate Paleontology, 10(1): 80-85.

only point at which the wing could be folded back was at the pulley joint between metacarpal and flight digit. Even if the humerus was pulled as far back and the elbow and hand joint flexed as far as possible, bipedal pterosaurs must to an extent have had to walk with arms outspread.

It is obvious that this required both an open space as habitat and also that the creatures must have had considerable balancing problems on the ground. A small gust of wind would have been enough to blow them over.

For all these reasons we must assume that pterosaurs, if they ever landed on level ground, must have moved using four feet, in other words in a quadrupedal fashion. Of course the forelimbs were not well adapted for this, on the one hand because the humerus could not be moved into a vertical position, and on the other because the hand with its three small, clawed fingers was better adapted to climbing than to walking. But the humerus could rotate forward around its longitudinal axis, thus bringing the lower arm and above all the metacarpus into a vertical position. Perhaps pterosaurs did not support themselves on their small fingers, but on the knuckles, with the flight digit folded back.

Thus we have a picture of a quadrupedal pterosaur bracing its body upwards when walking, pushing the body forwards with laterally directed hindlimbs and moving forwards slowly, somewhat clumsily, with its broad and bulky forelimbs. This was certainly the exception and not the rule, but was needed for finding hiding places, when breeding, when building a nest and when looking after young.

Thus pterosaurs were not bat-like on the ground, but pterosaur-like. Between the early rhamphorhynchoids with their relatively long hind legs, and the later forms with hind legs that had developed rather less strongly, there were differences in proportion suggesting that locomotion on the ground was quadrupedal in all cases, but better executed in some than in others. Pterosaurs' hind legs were primarily an aid to flight, because the upper leg at least was integrated into the flight membrane, and fulfilled an important aerodynamic function.

Pterosaurs were adapted to flight to an extreme extent. They spent their active life in the air and were presumably pretty helpless if they had to land on flat ground. Probably they simply avoided landing on a flat surface. Of course this did not condemn them to a 'Flying Dutchman existence'. They must have rested and bred on cliffs and rocks, where they could hang with their sharp, hook-shaped claws on hands and feet. To take off they only needed to swing themselves into the air. They did not need to achieve the necessary take-off speed by taking a run on two legs.

Pterosaurs could probably take off from the ground by standing on their hind legs and facing into the wind with outspread wings. A simultaneous jump and stroke of the wings raised them into the air. This was more easily possible for early pterosaurs like *Dimorphodon* and *Pterodactylus*, as they were smaller and lighter and had relatively long hind legs.

As a rule however, they too, like the great pterosaurs of the Cretaceous, probably took off when hanging from a raised point by their strong digital claws. It is not certain whether they could also hang head down on branches and rocky protrusions, like bats. The long-tailed Rhamphorhynchoidea would have found their long, stiff tails a great hindrance in doing this. Possibly the small pterosaurs of the Jurassic, as reconstructed very convincingly by Othenio Abel, could have rested in this position.[11]

Direct proof of the nature of pterosaurs' terrestrial locomotion would be provided by their tracks preserved in fossil form. Palaeoichnology is the branch of science concerned with the study of such track impressions, which are known in the cases of many reptiles, including dinosaurs. Fossil trackways provide much information about the maker of the footprints, e.g. whether it walked on two or four legs.

**On All-Fours (below)**
This is a skeletal reconstruction of *Anhanguera* in a quadrupedal stance. This pterosaur had a wing span of 13ft (4m), and the drawing shows the marked disproportion between fore and hind legs. Such an animal would have moved clumsily on all-fours, but locomotion on the ground would have been possible.

**Below:** On the ground a bat is almost helpless, and can only creep along on all-fours pushing its body forward on its stomach. Pterosaurs could certainly move more confidently on the ground than bats. They could lift their bodies off the ground, at least, and walk in a semi-erect manner on four legs.

**Above:** That *Pterodactylus* did not move like a bat on the ground is shown by this life restoration suggested by the ideas of Manfred Reichel. Walking on the ground must have been possible on all-fours, although the forelimbs, especially the hands, were designed for climbing rather than walking.

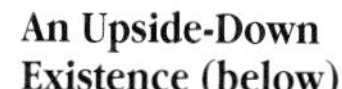


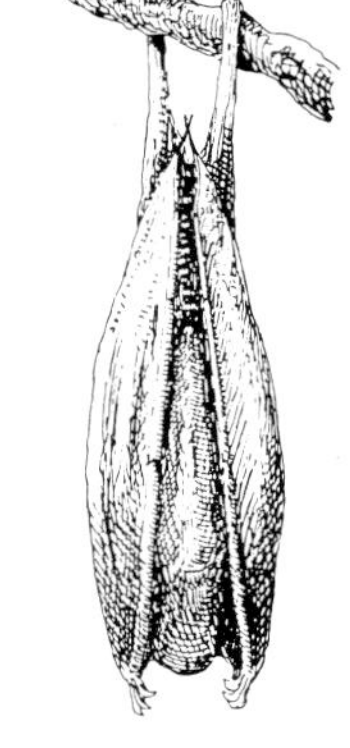

**Just Hanging Around (left)**
Othenio Abel also published this life restoration showing a sleeping *Pterodactylus* enveloped in its wing membranes and hanging upside down from a branch by its feet in a bat-like manner. This seems a convincing posture for a short-tailed pterosaur like *Pterodactylus*. A long-tailed rhamphorhynchoid would have had greater problems, however.

**An Upside-Down Existence (below)**
The manner in which the flying fox (*Pteropus celaeno*, a species of fruit bat) can climb upside down (below right) led the Viennese palaeobiologist Othenio Abel to the suggestion that *Pterodactylus* (below) could have climbed in the same way. It is shown in this drawing from 1925 hanging upside down from the branches of a tree, holding on securely with the claws of its feet and hands.

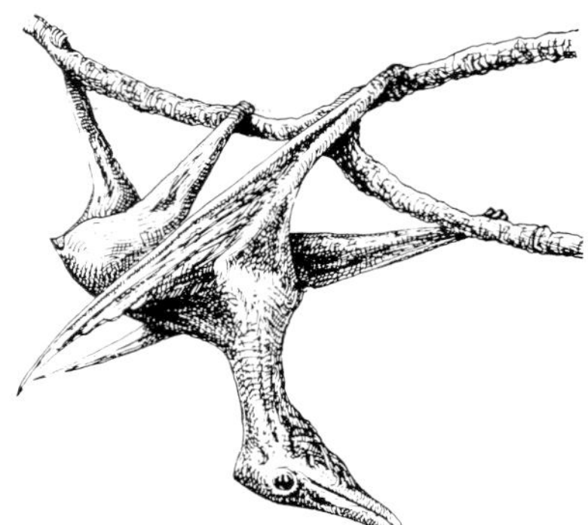

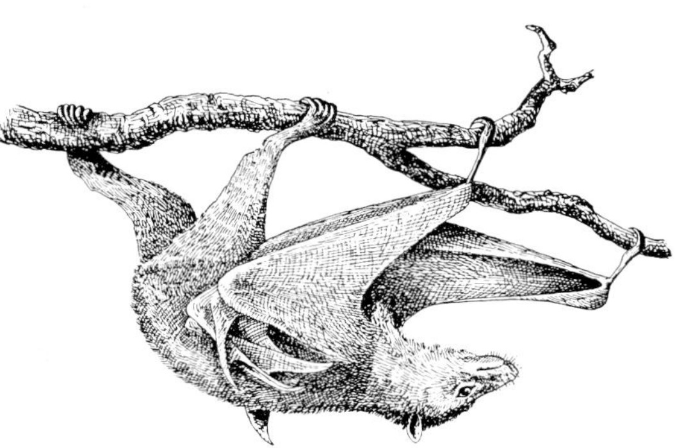

**Left:** *Pterodactylus* about to take off from its resting position. This painting by Neave Parker assumed that this pterosaur could hang upside down; to take off, it only needed to drop from the branch, develop forward speed and become airborne.

**Rhamphorhynchus on All-Fours (left)**
One of the earliest restorations of *Rhamphorhynchus* walking on all-fours was this one by Riou that was reproduced in L. Figuier's *La Terre avant le Déluge*, a book published in Paris in 1863. This interpretation was inspired by fossil trackways found in the Solnhofen limestone in Bavaria which seemed to show foot and tail prints of pterosaurs.

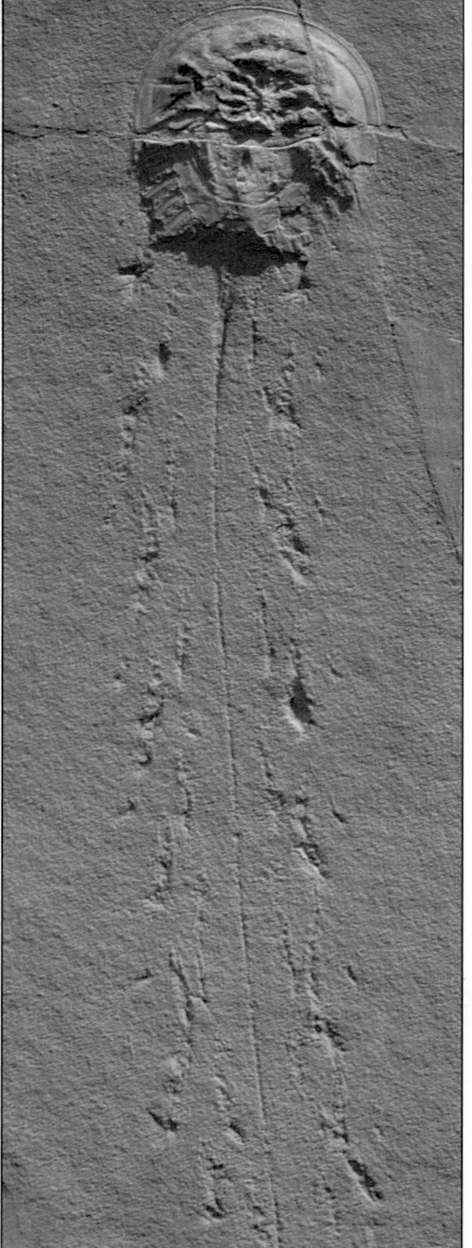

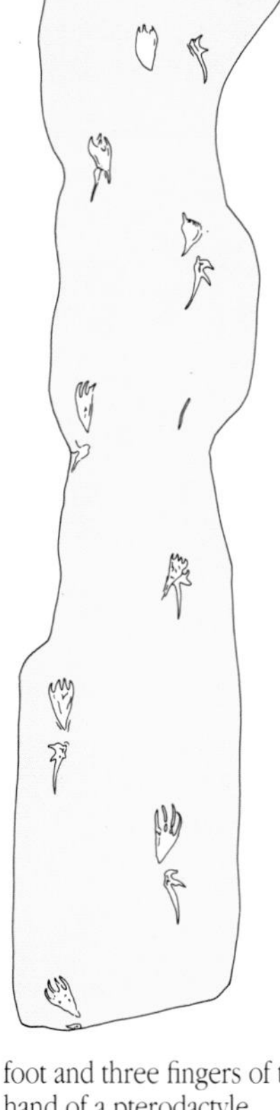

**A Fossil Track (right)**
This is the supposed pterodactyle trackway of *Pteraichnus* (wing track) identified by W.L. Stokes from the Morrison formation of Arizona. Later the tracks were interpreted as those of a crocodilian rather than those of a pterosaur.

**Left:** This fossil track helped the American K.E. Caster clear up further confusion. The trackmaker was the horseshoe crab, which is here fossilized at the end of the track. The middle line was made by its spiny tail, and not by that of *Rhamphorhynchus* as previously believed.

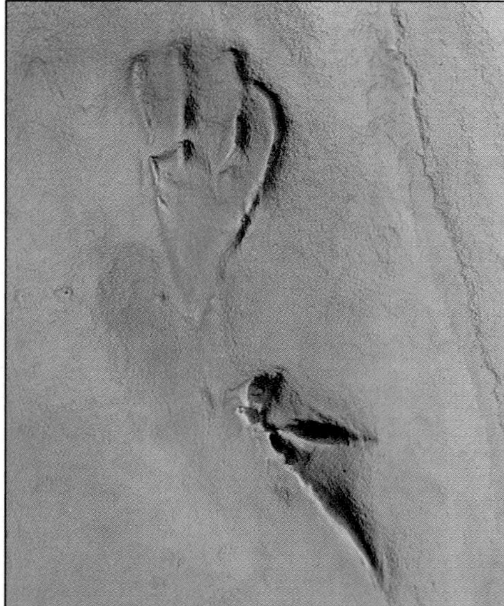

**Below:** This is a close-up of one of the *Pteraichnus* tracks (see drawing above), which was interpreted as the imprint of a four-toed foot and three fingers of the hand of a pterodactyle. However, one would expect pterosaur hands to be more widely spaced than this.

Even in the nineteenth century tracks on the surface of the Solnhofen limestone were interpreted as foot- and tailprints of pterosaurs.[34] It later emerged that they were made by the horseshoe crab: the creature itself is sometimes found at the end of its trail.

Various fossil footprints from the North American Jurassic have been interpreted as pterosaur tracks. In 1957 W.L. Stokes described a track from the Upper Jurassic Morrison strata of Arizona as *Pteraichnus saltwashensis*, and ascribed it to a quadruped pterodactyloid.[35] Later however it was convincingly argued that these tracks were possibly not made by a pterosaur, but by a member of the crocodile family.[36] It has also been proved that other ostensible pterosaur tracks could not have been made by pterosaurs.[37]

## Could Pterosaurs Swim?

H.G. Seeley was the first to propose that pterosaurs could swim. As a proof of this, webs can be seen between their long toes: they survived as prints in some of the Solnhofen specimens.[38]

It is to be expected that flying animals that feed on fish must inevitably have to come into contact with water, and are sometimes compelled to settle upon it. It can hardly be assumed that pterosaurs are an exception to this rule and fed only on flying fish, which they caught in flight just above the surface of the

34 Figuier, L., 1863. *La Terre avant le déluge.* Paris.
35 Stokes W.L., 1957. *Pterodactyl tracks from the Morrison Formation.* Journal of Paleontology, 31: 952-954.
Stokes, W.L. and Madsen Jr., J.H., 1979. *Environmental significance of pterosaur tracks in the Navajo Sandstone (Jurassic) Grand County, Utah.* Brigham Young University Studies, 26 (2): 21-26.
Logue, T.J., 1977. *Preliminary investigation of pterodactyl tracks at Alcora, Wyoming.* The Wyoming Geological Association Earth Science Bulletin, 10 (2): 29-30.
36 Padian, K. and Olsen, P.E., 1984. *The fossil trackway Pteraichnus: not pterosaurian, but crocodilian.* Journal of Paleontology, 58 (1): 178-184.
37 Unwin, D.M., 1989. *A Predictive Method for the Identification of Vertebrate Ichnites and its Application to Pterosaur Tracks.* In Gilette, D.D. and Lockley, M.G. (eds.) *Dinosaur Tracks and Traces,* Cambridge University Press: 259-274.
38 Broili, F., 1927. *Ein Exemplar von Rhamphorhynchus mit Resten von Schwimmhaut.* Sitzungsberichte der Bayerischen Akademie der Wissenschaften, math.-naturwiss. Abt., 1927: 29-48; Munich.
Döderlein, L., 1929. *Über Rhamphorhynchus und sein Schwanzsegel.* Sitzungsberichte der Bayerischen Akademie der Wissenschaften, math.-naturwiss. Klasse, 1929: 1-46; Munich.

water. It is even suggested that some long-tailed pterosaurs dived into the water like gannets and hunted fish beneath the surface.[39] But the argument against this is that pterosaurs could not hold their wings as close to their bodies as divers today. Thus the flight membrane would have been a great hindrance. Who would put on a flapping raincoat then dive in for a swim?

Fishing in flight just above the water was probably achieved by a rapid forward thrust of the long head and seizing the prey with the pointed jaws. In the course of this the tip of the beak dipped in the water at times and was drawn through a stretch of water. Many of the large pterosaurs, like *Tropeognathus* for example, even developed keel-like bony crests on their upper and lower jaw, in order to be subject to the lowest possible water resistance during this phase.

Another kind of fishing was achieved by skimming the surface of the water with the lower jaw, the long, narrow horn sheath of which dipped into the water in flight, rather like the modern black skimmer.

If pterosaurs landed on the water in the course of fishing, they could raise themselves into the air again from the crest of a wave with frog-like, simultaneous swimming thrusts of their feet. The foot digits were opened wide during this procedure to spread the webs. In the rhamphorhynchoids the very long, sideways pointing fifth digit spread an additional web which allowed the feet to function as an effective paddle. It is possible that the long tail was also used as a paddle in the water, but less probable that it was of any use when taking off from the water. The vertically oriented tail membrane was unsuitable for this.

**Fishing on the Wing (right)**
This scene shows *Tropeognathus* fishing near the coast of the early Cretaceous sea in South America. It is thought that the bony crests that were developed on its upper and lower jaws served to minimize hydrodynamic resistance as its beak dragged through the water when it plucked a fish from beneath the surface.

## Feeding Habits

Most pterosaurs so far known lived near water, on the sea coast and on islands and lakes. They fed on aquatic organisms. Probably they populated the coasts of the Mesozoic seas.

Judging by their dentition, some of them must have been specialized feeders, like for example the Jurassic pterosaurs *Ctenochasma, Gnathosaurus* and *Huanhepterus*. They had numerous long, slender teeth in their long jaws, and used them to filter small aquatic organisms like the larvae of crustaceans out of the water. An extreme example of this was the short-tailed pterosaur *Pterodaustro* from the Lower Cretaceous of Argentina. Its lower jaw had a set of long, bristle-like 'teeth', which must have functioned like the baleen of a whale. The jaw is bent upwards at the front and formed what amounted to a filter basket. *Pterodaustro*'s upper jaw contained only short, blunt teeth, used to break down the content of this filter basket into even smaller pieces.

It is not likely that these filter feeders collected their food in flight, pulling the lower jaw through the water like a fishing net. The forces exerted would inevitably have forced the lower jaw backwards, causing stalling. It is more probable that filter feeders simply stood in the water and dabbled for small animals and algae, as flamingos do.

Fossilized stomach contents of some pterosaurs such as *Eudimorphodon*, *Rhamphorhynchus*, *Pterodactylus* and *Pteranodon*, have been found, these being the remains of the last meal before they died. In all cases they are remains of fish. In the case of the Triassic pterosaur *Eudimorphodon* the contents of the stomach were the hard, shiny scales of small ganoid fish.[39] In many cases the teeth of this long-tailed pterosaur are extraordinarily worn by chewing. This is easily explained by the fact that the hard armour of scales had to be bitten through when the fish were caught. The indigestible hard parts, bones and scales, were spat out again as pellets.

39. Wild, R., 1978. *Die Flugsaurier (Reptilia, Pterosauria) aus der oberen Trias von Cene bei Bergamo, Italien.* Bolletino della Società Paleontologica Italiana, 17 (2): 237.

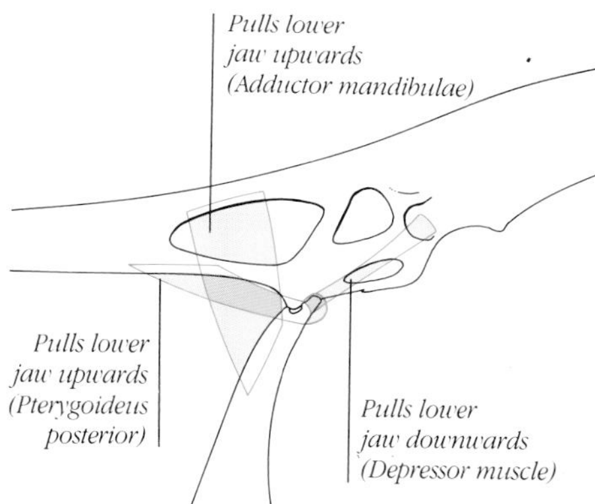


**Jaw Muscles (above)**
The jaw musculature of pterosaurs consisted of especially strong adductor muscles for pulling the lower jaw upwards. This was vital to close the beak when fishing on the wing. The joints of the jaw permitted the beak to be opened to a considerable width.

**Right:** A foot skeleton of *Pterodactylus* from Solnhofen with impressions of webs between the long toes preserved. The toes could be widely spread and formed a sturdy paddle which might propel the pterosaur on water.

**Webbed Feet (below)**
The foot skeleton of *Rhamphorhynchus* (left) and *Pterodactylus* (right). The shaded area shows where the imprints of webs were preserved.

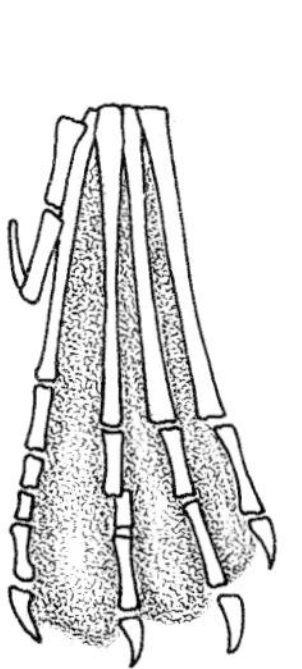

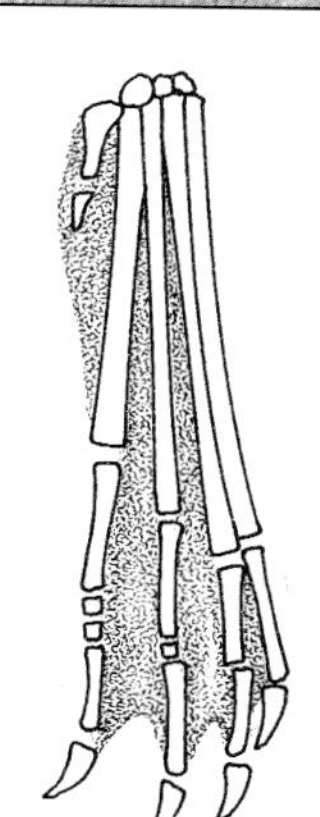

**Below:** Some layers of Solnhofen limestone are covered by small fishes of the genus *Leptolepides*. These must have been an easy prey for pterosaurs fishing on the wing. The indigestible hard parts of those bony fishes were probably vomited up as pellets by pterosaurs after the nutritious parts had been digested. The hard scales covering such fish were evidently quite hard to bite through, as the teeth of some fish-eating pterosaurs show signs of much wear.

**Left:** It is very rare to find stomach contents fossilized with the skeleton of a pterosaur. However, in the case of this small *Rhamphorhynchus* from Solnhofen, its last supper is preserved with the body. The remains of a small fish, probably the common bony fish *Leptolepides* which is pictured above, can be identified. A drawing of this specimen which identifies the various elements is included on the following page.

The dsungaripterids from the Lower Cretaceous of Asia, *Dsungaripterus* and *Phobetor*, with their tweezer-like pointed beak and strong crushing teeth either fed on hard-scaled fish as well, or like shore birds looked for molluscs, snails and crabs, whose hard shells they broke open with their strong teeth.

Half-digested remains of a small bony fish that had apparently been swallowed whole, head first, were found in the stomach of a *Rhamphorhynchus* from the Solnhofen limestone. There were also other remains of food in the stomach of the pterosaur, in the form of small, elongated objects that have so far not been identified. They suggest that *Rhamphorhynchus* did not eat only fish.

Remains of fish were also found in the great *Pteranodon* from the Cretaceous of Kansas. Barnum Brown, at the time Curator Emeritus of the American Museum of Natural History in New York, reported on this in 1943: 'A lower jaw recently prepared in the American Museum contained the remains of a last supper — backbones of two species of fishes and the joint of a crustacean, lying in the position of the throat pouch when death overtook the animal.'[40]

The jaws of fish-eating pterosaurs are always long. The *Rhamphorhynchus* species have long teeth directed forwards, making rapid seizure of slippery fish possible. It is striking that the front ends of the long jaws of many pterosaurs are very narrow and laterally compressed, in both the toothed and toothless forms. The tips of the jaws must have had horn beaks above them that have not survived in fossil form.

Examination of the mechanics of the articulation of the jaw have shown that pterosaurs could open their beaks very wide, and that when this happened the branches of the jaw splayed out, probably to increase the size of the throat pouch opening, as in the pelican.[41] Perhaps food was predigested in this, or stored, and brought back to the nest to feed the young.

Many pterosaurs seem to have fished with the lower jaw hanging, like the black skimmer, and many others by rapidly thrusting their pointed jaw into the water. *Pterodactylus* with its very long slender jaws and short, cone-

40 Brown, B., 1943. *Flying Reptiles.* Natural History, 52 (3): 104-111; American Museum, New York.

41 Wellnhofer, P., 1980. *Flugsaurierreste aus der Gosau-Kreide von Muthmannsdorf (Niederösterreich) – ein Beitrag zur Kiefermechanik der Pterosaurier.* Mitteilungen der Bayerischen Staatssammlung für Paläontologie und historische Geologie, 20: 95-112; Munich.

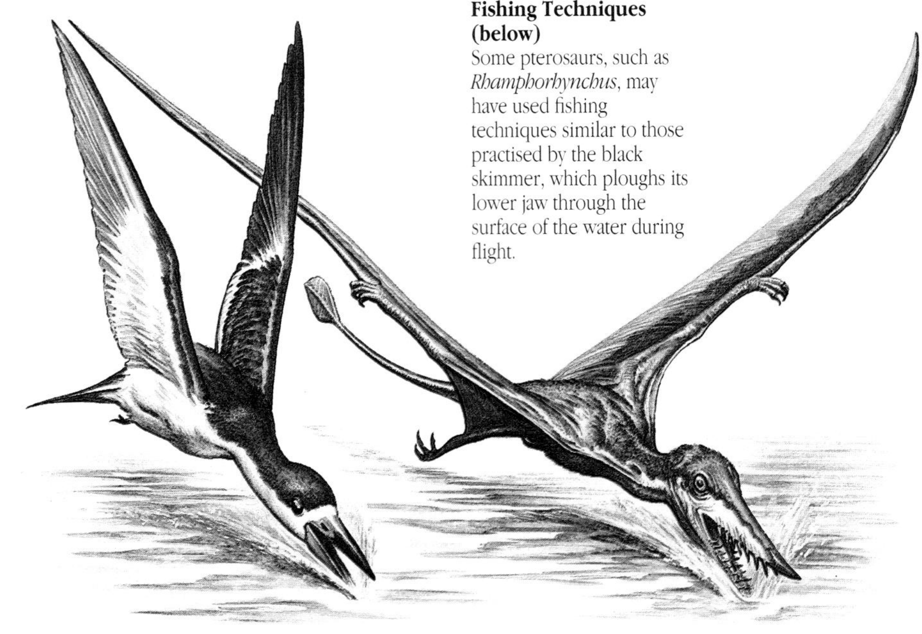

**Fishing Techniques (below)**
Some pterosaurs, such as *Rhamphorhynchus*, may have used fishing techniques similar to those practised by the black skimmer, which ploughs its lower jaw through the surface of the water during flight.

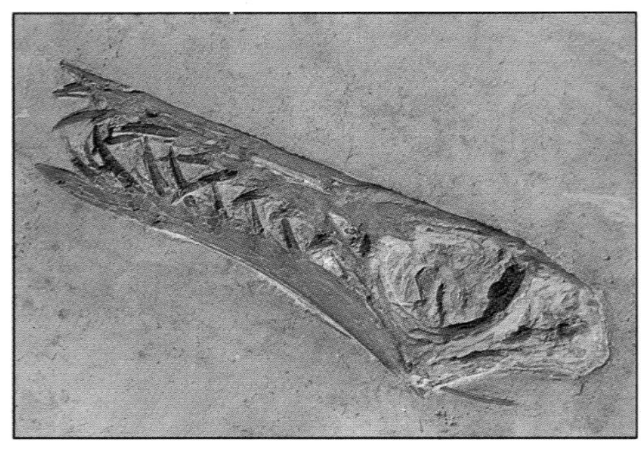

**Above:** This skull of *Rhamphorhynchus* from the Solnhofen limestone shows its long, curved, sharply pointed, intermeshing teeth which must have formed an extremely effective gripping tool for snatching slippery prey, like fish, out of the water. The jaws of fish-eating pterosaurs are always long like this.

**Left:** The lower jaw of *Rhamphorhynchus muensteri* is equipped with long teeth which point forwards, and has a pointed front end which was probably covered by a horny beak. This shape of jaw suits a creature that must stab it in the water after fish.

**Above:** The lower jaw of *Rhamphorhynchus longicaudus* has a flattened, laterally compressed front end, which suggests that it served the same purpose as that of the black skimmer which dips its lower jaw in the water as it skims over the surface.

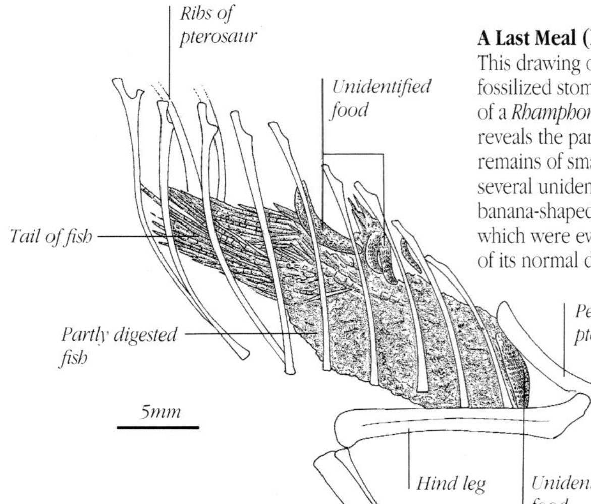


**A Last Meal (left)**
This drawing of the fossilized stomach contents of a *Rhamphorhynchus* reveals the partly digested remains of small fish, and several unidentified, banana-shaped objects which were evidently part of its normal diet also.

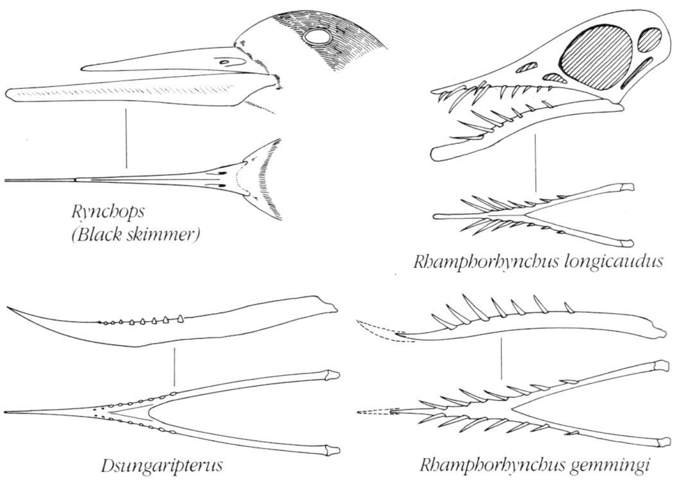

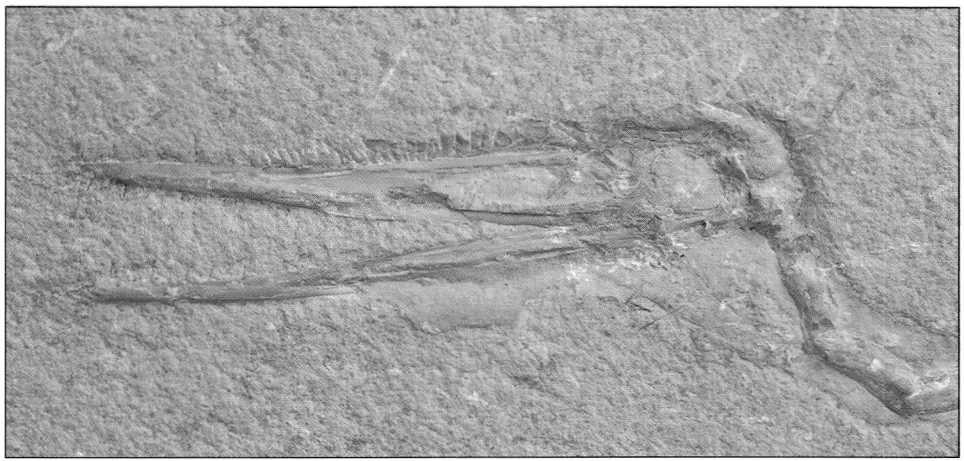

**Above:** Fishing pterosaurs had a throat pouch similar to pelicans for storing and predigesting fish, and possibly carrying it long distances to feed their young. Impressions of skin below the lower jaw of this *Pterodactylus* indicate the presence of such a throat sack. When its jaws were opened, the branches of the lower jaw splayed out causing the pouch to open.

**Above:** Pterosaurs with broad mouths and short heads, such as *Anurognathus* and *Batrachognathus*, were probably insect feeders. Fossil insects such as this dragonfly (*Cymatophlebia*) are abundant in the same fossil deposits.

**Probing for Food (below)**
*Pterodactylus* probing for a worm, after the idea of R.T. Bakker. Its narrow beak may well have been used in this way, although the walking abilities required were probably not sufficiently developed.

**Specialized Beaks (left)**
The lower beak of the black skimmer is laterally compressed and flattened, and extends beyond the upper beak. So, the knife-like front end of the lower beak encounters little resistance when cleaving through the water for small fish and crustaceans. The front end of the lower jaw of *Rhamphorhynchus longicaudus* is similar in shape. Other pterosaurs, like *Rh. gemmingi* or *Dsungaripterus*, also exhibit lower jaws whose front ends are elongated and pointed.

shaped teeth could also have fished, but probably lived mainly on small marine creatures. R.T. Bakker even thought it possible that it was an 'airborne worm tweezer'. 'It may well have probed the sand flat like a Jurassic sandpiper, poking its long snout into the burrows of polychaete worms, shrimp-like crustaceans, and sand fleas.'[42]

Whether the giant Texan pterosaur *Quetzalcoatlus* was a carrion eater who fed on dinosaur carcasses has never been proved, and is in fact rather improbable. Its long neck with extremely elongated cervical vertebrae was certainly not as flexible as would have been desirable for vulture-like gutting of dinosaur cadavers. Its long, tweezer-pointed and toothless jaws are much more suggestive of a diet of fish, though against this assumption must be set the great distance of the Texan fossil sites from the coast at the time, which was 250 miles (400km) away. Wann Langston therefore thought that *Quetzalcoatlus* used its slender beak to probe for molluscs and arthropods in shallow flood basins. There are numerous traces of burrowing animals in the strata in which fossils were found.[43]

A third group of nutrition specialists among the pterosaurs were the insectivores. Modern vertebrates that catch flying insects all have a broad mouth, like microchiroptera, or small bats, and various insectivorous birds like swallows, swifts and nightjars. Two Upper Jurassic pterosaur genera, *Anurognathus* and *Batrachognathus*, have a tall, short skull and a broad mouth slit with short, peglike teeth. It is to be assumed that both genera fed on flying insects which they caught in their mouths in flight. They must have been agile and skilful fliers to do this. There was certainly no lack of insects. Numerous insects, including mayflies (Ephemoptera), dragonflies, cicadas, beetles, wood wasps, caddice flies and flies, have been found in the same strata in the Solnhofen limestone and also in the Karatau lake deposits in Kazakhstan.

So far there are no known fruit-eating pterosaurs. It has been assumed that, especially in the Cretaceous when the first higher flowering plants appeared, it was pterosaurs in particular who distributed the seeds, as bird fauna were still relatively sparse at the time. Such fruit-eating pterosaurs probably lived further inland in higher regions subject to weathering and erosion, and thus with less chance of fossilization. If there were fruit-eaters — which is highly probable — we are unlikely ever to find their fossil remains.

## Reproduction

Did pterosaurs lay eggs, or give birth to living young? The likely answer is that they laid eggs, a method of reproduction typical of both cold-blooded reptiles and warm-blooded birds. Even in the nineteenth century some fossil eggs were interpreted as pterosaur eggs.

Thus as early as 1860 Professor J. Buckman reported the discovery of fossilized eggs in a quarry near Cirencester in Gloucestershire, England, in Great Oolite (Middle Jurassic) strata.[44] Buckman described the find 'as a cluster of the remains of at least eight eggs, of a uniformly ovate, not ovoid shape.' A single egg was 1·75in (44mm) long, and 1·1in (28mm) broad. The shell was only 0·01in (0·3mm) thick, and they seem to have been pliable. They were filled with calcite crystals. Buckman himself did not associate these eggs with pterosaurs, but he recognized they were reptile eggs, and named them *Oolithes bathonicae*.

In 1871 fossil eggs were found in the Stonesfield slate (Middle Jurassic) of Oxfordshire, England, and interpreted as tortoise eggs.[45] But as pterosaur bones (*Rhamphocephalus*) had also been found in the Stonesfield slate, H.G. Seeley assumed that they could also be the eggs of these pterosaurs. They are globular in form and about 0·75in (19mm) in diameter. They were named *Oolithes sphaericus*.

42 Bakker, R.T., 1986. *The Dinosaur Heresies*. 481 pp.; W. Morrow and Co., Inc., New York.

43 Langston Jr., W., 1981. *Pterosaurs*. Scientific American, 244 (2): 122-136.

44 Buckman, J., 1860. *On some fossil reptilian eggs from the Great Oolite of Cirencester*. Quarterly Journal of the Geological Society of London, 16: 107-110.

45 Carruthers, W., 1871. *On some supposed vegetable fossils*. Quarterly Journal of the Geological Society of London, 27: 443-449.
The fossil eggs from the Stonesfield Slate were originally taken to be fruit: '. . . and they so closely resembled the aspect of the ripe seed of a chestnut that it is not to be wondered that they are always placed among vegetable fossils in museums.'

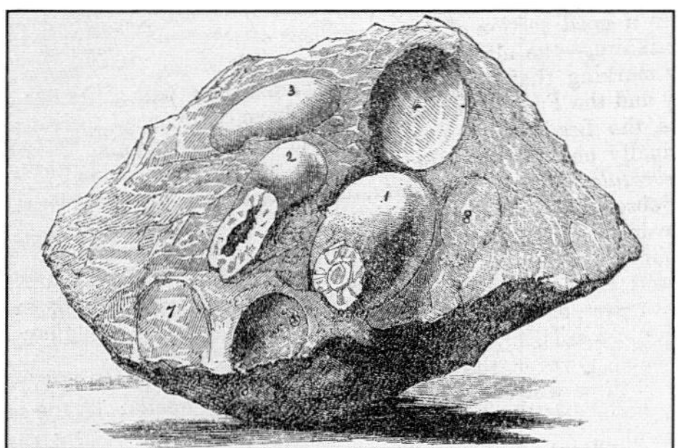

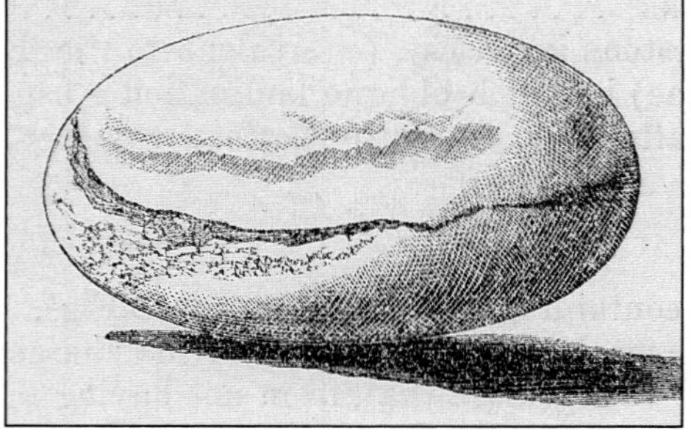

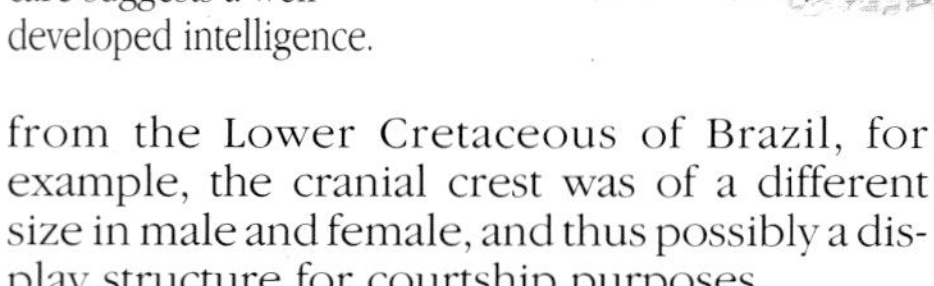

**Fossil Eggs (above)**
A block with eight fossil eggs from the Great Oolithe (middle Jurassic) of Gloucestershire was described by Professor J. Buckman in 1860. They were initially thought to be the fossil remains of pterosaur eggs.

**A Single Egg (above right)**
One of the eggs from the Great Oolithe was separated from the rock and measured accurately. There is no convincing evidence, however, that these eggs were actually laid by female pterosaurs.

**Feeding the Young (right)**
This reconstruction shows a conjectural posture (after a drawing by Peter Schouten, 1983) illustrating how *Ornithocheirus* may have fed its young. The parent pterosaur is seen having just returned from fishing with the prey stored in its throat pouch. The young individual thrusts its beak deep into its parent's jaws to pick the food out of the pouch. It may also be fed by food that is regurgitated by the adult. Such parental care suggests a well developed intelligence.

Examination of the shell structure of these eggs in 1928 revealed that they were certainly reptile eggs, but that it is not possible to assign them to pterosaurs.[46]

Fragments of eggshells which may come from giant pterosaurs came to light for the first time in 1989 at the site at which *Quetzalcoatlus* sp. was found, in the Upper Cretaceous sediments of the Big Bend National Park in Texas, but at the time of writing there is no positive proof that they were associated with them.

So far there have been no fossil finds of pterosaurs with eggs or embryos in their bodies, as is known in ichthyosaurs of the Jurassic. We do not even have a direct indication of the sex of the individuals, of sexual dimorphism, to enable us to decide whether we are dealing with male or female animals.

However, it is very strongly supposed that in the case of certain species of *Rhamphorhynchus* from the Solnhofen strata, of which we have enough skeleton specimens for statistical investigation, that there are two forms for the two sexes. One type has a relatively long skull and wings, the other has a relatively short skull and wings.[47] As both types occur with approximately equal frequency, one can conclude that here we can distinguish male animals, perhaps those with a longer skull and wings, and female animals, perhaps those with a shorter skull and wings.

Sexual dimorphism has also been assumed in the case of *Pteranodon* from the Upper Cretaceous of Kansas. On the basis of pelvic morphology it was possible to identify a smaller form with a smaller cranial crest and large pelvic canal as female and a large form with a large cranial crest and small pelvic canal as male.[48] The small, presumably female individuals occur three times as frequently as the large, presumably male ones.

It can also be assumed that in other Cretaceous pterosaurs as well, like *Anhanguera* from the Lower Cretaceous of Brazil, for example, the cranial crest was of a different size in male and female, and thus possibly a display structure for courtship purposes.

When one considers the small body and relatively small pelvic canal of pterosaurs, the eggs must have been relatively small as well. Probably the females could produce few, or maybe only a single, egg. It would be illogical for a flying animal, organized for extreme lightness of body, to be weighed down by a large quantity of eggs.[49]

As they were warm-blooded and hairy, it is entirely possible that they hatched their eggs themselves. This would mean that pterosaurs would have paired for a season, or maybe for their whole lives, as birds do, and that the male would have had to feed the female from his throat pouch. This highly developed social behaviour required higher intelligence than is displayed by modern reptiles, who hardly practise care for the brood at all. This assumption is well supported by the bird-like structure of the brain.

But pterosaurs could equally well have laid their eggs in a nest built in a high niche in the rock facing the sun. The warm Mesozoic climate would then have hatched the eggs. In either case, a pterosaur hatchling will have been very small, and certainly not capable of flight. Thus they could not have gone in search of food themselves. This means in its turn that the parents had to deal with bringing up their young, fetch food for them and feed them. A.J. Desmond assumes that pterosaurs must have had hatching colonies, in which the vulnerable chicks were protected by one or two guard pterosaurs.[50]

## The Growing Pterosaur

It has been possible to reconstruct the growth pattern of pterosaurs on the basis of statistical investigations of *Pterodactylus* species from the Solnhofen limestone. In the case of *Pterodactylus kochi* for example, the smallest, and therefore youngest, individual had a wing span of only 7·5in (19cm), the largest, and thus oldest, a wing span of 2·2ft (67·5cm). A continuous growth series can be assembled in between. It turned out that not all elements of the skeleton grew at the same speed, but that for example the skull grew more quickly in the young animal and is thus relatively larger than in the older and adult individuals. Also the eye socket is much larger in proportion to the skull in the young animals than in the older ones. A growth pattern of this kind corresponds entirely to the customary scheme in vertebrates, and is similar in crocodiles, birds and man.

As well as these changing proportions in individual parts of the skeleton the degree of ossification (bone formation) also increases as the individual grows. For example in young pterosaurs the tiny phalanges in the third and fourth digits of the foot were still cartilagenous, for which reason they are not preserved as fossils, and so corresponding gaps are left in these digits. It was not until the animals were older that they ossified and were then preserved as fossils.[51]

Other skeletal bones as well, like carpals and tarsals, scapulocoracoid, pelvis, notarium and the bones of the skull were still separate in youth and are fused firmly with each other only with increasing age. Thus juvenile and adult animals can be distinguished by the degree of

46 Straelen, V. van, 1928. *Les oeufs de reptiles fossiles.* Palaeobiologica, 1: 295-305.

47 Wellnhofer, P., 1975. *Die Rhamphorhynchoidea (Pterosauria) der Oberjura-Plattenkalke Süddeutschlands. Teil III: Palökologie und Stammesgeschichte.* Palaeontographica (A), 149: 1-30; Stuttgart.

48 Bennett, S.C., 1987. *Sexual dimorphism in the pterosaur Pteranodon.* Journal of Vertebrate Paleontology, 7, Supplement to Number 3: 9.

49 Wiman, C., 1924. *Aus dem Leben der Flugsaurier.* Bulletin of the Geological Institute Uppsala, 19: 115-127.

50 Desmond, A.J., 1975. *The Hot-Blooded Dinosaurs.* p.171; Blond and Briggs, London.

51 Wellnhofer, P., 1970. *Die Pterodactyloidea (Pterosauria) der Oberjura-Plattenkalke Süddeutschlands.* Abhandlungen der Bayerischen Akademie der Wissenschaften, math.-naturwiss. Klasse, Neue Folge, 141: 113 pp.; Munich.

**Right:** The extremely good fossil preservation in the Solnhofen limestone has made it possible not only to distinguish the relatively tough wing membranes of pterosaurs, but also the imprints of body skin and hairs. This is a section of a *Rhamphorhynchus* skin with clearly identifiable imprints of short hairs and hair clusters. Fine, needlepoint impressions indicate hair papillae.

**Above and right:** These photographs allow us to compare the skulls of a half-grown baby (above) and a fully grown adult *Pterodactylus antiquus* (right). The skulls exhibit markedly different proportions. The juvenile individual has a shorter beak and a relatively larger eye socket than the adult. The skull lengths are 1·73in (44mm) and 4·25in (108mm) respectively. Apparently the skulls of young *Pterodactylus* grew at a faster rate than other parts of the skeleton.

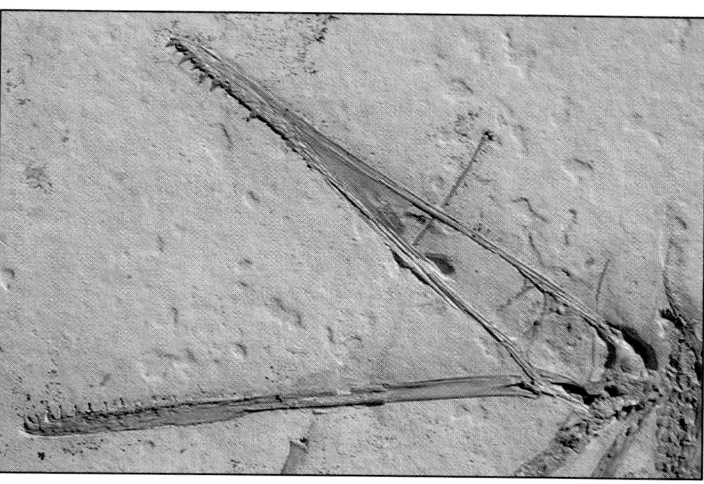

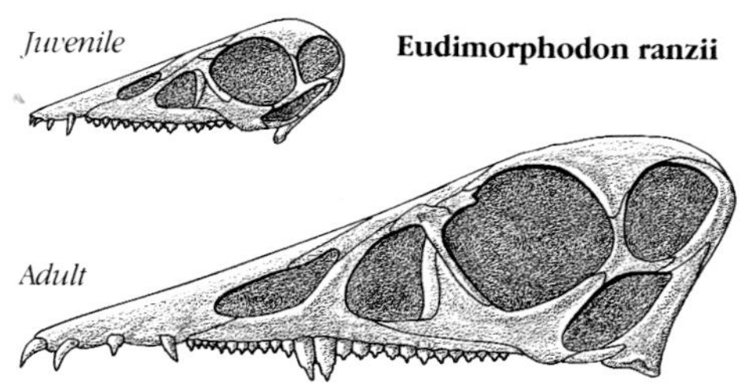


**Differing Skulls (above)** The skulls of young and adult individuals of the Triassic *Eudimorphodon* from Northern Italy were also found to exhibit different proportions. In the young animal the skull is smaller, the beak shorter, the eye socket relatively larger, and the number of teeth less than in the adult.

ossification, and species with small adults distinguished from those with large adults.

A striking juvenile feature is also dentition. Because of the shortness of the jaw young pterosaurs have fewer and smaller teeth than adults. In the Italian Upper Triassic *Eudimorphodon* the teeth of the young animals are hardly worn in contrast with those of the adults. This leads to the assumption that these pterosaurs, unlike their parents, did not eat fish with hard scales, but may have been insectivorous.[52]

At the end of a number of long bones of non-adult pterosaurs are so-called epiphyses, which as in birds are centres of ossification at which the longitudinal growth of long bones takes place. This leads one to assume that pterosaurs grew like birds, and reached their specific final size relatively early. Reptile-like growth throughout the whole life span would sooner or later have led to a point at which factors like body weight, muscular performance and wing area, significant parameters in flying animals, would have exceeded a critical point.

Thus pterosaurs can definitely be compared with birds in their reproductive behaviour and growth. All the signs point to their having been egg-laying, warm-blooded, intelligent flying animals with a growth pattern and social behaviour similar to modern birds.

## Physiology

It was conjectured even in the nineteenth century that pterosaurs were warm-blooded. Many naturalists took them to be water-birds, bats or marsupials. August Goldfuss, the Bonn professor of zoology and mineralogy, thought he found prints of hair in a Solnhofen pterosaur in 1831. He wrote: 'According to this *Pterodactylus* was not like the reptiles, with scales and plates, but had a pelt of soft hairs almost an inch long, perhaps even covered with feathers in some places.'[53]

In 1870 H.G. Seeley also suggested that pterosaurs had a covering of hair, like bats, and he concluded that they were warm-blooded because of their bird-like behaviour.[54]

In 1908, Karl Wanderer of the University of Munich examined the pterosaurs in the Dresdener Museum. He was familiar with the specimen on which Goldfuss thought that he had seen hair, but reasoned that these impressions were nothing more than unevenness on the surface of the stone. On the other hand he did find a Solnhofen *Rhamphorhynchus* with numerous pits like needle pricks between which fine, short stripes ran, but did not at first associate them with hair.[55] It was not until Ferdinand Broili examined this specimen again in 1927 that these hollows and stripes on the surface of the stone were interpreted as prints of hair follicles and tufts of hair.[56] Individual hairs, apparently stuck together, could be followed up to a length of about a third of an inch (7-8mm). He established that there was body skin with hair at several points on the body. These were to be found above the skull in the form of a hairy crest of skin about 1·6in (40mm) long and 0·7in (18mm) high, on both sides of the neck, on the wing between the humerus and the lower part of the arm, and on the rear side of the lower arm down to the first wing phalanx. There were no hair follicles on the flight membrane itself, which seems to have been largely naked. Later Broili was also able to confirm a covering of hair in *Dorygnathus* from the Liassic and *Pterodactylus* from Solnhofen. Several more specimens of *Rhamphorhynchus* from Solnhofen have come to light in which remains of skin with hair have been found. Here the hairs are very short, only 0·1in (2-3mm) long and between 0·004in and 0·002in (0·1mm – 0·05mm) thick. They seem to have had a thin central channel running through them.[47]

In 1970 the zoologist A.G. Sharov of the Moscow Academy of Science discovered the skeleton of a pterosaur during fossil investigations in Upper Jurassic lake deposits in the Karatau mountains in the Soviet republic of Kazakhstan. The body skin and flight membranes of this skeleton had survived in extraordinarily good condition. The Karatau fossil strata are fine-grained sediments similar to the flaggy limestones of Solnhofen and Eichstätt in Bavaria, and like these have provided a large quantity of fossils in outstanding condition.

Close examination of the Russian pterosaur revealed that the creature's body must have been covered with thick fur, consisting of fairly thick hairs up to a quarter of an inch (6mm) long. They grew somewhat more sparsely on the flight membrane, the digits of the hand and on the webs between the foot digits, while the

52 Wild, R., 1984. *Flugsaurier aus der Obertrias von Italien.* Naturwissenschaften, 71: 1-11; Springer Verlag.

53 Goldfuss A., 1831. *Beiträge zur Kenntnis verschiedener Reptilien der Vorzeit.* Nova Acta Academiae Leopoldinae Carolinae, 15: 61-128; Breslau and Bonn.

54 Seeley, H.G., 1870. *The Ornithosauria: An elementary study of the bones of Pterodactyles.* 130 pp.; Cambridge.

55 Wanderer, K., 1908. *Rhamphorhynchus Gemmingi H. v. Meyer. Ein Exemplar mit teilweise erhaltener Flughaut aus dem kgl. Mineralog.-Geol. Museum zu Dresden.* Palaeontographica, 55: 195-216; Stuttgart.

56 Broili, F., 1927. *Ein Rhamphorhynchus mit Spuren von Haarbedeckung.* Sitzungsberichte der Bayerischen Akademie der Wissenschaften, math.-naturwiss. Abt., 1927: 49-67; Munich.

Broili, F., 1938. *Beobachtungen an Pterodactylus.* Sitzungsberichte der Bayerischen Akademie der Wissenschaften, math.-naturwiss. Klasse, 1938: 139-154; Munich.

Broili, F., 1939. *Ein Dorygnathus mit Hautresten.* Sitzungsberichte der Bayerischen Akademie der Wissenschaften, math.-naturwiss. Klasse, 1939: 129-132; Munich.

long tail was apparently completely naked. Sharov named the animal *Sordes pilosus*, which means something like 'hairy devil'.[57]

Direct proof of a hair-like body covering seems to have confirmed the warm-bloodedness of pterosaurs once and for all, as only mammals, i.e. warm-blooded creatures, have hair today. What has not been explained is the nature of pterosaur hairs, and how they came into being. Probably they developed from reptile scales, like the feathers of birds, and are not homologous with mammal hairs. Their function must have been the same, however: protection against heat loss.

The majority of pterosaurs were actively flying animals. Flight requires high energy levels. This energy can only be generated by efficient circulation of the blood, effective respiration and thus a high metabolic rate. It is possible that the heart already had four completely separate chambers, in order to provide the muscles with sufficient oxygen-rich blood. In flying vertebrates, birds and bats, this kind of physiology goes hand in hand with a high body temperature, which has to be kept stable for optimum biological functioning.

Typical cold-blooded reptiles, like lizards, for example, have a body temperature corresponding to the ambient external temperature. They are stiff and lethargic when it is cool, and are only fully agile when they are warmed up by the sun. Warm-blooded creatures need an insulating body covering, to avoid heat loss if the ambient air temperature is lower. This was especially important for pterosaurs with their large wing membranes and small bodies, as they had an unfavourable surface/volume ratio from a thermophysiological point of view. In addition to this, their flight activities have to be considered: as Carl Wiman put it, this was so expensive that it could only be financed by warm-bloodedness.

Something else that speaks for the warm-bloodedness of pterosaurs could be the so-called pneumaticity of their bones. In birds air flows out of the lungs into a system of air sacks which surround all the internal organs of the body. Extensions of the air sacks often continue into the vertebrae and the limb bones, by means of small openings in the walls of the bones, the so-called pneumatic foramina. In pterosaurs, and in large ones in particular, air pores of this kind are also to be found in vertebrae and long bones. Presumably through them air sacks entered the bones, as in birds.

The significance of these air sacks was probably that inhaled air was warmed up, thus increasing lift force and reducing the specific weight of the bones. As well as this they cushioned the internal organs and cooled the interior of the body, i.e. freed it from excess heat and prevented overheating as a result of muscular activity while flying.

It is further striking that most pterosaurs have been found with nothing in their stomachs. Because of their high energy requirements when flying, birds require large quantities of nourishing food. Bats too eat incredible quantities of insects relative to their body weight. Pterosaurs also had to eat a great deal because of their flying, which required high energy levels. This means that digestion must have been rapid, more rapid than in cold-blooded reptiles, which explains why the stomachs of pterosaur fossils rarely contain the remains of food.

If we add to observations such as the existence of hair and air sacks, and high food requirements, the fact that pterosaurs grew rapidly, as seen from the presence of epiphyses, then we are establishing characteristics typical of modern warm-blooded creatures, birds and mammals, but not of reptiles. These are cold-blooded, have scales, no air sacks, need less food and grow slowly.

Thus there are strong reasons for thinking that pterosaurs were warm-blooded. If that was the case, they were able to settle in higher geographical latitudes, as is shown by recent fossil finds from Australia and New Zealand, and live in a cooler climate. On the other hand they would have had to undertake parental care sooner, warming their young with their bodies and keeping them under their protecting and warming flight membranes, and perhaps even hatching their eggs themselves.

## The Pterosaur Brain

Pterosaurs differ from typical reptiles not only in their warm-bloodedness, but also in the form of their brain. The size and shape of the brain of fossil vertebrates can be reconstructed from casts of the skull cavity. Under favourable conditions the cast of the brain itself occurs in fossil form, as an endocast, when the brain case has filled with sediment which then petrifies. In pterosaurs the shape of such an interior cast is so like a brain that one can assume that as in birds, the brain filled the whole brain case. In modern reptiles it only fills half its cavity.

Even in the nineteenth century H.G. Seeley used fossil skull fragments from the Cretaceous Cambridge Greensand to show that the

57 Sharov, A.G., 1971. *New flying reptiles from the Mesozoic deposits of Kazakhstan and Kirghizia.* Trudy of the Paleontological Institute of the Academy of Sciences U.S.S.R., 130: 104-113; Moscow. (In Russian)

**Left:** A section of the fossil slab with a specimen of *Sordes pilosus* showing part of the wing finger with a narrow strip of the wing membrane, and a dark area representing body skin covered with hairs. These reptilian hairs must have derived from scales, and so are unlike the hairs of mammals. Nevertheless, they must have had the same function: to protect the animal from heat loss.

**Left:** Several specimens of *Sordes* have been found associated with parts of the wing membranes, the body skin and the body covering consisting of a dense fur of short hairs. The first of these spectacular discoveries was described by the Moscow zoologist A.G. Sharov in 1971.

**Right**: The presence of pneumatic foramina in the long bones of larger pterosaurs, such as in this *Santanadactylus* wing metacarpal, suggests an air bag system similar to that of birds. Extensions of the air sacks which fill the body cavities enter the hollow bones.

pterosaur brain was bird-like. Since then there have been numerous other finds pointing in the same direction, these finds including those of the genera *Parapsicephalus*, *Rhamphorhynchus*, *Pterodactylus* and *Pteranodon*. Tilly Edinger in particular was able to demonstrate that many features of the pterosaur brain are very like those of birds.[58]

As in modern birds the pterosaur brain rises obliquely forwards in the skull. The foremost protrusion of the fore brain, the olfactory lobes, important for the sense of smell, is small. This suggests very limited development of the sense of smell. In crocodiles for example these olfactory lobes are very long, but short in birds as well. The fore brain consists of two large, upwardly bulging hemispheres. It grew broader as pterosaurs evolved. In early pterosaurs its proportions were more reptilian, the fore brain was longer than it was broad, but in more advanced pterosaurs like *Rhamphorhynchus* and *Pteranodon* it is broader than it is long, thus reaching similar proportions to modern birds. In them it is the seat of an association centre, in which complex instinctive actions are controlled. *Pterodactylus*' fore brain had two furrows, which are a definite avian characteristic. It is possible that they had formed in older pterosaurs as well.

Another definitely bird-like quality is that the optic lobes of the mid-brain are no longer in contact on their mid-line, as in reptiles, but have been forced apart by the cerebellum, which has extended between them, and therefore they have been shifted to both sides and downwards. Their relatively large volume indicates that pterosaurs must have had outstanding optical capabilities. This is also indirectly confirmed by the generally large size of the eye sockets. For flying animals who catch living prey in flight this is a requirement of life, and a decisive selective advantage.

The cerebellum of pterosaurs bulges up between the optic lobes and is like the cerebellum of birds in this respect. This is quite clearly one of the characteristics which distinguishes pterosaurs from all other reptiles. However, the pterosaur cerebellum is smaller than that of birds in volume. It also does not have the transverse furrows typical of birds. Side appendages to the cerebellum, the so-called flocculi, are developed as in birds. They are used to regulate balance in flight.

The fact that the form of the pterosaur brain is more like the brain of birds than that of reptiles is evidence to support the bird-like lifestyle of the pterosaurs. In pterosaurs the size of the cerebellum is at the upper limit of variabilty for reptiles, and at the lower limit for birds. It is extraordinarily important for the regulation and co-ordination of motor activity. Apparently very similar brain structures necessary for a flying lifestyle originated independently in birds and pterosaurs.

However, in terms of the size of their brain relative to body volume, pterosaurs were still in the realms of modern reptiles. There is probably no connection between relative brain size and body temperature. All the same, the brains of modern warm-blooded creatures, mammals and birds, are on average ten-times bigger than those of modern living cold-blooded vertebrates, in other words reptiles, amphibians and fish. Ptersosaurs come in between. Chicago palaeontologist J. Hopson conjectured that relative brain size 'reflects the plasticity of behaviour and also the intelligence of an animal', and that this is 'perhaps directly related to the overall activity characteristic of the animal' and thus to its energy balance.[59]

58 Edinger, T., 1927. *Das Gehirn der Pterosaurier.* Zeitschrift für Anatomie und Entwicklungsgeschichte, 83 (1/3): 105-112; Munich and Berlin.
Edinger, T., 1941. *The Brain of Pterodactylus.* American Journal of Science, 239: 665-682; Washington.

59 Hopson, J.A., 1977. *Relative brain size and behavior in archosaurian reptiles.* Annual Review of Ecology and Systematics, 8: 429-448.

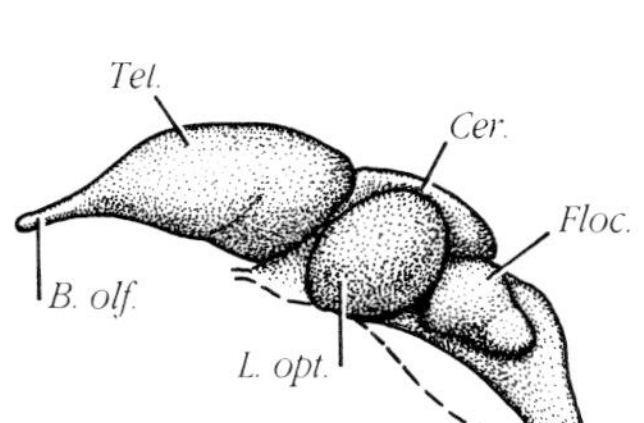
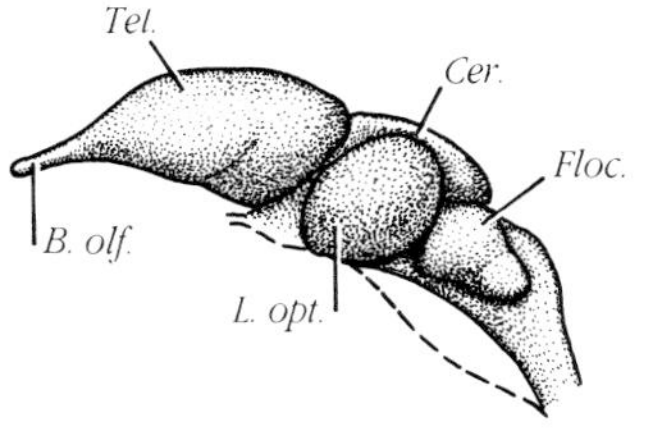


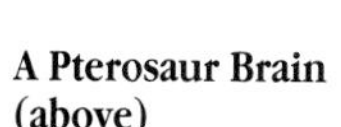
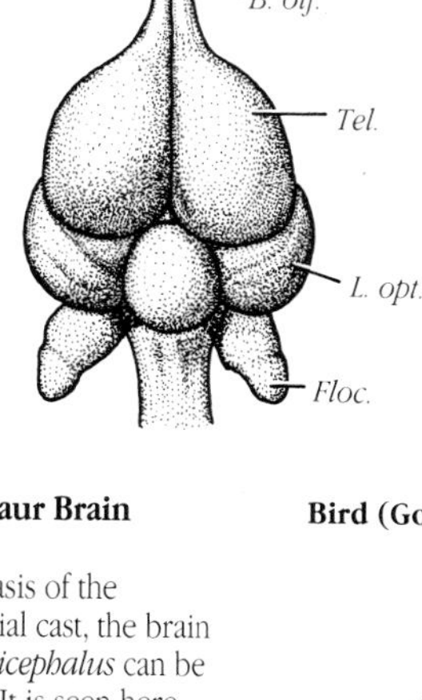


**A Pterosaur Brain (above)**
On the basis of the endocranial cast, the brain of *Parapsicephalus* can be restored. It is seen here from its left side (left) and from above (right). The abbreviations annotating the drawing mean: B. olf.: olfactory bulbs, responsible for the sense of smell; Cer.: cerebellum, the hindbrain, responsible for the co-ordination and regulation of movement; Floc.: flocculi, important for the maintenance of equilibrium, direction and orientation during flight; L. opt.: optic lobes, midbrain, responsible for the sense of vision; Tel.: telencephalon, forebrain, centre of association and control of complex instinctive actions.

**Above:** Endocranial casts of pterosaurs sometimes reveal a duplicate copy of the brain, because they are the petrified sedimentary infillings of the brain case. One of the best examples is the skull of *Parapsicephalus* found in the 1880's in the Liassic Alum shales near Whitby on the Yorkshire coast. The natural cast of its brain is seen here from above, and shows both hemispheres of the forebrain. The forebrain and hindbrain of pterosaurs are larger than those of reptiles such as crocodiles, but less developed than those of birds, as the diagram (right) reveals.

**Bird (Goose)**

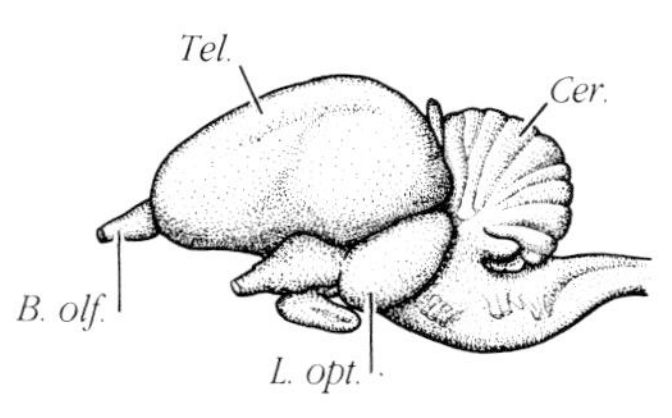


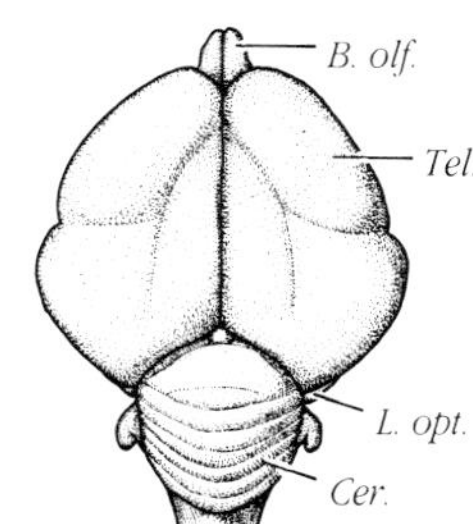


**Pterosaur (Pterodactylus)**

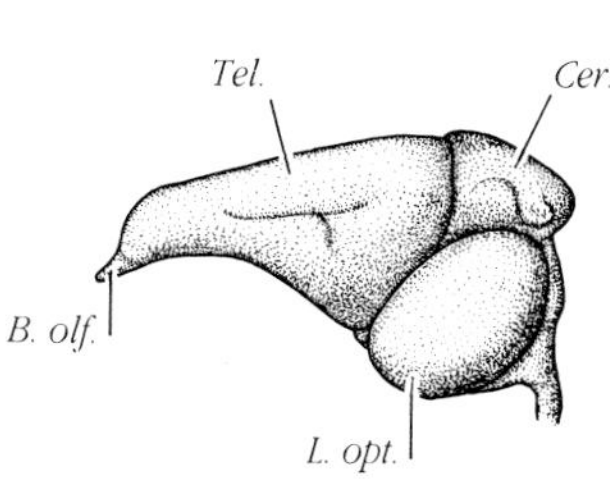


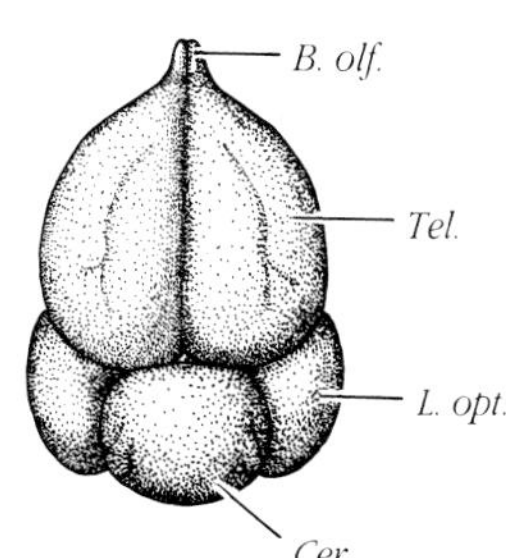
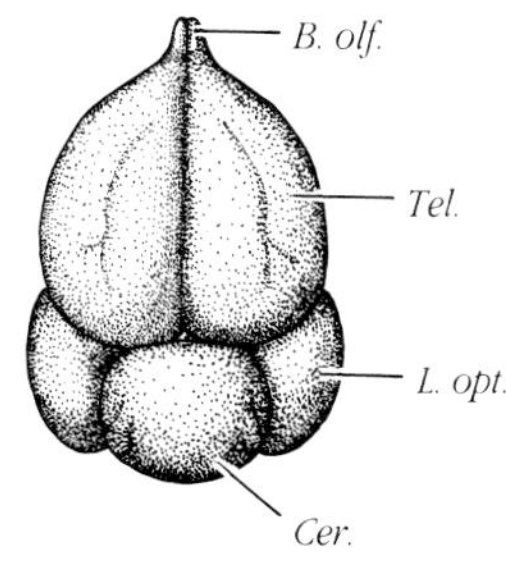


**Crocodile (Alligator)**

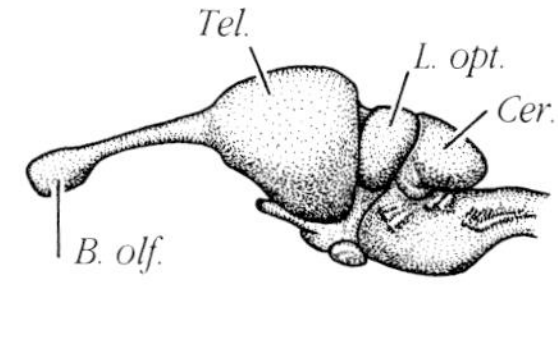


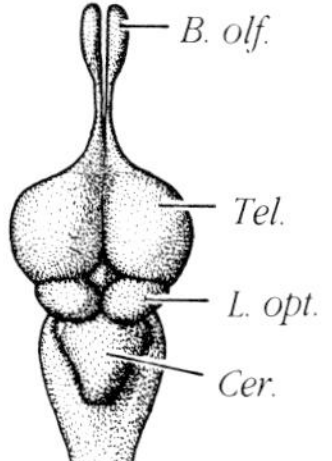


**Brain Comparisons (right)**
These drawings compare the brains of a goose, a pterosaur (*Pterodactylus*), and an alligator in left lateral and dorsal views. The pterosaurian brain is intermediate in relative size and shape between reptiles and birds.

# EXTINCTION OF THE PTEROSAURS

Extinction of animals, plants and evolutionary lines is a quite normal and natural process in the history of life on Earth. It is a natural balance to the emergence and evolution of new species and life forms. Palaeontologists can show, on the basis of the fossil record, that extinction occurred so frequently and regularly in the course of the history of the Earth that it must be seen as a necessary factor in the evolution of life.

However, as well as this more or less constant process of dying out over millions of years there have also been times in which the extinction rate has been higher; evolutionary crises, as it were, in which many groups of organisms disappeared from the Earth within a relatively short space of time. This often seems to have happened so quickly and so thoroughly that one is tempted to think of global catastrophes that might have caused 'mass extinction' of this kind. There have been many such periods of crisis in the geological past. Certainly one of the most spectacular was at the turn from the Mesozoic to the Cenozoic Era. Pterosaurs were victims of this striking extinctión of many animal forms on the Cretaceous-Tertiary boundary.

It was not just the pterosaurs, however, but also dinosaurs, marine reptile groups like plesiosaurs, ichthyosaurs and mosasaurs, and many invertebrate marine animals from various molluscs to protozoa, who died out 65 million years ago. The reasons for this 'mass extinction' at the end of the Cretaceous have not yet been completely established. Do we have to assume a single, possibly global catastrophe like the impact of an asteroid from space for all these animal groups?[1] Or did pterosaurs die out for different reasons from dinosaurs?

In order to answer this we must look at the evolution of pterosaurs, their rise, the period in which they flourished, and their decline. Here the main problem is the paucity of the fossil record, especially for pterosaurs; their bones were very fragile, and generally only became fossilized in aquatic sedimentation basins; they are simply not documented in terrestrial habitats.

In evaluating the approximately 40 genera and 100 species of pterosaur known from the Triassic, Jurassic and Cretaceous, one thing is clear: after modest beginnings in the late Triassic (220 million years ago), they first flourished, in very diverse forms, in the late Jurassic (150 million years ago). Long-tailed pterosaurs, the Rhamphorhynchoidea, had in various evolutionary lines reached the pinnacle and at the same time the end of their evolution. At the same time short-tailed pterosaurs, the Pterodactyloidea, appeared and occupied various 'ecological niches' in several adaptive types. These 'more modern', more successful, because better adapted Pterodactyloidea of the Jurassic were the parent group of the later Cretaceous pterosaurs. The Rhamphorhynchoidea were driven out by them, and finally became extinct at the turn from the Jurassic to the Cretaceous, after a few lines had already died out earlier, like Eudimorphodontidae and Dimorphodontidae, for example.

Pterosaurs became more diverse in the Lower Cretaceous, and flourished again in the middle Cretaceous, with a large number of toothed forms. Toothless pterosaurs, which were to dominate in the late Cretaceous, only appear as isolated specimens. Before this all the toothed forms had died out completely. A typical evolutionary trend of the toothless Pterodactyloidea of the Upper Cretaceous is a general increase in size. Three families can be shown to have existed with certainty in the latest Cretaceous period: Pteranodontidae, Nyctosauridae and Azhdarchidae. The azhdarchids were the last to survive: the genus *Quetzalcoatlus* was extant at the end of the Cretaceous. As we have seen, the Azhdarchidae were large to very large, toothless and highly specialized pterosaurs.

Thus the history of pterosaurs included two periods in which they flourished, in the late Jurassic and the middle Cretaceous, and three extinction events, at the Jurassic/Cretaceous boundary, in the early Cretaceous and finally at the Cretaceous/Tertiary boundary.[2]

Thus a clearly differentiated picture of pterosaur extinction patterns emerges, with an

---

1 Alvarez, L., Alvarez, W., Asaro, F. and Michel, H.V., 1980. *Extraterrestrial cause for the Cretaceous-Tertiary extinction.* Science, 208: 1096-1108.
Taking as their departure point the unusually high concentrations of the rare metal iridium in Cretaceous/Tertiary boundary strata, Alvarez and his team concluded that an extra-terrestrial asteroid six miles (10km) in diameter crashed into the Earth 65 million years ago. They suggest that dust swept up into the atmosphere by this collision would have blocked out the sun for months or even years, leading to consequent cooling of the Earth and damage to vegetation as a result of interrupted photosynthesis in plants. This catastrophic event would have had so deleterious an effect on the Earth's biosphere in so short a time that it could have brought about the extinction of dinosaurs and other animal groups at this time.

2 Unwin, D.M., 1987. *Pterosaur extinction: nature and causes.* Mémoires de la Société géologique de France, N.S. 150: 105-111.

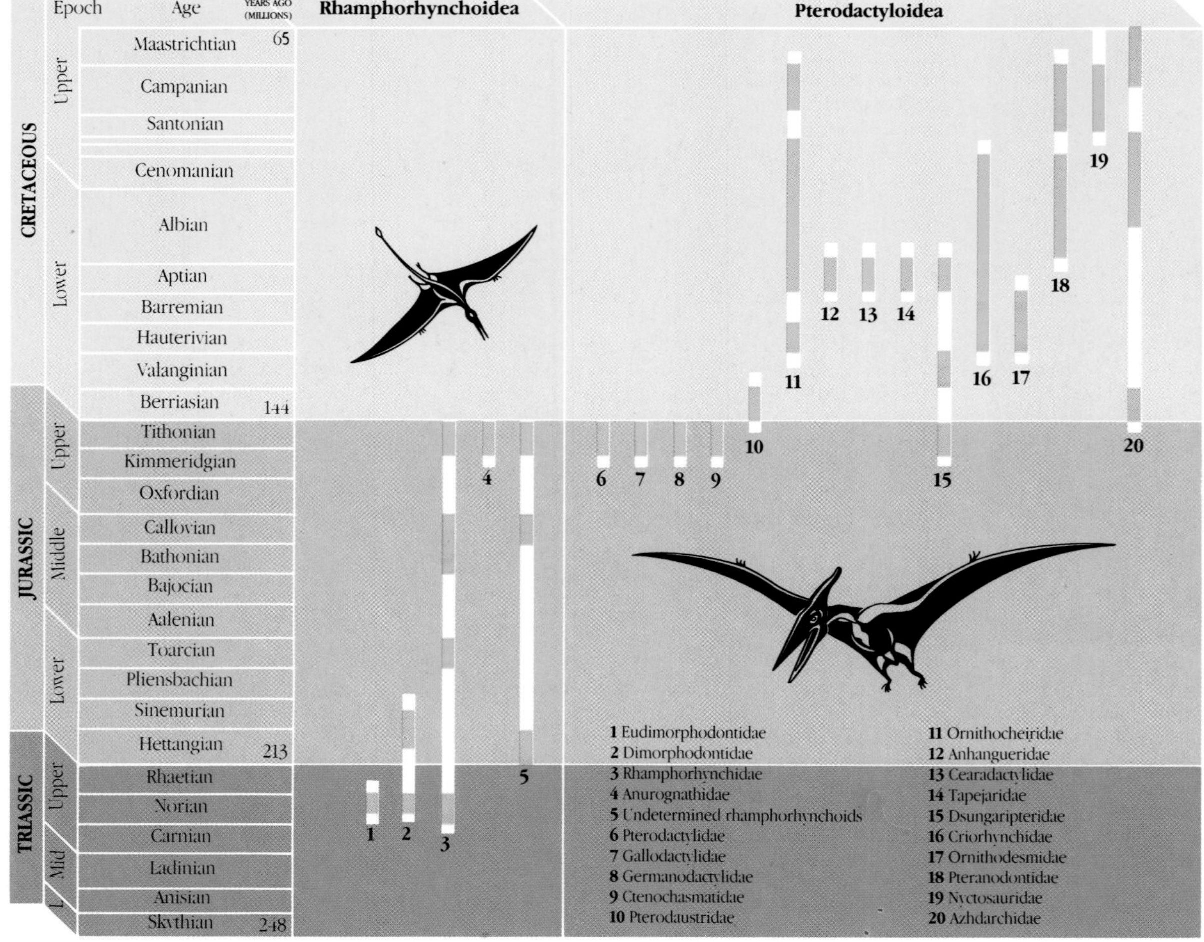


**Extinction Patterns (left)**
The fossil record of pterosaurs demonstrates a gradual pattern of origins and extinctions throughout their evolutionary history. In this diagram each bar represents a pterosaur family, the black sections showing where it is documented by fossils. The first pterosaurs, the rhamphorhynchoids, appear by late Triassic times with three different families. Two of these survive into the Jurassic, one until the late Jurassic. At the same time the pterodactyloids appear. They must be derived from unknown Jurassic rhamphorhynchoids. At the end of the Jurassic, a first extinction event can be recognized. During the Lower Cretaceous at least ten families of pterodactyloids can be recorded, indicating a high degree of diversity in Middle Cretaceous times. However, all these familes bar one, the Azhdarchidae, had become extinct prior to Maastrichtian times. It seems that the extinction pattern was a gradual decline rather than one single catastrophe.

evident but gradual decline towards the end. There is nothing to suggest a sudden 'mass extinction' brought about by a particular catastrophe. These findings correspond completely with the course of evolution palaeontologists have observed in other animal groups, like dinosaurs, for example.

Thus we must formulate the question about the extinction of pterosaurs rather more precisely: 'Why did the *last* pterosaurs become extinct on the Cretaceous/Tertiary boundary'? This event, however natural it may have been, was not an inevitable fate that can be taken for granted. Other reptile contemporaries of the pterosaurs, like crocodiles and turtles, did not become extinct at that time, but have survived to the present day. Thus there must have been factors peculiar to the pterosaurs.

We are possibly nearer to the truth if we ask: 'Why did crocodiles survive, but not pterosaurs?' Modern crocodiles are not essentially different from crocodiles of the Cretaceous, or even the Jurassic, i.e. their structure has hardly changed over all those millions of years. The evolution of crocodiles did not lead to any extreme special adaptations, they can be considered a 'conservative' reptile group. The lack of extreme specialization was their survival strategy, allowing them to accommodate themselves more easily to changing conditions.

Things were very different for the pterosaurs. They were not only generally adapted to a flying lifestyle to an extreme extent, but they also developed special adaptations to quite particular environmental conditions as well. Towards the end of the Cretaceous came the additional factor of their 'megalomania', which led to an increase in size that touched the boundaries of the possible for a flying animal. Evolution that led to such gigantic, but successful flying animals, was only possible under optimum life and environmental conditions.

Even relatively minor changes to these external conditions could disturb this equilibrium and endanger the continued existence of populations and entire species. The great long-necked, toothless azhdarchids with wing spans from 13 to 40ft (4 to 12m), had long bones that were extremely thin-walled and hollow. This structure was intended solely for weight reduction. The bones were hardly suitable to support high mechanical loads. Apparently they were adapted to climatic conditions appropriate to this skeletal structure.

As Bramwell and Whitfield discovered, *Pteranodon*, with flight speeds of 23ft/s to 46ft/s (7m/s to 14m/s), was outstandingly adapted to soaring in a light wind.[3] It is to be assumed that this was similarly true of *Quetzalcoatlus*, *Titanopteryx* and *Azhdarcho*, and that an increase of wind speed of only 16·4ft/s (5m/s) would have been enough to make flying absolutely impossible for giant pterosaurs.

A change in the average wind speed could have been caused by global cooling, with clear temperature differences between the poles and the equator, and the consequent emergence of seasonality. Longer periods of the year with higher wind speeds, during which giant pterosaurs were unable to fly, would have sufficed to weaken populations to the extent that they would have sunk beneath the critical minimum number of individuals, and thus that they were condemned to extinction.

3 Bramwell, C.D. and Whitfield, G.R., 1974. *Biomechanics of Pteranodon*. Philosophical Transactions of the Royal Society London, (B), 267: 503-581.

**Above:** The sedimentary sequence in the Big Bend National Park in West Texas reveals a continuous transition from the uppermost Cretaceous Javelina Formation to the lowermost Tertiary Black Peaks Formation, indicated by the purple-coloured bands. Sometime during the deposition of the Javelina Formation, the last pterosaurs went extinct.

And indeed there are geological and palaeontological signs of deterioration of the climate in the late Cretaceous.[4] It is assumed that in the period between the late Cretaceous and the early Tertiary the average annual temperature on Earth dropped by 50°F (10°C). This cooling need not necessarily have had extraterrestrial causes. The geological history of the Earth teaches us that it was just at the Cretaceous/Tertiary boundary that large areas of continental shelf, shallow seas in other words, dried up, or, as geologists put it, marine regression took place. This was caused by plate tectonics, movements of parts of the Earth's crust, which brought new oceans into being. Thus for example South America and Africa drifted apart (which they are incidentally still doing), and in the same way North America and Eurasia split apart. Thus the North and South Atlantic were created, and with this a system of marine currents which had a considerable influence on climate and weather conditions, as they still do today. It is in these climatic changes that we should look for the cause of the extinction of the last pterosaurs.

The evolutionary process that led to the giant pterosaurs of the late Cretaceous was a one-way street that finally became a cul-de-sac, or indeed a trap, from which there was no way back. In order to survive, pterosaurs would have had to renounce their specialization. In particular they would have had to become smaller, develop bones with thicker walls, and acquire flapping flight again. This was not possible. It would have contradicted what is recognized as a basic rule of biology, that of the non-reversibility of evolution.

After the disappearance of the last pterosaurs 65 million years ago, birds began to assert themselves more strongly in the Tertiary. Of course there was already a whole series of birds in the late Cretaceous, which were clearly little affected by the climatic crisis at the Cretaceous/Tertiary boundary. It was often assumed that birds had driven out the last pterosaurs in competition and thus brought about their extinction. Certainly the number of species of bird and their diversity had increased towards the end of the Cretaceous, while that of pterosaurs had steadily declined.[5] But probably Cretaceous birds, like the diver *Hesperornis*, had a different way of life from pterosaurs, and were thus not really in biological competition with them. Birds like gulls or petrels did not appear until the early Tertiary.

Thus the extinction of pterosaurs is marked by a gradual decline in their diversity during the Upper Cretaceous. Late Cretaceous pterosaurs were highly specialized giant forms, and their end was brought about by deterioration of the climate. This is adequately explained by geological factors which resulted from the internal dynamics of the Earth. Even if a meteor or an asteroid had crashed on Earth 65 million years ago, it could probably scarcely have influenced the long-term, entirely normal process of pterosaur extinction.

4 Van Valen, L. and Sloan, R.E., 1977. *Ecology and the extinction of dinosaurs*. Evolutionary Theory, 2: 37-64.

5 Unwin, D.M., 1987. *Extinction and survival in birds*. In *Extinction and Survival in the Fossil Record* (ed. G.P. Larwood), Systematics Association Special Volume No. 34; Clarendon Press, Oxford. Unwin suggested that birds probably began to compete with pterosaurs at about the time of the early Cretaceous. 'It would appear that, owing to their more flexible bauplan, birds were more successful, and by the late Cretaceous they appear to have filled virtually all niches, except for those where their avian bauplan was of no particular advantage. These were the niches occupied by large ocean-going forms such as *Pteranodon* and possibly *Quetzalcoatlus*.'

**Right:** Life in the Liassic Sea as reconstructed by de la Bèche, and, in 1846, reproduced in F.J. Pictet's *Traité élémentaire de Paléontologie.* The sea is populated by numerous types of marine animal, while pterosaurs fly in the air. They are regarded as bat-like, with their wing membranes extending down to their feet and tails.

**Left:** In this restoration by Riou we see a Jurassic landscape. Individual *Pterodactylus* are here shown flying to catch a dragonfly on the wing, and sitting upright in a resting position in the background. This scene was repeatedly published in several editions of L. Figuier's *La Terre avant le Déluge* from 1863 on, and in O. Fraas' *Vor der Sündflut* in 1866. Both were popular books of their time.

Attempts to reconstruct pterosaurs as they appeared in life were first undertaken in the very early nineteenth century. We have reconstruction drawings by August Goldfuss dating from the year 1831,[1] by William Buckland in his contribution to the *Bridgewater Treatises* of 1836,[2] and by Thomas Hawkins, who represented pterosaurs as well as great marine reptiles in fatal conflict in his *Book of the Great Sea-Dragons* dating from 1840.[3] Curiously they have bat-like wings and are apparently behaving as carrion feeders. Othenio Abel, Professor of Palaeobiology at the University of Vienna and an expert on the reconstruction of prehistoric vertebrates, was reminded by this picture of 'a ghostly figure of one of Breughel's hells'.

**Right:** The frontispiece of Thomas Hawkins' *Book of the Great Sea-Dragons* of 1840 is an engraving by John Martin which reveals his vision of the primeval antediluvian world. Marine saurians are locked in mortal combat, and toothed pterosaurs with bat-like wings are shown as carrion feeders scavenging on a carcass. Such early reconstructions look more like grotesque caricatures rather than life restorations based on careful scientific research.

Another, likewise very imaginative representation of living pterosaurs was given by de la Bèche. This was a so-called menagerie picture of life in the Liassic ocean, reproduced by F.J. Pictet in 1846.[4] The water is absolutely teeming with ichthyosaurs, plesiosaurs, crocodiles and fish, and there are a few pterosaurs in the air, with flight membranes that were again bat-like, extending right to their feet. They are also shown with a flight membrane between their hind legs and tails This reconstruction can be seen at the top left of the facing page.

Two very peculiar portraits of pterosaurs had appeared at an even earlier stage, intended to express that pterosaurs were not reptiles. One was a drawing by Munich zoologist Johann Wagler dating from 1830, showing *Pterodactylus* as a swimming creature, using its wings like long penguin flippers.[5] Wagler believed that pterosaurs and other marine reptiles belonged to a separate class of vertebrate, which he named Gryphi.

The other portrait was by the English zoologist Edward Newman, who in 1843 classified pterosaurs as carnivorous flying marsupials.[6] After A. Goldfuss thought he had found hair on his Solnhofen *Scaphognathus* in 1831, Newman was convinced that pterosaurs could not be reptiles, as reptiles have scales by definition. He was additionally aware of the controversy over part of the jaw of an opossum from the Jurassic Stonesfield Slate that Buckland had described 30 years earlier (in fact the first mammal found in Mesozoic strata), in the same strata as the pterosaurs appeared. He therefore believed that he should be permitted to reconstruct pterosaurs as hairy, flying marsupials. Thus in his view they were mammals, a kind of hairy marsupial bat, warm-blooded, with pretty little ears, and certainly not cold-blooded, lethargic reptiles.

Later life restorations of pterosaurs on a more scientific basis appeared. Representations worthy of mention are those by O.C. Marsh dating from 1882,[7] by K.A. Zittel in the same year,[8] and in particular by H.G. Seeley, who in his book *Dragons of the Air* dating from

1 Goldfuss, A., 1831. *Beiträge zur Kenntnis verschiedener Reptilien der Vorwelt.* Nova Acta Academiae Leopoldinae, 15: 61-128. Goldfuss, who had studied the *Scaphognathus* from the Solnhofen strata of Bavaria, was of the opinion that pterosaurs used their claws to climb rock walls and cliffs, or trees as well. He also believed that they flew close to the water, to catch insects or aquatic creatures.

2 Buckland, W., 1836. *Geology and Mineralogy, Considered with reference to Natural Theology,* I: 224-225, in volume 5 of *The Bridgewater Treatises on the Power Wisdom and Goodness of God as manifested in the Creation.* London.

3 Hawkins, T., 1840. *The Book of the Great Sea-Dragons, Ichthyosauri and Plesiosauri, Gedolim Taninim of Moses, Extinct Monsters of the Ancient Earth.* London.
The frontispiece to Hawkins' book was engraved by John Martin. Hawkins was a tireless collector, who carried away specimens by the quarryload. We owe some of the best marine reptile fossils from the Dorset coast of southern England to him; they found their way in to the Natural History Museum in London, where they can still be seen today. Hawkins was an eccentric and considered these fossil creatures to be an early creation by Jehovah. 'They perpetuate a Designe no longer in use', he wrote. In his opinion marine reptiles did not even belong to the animal kingdom. Thus he created a new kingdom for them, the 'Gedolim Taninim'.

4 Pictet, F.J., 1846. *Traité élémentaire de Paléontologie.* Geneva.

5 Wagler, J.G., 1830. *Das natürliche System der Amphibien.* München, Stuttgart, Tübingen.

6 Newman, E., 1843. *Note on the pterodactyle tribe considered as marsupial bats.* The Zoologist, I: 129-131..

7 Marsh, O.C., 1882. *The wings of Pterodactyles.* American Journal of Science, 23: 251-256.

**Left:** The life restorations of pterosaurs by Zdeněk Burian are still among the best reconstructions of their habits and patterns of behaviour as we imagine them to be. Here Jurassic *Pterodactylus* is shown fishing.

**Above:** A life restoration of pterosaurs from N. Hutchinson's book *Extinct Monsters* of 1910. The pterosaurs shown, (l to r) *Pterodactylus*, *Rhamphorhynchus* and *Dimorphodon* are not all actually from the same geological age.

**Below:** A reconstruction of *Rhamphorhynchus* by the late Professor Manfred Reichel of Basel University. Reichel's restorations were based on thorough scientific study informed by a life-long passion for bird-watching.

1901 produced numerous portraits of various pterosaurs of the Jurassic and the Cretaceous known at the time.[9]

There were, however, great divergences of view about matters like the extent of the pterosaur flight membrane, and scientists are still not agreed about this question. An example of a large flight membrane is the image given by N. Hutchinson in his book *Extinct Monsters*.[10] This is also a 'menagerie picture', in which various species from different geological ages were thrown together: *Dimorphodon*, from the earliest Jurassic here becomes a contemporary of *Rhamphorhynchus* and *Pterodactylus* from the late Jurassic, while in reality they lived at least 50 million years apart. In all of them a flight membrane extending to the feet and including the tail was assumed (see the illustration at top right).

A highlight in the reconstruction of prehistoric vertebrates are the standard works of Othenio Abel, who from 1907 concerned himself with the structure, appearance and life style of pterosaurs.[11] More recently the Czech artist Z. Burian, working with Professor Augusta in Prague, and also M. Reichel, professor at the University of Basel, have produced outstanding portraits of pterosaurs, which also appear correct from a biological point of view, and thus life-like.[12]

**Left:** Othenio Abel (1875-1946) established palaeobiology as an independent field of research. He also studied the pterosaur fossils in detail and strove to understand their life styles and behavioural habits as living animals.

8 Zittel, K.A., 1882. *Über Flugsaurier aus dem lithographischen Schiefer Bayerns.* Palaeontographica, 29: 47-80; Stuttgart.
9 Seeley, H.G., 1901. *Dragons of the Air.* Reprinted 1967, Dover paperback; New York.
10 Hutchinson, N., 1910. *Extinct Monsters.* London.
11 Abel, O., 1907. *Bau und Lebensweise der Flugsaurier.* Verhandlungen der Kaiserlichen und Königlichen zoologisch-botanischen Gesellschaft Wien, pp. 253-254; Vienna.
Abel, O., 1919. *Neue Rekonstruktion der Flugsauriergattungen Pterodactylus und Rhamphorhynchus.* Naturwissenschaften, 7 (37); 661-665; Berlin.
Abel, O., 1925. *Geschichte und Methode der Rekonstruktion vorzeitlicher Wirbeltiere.* 327 pp.; G. Fischer, Jena.
Abel, O., 1927. *Lebensbilder aus der Tierwelt der Vorzeit.* 2nd edition, 714 pp.; G. Fischer, Jena.
12 Augusta, J. and Burian, Z., 1961. *Flugsaurier und Urvögel.* Artia, Prague.
Reichel, M., 1985. *1896-1984, dessins.* 60 pp., edited by L. Hottinger, Geologisches Institut der Universität Basel.

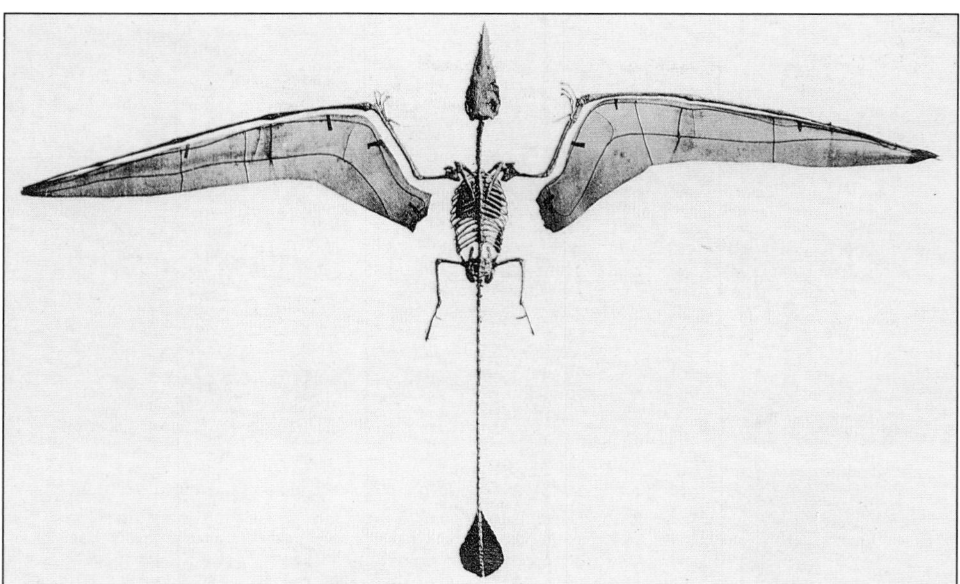

**Above:** The first attempt to build a model of a pterosaur was made by Munich Professor Ernst Stromer in 1913. His model was based on fossils of *Rhamphorhynchus* from the Solnhofen limestone.

All these reconstructions were in the form of drawings, but an important step was taken when pterosaurs were reconstructed three-dimensionally as well, both their skeletons and their bodies, and indeed even as flying models, as passively gliding or finally also actively flying 'artificial' pterosaurs.

## Skeletal Models

In 1913 the Munich palaeontologist E. Stromer was one of the first to attempt to reconstruct the skeleton of the Solnhofen long-tailed pterosaur *Rhamphorhynchus*.[13] His model was made of wood, rubber and modelling wax, and mounted on a wire frame.

C. Bramwell and G. Whitfield made a skeletal model of *Pteranodon* in 1974, to test the possibilities of movement in the wing skeleton on a small scale. It was a purely functional model, made of balsa wood.[14]

M. Reichel of the University of Basel in Switzerland was one of the first to make a life-size model of a *Pteranodon* skeleton, made of wood and now exhibited in the Naturhistorisches Museum in Basle.

13 Stromer, E., 1910. *Bemerkungen zur Rekonstruktion eines Flugsaurier-Skelettes.* Monatsberichte der deutschen Geologischen Gesellschaft, 62 (1): 85-91.
Stromer, E., 1913. *Rekonstruktion des Flugsauriers Rhamphorhynchus Gemmingi H.v.M.* Neues Jahrbuch für Mineralogie, Geologie und Paläontologie, 2: 49-68.

14 Bramwell, C.D. and Whitfield, G.R., 1974. *Biomechanics of Pteranodon.* Philosophical Transactions of the Royal Society London, B, 267: 503-581.

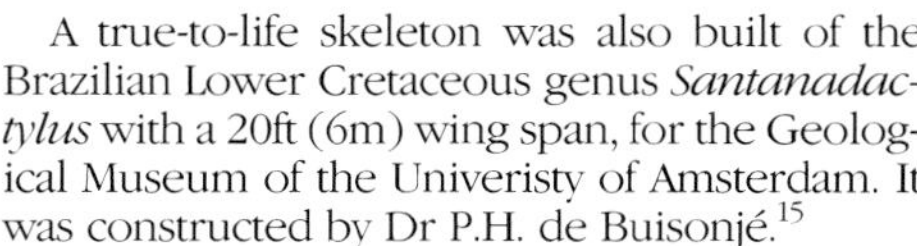

A true-to-life skeleton was also built of the Brazilian Lower Cretaceous genus *Santanadactylus* with a 20ft (6m) wing span, for the Geological Museum of the Univeristy of Amsterdam. It was constructed by Dr P.H. de Buisonjé.[15]

In 1972 the author made a life-size skeletal model of a Solnhofen *Rhamphorhynchus*. This was based on a fossil from the Carnegie Museum of Natural History in Pittsburgh, USA, bought in 1903 with a large fossil collection belonging to the Belgian Baron de Bayet.[16] The skeletal model consists of 50 bones and skeletal sections. They were shaped first of all from wax, on wire with cotton wrapped round it. Plaster, wood and lead were also used to make skull, teeth and pelvis. After this the shaped

15 Buisonjé, P.H. de, 1981. *Santanadactylus brasilensis: Skelet-reconstructie van een vliegend reptiel met zes meter vlucht.* Gea, 14 (2): 37-49.
16 Wellnhofer, P., 1973. *Flying Reptiles in the Bayet Collection.* Carnegie Magazine, January 1973: 11-15; Pittsburgh.

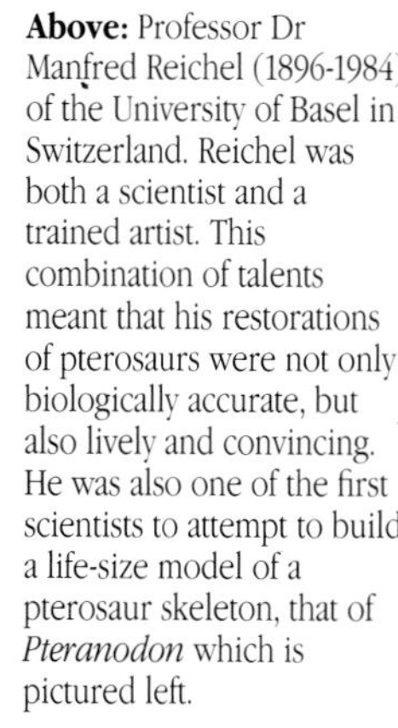

**Above:** Professor Dr Manfred Reichel (1896-1984) of the University of Basel in Switzerland. Reichel was both a scientist and a trained artist. This combination of talents meant that his restorations of pterosaurs were not only biologically accurate, but also lively and convincing. He was also one of the first scientists to attempt to build a life-size model of a pterosaur skeleton, that of *Pteranodon* which is pictured left.

**Left:** This is the skeletal restoration of a life-sized *Pteranodon* that was built by Professor Manfred Reichel. The skeleton is carved out of wood and mounted in the flight position. It is now on display in the Naturhistorisches Museum in Basel, Switzerland, which is where this photograph was taken.

**Right:** A skeletal model of *Rhamphorhynchus* based on a Solnhofen specimen in the Carnegie Museum of Natural History, Pittsburgh. It was built by the author in 1972. It consists of fifty bones and skeletal sections, which were modelled out of beeswax mounted on a cotton and wire, wood and lead framework. The model was finally cast in epoxy resin.

bones were cast in artificial resin, and assembled to make a skeleton in flying position. To put together a dinosaur skeleton you need heavy lifting gear, crane and welding torch, but the *Rhamphorhynchus* skeleton was assembled using tweezers, magnifying glass and glue. The pterosaur had a wing span of about 3ft (98cm) and was used as the basis for a later flesh restoration, showing the animal in flight position, at the moment when it is plunging down to catch a fish.

This three-dimensional model also made it possible to calculate the weight of a living *Rhamphorhynchus*. First the volume was determined, and multiplied by the specific weight of living tissue, 0·9. The result, 17oz (484g), was surprisingly low. A herring gull with the same wing span weighs twice as much!

In 1981 a model of a *Pteranodon* skeleton with a wing span of 23ft (7m) was made for exhibition purposes in the Paläontologisches Museum in Munich, and it still hangs in the great hall of this museum, in flight position. As a test it was previously lifted into the air by a builders' crane, so that for a short time the skeleton could be seen flying over the roofs of Munich. It is not until you see it high above you in the air that you realize how small the actual body of *Pteranodon* was, and how extremely long the wings were in comparison.

### Life Restorations

The Crystal Palace, the largest iron-framed glass building of its time, was built in London's Hyde Park to house the Great Exhibition of 1851. At the end of this international trade fair for technical products the Crystal Palace was dismantled and rebuilt in Sydenham in South London. It was set in a landscaped park, and

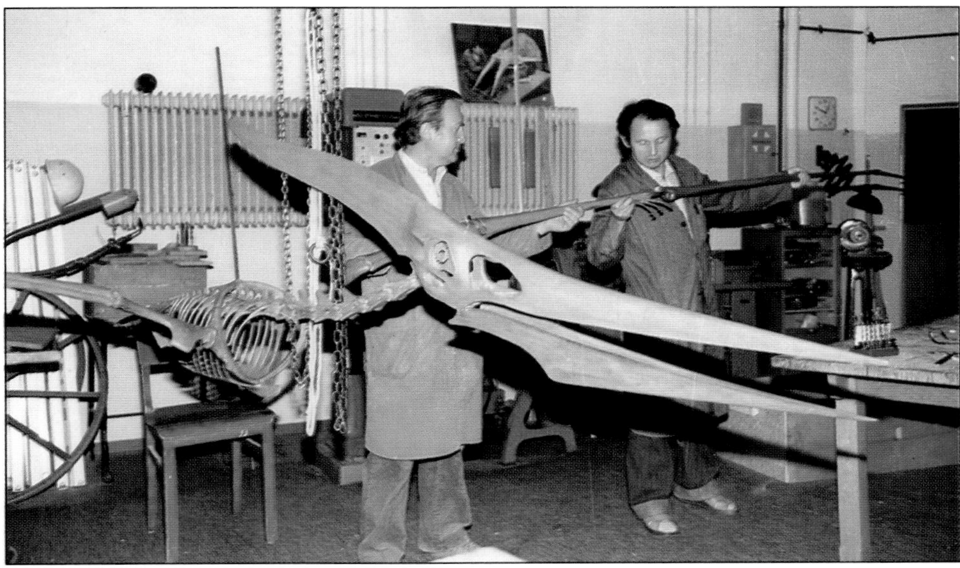

**Above:** Mounting of a life-sized skeletal reconstruction of *Pteranodon* in the workshop of the Munich Palaeontological Museum. Preparator Leonhard Bimmer (left) did much of the modelling of the bones and skull, and Ernst Schmieja (right) constructed the internal metal supporting framework. The skeleton is seen shortly before a 'test flight' in the spring of 1981 during which it was lifted into the air by a construction crane in the vicinity of the Museum.

**Left:** The *Pteranodon* skeleton replica in its final destination: the Great Hall of the Palaeontological Museum in Munich. It is on display hanging high above visitors' heads, suspended by a thin steel wire from the metal frame of the Museum's glass roof.

intended to serve as a permanent exhibition for arts and science.

It is said to have been Prince Albert, Queen Victoria's consort, who suggested that the park in Sydenham should be decorated with reconstructed prehistoric animals. Thus the animal painter and sculptor Benjamin Waterhouse Hawkins was commissioned to take on this task. After studying Richard Owen's monographs he decided to bring the giant reptiles of the Mesozoic back to life. Hawkins and Owen worked closely together, with Hawkins making the reconstructions to Owen's instructions. He made enormous clay moulds, from which he produced the casts. Thus the dinosaurs known at the time gradually came into being, *Iguanodon*, *Hylaeosaurus* and *Megalosaurus*, marine reptiles like ichthyosaurs, plesiosaurs and mosasaurs, and also crocodiles. Hawkins also constructed two large pterosaurs, which still sit majestically on a rock today, one with outspread wings, as if about to fly away, the other with folded wings. Queen Victoria and Prince Albert reopened the Crystal Palace in Sydenham on 10 June 1854, and they and 40,000 visitors greatly admired the animals reconstructed by Hawkins and Owen.[17]

The two Sydenham pterosaurs dating from 1854 were the first attempt at three-dimensional life restoration. Since then many museums and dinosaur parks have made life restorations of pterosaurs for exhibition purposes, like for example models of *Pteranodon* in the Haus der Natur in Salzburg, Austria, in the Museo Civico di Storia Naturale in Milan, Italy,[18] and in the Museum of Victoria in Melbourne, Australia. There is also a large *Pteranodon* hanging in the entrance hall of the Bäumlihof grammar school in Basel, Switzerland, with a wing span of about 26·3ft (8m). This excellently reconstructed model was built in aluminium and various plastics by D. Oppliger and C. Schärler, working to ideas by Professor Manfred Reichel. It only weighs 44lb (20kg), and must thus be fairly close to the weight of a live *Pteranodon*.

In the Zigong Dinosaur Museum in Dashanpu, Sichuan Province, China, is a life model of an *Angustinaripterus* from the middle Jurassic of Zigong, on display.

Life-size models of *Rhamphorhynchus* can be seen moving as a mobile in the hall of the Paläontologisches Museum in Munich.

There is a model of an 'automatic', that is to say moving *Dimorphodon* from the Lower Lias of Dorset in 'The Changing Earth' gallery of the City of Bristol Museum and Art Gallery in England. Nicknamed Didi, it was the star of a 1985 BBC TV 'Wildlife on One' series.

There is a model of a *Dorygnathus* from the Upper Lias of Banz in Upper Franconia in the 'Petrefaktensammlung' of the former monastery of Banz. It is based on pterosaur bones found by Carl Theodori in 1830 in the neighbourhood of the monastery and described as *'Pterodactylus' banthensis.*

There is a life restoration of the filter eater *Pterodaustro* in the Museo Argentino de Ciencias Naturales in Buenos Aires, Argentina. This model was built by the Argentinian artist José

17 Desmond, A.J., 1975. *The Hot-Blooded Dinosaurs. A Revolution in Palaeontology.* Blond and Briggs, London.

18 Pinna, G., 1973. *La riconstruzione di uno Pteranodonte (Pteranodon ingens Marsh) esposta nel Museo Civico di Storia Naturale di Milano.* Natura, 64 (1): 35-39; Milan.

**Above:** Waterhouse Hawkins' studio as it appeared in 1853. Here Hawkins and Owen must have built the pterodactyls, the first three-dimensional life restorations of pterosaurs, which were put on display in the Crystal Palace Park at Sydenham.

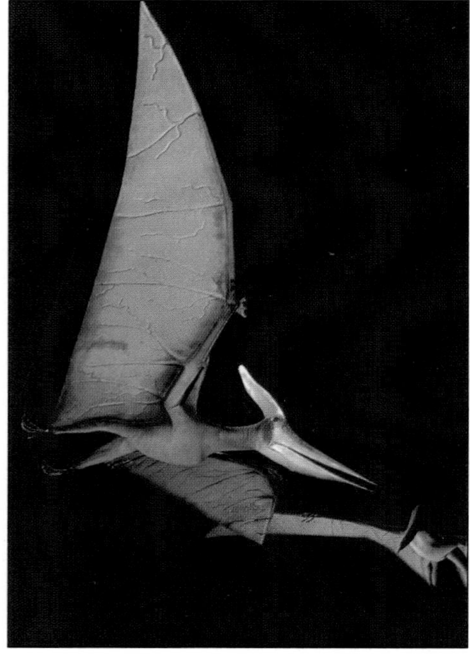

**Above:** These are life restorations of *Pteranodon* which are to be seen hanging in the McCoy Hall of the Museum of Victoria in Melbourne, Australia. It is interesting to compare the width of the wing with that of another *Pteranodon* model, seen below.

**Above:** This model of *Pteranodon* was built by D. Oppliger and C. Schärler under the direction of Professor Manfred Reichel. Its weight is only 44lb (20kg) which is reckoned to be close to the actual weight of the living animal. It hangs in the hall of Bäumlihof Gymnasium in Basel, Switzerland.

**Left:** The pterodactyls built by Owen and Hawkins as illustrated in the *Guide to the Crystal Palace and Park* by S. Phillips in 1856. These models were part of a display opened by Queen Victoria and Prince Albert at Sydenham in 1854.

**Left:** These models of *Quetzalcoatlus* were built by Matt B. Smith, and are now on display in the Museum of the Rockies.

**Above:** 'Didi', the mechanically movable life model of *Dimorphodon* that appeared in the BBC's 'Wildlife on One' series.

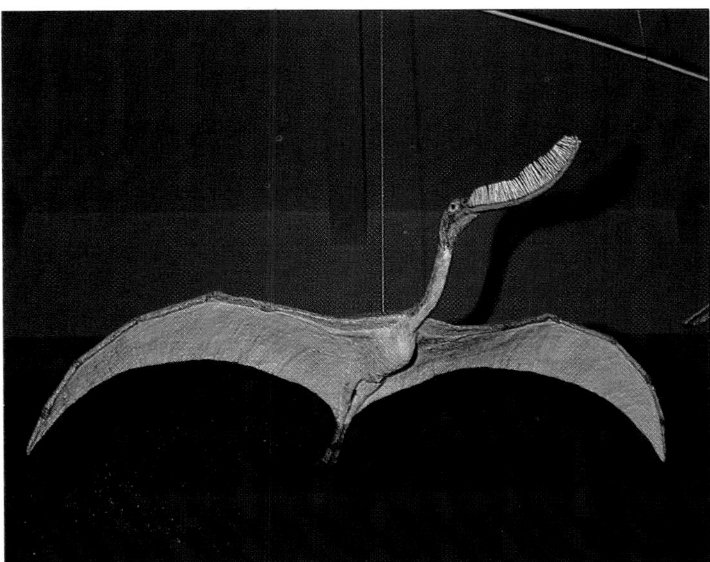

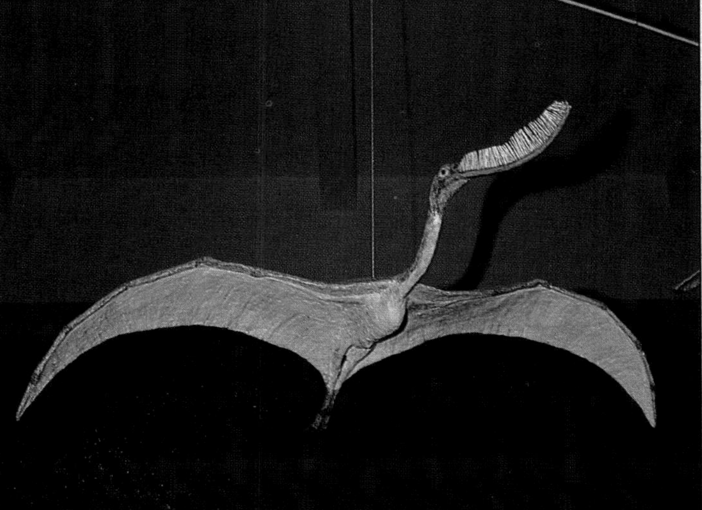

**Above:** This life-size model of *Quetzalcoatlus* was built a few years ago in Washington DC, and now hangs in the US Museum of Natural History.

**Left:** *Pterodaustro*, the 'flamingo pterosaur' from the Lower Cretaceous of Argentina. This life model of the filter feeder is on display in the Museo Argentino de Ciencias Naturales in Buenos Aires.

**Below:** The author modelling a life restoration of *Rhamphorhynchus*. It is constructed with fully extended wings on the basis of the skeletal restoration shown on page 171.

Luis Gómez on the basis of the original fossil material of this 'flamingo pterosaur' from the Lower Cretaceous strata of San Luis.

Finally, life restorations of the giant Texan pterosaur *Quetzalcoatlus* have been constructed in recent years, in the National Museum of Natural History, Smithsonian Institution, in Washington DC, USA, in the New Mexico Museum of Natural History in Albuquerque, New Mexico, USA, and in the Museum of the Rockies in Bozeman, Montana.

## Flying Models

The first attempt to make a model of a pterosaur that actually flew was made by the zoologist and behavioural researcher Erich von Holst in 1956.[19] On the basis of the 'artificial' birds he built a flying model of a Solnhofen *Rhamphorhynchus* of balsa wood, wire and Japanese paper. The wings were moved up and down by means of an ingenious but simple rubber band mechanism, so that it could use flapping flight. The wing span was 4ft (1·2m). E. von Holst wrote as follows about building his *Rhamphorhynchus* model: 'For those interested in technical matters, here in conclusion is a short sketch of the motor that made the *Rhamphorhynchus* model capable of flight. It was placed in the shell of the body, which is made of Japanese paper stiffened with glue and consists essentially of a balsa wood tube, through which runs a strong rubber band attached at one end to the axis of the pulley, around which a nylon thread is wrapped. The thread runs over a wheel which is held in a

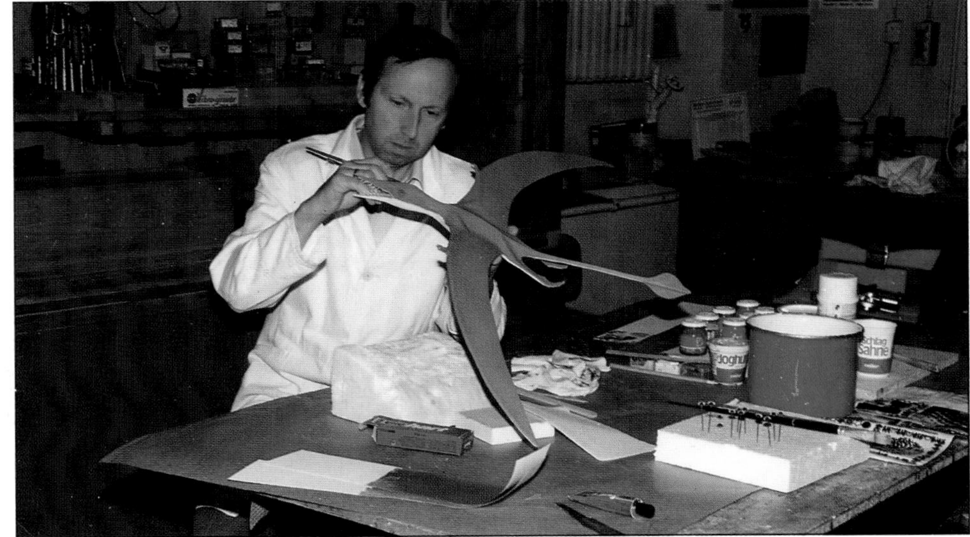

19 Holst, E. von, 1957. *Wie flog Rhamphorhynchus*. Natur und Volk, 87: 81-87; Frankfurt.

flexible position to a plate, the ends of the axis of which run out in two cranks which are connected by a rod to the arm section of the wing. When it is wound up the crank is turned, the thread taken from the pulley on to the plate and the rubber band subjected to torsion, causing the wing to flap up and down and at the same time swinging the wing arm around its horizontal axis, thus creating the twisting necessary for propulsion. The form of the plate regulates the distribution of force in the flap of the wing, the conical form of the pulley balances the tension in the rubber, so that all the 30 to 40 beats of the wing are executed with equal force. The model flies horizontally or at a climbing angle of up to 30° with two to three beats of the wing per second. This is followed by gliding flight. Turns are achieved by various positional angles of the wings.'

At the annual meeting of the Paläontologische Gesellschaft in Wilhelmshaven in autumn 1956 the model flew successfully. This experiment was not intended to produce a spectacular effect, but to clear up a question that was troubling scientists at the time, whether the terminal tail vane of *Rhamphorhynchus* was oriented horizontally or vertically in flight. The only possible solution to this question seemed to be by experiment. The result was that the model only flew when the tail membrane was horizontal, but crashed when it was vertical. Holst concluded from this that *Rhamphorhynchus*' tail membrane was not a rudder, but an elevator, regulating height.

In 1978 Stephen Winkworth, an Englishman who made model planes as a hobby, built a model of a *Pteranodon* which was capable of gliding like a model glider. Winkworth succeeded in building and flying first a small version with a wing span of 5ft (1·5m), and then a model that was twice as big. Then in 1985 he built a radio-controlled *Pteranodon* model with a wing span of 15ft (4·6m). His pterosaur models were static gliders, not capable of flapping flight.[20] The model was made of balsa-plywood, the feet were oriented vertically with spread digits, and served as a diagonal rudder. The radio-controlled *Pteranodon* flew excellently, and was the star of the BBC's scientific programme *Pterodactylus lives*, broadcast in January 1985. Winkworth's *Pteranodon* mastered its film role perfectly, and in good weather with a perfect wind for hang gliding, it flew by the Dorset cliffs where pterosaurs like *Dimorphodon* had circled 200 million years earlier.

But by far the most spectacular attempt to reconstruct a flying pterosaur was without a doubt the *Quetzalcoatlus* project, launched in America in 1984. The aim was to build a half-life-size flying model of the giant Texas pterosaur, thus with a wing span of 18ft (5·5m). It was intended not only to soar, but actively to move forwards by flapping its wings. This extraordinarily difficult project was taken on by the American aeronautical engineer Dr Paul MacCready and his team from AeroVironment Inc. in Monrovia, California.[21]

The actively flying *Quetzalcoatlus* model was intended for a film called 'On the Wing' for the Smithsonian Air and Space Museum in Washington D.C. The project was 'a large-format IMAX film exploring the dynamic relationship between natural and mechanical flight, contrasting the biological evolution of winged creatures with the technical innovation of man.'

The life-like, flying model of the giant pterosaur was to be the climax of the film, intended to fly realistically, move forwards by flapping

**A Flying Rhamphorhynchus (right)** In 1956 Professor Erich von Holst built a flying model of *Rhamphorhynchus* out of balsa wood, wire and rice paper. This drawing shows the power unit that flapped the wings. The mechanism was driven by a rubber band that could deliver up to 30 or 40 wings beats.

*Arm section of wings*
*Rod*
*Wheel*
*Rubber band*
*Pulley*
*Plate*
*Tube of balsa wood*

**Flapping Action (right)** These drawings show how von Holst's model of *Rhamphorhynchus* flapped its wings in flight. They beat at a frequency of two or three flaps a second. For aerodynamic reasons the tail membrane had to be oriented horizontally to keep the model airborne.

*Beginning downstroke*
*Downstroke*
*Beginning upstroke*
*Middle of upstroke*

**Left and below:** These photographs show Stephen Winkworth and his model of *Pteranodon* which was constructed as a glider with radio-controlled steering. The model was made of balsa wood and had a wing span of 15ft (4·6m). It flew successfully, and featured in a BBC TV programme in 1985 when it was seen soaring above the cliffs of the Dorset coast in southern England. Whether *Pteranodon* actually used its feet in life for steering itself, as the model did, remains open to question, however.

20 Winkworth, S., 1985. *Pteranodon.* Flug und Modelltechnik, 359, 990-993, Verlag für Technik und Handwerk, Baden-Baden.
Winkworth, S., 1985. *Pteranodon flies again.* New Scientist, 3 January 1985: 32-33.
21 MacCready, P., 1985. *The Great Pterodactyl Project.* Engineering and Science, November 1985: 18-24; CIT, Pasadena.
Dr Paul MacCready became internationally known in 1977 as the 'father of human-powered flight' when his 'Gossamer Condor' made the first controlled flight achieved by human muscle-power. Two years later he created the 'Gossamer Albatross', a 55lb (25kg) flying machine with a 96ft (30m) wing span, which crossed the English Channel using muscle power.
Parrish, M., 1986. *Flying as they did 65 million years ago.* Smithsonian, 16 (12): 72-81; Washington.

**Above, right and below:** In 1985 Dr Paul MacCready and his team from AeroVironment Inc. built a half-life-size replica of *Quetzalcoatlus* which flew by flapping its wings. The model had a wing span of 18ft (5·5m), weighed 44lb (20kg), and was capable of flying at 35mph (56km/h). It was flown successfully many times at Death Valley in California, but crashed on its first public flight in 1986.

its wings, be completely under control in a normal flying position, and fly for a few minutes under electric power.

In order to fulfil these conditions the AeroVironment engineers had to develop a special, computer-controlled auto-pilot system. To maintain a stable flight position the pterosaur had to move its head sideways, stretch its digits on the leading edge of the wing, and not only move its wings up and down, but also twist them and move them forwards and backwards.

After a series of small test models the 18ft (5·5m) flapping version was finally built. The *Quetzalcoatlus* model made its first successful flight on 1 December 1985, and early in 1986 made over 20 trouble-free flights in Death Valley in California. Each flight lasted about four minutes. These impressive, remote-controlled flights were captured for the film 'On the Wing', and can still be seen in the Air and Space Museum in Washington D.C. Unfortunately, on the occasion of its first public demonstration flight at Andrews Air Force Base near Washington on 17 May 1986, *Quetzalcoatlus* crashed shortly after take-off and was smashed to pieces.[22] Dr Wann Langston's eye witness report tells us that *Quetzalcoatlus*' last flight at Andrews Air Force Base went like this: the pterosaur took off without any problem in front of thousands of spectators. The model was winched into the air, assisted by a tail boom in the form of an aircraft tailplane for this climbing phase. This auxiliary element was normally discarded by remote control once the desired altitude had been reached and the reptile flew independently on, flapping its wings. For some unknown reason the tailplane came off a few seconds too early, at a height of about 400ft (120m). At this point, however, the auto-pilot in the head of the model was not switched on. Without automatic pilot the pterosaur got out of control and looped the loop. When it came out of this circle the automatic pilot finally started to work. But at the same moment a violent gust of wind blew the head so hard to one side that the neck broke, and *Quetzalcoatlus* crashed. The emergency parachute in the rear of the model did open, but only 60ft (18m) above the ground, so that a hard crash-landing was unavoidable. The model has since been restored, and is on show in the National Air and Space Museum, Washington D.C. There are no plans to make it capable of flight again. It is hoped that one day it will be possible to build an actual-size model of *Quetzalcoatlus*.

The model weighed 44lb (20kg), and flew at 35 mph (56km/h). It carried a radio receiver, autopilot system, sensors, 56 batteries and two electric motors to move the wings.[23]

The greatest difficulty in controlling the giant pterosaur was caused by the fact that these Cretaceous forms were tailless. Thus aerodynamically effective steering aids had to be developed. For taking off, which was achieved by means of a winch, the model needed an undercarriage and a tail-boom that was dropped when the correct height was reached, and floated down on a parachute.

Despite the final failure, Paul MacCready's *Quetzalcoatlus* was a wonderful enterprise, and it generated fascinating pictures of a flying giant pterosaur from the dim and distant past. You felt as though you have travelled 65 million years into the past, and like Conan Doyle's Professor Challenger were seeing a pterosaur flying with slowly flapping wings. Dr Langston summed it up: 'I think that in the air the *Quetzalcoatlus* model was probably very close to the living creature.'

---

22 Wellnhofer, P., 1986. *Die Saurier fliegen wieder.* Fossilien, 2/86: 73-79.
Wellnhofer, P., 1986. *Der Saurier flog wieder.* Fossilien, 6/86: 258-264.
Paul, G.S., 1987. *Pterodactyl habits – real and radio-controlled.* Nature, 328: 481.

23 Technical details of the *Quetzalcoatlus* model from a press release of the Smithsonian Institution's National Air and Space Museum:
*Control system:* On-board, eight channel radio receiver with an autopilot custom-built for QN (*Quetzalcoatlus northropi*). Three axis autopilot system. The autopilot receives information from the sensors during flight. The sensors consist of: a yaw vein below the neck; a pitch-rate gyro, and a yaw-rate gyro inside the body. The system uses a specially modified transmitter.
*Power system:* 56 sub-C NiCad batteries (6lb (2·7kg) total battery weight). Wing flapping by two 1-HP samarium-cobalt DC motors.
*Flapping rate:* 1·2 flapping cycles per second.
*Pilot commands by radio control:* Pitch attitude, turn rate, flapping amplitude, autopilot on/off, tailboom elevator, tailboom drop, head up/down, emergency parachute deploy.
*Construction:* The main structural elements are made from thin wall carbon fiber tubing. The wing spars are constructed with carbon fiber C-channel. The airfoil streamline shape of the wings is expanded polystyrene foam. Body, neck and head shells are modeled from Kevlar. Skin covering for the wings is rubber sheeting, ·003in thickness. Parts of the body use synthetic fur covering with the backing removed.

# OTHER FLYING VERTEBRATES

**Coelurosauravus (left)**
*Coelurosauravus* was a lizard-like, insect-eating reptile that could use its wing membranes supported by 21 elongated ribs for gliding from trees. Skeletal remains of this gliding reptile, the oldest in the fossil record, were discovered in Upper Permian marine deposits.

**Icarosaurus (right)**
Like *Coelurosauravus*, *Icarosaurus* was able to glide by means of a membrane of skin that was supported by a series of elongated ribs. Dr E.H. Colbert described the fossil, naming the genus after Icarus, the ill-fated son of Daedalus in Greek mythology.

In the course of their evolutionary history vertebrates often succeeded in conquering gravity and – at least for a time – raising themselves from the ground and using the air to move about in. Fish evolved species of flying fish and amphibians flying frogs, which could glide through the air for short distances, but it was above all reptiles, birds and mammals which produced effective flying forms in the course of the history of the Earth.

## Gliding Reptiles

Small gliding reptiles are known as early as the Palaeozoic (late Permian), named *Daedalosaurus* by Dr Robert Carroll of McGill University in Montreal, after Daedalus in Greek legend, who managed to escape from captivity in Crete by flying with wings he had built himself. The fossilized skeletal remains of *Daedalosaurus* were found on Madagascar. They were not quite complete, but showed very characteristically elongated ribs, 21 on each side of the body, used to support a gliding membrane.[1] This lizard-like animal had a long tail and was about 16in (40cm) long. The span of the open 'wings' was about 13in (33cm). In its body structure *Daedalosaurus* is reminiscent of the modern flying dragon *Draco* from the agamid family, which today lives in South-East Asia. *Draco* has large wing-like flaps of skin on its flanks, supported on each side by five to seven elongated ribs. These skin wings are usually folded sideways flat against the body, so that they do not hinder the animal when it is climbing trees. They are spread by pulling the moveable ribs forwards, and then the flying dragon can glide from tree to tree. Flights of up to 200ft (60m) have been observed.

Fossil remains have been found in Germany, England and Madagascar of another gliding reptile from the late Permian that is also related to *Daedalosaurus*.[2] It was named *Coelurosauravus* (hollow-tail-reptile). The rare skeletal remains from the so-called Kupferschiefer (late Permian) of Germany were formerly known as *Weigeltisaurus*, after Prof. J. Weigelt of Halle.

Similar too were two other fossil gliding lizards discovered in late Triassic rocks, *Kuehneosaurus*, named after Prof. W. Kühne, from the Bristol Channel area in Great Britain,[3] and *Icarosaurus*, named after Daedalus' son Icarus, from New Jersey, USA.[4] Their wings were also supported by long ribs, although there were only 10 to 11 pairs, meaning that the rib wings were narrower in shape. Perhaps they could also fold their wings back when climbing up tree trunks to catch insects. In any case this great area of skin, which certainly contained blood vessels, must have had a significant effect on heat regulation. The living *Draco* uses its wings, magnificently coloured in orange and red and blue with black patches on the underside, in courtship display.

In the same article in which Moscow zoologist A.G. Sharov described the hairy pterosaur *Sordes pilosus* from the Upper Jurassic of Kazakhstan in the Soviet Union, he also reported on two fossil reptile finds from late Triassic sediments in Kirghizia.[5] These two were gliding reptiles, but they had developed completely different 'wings' from the rib

1 Carroll, R.L., 1978. *A Gliding Reptile from the Upper Permian of Madagascar.* Palaeontographica Africana, 21: 143-159.
Evans, S.E., 1982. *The gliding reptiles of the Upper Permian.* Zoological Journal of the Linnean Society, 76: 97-123; London.

2 Schaumberg, G., 1976. *Zwei Reptilneufunde (Weigeltisaurus Kuhn (?), Lepidosauria (?), Reptilia) aus dem Kupferschiefer von Richelsdorf (Perm, Hessen).* Philippia, 3 (1): 3-8; Kassel.
Evans, S.E. and Haubold, H., 1987. *A review of the Upper Permian genera Coelurosauravus, Weigeltisaurus and Gracilisaurus (Reptilia, Diapsida).* Zoological Journal of the Linnean Society, 90: 275-303; London.

3 Robinson, P.L., 1962. *Gliding lizards from the Upper Keuper of Great Britain.* Proceedings of the Geological Society London, 1601: 137-146.

4 Colbert, E.H., 1970. *The Triassic gliding reptile Icarosaurus.* Bulletin of the American Museum of Natural History, 143 (2): 85-142; New York.

5 Sharov, A.G., 1971. *New flying reptiles from the Mesozoic of Kazakhstan and Kirghizia.* Trudy of the Palaeontological Institute, Akademia Nauk, USSR, 130: 104-113; Moscow (in Russian).

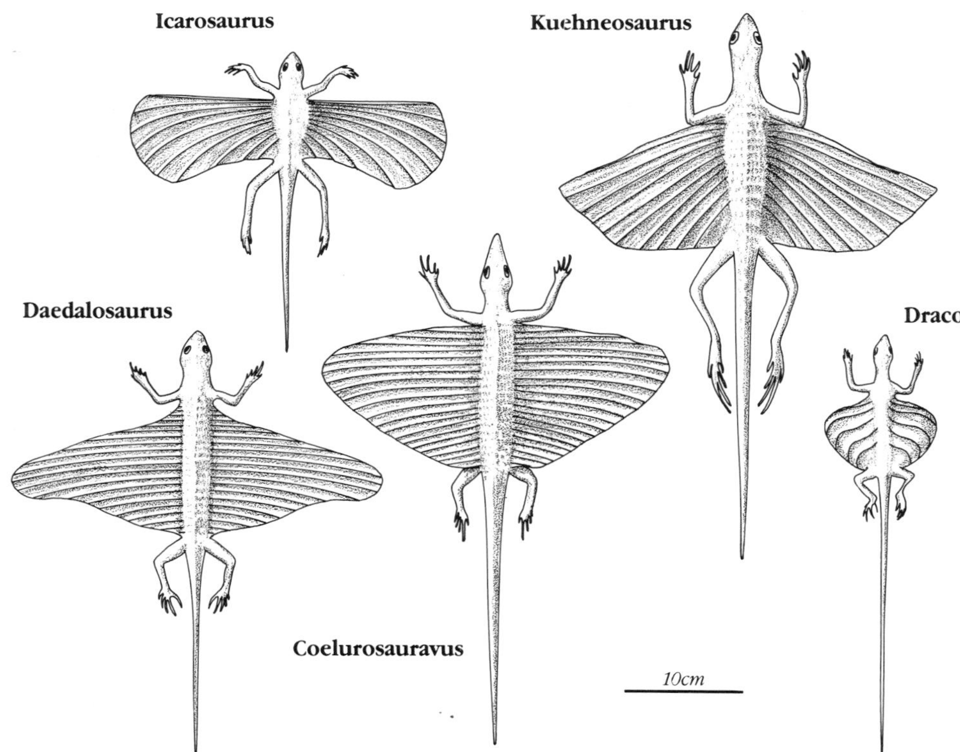


**Ancient Gliding Reptiles (left)**
These drawings compare gliding reptiles of the late Permian, *Daedalosaurus* and *Coelurosauravus*, and of the late Triassic, *Icarosaurus* and *Kuehneosaurus*, with the living *Draco*, the Flying Dragon, an agamid lizard from South-East Asia. The thoracic ribs of all these diapsid reptiles are greatly elongated in order to support a gliding membrane which is stretched across them, so enabling these arboreal animals to glide from one tree to another, or from a branch down to the ground.

**Above:** Three schoolboys found this specimen of *Icarosaurus siefkeri* in a piece of Upper Triassic shale while they were exploring an old quarry in New Jersey, across the Hudson River from Manhatten, New York. It was studied by E.H. Colbert.

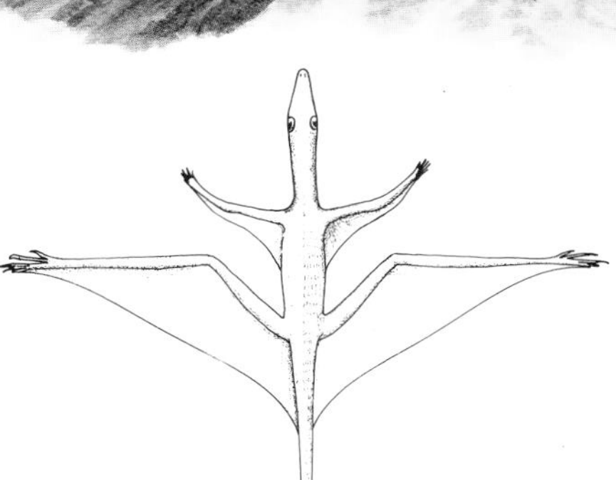

**Sharovipteryx (above)** This life restoration of *Sharovipteryx* from the Upper Triassic of Kirghizia shows its hind legs fully extended as if in gliding position. Tentatively, narrow gliding membranes are suggested behind the forelimbs.

**Right:** This fossil of *Sharovipteryx* shows the skeletal remains of a slender reptile with very long hind legs and a long tail. Between the legs, imprints of a gliding membrane are preserved indicating that this was a gliding reptile.

**Longisquama (below)** *Longisquama* had a unique gliding adaptation. A double series of long scale-like appendages were developed along its back. They could be folded and unfolded like the wings of a butterfly to form a continuous wing area.

gliders *Daedalosaurus*, *Coelurosauravus*, *Kuehneosaurus* and *Icarosaurus* described above.

Sharov named the first reptile *Podopteryx* (leg wing), because it had flight membranes between its long hind legs and tail. The flight membrane survived as imprints on the rock surface of the fossil slab. Later however it turned out that the name *Podopteryx* had been assigned to a fish a hundred years before. Thus the reptile from Kirghizia had to be given a new name. In honour of Dr Sharov it was very suitably named *Sharovipteryx* (Sharov wing).[6]

*Sharovipteryx* was a slim reptile about 10in (25cm) long, with a relatively long neck and enormously long hind legs, but very small front legs. A triangular flight membrane could be stretched between the long hind legs and the front section of the tail, real leg wings in fact. Certainly *Sharovipteryx* was not in a position to flap these leg wings, and fly actively, but it could probably glide for a certain distance. In flight the upper legs were spread slightly forwards and the lower legs and feet spread at a right angle from the body to the side. It is possible that flaps of skin had developed on the flanks or the back edge of the forelimbs, to stabilize gliding flight.[7]

The second reptile described by Sharov from the late Triassic of Kirghizia he named *Longisquama* (long scale), because of a row of enormously elongated scale-like appendages along the back. Its osteological characteristics suggested that the reptile was a small pseudosuchian. The animal is relatively small, about 4 to 5in (10 to 12·5cm) long. The appendages on the back are longer than the body and arranged in a double row one behind the other. They could apparently be folded upward like a butterfly wing and folded down to the sides. In this position they formed horizontal gliding surfaces, a kind of wing.[8] Each scale-shaped appendage consists of a very long, very thin shaft, broadening towards the distal end and bent backwards. Probably each pair of these appendages corresponds to a dorsal vertebra, thus 10 pairs, in close sequence and overlapping at their edges, which could create a continuous wing surface.

*Longisquama* was presumably also an arboreal reptile that certainly did not use its wings for flapping flight, but probably for gliding. It thus documents a unique solution to the problem of gliding flight, and together with the other gliders *Daedalosaurus, Coelurosauravus, Icarosaurus, Kuehneosaurus* and *Sharovipteryx*, shows that even in the later Permian and Triassic there was a very wide range of aerial adaptations among the various reptile

6 Cowen, R., 1981. *Homonyms of Podopteryx*. Journal of Palaeontology, 55: 483.

7 Gans, C., Darevski, I. and Tatarinov, L.P., 1987. *Sharovipteryx, a reptilian glider?* Paleobiology, 13 (4): 415-426.

8 Haubold, H. and Buffetaut, E., 1987. *Une nouvelle interprétation de Longisquama insignis, reptile énigmatique du Trias supérieur d'Asie central.* Comptes Rendus Académie des Sciences, Paris, 305 (II): 65-70.

groups, long before the radiation of the actively flying vertebrates, i.e pterosaurs, birds and bats.

## Birds

Early adaptations of vertebrates to flying in the air produced only gliding, i.e. passive exploitation of lift and drag forces, created by static aerodynamic surfaces on the body or the limbs. But in the course of vertebrate evolution the ability to fly actively emerged as well, in other words powered flapping flight achieved by muscle power.

Active vertebrate fliers are always distinguished from passive gliders by the fact that their pectoral girdle and forelimb are turned into flying apparatus, or wings. Gliders retain their four legs, and the wings are an additional feature. Active fliers always acquired wings at the cost of their forelegs.

As is shown in this book, pterosaurs were the first vertebrates to develop active flight. The second group were the birds, who did not appear until the pterosaurs had already achieved a high degree of diversity and worldwide distribution. The oldest fossil bird known today was *Archaeopteryx* (ancient wing). It lived in the late Jurassic, about 150 million years ago, and was a contemporary of pterosaurs and dinosaurs. To date six remains of fossil skeletons of this primeval bird have been found. They all came from the Solnhofen limestone of Bavaria and are considered the most important and famous fossil finds of all for evolutionary research.

As early as 1860 workers in the Solnhofen quarry found the imprint of a small bird's feather. At the time this was the first sign that birds must have existed in the Jurassic. The oldest fossil remains of birds were known only from much more recent Tertiary strata. The Solnhofen bird's feather was about 2·5in (6cm) long, with the same structure as a modern feather, down to the finest details. Hermann von Meyer, then the leading expert on fossil vertebrates in Germany, named the bird from which this feather had fallen *Archaeopteryx lithographica*, the 'ancient wing from the lithographic limestone'.[9] At the time Solnhofen limestone slabs were used for lithography more than anything else.

In the very next year, 1861, a complete skeleton of this primeval bird was found near Solnhofen. Feathers were again imprinted on the surface of the rock in the region of the wings and the long vertebral tail. The rare and valuable fossil immediately came into possession of Carl Haeberlein, a country doctor in nearby Pappenheim, who shortly afterwards sold it to the British Museum (Natural History) in London for £700. There it was studied by Richard Owen, who published a precise description of it in 1863.[10]

Further specimens of *Archaeopteryx* came to light in 1876, 1951, 1956 and 1987. They are now in museums in Berlin, Eichstätt and Solnhofen.[11] One find is still in a private collection. There are also skeletal remains from Solnhofen limestone interpreted as a pterosaur by Hermann von Meyer in 1857, and given the name *Pterodactylus crassipes*.[12] This is the 'Haarlem specimen', first recognized as *Archaeopteryx* by John Ostrom in 1970.[13]

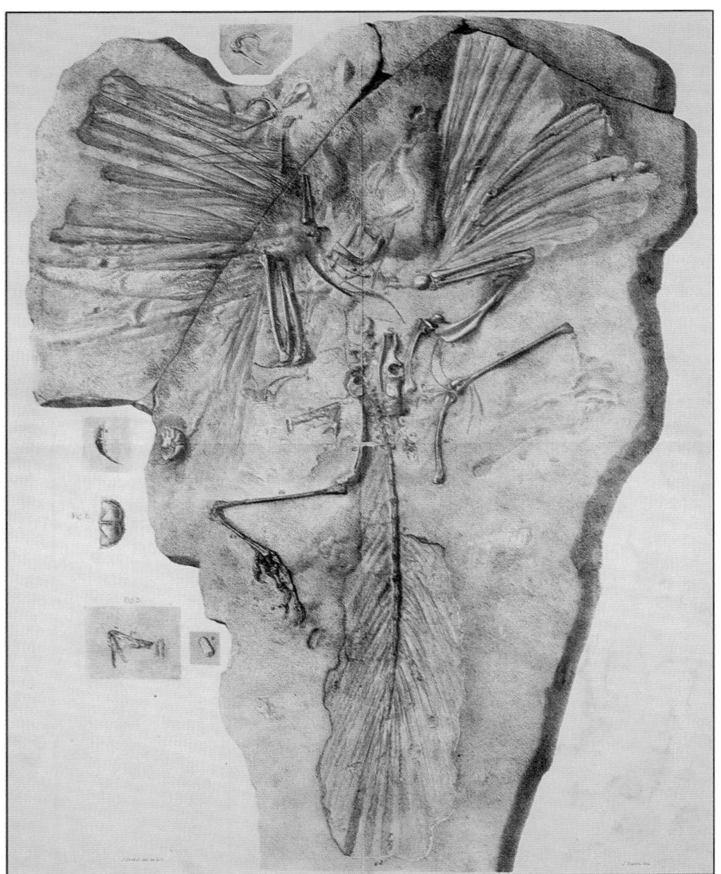

**Left:** This is Sir Richard Owen's lithograph of the London specimen of *Archaeopteryx* which appeared in his 1863 description of that specimen. It was found in 1861 near Solnhofen, purchased by Dr Carl Haeberlein in Pappenheim, and eventually sold to the British Museum (Natural History) in London. The skeletal remains were associated with impressions of feathers and so Owen classified it as a bird, though a primitive one, rather than as a transitional form halfway between reptiles and birds as the Darwinists saw it.

**Below:** This fossil feather of a primeval bird, later named *Archaeopteryx*, was discovered in the Solnhofen limestone in 1860. It was the first evidence of the existence of birds in periods older than the Tertiary. The details of the feather are preserved as black dendritic material rather than by impression in the sedimentary surface.

What are the particular features of this primeval bird *Archaeopteryx*? As it is the oldest bird known to man, one naturally expects it to provide indications of its origin and the origin of avian flight. In fact this bird has many characteristics that could be evidence of its evolutionary history, and its possible ancestors. Even early researchers noticed that the creature had bird's feathers, so must have been a bird, but it also had small teeth in its jaws, claws which it could move freely on its wings and a long tail made up of many vertebrae, all reptilian characteristics not known in modern birds. This mosaic of primitive and advanced characters led Sir Gavin de Beer to suggest a mosaic mode of evolution.[14] This made *Archaeopteryx* a transitional form, or a 'missing link' between two different animal classes, reptiles and birds. It is easy to under-

9 Meyer, H. von, 1861. *Archaeopteryx lithographica (Vogelfeder) und Pterodactylus von Solnhofen.* Neues Jahrbuch für Mineralogie, Geologie und Paläontologie, 1861: 678-679; Stuttgart.

10 Owen, R., 1863. *On the Archaeopteryx of von Meyer, with a description of the fossil remains of a long-tailed species from the lithographic stone of Solnhofen.* Philosophical Transactions, 153: 33-47; London. This is the first description of the 'London specimen' housed in the Natural History Museum.

11 Dames, W., 1884. *Ueber Archaeopteryx.* Palaeontologische Abhandlungen, 2 (3): 119-198; Berlin. Description of the 'Berlin specimen' in the Naturkundemuseum of Humboldt University, Berlin.
Heller, F., 1959. *Ein dritter Archaeopteryx-Fund aus den Solnhofener Plattenkalken von Langenaltheim/ Mfr.* Erlanger Geologische Abhandlungen, 31: 1-25; Erlangen. Description of the 'Maxberg specimen', still in a private collection.
Mayr, F.X., 1973. *Ein neuer Archaeopteryx-Fund.* Paläontologische Zeitschrift, 47: 17-24; Stuttgart.
Wellnhofer, P., 1974. *Das fünfte Skelettexemplar von Archaeopteryx.* Palaeontographica, A, 147: 169-216; Stuttgart. Description of the 'Eichstätt specimen' in the Jura-Museum in Eichstätt, Bavaria.
Wellnhofer, P., 1988. *Ein neues Exemplar von Archaeopteryx.* Archaeopteryx, 6: 1-30; Eichstätt. Description of the 'Solnhofen specimen' in the Bürgermeister Müller Museum in Solnhofen.

12 Meyer, H. von, 1857. *Beiträge zur näheren Kenntnis fossiler Reptilien.* Neues Jahrbuch für Mineralogie, Geologie und Paläontologie, 1857: 437; Stuttgart.
Meyer, H. von, 1860. *Zur Fauna der Vorwelt. Reptilien aus dem lithographischen Schiefer in Deutschland und Frankreich.* Frankfurt. Description of *Pterodactylus crassipes*, later to be recognized as *Archaeopteryx*, the 'Haarlem specimen' by J.H. Ostrom.

13 Ostrom, J.H., 1970. *Archaeopteryx: Notice of a 'new' specimen.* Science, 170: 537-538; Washington.
Ostrom, J.H., 1972. *Description of the Archaeopteryx specimen in the Teyler Museum, Haarlem.* Proceedings of the Koninklijke Nederlandse Akademie van Wetenschappen, B, 75: 289-305; Amsterdam.

14 De Beer, G., 1954. *Archaeopteryx lithographica: a study based on the British Museum specimen.* 68 pp., London, British Museum (Natural History).

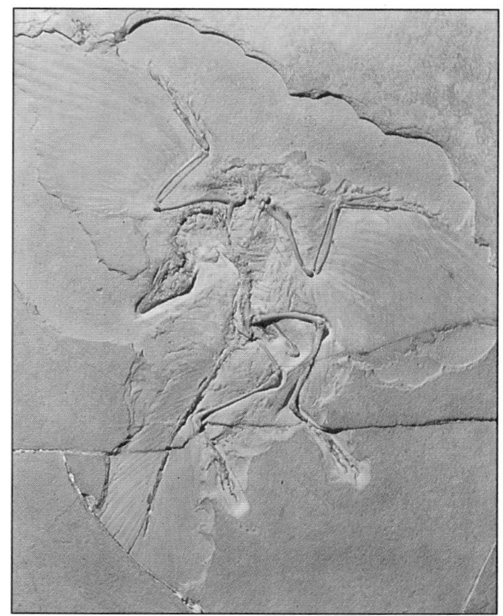

**Left and below left:** The 'Berlin specimen' of *Archaeopteryx* (left), discovered in 1876, reveals the sharp imprints of the feathered wings and tail in fine detail. The 'Solnhofen specimen' (below left) was discovered in the private collection of the former mayor of Solnhofen, F. Müller, in 1987. It had been mistaken for the small dinosaur *Compsognathus*.

**Above:** Charles Darwin had hypothesized that birds must have developed from reptiles. The discovery of *Archaeopteryx* in 1861 provided evidence of just such an evolution: the intermediate reptile-bird was the 'missing link' in the fossil record.

stand that the discovery of such important proof of Charles Darwin's theory of evolution, only two years after the appearance of his famous book *On the Origin of Species* in 1859, caused a considerable stir.[15] *Archaeopteryx* immediately unleashed heated debate between anti-Darwinists like Richard Owen or Andreas Wagner in Munich, and Thomas Henry Huxley, Darwin's 'bulldog'.[16]

Precise analysis of the skeletal remains of *Archaeopteryx* so far known shows a high degree of correspondence in many osteological details with certain predatory dinosaurs, the Theropoda ('beast feet'). John Ostrom of Yale University in New Haven was from 1973 a particular proponent of the ideas of theropod ancestry,[17] and he produced many sound reasons for this. The structure of pelvis and hind legs, and osteological features of arm, foot and skull in particular suggest a clear relationship with dinosaurs like *Deinonychus, Ornitholestes* or *Compsognathus. Archaeopteryx*' dinosaur characteristics are so convincing that some palaeontologists would like to classify the birds as Dinosauria.[18] Despite this some specialists are of the opinion that *Archaeopteryx* and thus birds as well are descended from another group of reptiles, namely the pseudosuchians of the Triassic. As the pseudosuchians are also considered ancestors of the later archosaurs, and thus also of dinosaurs, this dispute is reduced to the question of whether birds were descended directly from the pseudosuchians, or indirectly, via the dinosaurs. These and other opposing viewpoints were discussed at the first International *Archaeopteryx* Conference in Eichstätt, not far from Solnhofen in 1984.[19]

## Origin of Feathers

The only genuine and exclusive bird characteristic of *Archaeopteryx* is its feathers. The wing feathers are already very modern, and asymmetrical in form, which only makes sense if they had an aerodynamic function, as in modern birds capable of flight.[20] Feathers played a key role in the development of flight. It is generally accepted that birds' feathers developed from reptile scales. *Archaeopteryx*' still unknown ancestor, the hypothetical *Proavis*, must also have had a feather-like body-covering, and that even before flight was achieved. The question therefore arises, what was the primary function of these feathers? Were they a protection against cooling for creatures that were already warm-blooded, or the reverse, a shield against excessive irradiation by the sun for cold-blooded animals, a protection against overheating? Were the long, feathered forearms intended for display and fighting, or as fly-swatters for catching insects?

15 Darwin, C., 1859. *On the Origin of Species by Means of Natural Selection, or the Preservation of Favoured Races in the Struggle for Life.* London.

16 The debate on the significance of *Archaeopteryx* is presented in a most interesting and readable fashion in the following two books:
Desmond, A.J., 1975. *The hot-blooded dinosaurs.* p.134 ff., Blond and Briggs, London.
Wilford, J.N., 1985. *The Riddle of the Dinosaurs.* p.71 ff., Knopf Inc., New York.

17 Ostrom, J.H., 1973. *The ancestry of birds.* Nature, 242: 136; London.
Ostrom, J.H., 1976. *Archaeopteryx and the origin of birds.* Biological Journal of the Linnean Society, 8: 91-182; London.

18 Bakker, R.T. and Galton, P.M., 1974. *Dinosaur monophyly and a new class of vertebrates.* Nature, 248: 168-172; London.

19 Hecht, M.K., Ostrom, J.H., Viohl, G. and Wellnhofer, P. (editors), 1985. *The Beginnings of Birds. Proceedings of the International Archaeopteryx Conference Eichstätt, 1984.* 38 contributions, 382 pp., Freunde des Jura-Museums, Eichstätt.

20 Feduccia, A., and Tordoff. H.B., 1979. *Feathers of Archaeopteryx: asymmetric vane indicates aerodynamic function.* Science, 203: 1021-1022; Washington.

**Archaeopteryx**

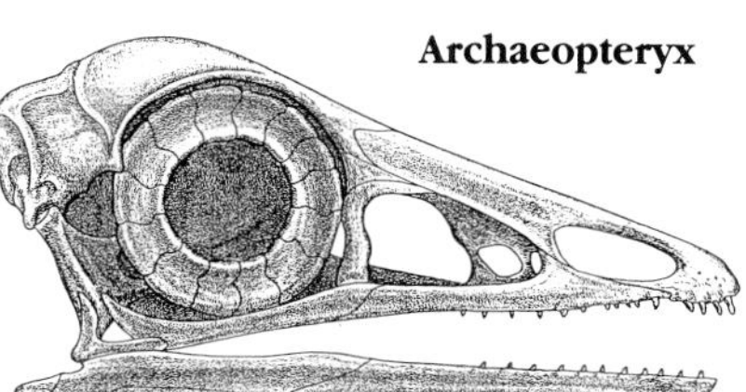

**Compsognathus**

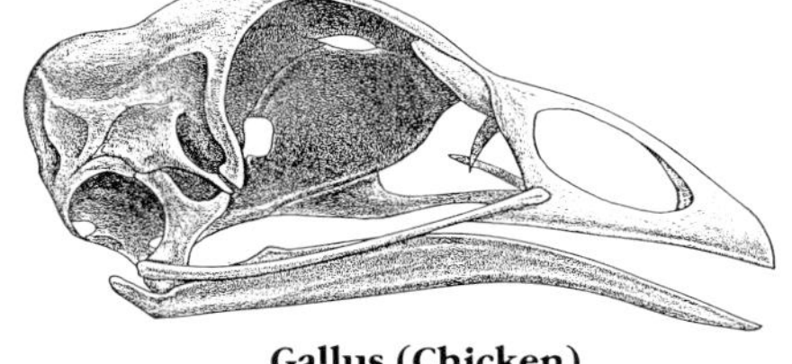

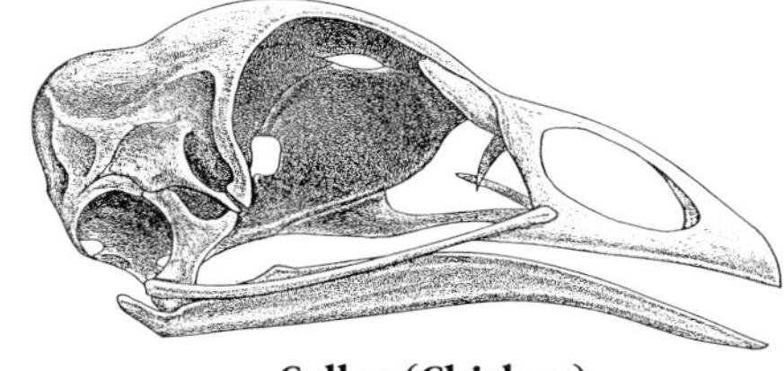

**Gallus (Chicken)**

**Skull Comparisons (above right)**
These drawings allow us to compare the reconstruction of the skull of *Archaeopteryx* (above), with the skull of a small theropod dinosaur, *Compsognathus* (above right), and an extant bird, a chicken (lower right). The teeth and the openings in front of the eye socket that we see in the skull of *Archaeopteryx* are reptilian features i.e. archosaurian characteristics. They are also present in *Compsognathus*, while modern birds by contrast lack teeth and have horny bills. However, the large eye socket and roomy braincase appear more bird-like than reptilian in nature, although small theropod dinosaurs also had large eye sockets. *Archaeopteryx* thus seems to occupy an intermediate evolutionary position between dinosaurs and birds, a view which is now widely accepted.

Were the outspread wings a kind of canopy to shade the surface of the water and so eliminate reflections when looking for food below the surface, or were the feathers primarily intended to have a water-repellent effect? There is still no satisfactory answer to these questions.

## Evolution of Flight in Birds

There are different opinions about the evolution of bird flight, just as there are about the ancestry of birds. Essentially today there are two opposing theories, the arboreal theory and the cursorial theory.

The cursorial theory postulates that avian flight developed from the ground up. Its principal proponents like S.W. Williston (1879), Baron F. Nopcsa (1907) and J.H. Ostrom today argue that osteological peculiarities of pelvis and hind legs in particular of *Archaeopteryx* show that it was a typical biped. In John Ostrom's words (1985): 'In summary, it is my conviction that *Archaeopteryx* was still learning to fly – from the ground up – and that avian flight began in a running, leaping, ground-dwelling biped.'[21] The primeval bird began to flap its wings as it leapt up to catch insects in flight. Enlargement of the feathered area led to bigger and longer jumps, bringing with it a selection advantage that gradually led to active flapping flight.

This cursorial theory is completely opposed to the conventional arboreal theory, according to which flight must have developed from the trees down. This theory was postulated by the Danish scientist G. Heilmann in particular,[22] and is recognized by many biologists today. Its supporters' principal objection to the cursorial theory is that the energy requirements for fast running and simultaneous wing flapping are very high, and additionally that flight from the ground up is against the force of gravity. Gliding from the trees down needs much less energy, as it exploits the Earth's pull. Transport costs in terms of energy are further reduced if the animal extends its gliding flights by flapping its wings, and can thus enlarge its radius of action, for example when looking for food.

A further point is that *Archaeopteryx*' digital claws are highly curved, and had extremely sharp points. The toe claws were less curved but also had pointed horn claws, ideally adapted to climbing up tree trunks. *Archaeopteryx* could support itself with its long rigid tail when doing this. Birds that live exclusively on the ground and run on two legs have very worn claws.

Walter Bock, professor at Columbia University, New York, has postulated several stages that could have led to active flight in birds.[23] He assumes that small reptiles, 'protobirds', started to live in trees to hide, to sleep and possibly to nest. In the cool environment of the tree-tops they developed warm-bloodedness and feathers as insulation. Elongation of the feathers on the arms at first only served to soften falls to the ground by an increase in surface area. This was the start of the evolution of wings, which finally led via a parachute and gliding stage to active flapping flight, a stage

21 Ostrom, J.H., 1985. *The Meaning of Archaeopteryx*. in ref. 19: 161-176.

22 Heilmann, G., 1926. *The Origin of Birds*. 210 pp., Appleton, New York.

23 Bock, W.J., 1985. *The Arboreal Theory for the Origin of Birds*. in ref. 19: 199-207.

**Archaeopteryx in Action (above)**
This life restoration shows *Archaeopteryx* flying down from a tree, running on the ground, and climbing up another tree assisted by the sharp claws on its fingers and toes. In this way of life both arboreal and cursorial adaptations could be exploited to advantage, and were in fact mutually complementary.

3-clawed hand
Long forelimbs with wing-like proportion
Reptilian teeth
Long bony tail
Furcula ('Wishbone')
Reptilian gastralia
Dinosaur-like pubis
Reversed 1st toe
Metatarsals not fused

**Archaeopteryx**

**Skeletal Comparisons (right and below)**
Here *Archaeopteryx* is compared to *Compsognathus* and a chicken. *Archaeopteryx* more closely resembles *Compsognathus* in build, especially with regard to the skull, vertebral column, pelvis and hind legs. The main difference lies in the longer forelimbs which have developed to bear feathers and form wings. Another avian feature is the presence of a 'wishbone'. In the chicken, the bony tail is greatly reduced. Other modifications are clearly linked to the aerial way of life and include a large breastbone to which the shoulder girdle is anchored, and fused clawless fingers on the hand.

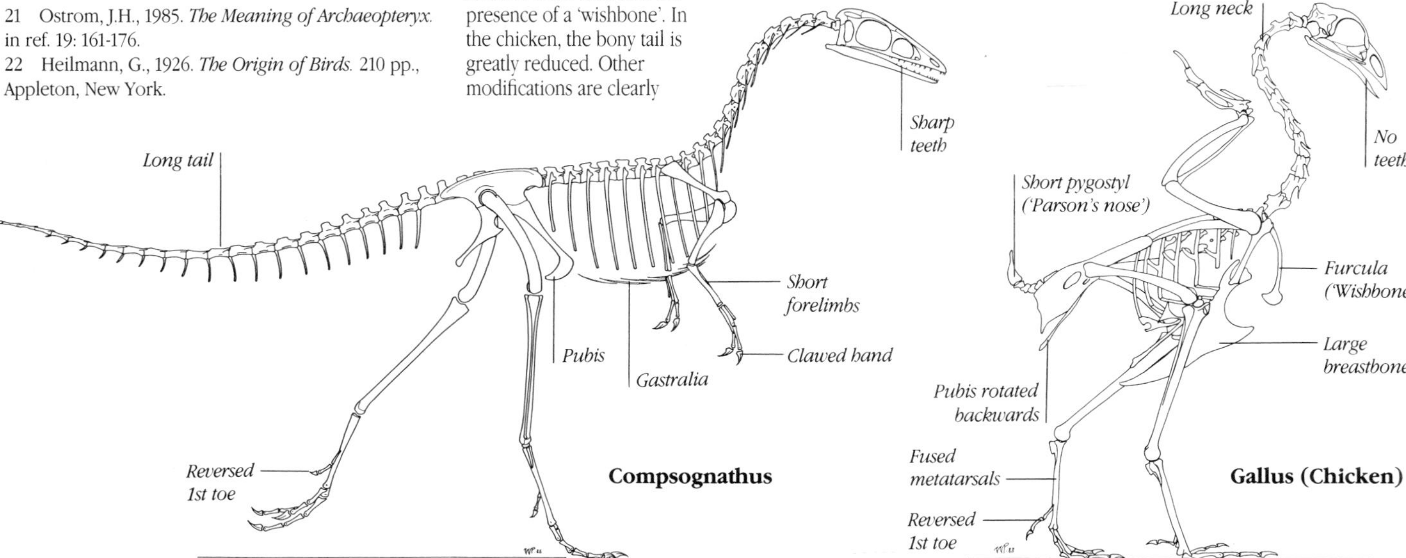

that had certainly already been reached in the case of *Archaeopteryx*.

It is nevertheless to be assumed that the Solnhofen primeval birds were still poor fliers. Their flight muscles cannot have been as well developed as those of modern birds, as they still did not have a breastbone for attachment of the pectoral muscles responsible for the downstroke of the wings.[24]

## Other Fossil Birds

How did the evolution of birds proceed after *Archaeopteryx*? Unfortunately in the early Cretaceous there are great gaps in the fossil record. Recently remains of fossil skeletons of birds, some of them with feathers, were discovered in Spain.[25] They are about 125 million years old, thus 25 million years younger than *Archaeopteryx*. It was a small bird, already with an ossified sternum, and also a shortened tail, in which the last vertebrae had fused to form a Parson's nose (a so-called pygostyl), although the pelvis and other characteristics were still 'primitively' reptilian. This can be regarded as an intermediate form between *Archaeopteryx* and modern birds.

Another primitive bird, the genus *Ambiortus*, was found in Lower Cretacous sediments in Mongolia. It too shows a mosaic pattern of archaic and advanced characteristics. *Ambiortus* must already have been able to fly well, as it too had an ossified sternum.[26]

Analysis of these early fossil skeletons makes it quite clear that the evolution of birds was directed primarily at improving flight qualities. It enabled birds to spread world-wide even in the Cretaceous: fossil remains of Cretaceous birds have been found in America, Europe, Africa, Asia and Australia.

Skeletal remains that were in good condition and fairly complete were removed from the Niobrara Chalk of West Kansas, USA. These were the late Cretaceous strata that produced the great pterosaurs *Pteranodon* and *Nyctosaurus*. O.C. Marsh found the first bird bones during his first expedition to the Western USA in 1870.[27] More complete skeletons came to light in subsequent years, of two different types, *Ichthyornis* (fish bird), the Cretaceous 'gull', which was capable of flight, and the diver *Hesperornis* (bird of the West), which was incapable of flight. Both had teeth in their jaws, for which reason O.C. Marsh classified them as toothed birds (Odontornithes) in a major monograph written in 1880. Another genus, *Baptornis* was recognized from there, besides *Hesperornis*.[28]

Even in the Upper Cretaceous ancestors of modern bird orders are found. But it is not until the early Tertiary, about 50 million years ago, that the first great radiation, or splitting into many different orders and families, took

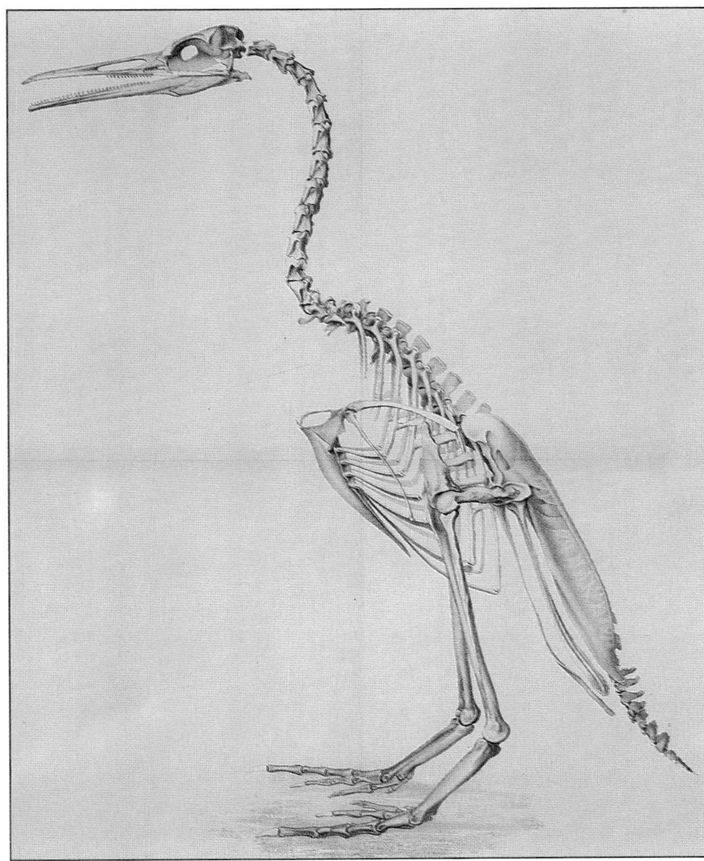

**Left:** The toothed diving bird *Hesperornis* occurs in the same fossil deposits in the Niobrara Chalk of West Kansas as *Ichthyornis* (right). It was a large, flightless bird, well adapted for diving. This restoration is from O.C. Marsh's 1880 monograph *On the Extinct Toothed Birds of North America*.

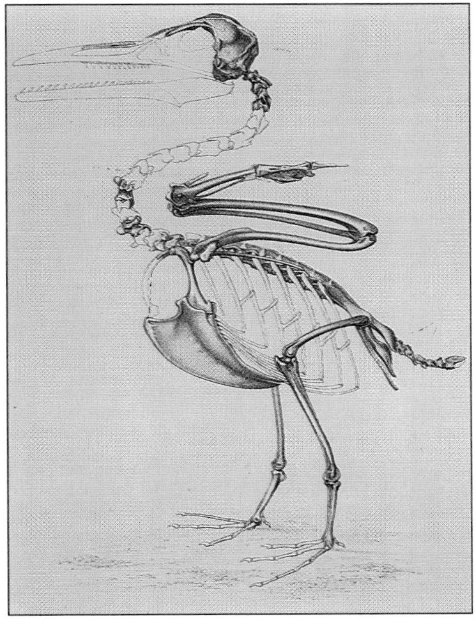

**Right:** Another skeletal restoration from Marsh's 1880 monograph, *Ichthyornis* was a primitive flying bird of the size and life style of a modern gull. These birds must have lived in large flocks on the coast of the Cretaceous mid-continental seaway.

**Baptornis (below)**
The toothed diving bird *Baptornis* from the Kansas Niobrara Chalk was closely related to *Hesperornis* which was recognized by O.C. Marsh in 1877. It had a very long neck, reduced wings, and large webbed feet that it used to propel itself through the water.

24 Feduccia, A., 1980. *The Age of Birds.* Harvard University Press, Cambridge, Mass. German translation entitled *Es begann am Jura-Meer. Die faszinierende Stammesgeschichte der Vögel.* Gerstenberg-Verlag, Hildesheim, 1984.
Wellnhofer, P., 1989. *Archaeopteryx.* Spektrum der Wissenschaft, 9, 1989.
Wellnhofer, P., 1990. *Archaeopteryx.* Scientific American, 262 (5): 70-77; Washington.

25 Sanz, J.L., Bonaparte, J.F. and Lacasa, A., 1988. *Unusual Early Cretaceous birds from Spain.* Nature, 331: 433-435; London.

26 Kurochkin, E.N., 1985. *A True Carinate Bird from Lower Cretaceous Deposits in Mongolia and Other Evidence of Early Cretaceous Birds in Asia.* Cretaceous Research, 6: 271-278; London.

27 Marsh, O.C., 1880. *Odontornithes: a monograph on the extinct toothed birds of North America.* Report of the US Geological Exploration of the Fortieth Parallel, no. 7; Washington.

28 Martin, L.D. and Tate, J., Jr., 1976. *The skeleton of Baptornis advenus (Aves: Hesperornithiformes).* Smithsonian Contributions to Paleobiology, 27: 35-66; Washington.

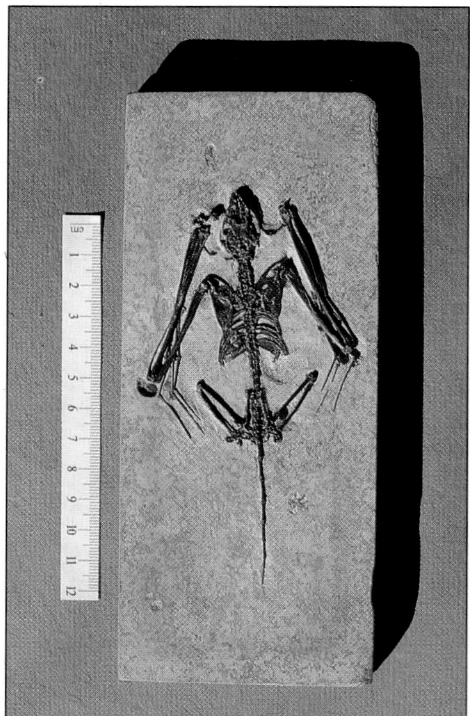

**Above:** *Icaronycteris* from early Tertiary lake deposits in Wyoming is regarded as the oldest known bat. The fossil shows the complete skeleton preserved with the long wing bones folded, and an unusual long tail. This fine specimen resides in the Yale Peabody Museum.

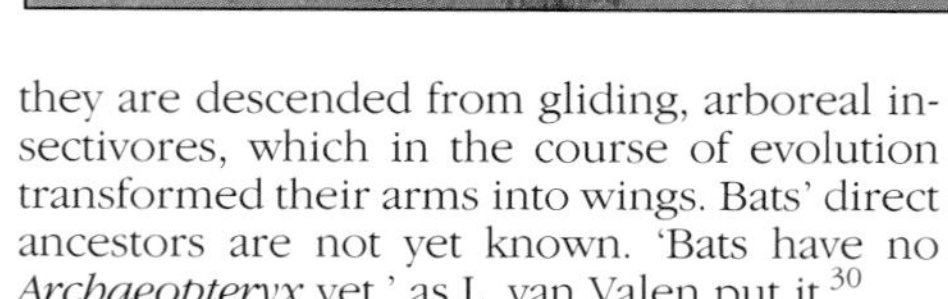

**Right:** Several genera of bats have been found in Lower Tertiary lake deposits in Germany. This is *Archaeonycteris* from the famous Messel pit near Darmstadt. In this oil shale soft parts, including even stomach contents, are preserved. The Messel bats were insect eaters.

place in birds. Very different habitats were occupied in the course of this, including those vacated by pterosaurs at the end of the Cretaceous. The last to emerge were the Passeriformes, in the late Tertiary.

From modest beginnings in the Jurassic, 150 million years ago, documented by the unique *Archaeopteryx* specimens from Solnhofen, 8,700 species of bird have now evolved, from the tiny humming-bird with a wing span of 3in (7·5cm) to the albatross with a wing span of 11ft (3·4m). During the last Ice Age there were far larger birds, however. The largest so far known is the extinct giant vulture *Argentavis* (Argentina bird). From head to foot it was 5ft (1·5m) long and had a wing span of 24ft (7·3m).[29] Thus it was just as big as *Pteranodon* from the Niobrara Chalk of Kansas, but certainly heavier than these pterosaurs.

## Bats

There are various mammal groups that developed powers of gliding independently of one another, like for example flying lemurs and flying squirrels, or marsupials like honey gliders and greater gliding phalangers. However, bats were the only mammals to have developed active flapping flight. It is assumed that they are descended from gliding, arboreal insectivores, which in the course of evolution transformed their arms into wings. Bats' direct ancestors are not yet known. 'Bats have no *Archaeopteryx* yet,' as L. van Valen put it.[30]

In the fossil record bats do not appear until the early Tertiary. The oldest bat is *Icaronycteris* from the lake deposits of the Green River Formation in Wyoming, USA, which are about 50 million years old.[31] Some bat genera from Eocene deposits in Germany, like the lignite mines of the Geiseltal near Halle, and from lake sediments from the Messel pit near Darmstadt, the genus *Archaeonycteris*, for example, are almost as old. Even in these early forms one finds structures in the auditory region that prove that they already had echo location or sonar, like modern bats. This made them able to hunt for insects at twilight or even at night.

Bats are able to emit pulses of very high-pitched sound at short intervals, usually 10 to 200 times a second. When these sound signals meet an obstacle or a flying insect, they are reflected, and received by the bat's sensitive ears. This echo serves to localize prey, and is an aid to navigation in a three-dimensional airspace. This extreme specialization meant that bats could conquer their own ecological niches, and assert themselves *vis-à-vis* birds.[32]

Even the oldest bats have the typical skeletal structure of their order. The four outer digits (II-V) of their hand are enormously elongated and form an inner support for the wing surface. This is made up of a thin, almost naked membrane, extending down to the feet. Because the long fingers are an integral part of the wing, and can spread and fold it, bats have much greater wing manoeuvrability than pterosaurs, in which the flight membrane is spread by a single digit. Bats' flight membrane contains blood vessels and has muscle fibres running through it. They do not have the internal reinforcement fibres typical of pterosaurs. There is also a membrane between the hind legs and the tail, supported by a special bone, the calcar, originating at the ankle of the foot.

The first hand digit, the thumb, is short in all bats, and has a claw. The normal rest position is hanging by the feet, with the head downwards. They sleep in this position during the day, and hibernate in moderate zones. Then the wings are pulled tight round the body, which is completely wrapped up in the flight membranes.

On the ground bats become genuine quadrupeds. They fold their flight membranes and

29 Campbell, K.E., Jr., 1980. *The world's largest flying bird.* Terra, 19 (2): 20-23; Los Angeles.
Campbell. K.E., Jr. and Tonni, E.P., 1980. *A new genus of Teratorn from the Huayquerian of Argentina (Aves: Teratornithidae).* Contributions in Science, 330: 59-68; Los Angeles.

30 Van Valen, L., 1979. *The evolution of bats.* Evolutionary Theory, 4: 103-121.
31 Jepsen, G.L., 1966. *Early Eocene bat from Wyoming.* Science, 154: 1333-1339; Washington.
32 Novacek, M.J., 1985. *Evidence for echolocation in the oldest known bats.* Nature, 315: 140-141; London.
Further reading on bats:
Norberg, U.M. and Rayner, J.M.V., 1987. *Ecological morphology in bats (Mammalia; Chiroptera): wing adaptations, flight performance, foraging strategy and echolocation.* Philosophical Transactions of the Royal Society of London, B, 316: 335-427.
Fenton, M.B., Racey, P.A. and Rayner, J.M.V. (editors), 1987. *Recent Advances in the Study of Bats,* Cambridge University Press.
Nachtigall, W. (editor), 1986. *Biona Report 5, Bat flight – Fledermausflug,* Gustav Fischer Verlag, Stuttgart.

rest their fore feet on the ground on an upholstered pad on the wrist and support themselves on the soles of their hind feet. The hind legs stand off laterally from the body. Bats are by no means as awkward when moving on the ground as is often assumed. Many species are even nimble runners. But above all bats are excellent climbers. The clawed, freely-moving thumb plays an important part in this. On vertical walls the animal pulls itself upwards by its thumb claws and supports itself with the clawed toes.

Bats (Chiroptera) are a distinct order of mammal. Two suborders are distinguished, Microchiroptera, predominantly insectivorous, and Megachiroptera, mainly fruit eaters, like fruit bats and flying foxes. The latter do not appear in the fossil record until the middle to late Tertiary. Both suborders probably go back to a common ancestral form, as yet unknown, in the earliest Tertiary or latest Cretaceous.

About 800 species of bat are known today. They live all over the world except in the polar regions, but preferably in the tropics. As well as fruit and insect eaters there are nectar drinkers, carnivores which eat small animals or even other bats, and fish eaters, who catch their prey from the water with their feet in flight. Genuine vampire bats are bloodsuckers.

Bats vary considerably in size. Pipistrelles have a wing span of only 7in (18cm), while the Java flying fox reaches a wing span of 4ft (1·2m) and more. Bats are mammals, and thus give birth to living young, usually only one, on rare occasions two. At first they are entirely dependent on the mother, and are suckled. Later they make themselves independent of the mother and learn to fly and hunt for food for themselves.

Today there are many endangered species of both birds and bats. This is due to the activities of man who, within a very short time, introduced a new factor into the evolutionary process of the biosphere, also affecting many natural environments of birds and bats. It is to be hoped that these fascinating flying vertebrates with their long evolutionary history will be saved by an increasing awareness of our human responsibility for life on Earth.

**Below:** This portrait of a Bechstein's bat shows very clearly the wing membrane, supported by the elongated fingers, joining the body and hind legs down to the ankle, the so-called chiropatagium. A small, triangular membrane, the propatagium, extends between the upper and lower arm, while a further membrane, the uropatagium, joins the legs and tail.

**Icaronycteris (right)**
The skeletal restoration of *Icaronycteris*, the oldest known bat in the fossil record, shows that its bauplan had quite a modern appearance. Although about 50 million years old, it has no 'primitive' or intermediate features which would point to a particular ancestor for bats. The wing skeleton typically shows the greatly elongated bones of the upper arm, the lower arm and the four outer fingers which in life were enclosed within a thin membrane of skin that extended to the body and hind legs. The long tail was probably totally enclosed in a membrane between the hind legs. The thumb bearing a claw remained free, and could be used for climbing and hooking on to rocks or trees. The dentition points to a diet of insects. Recent studies indicate that even these oldest bats had an echolocation system like modern bats for orientation in the dark and the location of prey insects.

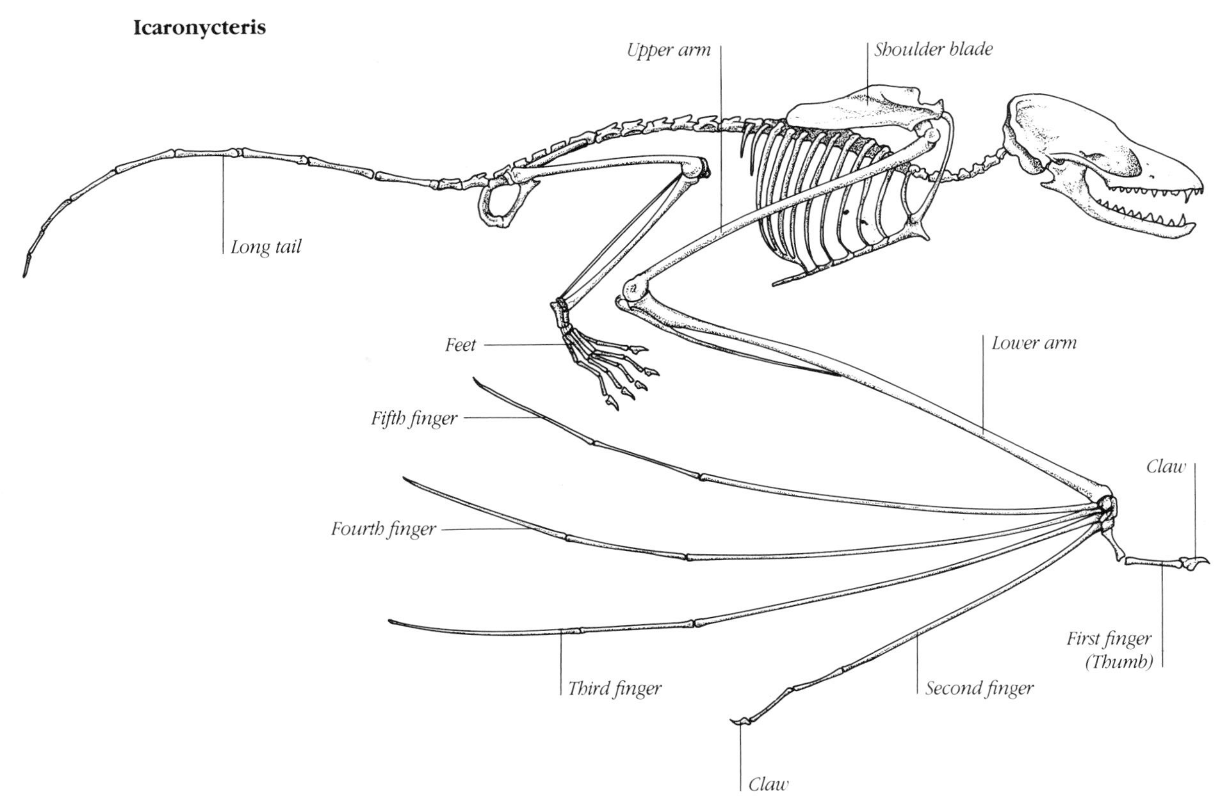

# CROCODILES

The crocodiles are a remarkable group of reptiles which, like the pterosaurs, are quite close relatives of the dinosaurs; they appear to have evolved from archosaurian ancestors during the late Triassic. However, their history is very different from that of the pterosaurs and dinosaurs because crocodiles have survived right through to the present day. For some reason they avoided the extinctions that affected so many groups of animals at the end of the Cretaceous. One of the most notable characters of this group is its enormous conservatism. Once crocodiles appeared in the Triassic Period as moderate to large-sized semi-aquatic predators their fate was sealed, and they have changed relatively little in body-form since then.

Modern crocodilians are found in tropical and subtropical environments and are of two major types. One group, the crocodylids, consists of the crocodiles and alligators of almost world-wide distribution; the gavialids comprise the slender-snouted fish-eating gavials (gharials) of India.

The ferocious alligators and crocodiles have relatively broad diets taking fish, large vertebrates (including humans!) and carrion whenever possible. Large vertebrates are generally caught in or near water by stealth. The attributes that allow crocodilians to feed in this way summarise many of their typical features. Crocodilians are long-bodied reptiles with a long and extremely powerful tail which is used for swimming, and as a defensive lash on land. The limbs are relatively short in proportion to their body length and are used for manoeuvring and steering in water. On land crocodiles and alligators mostly walk with a slow, measured stride with the belly held quite high off the ground. Although their legs do not seem particularly powerful, crocodiles are capable of short bursts of fast running on land either to catch prey or return quickly to the water. While these comments apply to adult crocodiles, this is not true of young crocodilians; these by contrast have disproportionately long legs and are remarkably active on land as well as in the water. Unlike the adults, young crocodiles feed on small vertebrates (frogs, fish) and a variety of insects and can, on occasions, even be found climbing in low shrubs in pursuit of their prey! Adults use the powerful tail to swim close to potential prey, they remain almost completely submerged, with just eyes and nostrils breaking the water. The eyes are specially positioned on top of the skull, and the nostrils are similarly located right at the tip of the snout and have special valves to close them off when the animals are completely submerged. Crocodiles also have a special bony roof to the mouth so that the air passage from the nostrils to the lungs is separated from the mouth—a neat way of avoiding drowning when trying to breathe while semi-submerged. The jaws of crocodiles are long and lined with large conical teeth which are very deeply rooted in the jaws. These jaws and teeth are well suited to overcoming large active prey such as wild pigs or antelope; the skull is also very heavily constructed in order to withstand the severe stresses and strains of violently struggling animals. Once killed, either directly or by drowning, the prey generally has to be dismembered prior to swallowing. This is done in a variety of ways: moderate-sized prey tends to be lifted out of the water and vigorously shaken from side to side until it is torn into pieces that can be swallowed with ease; larger prey are more difficult and their carcasses are often wedged under rocks or fallen trees beneath water. This

**Above:** Contemporary crocodiles are ferocious predators in tropical lakes and streams. Their prey ranges from large fish that are swallowed whole to much larger animals, such as antelopes, which are usually caught at water-holes when they come down to drink. Crocodiles are not able to chew off large pieces of meat as a lion can, so they have to tear such carcasses apart underwater. The crocodiles are one of the existing links to the Mesozoic Era. They survived the mass-extinction at the end of the Cretaceous.

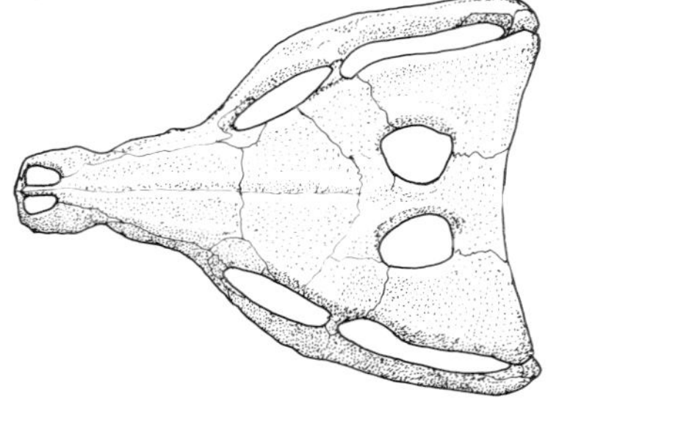

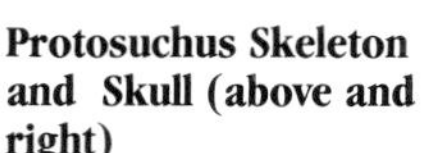

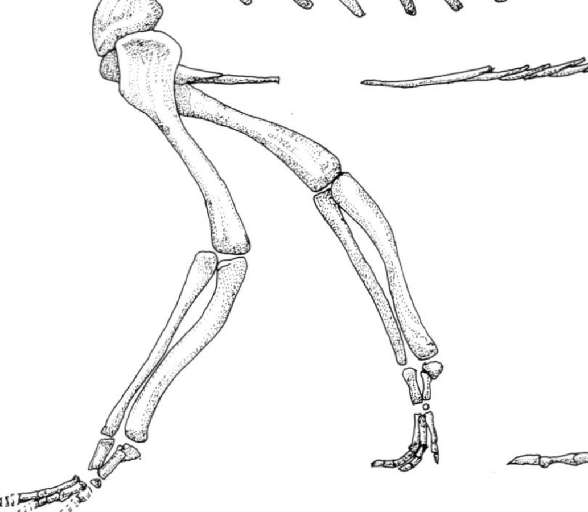

**Protosuchus Skeleton and Skull (above and right)**
These two reconstructions of the late Triassic crocodile *Protosuchus* are based on the work of Charles Mook and Edwin Colbert. Compared with modern crocodilians, *Protosuchus* is rather unusual. Its head is low and broad, and the snout, which is so typically long in modern forms, is really quite short and narrow. The remainder of the skeleton is also noteworthy. This was a small animal (c. 3·3ft, 1m long) and it had a slender build with a short trunk and long legs that lifted the belly quite high off the ground. Its back was armour-plated quite extensively (not shown here). *Protosuchus* may have spent much of its time on land.

**Above:** The little-known and studied gharial (*Gavialis gangeticus*) is an exclusively fish-eating crocodilian. Note the long snout lined with sharp teeth for gripping slippery fish. The lump on the tip of the snout develops in mature individuals.

**Left:** Crocodilians are very agile when young, chasing and catching insects in particular. This habit even takes them into trees in pursuit of prey. This young alligator has obviously graduated to larger prey but is being rather ambitious in his attempt to catch this fledgling egret.

allows the crocodile to take a firm hold of a desired portion (such as a leg) and then twist violently round and round underwater, using legs and tail, until the piece is torn off. All these peculiar manoeuvres are necessary because crocodiles have stabbing teeth rather than slicing teeth, and are therefore unable to chew off pieces of any prey too big to be swallowed whole.

Another notable feature of crocodiles and alligators is the heavy bony armour-plating of their backs. The body armour is undoubtedly valuable protection against predators, particularly for younger crocodiles which may be preyed upon by birds and large monitor lizards. The need for well-developed armour in adults is less obvious because there are no natural predators of these animals, and presumably simply reflects its importance for the young animals. However, another rather unexpected 'use' for body armour seems to be emerging from recent work by Frey and Reiss in Tübingen. They have demonstrated that the body armour is firmly attached to the muscles and bones of the back and lends a great deal of support to this area of the back above the hips during locomotion on land. In fact, it could be that the development of body armour down the back was a crucial step in the evolutionary line that in the Triassic led to the dinosaurs appearing on land.

Gharials (or gavials) are a peculiar group of fish-eating crocodiles which are today restricted to Indian rivers. They are quite large animals characterised by a very long and narrow snout fringed with even, sharply-pointed teeth. These adaptations are ideally suited to fish-eating and are not seen developed to quite the same degree in other living crocodiles.

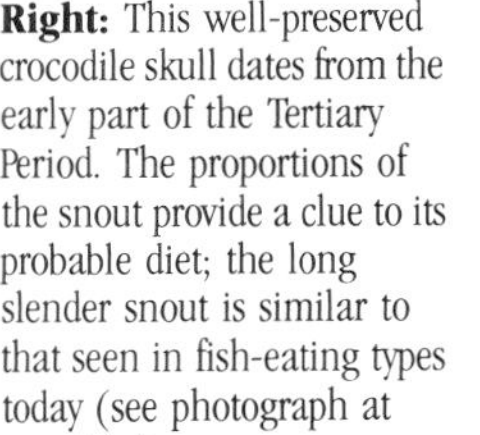

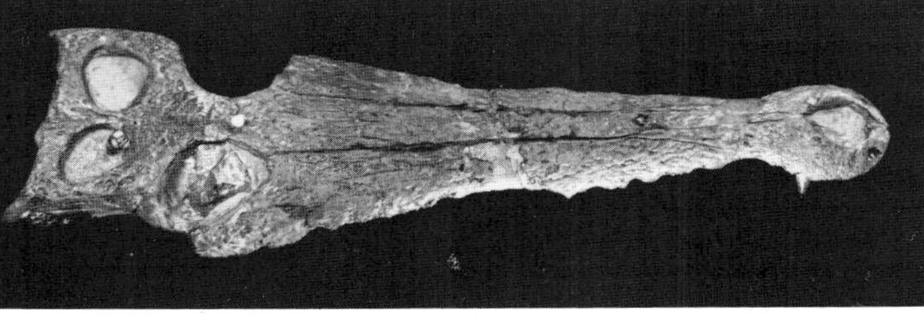

**Right:** This well-preserved crocodile skull dates from the early part of the Tertiary Period. The proportions of the snout provide a clue to its probable diet; the long slender snout is similar to that seen in fish-eating types today (see photograph at top right).

## Mesozoic Crocodilians

In the Mesozoic, crocodilians of various sorts are known, some from very well preserved fossil material. Some such examples are described below. *Protosuchus* ('first crocodile') is a small (3·3ft, 1m long) primitive crocodilian from the late Triassic or possibly early Jurassic of Arizona. It was first described by Barnum Brown in the 1930s from material originally collected by Navajo Indians and later from more fossils including 6 partial skeletons. In 1951 Professor Edwin Colbert and Charles Mook described the best material of *Protosuchus*. *Protosuchus* has rather different proportions from modern crocodiles. The head is quite short and broad, with a rather narrow snout. The neck and back are also short and the tail is of only moderate length—generally a much more 'compact' creature than those of today. The limbs accentuate the differences as well; as in all archosaurs the hindlimbs are longer than the forelimbs, but again the limbs are remarkably long for a crocodilian.

*Protosuchus* was evidently primarily a terrestrial crocodilian, an active land-living predator. This conclusion accords not only with the proportions of the body and limbs, but also with the head which has eyes and nostrils positioned on the side of the head rather than on top as in modern crocodilians.

*Orthosuchus* ('straight crocodile') is another early crocodilian, this time from the late Triassic of Lesotho (southern Africa). *Orthosuchus* was discovered by a team of collectors from the South African Museum (Cape Town) in 1963. Described in detail in 1975 by Dr Diane Nash (Bath, UK) *Orthosuchus* bears a strong resemblance to *Protosuchus* in its general proportions. Again it is rather a short-bodied creature. However, its limbs appear somewhat shorter than those of *Protosuchus* and there is less disparity between fore and hindlimbs. The skull has a rather unusual pattern of teeth compared with that of *Protosuchus,* but otherwise its proportions are remarkably similar. Nash proposed that the narrow-snouted form of the skull and relatively feeble teeth may indicate that *Orthosuchus* preyed upon fish rather than larger terrestrial vertebrates and suggested, albeit tentatively, that *Orthosuchus* may have inhabited swampy areas to avoid competition with early carnivorous dinosaurs and large predatory thecodontians.

More typical crocodilians are found in the Jurassic Period. *Teleosaurus* ('end reptile') and *Steneosaurus* ('narrow reptile') are two reasonably well-known early Jurassic forms. These types of crocodile appear to have been marine or possibly estuarine inhabitants. They have typical long-bodied crocodile-like bodies, and have notably elongate snouts lined with thin sharp teeth indicating that they were primarily fish eaters. Despite their obvious preference for the aquatic habitat, these forms retained the typical heavily-armoured body and well-developed limbs and feet—unlike the next type.

*Metriorhynchus* ('long snout') and *Geosaurus* ('rock reptile') are members of a very distinctive group of Jurassic crocodilians sometimes referred to as thallatosuchians ('sea crocodiles'). These long-snouted, presumably fish-eating crocodilians were completely un-armoured and their limbs were modified into turtle-like flippers or paddles. The paddle-like limbs, however, were not the main propulsive organs; this was the tail which was similarly modified into fish-like form by the development of a tail fin. The end of the tail was bent sharply downward in order to strengthen the fin in the same way as in the tail fins of the dolphin-like ichthyosaurs (see pages 368-370). For some reason these 'sea crocodiles' were not particularly successful because they seem to have gone extinct in late Jurassic times.

Modern types of crocodile begin to appear toward the end of the Jurassic Period in the form of crocodiles such as *Goniopholis* a 6·5-10ft (2-3m) long, reasonably typical crocodile which is found fairly widespread across Europe at about this time. Two rather fine *Goniopholis* skeletons were found at Bernissart among the many *Iguanodon* carcasses. Whether *Goniopholis* was actually scavenging the carcasses or was merely preserved there by accident is impossible to decide.

In addition to *Goniopholis,* another interesting crocodilian specimen was found among the *Iguanodon* carcasses at Bernissart. This tiny crocodilian, less than 3ft (1m) long, was named *Bernissartia* by Louis Dollo in 1885. *Bernissartia* was small but well-armoured, and had rather peculiar teeth in its jaws. The front teeth were normal simple spikes; the posterior teeth, however, were unusually broad and flattened—

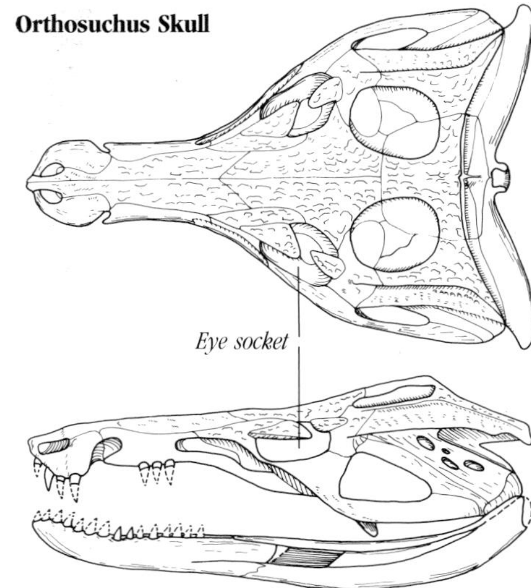


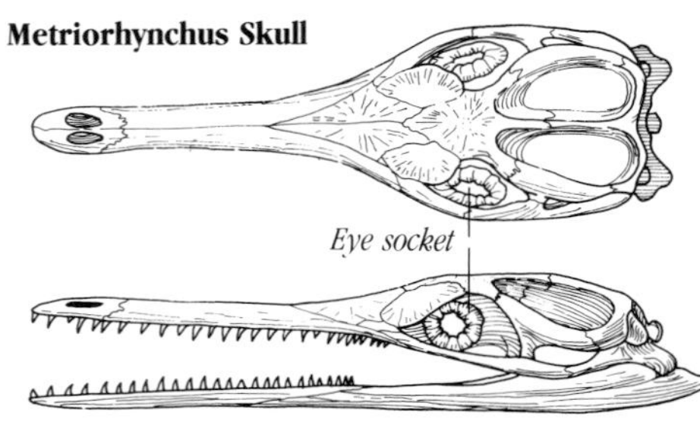


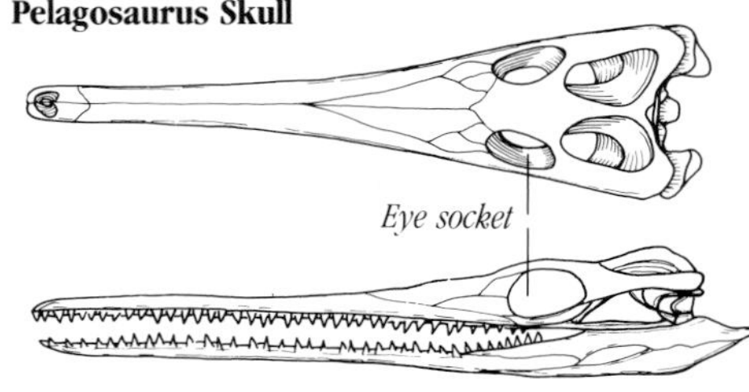


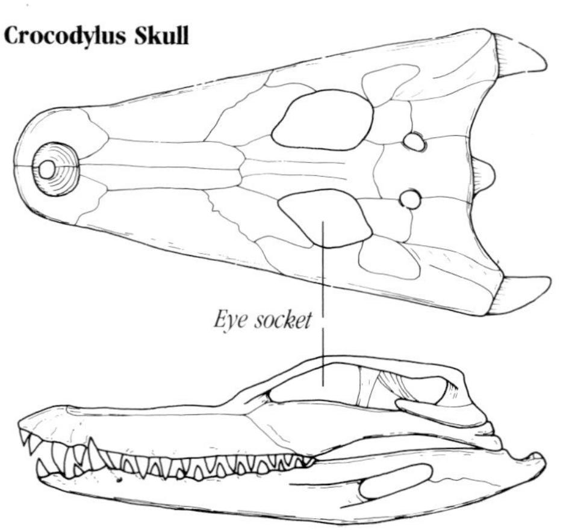


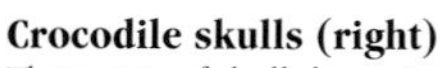

**Crocodile skulls (right)**
The variety of skull shapes in crocodilians can be appreciated here. *Orthosuchus* from the late Triassic of southern Africa is broad and short-snouted as is *Protosuchus* (page 364). *Metriorhynchus* and *Pelagosaurus* show an extreme elongation of the snout that suggests a fish diet, while *Crocodylus* is a broad and powerful general predator.

**Left:** This fossilised bony armour plate (or scute) of *Diplocynodon* is typically crocodilian having a rough and pitted texture.

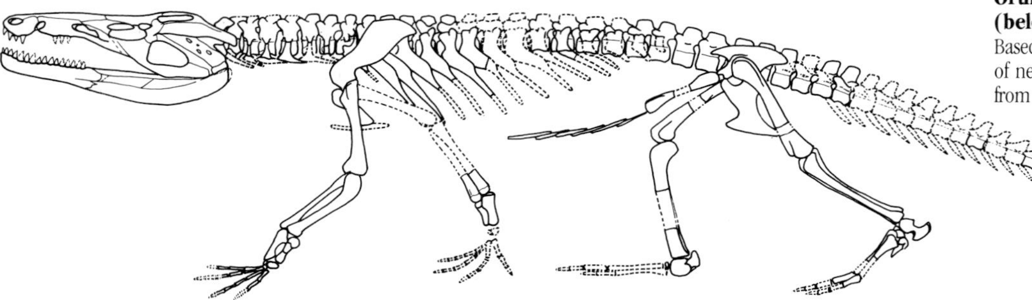

**Orthosuchus Skeleton (below)**
Based on Diane Nash's study of new material collected from Southern Africa in the 1960s, this reconstruction of *Orthosuchus* is broadly similar to *Protosuchus* (page 364). The jaws and rather feeble teeth suggest that *Orthosuchus* was a swamp-dweller feeding on fish, rather than a land-living predator.

shaped more like crushing plates than piercing teeth. Perhaps these unusual little crocodiles had a varied diet including shellfish. The blunt posterior teeth may have served as crushing plates to crack open the hard shells of clams, while the sharp front teeth could be used for grasping more conventional soft-bodied prey such as fish.

During the Cretaceous Period, the crocodilians were very abundant and widespread, far more so than today. This probably reflects the fact that the conditions were much milder than they are at the present time. Records of warmth-loving plants from the Mesozoic Era indicate that tropical or subtropical conditions extended into the temperate and subarctic regions of today.

One of the most remarkable of the Cretaceous crocodiles comes from the Rio Grande in Texas. Named *Deinosuchus* ('terrible crocodile') or *Phobosuchus* ('fearsome crocodile') this is the largest crocodile so far found. Although incomplete, *Deinosuchus* had a skull measuring 6ft (1·8m) in length. If this creature had the proportions of a typical crocodile then it may have attained a length of 40-50ft (12-15m). It seems quite possible that *Deinosuchus* preyed upon dinosaurs in the late Cretaceous. *Deinosuchus* was either a typical amphibious crocodile preying upon occasional wading sauropods or hadrosaurs, or as some have proposed it may have been a short-bodied, longer-legged terrestrial predator of dinosaurs. It would obviously be interesting to find more remains of this remarkable crocodilian.

## Recent Crocodilians

In addition to the comments already made about living crocodiles, a few other points need to be considered because they have a bearing on later sections of this book concerned with the origin of dinosaurs (page 170) and the debate on the physiology of dinosaurs (page 172).

**Crocodile ankles** As was mentioned earlier, crocodiles are able to adopt an unusually high gait when they walk (i.e. the belly is held very high off the ground). As a result the legs are drawn in very nearly underneath the body. This so-called 'semi-erect' position is a more efficient method of walking than the sprawling posture used by most other reptiles in which the belly is very close to the ground and the legs splay outward. However, in order to walk like this crocodiles have developed rather special ankle joints which have a special swivel section in the middle; this permits powerful twisting movements to occur at the ankle during the 'high walk'. As was seen (page 36), the unusual ankle and 'high walk' of the crocodile figure large in the origin of dinosaur walking methods.

**Crocodilian behaviour** It has often been alleged in the past that reptiles are rather 'simple' creatures and therefore incapable of the complex types of behaviour seen in living mammals and birds. On this basis it has been argued that as several types of dinosaur seem to show evidence of complex behaviour, dinosaurs must be more like mammals and birds than reptiles.

Hugh Cott, an authority on crocodilians, has been able to show quite conclusively that crocodiles are capable of very complex behaviour indeed. One of the best examples of such behaviour is the exhibition of parental care in the Nile crocodile. In this species the hatchling crocodiles call to their parents from the nest mound. This stimulates the parent crocodiles to break open the nest and release the young; these are then carried in the jaws of the parents to special 'nurseries' where their growth and development is watched over to prevent predators from taking the young. They are finally released when they are large enough to defend themselves against potential predators. All this information is comparatively recent work based on the field observations of Hugh Cott who has done more than anyone else to further our understanding of these remarkable animals. Its implications with regard to our view of dinosaurs and their possible behavioural patterns as well as those of living reptiles have been of great value.

**Above:** *Bernissartia fagesii;* this remarkable little crocodile was found among the *Iguanodon* skeletons at Bernissart. It may have been scavenging the flesh of the dinosaur carcasses when it was buried. However, the blunt rear teeth may point to a diet of shellfish. It was named after Gustav Fagès, the manager of the mine at Bernissart.

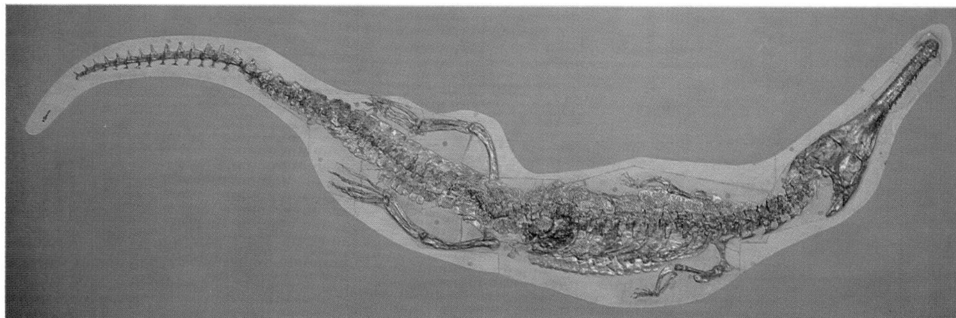

**Right:** *Steneosaurus,* a Jurassic crocodile, is typical of a variety that became well adapted to a purely aquatic way of life in the Mesozoic. Note the long body well suited to swimming, and the relatively small forelimbs. A diet of fish is indicated by the long snout. This was most probably an estuarine rather than an ocean-going form.

# Marine Reptiles

In addition to the various archosaurian types of reptile (pterosaurs and crocodiles), a number of other groups of reptiles co-existed with the dinosaurs during the Mesozoic Era. Many of these were aquatic forms of considerable variety. Representatives of these types of reptile are described below.

## Ichthyosaurs

Of all the varied reptilian types the ichthyosaurs ('fish reptiles') are by far the most highly adapted to an aquatic life-style. They seem to have occupied the niche now taken by porpoises of the present day. The earliest ichthyosaurs date back to the late Triassic. Even these, however, are clearly ichthyosaurs and give few clues to the earlier origin of these reptiles. Ichthyosaurs were particularly abundant in the Jurassic Period, although their remains extend into the late Cretaceous as well.

*Mixosaurus* ('mixed reptile') from the late Triassic is an early ichthyosaur that already possesses a full range of ichthyosaur characteristics. The head is drawn out into a long thin snout fringed with small spiky teeth; the eyes are unusually large and supported by a circular array of bones which probably improved the focusing abilities. The body is smooth and streamlined for efficient movement through the water and the neck is notably absent in profile view; this was achieved by great compression of the neck vertebrae (a similar phenomenon is seen in porpoises today). The limbs are modified into paddles which may have been used for steering rather than for propulsion. The tail is long and tapering, but near its base the spines are notably elongate suggesting the presence of an auxiliary fin to assist the propulsive action of the tail.

*Temnodontosaurus* ('cutting toothed reptile') is an example of an early Jurassic ichthyosaur; it was one of the largest of all ichthyosaurs, some individuals reaching lengths of as much as 30ft (9m). Originally described as *Ichthyosaurus* on the basis of a single tooth by William Conybeare in 1822, the original has unfortunately been lost. In his review of lower Jurassic ichthyosaurs of Britain Dr Chris McGowan (Ontario) designated another complete skeleton from a similar locality as a new representative of this genus. The form of this ichthyosaur is little different from that of *Mixosaurus* except that its snout has a greater number of teeth, the eye is a little larger and, most notably the tail has a more fish-like shape. Instead of the enlarged fin near the base of the tail of *Mixosaurus, Temnodontosaurus* has its tail bones curved down near their tip to support a broad paddle-like fin. Skin impressions of several ichthyosaurs have been found at several localities in southern Germany which reveal that the tail 'fluke' also extended upward, and was presumably supported by a stiffened bar of tissue. A fish-like dorsal fin was also present along the back to improve stability.

*Ophthalmosaurus* ('eye reptile'), also from the Jurassic, was named for the particularly large size of its eyes. Although typically ichthyosaurian, *Ophthalmosaurus* is notable for its apparent total lack of teeth.

Our knowledge of the feeding and reproductive habits of ichthyosaurs has been improved by the discovery of several beautifully-preserved ichthyosaur skeletons which include the fossilized soft tissues within the rib cage. Examination of these reveals that ichthyosaurs fed upon cephalopods, fish and occasionally pterosaurs. Several skeletons have also revealed the presence of embryos within the body cavity of a mother ichthyosaur; one such appears to have been preserved at the moment of birth of the young baby! As in porpoises, the baby was born tail first. The necessity of bearing live young, rather than laying eggs as many reptiles do, reflects the fact that ichthyosaurs were so highly adapted to life in the water that they were unable even to crawl onto land to lay their eggs in the manner of living turtles.

## Plesiosaurs

Plesiosaurs ('ribbon reptiles') are another very important group of marine reptiles of the Mesozoic. Less obviously fish-like than the ichthyosaurs, they were nevertheless well

**Above:** This finely preserved fossil of *Ichthyosaurus acutirostris* shows not only the details of the skeleton (including the 'kink' in the tail), but also the outline of the skin.

**Ichthyosaur Skull**

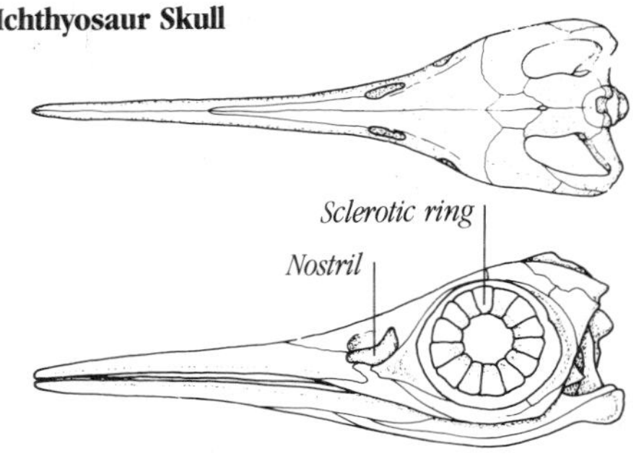


**Ophthalmosaurus Skull (above right)**
The skull of this Jurassic ichthyosaur has a very long, slender, toothless snout, and a large eye socket with a ring of bony plates.

**Plesiosaur Skull**

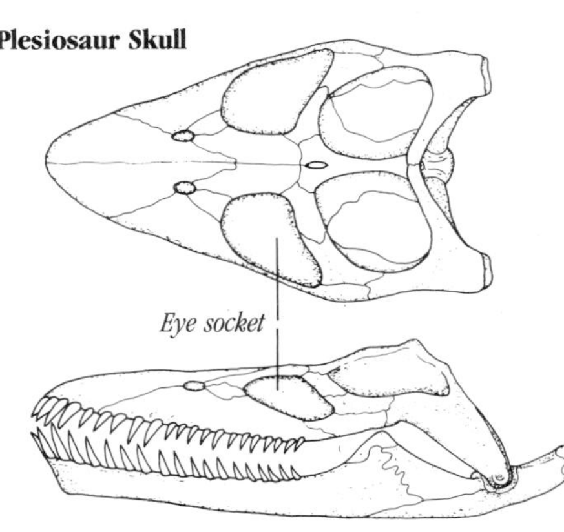


**Plesiosaur Skull (below right)**
This is a typical plesiosaur skull. The snout is broad and flat, and armed with large teeth. These creatures may have fed on fish.

**Ichthyosaur**

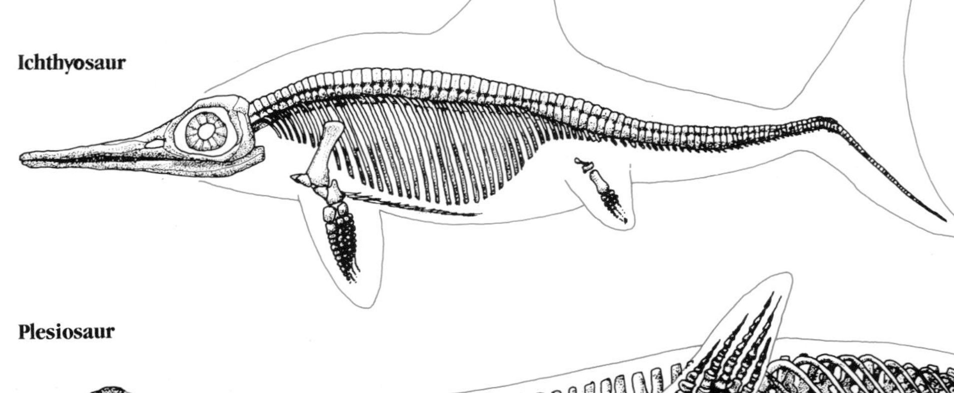

**Ichthyosaur Skeleton (below)**
Many ichthyosaur skeletons have been found. The streamlined body shape is very similar to that of fast-swimming porpoises.

**Plesiosaur**

**Cryptoclidus (below)**
This long-necked plesiosaur is shown in a fast swimming position with front flippers fully raised ready to be swept downwards powerfully. (Reconstruction based on the work of Dr David Brown).

adapted for a marine existence. Unlike the ichthyosaurs, many plesiosaurs have relatively short tails and long necks. The body is broad and quite compact with closely-set strong ribs and well-developed gastralia lining the belly area. The limbs are also very large and bear well-developed paddles which were undoubtedly their main means of propulsion. A careful study of plesiosaur paddles and limb girdles by Dr Jane Robinson revealed that instead of being pulled backward and forward like the oars of a rowing boat,the paddles were flapped up and down much like the 'wings' of a penguin or the paddles of a turtle.

The long-necked or 'plesiosauroid' plesiosaurs, such as *Elasmosaurus* ('plated reptile') and *Plesiosaurus* ('ribbon reptile') had relatively small heads armed with sharply-pointed teeth. Most probably these were fish-eaters using the neck rather like a sling to 'throw' the head at the prey in a very rapid darting movement.

Short-necked or 'pliosauroid' plesiosaurs seem to have been more like the killer whales of today. Powerfully built with enormous heads—one particularly large pliosauroid, *Kronosaurus* ('time reptile') from Queensland, Australia, has a head nearly 8ft (2·4m) long—these animals must have been formidable predators of most aquatic creatures including other plesiosaurs, ichthyosaurs (if it could catch them!), giant turtles and large ammonites. They lived at the same time as the mosasaurs.

On a historical note, *Elasmosaurus*, a very long-necked Cretaceous 'plesiosauroid' from Kansas, may well have been the unwitting cause of the bitter but highly productive feud between O. C. Marsh and E. D. Cope. According to Adrian Desmond who has researched the history of the Marsh-Cope feud, the event which sparked off the aggressively competitive spirit between these two men occurred after Cope had described the newly-discovered skeleton of *Elasmosaurus* in 1868. In so doing he had mistakenly placed the head of the animal on the tip of its tail! At a meeting between Marsh and Cope, Marsh was able to demonstrate to Cope that he had made this rather important mistake. Cope, a man of fiery disposition, found his own mistake hard to bear and this event irrevocably soured what had up to that time been a fairly cordial relationship between these two men.

## Placodonts and Mosasaurs

Placodonts ('flat teeth') are a rather odd group of Triassic reptiles that seem to have taken to a mollusc diet very early on.The neck and trunk of these creatures is relatively short and generally covered in well-developed bony armour. The tail is fairly short and was evidently not always used for swimming. The limbs are short and powerful. Evidently these animals walked across the sea floor and used their claws

**Above:** This well-preserved plesiosaur skull, which is fossilised in a slab of limestone, is in the British Museum (Natural History) collection. Note the large, sharply-pointed teeth.

**Above:** The skeleton of the 10ft (3m) long plesiosaur *Cryptoclidus oxoniensis* as it used to be mounted in the Marine Reptile gallery of the British Museum (Natural History).

**Placochelys (below)**
This placodont reptile skeleton shows clearly the generally turtle-like nature of these creatures. The back was very heavily armoured. The legs were flipper-like.

**Placodont Skulls (below and right)**
The head of *Placochelys* (below left) is very short-jawed and powerfully constructed. The teeth are short and block-like. Their absence from the front of the jaws suggests this area was covered by a horny beak. The skull of *Placodus* is seen in side view and looking into the roof of the mouth with the lower jaw removed (bottom). *Placodus* retains peg-like teeth at the front of the jaws, which were used to pluck shellfish from river beds. These would have been cracked open by the massive crushing teeth.

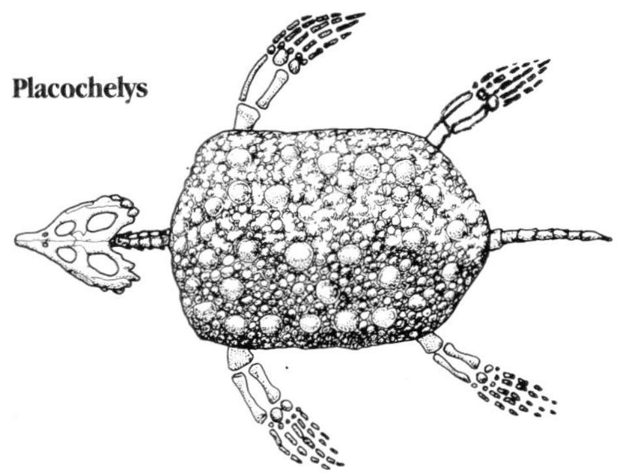


**Placochelys Skull**

*Eye socket*

**Placodus Skeleton (below)**
With its armour plating removed, *Placodus* looks much like other reptiles. Its body is quite short and is supported by powerful legs that splay outwards.

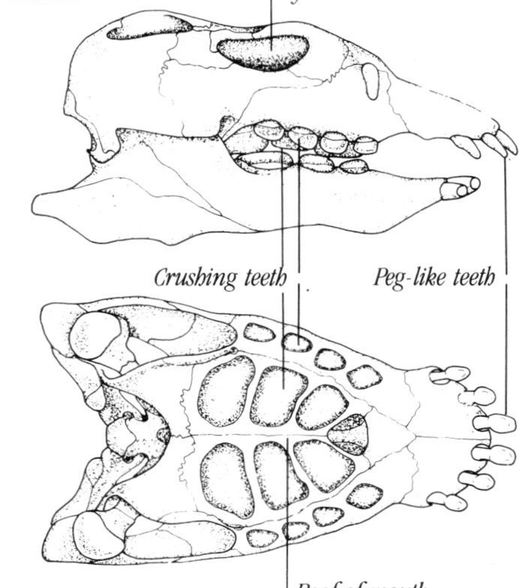


**Placodus**

to prize clams and suchlike from rocky ledges or crevices.

The head betrays their preference for shellfish quite clearly. The teeth are highly modified. At the front of the jaws they are blunt and forwardly-pointing in order to grasp potential food; behind these teeth the sides of the jaws and roof of the mouth are covered by large, flat crushing plates. The skull also has large areas at the back for the attachment of powerful muscles to operate the jaws. These features all clearly point to a diet of hard-shelled molluscs, such as clams or mussels. The extraordinary degree of armour plating found in these animals presumably reflects the fact that they were slow-moving and therefore open to attack from various aquatic predators.

Mosasaurs ('reptiles from the Meuse') were very large (15-30ft, 4·5-9m long) marine lizards that evolved in the late Cretaceous. They are especially abundant in the Cretaceous rocks of northern Europe (Maastricht, Holland) and Kansas (USA).

The head is long and the jaws armed with long, sharp fangs—a standard pattern for most aquatic predators. The neck is quite short and the body behind particularly long and slender. As in ichthyosaurs the tail was the main swimming organ, while the limbs, which are paddle-like, were used for steering. The feet and hands have long, delicate toes which were probably webbed.

In the shape and arrangement of its bones, the skull is very similar to that of living monitor lizards. Such similarities even extend to the structure of the lower jaw, which has an extra joint half way along its length. Because of these similarities, it is suspected that living monitor lizards are close relatives of the mosasaurs.

Mosasaurs may well have been fish eaters but many were sufficiently large to have taken a whole range of large vertebrate prey. One or two mosasaurs show slightly unusual types of teeth: for example *Globidens* ('globe tooth') has rather flattened teeth which may well reveal a placodont-like predilection for shellfish.

## Turtles

The earliest turtles are Triassic. A good example of a Triassic turtle is *Proganochelys* ('first turtle'). In the same way as modern turtles and tortoises, *Proganochelys* had a well-developed bony carapace; however, it seems unlikely that the head, tail or legs could be withdrawn inside the shell. Again like modern turtles, this Triassic type had a horny beak covering its jaws; however *unlike* modern forms it did retain some teeth on the roof of its mouth; the teeth may have helped to hold slippery fish in the mouth before they were swallowed.

One of the most impressive of dinosaur contemporaries among the turtles was *Archelon* ('ancient turtle'). This Cretaceous turtle grew to over 12ft (3·6m) in length. Its carapace was well developed and its flipper-like limbs were very large. A well-developed shell would have been absolutely essential to a Cretaceous turtle given the profusion of large marine predators at this time.

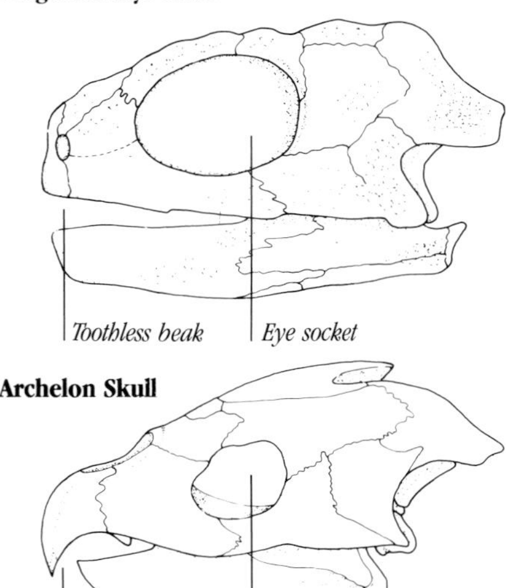


**Above:** Here we see the 'business end' of a late Cretaceous mosasaur. Apparently quite close relatives of the living monitor lizards, these must have been savage predators in the Cretaceous seas. The large head is armed with pointed teeth, while the limbs are modified into swimming flippers.

**Below:** *Protostega gigas* is a large marine turtle on display in the Smithsonian Institution, Washington D.C. Note the large flippers and poorly developed shell.

**Below:** A very well preserved shell of the turtle *Pleurosternon bullocki*. Turtle fossils are often either skulls or shells, rarely both together.

**Turtle Skulls (above)** *Proganochelys* (top) is an early turtle of the Triassic Period. The skull is already typically turtle-like with toothless horn-covered jaws, large eyes and a short head. *Archelon* (lower) was a gigantic late Cretaceous form. The hooked beak suggests it may have fed on slow-moving shellfish.

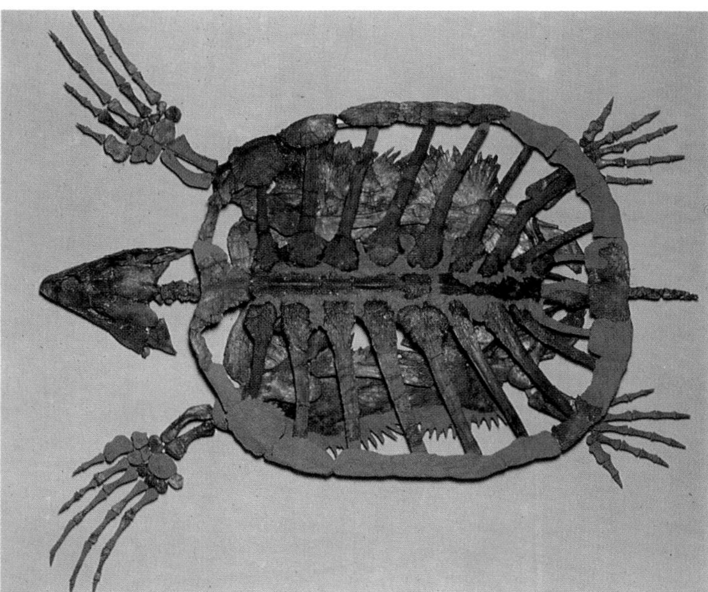

# Lizards & Snakes

The lizards and snakes are by far the most successful of modern reptiles, with about 6,000 species alive today. The first lizards appear in late Triassic rocks and these relatively small, agile, insectivorous creatures have remained virtually unchanged to the present day – apart from some relatively short-lived variants (notably the large predatory mosasaurs mentioned earlier).

The 'secret' of the success of lizards is hard to define with certainty. One factor may be that the typical shape of lizards (slender, long-bodied, sprawling legs, small head) ideally suits them to particular ecological niches; they are just better at being 'lizards' than anything else! However, side-stepping the circularity of that last proposition, one of the most popular explanations for their success over the past 200 million years is based on an analysis of the way in which the skull and jaw bones are linked together in a movable chain of bones.

One of the key innovations in lizard design – in fact it is the only significant change that has taken place if you compare the very earliest reptiles to lizards – can be found on the side of the head. The arch of bone possessed by non-lizard reptiles, marked (J) below, has disappeared (compare the drawings of *Sphenodon* and *Kuehneosaurus*). The result of this change is quite profound since the removal of bone J now permits the bone Q (a pillar-like bone that forms the joint with the lower jaw) to swing backward and forward. This means first of all that the lower jaw can be slid fore and aft. Secondly, movement of Q also operates a series of joints within the skull of the lizard. The net result of this series of interlinked joints is that the snout can be raised and lowered. It would appear that the development of this mobility both in the lower and the upper jaws of lizards was very important. Perhaps it allowed lizards to feed more effectively on insects (the staple diet of many lizards) by allowing them greater precision of jaw closure. This unusual hingeing system may also have acted as a type of a 'shock-absorber' in the skull; this may have been of some value since it would tend to cushion the lizard's brain against the jarring effect caused by snapping the jaws shut on its prey. The violent snapping action of the jaws is a necessary adaptation both to catch very fast-moving insects, and also to crack open their hard external skeletons. Whatever the true explanation is, it seems inevitable that mobility of the jaws was of considerable value because it is developed in almost all living lizards.

The fossil record of lizards is poor, largely because lizards tend to live in dry uplands away from the areas that are most likely to produce fossils, and because they are so small and their skeletons are consequently very easily destroyed. Nevertheless, several fossil lizards are known. One of these is *Kuehneosaurus* ('Kühne's reptile') from the late Triassic of Britain. Despite its early appearance, this was already a highly specialised gliding lizard; its ribs are enormously elongate and formed gliding membranes which allowed the animal to glide from tree-to-tree. A small living lizard from Malaya (*Draco volans*, 'flying dragon') has similar long ribs which are also used for gliding.

## Snakes

Snakes have an even worse fossil record than lizards. The first remains of snakes are known from the late Cretaceous of North America (*Coniophis*, 'Coniacian snake') and Patagonia (*Dinilysia*, 'terrible destroyer').

The main differences between lizards and snakes are fairly technical anatomical ones. Simple features such as the absence of legs are not sufficiently precise because there are several legless lizards ('slow-worms', 'glass-snakes' etc). One particular feature can be mentioned because it continues a trend seen in the lizards. This relates to the flexibility of the skull bones. If we compare a lizard and snake skull, we can see that not only has bone J been lost but also the arch of bone above it (U) has gone. As a result, the bone (Q) which supports the lower jaw has only the flimsiest attachment to the skull – giving a great deal of mobility to the lower jaw. In addition both sides of the lower jaw are separate, and the skull bones are even more loosely joined together than those of the lizard. The result of these changes has been to make the whole snake head incredibly flexible, so allowing it to swallow very large animal prey.

The other notable feature of snakes is the variety of methods that they use for killing their prey. The large boas, pythons and anacondas use constriction to suffocate their prey. Other types of snake (notably the viper family) are able to inject deadly venoms into their victims. Some venomous snakes have permanently erect fangs, either at the rear of the jaws (back-fanged snakes), or at the front (elapids). The most specialised fangs are those of the vipers. The teeth at the front of their mouths are specially modified in the form of hypodermic needles through which they can squirt venom from glands in the roof of the mouth. When not in use, the fangs may be folded back against the roof of the mouth. However, when they are about to make a 'strike' the fangs are swung forward through the action of the jointed bones of the skull roof. Whether vipers had evolved in late Cretaceous times when snakes first appeared is uncertain.

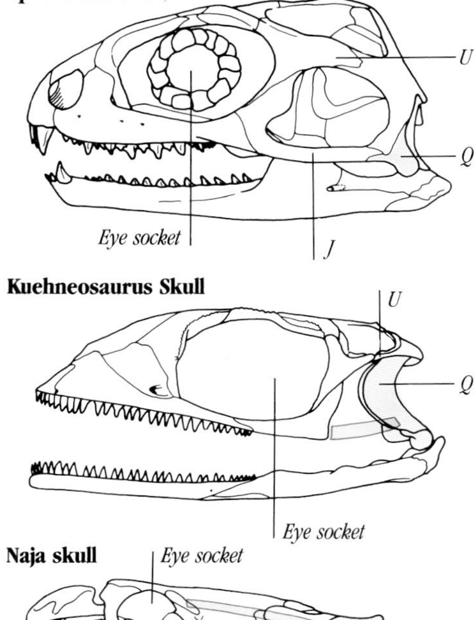


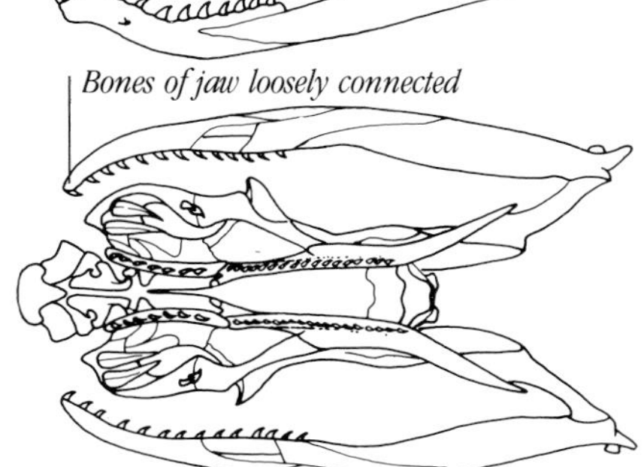


**Lizard and Snake Skulls (above)**
*Sphenodon* (top) shows the typical skull shape of an early lizard. Note the positions of the bony arches J (jugal) and U (upper temporal) and the bone Q (quadrate) which forms part of the jaw joint. *Kuehneosaurus* is an early true lizard. Note that J has been lost leaving bone Q free to swing backwards and forwards. The snake skull (bottom drawings) shows that arches J and U have both been lost. Both sides of the lower jaw are separate, while the skull bones are loosely connected, features which allow the snake to swallow large prey.

**Lizard Skull Flexing**

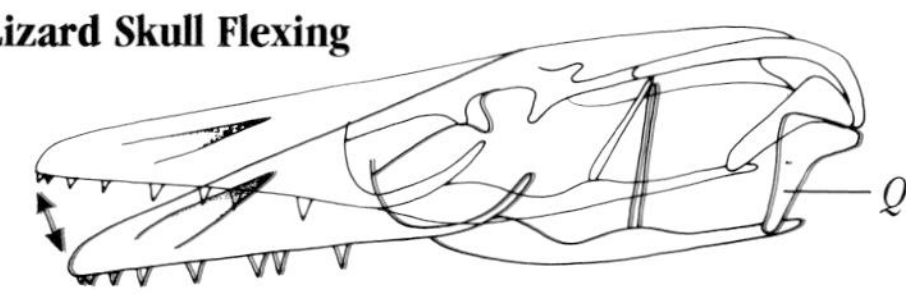


**Lizard Skull Movements (above)**
The ability of bone Q to move to and fro is used by lizards to tilt the snout up and down. The mechanism allows them to feed very efficiently.

**Below:** This photograph shows the front portion of the skeleton of *Pleurosaurus goldfussi*, a small lizard-like reptile from the late Jurassic Period. Compare the shape of the skull with the drawings on this page.

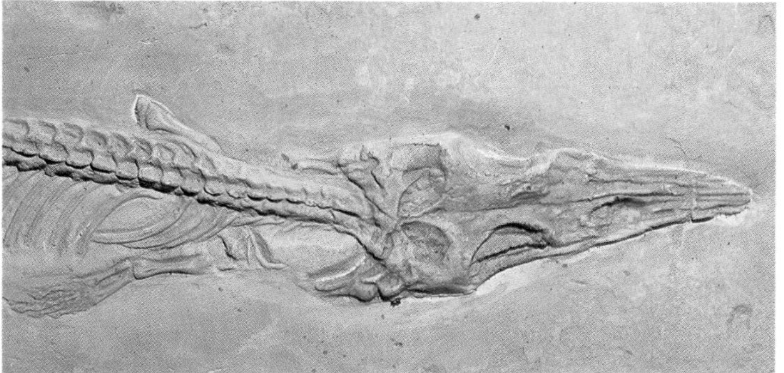

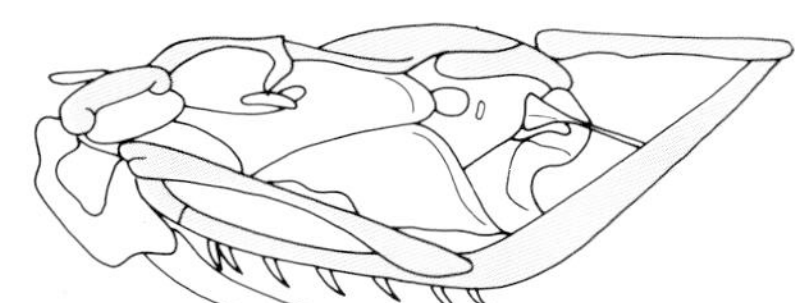

**Viperid Fang Erection**

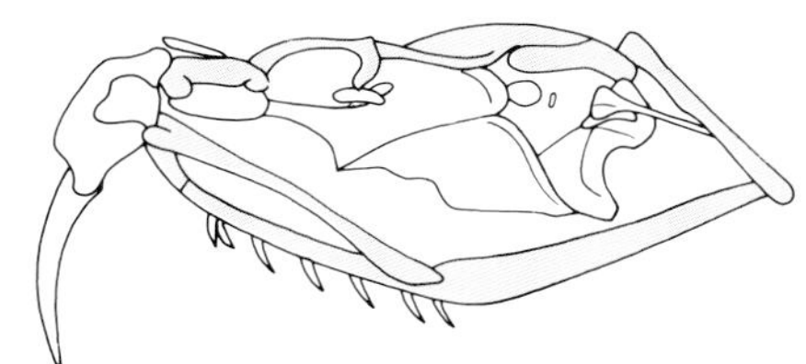

**Snake Fangs (above)**
The flexibility of skull developed by lizards was further adapted in two ways by snakes: allowing them to swallow large prey, and to deploy erectile fangs to inject venom into a victim. Seen here is the mechanism of fang erection (red). With jaws closed the fangs are folded back, but when the jaws open they swing forward ready to strike.

The last group of dinosaur contemporaries that we shall be looking at are the mammal-like reptiles and mammals. These represent a very important group of animals in the fossil record. The mammal-like reptiles were particularly abundant in the Permian and early part of the Triassic but rapidly declined in abundance towards the close of the Triassic Period. The disappearance of the mammal-like reptiles at the end of the Triassic heralds the arrival of two new groups: the dinosaurs which rapidly rise to dominate the land for the remaining 140 million years or so of the Mesozoic Era; and, the first true mammals. Rather than being large, dominant creatures as they are today, these early mammals were small, shrew-like, probably nocturnal, insectivorous creatures and so they remained throughout the remainder of the Mesozoic Era — literally and figuratively in the shadow of the dinosaurs. So far as we can tell, things might have continued like this right up to the present day had it not been for the mysterious event which occurred at the end of the Cretaceous Period. At this time, 64 million years ago, the dinosaurs quite suddenly went extinct, as did a variety of other creatures. However, from the point of view of the mammals which somehow survived the Cretaceous extinction event, the most important feature was the disappearance of the dinosaurs, because within the space of a few million years the mammals underwent a quite spectacular evolutionary radiation. Not only did they evolve into large land-living animals of all shapes and sizes, they also evolved into sea creatures — the whales and dolphins, seals and sea cows — and invaded the air in the form of bats. The enormity of this radiation makes it seem as though it represents the pent-up 'energy' of 140 million years of mammals waiting in the wings for the dinosaurs finally to leave the stage. A part of the wide radiation of mammals in the early Tertiary included some fairly small, almost rat-like creatures which are of particular interest to us because they were the first primates, a group from which our own human species was eventually to arise a mere 2-3 million years ago.

So, even though the mammals were relatively insignificant elements of the terrestrial fauna during the Jurassic and Cretaceous Periods, they are nevertheless an extremely important group in the fossil record and both they and their ancestors, the mammal-like reptiles, deserve some consideration.

## Pelycosaurs

The earliest known mammal-like reptiles are called pelycosaurs ('sail reptiles') and are first found in rocks of late Carboniferous age. *Archaeothyris* ('ancient opening') is a very early representative which is known from very fragmentary remains from Nova Scotia. In its general features it is small and lizard-like — much like most of the other small insectivorous early reptiles. It does, however, bear one particular distinguishing feature which is the small single opening on the side of the skull just behind the eye. This one character sets this little reptile apart from all others of the time, because it is found only in the synapsids or mammal-like reptiles and, in a highly modified form, in mammals too.

From these small beginnings, the pelycosaurs evolved into some of the dominant terrestrial animals of the early Permian. Pelycosaurs are particularly common fossils in the early Permian 'Red Bed' rocks of Texas and neighbouring areas of the USA. There appear to be three main types of pelycosaur, the large long-bodied and long-snouted ophiacodonts (named after *Ophiacodon* or 'snake tooth') of which *Varannosaurus* ('monitor lizard reptile') is a good example. The relatively long snout and rather small spiky teeth have been interpreted by many as indicating an aquatic, fish-eating way of life. The other two groups are far better known and quite spectacular animals: the sphenacodonts (*Dimetrodon*) and the edaphosaurs (*Edaphosaurus*).

*Dimetrodon* ('two long teeth') was a large predatory creature of the early Permian. Compared with *Varannosaurus*, it has a much shorter, deeper skull, the jaws of which are armed with large sharp-edged teeth. The remainder of the skeleton is very similar to that of *Varannosaurus* except that the dorsal spines are enormously long giving the appearance of a large fan perched on the back.

One early suggestion was that this sail-like structure was literally used as a sail so that these animals could swim more easily. This idea was not taken at all seriously. The most favoured explanation is that the sail of *Dimetrodon* was

**Archaeothyris Skull**

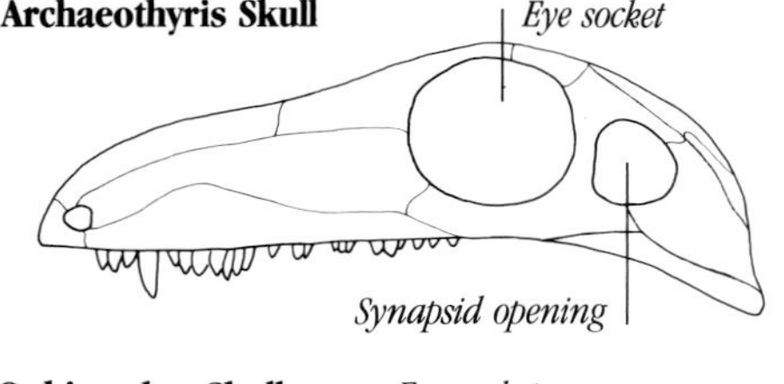


**Ophiacodon Skull**

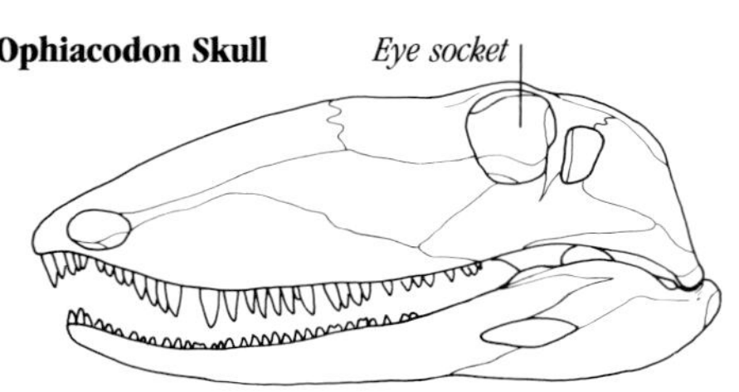

**Left:** This view of *Varanops brevirostris* clearly shows the classic sprawling posture of a typical pelycosaur. Even though the legs are quite long, their splayed position means that the belly is low-slung.

**Right:** This magnificent skeleton from the Field Museum of Natural History, Chicago, shows a victim's-eye view of the ferocious *Dimetrodon grandis*. Note the large skull and jaws befitting a fierce predator such as this.

**Pelycosaur Skulls (above)**
*Archaeothyris* (top)is the earliest well-described pelycosaur, a small lizard-like creature of the late Carboniferous. *Ophiacodon* (bottom) from the Permian is a larger form that was clearly a predator. It may have been aquatic.

**Edaphosaurus Skull**

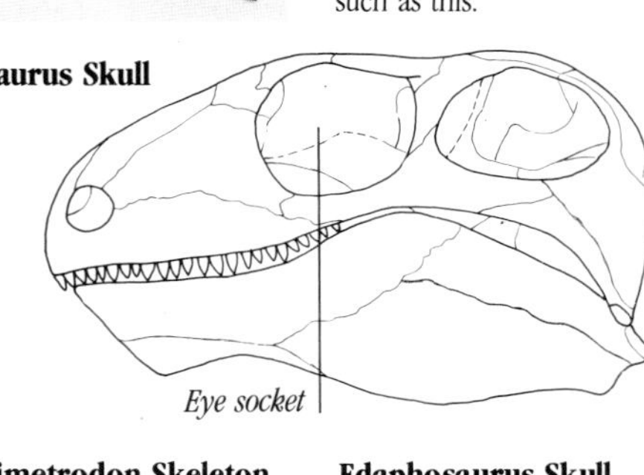


**Dimetrodon Skeleton (left)**
This reconstruction shows all the main anatomical attributes of this sail-backed sphenacodont: the large head, sprawling limbs, and tall 'sail' of spines.

**Edaphosaurus Skull (above)**
Similar in overall size to *Dimetrodon, Edaphosaurus* was however an herbivore. The teeth are blunt and modified to form large grinding plates for crushing plants.

involved in body temperature regulation (see also *Spinosaurus, Ouranosaurus* and stegosaurids). The spines were undoubtedly covered by thin skin, and by controlling the amount of blood flowing through the sail it could have acted as either a solar panel: the heat from the Sun falling on the sail warming the blood and the body; or as a radiator: in the case of the animal being too warm, the blood in the sail could be cooled either in a breeze or in the shade so that the body temperature could be lowered very quickly. Calculations have been made in order to estimate how long it would take reptiles of the size of *Dimetrodon*—with or without a sail—to warm up in the morning by basking in the Sun. The answer seems to be that possesing a sail allows a reptile to warm itself much more quickly. This may well have been a distinct advantage to early Permian predators.

*Edaphosaurus* ('Earth reptile') also from the early Permian, was another large-sailed pelycosaur. *Edaphosaurus*, however, was an herbivore; the skull is again short, but its teeth are shorter and blunter than those of *Dimetrodon*, and the inner sides of the jaws are modified in the form of large food-grinding knobbly tooth plates. These features indicate that *Edaphosaurus* fed on tough vegetation. Another peculiarity lies in the structure of the sail.Unlike the spines of *Dimetrodon* which are quite smooth, those of *Edaphosaurus* are very knobbly; this feature may have increased surface area and therefore the efficiency of its temperature-regulating sail.

At the very beginning of the late Permian, a fairly dramatic change seems to take place among these early mammal-like reptiles. The pelycosaurs which were so abundant in early times dwindled and rapidly became extinct and their place seems to have been taken by another type of mammal-like reptile group known as the therapsids.

## Therapsids

The therapsids ('beast arch') were a varied group of mammal-like reptiles which differ from the earlier pelycosaurs in a number of ways. One of the most obvious changes is in the body proportions and posture. Therapsids tend to have relatively short tails, unlike the long lizard-like tails of pelycosaurs. Their limbs are rather longer and could be held not only in the sprawled position, but also in a much more efficient position tucked beneath the body. This 'dual or variable gait' as it is known is very similar to that of crocodiles. The combination of a short-tailed, rather compact body with the

**Above:** Another very fine exhibit from the Field Museum, Chicago, this is the herbivorous sail-backed pelycosaur, *Edaphosaurus poconias.* The spines of the sail are quite distinct from those of *Dimetrodon;* they are very knobbly, a feature that may have increased the surface area, and thus the efficiency, of the sail.

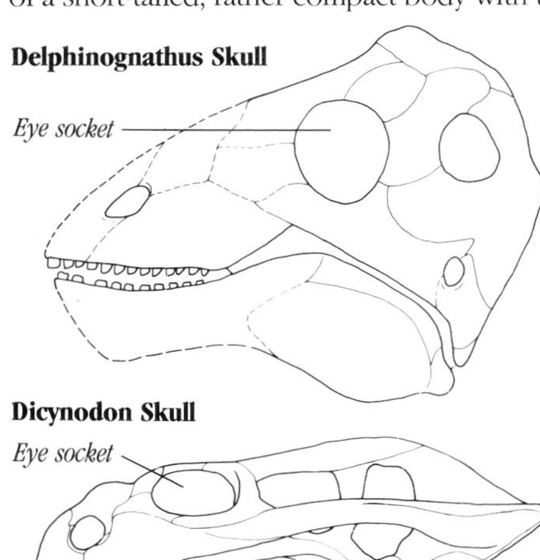


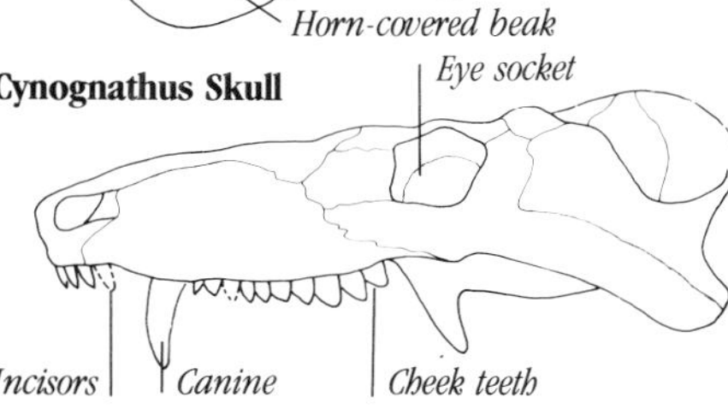




**Therapsid Skulls (right)** *Delphinognathus* (top) shows the fairly typical skull shape of an early Permian therapsid. The head is heavily-built and sloping; the teeth are large and chisel-like. *Dicynodon* (middle) is typical of the dicynodont therapsids which were very abundant in the late Permian and Triassic. Apart from the large 'eye-teeth', their jaws were toothless and no doubt covered in a horny sheath. These creatures were about the size of modern sheep.

**Cynognathus Skull (above and left)** The two illustrations of *Cynognathus* show that this was an advanced carnivore. The teeth are differentiated into small incisors at the front, large canines behind, and broader, sharp-edged slicing teeth at the back. The similarity to a modern dog is quite striking.

variable gait potential of the legs seems to represent a major advance over the arrangements seen in pelycosaurs, and suggests that these may have been much more active types of animal.

Increased activity is also probably reflected in the structure of the jaws and teeth of the therapsids. Some of the early carnivores such as *Lycaenops* ('wolf-face') of the late Permian had large heads and teeth which are specialised for dealing with large prey. *Lycaenops* has small nipping teeth at the tip of the jaws, but immediately behind these are a pair of huge stabbing teeth, followed by a few smaller chewing teeth. As the name of this predator suggests, these are indeed rather wolf-like creatures, and their long legs would have made them quite fast runners.

Various sabre-toothed therapsids resembling *Lycaenops* appeared during the late Permian but they do not appear to survive beyond the close of the Permian Period.

Alongside these fearsome predators are found a peculiar assortment of herbivores. Some early forms developed stout, powerful bodies, large knobbly heads and blunt chipping teeth and were known as dinocephalians ('terrible heads') because of their rather grotesque appearance. These were, however, relatively short lived and were replaced by another equally odd group of herbivores known as dicynodonts ('two dog teeth').

Dicynodonts were extremely numerous in late Permian times and in fact persist in fewer numbers right into the late Triassic. Their body form is surprisingly constant featuring relatively short, stout legs, and a barrel-like body. Their heads, however, are the most interesting part.

The name dicynodont refers to the fact that most of them only had two large tusks in the upper jaw. All their other teeth were lost (except in one or two rather primitive forms) and were replaced by a turtle-like horny beak. This was evidently a very successful ploy judging by their great abundance in late Permian rocks. It would appear that the jaws of these creatures were very versatile and able to cope with most types of vegetation. This may have been assisted by the extraordinary mobility (both fore and aft, and side to side) of the lower jaw.

At the end of the Permian the majority of carnivorous therapsids and many of the herbivorous therapsids (excluding the dicynodonts) had gone extinct. These were in turn replaced by yet another group of mammal-like reptiles, this time known as cynodonts ('dog teeth').

## Cynodonts

A few cynodonts appear in the latest Permian but they first begin to be abundant in early Triassic times. This time the changes which distinguish therapsids from cynodonts are much more subtle. From our point of view the most important changes are to be found in the jaws and teeth. The teeth are even more specialised than those of therapsids, being divided into small sharp incisors at the tip of the jaws, a large stabbing canine tooth, and behind this a row of complex cheek teeth. Unlike typical reptiles, each cheek tooth has a broad crown which develops a series of blunt points. This arrangement allowed the cynodonts to chew their food very efficiently, unlike most other reptiles. The teeth in the lower jaw are also lodged in a large single bone to which all the jaw muscles are attached; this is a much stronger arrangement than that of earlier mammal-like reptiles. Finally the complicated cheek teeth made it necessary for the jaw muscles to be not only powerful, but also quite sophisticated in order that opposing teeth could be brought together powerfully and in exactly the right position for the most effective cutting or crushing action.

These changes give a vivid impression of cynodonts as highly active and very efficient animals of the Triassic. They evolved not only into small, agile carnivores such as *Probelesodon* ('before lovely tooth') from South America, but also various herbivorous, lightly-built types. Towards the end of the Triassic, however, even the active and versatile cynodonts declined and

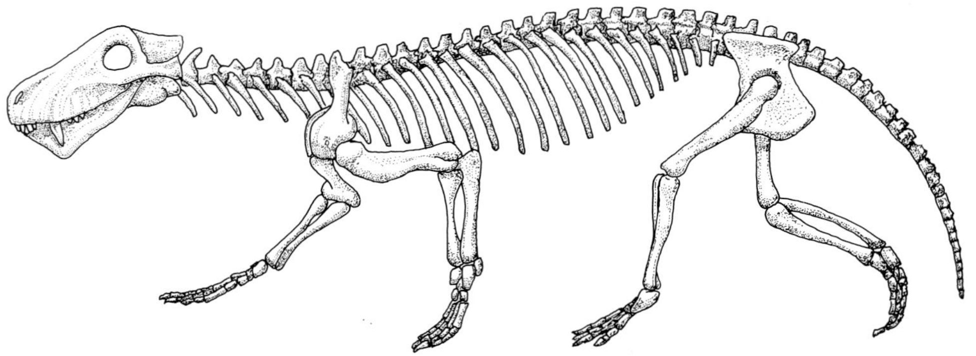

**Lycaenops (above)**
This was a therapsid mammal-like reptile of the late Permian. As can be seen here the skeleton is much less lizard-like than that of a pelycosaur. The legs are tucked in beneath the body and the tail is quite short. The large stabbing teeth reveal that *Lycaenops* was a carnivorous predator.

**Below:** *Aulacocephalodon peavoti* was a dicynodont mammal-like reptile. Therapsids like this were particularly abundant in the late Permian and Triassic. This was a rather unprepossessing creature to look at, with stout legs and a tubby body. It was an herbivore, the prey of animals like *Lycaenops*.

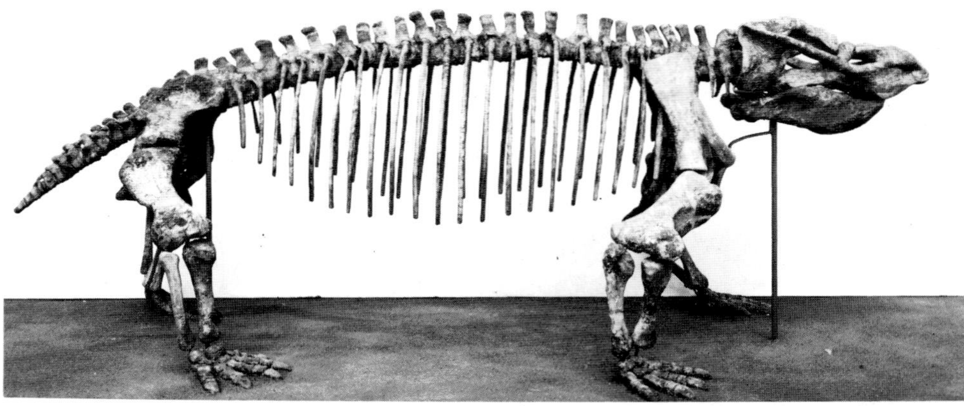

**Probelesodon (below and bottom)**
One of the more advanced types of cynodont, *Probelesodon* from South America was a small, nimble predator. The photograph of the finely preserved skull (bottom) shows the large spaces behind the eyes for the jaw muscles.

**Morganucodon Skull (right)**
A close relative of *Megazostrodon*, *Morganucodon* remains come from South Wales. This is an early mammal, and the drawing shows clearly the four types of teeth. It is based on the work of Dr Mussett and Professor Kermack.

**Morganucodon Skull**

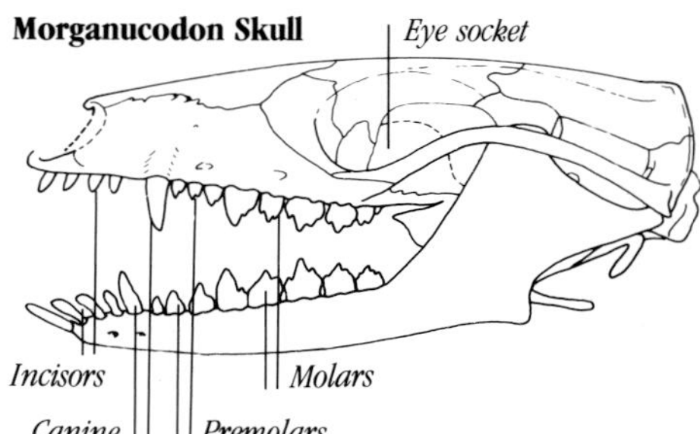


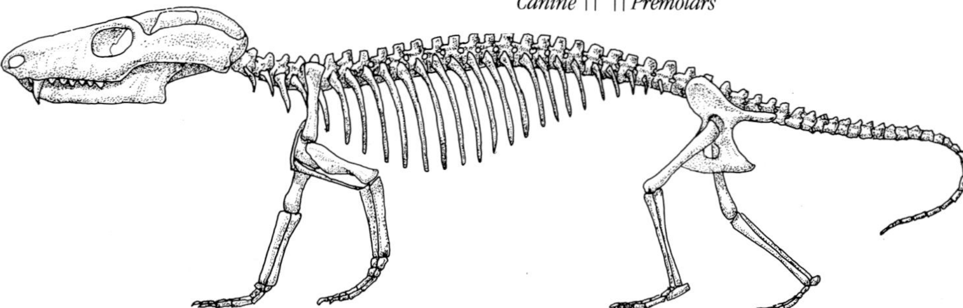

**Above:** This living rufous spectacled elephant shrew (*Elephantulus rufescens*) is an animal which we believe exists in a very similar way to Mesozoic mammals such as *Megazostrodon* (below left) and *Morganucodon* (opposite page). Nocturnal, it spends its time scurrying in search of insects. Great sensitivity and agility are absolutely essential for this style of life.

**Left:** This model of *Megazostrodon* comes from a display in the British Museum (Natural History). It shows the strong resemblance between this early mammal and modern shrews.

**Megazostrodon Skeleton (left)**
The real breakthrough in our understanding of early mammals came with the chance discovery by Dr Ione Rudner of a partial skeleton and skull of this tiny creature in 1966. The skeleton (based on the work of Jenkins and Parrington) looks like that of an agile insectivore.

went extinct. This final phase in the evolution of the mammal-like reptiles marked the time of the rise of two groups: the true mammals and the dinosaurs.

## Mammals

Living mammals are quite distinct from the reptiles of today. Briefly summarised the main differences are as follows. Reptiles have scaly skin, lay eggs, rely on the Sun to warm their bodies and have relatively simple teeth. Mammals in contrast have soft hair-covered skin, bear live young (except for the duck-billed platypus and spiny echidna of S. E. Asia and Australia), suckle their young on mothers' milk, generate their own body heat rather than relying on the Sun, and have complicated teeth.

Turning to the fossil record, these clear-cut differences become blurred, or at least extremely difficult to establish, since they are dependent mostly upon soft anatomical features (skin structure, hair, mammary glands, and body temperature control), none of which preserve in fossils. As a result, the first true mammals are recognised as fossils almost by weight of opinion, rather than anything more scientific.

One of the best preserved early mammals is a creature named *Megazostrodon* ('big girdled tooth') which was found in Lesotho in 1966. *Megazostrodon* was a tiny shrew-like creature. So far as we can tell it was an early mammal. Some of the reasons for believing this can be found in its jaws and teeth. The teeth are divided into four types (incisors, canines, premolars and molars). Unlike the cynodonts which have simple cheek teeth, those of *Megazostrodon* fall into premolar and molar types. This implies that *Megazostrodon* had a 'milk set' and a 'permanent set' of teeth only, rather than the continuously replaced teeth of reptiles; this also implies that *Megazostrodon* may have suckled its young on milk—a key mammalian character. The molar teeth also show very precise wear surfaces caused by opposing teeth rubbing past one another; this precision bite is another mammal character.

These features, and a few other more technical ones, make it highly probable that *Megazostrodon* was a very early mammal. The combination of large eyes, a long nose, sharp spiky teeth, and nimble limbs suggests that *Megazostrodon* and many other early mammals of the Triassic, Jurassic and Cretaceous were nocturnal insectivores, little different in most respects from living shrews.

**Mammal features in advanced cynodonts** Several of the later cynodonts show many very mammal-like features, notably complex teeth, great agility etc, and they may indeed have been very mammal-like in appearance. Many palaeontologists have speculated on the possibility that cynodonts might have generated their own body heat and had hair-covered skin rather than scaly bodies.

The curiously cyclical nature of origin, radiation and extinction in the evolution of the mammal-like reptiles from pelycosaurs to therapsids, then cynodonts, finally culminating in late Triassic mammals was reviewed recently (1982) by Dr Tom Kemp (Oxford). This curious pattern may reflect how the process of evolution of animals as complex as living mammals may have had to occur in stepwise fashion from less biologically complex lizard-like pelycosaurs. In retrospect, each step appears to mark a distinct advance towards the ultimate mammalian condition.

# SYSTEMATICS AND MUSEUMS

Systematics is the arrangement of organisms into a certain system, thus a classification. The aim of this is to present the subdivisional units of the system in a hierarchic sequence, and to use this rank order to make family connections, the natural links, as clear as possible. In palaeontology it is inevitable that new fossil finds will make the systematics more precise, or even change them, with the result that the system for a particular group of organisms can only represent the present state of knowledge.

This is certainly true of pterosaurs. We have a fossil record of their evolution for a period of almost 160 million years, but their very diverse evolutionary lines can hardly be reliably connected together. Gaps in the fossil record are far too large, and important connecting links are missing. An additional problem is that in the case of pterosaurs there are no living representatives upon which we can draw for comparison, and we usually have to rely on very fragmentary fossil material. Thus attempts to reconstruct pterosaur family connections are always hypothetical.

Systematic arrangement of organisms is done by taxonomy. By naming the rank order within the system, taxonomy allows us to establish family connections. To this end taxonomy has certain concepts at its disposal, so-called taxa, which are allotted in hierarchical order, like for example 'class', 'order', 'family', 'genus' and 'species'. Thus taxonomy is used to express, for example, that species that are similar to each other, and which thus seem to be related, are put together in a genus, and in the same way genera into families, families into orders and orders into classes. To an extent these categories are not adequate, and individual taxa have been further subdivided, for example into 'subclass', 'suborder', 'subfamily' and 'subgenus'. As in biology, the standard unit in palaeontology is the 'species'.

It has already been shown in the earlier chapter on 'What Are Pterosaurs?' that there are and always have been various views about the systematics and taxonomy of pterosaurs. Thus pterosaurs were classified as an independent 'class' alongside the reptile class, as a 'subclass' alongside the archosaur subclass and as an 'order' alongside other orders of the subclass Archosauria. In order not to confuse the reader, I intend to list here all hitherto named taxa of pterosaurs, down to the genus, using the conventional systematics with the order Pterosauria within the subclass Archosauria, within the class Reptilia. In each case the name of the author is given after the name of the taxon, and the year in which he established it.

Order PTEROSAURIA Kaup 1834
- Suborder Rhamphorhynchoidea Plieninger 1901
  - Family Dimorphodontidae Seeley 1870
    - Genus *Dimorphodon* Owen 1859
    - Genus *Peteinosaurus* Wild 1978
  - Family Eudimorphodontidae Wellnhofer 1978
    - Genus *Eudimorphodon* Zambelli 1973
  - Family Rhamphorhynchidae Seeley 1870
    - Genus *Preondactylus* Wild 1984
    - Genus *Dorygnathus* Wagner 1860
    - Genus *Campylognathoides* Strand 1928
    - Genus *Rhamphorhynchus* H. von Meyer 1847

---

The purpose of this listing is to show the major museums and collections in the world where pterosaurs are housed and on display, either fossil specimens or models of skeletons and life restorations. This list cannot be complete, however, and includes naturally only institutions which are open to the public, and not the many private collections which may also contain important specimens. Wherever possible, the pterosaur genera which that particular collection holds are indicated, although these may not always be on open display.

## THE AMERICAS

### Argentina

**Fundación-Instituto Miguel Lillo,**
Universidad Nacional
Tucuman
*Pterodaustro*
*Puntanipterus*

**Museo Argentino de Ciencias Naturales**
'Bernardino Rivadavia'
Buenos Aires
*Pterodaustro*
*Herbstosaurus*

**Museo Municipal de Ciencias Naturales**
Mar del Plata
*Pterodaustro*

### Brazil

**Departmento Nacional Produción Mines (DNPM)**
Rio de Janeiro
*Anhanguera*
*Araripesaurus*
*Brasileodactylus*
and other pterosaurs from the Santana formation of Brazil

### Canada

**National Museum of Natural Sciences**
Ottawa,
Ontario

**Royal Ontario Museum**
Toronto,
Ontario

**Tyrrell Museum of Paleontology**
Drumheller,
Alberta

### United States of America

**Academy of Natural Sciences**
Philadelphia,
Pennsylvania
*Pteranodon*

**American Museum of Natural History**
New York, N.Y.
*Anhanguera*
*Nesodactylus*
*Pteranodon*
*Pterodactylus*
*Rhamphorhynchus*
*Santanadactylus*
*Tapejara*

**Carnegie Museum of Natural History**
Pittsburgh,
Pennsylvania
*Campylognathoides*
*Nyctosaurus*
*Pteranodon*
*Pterodactylus*
*Rhamphorhynchus*

**Field Museum of Natural History**
Chicago,
Illinois
*Nyctosaurus*
*Pteranodon*

**Fort Hays Kansas State University,** Sternberg Museum
Hays,
Kansas
*Nyctosaurus*
*Pteranodon*

**Museum of Comparative Zoology**
Harvard University
Cambridge,
Massachusetts
*Pterodactylus*
*Rhamphorhynchus*

**Museum of Natural History**
University of Kansas,
Lawrence,
Kansas
*Nyctosaurus*
*Pteranodon*

**Museum of Paleontology**
University of California,
Berkeley,
California
*Pteranodon*

**Museum of the Rockies**
Montana State University,
Bozeman,
Montana
*Quetzalcoatlus*, model

**New Mexico Museum of Natural History**
Albuquerque,
New Mexico
*Rhamphorhynchus*, models
*Pteranodon*, model
*Quetzalcoatlus*, model

**Peabody Museum**
Yale University,
New Haven,
Connecticut
*Comodactylus*
*Dermodactylus*
*Dimorphodon*
*Nyctosaurus*
*Pteranodon*
*Rhamphorhynchus*

**Texas Memorial Museum**
University of Texas,
Austin,
Texas
*Quetzalcoatlus*

**U.S National Museum of Natural History**
Smithsonian Institution,
Washington, D.C.
*Pteranodon*
*Rhamphorhynchus*

**Utah Museum of Natural History**
Salt Lake City, Utah
*Pteraichnus*

## ASIA AND AUSTRALIA

### Australia

**Museum of Victoria**
Melbourne
*Pteranodon*, model

**Queensland Museum**
Fortitude Valley,
Brisbane
Pterodactyloidea from the Lower Cretaceous of Queensland

### China

**Natural History Museum**
Institute of Vertebrate Palaeontology and Palaeoanthropology,
Beijing
*Dsungaripterus*
*Huanhepterus*
*Noripterus*

**Palaeontological Museum Zigong**
Beipei Museum,
Dashanpu,
Sichuan Province
*Angustinaripterus*

## EUROPE

### Austria

**Haus der Natur**
Salzburg
*Pteranodon*, model

**Naturhistorisches Museum Wien**
Vienna
*Dorygnathus*
*Pterodactylus*

### Denmark

**Geologisk Museum**
University of Kopenhagen,
Copenhagen
*Rhamphorhynchus*

### France

**Musée d'Histoire Naturelle**
Lyon
*Pterodactylus*

**Musée National d'Histoire Naturelle**
Paris
*Campylognathoides*
*Gallodactylus*

### Germany

**Bayerische Staatssammlung für Paläontologie und historische Geologie**
Paläontologisches Museum München,
Munich
*Anurognathus*
*Araripedactylus*
*Campylognathoides*
*Ctenochasma*
*Dorygnathus*
*Germanodactylus*
*Gnathosaurus*
*Pteranodon*, model
*Pterodactylus*
*Rhamphorhynchus*
*Santanadactylus*
*Tropeognathus*

**Bürgermeister-Müller-Museum**
Solnhofen
*Pterodactylus*
*Rhamphorhynchus*

**Geologisch-Paläontologisches Institut der Universität Bonn**
Bonn
*Scaphognathus*

**Geologisch-Paläontologisches Institut der Universität Heidelberg**
Heidelberg
*Rhamphorhynchus*

**Hessisches Landesmuseum**
Darmstadt
*Rhamphorhynchus*

**Institut und Museum für Geologie und Paläontologie der Universität Tübingen**
Tübingen
*Campylognathoides*
*Dorygnathus*
*Pterodactylus*
*Rhamphorhynchus*

**Jura-Museum**
Eichstätt
*Ctenochasma*
*Gnathosaurus*
*Pterodactylus*
*Rhamphorhynchus*

**Maxberg-Museum beim Solnhofener Aktienverein**
Solnhofen
*Pterodactylus*
*Rhamphorhynchus*
*Scaphognathus*

**Museum Bergèr**
Harthof near Eichstätt
*Pterodactylus*
*Rhamphorhynchus*

**Museum Hauff**
Holzmaden
*Dorygnathus*

**Museum Mensch und Natur**
Munich
*Rhamphorhynchus*, model
*Tropeognathus*

**Museum für Naturkunde**
Humboldt Universität,
Paläontologisches Museum
Berlin
*Dorygnathus*
*Pterodactylus*
*Rhamphorhynchus*

**Naturmuseum Senckenberg**
Frankfurt
*Pterodactylus*
*Rhamphorhynchus*

**Staatliches Museum für Naturkunde**
Museum am Löwentor,
Stuttgart
*Campylognathoides*
*Dorygnathus*

Genus *Odontorhynchus* Stolley 1936
Genus *Rhamphocephalus* Seeley 1880
Genus *Parapsicephalus* Arthaber 1919
Genus *Scaphognathus* Wagner 1861
Genus *Sordes* Sharov 1971
Genus *Angustinaripterus* He, Yan & Su 1983
Family Anurognathidae Kuhn 1967
Genus *Anurognathus* Döderlein 1923
Genus *Batrachognathus* Rjabinin 1948
Undetermined family of Rhamphorhynchoidea
Genus *Rhamphinion* Padian 1984
Genus *Herbstosaurus* Casamiquela 1975
Genus *Nesodactylus* Colbert 1969
Genus *Comodactylus* Galton 1981

Suborder Pterodactyloidea Plieninger 1901
Family Pterodactylidae Bonaparte 1838
Genus *Pterodactylus* Cuvier 1809
Family Gallodactylidae Fabre 1974
Genus *Gallodactylus* Fabre 1974
Family Germanodactylidae Young 1964
Genus *Germanodactylus* Young 1964
Family Ctenochasmatidae Nopcsa 1928
Genus *Ctenochasma* H. von Meyer 1852
Genus *Gnathosaurus* H. von Meyer 1834
Genus *Huanhepterus* Dong 1982
Family Pterodaustridae Bonaparte 1971
Genus *Pterodaustro* Bonaparte 1970
Family Dsungaripteridae Young 1964
Genus *Dsungaripterus* Young 1964
Genus *Noripterus* Young 1964
Genus *Phobetor* Bakhurina 1986
Genus *Puntanipterus* Bonaparte & Sanchez 1975
Family Ornithocheiridae Seeley 1870
Genus *Ornithocheirus* Seeley 1869
Genus *Araripesaurus* Price 1971
Genus *Santanadactylus* Buisonjé 1980
Genus *Brasileodactylus* Kellner 1984
Family Anhangueridae Campos & Kellner 1985
Genus *Anhanguera* Campos & Kellner 1985
Family Tapejaridae Kellner 1990
Genus *Tapejara* Kellner 1990
Genus *Tupuxuara* Kellner & Campos 1989
Family Cearadactylidae Wellnhofer 1991
Genus *Cearadactylus* Leonardi & Borgomanero 1985
Family Criorhynchidae Hooley 1914
Genus *Criorhynchus* Owen 1874
Genus *Tropeognathus* Wellnhofer 1987
Family Ornithodesmidae Hooley 1913
Genus *Ornithodesmus* Seeley 1887
Family Pteranodontidae Marsh 1876
Genus *Pteranodon* Marsh 1876
Genus *Ornithostoma* Seeley 1871
Family Nyctosauridae Williston 1903
Genus *Nyctosaurus* Marsh 1876
Family Azhdarchidae Nessov 1984
Genus *Azhdarcho* Nessov 1984
Genus *Titanopteryx* Arambourg 1959
Genus *Quetzalcoatlus* Lawson 1975
Genus *Doratorhynchus* Seeley 1875
Undetermined family of Pterodactyloidea
Genus *Dermodactylus* Marsh 1878
Genus *Mesadactylus* Jensen & Padian 1989
Genus *Araripedactylus* Wellnhofer 1977

*Pterodactylus*
*Rhamphorhynchus*

**Staatliches Museum für Mineralogie und Geologie**
Dresden
*Rhamphorhynchus*

**Petrefaktensammlung Kloster Banz**
Banz near Lichtenfels
*Dorygnathus*

**Italy**

**Museo Civico di Scienze Naturali**
Bergamo
*Eudimorphodon*
*Peteinosaurus*

**Museo Civico di Storia Naturale di Milano**
Milan
*Eudimorphodon*
*Pteranodon*, model

**Museo Civico di Storia Naturale di Venezia**
Venice
Pterodactyloidea from the Santana formation of Brazil

**Netherlands**

**Geological Institute of the University**
Amsterdam
*Santanadactylus*, model

**Rijksmuseum van Geologie en Mineralgie**
Leiden
*Pterodactylus*
*Rhamphorhynchus*

**Teyler's Museum**
Haarlem
*Pterodactylus*
*Rhamphorhynchus*

**Sweden**

**Palaeontological Museum, Uppsala University**
Uppsala
*Dorygnathus*
*Pterodactylus*

**Switzerland**

**Naturhistorisches Museum**
Basel
*Pteranodon*, model

**Paläontologisches Institut und Museum der Universität Zürich**
Zurich
*Pterodactylus*
*Rhamphorhynchus*
*Santanadactylus*

**United Kingdom**

**City Museum and Art Gallery**
Bristol
*Dimorphodon*, model

**Crystal Palace Park**
Sydenham,
London
Hawkin's pterodactyl models

**Lyme Regis (Philpot) Museum**
Lyme Regis,
Dorset
*Dimorphodon*

**Natural History Museum**
London
*Criorhynchus*
*Dimorphodon*
*Doratorhynchus*
*Ornithocheirus*
*Ornithodesmus*
*Parapsicephalus*
*Pterodactylus*
*Rhamphocephalus*
*Rhamphorhynchus*

**Sedgwick Museum**
Cambridge University,
Cambridge
*Criorhynchus*
*Ornithocheirus*

**USSR**

**Palaeontological Museum, Akademia Nauk**
Moscow
*Batrachognathus*
*Phobetor*
*Sordes*

**Zoological Museum, Akademia Nauk**
Leningrad
*Azhdarcho*

**Above:** This is the central hall of the Bavarian State Collection of Palaeontology and historical Geology in the city of Munich. This institute houses one of the finest collections of pterosaur fossils in the world, many of the specimens coming from Solnhofen limestone which is quarried in Bavaria.

## A

**Aberrant**
Unusual, out of the ordinary.
**Abraded**
Worn down.
**Absolute dating**
A means of estimating the age of rocks with some degree of accuracy using measurements of radiocactive isotopes.
**Adaptation**
Fitness in structure or function for a particular kind of environment; the process of becoming so adjusted.
**Adaptive radiation**
Diversification of organisms along various evolutionary lines adjusted to different environments.
**Adductor**
Closer (i.e. jaw adductor muscle is a jaw-closing muscle).
**Aerodynamics**
The study of the physical conditions of air currents and their effect on moving bodies.
**Aestivate**
To hide away and become inactive during periods of drought.
**Aëtosaurs**
Heavily-armoured, plant-eating archosaurs of the Triassic Period.
**Age**
Geological time unit as a subdivision of the periods, for example Maastrichtian Age of the Cretaceous Period.
**Agnathans**
Primitive, jawless, fish-like, aquatic animals, the earliest vertebrates.
**Aktinofibrils**
Strengthening membranes embedded in the flight membrane of pterosaurs.
**Algae**
Aquatic plants, both large and small.
**Alveoli**
Tooth sockets in the jaw bone.
**Ammonites**
Extinct tentacled molluscs related to squids, but with a coiled and chambered shell similar to the *Nautilus* today. Abundant in Mesozoic seas and used as index fossils.
**Amnion**
A membraneous sac filled with watery fluid that encloses the developing embryo in reptiles, birds and mammals.
**Amniotes**
Tetrapods whose embryos develop within an amniotic membrane, i.e. reptiles, birds and mammals.
**Amphibians**
Tetrapods whose embryos do not develop within an amniotic membrane and which have to pass through a larval stage in the water breathing through gills, e.g. toads, frogs and salamanders.
**Amphibious**
Able to live both in water and on land.
**Anapsids**
A reptile group characterised by having no skull openings behind the eye socket, including the living tortoises and turtles, but also the earliest reptiles.
**Angiosperms**
Flowering plants.
**Anterior**
Pertaining to the front of the body as opposed to posterior.
**Arboreal**
Living in trees.
**Archaeothyris**
The earliest pelycosaur.
**Archosaurs**
A grouping of reptiles based on certain shared skeletal features comprising dinosaurs, pterosaurs, thecodonts and crocodiles.
**Arthropods**
Invertebrate animals with jointed legs, e.g. insects, spiders, crabs, shrimps and some extinct groups.
**Articular facet**
A joint surface.
**Articulated**
Jointed together or jointed.
**Articulation**
A joint connecting bones.
**Asiamerica**
The land areas of Asia and America joined by a land bridge formed by the Bering Straits in the Mesozoic Era.
**Atlas**
The first vertebra of the neck which connects directly with the skull (from the Greek mythology, where the giant Atlas supports the world on his shoulders).
**Axial**
Trunk muscles in general are called axial muscles. In fishes much of the bulk of the body is formed by axial musculature.
**Axis**
The second neck vertebra about which the atlas rotates to turn the skull.

## B

**Bacteria**
Microscopically small organisms.
**Baleen**
The Baleen Whale *(Mystacoceti)* is a very large whale, up to 108ft (33m) in length, and has peculiar filtering lamellae on the palate in its mouth.
**Bauplan**
Construction plan or pattern.
**Belemnites**
Extinct molluscs, related to squids with a bullet-shaped, calcified guard or rostrum.
**Biosphere**
Zones of the earth in which living organisms exist, i.e. from the depths of the oceans up to the highest mountains.
**Biostratigraphy**
The study of rocks by dating their origin with containing fossils, i.e. index fossils.
**Biozone**
Geological time unit defined by the life time of the species of an index fossil.
**Biped**
An animal that stands and walks on its hind legs.
**Bitumen**
Natural inflammable substance composed of a mixture of hydrocarbons, for example petroleum, asphalts and natural mineral waxes.
**Bivalves**
Mussels, two-sided molluscs, e.g. clams and oysters.
**BM (NH)**
British Museum (Natural History)
**Botany**
The science dealing with the study of plants.
**Brachiopatagium**
The main flight membrane of the pterosaur wing.
**Brachiopods**
Shelled sea creatures that look a little like mussels but are not closely related.
**Browsers**
Those animals that feed on high foliage (shrubs and trees).
**Burlap**
Strips of hessian sacking soaked in plaster-of-Paris and used to bandage fossils in the field.

## C

**Cadaver**
A carcass of a dead animal.
**Calcite**
A mineral found abundantly in the Earth's crust as a variant of chalk ($CaCO_3$).
**Cambrian Period**
The most ancient of the Palaeozoic time zones. Rocks from this period show the first trace of fairly complicated animal life.
**Cantilever**
A beam or lever that projects outward from its support (e.g. the tail of a dinosaur projects from the pelvis as a cantilever and so balances the front part of the body).
**Caput**
The articular upper end (head) of the upper arm (humerus) or the upper leg (femur).
**Carapace**
A hard outer covering to the body, such as the shell of a tortoise.
**Carboniferous**
A geological time period in the Palaeozoic Era; it lasted from 360-286 million years ago. In this period the main coal deposits were formed.
**Carina**
A keel, here on the breastbone of pterosaurs.
**Carpals**
Small bones forming the wrist.
**Carpus**
The wrist.
**Cartilage**
Organic tissue connected with skeletal functions, for example in joints. In embryonic and juvenile stages of vertebrates bones are preformed as cartilage and develop into bone substance during growth.
**Caudal**
Pertaining to the tail, or posterior part of the body.
**Cellulose**
Chemical that forms the bulk of plant cell walls - tough and indigestible to most animals.
**Cenozoic/Kainozoic**
'Recent life': the geological era after the Mesozoic, comprising the Tertiary and Quaternary Periods, i.e. the last 65 million years.

**Cerebellum**
The hindbrain, which is principally concerned with co-ordination of movements.
**Cervical**
Pertaining to the neck.
**Champsosaurs**
Early aquatic lizard-like reptiles.
**Chevrons**
V- or Y-shaped bones attached to the lower side of the tail vertebrae. Anatomists call them haemapophyses.
**Cladogram**
A diagram representing the family tree of groups of organisms.
**Class**
A major category of organisms below the Phylum and above the Order, as for example the classes Amphibia, Reptilia, Mammalia and Aves (birds).
**Classification**
The process of ordering or cataloguing organisms into groups which are related by descent.
**Clavicle**
A bone in the shoulder girdle, the collar bone.
**Collagen**
A protein that forms fine, tough strands which make up ligaments and tendons and strengthens bones.
**Colonial**
Living together in colonies of like individuals.
**Community**
The local environment of an organism.
**Comparative anatomy**
A branch of biology which depends upon the ability to compare and contrast the attributes of one animal with another so that a greater overall understanding may be achieved.
**Comparative dating**
A technique for estimating the age of rocks based on their characteristic fossils; these can be compared with those from rocks elsewhere, as similarly aged rocks are expected to have similar fossil species.
**Concretion**
A hard, compact, rounded mass of rock, also called a nodule, formed by orderly and localized precipitation from aqueous solution, often about a centre, such as a bone.
**Conifers**
Cone-bearing trees such as firs, pines and yews.
**Conservation**
The procedure used to ensure that a fossil once excavated does not deteriorate.
**Continental Drift**
The phenomenon of continental movement (Drift) on tectonic plates in the Earth's crust.
**Coprolite**
Fossilised dung.
**Coracoid**
A prominent bone in the shoulder girdle of reptiles and many other vertebrates. In pterosaurs and birds it articulates with the breastbone.
**Cornea**
The horny skin of the eye.
**Coronoid process**
A tall prong of bone on the lower jaw for the attachment of jaw-closing muscles.
**Cranial**
Relating to the cranium or braincase.
**Cretaceous**
The last period in the Mesozoic Age. It lasted from 144-65 million years ago.
**Cristospina**
A crest at the lower side of the breastbone extending to the front into a spine, typical for pterosaurs.
**Crocodylids**
Alligators and crocodiles.
**Crurotarsal ankle**
Ankle structure in which the hinge between leg and foot has a sharp twist to allow the foot to swivel.
**Cursorial**
With slender limbs adapted to running.
**Cycads**
Squat, rather palm-tree-like plants that were particularly abundant in the Mesozoic Era.
**Cynodonts**
Advanced types of mammal-like reptiles of the Triassic Period.

## D

**Decay**
To rot, disintegrate (see also **radioactive decay**).
**Dendrochronology**
The study of annual growth rings of trees for dating of the recent past.
**Dentition**
Teeth.
**Deposit (geological)**
Accumulation of rock.
**Depyritisation**
The chemical process (which can severely damage fossil specimens) whereby iron pyrites spontaneously converts into iron sulphate and acids.
**Dermal bone**
Bone formed within the skin.
**Description**
Here the scientific description of fossil specimens, the results of their detailed study with conclusions concerning their anatomy determination, relationships, origin and functional morphology.
**Diapsids**
A reptile group characterised by having two skull openings behind each eye socket. Diapsids include the pterosaurs, crocodiles, dinosaurs, thecodonts as well as snakes and lizards and their ancestors.
**Dicynodonts**
Curious pig-like therapsids of the Permian and Triassic Periods, often with just two tusks in the upper jaw.
**Digit**
Finger (on the hand) and toe (on the foot).
**Digitigrade**
Walking on the digits, as opposed to plantigrade.
**Dimorphism**
The characteristic of having two forms, usually sexual. If males and females of the same species look different, then the species exhibits sexual dimorphism.
**Dinosaurs**
A group of archosaurian land-living reptiles with an erect gait. They lived in the Mesozoic Era and became extinct at the end of the Cretaceous Period 65 million years ago. Dinosaurs can be classified in two orders: Saurischia and Ornithischia. The name means 'terrible lizard'.
**'Dinosauroid'**
Dale Russell's name for his imaginative reconstruction of how the theropod dinosaur *Stenonychosaurus* might have looked if it had not gone extinct 64 million years ago.
**Disarticulated**
Pulled apart, broken up.
**Dispersal**
The process of spreading out, in a geographic sense.
**Distal**
Furthest from the point of attachment to the body (opposite of proximal).
**Diurnal**
Active during daylight hours (as opposed to nocturnal).
**Divergence**
Moving away from, changing in form in an evolutionary sense.
**Dogger**
The middle epoch of the Jurassic Period (= Middle Jurassic), following the Lias and followed by the Malm. It lasted from 188-163 million years ago.
**Dorsal**
From above (opposite of ventral).

## E

**Echinoderms**
Sea urchins and their relatives.
**Ecology**
The science which is the study of the relationship between organisms and their environment.
**Ectothermic**
'Cold-blooded' - relying mainly on external sources of heat (i.e. the Sun's rays) to maintain an even working body temperature.
**Embryo**
An animal in its earliest stages of development.
**Endocast**
A sediment in-fill of a cavity, for example the brain cavity, then also called endocranial cast.
**Endocranial cavity**
The cavity in the skull for the brain and associated soft parts.
**Endothermic**
'Warm-blooded' - being able to generate heat internally by means of chemical reactions in order to regulate the body temperature.
**Eosuchia**
A group of early diapsid reptiles which gave rise to archosaurs, lizards and snakes.
**Epaxial**
Dorsal trunk muscles running the length of the body are known as epaxial muscles.
**Epidermis**
The outer layer of the skin.

**Epiphysis**
An accessory centre of ossification at the ends of long bones forming the articular regions. Between epiphysis and shaft there is a long persistent band of cartilage which is continuously growing and being replaced by bone until epiphysis and shaft are united by bone and growth is over. This growth pattern is found in mammals, birds and to a limited extent also in reptiles.
**Epoccipital**
Small bone edging the frill on the skulls of ceratopian dinosaurs.
**Era**
Geological time unit, for example Palaeozoic, Mesozoic or Cenozoic Eras.
**Erosion**
The result of weathering on exposed rocks.
**Ethnology**
Science dealing with the history and culture of peoples.
**Euramerica**
The land areas of Europe and America which were joined for much of the Mesozoic Era.
**Eurasia**
The land areas of Europe and Asia joined as they are today.
**Euryapsids**
A reptile group, exclusively aquatic and now extinct, e.g. plesiosaurs and ichthyosaurs, characterised by having a single opening (temporal fenestra) high up on the side of the skull behind the eye socket.
**Evolution**
The development of plants and animals through geological time, and the way that this development has come about. Organisms evolve, or develop, as a result of changes in their living conditions.
**Evolve**
To change in form or appearance over successive generations.
**Exapophyses**
Bony processes low on the front and back of the neck vertebrae of pterosaurs which form additional joints for the strengthening of the long neck.
**Exposure**
An area where bare rock is exposed to the erosive action of the weather.
**Extensor tendon**
The tendon of a muscle which straightens a joint, as opposed to a flexor tendon.
**Extinction**
The death of a species.

## F

**Family**
A grouping of similar closely related genera.
**Fauna**
Animals, as opposed to flora (plants).
**Femur**
The long bone in the upper leg or thigh-bone.
**Fenestra**
This is a window-like opening found in the skull.
**Fibula**
The smaller of the two bones of the lower leg or shin.
**Flexion**
Bending of a joint, as opposed to extension.
**Flexor tendon**
The tendon of a muscle which bends a joint, as opposed to an extensor tendon which straightens it.
**Flocculi**
Small, lateral appendages of the hindbrain (cerebellum), especially concerned with equilibrium and closely connected with the inner ear.
**Flora**
Plants, as opposed to fauna (animals).
**Foliage**
Leaves, branches and twigs.
**Foramen magnum**
The opening in the brain case of the skull through which the spinal cord penetrates into the spinal canal.
**Forelimbs**
Front legs or arms/wings.
**Fossil**
The preserved remains of plants or animals that lived in the geological past turned to stone. Fossils can be millions of years old.
**Fossiliferous**
Fossil-bearing.
**Fossilisation**
The process that leads to the formation of fossils.
**The Fossil Record**
The history of life on Earth as revealed by fossil remains.
**Furcula**
The 'wish-bone' of birds.
**Fused**
Joined, welded together very firmly.

## G

**Gait**
Characteristics of movement.
**Ganoid fish**
A group of fishes with enamel-like scales, very common in the Mesozoic Era.
**Gastralia**
Belly ribs.
**'Gastric mill'**
A muscular portion of the stomach used to grind up food - often with the assistance of gastroliths or 'stomach stones'.
**Gastroliths**
'Stomach stones' used either for pounding up food or as ballast.
**Gastric pellet**
Stomach pellet, containing indigestible parts of the diet, for example bones, which is vomited up.
**Gavialids**
Slender-snouted, fish-eating crocodiles of India.
**Genealogy**
The study of family-trees.
**Genus (pl. genera)**
A group of closely related species of plants or animals.
**Geographical distribution**
The localities where an animal or plant may be found.
**Geological timescale**
A timescale of the history of the Earth arrived at by a combination of comparative and absolute dating of rocks and their fossils worldwide.
**Geologist**
A person who studies rocks.
**Geology**
The science which treats of the history of the Earth, the composition and structure of the Earth's crust.
**Ginkgo**
The maidenhair tree of East Asia, the sole survivor of a once abundant group of gymnosperm trees.
**Gizzard**
As **'gastric mill'**.
**Glenoid fossa**
The shoulder joint on the shoulder girdle.
**Gondwana**
The 'southern continents' of the Triassic Period, comprising South America, Africa, India, Antarctica and Australia.
**Graptolites**
Curious fossils, especially in Palaeozoic rocks, that look like scratch marks made by a saw.
**Graviportal**
Slow-moving, lumbering.
**Grazers**
Those animals that feed on grasses (and other low-lying vegetation).
**Gymnosperms**
Non-flowering plants (in general).

## H

**Hadrosaurine**
Non-crested hadrosaurid.
**Hindlimbs**
Back or rear legs.
**Histology**
The study of the fine structure of body tissues.
**Humerus**
Upper arm bone.
**Hyperextended**
Over-straightened, bent backwards upon itself.

## I

**Ichnology**
The study of footprints as preserved in rocks.
**Ichthyosaurs**
Marine reptiles of the Mesozoic Era; these were the most highly specialised of swimming reptiles with streamlined, dolphin-shaped bodies.
**Ilium**
One of the bones of the pelvis; the ilium is connected to the vertebral column (backbone) via the sacral ribs.
**Index fossil**
Fossils of species which had a relatively short life span and a wide geographical distribution. They are extremely useful as geological time-markers (see biostratigraphy).
**Infraorder**
A category smaller than Suborder but bigger than Family; used in the classification of animals.

**Insectivores**
Insect-eaters.
**Interclavicle**
A bone in the anterior median part of the chest region between the proximal ends of the two clavicles ('collar bones').
**Iridium**
A heavy metal element found in meteorites and the Earth's core.
**Iron pyrites**
'Fool's gold'; an iron-based mineral that occurs widely in all types of rocks.
**Ischium**
One of the bones of the pelvis; it points downward and backward from the hip socket.
**Isotope**
One of a set of chemically identical types of atom which differ in their weight and stability. Unstable isotopes are radioactive and 'decay' to form more stable isotopes. Isotope analysis is used in dating some types of rocks.
**IVPP**
Institute of Vertebrate Palaeontology and Palaeoanthropology, Beijing, China.

## J

**Jurassic**
The middle period of the Mesozoic Era, following the Triassic and followed by the Cretaceous Periods. The Jurassic lasted from 213-144 million years ago.

## K

**Keratine**
A horny substance which is the basic material of horns, claws and hair in animals.
**Kinematics**
The study of movement by a system of links and joints.
**Kuehneosaurus**
An early gliding lizard which lived during the Triassic Period.

## L

**Lambeosaurine**
Relating to hadrosaurids with large tubular crests on skull.
**Lateral**
From the outside; external (opposite of medial).
**Laurasia**
The 'northern continents' in the Triassic Period, comprising North America, Europe and Asia. Separated from Gondwana by Tethys.
**Lepidosaurs**
Snakes and lizards.
**Lias**
The first epoch of the Jurassic Period (= Lower Jurassic); it lasted from 213-188 million years ago.
**Ligaments**
Tough sheets or threads of collagen (protein) which support joints between bones.
**Limestone**
Rock largely composed of calcium carbonate ($CaC0_3$).
**Loess**
Windblown dust of the Ice Age, a highly calcareous, fine-grained blanket deposit of mostly yellowish marl or loam, covering areas extending from North-central Europe to eastern China as well as in the Mississippi Valley and Pacific Northwest of the US.

## M

**Macroevolution**
Large-scale evolutionary change.
**Malm**
The third epoch of the Jurassic Period (= Upper Jurassic); it lasted from 163-144 million years ago.
**Mammal**
A warm-blooded animal with hair that gives birth to young and produces milk to feed them. Examples are mice, rabbits, elephants, and humans.
**Mantle**
The region of the Earth's interior between the outer crust and the core.
**Marl**
Limestone with a high content of clay.
**Marsupials**
Mammals that bear live young that develop in a pouch on the mother's body. Examples include kangaroos, wombats, and koalas in Australia, and opossums in South America.
**Mass-extinction**
The simultaneous extinction of a whole range of species.
**Medial**
From the inside or inner (opposite of lateral).
**Median**
The middle plane of a body.
**Mesotarsal ankle**
Ankle structure in which the hinge line between leg and foot runs between the proximal and distal series of the tarsal bones allowing a fully-erect leg posture.
**Mesozoic**
'Middle life': the middle Era between the Palaeozoic and the Cenozoic Eras. It lasted from 248-65 million years ago and is referred to colloquially as the 'Age of Reptiles'. The Mesozoic Era incorporates the Triassic, Jurassic and Cretaceous Periods.
**Metabolic level**
The intensity of the chemical processes within the body, i.e. the breakdown of food to release energy. A high metabolic level entails the ability to release more energy and with greater speed, involving an increased uptake of oxygen to 'burn' the food. Chemical reactions are slower if the temperature drops. Most reptiles are capable of short bursts of fast metabolism, but they are unable to sustain it because their body temperature is dependent on the surrounding air temperature. They have a low metabolic level. On the other hand, the warm-blooded mammals and birds are able to maintain a constant high body temperature, and can therefore sustain an increased energy output; they have a higher metabolic level.
**Metacarpals**
Long bones in the upper part of the hand, between the wrist and the digits (fingers). In pterosaurs the wing metacarpal supports the wing finger, is strongly developed and, in pterodactyloids, greatly elongated.
**Metatarsals**
Long bones in the upper part of the foot, between the ankle and the digits (toes).
**Monophyletic**
A single origin for a group of animals, originating from a common ancestor.
**Morphology**
The study of the form and shape.
**Mosasaurs**
Marine reptiles which lived in the Cretaceous Period. Large predators of the sea, these forms appear to be relatives of modern monitor lizards. They were first excavated near the River Maas in the Netherlands, hence their name.
**Musculature**
The arrangement of muscles of an animal.
**Muzzle**
The front part of the head around the jaws and nostrils.

## N

**Natural selection**
The notion that those organisms that are best adapted to prevailing conditions will survive to perpetuate their kind, i.e. the environment 'selects' the fittest organisms. A quintesssential part of Charles Darwin's *Theory of Evolution*.
**Neural spine**
A bone spine rising above a vertebra providing surface areas for the attachment of muscles and ligaments and protecting the spinal cord.
**Nocturnal**
Being active at night, rather than during daylight hours.
**Notarium**
A fusion of several anterior dorsal vertebrae to form a solid vertebral block. A notarium is commonly developed in large Cretaceous pterosaurs in order to provide a firm base for the strongly-developed shoulder girdle and for the origin of wing muscles.
**Nuchal ligaments**
Neck ligaments (from *ligamentum nuchae*).

## O

**Occipital condyle**
A ball-like process of a bone constituting a part of the back of the skull. The occipital condyle fits in a socket in the front of the anterior neck vertebrae thus forming the joint between the neck and the skull.
**Olfactory lobes**
The region of the vertebrate forebrain concerned with the sense of smell.
**Omnivore**
An animal with a diet of both plant and animal food.

**Orbital**
Pertaining to the eye socket (orbit).
**Order**
A grouping of animals that includes a variety of similar, related families.
**Ornithischian**
One of the two major Orders of dinosaurs (see also **saurischian**) which is based on hip structure. In ornithischians the pubis lies parallel to the ischium (as in birds). The group is entirely herbivorous and includes ornithopods, stegosaurs, ceratopians, ankylosaurs and pachycephalosaurs.
**Ornithosuchids**
Large thecodontian archosaurs of the Late Triassic.
**Ossified**
Composed of bone.
**Osteology**
The study of bones and skeletons.
**Ovate**
Equally oval in cross- and length-sections.
**Overburden**
The rock lying directly above a fossil that is in the process of being excavated.
**Ovoid**
Egg-shaped.

## P

**Pachyderm**
Literally 'thick-skinned' mammals, such as the rhinoceros, hippopotamus and elephant living today.
**Palaeography**
The study of the geographical distribution of continents and oceans in each geological period of the history of the Earth.
**Palaeoichnology**
The study of footprints of fossil animals as preserved in rocks.
**Palaeolatitude**
The changing position of the continents during the history of the Earth means that a particular site had also a different latitude on the globe in former geological periods, called palaeolatitude.
**Palaeomagnetism**
The magnetic bearing left in rocks from the time when they first solidified.
**Palaeoneurology**
The study of fossil brains.
**Palaeontologist**
A scientist who studies fossils as documents of the history of life on Earth.
**Palaeontology**
Science dealing with the life of past geological periods as based on the study of fossils.
**Palaeozoic**
'Ancient life': the era before the Mesozoic, between 590-248 million years ago, comprising the Cambrian, Ordovician, Silurian, Devonian, Carboniferous and Permian Periods. This was the Era *before* the dinosaurs, who lived in the Mesozoic.
**Palpebral**
Small bone found in the rim of the eye socket, especially in ornithischian dinosaurs.
**Pangaea**
The enormous supercontinent formed in late Permian times when all the continents of the Earth collided.
**Para-sacral spines**
Bony spikes projecting from the hip region in stegosaurs.
**Pareiasaurids**
Large, early plant-eating reptiles of the Permian Period.
**Parietal**
A bone (or pair of bones) forming the roof of the skull, between the frontal and the occipital.
**Passeriformes**
Order of birds, the sparrows.
**Pathological**
Relating to the study of disease.
**Pectoral girdle**
The shoulder girdle.
**Pelvis**
The hip bones collectively, the basin.
**Pelycosaurs**
Mammal-like reptiles of the Carboniferous and Permian Periods; some have distinctive 'sails' on their backs.
**Percolate**
To penetrate gradually with water (and dissolved minerals).
**Permian**
The last period of the Palaeozoic Era, following the Carboniferous and followed by the Triassic Periods. It lasted from 286-248 million years ago.
**Permineralisation**
The deposition of minerals inside a bony fossil.
**Petrification**
'Turning to stone': the replacement by minerals, of the original tissues of a fossilised organism, so that it becomes stone-like in nature.
**Phalanx (pl. phalanges)**
The (usually) small bones in the fingers and toes of vertebrates. In pterosaurs the phalanges of the wing finger are greatly elongated and strongly developed in order to support the wing membrane.
**Phanerozoic**
'Visible life': the time on Earth between 600 million years ago and today during which recognisable animal and plant remains are known.
**Photoelastic studies**
The use of light to measure the flexibility of materials.
**Phylogeny**
Evolutionary development of organisms during the history of their family tree.
**Phylum**
One of the major groupings of the Animal Kingdom.
**Physiology**
The study of the processes of life in animals and plants.
**Phytosaurs**
Early crocodile-like archosaurs of the Triassic.
**Piscivorous**
Feeding upon fish.
**Placodonts**
Marine, turtle-like, heavily-armoured reptiles of the Triassic Period that fed on shellfish, which they crushed with their flattened, plate-like teeth.
**Plantigrade**
Walking on the soles of the feet, in contrast to digitigrade (= walking on the toes).
**Plate tectonics**
The study of the large plates which make up the Earth's crust, and their relative movements.
**Plenum**
A concept used in religious teaching which is founded on the idea that the Creator formed all Earthly life in its infinite variety on just one occasion, thereby excluding the possibility of extinctions.
**Plesiosaurs**
Aquatic reptiles of the Mesozoic Era which swam by using their flipper-like feet.
**Pleurocoel**
A cavity in the sides of vertebrae.
**Pneumatic foramen**
A small opening in some bones of pterosaurs and birds through which extensions of the lung sac penetrated.
**Pneumaticity**
The condition of hollow bones with pneumatic foramina.
**'Polywachs'**
Polyethylene glycol granules, used in the conservation of fossil bones.
**Posterior**
Pertaining to the back of the body, as opposed to anterior.
**Posture**
Normal standing or walking position of an animal.
**Precambrian**
Referring to the vast period of time (before the Cambrian Period) that elapsed while the Earth cooled and became a solid planet which eventually developed its own climate and ecosystems with simple forms of life (4,500-600 million years ago).
**Predatory**
Preying upon other animals, referring to a hunting-and-killing style of life.
**Predentary bone**
A small crescent-shaped bone found at the tip of the lower jaw in ornithischian dinosaurs alone.
**Premaxilla**
A paired bone at the front of the upper jaw of nearly all vertebrates.
**Preorbital**
Pertaining to the front of the orbit or eye socket. The preorbital opening lies in front of the orbit and is a diagnostic character of archosaurs.
**Prepubis**
A pelvic bone attached to the lower end of the pubis in pterosaurs.
**Preservation**
The general condition or 'state' (of a fossil specimen).
**Primeval**
Ancient, original, ancestral.
**Process**
A bony projection (in an anatomical sense).
**Procoelous**
The condition in a vertebra when the surface of the joint at the front is concave and convex at the back (opposite to opisthocoelous).
**Procolophonids**
Small, primitive, plant-eating reptiles of the

Permian Period.

**Profile**
A sequence of rock strata (in a geological sense).

**Prolacertilians**
These are the primitive lizard-like, diapsid reptiles of the Early Triassic period considered by some to be ancestral to the lizards.

**Propatagium**
A small wing membrane in pterosaurs and bats found between neck, upper and lower arm.

**Proterosuchians**
Hook-nosed, crocodile-like thecodontians of the late Permian Period.

**Protozoans**
Single-celled, microscopically small animals; the earliest and most primitive animals known on Earth.

**Proximal**
Nearest to the point of attachment to the body (opposite of distal).

**Pterodactyloid**
Pertaining to the suborder Pterodactyloidea.

**Pterodactyloidea**
A major grouping (suborder) of pterosaur families, the short-tailed pterosaurs, which lived from the Late Jurassic to the end of the Cretaceous.

**Pteroid bone**
A small slender bone arising from the wrist in pterosaurs. It supported the leading edge of the propatagium.

**Pterosaurs**
The flying reptiles of the Mesozoic Era considered to be an order of the archosaurs and thus distant cousins of the dinosaurs and crocodiles. Pterosaurs include the two suborders Rhamphorhynchoidea, the long-tailed pterosaurs, and the Pterodactyloidea, the short-tailed pterosaurs.

**Pubis**
This is one of the bones of the pelvis, usually pointing forward and downward from the hip socket. In ornithischain dinosaurs, segnosaurids and birds, the publis is found lying parallel to the ischium. In pterosaurs this element is mostly fused with the ischium, thus forming the ischiopubis.

**Pygostyl**
Fused tail vertebrae of birds, also called 'Parson's nose'.

**'Pyrite disease'**
Spontaneous destruction of fossil specimens which contain high concentrations of iron pyrites.

## Q

**Quadrate**
A bone in the skull of vertebrates with which the lower jaw articulates.

**Quadruped**
This is an animal that stands and walks on all fours.

**Quaternary**
The recent prehistoric past which has been dominated by the arrival of Man; the period following the Tertiary Period; the last 2 million years.

## R

**Radiation**
Branching out from a common centre; diversification along various evolutionary lines from a common ancestral stock.

**Radioactive decay**
The disintegration of an unstable isotope into a more stable isotope with the production of radiation (energy).

**Radiometrics**
Measurement of radioactive decay.

**Radius**
One of the two forearm bones (see also ulna).

**Recurved**
Curved backwards (of teeth).

**Reptile**
Usually cold-blooded, egg-laying vertebrates covered with scales, for example the living crocodiles, turtles, lizards and snakes. In the Mesozoic Period reptiles were much more diverse and included very different forms, such as ichthyosaurs, plesiosaurs, placodonts, dinosaurs and pterosaurs. Some of them may even have been warm-blooded, as the pterosaurs.

**Resonator**
A device for increasing sound levels by vibrating in sympathy with the source of the sound.

**Rhamphorhynchid**
Pertaining to the family Rhamphorhynchidae.

**Rhamphorhynchoid**
Pertaining to the suborder Rhamphorhynchoidea.

**Rhamphorhynchoidea**
A major grouping (suborder) of pterosaur families, the long-tailed pterosaurs, which lived from the Late Triassic to the Late Jurassic.

Rhynchocephalia
A group of lizard-like reptiles widely distributed in the Mesozoic Era. The only living representative is the tuatara of New Zealand.

**Rhynchosaurs**
Squat, pig-like, plant-eating reptiles with a hooked beak that lived in late Triassic times.

**'Ridges'**
High mountain ranges on the sea-floor, marking the point where new sea-floor is emerging from the interior of the Earth.

**Rigor mortis**
Stiffening of the body following death.

**Rostral bone**
A bone found at the tip of the upper jaw in ceratopian dinosaurs only.

**Rutting**
Mating behaviour of deer.

## S

**Sacral ribs**
Special strong ribs that connect the vertebral column to the pelvis.

**Sacrum**
The region of the backbone which is attached to the pelvis by means of sacral ribs.

**Sagittal**
Parallel to the medial (or middle) plane in an anatomical sense.

**Saurian**
Reptile, from the Greek, meaning 'lizard'.

**Saurischian**
One major grouping of the dinosaurs (based on hip structure) in which the pubis is long and points forward and downward from the hip socket; includes the carnivorous theropods and the herbivorous sauropodomorphs.

**Saurolophine**
Referring to hadrosaurids with slender spikes on head.

**Sauropodomorphs**
Large herbivorous saurischian dinosaurs including the prosauropods and sauropods.

**Scapula**
The shoulder blade.

**Scapulocoracoid**
A hook-like bone, the shoulder girdle in pterosaurs, composed of the scapula and the coracoid.

**Sclerotic ring/Sclerotic ossicles**
A ring of flat bones lying in the eye-ball (the sclera or 'white' of the eye) providing additional strength.

**Scutes**
Bony or horny plates embedded in the skin, particularly of reptiles.

**Sedimentary rocks**
Rocks that have formed from sediments such as sands and clays.

**Sedimentation**
The process of forming and accumulating sediment in layers.

**Serrated**
With a notched edge like the cutting edge of a saw.

**Shales**
A rock type composed mainly of clay that splits into thin wafers.

**Silica**
One of several abundant minerals in the Earth's crust based on the element silicon.

**Silt**
Grains, or finely broken pieces of rock that slowly settle out of water.

**Sinuses**
Spaces within the body.

**Solar-panels**
Flat surfaces that are able to absorb the warmth of the Sun.

**Specialised**
Modified in a particular way.

**Species**
The basic unit of biological classification, a group of animals which can breed together - something which is impossible to prove in fossils. *Pterodactylus antiquus* is a species. There may be many species in a genus (*Pterodactylus* is the genus).

**Squamosal**
A bone near the top rear corner of a reptile skull. In ceratopians it is greatly enlarged to form part of the frill.

**Stem reptiles**
A group of early, primitive reptiles which lived in the Carboniferous Period and are considered to be the ancestors of most later reptiles.

**Stereoscopic**
Relating to an ability to perceive a three-dimensional image.

**Sternum**
Breastbone.
**Stratigraphy**
The study of the pattern of rock layers (strata) and their chronological sequence.
**Stratum (pl. strata)**
A layer of (usually sedimentary) rock.
**Stromatolites**
Banded rocks that were made by blue-green algae; abundant in the Precambrian in particular.
**Suborder**
A category smaller than Order but bigger than Infraorder; used in the classification of animals.
**Supercontinents**
Extra large continents formed by the joining together of several continental areas e.g. Laurasia, Gondwana, Pangaea.
**Supernova**
The last phase in the life of certain types of star, when it annihilates itself in an enormous explosion.
**Superorder**
A category bigger than Order but smaller than Class; used in the classification of animals.
**Supraoccipital**
The upper bony element at the back of the skull in many reptiles.
**Suture**
A line where bones meet.
**Synapsids**
A reptile group characterised by a single opening low down on the skull behind the eye socket; they include the pelycosaurs and the mammal-like reptiles of the Permian and Triassic Periods.
**Synsacrum**
The fused sacral and posterior dorsal vertebrae in birds and some pterosaurs.
**Systematics**
The arrangement of groups (taxa) of organisms (plants and animals) according to their phylogenetic relationships.

## T

**Talons**
Sharp claws.
**Taphonomy**
The study of the processes of decay and fossilisation in order to understand the circumstances that may have led to organisms being preserved in particular ways.
**Tarsals**
Small bones forming the ankle.
**Tarsus**
The ankle.
**Taxon (pl. taxa)**
A systematic unit of classification of plants and animals of any category, for example species, genus, family, order or class.
**Taxonomy**
Science of the grouping and subdivision of organisms according to their distinct categories (taxa).
**Temporal opening**
An opening in the temporal region of the skull behind the eye socket, also called temporal fenestra.
**Termitarium**
A termite mound.
**Tertiary**
The first period in the Cenozoic Era, following the Cretaceous Period and followed by the Quaternary Period. It lasted from 65-2 million years ago and charts the rise of mammals and birds.
**Tethys**
A sea which in former times separated Laurasia from Gondwana. A remnant of this seaway is the Mediterranean.
**Tetrapods**
Vertebrates with four limbs, e.g. amphibians, reptiles, mammals *and* birds.
**Thecodonts**
Early archosaurian reptiles of the Permian and Triassic Periods, with socketed teeth. The group from which most of the more advanced archosaurs evolved.
**Therapsids**
Mammal-like reptiles of the late Permian and early Triassic Periods.
**Thoracic**
Pertaining to the thorax or chest.
**Theropods**
A wide range of predatory saurischian dinosaurs, most of which were bipedal; commonly divided into two artificial groupings as 'coelurosaurs' (small theropods) and 'carnosaurs' (big theropods).
**Tibia**
One of the two bones of the lower leg, the shin bone; usually the larger of the two, the other being the fibula.
**Tibiotarsus**
A single bone composed of the tibia and the proximal series of the tarsal bones of the ankle; a normal condition in birds and advanced pterosaurs.
**Tooth battery**
A large number of interlocking teeth arranged in a jaw to form a cutting or grinding surface.
**'Trenches'**
Deep gullies found at the edges of tectonic plates where ocean crust is sinking back into the mantle.
**Triassic**
The first period of the Mesozoic Era, following the Permian and followed by the Jurassic Periods. It lasted from 248-213 million years ago. The pterosaurs, dinosaurs and many other reptilian groups appeared towards its close.
**Tripodal**
Of, or with, three feet.
**Trochanter**
A bony lump on the femur to which muscles are attached.
**Trochlea**
The pulley-shaped distal articular end of the upper arm (humerus) against the forearm (radius and ulna).
**Tuatara**
Lizard-like reptile (*Sphenodon punctatus*) of New Zealand, the only living representative of the rhynchocephalians, a group widely distributed in the Mesozoic Era.

## U

**Ulna**
One of the two long bones in the forearm or front leg of a tetrapod; the other being the radius.
**Uropatagium**
A skin membrane stretched between the tail and hind legs of bats; probably not present in pterosaurs.

## V

**'Variable gait'**
The ability to walk in a number of ways depending upon how the legs are positioned.
**Variation**
The range of appearance of organisms of the same general type of species.
**Varve**
A sedimentary layer deposited in a body of still water within one year, usually by meltwater streams in a glacial lake in front of a glacier. A glacial varve includes a light-coloured summer layer and a dark-coloured winter layer. By counting the varves the ages of Quaternary glacial deposits can be measured.
**Vascular**
Of or relating to the blood.
**Ventral**
From beneath (opposite of dorsal).
**Vertebra**
An individual bone of the back (vertebral column = backbone). The backbone is made up of many vertebrae.
**Vertebrates**
Backboned animals, e.g. fish, amphibians, reptiles, birds and mammals.
**Viscera**
The internal organs, the intestines.

## W

**Wealden**
An area of south east England comprised of rocks of early Cretaceous age.

## Z

**Zoology**
The science of the study of animals.
**Zygapophyses**
Processes on the vertebrae which articulate with the corresponding processes of the neighbouring vertebrae, and prevent them from slipping apart.

# INDEX

Page references set in **bold** type refer to subjects that are mentioned in illustration captions.

## C

# D

## G



## H

## M

## N



## O

# T

The publishers wish to thank the many private individuals, museum photographic archives and picture agencies who have generously supplied photographs for inclusion in this book, and by courtesy of whom they are reproduced. All photographs are here credited by page number.

**The Academy of Natural Sciences,** Philadelphia: 12 top left; 120 upper
**ARDEA:** 371 (Pat Morris); 175 right (Pat Morris)
**S.K.H. Herzog Albrecht von Bayern:** 202 upper
**J. Augusta and Z. Burian, Artia Verlag,** Prague: 188 both; 349 middle left
**Bayerische Akademie der Wissen schaften,** Munich: 204 lower
**Bayerische Staatsammlung für Paläontologie und historische Geologie,** Munich (Photographer: Franz Höck): 42; 191 lower; 192/3 all; 197 middle; 203 upper; 205 both upper and bottom; 217 middle right and bottom left; 228; 229; 259 middle; 261; 262; 268; 269 upper; 297 bottom; 304 all photographs; 305 top, middle left and lower right; 306 all photographs; 307 top left and right, bottom left and right; 329 upper; 351 top; 353 bottom right; 362 upper right; 377
**C. Bennett:** 216 bottom
**W.T. Blows:** 18 top left; 49 lower; 120 middle (D. Tanke); 144 middle
**J.F. Bonaparte:** 311; 312; 353 middle right
**Brigham Young University:** 91 left and lower right (Mark Philbrick)
**British Museum (Natural History),** courtesy of the Trustees: 35; 48 lower; 61 middle; 67 upper; 72 upper; 109 lower right; 120 lower; 127 upper left; 133 lower; 150 both; 162; 169 upper left; 175 left; 181 upper; 184-5; 367 lower; 369 left; 370 lower right
**Carnegie Museum of Natural History:** 18/9; 90; 108/9
**China Ocean Press,** Beijing: 260 top and bottom; 284 bottom; 297 top
**City of Bristol Museum:** 353 top left
**Bruce Coleman Ltd:** 33 (WWF/Hirsch and Müller); 43 lower (Hans Reinhard); 48 upper (Jen and Des Bartlett); 52 left (Joseph van Wormer); 97 (Gerald Cubitt); 102 left (Udo Hirsch); 102 right (Masood Qureshi); 109 upper (Gunter Ziesler); 139 lower right (Bob Campbell); 145 upper (Hans Reinhard); 174 upper (Jen and Des Bartlett); 364 (Norman Myers); 365 upper left (Donn Renn); 365 upper right (Peter Jackson); 375 upper (Mark Boulton)
**Martin Cowley:** 219 lower right; 355 all photographs
**Daily Mirror Syndication International:** 9 (part of montage)
**R. Delun:** 218 top right (Franz Höck)
**Denver Museum of Natural History** Photo Archives: 22 top; 85 upper; 156 upper right
**Dong Zhiming:** 285; 300 top; 301 top
**K. Ehrenberg:** 349 bottom
**Express Newspapers:** 9 (part of montage)
**Field Museum of Natural History,** Chicago: 132; 372; 373 upper and lower left; 374 upper
**Fort Worth Museum of Science and History:** 174 lower
**Foto-Wagner,** Furth im Wald: 200-201
**K.A. Frickhinger:** 253 lower
**Geological Institute of Basel:** 350 middle
**GeoScience Features:** 170/1
**Hasselblad:** 16 upper
**Dietrich Herm:** 201 upper
**K.H. Hilpert:** 25 lower
**F. Höck:** 238 upper; 339 lower right; 342; 358 upper
**H. Hofer:** 218 top left (Franz Höck)
**N. Hutchinson:** 213 lower
**Stephen Hutt,** Museum of Isle of Wight Geology: 18 top right; 108 upper
**Imitor:** 8 top; 10 all excluding middle left; 12 top middle and top right; 171 upper right; 173; 177; 178 uppr right; 179; 208 top left; 209 top left; 215 upper; 216 top; 289; 293 top; 326 middle; 365 bottom; 366; 368; 369 right; 374 lower; 375 lower
**Institute of Palaeobiology,** Warsaw: 13 lower; 49 upper; 61 lower; 73 upper; 84; 96/7; 150/1; 169 lower left
**Institute of Vertebrate Palaeontology and Palaeoanthropology,** Beijing/Dong Zhiming: 126; 133 upper left
**Institut Royal des Sciences Naturelles de Belgique:** 12 lower; 22 lower; 25 both upper; 26 upper (E. Casier); 28; 28/9; 31 upper; 32 (L. Dollo); 32/3; 357 upper
**Institut und Museum für Geologie und Paläontologie,** Tübingen: 211 upper; 265; 276 bottom
**G. Jakob:** 195 lower
**Jet Propulsion Laboratory/NASA:** 16 lower
**A.W.A. Kellner:** 194 lower left; 302 bottom; 303 both; 305 bottom left and middle right skull; 307 middle right; 310 top and middle right
**A. Kistner:** 202 lower
**E. Kuhn-Schnyder:** 203 lower right
**S.M. Kurzanov,** Moscow Academy of Sciences: 37 top right; 52 left; 72 lower; 114 lower; 115 upper; 127 upper rightp; 132/3; 133 upper right; 169 upper and lower right (all photographs by A.N. Tarassenco)
**Frank Lane Picture Agency:** 333 (Christiana Calvalho); 335 bottom (Bob Langrish); 337 bottom left (Chris Newton); 363 top right (Silvestris)
**W. Langston Jr:** 323
**Los Angeles County Natural History Museum:** 66/7
**Dr James H. Madsen:** 19 lower
**The Mansell Collection:** 11 lower; 20
**Masberg Museum,** Solnhofen: 271
**Dr. A.C. Milner:** 13 top; 24/5; 67 lower; 79 upper left and right; 85 lower; 156 lower right; 157
**Pat Morris Photographic:** 34/5 lower; 91 lower middle; 178 lower right; 370 upper
**Museo Civico di Storia Naturale,** Venice: 115 lower (E. Ruffert)
**Museum Hauff,** Holzmaden: 253 top right
**Museum of the Rockies,** Bozeman: 353 middle left
**Natural History Museum,** London: 208 top right; 249 upper; 263 top; 288; 295 top right; 338 top left
**Naturhistorisches Museum, Vienna:** 330
**NHPA:** 34/5 upper (G.I. Bernard); 172 lower (G.I. Bernard)
**F. Nopcsa:** 238 lower (Franz Höck)
**Dr D.B. Norman:** 8 middle; 11 top right; 19 top; 26 lower; 27 top left; 29; 31 lower; 36; 103 lower; 108 lower left; 158; 159 both; 171 upper left
**NRAO** (National Radio Astronomy Observatory): 180/1
**Nucolorvue Productions Pty Ltd:** 352 top right
**J.H. Ostrum:** 314 top
**Oxford University Museum:** 10 middle left; 11 top left
**Palaeontological Institute,** Moscow: 281 upper; 282; 284 upper; 357 middle
**Peabody Museum of Natural History,** Yale University: 61 top right; 145 lower; 215 lower; 315 top, middle left and right; 317
**Queensland Museum,** Fortitude Valley: 302 top middle and right
**Science Photo Library:** 178 upper left (Martin Dohrn); 219 upper right (Martin Dohrn/Stephen Winkworth); 354 middle and bottom right (Martin Dohrn/Stephen Winkworth); 373 lower right (Sinclair Stammers)
**Senckenberg Museum,** Frankfurt: 114 upper; 139 upper; 172/3 (all photographs by E. Haupt); 190 upper and middle right; 263 lower
**Smithsonian Institution:** 8/9; 37 top left; 138 lower right; 139 lower left; 353 top right; 370 lower left
**South African Museum,** Cape Town: 78 upper; 79 lower right; 103 upper
**Staatliches Museum für Naturkunde,** Stuttgart: 253 top left (H. Lumpe); 256 top (H. Lumpe)
**Stadtarchiv Munich:** 204 upper
**E. Stromer:** 350 top
**The Sun:** 9 (part of montage)
**D. Tanke:** 120 middle (via W.T. Blows)
**Texas Memorial Museum,** Austin: 321 middle right and bottom
**Tübingen University,** Museum for Geology and Palaeontology: 78/9
**Tyrrell Museum of Palaeontology,** Alberta: 42/3; 60/1; 73 lower; 120/1; 126/7; 138 lower left; 144 upper
**D. Unwin:** 281 lower; 300 middle right; 344 middle and bottom left
**US Department of the Interior,** National Park Service: 84/5; 91 upper right; 156 upper left
**US Naval Observatory:** 181 lower
**G. Viohl:** 195 upper middle
**Peter Wellnhofer:** 191 upper; 194 uper left; 197 upper; 201 lower;; 209 lower left; 210 upper; 226; 231 both; 232; 233; 234; 235; 236; 237; 257 258; 259 top right; 264; 269 lower; 273; 275; 276 upper left and right; 277 middle right and lower right; 280 both; 287; 301 bottom; 310 bottom; 315 bottom; 316; 320; 321 top left and right; 324 all photographs; 328; 329 botton; 331; 332 all photographs; 344 bottom right; 345; 347; 350 bottom; 351 middle and bottom; 352 middle; 357 top right; 358 lower; 359 all photographs; 362 upper left
**R. Wild:** 239; 242; 243; 246; 247

**O. Abel:** 109 *Hypsilophodon* foot; 333 lower right; 337 lower right and bottom right.
**R. Barsbold:** 47 *Oviraptor* shoulder and middle skull; 148 *Stegoceras* teeth
**R. Barsbold and A. Perle:** 53 *Segnosaurus, Adasaurus* and *Erlikosaurus*
**A. Bartholomai and R. Molnar:** 112 *Muttaburrasaurus*
**C. Bennett:** 331 middle
**J. Bonaparte:** 36 *Saurosuchus*; 77 *Coloradia* skull; 222 upper; 222 lower (redrawn by John Sibbick); 311 (redrawn)
**J. Bonaparte and J. Powell:** 53 *Noasaurus*; 94 *Saltasaurus* and *Laplatasaurus*
**M. Borsuk-Bialynicka:** 95 *Opisthocoelicaudia*
**C.D. Bramwell and G.R. Whitfield:** 218 middle left and right (Geoff Denney)
**B. Brown and E.M. Schlajiker:** 130 *Protoceratops* skull
**D.S. Brown:** 358-9 *Cryptoclidus*
**W. Buckland:** 208 bottom (BMNH); 326 bottom (BMNH)
**J. Buckman:** 342 top left and top middle
**Z. Burian:** 188 both; 349 middle left
**C. Camp:** 53 *Segisaurus*
**K. Carpenter:** 166-7 *Euoplocephalus* skeleton
**R. Carroll:** 224 bottom (redrawn by John Sibbick)
**A.J. Charig:** 35 postures; 36 hip joints; 76 *Plateosaurus* tooth; 95 *Cetiosauriscus* chevron
**A.J. Charig and A.W. Crompton:** 100-1 *Heterodontosaurus* skull
**E.H. Colbert:** 40-1 *Coelophysis*; 285 lower right (redrawn); 286 bottom (redrawn)
**E.H. Colbert and C.C. Mook:** 354-5 *Protosuchus*
**W.P. Coombs:** 162-3 nodosaur shoulder blade, *Panoplosaurus* skulls and skull sections, *Sauropelta* tail; 166-7 *Euoplocephalus* skulls and skull sections, *Ankylosaurus* tail club, shoulder and hip muscles
**M. Cooper:** 95 *Vulcanodon*
**G. Cuvier:** 206 upper
**De La Beche:** 349 top left (in F.J.Pictet, 1846)
**P. Dodson:** 107 *Tenontosaurus* hand and foot; 125 *Corythosaurus* and *Lambeosaurus* skulls; 133 *Protoceratops* skulls (after B.Brown and E.M.Schlajiker)
**Dong Zhiming:** 53 *Shanshanosaurus*; 65 *Yangchuanosaurus*; 94 *Omeisaurus*; 285 upper left and right (redrawn)
**C.F. Eaton:** 216 middle (redrawn); 230 bottom (redrawn)
**R.F. Ewer:** 34 *Euparkeria*; 223 upper left and right
**L. Figuier:** 338 middle top
**T. Frazzetta:** 360-1 lizard skull flexing
**E. Frey and J. Riess:** 328 top (redrawn)
**P.M. Galton:** 286 top (redrawn); 76-7 anchisaurid posture, *Plateosaurus* hand (redrawn) and foot (redrawn); 100 *Lesothosaurus* skeleton; 106-7 *Hypsilophodon, Dryosaurus* skull
**P.M. Galton and P. Watts:** 149 *Pachycephalosaurus* skull
**C.W. Gilmore:** 64-5 *Ceratosaurus* skeleton and hip, *Allosaurus* skull and vertebrae; 83 *Apatosaurus* vertebrae; 88-9 *Camarasaurus*; 112 *Camptosaurus*; 118 *Bactrosaurus* skull; 136-7 *Centrosaurus* skeleton, hand and foot; 154-5 *Stegosaurus*; 156 *Stegosaurus* skeleton
**A. Goldfuss:** 206 lower; 207 upper left
**Mark Hallett:** 30 *Iguanodon* reconstructions
**G. Heilmann:** 115 *Iguanodon* feeding; 176 *Euparkeria, Archaeopteryx* and pigeon skulls, pigeon skeleton (redrawn)
**W. Hennig:** 154 *Kentrosaurus*
**W.J. Holland:** 82-3 *Diplodocus* skeleton (redrawn), skull, hand and foot
**E.v. Holst:** 219 top left (redrawn); 354 top (redrawn)
**J. Horner:** 118-9 *Edmontosaurus* skeleton (redrawn)
**F. Howse:** 293 bottom right (redrawn)
**F.von Huehne:** 76-7 *Plateosaurus* skeleton and skull
**N. Hutchinson:** 349 top right
**F.von Huehne:** 89 *Brachiosaurus* hand; 221 bottom (redrawn)
**Illustrated London News** (1853): 352 top left
**S. Jain:** 94 *Barapasaurus*
**W. Janensch:** 88-9 *Brachiosaurus* skeleton, skull, rib and vertebrae
**F. Jenkins and R. Parrington:** 377 *Megazostrodon* (redrawn)
**J. Jensen and K. Padian:** 286 middle (redrawn)
**T.S.Kemp:** 363 *Delphinognathus, Dimetrodon* and *Cynognathus* skulls; 376 *Probelesodon*
**D.M. Kermack and K.A. Kermack:** 376 *Morganucodon* (redrawn)
**A. Kircher:** 200 lower
**B. Kurten:** 356 *Pelagosaurus*
**S.M. Kurzanov:** 52 *Avimimus*
**L. Lambe:** 118-9 *Edmontosaurus* skull; 148-9 *Stegoceras* skeleton (redrawn) and skull (redrawn)
**R.S. Lull:** 142-3 *Chasmosaurus* pelvis, *Torosaurus, Pentaceratops* and *Anchiceratops* skulls; 162-3 *Nodosaurus* skeleton (redrawn)
**R.S. Lull and C.W. Gilmore:** 142-3 *Chasmosaurus* skeleton (redrawn)
**R.S. Lull and N. Wright:** 118-9 hadrosaur pelves, *Kritosaurus* skull (redrawn), *Anatosaurus* skull (redrawn); 125 *Prosaurolophus* and *Saurolophus* skulls
**W.N. McFarland, F.H. Pough, J.B. Heiser and T.J. Cade:** 361 *Naja* skull
**J. Madsen:** 64 *Allosaurus* hand and foot
**A. Maleev:** 71 *Tyrannosaurus* hand and foot, *Tarbosaurus* skull
**G. Mantell:** 209 upper right (BMNH)
**O.C. Marsh:** 64 *Ceratosaurus* skull; 77 *Anchisaurus* skeleton and skull; 83 *Apatosaurus* skeleton (redrawn); 137 *Triceratops* skull; 217 middle left; 361 middle left and right (Franz Höck)
**J. Martin:** 348 lower (in Th. Hawkins, 1840)
**T. Maryanska:** 166 *Pinacosaurus* and *Saichania* skulls
**T. Maryanska and H. Osmolska:** 149 *Homalocephale* pelvis, vertebrae and skull, *Prenocephale* skulls
**H.v. Meyer:** 211 lower; 212 upper and 213 upper (Franz Höck)
**D. Nash:** 356 *Orthosuchus*
**B.H. Newman:** 70-1 *Tyrannosaurus* skeleton (redrawn); 73 *Tyrannosaurus* rising from ground (redrawn); 159 *Scelidosaurus* skeleton from a photograph
**E. Newman:** 207 bottom right
**E.T. Newton:** 212 lower (Franz Höck)
**F. Nopcsa:** 163 *Polacanthus* skeleton; 239 upper
**D.B. Norman:** 27 *Iguanodon*; 28-9 *Iguanodon*; 30-1 *Iguanodon*; 32-3 *Iguanodon*; 47 shoulders and hips; 58 head, skull and shoulder musculature; 112-3 *Iguanodon*; 118 hadrosaurid teeth; 143 shoulder musculature
**J. Nowinski:** 82 *Nemegtosaurus, Dicraeosaurus* and *Antarctosaurus* skulls
**H.F. Osborn:** 41 *Ornitholestes*; 47 *Oviraptor* top skull; 58 *Velociraptor* skull; 71 *Tyrannosaurus* pelvis; 130 *Psittacosaurus* skeleton; 176 *Ornitholestes*
**H. Osmolkska:** 47 *Oviraptor* bottom skull; 52 *Elmisaurus*; 131 *Bagaceratops* skull
**J.H. Ostrom:** 9 *Compsognathus* hip; 40-1 *Compsognathus*; 58-9 *Deinonychus*; 106 *Tenontosaurus* skull; 125 *Parasaurolophus* skulls, sections through crests (redrawn); 130-1 ceratopian teeth; 176 *Archaeopteryx*
**R. Owen:** 214 upper (Franz Höck); 248 lower; 249 lower; 290 top (redrawn); 292 middle and bottom (redrawn); 293 middle and bottom left (redrawn); 358 upper (Franz Höck)
**K. Padian:** 259 (redrawn); 352-3 *Dimorphodon*
**N. Parker:** 338 top left
**C.W. Parks:** 119 *Edmontosaurus* hand and foot; 124-5 *Parasaurolophus* skeleton (redrawn)
**C.J. Pennycuik:** 328 middle (redrawn)
**D.S. Peters and W.F. Gutmann:** 224 top (redrawn)
**S. Phillips:** 352 bottom left
**L.I. Price:** 189 lower; 302 (redrawn)
**M. Reichel:** 317 lower left and right (redrawn); 349 middle right
**R. Reisz:** 34 *Petrolacosaurus*; 220 lower (P.Wellnhofer); 363-3 *Archaeothyris*
**Riou:** 348 upper (in O. Fraas, 1866)
**A.S. Romer:** 46 *Struthiomimus* foot; 352-3 *Rhamphorhynchus* (redrawn) and *Pteranodon* (redrawn); 356 *Metriorhynchus*; 358-9 *Ophthalmosaurus*, ichthyosaur, plesiosaur skull, *Placodus, Placochelys*; 360-1 *Proganochelys, Archelon, Sphenodon, Kuehneosaurus*, snake fangs; 376-7 *Lycaenops*
**A.S. Romer and L. Price:** 362-3 *Ophiacodon, Dimetrodon* and *Edaphosaurus* skull
**A.K. Rozhdestvensky:** 53 *Therizinosaurus*
**A.G. Russell and E. Nicholls:** 46 *Struthiomimus* hand and gastralia
**D. Russell:** 46-7 *Struthiomimus* skeleton (redrawn) and skull, *Dromiceiomimus* skull; 70-1 *Allosaurus* hatchling, *Albertosaurus* and *Daspletosaurus* skulls
**D. Russell and R. Seguin:** 55 'dinosauroid' (redrawn)
**A.P. Santa-Luca:** 9 *Heterodontosaurus* hip; 100-1 *Heterodontosaurus* skeleton, hip, hand and foot
**W. Schäfer:** 193 lower left (redrawn)
**H.G. Seeley:** 94 *Ornithopsis*; 214 lower
**John Sibbick:** 222 bottom; 224 bottom; 229 top, middle left and bottom; 247 middle right; 252 lower; 296 bottom (after E. Thenius); 324; 334 (after C. Bramwell and G. Whitfield); 340 top (after P. Wellnhofer); 341 bottom (after R.T. Bakker); 342 (after P. Schouten); 356 top; 357 top left and bottom (after H. Haubold and E. Buffetaut); 360 top; 361 bottom
**S.T.v. Soemmerrring:** 203 lower left; 205 middle left and right
**C.M. Sternberg:** 130-1 *Protoceratops* skeleton (redrawn); 137 *Styracosaurus* skull
**P. Taquet:** 112-3 *Ouranosaurus* skeleton and skull (redrawn)
**C. Theodori:** 210 lower
**R.A. Thulborn:** 36 ankle structures (redrawn); 101 *Lesothosaurus* skull (redrawn)
**G. Wagler:** 207 middle
**S.P. Welles:** 65 *Dilophosaurus*
**M. Wellnhofer:** 190 lower (Geoff Denney)
**Peter Wellnhofer:** 189 upper (Geoff Denney); 196 (Geoff Denney); 197 both; 198 (Geoff Denney); 199 (Geoff Denney); 220 upper; 221 upper; 222 middle (Geoff Denney); 223 lower (Geoff Denney); 225 (slightly changed after R. Wild); 226 all artwork; 227 all artwork; 229 middle right; 230 top and middle; 231 all artwork; 232 all artwork; 233 all artwork; 234 all artwork; 235 all artwork; 236 all artwork; 237 all artwork; 242 portrait; 247 both skulls; 250 portrait and skull; 252 upper; 254 skull; 255 portrait; 257 all artwork; 258; 260; 261; 264; 265 all artwork; 266 skulls; 267 portrait; 268 all artwork; 272 all artwork; 273 all artwork; 276 all artwork; 277; 279 portrait and skull; 280; 281; 284; 292 skull; 293 skull; 296 all skeletal drawings; 299 skull and portrait; 300 skull; 301 lower right; 304; 305; 306 both artworks; 307; 308 skull and portrait; 309 jaw; 310; 313 portraits; 316; 319 portrait and skull; 327; 328 bottom; 330 bottom; 331 top and bottom right; 332; 333 lower left; 335; 336 all artwork; 337 top left (after M. Reichel) and middle; 338 middle; 339 both artworks; 340 bottom left and right; 343 (after R. Wild); 345 all artworks; 346 (Geoff Denney); 354 middle sequence; 356 bottom; 357 middle left; 359 skulls; 360 skeletons; 363 bottom (after Novacek 1987)
**R. Wild:** 239 lower; 240 top; 242 all skeletal artwork; 243 all artwork; 246 all artwork; 247 top left and bottom left
**S.W. Williston:** 217 top left; 320 (redrawn)
**A.S. Woodward:** 95 *Cetiosauriscus* skeleton
**C.C. Young:** 300 middle left (redrawn); 301 upper left (redrawn)
**K.A. Zittel:** 217 upper right

The pterosaur specimens figured in this book are housed in many different museums and collections around the world. The following listing, arranged in alphabetical order of the cities, is intended to help the interested reader to locate these specimens.

**Austin, USA:** Texas Memorial Museum, University of Texas, Austin, Texas: 321 upper left; 321 middle right.
**Banz, Germany:** Petrefaktensammlung Kloster Banz, Lichtenfels: 210 bottom.
**Beijing, China:** Institute of Vertebrate Palaeontology and Palaeoanthropology, Academia Sinica, Beijing: 285 upper left; 297 bottom; 300 top; 301 top left; 301 top right.
**Bergamo, Italy:** Museo Civico di Scienze Naturali, Bergamo: 239 lower right; 242 top; 242 bottom; 246 upper left; 246 bottom; 247 upper left.
**Berlin, Germany:** Museum für Naturkunde an der Humboldt-Universität, Berlin: 368 lower; 369 top left.
**Bochum, Germany:** Collection Helmut Leich, Bochum: 332 lower right; 343 upper right.
**Bonn, Germany:** Geologisch-Paläontologisches Institut der Universität, Bonn: 207 upper left; 272 top.
**Brisbane, Australia:** Queensland Museum, Fortitude Valley, Queensland: 302 upper middle; 302 upper right.
**Cambridge, England:** Sedgwick Museum, University of Cambridge: 290 upper right; 293 lower left.
**Chicago, USA:** Field Museum of Natural History, Chicago, Illinois: 320 upper right.
**Curitiba, Brazil:** Collection Guido Borgomanero, Curitiba: 307 middle right.
**Dashanpu, China:** Palaeontological Museum, Zigong, Beipei Museum, Dashanpu, Sichuan: 260 upper right.
**Eichstätt, Germany:** Jura-Museum, Eichstätt: 264 middle left; 277 lower right; 280 middle left.
Collection Karl Strobl, Eichstätt: 339 lower right.
**Frankfurt, Germany:** Naturmuseum Senckenberg, Frankfurt am Main: 190 top; 263 middle.
**Haarlem, The Netherlands:** Teyler's Museum, Haarlem: 191 bottom; 212 top; 213 top; 343 upper left.
**Hays, USA:** Sternberg Memorial Museum, Fort Hays State University, Hays, Kansas: 316 middle left.
**Leningrad, USSR:** Palaeontological Institute of the University, Leningrad: 301 lower right.
**London, England:** Natural History Museum, London: 195 upper right; 208 bottom; 212 bottom; 249 top; 259 middle; 263 top; 288 middle; 292 bottom; 292 middle right; 293 middle left; 293 bottom right; 295 upper right; 296 middle left; 345 lower left; 358 upper.
**Milan, Italy:** Museo Civico di Storia Naturale, Milano: 243 lower right.
**Moscow, USSR:** Palaeontological Musem, Moscow: 281 upper left; 281 lower right; 282 upper right; 284 upper left; 300 middle right; 344 lower left; 357 middle.
**Munich, Germany:** Bayerische Staatsammlung für Paläontologie und historische Geologie, München: 192 top; 192 bottom; 193 middle; 193 lower right; 194 upper right; 203 top; 205 upper right; 217 middle right; 228 top; 231 upper right; 231 middle; 232 upper left; 233 middle right; 234 middle; 235 middle right; 236 top; 236 middle left; 237 middle left; 237 lower left; 262 top; 262 bottom; 264 middle right; 264 lower left; 268 lower right; 269 top; 273 upper left; 275 upper left; 276 top; 277 upper right; 280 upper left; 304 top; 304 lower middle; 305 upper left; 307 upper right; 307 bottom left; 307 bottom right; 309 upper left; 328 middle; 329 middle; 329 bottom; 331 lower left; 332 top; 332 middle; 336 upper left; 336 middle; 338 lower left; 339 middle left; 339 middle right; 340 middle; 340 middle right; 340 lower middle; 341 upper left; 341 middle left; 343 middle; 344 lower right; 362 top right.
**New Haven, USA:** Peabody Museum of Natural History, Yale University, New Haven, Connecticut: 191 top; 216 bottom; 229 middle right; 285 lower right; 286 upper right; 315 middle left; 315 middle right; 317 top; 362 top left.
**New York, USA:** American Museum of Natural History, New York, N.Y.: 269 lower left; 286 lower right; 287 bottom; 305 top; 305 lower right; 306 upper right; 306 middle; 306 lower left; 307 upper left; 310 bottom left; 315 lower left; 316 top; 357 top right.
**Paris, France:** Musée National d'Histoire Naturelle, Paris: 301 lower middle.
**Pittsburgh, USA:** Carnegie Museum of Natural History, Pittsburgh, Pennsylvania: 257 top.
**Provo, USA:** Brigham Young University, Provo, Utah: 286 middle right.
**Rio de Janeiro, Brazil:** Departamento Nacional Producíon Mines (DNPM), Rio de Janeiro: 189 bottom; 302 lower right; 303 lower right; 305 upper right; 305 lower middle left.
**Salt Lake City, USA:** Utah Museum of Natural History, University of Utah, Salt Lake City, Utah: 338 lower middle.
**Solnhofen, Germany:** Bürgermeister-Müller-Museum, Solnhofen: 359 middle left.
Maxberg-Museum, Solnhofen: 271 upper right.
**Stuttgart, Germany:** Staatliches Museum für Naturkunde, Stuttgart: 253 upper left; 256 top.
**Tübingen, Germany:** Institut für Geologie und Paläontologie der Universität, Tübingen: 211 top; 265 middle left.
**Tucuman, Argentina:** Instituto-Fundacíon Miguel Lillo, Universidad Nacional, Tucuman: 311 top; 314 top.
**Udine, Italy:** Museo Friuliano di Storia Naturale, Udine: 247 middle left; 247 bottom.
**Uppsala, Sweden:** Palaeontological Museum Uppsala: 253 lower right.
**Vienna, Austria:** Geological Institute of the University, Wien: 296 upper right; 296 middle right.
Naturhistorisches Musem, Wien: 330 upper left.